E

HOW T

1. OPEN THIS FLAP
2. TURN TO THE COUN
3. COMPARE THE SIGNS FOR EXPLANATION

FRANÇAIS 

COMMENT INTERPRETER LES SYMBOLES

① OUVRIR CE VOLET

② REPORTEZ-VOUS AU PAYS QUI VOUS INTERESSE

③ COMPAREZ LES SIGNES POUR EN AVOIR L'EXPLICATION

DEUTSCH 

ANLEITUNG ZUR BENUTZUNG DER ZEICHEN

1. ÖFFNEN SIE DIESES FALTBLATT
2. SUCHEN SIE DAS LAND ÜBER WELCHES SIE AUSKÜNFTE HABEN MÖCHTEN
3. VERGLEICHEN SIE DIE ZEICHEN FÜR ERKLÄRUNG

ESPAÑOL 

COMO UTILIZAR LOS SIMBOLOS

① ABRA ESTA SOLAPA

② BUSQUE EL PAIS QUE LE INTERESA

③ COMPARE LOS SIMBOLOS PARA OBTENER SU EXPLICACION

EXPLICACION DE LOS SIMBOLOS

Albergues que participan en el Plan de Normas Garantizadas

▲	Categoría Normal
△	Categoría Sencilla

	Número de teléfono
	Número de fax
	Dirección de e-mail
	Dirección Internet
Open Dates:	Fechas de apertura
	Albergue abierto todo el año
Open Hours:	Horas de apertura
	Albergue abierto 24 horas
Reservations:	Información sobre reservas
	Es recomendable reservar
	Reservas online en HIhostels.com (ver la Introducción para más información)
	Albergue participante en el programa FreeNites & More (ver la Introducción para más información)
CC	Se admiten tarjetas de crédito
Beds:	Número total de camas
	Número de habitaciones con número de camas indicado
	Camas de estilo japonés
Price (range):	Tarifas mínima y máxima (tarifas sujetas a cambio)
BB inc	Desayuno incluido en el precio
	Sábanas incluidas en el precio
	Sábanas disponibles abonando un suplemento

Facilities:	Instalaciones y prestaciones que ofrece el albergue
	Preparado para uso de disminuidos físicos
	Se admiten grupos
	Hay habitaciones familiares
	Sólo para mujeres
	Sólo para hombres
	Se sirven todas las comidas (a menos que se indique lo contrario):
B	Desayuno
L	Comida
D	Cena
	Cocina para uso de los huéspedes
	Bar-Cafetería
	Cobertizo para bicicletas en el albergue
	Se pueden obtener descuentos a través del albergue
	Sala(s) común(es) en el albergue
TV	Salón de TV en el albergue
	Biblioteca para uso de los socios
	Acceso a Internet en el albergue
	Sala(s) de conferencias
	Posibilidad de lavar la ropa/Lavandería en el albergue o cerca de él
	Lugar donde guardar el equipaje/consigna para socios
	Pequeña tienda en el albergue o cerca de él
	Casillas/armarios con cerradura en el albergue
	Aire acondicionado
	Ascensor en el albergue
P	Aparcamiento en el albergue o cerca de él
i	Información turística
	Cambio de divisas en el albergue o cerca de él
	Jardín en el albergue
	Parque infantil en el albergue

Directions:	Cómo llegar al abergue: Medios de transporte
2NE	Dirección y distancia aproximada en km. en línea recta desde el centro de la ciudad hasta el albergue.
	Aeropuerto más cercano
A	Autobús desde/para el aeropuerto
	Puerto: Nombre y distancia desde el centro de la ciudad
	Tren: Estación más cercana y distancia hasta el albergue
	Autobús (desde el centro de la ciudad): N^os^, parada y distancia hasta el albergue
	Tranvía o trolebús (desde el centro de la ciudad): N^os^, parada y distancia hasta el albergue
U	Metro: Nombre de la línea, nombre de la estación y distancia hasta el albergue
	Parada de autobús
	Parada de tranvía
ap	Apeadero

Attractions:	Actividades que ofrecen el albergue y sus alrededores
	Playa en el albergue o cerca de él
	Zona de esquí de fondo
	Zona de marcha/senderismo
	Natación en el albergue o cerca de él
	Instalaciones deportivas en el albergue o cerca de él
Mon Tue	Lunes Martes
Wed Thur	Miércoles Jueves
Fri Sat	Viernes Sábado
Sun	Domingo
Ave Hwy	Avenida Autopista
Rd St	Carretera Calle
Su Wi	Verano Invierno

EXPLANATION OF SIGNS

Hostels within the Assured Standards Scheme

▲	Standard Grade
△	Simple Grade
	Telephone number
	Facsimile number
	E-mail address
	Web Address
Open Dates:	Dates hostel open
	Hostel open all year
Open Hours:	Times hostel open
	Hostel open 24 hours
Reservations:	Reservation Information
R	Reservation recommended
HI	Online reservations with HIhostels.com (see main introduction for details)
FNM	FreeNites & More participating hostel (see main introduction for details)
CC	Credit cards accepted
Beds:	Total number of beds
1 - 6+	Number of rooms containing indicated number of beds
	Japanese style beds
Price (range):	Overnight fee (prices are subject to change)
BB inc	Breakfast included in Overnight Fee
	Linen included in fee
	Linen can be hired
Facilities:	Facilities available at the hostel
	Suitable for wheelchair users
	Groups welcome
	Family rooms available
	Female only
	Male only
	All meals available (unless otherwise specified):
B	Breakfast
L	Lunch
D	Dinner (evening meal)
	Self catering facilities provided
	Café/Bar available
	Cycle Store at hostel
	Discounts & Concessions available
	Common room(s) in hostel
TV	TV room in hostel
	Library for members' use
	Internet Access at hostel
	Conference room(s)
	Laundry facilities available at or near the hostel
	Luggage storage for members
	Basic store available at or near the hostel
	Lockers available at hostel
	Air Conditioning
	Lift in hostel
P	Parking facilities available at or near the hostel
i	Tourist Information
	Currency Exchange at or near hostel
	Garden at hostel
	Playground at hostel
Directions:	Transport for getting to & from the hostel
2NE	Direction and approximate distance in km in straight line from city centre to hostel
	Nearest major Airport
A	Airport bus
	Harbour/Port: Name and distance from City Centre
	Train: nearest Station and distance to hostel
	Bus (from City Centre): No/Nos, alighting point and distance to hostel
	Tram or trolley bus (from City Centre): No/Nos, alighting point and distance to hostel
U	Underground: Line name, Station name and distance to hostel
	Bus Stop
	Tram Stop
ap	alighting point
Attractions:	Attractions at the hostel or in the surrounding area
	Beach at or near hostel
	Skiing area
	Hiking area
	Swimming at or near hostel
	Sports facilities at or near hostel
Mon Tue	Monday Tuesday
Wed Thur	Wednesday Thursday
Fri Sat Sun	Friday Saturday Sunday
Ave Hwy	Avenue Highway
Rd St	Road Street
Su Wi	Summer Winter

EXPLICATION DES SYMBOLES

Auberges participant au Plan pour la Garantie des Normes en Auberge

▲	Catégorie Normale
△	Catégorie Simple
	Numéro de téléphone
	Numéro de facsimilé
	Adresse e-mail
	Adresse Internet
Open Dates:	Dates d'ouverture de l'auberge
12	Auberge ouverte toute l'année
Open Hours:	Heures d'ouverture de l'auberge
	Auberge ouverte 24 h sur 24
Reservations:	Renseignements sur les réservations
R	Réservation recommandée
HI	Réservations en ligne avec HIhostels.com (voir l'introduction générale pour en savoir plus)
FNM	Auberge participant au programme FreeNites & More (voir l'introduction générale pour en savoir plus)
CC	Les cartes de crédit sont acceptées
Beds:	Nombre de lits
1 - 6+	Nombre de chambres au nombre indiqué de lits
	Lits de style japonais
Price (range):	Tarif pour une nuitée (les tarifs sont donnés sous réserve de modifications)
BB inc	Petit déjeuner compris dans le prix de la nuitée
	Draps compris
	Location de draps
Facilities:	Prestations offertes par l'auberge
	Convient aux ajistes en fauteuil roulant
	Accueil des Groupes
	Chambres familiales disponibles
	Réservé aux femmes
	Réservé aux hommes
	Tous les repas sont disponibles (sauf indication contraire):
B	Petit déjeuner
L	Déjeuner
D	Dîner (repas du soir)
	Cuisine à la disposition des membres
	Café/Bar disponibles
	Abri vélo à l'auberge
	Remises disponibles
	Salle(s) commune(s) à l'auberge
TV	Salle de télévision à l'auberge
	Bibliothèque pour adhérents
	Accès à l'Internet à l'auberge
	Salle(s) de réunion
	Laverie à ou près de l'auberge
	Dépôt de bagages pour adhérents
	Petit magasin à votre service à ou près de l'auberge
	Casiers individuels à l'auberge
	Climatisation
	Ascenseur à l'auberge
P	Possibilités de parking à ou près de l'auberge
i	Informations touristiques
	Bureau de change à ou près de l'auberge
	Jardin à l'auberge
	Terrain de jeu à l'auberge
Directions:	Moyens de transport et indications pour se rendre à l'auberge
2NE	Direction et distance approximative en km en ligne droite du centre-ville à l'auberge
	Aéroport principal le plus proche
A	Autobus pour l'aéroport
	Port: Nom et distance à partir du centre-ville
	Train: gare la plus proche et distance jusqu'à l'auberge
	Bus (à partir du centre-ville): No/Nos, point d'arrivée et distance jusqu'à l'auberge
	Trams ou trolleys (à partir du centre-ville): No/Nos, point d'arrivée et distance jusqu'à l'auberge
U	Métro: Nom de la ligne, nom de la station et distance jusqu'à l'auberge
	Arrêt de bus
	Arrêt de tram
ap	point d'arrivée
Attractions:	Attraits touristiques de l'auberge et de la région
	Plage à ou près de l'auberge
	Région de ski de fond
	Région de randonnée pédestre
	Natation à ou près de l'auberge
	Installations sportives à ou près de l'auberge
Mon Tue	Lundi Mardi
Wed Thur	Mercredi Jeudi
Fri Sat	Vendredi Samedi
Sun	Dimanche
Ave Hwy	Avenue Autoroute
Rd St	Route Rue
Su Wi	Eté Hiver

ZEICHENERKLÄRUNG

Herbergen mit garantierten Qualitätsstandards

▲	Normaler Standard
△	Einfacher Standard

t	Telefonnummer
f	Telefaxnummer
e	Email-Adresse
w	Web-Adresse
Open Dates:	Herberge geöffnet (Tage)
12	Herberge ganzjährig geöffnet
Open Hours:	Herberge geöffnet (Zeiten)
	Herberge 24 Stunden geöffnet
Reservations:	Reservierungsinformationen
R	Reservierung empfohlen
HI	Reservierungen per Internet bei HIhostels.com (Einzelheiten dazu im Einführungsteil
FNM	Herbergen, die bei FreeNites & More mitmachen (Einzelheiten dazu im Einführungsteil)
CC	Kreditkarten werden akzeptiert
Beds:	Bettenzahl
1 - 6+	Anzahl der Räume mit entsprechender Bettenausstattung
	Betten im japanischen Stil
Price (range):	Übernachtungspreise (Preisänderungen sind vorbehalten)
BB inc	Frühstück ist im Übernachtungspreis enthalten
	Bettwäsche im Preis enthalten
	Bettwäsche kann ausgeliehen werden

Facilities:	Ausstattung in oder in der Nähe der Herberge
	Für Rollstuhlbenutzer geeignet
	Aufnahme von Gruppen
	Familienräume vorhanden
	Nur für Frauen
	Nur für Männer
	Mahlzeiten erhältlich (sofern nicht anders angegeben):
B	Frühstück
L	Mittagessen
D	Abendessen
	Küche für Mitglieder
	Café/Bar vorhanden
	Fahrradschuppen vorhanden
	Rabatte & Konzessionen erhältlich
	Gemeinschaftsraum vorhanden
TV	Fernsehraum in der Herberge
	ruhiger Leseraum vorhanden
	Internet-Zugang in der Herberge
	Tagungsräume
	Einrichtungen zur Wäschepflege in (oder in der Nähe) der Herberge
	Gepäckaufbewahrung für Mitglieder
	Kleines Geschäft in (oder in der Nähe) der Herberge
	Schließfächer vorhanden
	Klimaanlage
	Personenaufzug in der Herberge
P	Parkmöglichkeiten in (oder in der Nähe) der Herberge
i	Touristeninformation
	Geldwechsel in oder in der Nähe der Herberge möglich
	Garten vorhanden
	Spielplatz vorhanden

Directions:	Verkehrsanbindung zu und von der Herberge
2 NE	Richtung und ungefähre Entfernung in km vom Stadtzentrum bis zur Herberge (Luftlinie)
	Nächster größerer Flughafen
A	Flughafenbus
	Hafen: Name und Entfernung vom Stadtzentrum
	Eisenbahn: nächster Bahnhof und Entfernung bis zur Herberge
	Bus (vom Stadtzentrum): Nummer(n), günstigste Haltestelle und Entfernung bis zur Herberge
	Straßenbahn oder O-Bus (vom Stadtzentrum): Nummer(n), günstigste Haltestelle und Entfernung bis zur Herberge
U	U-Bahn: Name der Linie, Name der Haltestelle und Entfernung bis zur Herberge
	Bus-Haltestelle
	Straßenbahn-Haltestelle
ap	günstigste Haltestelle

Attractions:	Attraktionen in der Herberge oder in der Umgebung
	Strand in der Nähe der Herberge
	Ski-Gebiet
	Gebiet zum Wandern
	Schwimmbad in oder in der Nähe der Herberge
	Sporteinrichtungen in oder nahe der Herberge
Mon Tue	Montag Dienstag
Wed Thur	Mittwoch Donnerstag
Fri Sat Sun	Freitag Samstag Sonntag
Ave Hwy	Allee Landstraße
Rd St	Straße
Su Wi	Sommer Winter

 Typeset in England by Elanders (UK) Limited. Printed in Poland by Elanders Polska Sp.zo.o.

Cover Design, Hostelling International advertisements, Inside Front Cover, pages 1-32 & "We want to hear from you" pages designed by Elanders (UK) Ltd.

IYHF acknowledges the help of Member Associations in providing photographs for pages 1-16.

In pursuance of the Environmental Charter adopted by IYHF's 39th International Conference, this book has been produced using only paper from environment-friendly sources. The Nordic Council of Ministers decided in November 1989 to introduce common Nordic environmental labelling of products. Today, the 'Swan' is the only existing environmental label for printed matter in Europe. The criteria is set with this main target area:

The effect on the environment is minimised within the production process.

The product itself:

This product is 100% recyclable.

The ink, varnish and glue does not contain chemicals classified as environmentally hazardous according to EU directives.

The paper used is produced with low environmental impact (emissions) not with chemicals classified as environmentally hazardous according to EU directives.

Published in 2005 by
International Youth Hostel Federation
International Office, 2nd Floor, Gate House, Fretherne Road,
Welwyn Garden City,
Hertfordshire, AL8 6RD, England

Registered under the Charity Act in England.

Distributed through Hostelling International outlets worldwide.

"Hostelling International" is the brand name of Youth Hostelling Worldwide

The Official International Youth Hostels Guide 2006

Hostelling International is the brand name of the International Youth Hostel Federation, the organisation that represents Youth Hostel Associations worldwide.

The information supplied in this Guide has been supplied by the Youth Hostel Associations of each country represented. Every effort has been made to ensure that it is correct, and Hostelling International accepts no responsibility for any inaccuracies or for changes subsequent to publication.

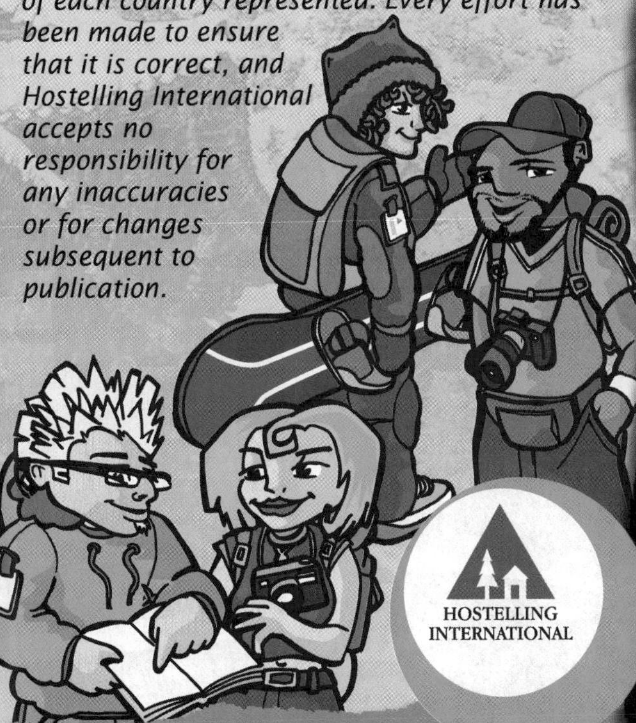

Welcome - Bienvenue - Willkommen - Bienvenido

For further information either contact your local Youth Hostel Association (YHA) or visit **www.HIhostels.com.**

ISBN 0 901496 66 9

SNAPSHOTS OF THE WORLD

Blida Youth Hostel - Algeria

Malka Youth Hostel, Tilcara - Argentina

Sydney Beachouse, Collaroy - Australia

Banff Alpine Centre - Canada

Mechelen Youth Hostel, De Zandpoort - Belgium

Hostel Hütteldorf, Vienna - Austria

Curitiba Youth Hostel - Brazil

DANHOSTEL
Copenhagen City
- Denmark

Toruma Youth Hostel,
San José - Costa Rica

Yangshuo Youth
Hostel - China

Pula Youth Hostel
- Croatia

Jockey Club
Mt Davis
Youth Hostel
- Hong Kong

Valdiva Youth Hostel,
Buenos Aires - Chile

Hurghada Youth Hostel - Egypt

SNAPSHOTS OF THE WORLD

PASEO RELÁMPAGO POR EL MUNDO - FOTOGRAFISCHE EINDRÜCKE AUS ALLER WELT - CARTES POSTALES DU MONDE

Lee Valley Youth Hostel - England

Country Hotel SaimaanSydän, Rantasalmi- Finland

Biarritz Youth Hostel - France

Hostel Marco Polo, Budapest - Hungary

Rostock Youth Hostel - Germany

Reykjavik City Youth Hostel - Iceland

PASEO RELÁMPAGO POR EL MUNDO - FOTOGRAFISCHE EINDRÜCKE AUS ALLER WELT - CARTES POSTALES DU MONDE

SNAPSHOTS OF THE WORLD

SNAPSHOTS OF THE WORLD

PASEO RELÁMPAGO POR EL MUNDO - FOTOGRAFISCHE EINDRÜCKE AUS ALLER WELT - CARTES POSTALES DU MONDE

New Delhi International Hostel - India

Cork International Youth Hostel - Republic of Ireland

Nairobi Youth Hostel - Kenya

Okinawa Yout[h] Hostel - Japa[n]

Villa Camerata, Florence - Italy

Whitepark Bay Youth Hostel - Northern Ireland

Massada Youth Hostel - Israel

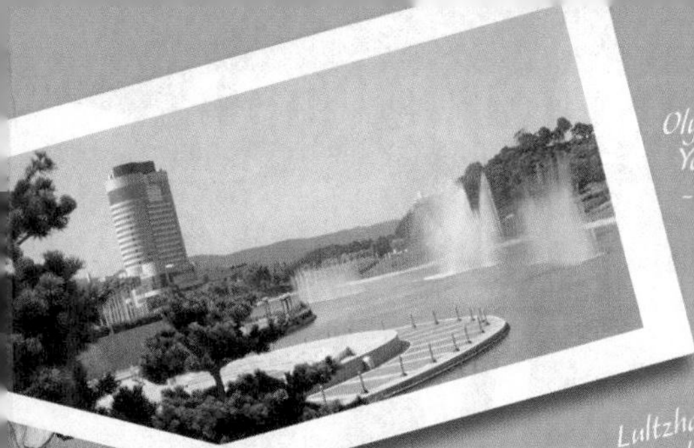

Olympic Parktel Youth Hostel, Seoul - South Korea

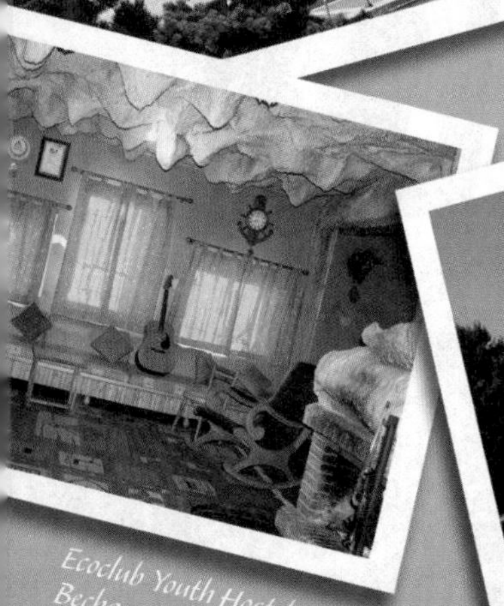

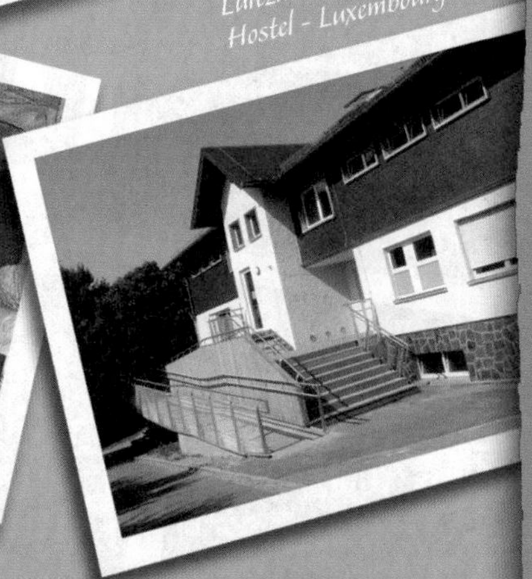

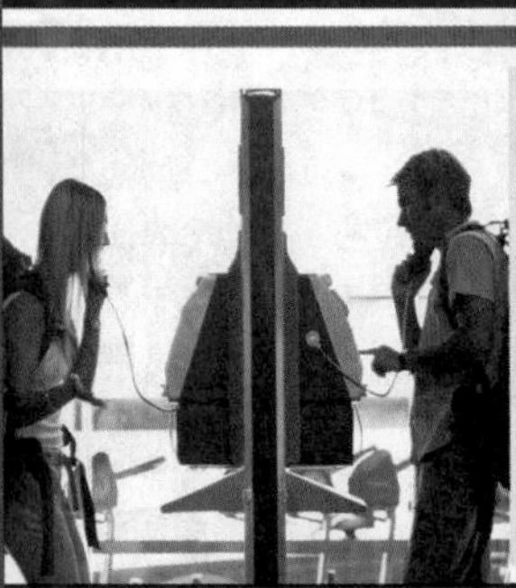

Lultzhausen Youth Hostel - Luxembourg

Ecoclub Youth Hostel, Becharre - Lebanon

PASEO RELÁMPAGO POR EL MUNDO - FOTOGRAFISCHE EINDRÜCKE AUS ALLER WELT - CARTES POSTALES DU MONDE

SNAPSHOTS OF THE WORLD

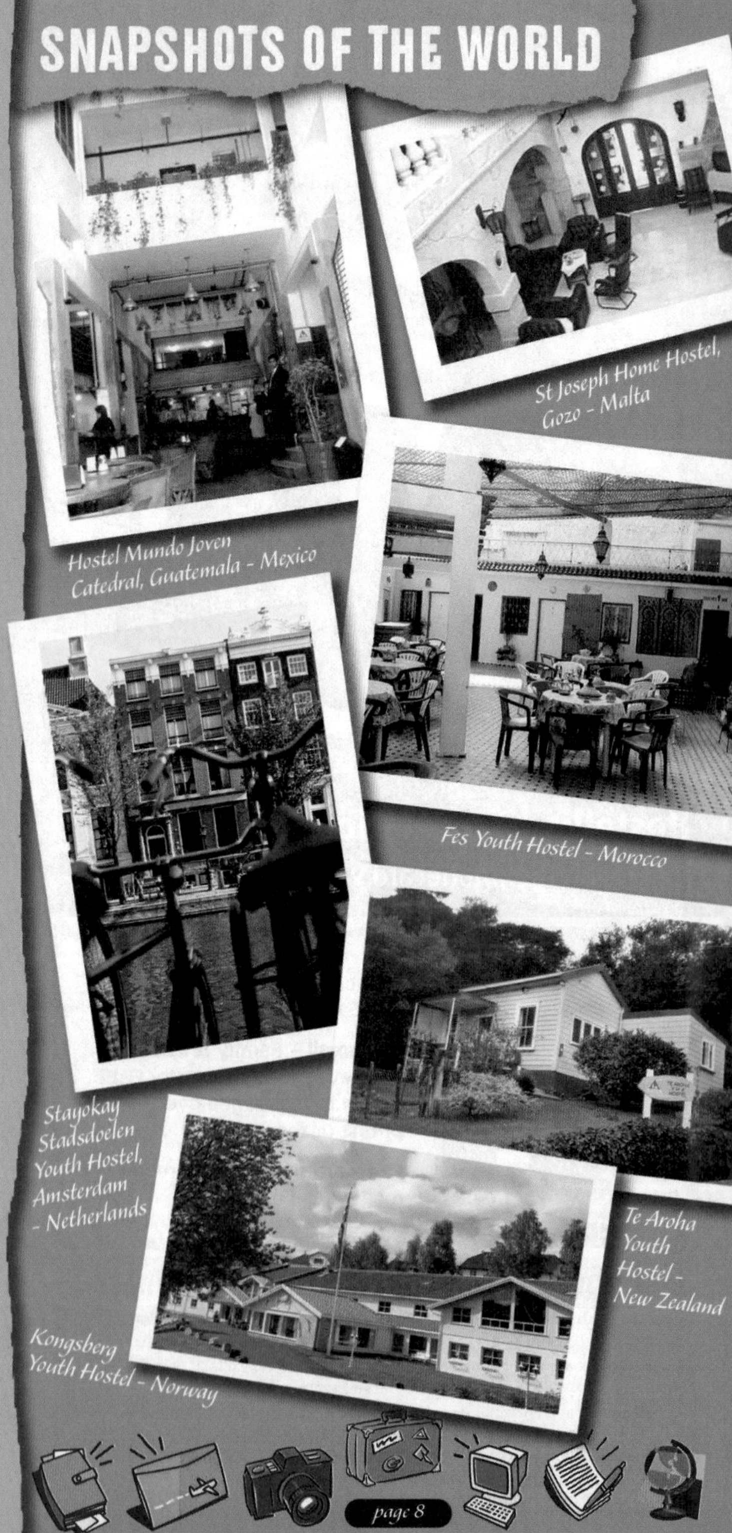

Hostel Mundo Joven Catedral, Guatemala - Mexico

St Joseph Home Hostel, Gozo - Malta

Fes Youth Hostel - Morocco

Stayokay Stadsdoelen Youth Hostel, Amsterdam - Netherlands

Te Aroha Youth Hostel - New Zealand

Kongsberg Youth Hostel - Norway

SNAPSHOTS OF THE WORLD

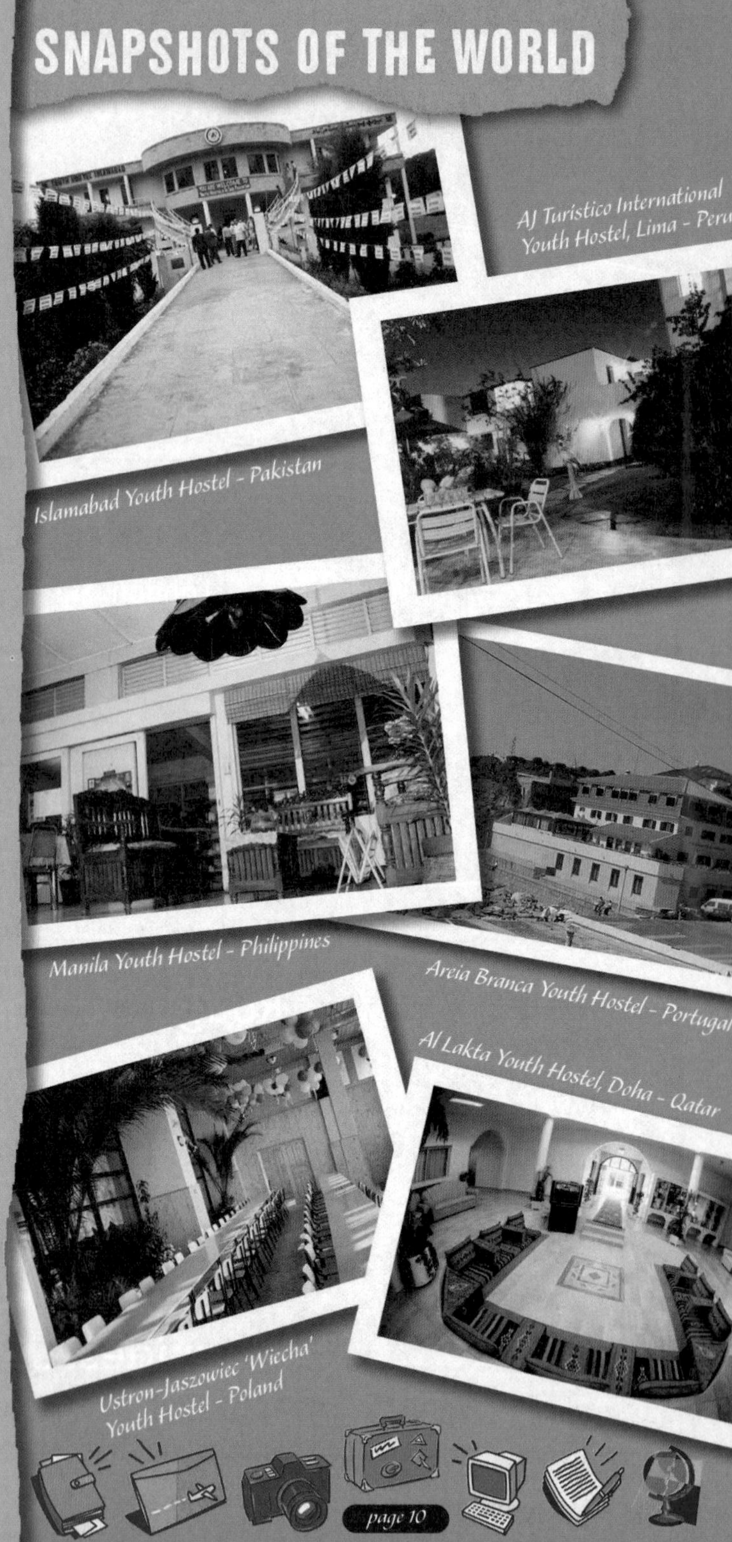

AJ Turistico International Youth Hostel, Lima - Peru

Islamabad Youth Hostel - Pakistan

Manila Youth Hostel - Philippines

Areia Branca Youth Hostel - Portugal

Al Lakta Youth Hostel, Doha - Qatar

Ustron-Jaszowiec 'Wiecha' Youth Hostel - Poland

Damman Youth Hostel - Saudi Arabia

Cluj-Napoca Retro Hostel - Romania

Uig Youth Hostel, Isle of Skye - Scotland

Bledec Youth Hostel - Slovenia

Ebbamåla Bruk Youth Hostel - Sweden

Altafulla Youth Hostel - Spain

SNAPSHOTS OF THE WORLD

PASEO RELÁMPAGO POR EL MUNDO - FOTOGRAFISCHE EINDRÜCKE AUS ALLER WELT - CARTES POSTALES DU MONDE

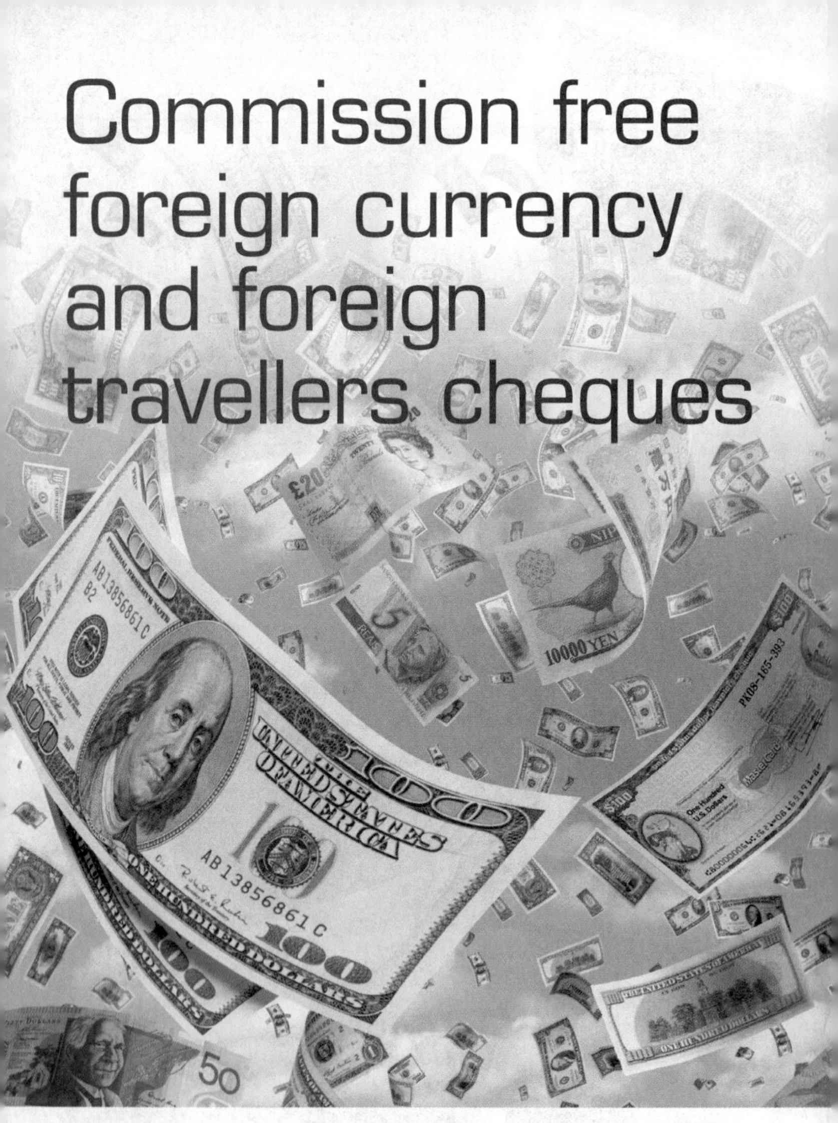

SNAPSHOTS OF THE WORLD

PASEO RELÁMPAGO POR EL MUNDO - FOTOGRAFISCHE EINDRÜCKE AUS ALLER WELT - CARTES POSTALES DU MONDE

Introduction to Hostelling International

Welcome to the unique world of Hostelling International - where you can enjoy a world of adventure and a good night's sleep in friendly surroundings at an affordable price.

Hostelling International is the largest, most experienced network dedicated to travellers of all ages. You can find out more at **www.HIhostels.com.**

For budget accommodation you can trust, look for the triangle symbol.

English

How to use this Guide

This guide is organised in two parts - see Contents for full details.

In the **Introduction** you will find general information about Hostelling International such as: online booking at **www.HIhostels.com**, member benefits including a vast range of discounts, Hostelling International Assured Standards and international emergency telephone numbers.

The **Hostel Directory** is an alphabetical listing, by country and town, of hostels belonging to full members of the International Youth Hostel Federation. Symbols indicate hostel opening times, prices, facilities etc. - these are explained in the fold-out section at the front of this Guide. At the end of the directory you will find an alphabetical listing, by country, of supplementary accommodation provided by affiliate organisations.

Throughout this book you will find a selection of useful tips supplied by Culture Smart! guides, the definitive guides to customs and etiquette. Containing essential information, not found in other guides, these guides have already saved many travellers from embarrassing and sometimes dangerous situations. To purchase a guide for the country of your choice visit **www.culturesmartguides.co.uk.**

HIhostels.com Bookings & Reservations

BOOK ONLINE AT www.HIhostels.com!

HIhostels.com offers simple, low-cost bookings up to 12 months in advance for hundreds of key hostels in over 80 countries worldwide. In this Guide, hostels which can be booked online display the HI symbol and are highlighted in blue. Each hostel has a unique ID number (eg 4014) so you can find them easily online.

Point your browser to **www.HIhostels.com to:**

- **Find out about a hostel** - including open dates and times, contact details, directions, facilities plus attractions nearby.
- **Check *real time* bed availability** over the next 12 months.
- **Book accommodation** in advance.
- **Learn about the countries** you plan to visit

Secure online payment

Book at **www.HIhostels.com** using any of these cards:

Credit cards: 

Debit cards: 

SOLO

OTHER BOOKING INFORMATION

Advance booking is not essential, but it is advisable at busy times or in key cities; groups should book ahead of time. If you cannot access the internet, you can book in the following ways:

- global booking centres (see page 38)
- credit card booking centres (see below)
- by email, fax or letter (include an international postal reply coupon and self-addressed envelope) to your chosen hostel

If you make an advance booking without paying a deposit you will usually be required to arrive at the hostel by 1800 hours, unless a different time is agreed.

We know you will enjoy the hostel experience. You will certainly be able to afford it. We look forward to meeting you.

MAKE YOUR CREDIT CARD BOOKINGS AT THESE CENTRES:

Australia	☎ (2) 9261 1111
Canada	☎ (1) 800 663 5777 (within Canada only) www.HIhostels.ca (all others)
England & Wales	☎ (0870) 770 8868; 44 (0)1629 59270
Northern Ireland	☎ (28) 9032 4733
New Zealand	☎ 0064 3 379 9808
Scotland	☎ (0870) 1 55 32 55 www.syha.org.uk
Switzerland	☎ 00 41 (0)44 360 14 14
USA	☎ (301) 495-1240

Benefits of Membership

To stay at a Youth Hostel, you must become a member of your national Youth Hostel Association. If there is no national YHA in your country, you can purchase a Hostelling International Card or a Welcome Stamp. Membership is open to people of all ages and offers:

- 4,000 **accommodation** centres in 80 plus countries.
- **Activities,** programmes, events and the opportunity to **contribute to World Peace.**
- Thousands of **discounts** worldwide - see **page 777** and **www.HIhostels.com**
- **Reservations** up to 12 months ahead at **www.HIhostels.com - see page 18.**
- The opportunity to earn **FreeNites & More** points with our membership reward program.
- Low-cost **HI-eKit phonecard** and **HI Travel Insurance.**

FREENITES & MORE

FreeNites & More rewards you EVERY TIME you visit a participating hostel! Earn FNM points on overnight stays, meals, drinks - and redeem points for a FREE overnight etc. The more FNM points you earn, the more money you save! All HI members with a valid national or HI card who live in a participating country can join FreeNites & More.

For the most up-to-date list of these countries check out **www.HIhostels.com/FreeNites**

Wherever your adventure leads, the HI-eKit phonecard is the easiest way to make calls and receive messages worldwide - even from mobile/cell phones. Activate now at **www.HI.ekit.com** or call Customer Services - see page 36 for Access Numbers. Receive a US$10 calling bonus when you charge your card for US$20 or more!

Key benefits include:

- Low-cost international and long-distance calls
- Free Email - you can even listen to emails over the phone!
- SMS text messages from your HI-eKit email account
- 24-hour travel assistance
- 24-hour multi-lingual customer service
- Recharge your account any time, anywhere

HI TRAVEL INSURANCE

Whether you are skiing for a week or spending a year backpacking round the world, you want to be sure that if the unthinkable happens, help is just a 'phone call away. Hostelling International has teamed up with leading insurance provider Columbus Direct to bring you travel insurance products at affordable prices.Check out **www.columbusdirect.net/HI** - and discover just how much you can save.

YOUTH HOSTELLING FOR PEACE AND INTERNATIONAL UNDERSTANDING

Working with UNESCO (see page 774) on educational initiatives and supporting the United Nations "Decade for a Culture of Peace and Non-violence" Hostelling International is active throughout its Youth Hostels to educate people and promote peace concepts.

Find out how you can contribute at **www.HIhostels.com/peace**

Quality Standards You Can Count On

Hostelling International's Assured Standards Scheme means you can rely on a consistent level of services and facilities wherever you stay.

- **Welcome** - hostels are open to all. You will have access to essential facilities if the hostel closes for a period during the day.
- **Comfort** - a good night's sleep and sufficient washing/shower facilities. Meals, self-catering facilities and a food store are generally available.
- **Cleanliness** - the highest standards of hygiene.
- **Security** - for you and your possessions.
- **Privacy** - in showers, washing areas and toilets. Most hostels provide single sex dormitories - although if requested, a mixed sex dormitory may be offered to people travelling together.

Standards are monitored by Hostelling International and by you, the user. **There are Comment Cards at the back of this Guide and at www.HIhostels.com - tell us what you think!**

HOSTEL GRADES

▲ **Standard:** applies to the majority of hostels

△ **Simple:** applies to smaller hostels, or those in remote locations with simple facilities - you may find limited staffing and shorter opening hours.

Some hostels listed in this Guide are outside the Assured Standards Scheme - these provide accommodation in areas where it would not otherwise be available.

TRAVELLERS WITH DISABILITIES ♿

Hostelling International welcomes travellers with disabilities - hostels suitable for wheelchair access display the ♿ symbol in this Guide.

ENVIRONMENTAL CHARTER

Hostels adhere to the IYHF Environmental Charter. This lays down criteria for the consumption and conservation of resources, waste disposal and recycling, nature conservation and the provision of environmental education. You can find out more by visiting our website **www.HIhostels.com.**

Bienvenue à Hostelling International

Bienvenue au monde unique d'Hostelling International – là où vous attend tout un monde d'aventures et où vous pouvez passer une bonne nuit de sommeil dans un milieu accueillant et à des prix abordables.

Hostelling International est le plus grand réseau d'hébergements et celui qui a la plus longue expérience du service des voyageurs de tous les âges. Pour en savoir plus, consultez notre site Internet **www.HIhostels.com.**

Pour un hébergement économique auquel vous pouvez vous fier, suivez le triangle.

Comment se servir de ce guide

Ce guide se présente en deux parties. Voir l'index pour en savoir plus.

Dans **l'introduction**, vous trouverez des renseignements généraux sur Hostelling International tels que: les réservations en ligne sur **www.HIhostels.com**, les avantages de l'adhésion dont une vaste sélection de remises, les normes garanties Hostelling International et les numéros d'urgence internationaux.

Le **répertoire des auberges** est une liste alphabétique, par pays (selon leur nom en anglais, pour les besoins de cette édition internationale) et par ville, des auberges affiliées aux associations membres (à part entière) de la Fédération Internationale des Auberges de Jeunesse (IYHF). Des symboles indiquent les heures d'ouverture, les prix, les prestations fournies, etc. La signification de ces symboles est fournie dans le dépliant inséré en début d'ouvrage. A la fin du répertoire, vous trouverez une autre liste alphabétique, par pays (également selon leur désignation anglaise), contenant la liste des hébergements secondaires proposés par des organisations affiliées.

Dans ce manuel vous trouverez de nombreux trucs et astuces tirés des guides Culture Smart!, les meilleurs guides en matière de coutumes et d'étiquette. Véritables mines d'informations essentielles n'apparaissant pas dans d'autres publications, ces guides ont déjà permis à de nombreux voyageurs de se tirer de situations embarrassantes, voire dangereuses. Pour acheter un guide sur le pays de votre choix, rendez-vous sur **www.culturesmartguides.co.uk.**

Réservations

RÉSERVEZ EN LIGNE SUR www.HIhostels.com!

HIhostels.com propose un moyen simple et économique de réserver jusqu'à 12 mois à l'avance, dans des centaines d'auberges réparties dans plus de 80 pays dans le monde entier. Dans notre listing, les auberges que l'on peut réserver en ligne apparaissent sur fond bleu et sont indiquées par le symbole HI. Chacune de ces auberges sont indiquées par un numéro unique (par ex. 4014) pour que vous puissiez les trouver facilement sur le site.

Dirigez-vous sur **www.HIhostels.com** pour:

- **Vous renseigner sur une auberge** - horaires d'ouverture de l'établissement/de l'accueil, coordonnées indications pour trouver l'auberge, installations et prestations, ainsi que les choses à ne pas manquer dans la région.
- **Vérifier les disponibilités en lits *en temps réel*** sur les 12 mois suivants.
- **Réserver votre hébergement** à l'avance.
- **En savoir plus sur les pays** que vous projetez de visiter.

Paiement en ligne en toute sécurité

Réserver votre hébergement sur **www.HIhostel.com** en utilisant l'un des types de cartes suivants:

Cartes de crédit: VISA 

Cartes à prélèvement direct: DELTA  

AUTRES POINTS A NOTER SUR LES RESERVATIONS

Il n'est pas toujours nécessaire de réserver à l'avance, mais pendant les périodes de forte demande ou dans les grandes villes touristiques, nous vous conseillons vivement de le faire. Par ailleurs, les groupes doivent toujours réserver avant de se présenter. Si vous n'avez pas accès à l'Internet, il vous est possible de réserver par les moyens suivants:

- à l'un de nos nombreux centres de réservation (voir page 38),
- par carte de crédit dans certains centres de réservation (voir ci-dessous)
- par fax, par courrier ordinaire ou électronique en contactant l'auberge en question directement (si vous le faites par courrier, n'oubliez pas de joindre un coupon-réponse international, ainsi qu'une enveloppe à vos nom et adresse).

Si vous réservez sans verser d'arrhes, vous devrez normalement arriver à l'auberge avant 18h, à moins d'avoir convenu avec celle-ci d'une heure différente pour votre arrivée.

Nous sommes sûrs que votre expérience des auberges sera agréable. Elle sera de toute façon abordable. Nous sommes impatients de faire votre connaissance.

RESERVEZ PAR CARTE DE CREDIT AUPRES DES CENTRES SUIVANTS:

Angleterre et Pays de Galles	(0870) 770 8868; 44 (0)1629 59270
Australie	(2) 9261 1111
Canada	(1) 800 663 5777 (Canada uniquement) www.HIhostels.ca (tous les autres pays)
Ecosse	(0870) 1 55 32 55 www.syha.org.uk
Etats-Unis	(301) 495-1240
Irlande du Nord	(28) 9032 4733
Nouvelle Zélande	0064 3 379 9808
Suisse	00 41 (0)44 360 14 14

Les Avantages que vous apporte l'Adhésion

Afin d'être admis à séjourner dans une auberge de jeunesse, il vous faudra devenir membre de l'association d'auberges de jeunesse de votre pays. S'il n'existe pas d'association nationale dans votre pays, vous pouvez acheter une carte Hostelling International ou un Timbre de Bienvenue (Welcome Stamp) à votre arrivée à l'auberge.

L'adhésion est ouverte à tous, quel que soit votre âge, et vous propose:

- 4 000 **centres** d'hébergement dans plus de 80 pays.
- Des **activités**, animations et manifestations en tout genre, ainsi que **l'opportunité d'œuvrer pour la paix dans le monde.**
- Des milliers de **réductions** à travers le monde: consulter **la page 777** de ce guide ou **www.HIhostels.com**
- La possibilité de **réserver** jusqu'à douze mois à l'avance sur **www.HIhostels.com - voir aussi page 22.**
- La possibilité de gagner des points **FreeNites & More** grâce à notre programme de fidélisation pour adhérents
- **La carte téléphonique HI-eKit** et **l'assurance voyage HI** à des tarifs très compétitifs.

FREENITES & MORE

FreeNites & More vous récompense À CHAQUE FOIS que vous séjournez dans une auberge participante! Accumulez des points FNM sur des séjours, des repas, des boissons et échangez-les contre une nuitée GRATUITE etc. Plus vous gagnez de points FNM, plus vous économisez!

Tout titulaire d'une carte nationale d'adhérent ou d'une carte internationale HI en cours de validité, et résident de l'un des pays participants peut s'inscrire à FreeNites & More.

Pour la liste la plus à jour de ces pays, rendez-vous sur **www.HIhostels.com/FreeNites.**

LA CARTE TÉLÉPHONIQUE

Où que vous mène votre aventure, la carte téléphonique HI-eKit est le moyen le plus simple de faire des appels et de recevoir des messages partout dans le monde, même sur un téléphone portable. Activez dès maintenant votre compte à **www.HI.ekit.com**! Et recevez un bonus de 10$US lorsque vous alimenter votre carte de 20$ ou plus!

Visez un peu les avantages!

- Appels à l'étranger ou longue distance à tarifs réduits
- Courrier électronique gratuit – vous pouvez même écouter vos mails par téléphone!
- Messages en texto depuis votre compte courriel HI-eKit
- Assistance voyage 24h/24
- Service clientèle disponible en plusieurs langues 24h/24
- Alimentez votre compte n'importe où et n'importe quand!!

L'ASSURANCE VOYAGE HI

Que vous soyez en vacances de neige pour une semaine ou que vous passiez une année sabbatique à faire le tour du monde, il est préférable d'être sûr que, si l'impensable arrive, les secours seront à la portée d'un simple coup de fil. Hostelling International s'est associé à la compagnie d'assurance Columbus Direct pour vous proposer des assurances voyages à des prix abordables. Un petit coup d'œil sur leur site (**www.columbusdirect.net/HI**) vous donnera une idée des grandes économies que vous pourrez faire.

LES AUBERGES DE JEUNESSE POUR LA PAIX ET L'ENTENTE INTERNATIONALE

Œuvrant en collaboration avec l'UNESCO (voir page 774) sur des initiatives éducatives et en soutien à la «Décennie internationale pour une culture de la paix et de la non-violence», lancée par les Nations Unies, Hostelling International est actif à travers tout son réseau d'auberges pour éduquer les gens et promouvoir ses idéaux pacifiques.

Pour savoir comment contribuer à cette initiative, consultez **www.HIhostels.com/peace.**

Des Normes de Qualité qui vous sont garanties

Le Plan pour la Garantie des Normes en Auberges a été mis en place par Hostelling International pour vous assurer une qualité constante dans nos prestations et nos installations, quelle que soit l'auberge où vous séjournez.

- **Accueil** – Les auberges sont ouvertes à tous. L'accès à certaines parties de l'auberge vous est garanti, même si celle-ci ferme dans la journée.
- **Confort** - une bonne nuit de sommeil et des douches/lavabos en nombre suffisant. Une forme ou une autre de restauration est généralement disponible, ainsi qu'une cuisine équipée pour préparer ses propres repas et un magasin d'alimentation à l'auberge ou à proximité.
- **Propreté** – les plus strictes normes d'hygiène et de propreté.
- **Sécurité** – de votre personne et de vos biens.
- **Intimité** - dans les douches, les blocs sanitaires et les toilettes. La plupart des auberges proposent un hébergement dans des dortoirs non-mixtes, bien que certains établissements puissent offrir, sur demande, des chambres ou dortoirs mixtes à des groupes voyageant ensemble.

La présence de ces normes dans les auberges sera contrôlée par Hostelling International et par vous, les usagers. **Il y a des fiches-commentaires à la fin de ce guide et sur www.HIhostels.com – Dites-nous ce que vous en pensez!**

CATEGORIES D'AUBERGES

▲ **Standard:** s'applique à la majorité des auberges

△ **Simple:** s'applique aux établissements plus petits ou à ceux qui sont situés dans des lieux reculés et qui proposent donc des prestations plus simples: entre autre, le personnel y sera limité, ainsi que les heures d'ouverture.

Quelques-unes des auberges listées dans ce guide ne font pas partie du Plan de Garantie des Normes en Auberge. Celles-ci ont toutefois été inclues dans le guide parce qu'elles permettent de fournir un hébergement là où il y aurait eu une absence totale de structures économiques d'accueil.

VOYAGEURS HANDICAPES ♿

Hostelling International accueille les voyageurs handicapés – les auberges qui disposent d'installations facilitant l'accès aux fauteuils roulants sont indiquées par le symbole ♿.

CHARTE SUR L'ENVIRONNEMENT

Les auberges s'engagent à adhérer à la Charte sur l'Environnement de l'IYHF. Celle-ci dicte les critères de consommation et de préservation des ressources, d'élimination des déchets et de recyclage, de défense de l'environnement et prévoit également que les auberges devront jouer un rôle dans l'éducation écologique. Pour en savoir plus, rendez-nous visite sur notre site Web, à l'adresse suivante: **www.HIhostels.com.**

Einführung zu Hostelling International

Deutsch

Willkommen in der einzigartigen Welt von Hostelling International – wo man eine Welt voller Abenteuer und gute Übernachtung in gastfreundlicher Umgebung und zu erschwinglichen Preisen bekommt.

Hostelling International ist das größte und erfahrenste Netzwerk, das sich für Reisende jeden Alters - jung und alt - engagiert. Mehr darüber erfahren Sie auf unsere Website **www.HIhostels.com**.

Wenn Sie preisgünstige und bewährte Unterkünfte suchen, halten Sie nach dem Symbol mit dem Dreieck Ausschau.

Wie Sie diesen Führer benutzen

Dieser Führer besteht aus zwei Teilen – vollständige Angaben dazu finden Sie im Inhaltsverzeichnis.

In der **Einführung** finden Sie allgemeine Informationen über Hostelling International wie z.B. Internetbuchungen bei **www.HIhostels.com**, Vorteile für Mitglieder einschließlich einer großen Palette von Rabatten, "Garantierte Qualitätsstandards" bei Hostelling International und internationale Notrufnummern.

Das Herbergsverzeichnis ist eine alphabetisch nach Ländern und Orten angelegte Übersicht aller Herbergen von Vollmitgliedern der Internationalen Jugendherbergsföderation (IYHF). Symbole kennzeichnen Herbergsöffnungszeiten, Preise, Ausstattung usw. – die dazu gehörende Zeichenerklärung befindet sich im ausklappbaren Abschnitt am Anfang dieses Führers. Am Ende des Verzeichnisses gibt es noch eine alphabetisch nach Ländern geordnete Liste von zusätzlichen Übernachtungsmöglichkeiten angegliederter Organisationen.

In diesem Buch findet ihr eine Menge nützlicher Tipps, die von Culture Smart! Ratgeber - die klaren Ratgeber zu Brauch und Etikette - zusammengestellt wurden. Die Ratgeber, die wesentliche Informationen enthalten, die man in anderen Ratgebern nicht findet, haben schon viele Reisende vor peinlichen und manchmal gefährlichen Situationen gerettet. Um einen Ratgeber für ein Land eurer Wahl zu kaufen, besucht **www.culturesmartguides.co.uk.**

Deutsch

HIhostels.com Buchungen & Reservierungen

ONLINE BUCHEN BEI www.HIhostels.com!

Bei HIhostels.com Kann man einfach und günstig hunderte der besten Herbergen in über 80 Ländern bis zu 12 Monaten im Voraus buchen. In diesem Führer sind Herbergen, die über das Internet gebucht werden können, mit dem Symbol HI gekennzeichnet und blau hervorgehoben. Jede Herberge hat ihre unverwechselbare Kennzahl (z.B. 4014), sodass Sie die Herberge leicht online ausfindig machen können.

Gehen Sie mit Ihrem Browser zu **www.HIhostels.com** und mit nur wenigen Mausklicks können Sie schnell und leicht ...

- **Herbergsinformationen finden** – inklusive Öffnungsdaten, Rezeptions-Öffnungszeiten, Herbergsadressen und Kontaktdetails, Hinweise zur Anreise, Herbergsausstattung und nahegelegenen Sehenswürdigkeiten.
- **In *Echtzeit* die Betten-Verfügbarkeit** für die nächsten 12 Monate **überprüfen**.
- **Unterkunft** im Voraus **buchen** – und das ganz ohne Buchungsgebühr!
- **Sich über die Länder informieren,** die Sie besuchen möchten.

SICHERE BEZAHLUNG ONLINE

Wenn Sie bei **www.HIhostels.com** buchen, können Sie mit folgenden Karten bezahlen:

Kreditkarten: 

Bankkarten: 

WEITERE BUCHUNGSINFORMATIONEN

Vorausbuchungen sind nicht unbedingt notwendig, aber in Hauptreisezeiten oder in beliebten Städten sind sie zu empfehlen; Gruppen sollten möglichst immer rechtzeitig im Voraus buchen.

Falls Sie keinen Zugang zum Internet haben, können Sie Reservierungen folgendermaßen vornehmen:

- in weltweiten Buchungszentren (siehe Seite 38)
- mit Kreditkarte in einigen ausgewählten Buchungszentren (siehe unten)
- per E-mail, Fax oder Brief an die ausgewählte Herberge. Bei schriftlicher Buchung bitte einen internationalen Antwortkupon und adressierten Briefumschlag beilegen.

KREDITKARTEN-RESERVIERUNGEN BEI DIESEN ZENTREN:

Australien	☎ (2) 9261 1111
England & Wales	☎ (0870) 770 8868; 44 (0)1629 59270
Kanada	☎ (1) 800 663 5777 (nur innerhalb Kanadas) www.HIhostels.ca (für alle anderen)
Neuseeland	☎ 0064 3 379 9808
Nordirland	☎ (28) 9032 4733
Schottland	☎ (0870) 1 55 32 55 www.syha.org.uk
Schweiz	☎ 00 41 (0)44 360 14 14
USA	☎ (301) 495-1240

Bei Vorausbuchungen ohne Anzahlung sollten Sie vor 18.00 Uhr in der Herberge eintreffen, sofern keine andere Zeit vereinbart wurde.

Wir sind sicher, ein Herbergsaufenthalt wird Ihnen viel Freude machen. Auf jeden Fall können Sie sich diesen leisten. Wir freuen uns auf Ihren Besuch.

Vorteile der Mitgliedschaft

Um in einer Jugendherberge zu übernachten, müssen Sie Mitglied Ihres nationalen Jugendherbergsverbands (JHV) werden. Sollte Ihr Land keinen JHV haben, können Sie bei Ankunft in der Herberge einen HI Ausweis (Hostelling International Card) oder Begrüßungsmarken (Welcome Stamps) kaufen.

Mitgliedschaft können Personen aller Altersgruppen erwerben und die damit verbundenen Vorteile genießen wie:

- 4 000 **Herbergen** in über 80 Länderen,
- **Aktivitäten,** Programme, Veranstaltungen und die Gelegenheit, einen Beitrag zum Weltfrieden zu leisten,
- tausende von **Rabatten** weltweit – lesen Sie dazu **Seite 777** und bei **www.HIhostels.com**
- **Reservierungen** bis zu 12 Monaten im Voraus buchen bei **www.HIhostels.com - siehe dazu Seite 26.**
- die Möglichkeit, **FreeNites & More** Treuepunkte zu sammeln.
- preiswerte **HI-eKit Telefonkarte** und **HI Reiseversicherung.**

FREENITES & MORE

FreeNites & More belohnt Sie JEDES MAL, wenn Sie in einer beteiligten Herberge übernachten! Sammeln Sie FNM - Punkte für Übernachtungen, Mahlzeiten, Getränke – und lösen diese gegen eine KOSTENLOSE Übernachtung usw. ein. Je mehr FNM - Punkte Sie sammeln, desto mehr Geld sparen Sie! Alle HI-Mitglieder mit einem gültigen Mitgliedsausweis von HI oder ihrem nationalen Verband, die ihren Wohnsitz in einem der Teilnehmerländer haben, können bei FreeNites & More mitmachen.

Die aktuelle Liste dieser Länder finden Sie auf der Website **www.HIhostels.com/FreeNites**

TELEFONKARTE

Wohin auch immer Ihre Abenteuer Sie führen – die HI-eKit Telefonkarte ist der einfachste Weg zu telefonieren und Nachrichten zu erhalten. Und das weltweit – sogar mit dem Handy. Melden Sie sich bei **www.HI.ekit.com** an oder rufen Sie den Kundendienst an – auf Seite 36 finden Sie die Zugangsnummern. Wenn Sie Ihre Karte mit 20 US$ oder mehr aufladen, erhalten Sie einen Telefonbonus im Wert von 10 US$ als Geschenk!

Zu den wichtigsten Vorteilen gehören:

- Preisgünstige internationale und Ferngespräche
- Kostenlose Email – Sie können sogar Email über Telefon abrufen!
- SMS Textnachrichten von Ihrem HI-eKit Email-Konto
- 24-Stunden Reiseservice
- 24-Stunden mehrsprachiger Kundendienst
- Aufladen Ihres Kontos zu jeder beliebigen Zeit an jedem beliebigen Ort

HI REISEVERSICHERUNG

Ganz gleich, ob Sie eine Woche in den Skiurlaub fahren oder ein Jahr lang als Rucksacktourist um die Welt reisen – Sie brauchen die Gewissheit, dass im Notfall nur ein Telefonanruf genügt, um Hilfe zu holen. Hostelling International hat sich deshalb mit dem führenden Versicherungsunternehmen Columbus Direct zusammengetan und bietet Ihnen nun

Reiseversicherungsprodukte zu erschwinglichen Preisen. Sehen Sie selbst nach bei **www.columbusdirect.net/HI** – und überzeugen sich, wieviel Sie sparen können.

JUGENDHERBERGSBEWEGUNG FÜR FRIEDEN UND INTERNATIONALE VÖLKERVERSTÄNDIGUNG

Hostelling International arbeitet eng mit der UNESCO (siehe Seite 774) im Bereich Bildungsinitiativen zusammen und unterstützt das "Jahrzehnt für Frieden und Gewaltverzicht" der Vereinten Nationen. In allen seinen Jugendherbergen fördert HI den Friedensgedanken und wird bei der Erziehung junger Menschen zum Frieden aktiv.

Wie Sie Ihren Beitrag leisten können, ist bei **www.HIhostels.com/peace** nachzulesen.

Garantierte Qualitätsstandards

"Hostelling International Assured Standards Scheme " heißt, Sie können sich in unseren Herbergen auf einen gleichbleibenden Service- und Ausstattungsstandard verlassen – wo immer Sie auch übernachten.

- **Empfang** – Herbergen sind für alle Altersgruppen geöffnet. Sie können, wenn Sie es noch nicht sind, Mitglied werden und Reservierungen im Voraus buchen. Wenn die Herberge für einen Teil des Tages geschlossen ist, haben Sie trotzdem Zugang zu allen notwendigen Einrichtungen.
- **Komfort** – eine gute Nachtruhe (inklusive Verleih frischer Bettwäsche, falls nicht im Übernachtungspreis enthalten) und genügend Wasch- /Duscheinrichtungen. Mahlzeiten sowie Selbstversorgungseinrichtungen werden generell angeboten. Kleine Lebensmittelgeschäfte befinden sich meistens in Herbergsnähe.
- **Sauberkeit** – die höchsten Hygienestandards wo immer Sie reisen.
- **Sicherheit** – für Sie und Ihr Eigentum, inklusive Schließfächer für Gepäck und Wertsachen.
- **Privatsphäre** - in Duschen, Waschräumen und Toiletten. In unseren Herbergen gibt es überwiegend nach Geschlecht getrennte Schlafräume – aber auf Anfrage können auch gemeinsame Schlafräume für Gruppenreisende gebucht werden.

Qualitätstandards werden von Hostelling International und von Ihnen überwacht. **Im hinteren Teil dieses Führers und bei www.HIhostels.com finden Sie Hinweiskarten – sagen Sie uns Ihre Meinung!**

HERBERGSKATEGORIEN

▲ **Standard**: Gilt für den größten Teil der Herbergen

△ **Einfach**: Gilt für kleinere oder in ablegenen Gegenden befindliche Herbergen, in denen Sie einfache Einrichtungen, wenig Personal und beschränkte Öffnungszeiten vorfinden könnten.

Einige Herbergen in diesem Führer entsprechen nicht den Richtlinien des "Assured Standards Scheme" – dies sind Unterkünfte in Gebieten, wo es sonst keine anderen gibt.

REISENDE MIT BEHINDERUNGEN ♿

Hostelling International heißt Reisende mit Behinderungen willkommen – für Rollstuhlfahrer geeignete Jugendherbergen sind im Verzeichnis mit '♿' gekennzeichnet.

UMWELTCHARTA

Herbergen befolgen die Richtlinien der IYHF Umweltcharta. Diese schreibt die Kriterien für den Umgang mit Ressourcen, Abfallbeseitigung und Recycling, Umweltschutz und Förderung der Umweltschutzerziehung vor. Mehr darüber erfahren Sie auf unserer Webseite **www.HIhostels.com.**

Hostelling International – Introducción

Bienvenido al incomparable mundo de Hostelling International, donde disfrutarás de todo un mundo de aventuras, además de pasar una buena noche, en un ambiente acogedor y a precios asequibles.

Hostelling International es la red más extensa y con más experiencia del servicio a los viajeros de todas las edades. Para más información, visita **www.HIhostels.com.**

Si deseas alojamiento económico de confianza, busca el triángulo.

Cómo utilizar esta Guía

La presente guía ha sido elaborada en dos partes. Ver el índice para más información.

En la **introducción** encontrarás información general sobre Hostelling International, por ejemplo: reservas online en **www.HIhostels.com**, las ventajas de la afiliación, que incluyen una amplísima gama de descuentos, las normas de calidad garantizadas de Hostelling International y los números de teléfono de emergencia internacionales.

En el **listado de albergues** están catalogados alfabéticamente por país y por ciudad los albergues afiliados a las Asociaciones miembros de pleno derecho de la Federación Internacional de Albergues Juveniles (IYHF). Los símbolos indican las fechas y el horario de apertura de los albergues, sus tarifas, prestaciones, etc. En la página desplegable, al principio de la Guía, se explica el significado de cada símbolo. Al final del listado, en una sección aparte, se relacionan alfabéticamente por país otros establecimientos, administrados por organizaciones afiliadas, en los que también puedes alojarte.

Repartida por todo este volumen encontrarás una selección de útiles consejos a cargo de Culture Smart!, las guías de mayor autoridad en materia de costumbres y etiqueta. Estas recogen información indispensable de que carecen otras publicaciones de este tipo y gracias a la que numerosos viajeros se han librado de situaciones embarazosas e incluso peligrosas. Quienes deseen adquirir una guía para un país específico pueden hacerlo en **www.culturesmartguides.co.uk.**

Reservas a través de HIhostels.com

¡RESERVA ONLINE EN www.HIhostels.com!

Gracias al sencillo y económico servicio de reservas con el que cuenta HIhostels.com, se peuden realizer reservas hasta con 12 meses de antelación en cientos de albergues estratégicos de más de 80 países de todo el mundo. En nuestra Guía, los establecimientos en los que es posible reservar online llevan el símbolo HI y se destacan de los demás por su fondo azul. Cada albergue está dotado de un número de identificación (p.ej. 4014), por lo que te será fácil localizarlos en nuestra página web.

Dirígete a **www.HIhostels.com** para:

- **Informarte sobre un albergue:** datos tales como fechas y horarios de apertura, información de contacto, indicaciones para localizar el establecimiento, sus instalaciones y prestaciones, así como los lugares de interés cercanos al mismo.
- **Consultar la disponibilidad de plazas *en tiempo real*** con 12 meses de antelación.
- **Reservar tu alojamiento** antes de salir de viaje.
- **Informarte sobre los países** que piensas visitar.

PAGO SEGURO ONLINE

Puedes reservar en **www.HIhostels.com** mediante cualquiera de las siguientes tarjetas:

Tarjetas de crédito:  

Tarjetas de débito: 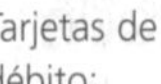   

RESERVAS – OTROS PUNTOS IMPORTANTES

No es imprescindible reservar con antelación, pero es recomendable hacerlo en temporada alta y en las grandes ciudades; los grupos en particular deben siempre reservar con tiempo. Si no dispones de acceso a Internet, puedes realizar tus reservas de las siguientes maneras:

- En nuestras centrales de reservas repartidas por todo el mundo (ver pág. 38)
- Con tarjeta de crédito, en determinadas centrales de reservas (ver más abajo)
- Enviando un e-mail, fax o carta (adjuntando un cupón internacional de respuesta pagada y un sobre con tu nombre y dirección) al albergue de tu elección.

RESERVA CON TARJETA DE CRÉDITO EN LAS SIGUENTES CENTRALES DE RESERVAS:

País	Teléfono
Australia	(2) 9261 1111
Canadá	(1) 800 663 5777 (dentro del Canadá solamente) www.HIhostels.ca (desde otros paises)
Escocia	(0870) 1 55 32 55 www.syha.org.uk
Estados Unidos	(301) 495-1240
Inglaterra y Gales	(0870) 770 8868; 44 (0)1629 59270
Irlanda del Norte	(28) 9032 4733
Nueva Zelanda	0064 3 379 9808
Suiza	00 41 (0)44 360 14 14

Si reservas con antelación sin abonar un depósito, normalmente deberás llegar al albergue antes de las 18 h, a menos que hayas concertado previamente otra hora de llegada.

Estamos seguros de que disfrutarás de tu estancia en nuestros albergues y de que no te saldrá cara la experiencia. Esperamos tener el agrado de tu visita.

Ventajas de la Afiliación

Para alojarte en nuestros albergues juveniles, deberás hacerte miembro de la Asociación de Albergues Juveniles del país en el que resides. Si no existe una Asociación de Albergues Juveniles en tu país, tendrás la oportunidad de adquirir una tarjeta Hostelling International o un "sello de bienvenida" (welcome stamp) en el albergue. El carné de alberguista es para personas de todas las edades y ofrece:

- 4.000 **centros** de alojamiento en más de 80 países.
- **Actividades,** programas y acontecimientos, así como la oportunidad de contribuir a la paz mundial.
- Miles de **descuentos** en todo el mundo: ver **pág. 777,** o bien **www.HIhostels.com**
- **Reservas** con un máximo de 12 meses de antelación a través de **www.HIhostels.com: ver pág. 30.**
- La posibilidad de acumular puntos **Freenites & More** gracias a nuestro plan de fidelización de miembros
- Los económicos **seguro de viaje HI** y **tarjeta telefónica HI-eKit.**

FREENITES & MORE

¡Nuestro programa FreeNites & More (noches gratuitas y más) te recompensa cada vez que te hospedas en un albergue participante! Puedes acumular puntos FNM al abonar tu alojamiento, comidas y bebidas, y canjear puntos por una noche gratis, etc. ¡Cuantos más puntos FNM acumulas, más dinero te ahorras! Todos los miembros de HI que sean titulares de un carné de alberguista nacional o una tarjeta HI vigentes y que residan en uno de los países participantes pueden adherirse a FreeNites & More.

Para ver la lista actualizada de estos países, consulta **www.HIhostels.com/FreeNites.**

TARJETA TELEFÓNICA

Dondequiera que te lleven tus viajes, la tarjeta telefónica HI-eKit es la forma más fácil de realizar llamadas y recibir mensajes en todo el mundo, incluso desde teléfonos móviles/celulares. Activa tu cuenta hoy mismo en **www.HI.ekit.com**, o llama al servicio de atención al cliente: en la página 36 encontrarás los números de acceso. Recibirás 10 $USA de regalo para hacer llamadas si ingresas 20 $USA o más en tu tarjeta.

Las principales ventajas de la tarjeta incluyen:

- Llamadas internacionales e interurbanas económicas
- Cuenta de e-mail gratuita; ¡puedes incluso escuchar tus correos electrónicos por teléfono!
- Mensajes de texto SMS desde tu cuenta de e-mail HI-eKit
- Servicio de asistencia turística las 24 horas del día
- Servicio multilingüe de asistencia al cliente las 24 horas del día
- La posibilidad de "recargar" tu cuenta en cualquier momento y desde cualquier lugar

SEGURO DE VIAJE HI

Tanto si se trata de una semana de vacaciones esquiando o de un año entero trotando mundos con la mochila al hombro, es importante saber que, si sucede lo peor, tienes ayuda al alcance de la mano. Hostelling International se ha unido a la importante compañía de seguros Columbus Direct para poder

ofrecerte seguros a precios asequibles.
Visita **www.columbusdirect.net/HI** y descubre lo mucho que te puedes ahorrar.

ALBERGUISMO JUVENIL PARA LA PAZ Y EL ENTENDIMIENTO INTERNACIONAL

Mediante su colaboración con la UNESCO (ver pág. 774) en iniciativas educativas y su apoyo a las Naciones Unidas dentro del marco de la "Década para una cultura de paz y no-violencia", Hostelling International está tomando parte activa, a través de sus albergues juveniles, en la educación de las personas y el fomento de los conceptos de la paz.

Para averiguar cómo puedes ayudar, consulta **www.HIhostels.com/peace.**

Unas Normas de Calidad Garantizadas

El Plan de las Normas Garantizadas ha sido instituido por Hostelling International para asegurarte un nivel uniforme de prestaciones e instalaciones, sea cual sea el albergue en el que te alojes.

- **Recibimiento:** Los albergues están abiertos a todos. En el caso de que el establecimiento cierre durante parte del día, tendrás acceso a las zonas más necesarias del mismo.
- **Comodidad:** una buena noche garantizada y suficientes lavabos y duchas. Normalmente, los albergues sirven comidas, están dotados de cocina para uso de los alberguistas y disponen de una tienda de comestibles.
- **Limpieza:** las más rigurosas normas de higiene.
- **Seguridad:** personal y de tus pertenencias.
- **Intimidad:** en las duchas, los lavabos y los aseos. El alojamiento en la mayoría de los albergues consiste en dormitorios múltiples no mixtos, aunque es posible que algunos establecimientos cuenten con habitaciones mixtas para quienes viajen juntos.

Estas normas son objeto de un seguimiento por parte de Hostelling International y por parte tuya, el usuario. **Al final de la Guía, así como en www.HIhostels.com, encontrarás unos impresos en los que puedes enviarnos tus comentarios. ¡Dinos lo que opinas!**

CATEGORÍAS DE LOS ALBERGUES

▲ **Normal:** se aplica a la mayoría de los albergues.

△ **Sencilla:** se aplica a los albergues más pequeños y a los situados en lugares remotos, cuyas instalaciones y prestaciones son sólo básicas. Por ejemplo, es posible que el personal y el horario de apertura sean limitados.

Algunos de los albergues relacionados en esta Guía no forman parte del Plan de las Normas Garantizadas. Han sido incluidos en ella porque están situados en lugares en los que no nos es posible ofrecer otro tipo de alojamiento.

VIAJEROS MINUSVÁLIDOS ♿

Los disminuidos físicos son bienvenidos en los albergues de Hostelling International. Los establecimientos que disponen de acceso para sillas de ruedas llevan el símbolo ♿ en la Guía.

NORMAS MEDIOAMBIENTALES

Los albergues deben cumplir las Normas Medioambientales de IYHF. Estas establecen los criterios relativos al consumo y la conservación de recursos, la eliminación de residuos y su reciclaje, la protección de la naturaleza y la provisión de educación medioambiental. Si deseas una explicación más detallada, consulta nuestra página Internet **www.HIhostels.com.**

Country	GMT	INT Code	Country Code	Medical	Police	Fire
Albania	+1/2	00	355	17	19	18
Algeria	+1	00	+213	118	17	14
Argentina	-3/-4	00	+54	103	101	100
Australia	+8/10	0011	+61	000	000	000
Austria	+1	00	+43	144	133	122
Bahrain	+3	00	+973	999	999	999
Bangladesh	+6	00	+880	500121-5, 5050525-29	8322501-8	9556666-7, 9555555-7
Belgium	+1	00	+32	100	101	100
Bolivia	-5/6	00	+591	118	110 (local) 120 (nat'l)	119
Brazil	-2/5	00	+55	192	190	193
Bulgaria	+2	00	+359	150	166	160
Canada	-3.5/11	001	+1	911	911	911
Chile	-4/6	00	+56	131	133	132
China - Guangdong	+8	00	+86	120	110	119
China - Hong Kong	+8	001	+852	999	999	999
Colombia	-5	009/007/005	+57	132	112	119
Costa Rica	-6	00	+506	911	911	911
Croatia	+1	00	+385	94	92	93
Czech Republic	+1	00	+420	155	158	150
Denmark	+1	00	+45	112	112	112
Ecuador	-5	00	+593	911	101	102
Egypt	+2	00	+20	123	122	180
Estonia	+2	00	+372	112	112/110	112
Faroe Islands	GMT	00	+298	000	000	000
Finland	+2	999/990	+358	112	10022	112
France	+1	00	+33	15	17	18
Germany	+1	00	+49	112	110	112
Greece	+2	00	+30	166	100	199
Guatemala	-6	00	+502	128	120/110	123/122
Hungary	+1	00	+36	104	107	105
Iceland	GMT	00	+354	112	112	112
India	+5.5	00	+91	102	100	101
Indonesia	+7/9	010	+62	118	110	113
Ireland - Republic	GMT	00	+353	999	999	999
Israel	+2	00	+972	101	100	102
Italy	+1	00	+39	118	112/113	115
Japan	+9	001	+81	119	110	119
Kenya	+3	0195	+254	999	999	999
Kuwait	+3	00	+965	777	777	777
Latvia	+2	00	+371	03	02	01
Lebanon	+2	00	+961	140	112	125
Libya	+2	00	+218	191	193	190
Lithuania	+2	00	+370	112	112	112
Luxembourg	+1	00	+352	112	113	112
Macedonia*	+1	99	+389	94	92	93

Country	GMT	INT Code	Country Code	Medical	Police	Fire
Malaysia	+8	00	+60	999	999	994
Malta	+1	00	+356	112	112	112
Mexico	-6/8	00	+52	080	080	080
Morocco	GMT	00	+212	15	19	15
Nepal	+5.45	00	+977-1	102	100	101
Netherlands	+1	00	+31	112	112	112
New Caledonia	+10	00	+687	15	17	18
New Zealand	+12	00	+64	111	111	111
Nicaragua	-6	001	+505	128	118	115
Norway	+1	00	+47	113	112	110
Pakistan	+5	00	+92	15	15	16
Panama	-5	001	+507	228-2187/ 231-2067/ 227-4122	104	103
Peru	-5	00	+51	105	105	116
Philippines	+8	00	+63	00632-8319 731	117	00632-8269 131
Poland	+1	0	+48	999	997	998
Portugal	GMT	00	+351	112	112	112
Qatar	+3	0	+974	999	999	999
Romania	+2	00	+40	961	955	981
Russia	+2/12	8-10	+7	03	02	01
Saudi Arabia	+3	00	+966	997	999	998
Serbia & Montenegro	+1	99	+381	94	92	93
Singapore	+8	001	+65	995	999	995
Slovakia	+2	00	+421	155	158	150
Slovenia	+1	00	+386	112	113	112
South Africa	+2	01	+27	10177	10111	10111
South Korea	+9	001/002	+82	119	112	119
Spain	+1	00	+34	061	091	112
Sudan	+3	00	+249	779500	780751	774444
Sweden	+1	00	+46	112	112	112
Switzerland	+1	00	+41	144	117	118
Taiwan	+8	002	+886	119	110	119
Thailand	+7	001	+66	1155	191	199
Tunisia	+1	00	+216	190	197	198
Turkey	+2	00	+90	112	155	110
UAE	+4	00	+971	999	999	999
Ukraine	+3	8-10	+380	03	02	01
United Kingdom	GMT	00	+44	999	999	999
Uruguay	-3	00	+598	911	911	911
USA	-5/9	011	+1	911	911	911
Venezuela	-4	00	+58	171	171	171

* Former Yugoslav Republic of Macedonia

Country	Access number
Argentina	0800-666-1409
Australia - Adelaide Economy - Brisbane Economy - Cairns Economy - Canberra Economy - Melbourne Economy - Perth Economy - Sydney Economy	1800-207-576 08-8121-8880 * 07-3102-8880 * 07-4049-0710 * 02-6100-8880 * 03-9010-0225* 08-9467-8880 * 02-8208-3000 *
Austria - Vienna Economy	0800-677-664 ¶ 01-928-0451 *
Bahamas	1800-389-0206
Belgium - Brussels Economy - Nationwide Economy	0800-49943 ¶ 02-400-6848 * 078-160-170 *
Brazil	0800-891-5825
Canada	1866-626-9724 ¶
Chile	800-800-014 §
China - China (North) - China (South)	10800-180-0072 » § 10800-713-0673 » § 10800-130-0559 » §
Colombia	01800-918-0096
Cyprus	8009-7169
Czech Republic	800-142-069
Denmark	8088-1909 ¶
Dominican Republic	1-888-751-8123 »
Finland	0800-112-010 »
France - Nationwide Economy - Nice Economy - Paris Economy - Francais	0805-113-721 ¶ 0820-60-0052 » * 04-89-12-00-32 * 01-70-70-03-95 * 0805-113-722 ¶
Germany - Berlin Economy - Frankfurt Economy - Munich Economy - Deutsch	0800-100-6492 ¶ 030-22153037 * 069-2222-3144 * 089-20303271 * 0800-100-6346 » §
Greece	00800-1809-201-2429 §
Hong Kong	800-967-389 »

Country	Access number
Hungary	06800-17053
Iceland	800-8326
India	000-800-100-3004 »
Indonesia	0018-030-113-663 » §
Ireland - Dublin Economy - Nationwide Economy	1800-992-363 ¶ 01-247-5181 * 1850-930-363 *
Israel	180-920-3300
Italy - Milan Economy - Italiano	800-985-675 ¶ 02-3601-0911 * 800-985-676 ¶
Japan	0053-112-1399 §
Latvia	800-2091
Luxembourg	800-22026 §
Macau	0800-275
Malaysia	1800-804-146
Mexico	01800-088-5000
Monaco	0800-913-588 §
Netherlands - Amsterdam Economy	0800-020-3235 ¶ 0207-133-472 *
Netherlands Antilles	0018-886-467-702 » §
New Zealand - Auckland Economy	0800-445-108 § 09-912-8211 *
Nicaragua	001-800-220-1402
Norway	800-11-357
Panama	001-800-201-2441
Peru	0800-520-08
Poland	00800-111-3535 §
Portugal	800-812-993 §
Puerto Rico	1800-531-9684 §
Russia	8-10-800-2092-1012 » §
Saipan	1800-952-9984 §
Singapore	800-120-3480
South Africa	0800-994-172
South Korea	0030-814-0226

* Economy numbers incur lower eKit charges but may incur local call charges.

§ Unavailable from mobile phones in some cases.

» Unavailable from payphones in some cases.

¶ Higher charges may be incurred from mobiles and payphones.

ARGENTINA

Red Argentina de Alojamiento para Jóvenes (RAAJ)

Bariloche – Tango Inn
Av. 12 de Octubre, 1915 Bariloche, Rio Negro.
t (54) (29) 44430707
f (54) (29) 44430707
e info@tangoinn.com

Buenos Aires – National Office
Florida 835, 3rd Floor, Of. 319, Buenos Aires.
t (54) (11) 45118712/23
f (54) (11) 43120089
e raaj@hostels.org.ar

Buenos Aires –
San Miguel de Tucumán 669, Provincia de Tucumán.
t (54) (381) 4201584
f (54) (381) 4241652
e info@tucumanhostel.com

AUSTRALIA

Australian Youth Hostels Association

Adelaide – YHA South Australia
135 Waymouth St, Adelaide, SA 5000.
t (61) (8) 84143000
f (61) (8) 84143014
e yha@yhasa.org.au

Brisbane – YHA Queensland
154 Roma Street, Brisbane, Queensland 4000.
t (61) (7) 32361681
f (61) (7) 32361702
e travel@yhaqld.org

Byron Bay – YHA Travel Byron
Corner Byron/Middleton Streets, Byron Bay NSW.
t (61) (2) 66855997
f (61) (2) 66858814
e travel@yhansw.org.au

Cairns – YHA Queensland
20-24 McLeod Street, Cairns, Queensland 4870.
t (61) (7) 40510772
f (61) (7) 40313158
e cairns_central@yhaqld.org

Canberra – YHA New South Wales
191 Dryandra Street, O'Connor, Canberra, ACT 2602.
t (61) (2) 62489155
f (61) (2) 62491731
e canberra@yhansw.org.au

Darwin - YHA Northern Territory
69 Mitchell Street, Darwin, NT 0801.
t (61) (8) 89813995
f (61) (8) 89816674
e yhant@yhant.org.au

Melbourne – YHA Victoria
Level 1, 377 Little Lonsdale Street, Melbourne, Victoria 3000.
t (61) (3) 96707991
f (61) (3) 96709840
e yha@yhavic.org.au

Perth – YHA Western Australia
236 William Street, Northbridge, Perth, Western Australia 6003.
t (61) (8) 94275100
f (61) (8) 94275177
e travel@yhawa.com.au

Sydney – YHA New South Wales
GPO Box 5276, 422 Kent St, Sydney, New South Wales 2001.
t (61) (2) 92611111
f (61) (2) 92611969
e yha@yhansw.org.au

Sydney – YHA Travel CBD
422 Kent Street, Sydney NSW 2000.
t (61) (2) 92611111
f (61) (2) 92611111
e travel@yhansw.org.au

Sydney – YHA Travel Central
11 Rawson Place, Sydney NSW.
t (61) (2) 92819444
f (61) (2) 92819311
e travel@yhansw.org.au

AUSTRIA

Österreichischer Jugendherbergsverband

Graz – International (ÖJHV)
Idlhofgasse 74, A-8020 Graz.
t (43) (316) 7083
f (43) (316) 7083-88
e jgh-graz@jgh.at

Klagenfurt – International
Neckheimgasse 6, 9020 Klagenfurt.
t (43) (463) 230019
f (43) (463) 230019-13
e oejhv-kaernten@oejhv.or.at

Salzburg –
Kaigasse 24, A5020 Salzburg.
t (43) (662) 841165
f (43) (662) 840164
e jhw.sbg@aon.at

Vienna – ÖJHV National Office
1010 Wien, Gonzagag.22.
t (43) (1) 5335353
f (43) (1) 5350861
e oejhv@chello.at

Österreichisches Jugendherbergswerk

Vienna – ÖJHW National Office
1010 Wien, Helferstorferstrasse 4.
t (43) (1) 5331833
f (43) (1) 533183385
e office@jungehotels.at; travel@supertramp.co.at

BELGIUM

Belgium - Les Auberges de Jeunesse

Brussels – LAJ - Les Auberges de Jeunesse
Rue de la Sablonnière 28,
B-1000 Brussels.
t (32) (2) 219 5676
f (32) (2) 219 1451
e info@laj.be
w www.laj.be

Belgium - Vlaamse Jeugdherbergcentrale

Antwerp – VJH National Office
Van Stralenstraat 40, B-2060 Antwerpen.
t (32) (3) 232 7218
f (32) (3) 231 8126
e vjh@vjh.be

BOLIVIA

Hostelling International Bolivia

Santa Cruz de la Sierra –
Avendia Roca y Coronado No. 34
t (591) (3) 3701294
e hostelling_international_bolivia@yahoo.com

BRAZIL

Federaçao Brasileira dos Albergues da Juventude

Helo Horizonte - FBAJ MG B/C
Rua Sergipe, 1449 Savassi,
Helo Horizonte/MG - 30-150-170.
t (55) (31) 32849958
f (55) (31) 32849958
e albergue@task.com.br

Porto Alegre – Regional Office
Rua Dos Andradas, 1137 S. 214,
Centro - Porto Alegre, RS CEP: 90020-008.
t (55) (51) 2283802
f (55) (51) 2265380
e turjovem@zaz.com.br

Rio de Janeiro – Regional Office
Rua da Assembleia No 10, Sala 1616,
Centro-CEP:20011-000, Rio de Janeiro.
t (55) (21) 5311085
f (55) (21) 5312234
e albergue@microlink.com.br

São Paulo – Regional Office
Rua Sete de Abril, 386-2° andar Centro,
CEP 01044-908, Sao Paulo - SP.
t (55) (11) 32580388
f (55) (11) 32580388209
e info@alberguesp.com.br

BULGARIA

USIT Colours Bulgaria

Sofia -
35 Vasil Levski Blvd, 1000 Sofia.
t (359) (2) 9211900
f (359) (2) 9819991
e sofia@usitcolours.bg

CANADA

Canadian Hostelling Association

Edmonton – HI Travel Shop
10926 - 88 Avenue, Edmonton,
Alberta T6G 0Z1.
t (1) (780) 439-3089
f (1) (780) 433-7781
e travelshop.na@hihostels.ca

Montréal – Boutique Tourisme Jeunesse
205 avenue Mont-Royal Est, Montreal (Québec) H2T 1P4.
t (1) (514) 844-0287
f (1) (514) 844-5246
e boutiqueqc@tourismejeunesse.org

Ottawa – National Office
400-205 Catherine Street, Ottawa, Ontario, K2P 1C3.
t (1) (613) 237-7884
f (1) (613) 237-7868
e info@hostellingintl.ca

Ottawa – Hostel Shop B/C
75 Nicholas Street, Ottawa, Ontario, K1N 7B9.
t (1) (613) 509-1400
f (1) (613) 235-9202
e hostel.shop@hihostels.ca

Québec – Boutique Tourisme Jeunesse
94 Boulevard René-Lénesque Ouest, Québec City, Québec G1R 2A4.
t (1) (418) 522-2552
f (1) (418) 522-2455
e boutiqueqc@tourismejeunesse.org

Toronto – International Travel
56 Church Street, Toronto, Ontario M5C 2G1.
t (1) (416) 363-0697 ext.15
f (1) (416) 368-6499
e hits@hihostels.ca

Vancouver – Regional Office
1155 West Pender Street, Suite 200, Vancouver, British Columbia, V6E 2P4.
t (1) (604) 684-7101
f (1) (604) 684-7181
e info.pm@hihostels.ca

CHILE

Asociación Chilena de Albergues Turísticos Juveniles

Santiago – National Office
Hernando de Aguirre 201, Of. 602, Providencia.
t (56) (2) 233-3220, 2555
f (56) (2) 233-3220
e histgoch@entel.chile.net

CHINA

Beijing, Shanghai and Guangdong Youth Hostel Associations of China

Beijing B/C
No. 10 building, Xuanwa Men Xi Da Jie, Xuanwu District, Beijing.
t (86) (10) 63151165
f (86) (10) 63151165
e bjyha@byecity.com

Guangzhou – c/o National Office
185 Huanshi Xi Road, Guangzhou, Guangdong Province.
t (86) (20) 86677422
f (86) (20) 86665039
e gdyhac@public.guangzhou.gd.cn

YHA China B/C
18C Ming Yue Ge Building, No. 20 Ming Yue Yi Road, Wu Yang Xin Cheng, Guangzhou 510600
t (86) (20) 87345080
e yha_china@hotmail.com

Hong Kong Youth Hostels Association

Hong Kong – National Office
Room 225, Block 19, Shek Kip Mei Estate, Shamshuipo, Kowloon, Hong Kong, SAR China.
t (852) 2788-1638
f (852) 2788-3105
e info@yha.org.hk

CROATIA

Croatian Youth Hostel Association

Zagreb – National Office
Dezmanova 9, 10000 Zagreb.
t (385) (1) 484-7474
f (385) (1) 484-7472
e travelsection@hfhs.hr

CZECH REPUBLIC

Česká hostelová asociace (CZYHA)

Brno – GTS Vachova B/C
Vachova 4, Brno 602 00.
t (420) 542221996
f (420) 542221001
e gts.brno@gtsint.cz

Ceske Budejovice – GTS Lannova B/C
Lannova 57, Ceske Budejovice 37021.
t (420) 387420420
f (420) 387426244
e gts.cb@gtsint.cz

Dejvice – GTS Bechynova B/C
Bechynova 3, Praha 6, Dejvice 160 00.
t (420) 224325235
f (420) 224325237
e gts.dejvicka@gtsint.cz

Hradec Kralove – GTS Celakovske'ho B/C
Celakovske'ho 623, Hradec Kralove 500 02.
t (420) 495515825
f (420) 495515827
e gts.hk@gtsint.cz

Liberec – GTS Husova B/C
Husova 75, Liberec 460 01.
t (420) 485353531
f (420) 485353537
e gts.liberec@gtsint.cz

Liberec – GTS Zamecnicka B/C
Zamecnicka 8, Liberec 460 01.
t (420) 485100908
f (420) 495515827
e liberec@gtsint.cz

Olomouc – GTS Olomouc B/C
Horni namesti 371/1, 772 00 Olomouc.
t (420) 585237190
f (420) 585237777
e gts.olomouc@gtsint.cz

Ostrava – GTS Denisova B/C
Denisova 5, Ostrava 702 00.
t (420) 596115324
f (420) 596115328
e gts.ostrava@gtsint.cz

Pardubice – GTS Studentska B/C
Studentska 519, Pardubice 530 09.
t (420) 466036685
f (420) 466036687
e gts.pardubice@gtsint.cz

Plzen – GTS Prazska B/C
Prazska 12, Plzen 301 00.
t (420) 377328621
f (420) 377235246
e gts.plzen@gtsint.cz

Prague – GTS International B/C
Letenska 1/118, Prague 1, 118 00
t (420) 257187100
f (420) 257535768
e callcentre@gtsint.cz

Prague – GTS Ve Smeckach B/C
Ve Smeckach 33, Prague 1, 110 00.
t (420) 222211204
f (420) 222211717
e gts.smecky@gtsint.cz

Prague – GTS Letiste B/C
Letiste Ruzyne - Terminal A,
Prague 6 16000.
t (420) 220113008
f (420) 220116788
e letiste@gtsint.cz

Usti nad Labem – GTS Parizska B/C
Parizska 10, Usti nad Labem 40001.
t (420) 475216467
f (420) 475216467
e gts.ul@gtsint.cz

Zlin – GTS Stefanikoova
Stefanikoova 2464, 760 01 Zlin.
t (420) 57 7223000
f (420) 577019034
e gts.zlin@gtsint.cz

DENMARK

DANHOSTEL Denmarks Vandrerhjem

Copenhagen – National Office
Hostelling International Denmark,
Vesterbrogade 39, DK1620, Copenhagen V.
t (45) 3331-3612
f (45) 3331-3626
e ldv@danhostel.dk

ECUADOR

Idiomas S.A.

Guayaquil –
Junín 203 y Panamá, Floor 2,
Of. 4, Guayaquil.
t (593) (4) 256-4488
f (593) (4) 256-3385
e hostelling@idiomas.com.ec

ENGLAND & WALES

Youth Hostels Association (England & Wales)

Credit/Debit Card Reservations only – Trevelyan House, Dimple Road, Matlock, Derbyshire DE4 3YH.

ⓣ (44) (1629) 592700

ⓕ (44) (870) 770 6127/(1629) 592627

ⓔ customerservices@yha.org.uk

ESTONIA

Estonian Youth Hostels Association

Tallinn – National Office
Narva mnt. 16-25, 10120 Tallinn.

ⓣ (372) 6461455

ⓕ (372) 6461595

ⓔ info@hostels.ee

FINLAND

Suomen Retkeilymajajärjestö-SRM

Helsinki – National Office
Yrjönkatu 38 B 15, 00100 Helsinki.

ⓣ (358) (9) 565-7150

ⓕ (358) (9) 565-7150

ⓔ info@srm.inet.fi

Vaasa –
Niemelantie, 65170 Vaasa.

ⓣ (358) (6) 3241-555

ⓕ (358) (6) 3241-501

ⓔ info@hostelvaasa.com

FRANCE

Fédération Unie des Auberges de Jeunesse

Paris – National Office
27 rue Pajol, 75018 Paris.

ⓣ (33) (1) 44898727

ⓕ (33) (1) 44898749

ⓔ fuaj@fuaj.org

GERMANY

Deutsches Jugendherbergswerk

Berlin – German Youth Hostels Association, Brandenburg Regional Office Service Team, Kluckstrasse 3, D-10785 Berlin.

ⓣ (49) (30) 2649520

ⓕ (49) (30) 26495210

ⓔ service@jugendherberge.de

Detmold – National Office
DJH Service GmbH, Bismarckstr.8, 32756 Detmold.

ⓣ (49) (5231) 7401-0

ⓕ (49) (5231) 740149

ⓔ info@djh.de

Dresden - Sachsen Regional Office
Maternistrasse 22, 01067 Dresden.

ⓣ (49) (351) 4942211

ⓕ (49) (351) 4942213

ⓔ servicecenter@djh-sachsen.de

Düsseldorf – Rheinland Regional Office
Postfach 110301, 40503 Düsseldorf.

ⓣ (49) (211) 5770321

ⓕ (49) (211) 579735

ⓔ service-center@djh-rheinland.de

Hamburg – Nordmark Regional Office
Rennbahnstrasse 100, 22111 Hamburg.

ⓣ (49) (40) 655995-0

ⓕ (49) (40) 62299552

ⓔ service@djh-nordmark.de

Munich – YH Munich-Neuhausen (Booking Center)
Wendl-Dietrich-Strasse 20, 80634 München.

ⓣ (49) (89) 131156

ⓕ (49) (89) 1678745

ⓔ jhmuenchen@djh-bayern.de

ⓦ www.muenchen-neuhausen.jugendherberge.de

HUNGARY

Magyarországi Ifjusági Szállások

Budapest – Mellow Mood
1077 Budapest, Baross tér 15, 3rd Floor 6.

ⓣ (36) (1) 4132065

ⓕ (36) (1) 3214851

ⓔ info@youthhostels.hu

INDIA

Youth Hostels Association of India

New Delhi - International Hostel
5 Nyaya Marg, Chanakyapuri, New Delhi.
t (91) (11) 26116285
f (91) (11) 24676349
e yhostel@del2.vsnl.net.in
w www.yhaindia.org

IRELAND - NORTHERN

Hostelling International - Northern Ireland

Belfast – National Office
22 Donegall Road, Belfast, BT12 5JN.
t (44) (28) 90315435
f (44) (28) 90439699
e info@hini.org.uk

IRELAND - REPUBLIC

An Óige

Dublin – Booking Centre
61 Mountjoy Street, Dublin 7.
t (353) (1) 830 1766
f (353) (1) 830 1600; 830 5808
e mailbox@anoige.ie

ISRAEL

Israel Youth Hostels Association

Jerusalem – National Office
Jerusalem 1 Shazar St,
International Convention Center,
PO Box 6001, Jerusalem 91060.
t (972) (2) 655-8400
f (972) (2) 655-8432
e iyha@iyha.org.il
w www.iyha.org.il

ITALY

Assoc. Italiana Alberghi per la Gioventù

Bergamo – Regional Office
Via Galileo Ferraris 1, 24123, Bergamo.
t (39) (035) 361724
f (39) (035) 361724
e hostebg@libero.it

Bologna – Regional Office
Via dell Unione n.6/a, 40126 Bologna.
t (39) (051) 224913
f (39) (051) 224913
e aig.emiliaromagna@ostellionline.org

Catania – Local Office
Via Andrea Costa 34/B,
951279 Catania, Sicily.
t (39) (095) 539853
f (39) (095) 539853
e aigcatania@iol.it

Florence – Regional Office
Viale Augusto Righi 2/4, 50137, Florence.
t (39) (055) 600315
f (39) (055) 610300
e aig.toscana@ostellionline.org

Genoa – Regional Office
Salita Salvatore Viale n. 1/8, 16128, Genova.
t (39) (010) 586407
f (39) (010) 586407
e aig.liguria@ostellionline.org

Naples – Regional Office
Salita della Grotta a Piedigrotta 23,
80122 Naples.
t (39) (081) 7611215
f (39) (081) 7612391
e aig.campania@ostellionline.org

Palermo – Regional Office
Via Plauto 27, 90148 Palermo.
t (39) (091) 534693
f (39) (091) 6912376
e aig.sicilia@ostellionline.org

Rome – National Office
Via Farini 48/50, 00184 Rome.
t (39) (06) 48907740
f (39) (06) 48987982
e info@ostellionline.org

Venice – Regional Office
Calle dei Amai 197/1 Santa Croce,
30135 Venezia.
t (39) (041) 5204414
f (39) (041) 5204034
e aig.veneto@ostellionline.org

JAPAN

Japan Youth Hostels Inc

Kyoto – Kyoto Youth Hostel Association
29 Uzumasa-Nakayamacho, Ukyo-ku,
Kyoto 616-8191.
t (81) (75) 462-9185
f (81) (75) 462-2289
e utano-yh@mbox.kyoto-inet.or.jp

Nagoya-Aichi –
Aichi Youth Hostel Association
Aichiken Seinen Kaikan,
18-8 Sakae 1 chome,
Naka-ku, Nagoya-shi 460-0008.
t (81) (52) 221-6080
f (81) (52) 221-6057

Osaka – Osaka Youth Hostel Association
C/O Shin Osaka YH, 10F Koko Plaza,
13-13, 1 Chome Higashinakajima,
Higashi-yodogawa-ku, Osaka-shi, Osaka
533-0033
t (81) (6) 6370-5427
f (81) (6) 6370-5428
e yhaosaka@osk3.3web.ne.jp

Tokyo – National Office (JYH)
9F Kanda Amerex building, 3-1-16,
Misaki-cho, Chiyoda-ku, Tokyo 101-0061.
t (81) (3) 3288-0260
f (81) (3) 3288-1490
e travel@jyh.or.jp

Tokyo – Tokyo Youth Hostels Association
2-21-4 Yanagibash Taito-Ku, Tokyo
111-0052.
t (81) (3) 3851-1121
f (81) (3) 3851-1130
e tokyo.yh@vesta.ocn.ne.jp

Tokyo-Yoyogi –
Tokyo-Yoyogi Youth Hostel
3-1 Yoyogi-Kamizono-cho, Shibuya-ku, 31,
Tokyo 151-0052.
t (81) (3) 3467-9163
f (81) (3) 3467-9417
e yoyogi@jyh.gr.jp

KOREA - SOUTH

Korea Youth Hostels Association

Seoul – National Office
Rm 408, Jeokseon Hyundai Bldg 80,
Jeokseon-dong, Jongno-gu, Seoul 110-756 .
t (82) (2) 725-3031
f (82) (2) 725-3031
e inform@kyha.or.kr

LATVIA

Riga – Hostelling Latvia
Siguldas pr 17-2, Riga LV 1014, Latvia.
t (371) 9218560
f (371) 7517006
e info@hostellinglatvia.com
w www.hostellinglatvia.com

LITHUANIA

Lithuanian Youth Hostels

Vilnius – National Office
Filaretai Youth Hostel
Filaretu Street 17, 01207 Vilnius.
t (370) (5) 2154627
f (370) (5) 2120149
e booking@lithuanianhostels.org

LUXEMBOURG

Centrale des Auberges de Jeunesse Luxembourgeoises

Luxembourg – Centrale des Auberges de Jeunesse
Luxembourgeoises 2, rue du Fort Olisy,
L-2261 Luxembourg.
t (352) 26 27 66 40
f (352) 26 27 66 42
e info@youthhostels.lu
w www.youthhostels.lu

MALAYSIA

Malaysian Youth Hostels Association

Kuala Lumpur – MSL Travel Centre
66, Jalan Putra, 50350 Kuala Lumpur.
t (60) (3) 40424722
f (60) (3) 40433707
e msl@po.jaring.my

MALTA

NSTS Student & Youth Travel

Valletta –
220 St Paul Street, Valletta VLT07.
Ⓣ (356) 2558 8000
Ⓕ (356) 2558 8200
Ⓔ nsts@nsts.org

MEXICO

Mexico City – Republica de Guatemala #4, Colonia Centro CP 06020.
Ⓣ (52) (55) 55 18 17 26
Ⓕ (52) (55) 54 10 34 42
Ⓔ reservations@hostellingmexico.com; info@hostellingmexico.com

NEW ZEALAND

Youth Hostels Association of New Zealand

Christchurch - National Office
PO Box 436, 166 Moorehouse Avenue, Christchurch.
Ⓣ (64) (3) 379 9970
Ⓕ (64) (3) 365 4415
Ⓔ info@yha.co.nz

NORWAY

Norske Vandrerhjem

Oslo – National Office
Torggata 1, N-0181 Oslo.
Ⓣ (47) (23) 139300
Ⓕ (47) (23) 139350
Ⓔ hostels@vandrerhjem.no

PERU

Asociación Peruana de Hostelling International

Lima – National Office
Avda Casimiro Ulloa 328,
San Antonio, Miraflores, Lima 18.
Ⓣ (51) (1) 2423068
Ⓕ (51) (1) 4448187
Ⓔ hostell@terra.com.pe

PORTUGAL

MOVIJOVEM

Lisbon – Movijovem - Mobilidade Juvenil
Rua Lúcio Azevedo 27, 1600-146 Lisbon.
Ⓣ (351) (21) 7232100
Ⓕ (351) (21) 7232101
Ⓔ movijovem@movijovem.pt
Ⓦ www.pousadasjuventude.pt

Lisbon – Movijovem - Portugal Youth Hostel Booking Centre
Av. Duque de Avila, 137 1069-017 Lisbon.
Ⓣ (351) 707 203030 (less than 10 persons); (351) 707 233233 (more than 10 persons)
Ⓕ (351) 213 568129
Ⓔ reservas@movijovem.pt
Ⓦ www.pousadasjuventude.pt

ROMANIA

Asociatia Youth Hostel România

Romania YHA B/C
400537 Cluj-Napoca, Casa de Cultura a Studentilor P-ta, Lucian Blaga nr. 1-3.
Ⓣ (40) (264) 586616; (745) 397292
Ⓕ (40) (264) 586616
Ⓔ office@HIhostels-Romania.ro

RUSSIA

St Petersburg –
Russian Youth Hostels, Sindbad Travel
3rd Sovetskaya Ulitsa 28, St Petersburg.
Ⓣ (7) (812) 329 8018; 327 8384
Ⓕ (7) (812) 329 8019
Ⓔ inquiries@ryh.ru

Moscow – InterAir Travel
Chistoprudny Blvd. 12A, Suite 420, 101000 Moscow.
Ⓣ (7) (95) 916-9364
Ⓕ (7) (95) 924-4968
Ⓔ info@world4u.ru

Moscow – STAR Travel
Leningradsky Prospect. 80/21, 3rd Floor, 125178 Moscow.
Ⓣ (7) (95) 797-9555
Ⓕ (7) (95) 797-9554
Ⓔ help@startravel.ru

SCOTLAND

Scottish Youth Hostels Association

Stirling – National Office
7 Glebe Crescent, Stirling, FF8 2JA.
ⓣ (44) (8701) 553255
ⓕ (44) (1786) 891350
ⓔ reservations@syha.org.uk

SINGAPORE

Singapore – STA Travel Pte Ltd
400 Orchard Rd, #07-02 Orchard Towers, Singapore 238875.
ⓣ (65) 67377188
ⓕ (65) 67372591
ⓔ osu@statravel.com.sg

SLOVAKIA

CKM SYTS

Bratislava – CKM 2000 Travel
Vysoka 32, 814 45 Bratislava.
ⓣ (421) (7) 52731018
ⓕ (421) (7) 52731025
ⓔ ckm2000@ckm.sk

SLOVENIA

Maribor – Slovenia Gaudeamus B/C
Gregorciceva 25, 2000 Maribor.
ⓣ (386) (2) 2502108
ⓕ (386) (2) 2502107
ⓔ info@gaudeamus.si

SOUTH AFRICA

Hostelling International - South Africa

Durban – Africa Wonderland Tours
19 Smith Street, Durban 4001, Natal.
ⓣ (27) (31) 3324944
ⓕ (27) (31) 3324551
ⓔ wonderland.durban@pixie.co.za

Johannesburg –
Africa Wonderland Tours
Inchanga Ranch, Inchanga Road, Witkoppen, 4 Ways, Johannesburg.
ⓣ (27) (11) 7081459
ⓕ (27) (11) 7081464
ⓔ wonderland@pixie.co.za

SPAIN

Red Española de Albergues Juveniles

Alicante – IVAJ
Rambla Mendéz Nuñez, 41 - Bajo - 03002 Alicante.
ⓣ (34) (966) 478120/21
ⓕ (34) (966) 478129
ⓔ turivaj@ivaj.gva.es

Barcelona – Alberg Mare de Déu de Montserrat - Booking Centre & Hostel
Passeig Mare De Deu Coll 41 - 51, 08023 Barcelona, Catalunya.
ⓣ (34) (93) 2105151
ⓕ (34) (93) 2100798
ⓔ alberg_Barcelona@tujuca.com

Barcelona – Sants B/C - Booking & Information Hostel Centre
Pl.Països Catalans, s/n (Estació Renfe-Local 62). 08014 Barcelona Catalunya.
ⓔ sants_booking@tujuca.com

Barcelona – Viatgeteca - Booking centre & Tourist information Centre
Passeig de Gràcia, 107 (Palau Robert), 08007 Barcelona, Catalunya.
ⓔ informacio@tujuca.com

Barcelona – XANASCAT - Catalonian Hostels Head Office
Carrer Rocafort 166-122, 08015 Barcelona, Catalunya.
ⓣ (34) (93) 4838363
ⓕ (34) (93) 4838350
ⓔ vendes@tujuca.com

Madrid – TIVE Office
c/Fernando el Católico 88, 28015 Madrid.
ⓣ (34) (91) 5437412
ⓕ (34) (91) 5440062
ⓔ tive.juventud@comadrid.es

Sevilla – Sevilla-Inturjoven B/C
C/Virgen de la Victoria, 46, E-41011 Sevilla.
ⓣ (34) (95) 5035800
ⓕ (34) (95) 5035848
ⓔ jmadrid@inturjoven.junta-andalucia.es

Valencia – IVAJ
C/Del Hospital, 11, 46001 Valencia.
t (34) (963) 985990
f (34) (963) 985920
e turivaj@ivaj.gva.es

SWEDEN

Swedish Tourist Association

Stockholm – National Office
Svenska Turistföreningen (STF)
Amiralitetshuset, Skeppsholmen,
PO Box 25, 101 20 Stockholm.
t (46) (8) 4632100
f (46) (8) 6781958
e info@stfturist.se
w www.stfturist.se

SWITZERLAND

Swiss Youth Hostels

Zurich – National Office
Swiss Youth Hostels,
Schaffhauserstrasse 14, Postfach CH-8042
Zurich.
t (41) (44) 360-1414
f (41) (44) 360-1460
e bookingoffice@youthhostel.ch
w www.youthhostel.ch

THAILAND

Thai Youth Hostels Association

Bangkok – National Office
25/14 Phitsanulok Road, Bangkok,
Dusit, 10300.
t (66) (0) 2628-7413 to 5
f (66) (0) 2628 7416
e bangkok@tyha.org; contact@tyha.org

UNITED STATES

Hostelling International – USA

Boston –
Eastern New England Council Travel Centre
1105 Commonwealth Avenue, Boston,
MA 02215.
t (1) (617) 719-0900
f (1) (617) 779-0904
e travelctr_hienec@juno.com

Los Angeles –
Los Angeles Council Travel Centre
1434 Second Street, Santa Monica,
CA 90401.
t (1) (310) 393-3413
f (1) (310) 393-1769
e reserve@hilosangeles.org

New York – HI-New York Hostel Shop
891 Amsterdam Avenue, New York,
NY 10025.
t (1) (212) 932-2300
f (1) (212) 932-2574
e reserve@hinewyork.org

Philadelphia –
Delaware Valley Council Travel Centre
624 South 3rd Street, Philadelphia,
PA 19147.
t (1) (215) 925-6004
f (1) (215) 925-4874
e hidvc@starlinx.com

San Francisco –
Golden Gate Council Travel Centre
425 Divisadero Street, Suite 307,
San Francisco, CA 74117-2242.
t (1) (415) 701-1320
f (1) (415) 863-3865
e travelsf@norcalhostels.org

St Louis – Gateway Council Travel Centre
7187 Manchester Road, St Louis,
MO 63143-2450.
t (1) (314) 644-4660
f (1) (314) 644-6192
e info@gatewayhiayh.org

Washington DC – National Office
8401 Colesville Road Suite 600,
Silver Spring, MD 20910.
t (1) (301) 495-1240
f (1) (301) 495-6697
e members@hiusa.org

URUGUAY

Hostelling International Uruguay

Canelones – National Office
Canelones 935, CP 11100.
t (598) (2) 9005749
f (598) (2) 9013587
e albergues@hosteluruguay.org
w www.hosteluruguay.org

Algeria

**Fédération Algérienne des Auberges de Jeunesse,
14, Rue Bouzar Boualem Boite Postale numéro 10,
Douaouda-Marine, Wilaya de TIPAZA, Algeria.**
t (213) (24) 407558; 407559
f (213) (24) 407557

A copy of the Hostel Directory for this Country can be obtained from:
The National Office.

National Tourist Authority/Board:	www.tourisme.dz
Capital:	Algiers
Language:	Arabic
Currency:	DA (dinar)
Population:	30,000,000
Size:	2,381,741 sq km
Telephone Country Code:	213
eKit Access Number:	Check www.hi.ekit.com for up to date Access Numbers

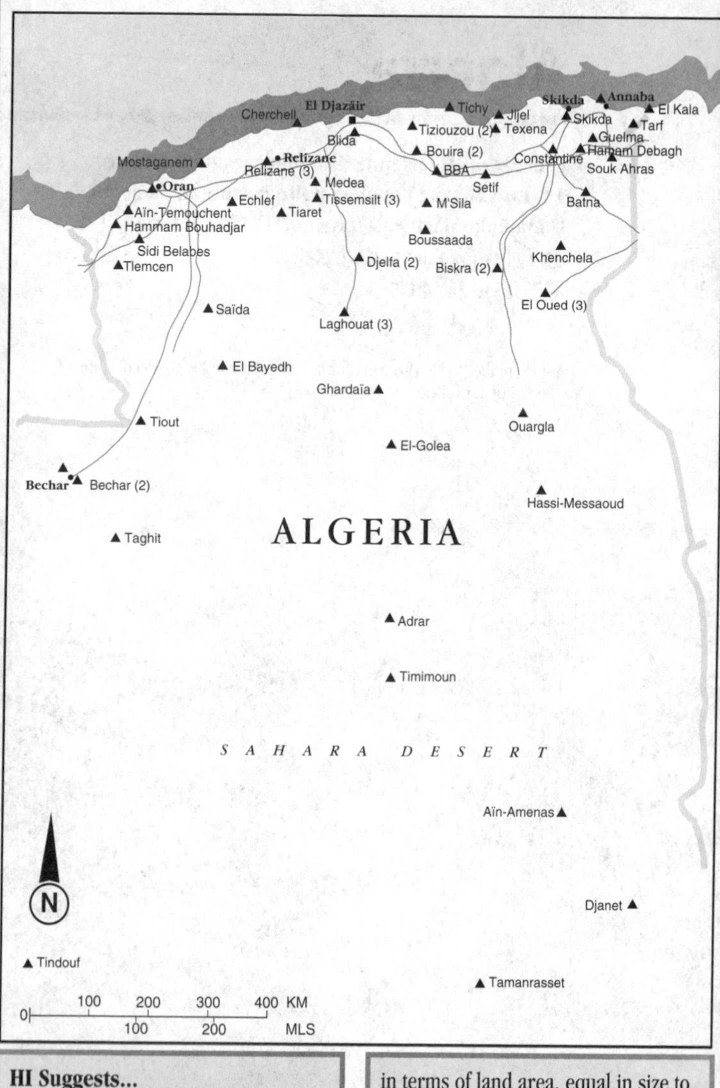

HI Suggests...

Algeria is situated along the North African coast, bordered by Tunisia, Libya, Niger, Mali, Mauritania and Morocco. It is the largest of the three countries (including Morocco and Tunisia), which form the region of western North Africa known traditionally as Al Maghrib ("the West"). It is also the second largest country in Africa, covering an area of nearly 2.5 million square miles, and the tenth largest country in the world in terms of land area, equal in size to Western Europe.

The Sahara is one of Algeria's most striking features; it covers 85% of the country and is relatively uninhabited. The area draws increasing numbers of winter tourists.

Local cooking often includes roast meat and couscous with a vegetable sauce. Main towns offer reasonable entertainment facilities, including discotheques, folk dancing and traditional music.

The great majority of the population are Sunni Muslims of Arab-Berber descent; Europeans, who before independence accounted for 10% of the total, now are only 1% of the population. Arabic is the official language, but French is widely spoken, and a sizable minority speaks a Berber language.

The capital city, Algiers, has been a port since Roman times and many impressive ruins can still be seen, such as those at Djemila and Tipaza. Along the coastal strip are the main towns and beach resorts and there lie some of the finest resorts; Zeralda is a beach resort with a holiday village and a replica nomad village. Tipaza has exceptional Roman, Punic and Christian ruins. There are two spectacular mountain ranges, which are a must see: the dramatic Hoggar massif, rising to almost 3000m (9800ft), and the Tassili N'Ajjer or 'Plateau of Chasms'.

You can find out a lot more on our website - a visit to www.HIhostels.com is essential for planning your trip!

Pour en savoir plus, rendez-vous sur notre site Internet, www.HIhostels.com une visite incontournable pour préparer votre voyage!

Viele weitere Informationen auf unserer Website: www.HIhostels.com - unverzichtbar für die Reiseplanung!

Puedes averiguar mucho más en nuestro sitio web. Es imprescindible que visites la página www.HIhostels.com para planear tu viaje.

▲ **Adrar** – Centre-Ville – 1001
Adrar-Centre-Ville, 01000 Adrar.
(49) 960899; 969212
Open Dates: x 50

△ ***Aïn-Amenas*** – *Aïn-Amenas – 1002*
BP245, Aïn-Amenas, Wilaya Illizi.
(29) 438159-60 (9) 438159
Open Dates: Imarenas 7km
1.8km x 50

△ ***Aïn-Temouchent*** – *Ville – 1003*
08 Duled Belaid Mohamed.
(43) 604114
Open Dates: Trebcen Zianide 80km; Oran Senia 70km Port D'Oran 75km
100m x 50

▲ **Annaba** – Centre-Ville – 1005
Sidi Brahim Annaba, 23000 Wilaya d'Annaba.
(38) 831041
Open Dates: Annaba (Mohamed Boutiaf) 10km Annaba 1.6km
500m 400m x 50
100m

▲ **Batna** – Centre-Ville – 1006
Hai-Enasr-Cite Du S Juillet, Batna.
(33) 869600 (33) 863807
Open Dates: Batna 25km 800m
1.5km x 50

△ ***Béchar*** – *1007*
ex Cantine Scolaire, Cité Riadi, 08000 Béchar.
(49) 810844
Open Dates: Bechar 7km 4.5km
4km x 50

△ ***Béchar*** – *Centre Ville – 1008*
Hai Essalem.
(49) 813407
Open Dates: Bechar 7km 4km
3km x 50

▲ **Biskra** – Centre-Ville – 1009
Cité des Moudjahidines, Biskra.
(33) 759232
Open Dates: Biskra 10km 500m
300m x 50

▲ **Biskra** – Elkantara – 1010
(33) 792142; 792552
Open Dates: Gare Routiere - Biskra Elkantara 50km x 70

▲ Blida – 1011
Route du Nouveau Stade, Blida.
(25) 430933
Open Dates: 2km 3km 0.4N x 50

△ *Bordj-Bou-Arreridj* – *Parc Attraction – 1012*
Ave du 24 Avril, Route de Setif, Bordj-Bou-Arreridj.
(35) 685687
Open Dates: 1.5km 0.5E x 30 (B)

△ *Bouira* – *Lakhdaria – 1014*
Lakhdaria BP 61 F W Bouira.
(26) 903031 (26) 901461
Open Dates: Houari Boumediene, Alger 60km 500m 200m x 30

▲ Bouira – Bouira – 1067
13 Rue Benabdauah Nohamed, 10000 Wilaya Bouira.
(26) 941049
Open Dates: Alger - Bouira 100km ap Alger - Bouira 100km x 80

△ *Boussaada* – *Centre-Ville – 1013*
Route de Biskra, BP 23, Wilaya de M'Sila.
(35) 522258; 524154
Open Dates: Boussaada 10km 300m x 50

▲ Cherchell – Centre-Ville – 1015
Route de Tenes, Wilaya de Tipasa.
(24) 439752 (24) 439752
Open Dates: 1.5km x 50

▲ Constantine – Centre-Ville – 1016
MJ Cité Filali, Constantine.
(31) 926186
Open Dates: Constantine 10km 4km 2km x 60

△ *Djanet* – *Aj du Tassili – 1017*
Auberge de Jeunesse, Djanet, Wilaya D'illizi.
(29) 470259 (29) 470260/61
Open Dates: Djanet Tiska 22km 6km 0.2NE x 50

△ *Djelfa* – *Centre-Ville – 1018*
Cite du 5 Juillet, Centre Parc Omnisport.
Open Dates: 2km x 50

△ *Djelfa* – *Ain Oussera – 1068*
A.J Ain Oussera, Wilaya Djelfa.
(27) 824904
Open Dates: Alger - Ain Oussera 200km Alger - Ain Oussera 200km x 50

▲ Echlef Centre Ville – Gare Ferroviaire – 1020
Echlef (Gare Ferroviaire).
(27) 777279
Open Dates: 200m 2km x 50

△ *Elbayedh* – *Centre-Ville – 1025*
Elbaydh Centreville.
(49) 718825 (49) 714112
Open Dates: 2km x 50

△ *El-Golea* – *1021*
Auberge de Jeunesse, El-Golea, Wilaya de Ghardaïa.
(29) 812038 (29) 814319
Open Dates: El Golea 13km; Ghardaia 2.7km 2km x 50

▲ El-Kala – Centre-Ville – 1022
Cité du 19 Juin, Wilaya de Tarf 36100.
(38) 661237
Open Dates: Annaba (Mohamed Boutiaf) 60km 800m x 40 500m

△ *El-Oued* – *AJ Taleb el Arabi – 1026*
El-Oued.
(32) 229521
Open Dates: Guemar 100km El Oued 80km x 50

△ *El-Oued* – *Djamaa – 1023*
BP 185. Djamaa Wilaya D'El Oued.
(32) 259853 (32) 259135
Open Dates: Touggourt 50km 800m 600m x 50

▲ **Tiout** – AJ De La Palmeraic – 1059
Wilaya de Naama.
(49) 768177
Open Dates: Mechria 80km
Naama 18km Naama 18km
x 50

△ ***Tissemsilt*** – *Bordj Bounaama – 1065*
Rue du 1 Novenbre Mi 18, Bordj Bounaama.
(46) 494580
Open Dates: Gare Routiere
Tissehfilt 60km x 70

△ ***Tissemsilt*** – *Centre-Ville – 1060*
Arib-Djillali, Tissemsilt.
(46) 470932
Open Dates: Bouchekif 40km
300m 0.7S x 50 R

△ ***Tissemsilt*** – *Teniet El Had – 1061*
(46) 482435
Open Dates: 30km x 38

▲ **Tiziouzou** – Boulila Amar – 1062
Rue Boulila Amar W Tiziouzou.
(26) 222943 (26) 228159
Open Dates: Houari Boumediene, Alger
100km 100km 600m x 50
R

△ ***Tiziouzou*** – *Tigzirt – 1063*
Tigzirt Wilaya, Tiziouzou.
(26) 258041 (26) 258942
Open Dates: Houari Boumediene,
Alger 140km 700m x 50
1 x
600m

▲ **Tlemcen** – Centre-Ville – 1064
Quartier Kebbasse Tlemcen.
(43) 207845 (43) 207845
Open Dates: Le Zianides 15km
A 15km x 50 R

Argentina

Hostelling International Argentina,
Florida 835 Piso 3 Of 319b, C1005AAQ, Buenos Aires, Argentina.

t (54) (11) 45118712
f (54) (11) 43120089
e hiargentina@hostels.org.ar
w www.HIhostels.com/argentina

Office Hours: Monday-Friday 09.00-18.00hrs

A copy of the Hostel Directory for this Country can be obtained from:
The National Office

National Tourist Authority/Board:	www.turismo.gov.ar
Capital:	Buenos Aires
Language:	Spanish
Currency:	Peso
Population:	37,000,000
Size:	3,800,000 sq km
Telephone Country Code:	54
eKit Access Number:	0800-666-1409

Second only in size to Brazil, and populated mostly by Europeans (nearly 40 million), Argentina is historically South America's most sophisticated country. It rejoices in a certain arrogance of culture and good fortune, believing itself to be the continent's 'best brand', by mimicking the panache of the British when playing polo and the snobbism of France in fashion and high society. The capital Buenos Aires, despite its vast population even vied with Paris as the place to visit if you were anybody.

Once the most prosperous country on the continent, built on the export of beef, hides and cereals, made possible by significant British investments in the late nineteenth and early twentieth centuries, it subsequently began to live beyond its means and was recently brought to its knees through bad management of the economy and the currency.

However it has started its recovery. Today, the country of the tango,

Colonel Peron and his wife Eva and the 'disappeared' is signalling a new beginning. Its spectacular natural beauty with the Andes in the west, the longest chain of mountains in the world, forming the border with Chile and Bolivia, remains as fabulous as ever.

A few other Top Tips from **CULTURE SMART!:**

- Argentines are hugely fashion-conscious and are ever ready to make a fashion statement whatever the context and the season, although in business a conservative approach is preferred.
- The Latin rather than the Anglo-Saxon heritage seems to dominate Argentine culture, giving them a warm and effusive nature with handshaking being backed up by kissing on the cheek. If men know each other well, they will also kiss each other hello.
- There are some taboo subjects best avoided, including the Malvinas-Falklands issue, the military dictatorship period and government corruption.
- Unsurprisingly beef is central to Argentine cooking and on all the menus. But pizza, pasta and ice-cream are also widely eaten, reflecting the country's significant Italian population. There is also an Andean Indian cuisine, dishes to be enjoyed including meat stews, and meat or cheese patties.

Culture Smart! Top Tips © Kuperard 2005

Cultural Top Tips supplied by Culture Smart! guides. These essential guides to customs and etiquette will help you steer clear of embarrassing gaffes and sensitive issues, enabling you to discover new cultures whilst developing new friendships. Order online at www.culturesmartguides.co.uk

You can find out a lot more on our website - a visit to www.HIhostels.com is essential for planning your trip!

Pour en savoir plus, rendez-vous sur notre site Internet, www.HIhostels.com une visite incontournable pour préparer votre voyage!

Viele weitere Informationen auf unserer Website: www.HIhostels.com - unverzichtbar für die Reiseplanung!

Puedes averiguar mucho más en nuestro sitio web. Es imprescindible que visites la página www.HIhostels.com para planear tu viaje.

▲ **Bariloche - Rio Negro** – Marcopolo Inn HI 2070
Salta 422
T (02944) 400105 F (02944) 400105
E info@marcopoloinn.com.ar
W www.marcopoloinn.com.ar
Open Dates: 12 ✈ 15km x 60 R

▲ **Bariloche - Rio Negro** – Tango Inn Hostel HI 2051
12 de Octubre 1915, Rio Negro, Bariloche.
T (02944) 430707 E info@tangoinn.com
W www.tangoinn.com
Open Dates: 12 ✈ 15km x 60 R

Buenos Aires – HI - Milhouse Hostel
2017
Hipolito Yrigoyen 959,
C1086AAO - Buenos Aires.
(011) 43459604 (011) 43435038
info@milhousehostel.com
www.milhousehostel.com
Open Dates: Open Times:
Beds: 150
Directions: 0.8E from city centre
Ministro Pistarini 35km A No 86 100m Puerto Nuevo 1km Retiro & Constitucion 1.2km U Line C 100m
R (BD) TV
i P

Buenos Aires – HI - Milhouse Hostel

Buenos Aires – Recoleta Hostel
2050
Libertad 1216.
(011) 48124419 (011) 48124419
info@trhostel.com.ar
www.trhostel.com.ar
Open Dates: Ministro Pistarini International 40km Puerto Nuevo 1km Retiro 1km 152,106, 200m U C-San Martin 500m x 71 R (B) TV i 8

Buenos Aires – St Nicholas Hostel
2028
Bartolome Mitre 1691.
(011) 43735920 (011) 43714364
info@snhostel.com www.snhostel.com
Open Dates: Jorge Newberry 4km Buenos Aires 2km Retiro 2km U Congress Linea A 200m x 48 R (B) TV i 8

Buenos Aires – Tango Backpackers Hostel 2029
Thames 2212.
(011) 47766871 (011) 47766871
info@tangobp.com www.tangobp.com
Open Dates: Jorge Newbery 2.5km A 160 100m Buenos Aires 4km Palermo 400m 38, 39, 67, 59, 29, 111, 152 300m U Plaza Italia Linea D 300m 3.5N x 40 R i

Buenos Aires... Travel Tips

- **For budget eats check out...** Milion, El Desnivel, Grant's, Siga La Vaca, Empire
- **For great nightlife try...** Niceto, Kilkeny, Pacha, Mint, La Catedral
- **Don't miss...** La Boca - Caminito, Plaza de Mayo, Recoleta, Puerto Madero, Palermo - Parque 3 de Febrero, Tigre, San Antonio De Areco

Cafayate - Salta – El Hospedaje Hostel – 2058
Salta No 13.
(03868) 421680
elhospedajehostel@yahoo.com.ar
www.hihostels.com/argentina
Open Dates: Salta City 180km x 37 i P

Calafate - Santa Cruz – Calafate Hostel
2071
Gobernador Moyano 1226
(02902) 492450
calafatehostel@cotecal.com.ar
www.calafatehostels.com
Open Dates: Calafate 20km x 180 R

Calafate - Santa Cruz – Del Glaciar Pioneros Hostel 2009
Los Pioneros 251
(02902) 491243 (02902) 491243
info@glaciar.com www.glaciar.com
Open Dates: Calafate 20km A Aerobus x 128 R CC (BD) 2 x i 8 P

Capitan Sarmiento - Buenos Aires – La Maria Paloma – 2085
Ruta Nac. N°8 km 142,5
(02478) 483282 (02478) 483282
info@lamariapaloma.com.ar
www.lamariapaloma.com.ar
Open Dates: x 20 R

▲ Puerto Madryn - Chubut – El Gualicho Hostel – 2042
Marcos A. Zar 480, Provincia de Chubut.
(02965) 454163
elgualicho@elgualichohostel.com.ar
www.hostels.org.ar
Open Dates: Luis Piedrabuena 500m x 40 (B)

*△ **Rodeo - San Juan** – Rancho Lamaral Hostel – 2061*
Santa Lucia s/n - Dique Cuesta del Viento, San Juan.
(0264) 156702088
rancholamaral@yahoo.com.ar
www.hostels.org.ar
Open Dates: La Chacritas 235km Las 20 de Junio Sa - Valle Del Sol x 35

▲ Rosario - Santa Fe – La Casona de Don Jaime 2079
Pte. Roca 1051
(0341) 5279964 (0341) 5279964
lacasonadedonjaime@yahoo.com.ar
www.youthhostelrosario.com.ar
Open Dates: x 30 (B)

▲ Salta – Backpacker's Hostel 2021
Buenos Aires 930, Provincia de Salta.
(0387) 4235910 (0387) 4235910
hostelsalta@backpackerssalta.com
www.backpackerssalta.com
Open Dates: 8km x 44

▲ Salta – Backpackers Soul – 2080
san juan 413
(0387) 4318944 (0387) 4318944
hostelsalta@backpackerssalta.com
www.hostels.org.ar
Open Dates: x 40

▲ San Juan - San Agustín del Valle Fértil – Valle de la Luna Hostel – 2081
Tucuman s/n entre San Luis y Libertador
(0261) 4255511; 4293460
(0261) 4255511; 4293460
info@campo-base.com.ar
www.hostelvalledelaluna.com.ar
Open Dates: x 20

▲ San Martín de los Andes - Neuquen – Puma Hostel 2026
A. Fosbery 535, Provincia de Neuquen.
(02972) 422443 (02972) 428544; 428545 puma@smandes.com.ar
http://www.pumahostel.com.ar
Open Dates: Campos Chapelco 20km Plumas Verdes 600m 04SE x 47

▲ San Rafael - Mendoza – Tierrasoles Hostel 2049
Alsina 245
(02627) 433449 (02627) 433449
info@tierrasoles.com.ar
www.hostels.org.ar
Open Dates: San Rafael 4km x 32

▲ San Salvador de Jujuy - Jujuy – Yok-Wahi Hostel – 2066
Lamadrid 168.
(0366) 4229608
reservas@yok-wahi.com.ar
www.hostels.org.ar
Open Dates: San Savador de Jujuy 30km x 24

▲ Susques - Jujuy – Pastos Chicos Hostel – 2055
Ruta 16 Susques- Jujuy- Argentina
(0388) 4229608
info@pastoschicos.com.ar
www.hostels.org.ar
Open Dates: San Salvador de Jujuy 237km x 50

▲ Tilcara - Jujuy – Malka Hostel – 2036
Calle San Martin s/n.
(0388) 4955197 (0388) 4955197
malka_tilcara@cootepal.com.ar
www.hostels.org.ar
Open Dates: El Cadillal 20km x 36 (B)

▲ Trevelín - Chubut – Casaverde Hostel – 2037
Los Alerces s/n, Provincia de Chubut.
(02945) 480091 (02945) 480091
casaverdehostel@ciudad.com.ar
www.hostels.org.ar
Open Dates: Esquel 40km Expreso Patagonico 20km 04E x 20 (B)

▲ **Tucumán** – Tucumán Hostel (HI) 2043
Buenos Aires 669, Provincia de Tucumán.
(0381) 4201584 (0381) 4241652
info@tucumanhostel.com
www.tucumanhostel.com
Open Dates: Aeropuerto Internacional Matienzo 12km A Transfer Express Mitre 1.2km x 40 R

▲ **Ushuaia** – Los Cormoranes Hostel (HI) 2056
Kamshem 788 , Province of Tierra del Fuego
(02901) 423459; 434305
loscormoranes@speedy.com.ar
www.hostels.org.ar
Open Dates: 7km 0.6N x 40 R (B) 8

▲ **Ushuaia** – Torre al Sur Hostel – 2038
Gobernador Paz 1437,
Provincia de Tierra del Fuego.
(02901) 430745; 437291 (02901) 437291 torrealsur@speedy.com.ar
www.hostels.org.ar
Open Dates: 3km x 40 R (B) TV P

▲ **Uspallata - Mendoza** – Hostel Internacional Uspallata – 2063
Ruta Nacional 7km 1141, S.
(0261) 4293220; 4257699
(0261) 4257699
reservas@hostels.org.ar
www.hostels.org.ar
Open Dates: x 46 R 8

▲ **Villa General Belgrano - Cordoba** – El Rincón Hostel – 2039
Calle Fleming s/n.
(03546) 461323 (03546) 461761
hostels@hostels.org.ar
www.hostels.org.ar
Open Dates: Cordoba 95km x 56 R P

▲ **Villa La Angostura - Neuquen** – Bajo Cero Hostel – 2044
Rio Caleufu 88, Provincia de Neuquen.
(02944) 495454 (02944) 495454
hostels@hostels.org.ar
www.hihostels.com/argentina
Open Dates: Bariloche 80km 1N x 44 R P

▲ **Villa La Angostura - Neuquen** – Hostel La Angostura – 2082
Calle Barbagelata 157
(0294) 4494834 (0294) 4494834
info@hostellaangostura.com.ar
www.hostellaangostura.com.ar
Open Dates: TV

▲ **Villa Mercedes - Corrientes** – Delicias Del Ibera (HI) 2064
Pujol 1162
(03773) 422508 (03773) 422508
reservas@hostels.org.ar
www.hihostels.org/argentina
Open Dates: Corrientes 260km x 11 R 8 P

▲ **Villa Paranacito - Entre Rios** – Top Malo Hostel – 2040
Ruta Prov. No.46 km 18,2
(03446) 495255 (03446) 495125
hostels@hostels.org.ar
www.hihostels.com/argentina
Open Dates: 2W x 32 TV P

▲ **Villa Traful - Neuquen** – Vulcanche Hostel – 2076
Ruta Provincial 61
(02944) 479028 (02944) 479028
vulcanche@ciudad.com.ar
www.vulcanche.com
Open Dates: R

▲ **Yala - Jujuy** – El Refujio Hostel – 2083
Ruta Nac. 9 Km 14
(0388) 4909344 (0388) 4909344
elrefugio@arnet.com.ar
www.hostels.org.ar
Open Dates: TV

Australia

YHA Australia Inc
PO Box 314,
Camperdown 1450,
New South Wales,
Australia.
t (61) (2) 95651699
f (61) (2) 95651325
e yha@yha.org.au
w www.yha.com.au

A copy of the Hostel Directory for this Country can be obtained from:
The National Office

National Tourist Authority/Board:	www.australia.com
Capital:	Canberra
Language:	English
Currency:	Australian dollar
Population:	20,264,082
Size:	7,692,030 sq km
Telephone Country Code:	61
eKit Access Number:	1800-207-576

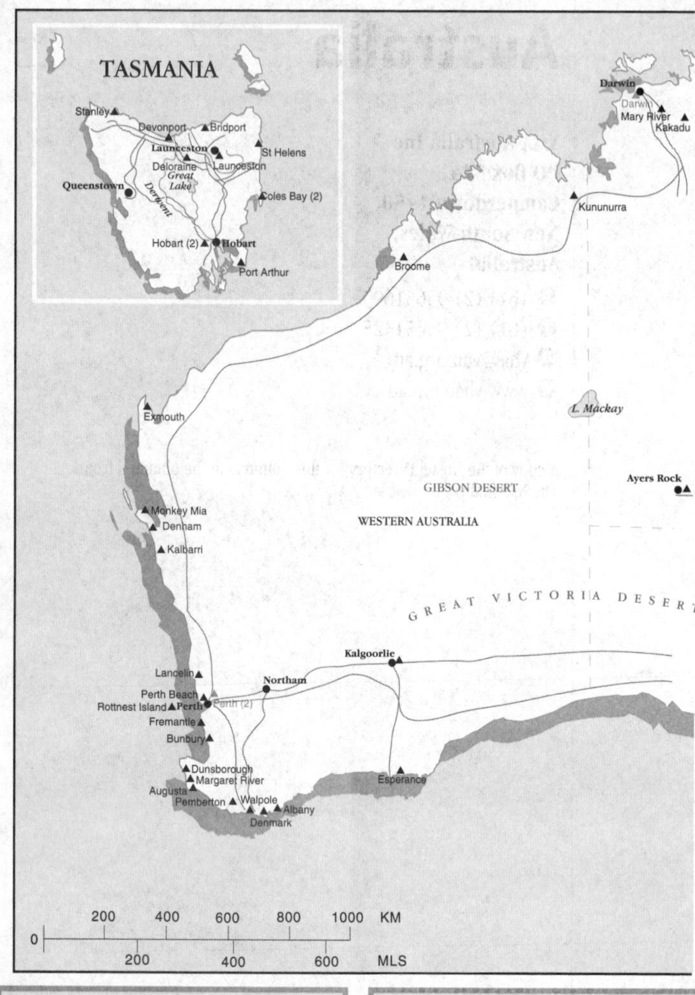

HI Suggests...

From the sparkling blue backdrop of Sydney Harbour, the blood red dust surrounding Uluru, the leafy green rainforests of the Daintree, and the endless miles of unspoilt golden beaches, Australia is as diverse as it is colourful. Whilst there are some that believe they may see a kangaroo hopping down the main street of Sydney, a visit to Australia is likely to dissolve some of the stereotypes of the land down under.

Australia is the sixth largest country in the world. It is about the same size as the 48 mainland states of the USA and 50 per cent bigger than Europe, but has the lowest population density in the world, with only two people per square kilometre. The majority of the 20 million population live in a handful of coastal cities, mostly within 20km of the ocean.

Australia's cities are destinations in their own right, each offering the visitor a new experience with its own sense of history and charm.

Sunny, sexy, sophisticated - Sydney is the shining star of the southern

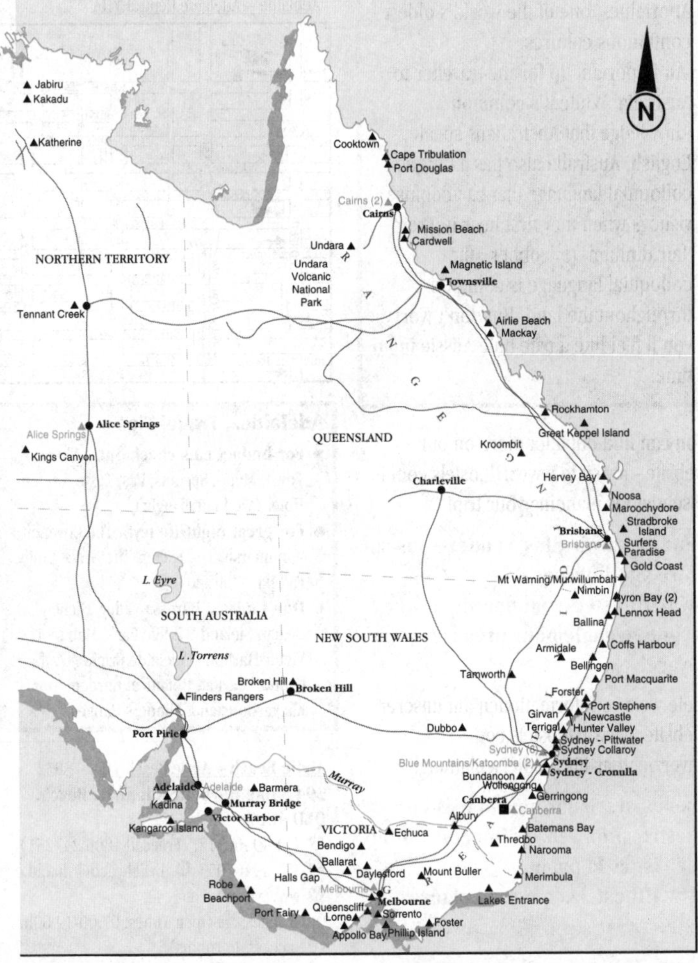

hemisphere, with the stunning Opera House and Sydney Harbour Bridge. Brisbane, in sun blessed Queensland is beautiful one day, perfect the next. Melbourne, Victoria's capital and cultural hub is known for the good things in life - fashion, food and sport. On the west coast in Perth, cool down with Swan River water sports, enjoy a glass of local wine or explore Kings Park. In South Australia, Adelaide is a graceful city of wide streets and elegant buildings, nestled between sea and hills. In the top end, Darwin is a vibrant, tropical capital city and acts as a gateway to key natural and cultural attractions. Hobart, island Tasmania's capital, has a stunning harbour and historic buildings.

Yet, Australia's big attraction is its natural beauty. There is the two thousand kilometre long Great Barrier Reef with its complex of islands and underwater splendour, and the brooding monolith of Uluru at Australia's heart, the outback. The outback is a vast land, often harsh and unforgiving, but with great beauty and variety. It is easy to be swept up with the mythical ceremonies of Australia's

Aborigines, one of the world's oldest continuous cultures.

An important tip for the traveller to Australia: While it's common knowledge that Australians speak English, Australia also has a unique colloquial language that can confuse visitors when they first hear it. From 'fair dinkum' to 'cobber', the colloquial language is common throughout the land. But don't worry, you'll feel like a true blue Aussie in no time.

You can find out a lot more on our website - a visit to www.HIhostels.com is essential for planning your trip!

Pour en savoir plus, rendez-vous sur notre site Internet, www.HIhostels.com une visite incontournable pour préparer votre voyage!

Viele weitere Informationen auf unserer Website: www.HIhostels.com - unverzichtbar für die Reiseplanung!

Puedes averiguar mucho más en nuestro sitio web. Es imprescindible que visites la página www.HIhostels.com para planear tu viaje.

Adelaide – Adelaide Central YHA Ⓗ 3024
135 Waymouth St, Adelaide, SA 5000.
Ⓣ (8) 84143010 ; (Freecall 1800 222942)
Ⓕ (8) 84143015
Ⓔ adlcentral@yhasa.org.au
Ⓦ www.yha.com.au
Open Dates: Open Times: access
Beds: 245 - 23x2 16x4 15x6
Price Range: from $23
Directions: 5km Central 2km
Coach Terminal 100m x 9
R CC 1 x

Adelaide – Adelaide Central YHA

Adelaide... Travel Tips

- **For budget eats check out...** China Town, Mapo, Sprouts, East Taste, Exeter Hotel (Wed curry night)
- **For great nightlife try...** The Govenor Windmarsh, The Exeter, The Grace Emily, Fad Bar, Zhivago
- **Don't miss...** Barossa Valley, Gleneig Beach, Cleland Wildlife Park, Hahndorf, Victor Harbour, Adelaide Cricket Oval, Central Market, Botanical Garden, Kangaroo Island, Flinders Ranges

Airlie Beach – Airlie Beach YHA – 3032
394 Shute Harbour Rd, Airlie Beach, QLD 4802.
Ⓣ (7) 49466312; (Freecall 1800 247251)
Ⓕ (7) 49467053 Ⓔ airliebeach@yhaqld.org
Ⓦ www.yha.com.au
Open Dates: Open Times: 07.00-19.00hrs (access to rooms)
Beds: 86 - 13x2 10x6
Price Range: from $22
Directions: Proserpine 45km
Proserpine 30km 300m
R CC
30m

Airlie Beach – Airlie Beach YHA

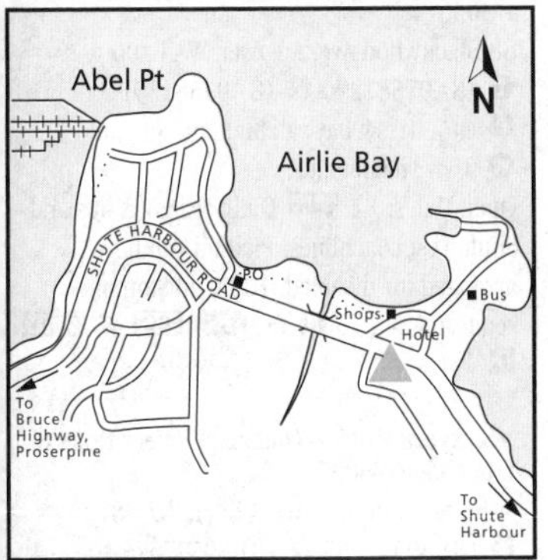

Airlie Beach... Travel Tips

- **For budget eats check out...** KC's Bar & Grill, Sidewalk Cantina, Mangrove Jacks, Sushi Hi, Cappa's
- **For great nightlife try...** The Juice Bar, Mama Africa, Beaches, Magnums, Morocco's
- **Don't miss...** Whitehaven Beach, 74 Islands of The Whitsundays, Great sailing, Diving, Cedar Creek Falls, Conway National Park, Airlie Lagoon, Whitsundays Great Walk

▲ **Albany** – Albany Bayview Backpackers YHA – 3033
49 Duke St, Albany, WA 6330.
(8) 98423388 (8) 98413949
albanyyha@westnet.com.au
www.yha.com.au
Open Dates: Daily Trans WA service from Perth. Phone hostel for free pick up.
Bus stop 500m x 52 500m 500m

▲ **Albury-Wodonga** – Albury Motor Village YHA – 3034
372 Wagga Rd (Hume Hwy), Lavington, NSW 2641.
(2) 60402999 (2) 60403160
albury@yhavic.org.au
www.yha.com.au
Open Dates: 6km 4.6km
Daily services stop across the road from the hostel at North Albury 4.6N x 24

Alice Springs – Pioneer YHA 3030
Corner of Parsons St and Leichhardt Terrace, Alice Springs, NT 0870.
(8) 89528855 (8) 89524144
alicepioneer@yhant.org.au
www.yha.com.au
Open Dates: Open Times: 07.30-20.30hrs
(Please ring if arriving after hours)
Beds: 110 - 4x 10x 3x 3x
Price Range: from $19
Directions: 0.1E from city centre
Alice Springs 15km Regular Services, ""Ghan"" Alice - Adelaide 2km x 2

Alice Springs – Pioneer YHA

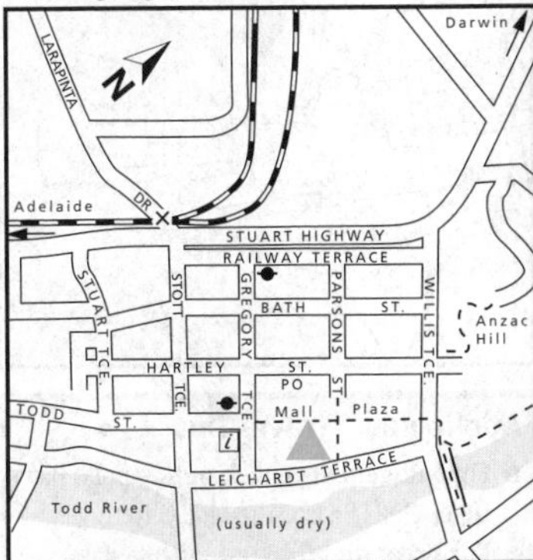

Alice Springs... Travel Tips

- **For budget eats check out...** Yeperenye & Alice Plaza Food Courts, Café Mediterranean Bar Doppio, Alfresco Café, Olive Tree, Pub Caf
- **For great nightlife try...** Sounds of Starlight Theatre, Red Centre Dreaming, Bojangles, Sean's Irish Bar, Firkin & Hound
- **Don't miss...** Sunrise Ballooning in the Desert, Alice Springs Desert Park, Aboriginal Art & Culture Centre, Camel Safaris, Reptile Centre, Uluru/Kata Tjuta National Park, National Pioneer Women's Hall of Fame, West Mac Donnell Ranges, Old Alice Springs Telegraph Station, School of The Air

Apollo Bay – Echo Beach YHA – 3168
5 Pascoe Street, Apollo Bay, VIC, 3233.
(3) 52377899
apollobay@yhavic.org.au
www.yha.com.au
Open Dates: Open Times: 08:00-12:00hrs; 17:00-22.00hrs
Beds: 72 - 8x1 8x2 6x4
Directions: 200m x 2

Apollo Bay – Echo Beach YHA

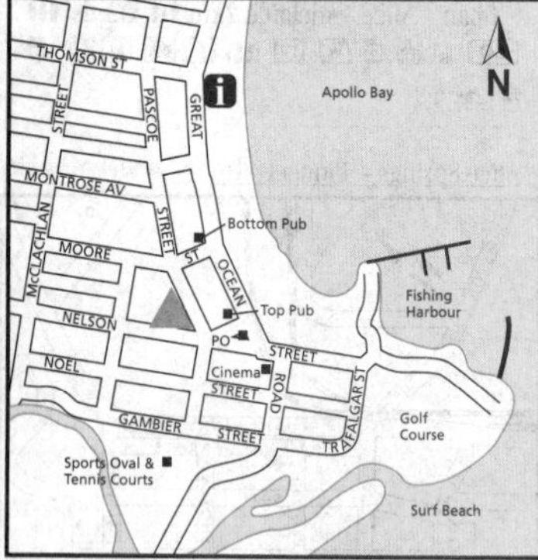

Apollo Bay... Travel Tips

- **For budget eats check out...** Apollo Bay Hotel, Buffs Bistro, The Blue Olive
- **For great nightlife try...** Apollo Bay Hotel, Apollo Bay Life Saving Club
- **Don't miss...** Old Cable Station Museum, Bass Strait Shell Museum, Otway Ranges, Tanbryn Gallery, Horseriding, Glowworm Tows at Melba Gully, The Great Ocean Road, Golf, Cape Otway Light Station, Mariners & Cape Patton Lookouts

▲ **Armidale** – Armidale YHA - Pembroke Tourist & Leisure Park – 3035
39 Waterfall Way, Armidale, NSW 2350.
(2) 67726470; (Freecall 1800 355578)
(2) 67729804
armidale@yhansw.org.au
www.yha.com.au
Open Dates: 4km 3km 2km
x 32

▲ **Augusta** – Baywatch Manor Resort YHA – 3036
88 Blackwood Ave, Augusta, WA 6290.
(8) 97581290 (8) 97581291
enquiries@baywatchmanor.com.au
www.yha.com.au
Open Dates: Daily TransWA bus and Southwest coachlines. Pick up can be arranged for disabled. 100m ap Stop on request x 36

▲ **Ayers Rock** – Outback Pioneer Hotel & YHA Lodge – 3037
Ayers Rock Resort, Ayers Rock, NT 0872.
(8) 89577605 (8) 89577615
reservations@voyages.com.au
www.yha.com.au
Open Dates: A Complimentary airport shuttle Interstate coaches drop off at reception x 168

▲ **Ballarat** – Sovereign Hill Lodge YHA – 3038
Magpie St, Sovereign Hill, Ballarat, VIC 3350.
(3) 53333409 (3) 53335861
ballarat@yhavic.org.au
www.yha.com.au
Open Dates: 3km 3km
x 12

▲ **Ballina** – Ballina Travellers Lodge YHA – 3039
36 Tamar St, Ballina, NSW 2478.
(2) 66866737 (2) 66866342
ballina@yhansw.org.au
www.yha.com.au
Open Dates: 4km 600m
3km x 18

▲ **Barmera** – Barmera Backpackers YHA – 3040
6 Bice Street, Barmera, SA 5345.
(8) 85883007 (8) 85883035
backpack@riverland.net.au
www.yha.com.au
Open Dates: 400m x 25

▲ **Batemans Bay** – Batemans Bay YHA – 3041
Corner of Old Princes Hwy and South Street, Batemans Bay, NSW 2536.
(2) 44724972 (2) 44724045
batemansbay@yhansw.org.au
www.yha.com.au
Open Dates: Moruya 20km 1km
1SE x 38

▲ **Beachport** – Beachport YHA – 3163
Beach Road, Beachport SA 5280.
(8) 87358197 (8) 87358197
beachportyha@bigpond.com
www.yha.com.au
Open Dates: 100m x 20

▲ **Bellingen** – Bellingen YHA – 3042
2 Short St, Bellingen, NSW 2454.
(2) 66551116 (2) 66551358
bellingen@yhansw.org.au
www.yha.com.au
Open Dates: Coffs Harbour 39km
Uranga. Free pick up on request 15km
Uranga. Free pick up on request 15km
0.1SE x 50

▲ **Bendigo** – Bendigo YHA – 3043
33 Creek St South, Bendigo, VIC 3550.
(3) 54437680 (3) 54437687
bendigo@yhavic.org.au
www.yha.com.au
Open Dates: 1km From coach/train station, walk down Edward Street. Turn left into Bath Lane, cross over Short Street. Hostel is 200 metres on the left. 0.4SW
x 26

Blue Mountains – Blue Mountains YHA
3029
207 Katoomba St, Katoomba, NSW 2780.
(2) 47821416 (2) 47826203
bluemountains@yhansw.org.au
www.yha.com.au
Open Dates: Open Times: 07.00-22.00hrs
Beds: 200 - 29x2 24x5 4x6
Price Range: from $24
Directions: Katoomba - hourly trains from/to Sydney 650m Daily services to/from Sydney and Adelaide 650m x 2

Blue Mountains – Blue Mountains YHA

▲ **Blue Mountains** – Hawkesbury Heights YHA – 3044
836 Hawkesbury Rd, Hawkesbury Heights, NSW 2777.
(2) 47545621 (2) 47545621
hawkesburyheights@yhansw.org.au
www.yha.com.au
Open Dates: Springwood 10km
3km x 12

Blue Mountains... Travel Tips

- **For budget eats check out...** Chork Dee Thai, Journey Café, The Dry Dock, The Hattery, Pizzaro
- **For great nightlife try...** Carrington Piano Bar, Clarendon Music Venue, Tris Elies Nightclub, Edge Cinema, Glow Worm Night Walk
- **Don't miss...** Three Sisters, Wentworth Falls, Govetts Leap, Jenolan Caves, Winter Magic Festival, Yulefest, Blue Folk Festival, National Park, Historic Villages, Antique Stores

---

▲ **Bridport** – Bridport Seaside Lodge Backpackers YHA – 3047
47 Main St, Bridport, TAS 7262.
(3) 63561585 (3) 63561585
bridportseasidelodge@hotmail.com
www.yha.com.au
Open Dates: Launceston 95km
Red Line coaches from Launceston to Scottsdale, then Stan's Coaches to Bridport. Twice daily, Mon to Fri only x 21

Brisbane – Brisbane City YHA 3001
392 Upper Roma St, Brisbane, QLD 4000.
(7) 32361004 (7) 32361947
brisbanecity@yhaqld.org
www.yha.com.au
Open Dates: Open Times: 06.30-23.00hrs
Beds: 160 - 35x2 10x3 3x4 4x5 5x6+
Price Range: from $23
Directions: Brisbane International 15km A Direct to hostel Roma Street 600m 600m ap Brisbane Transit Centre

Brisbane – Brisbane City YHA

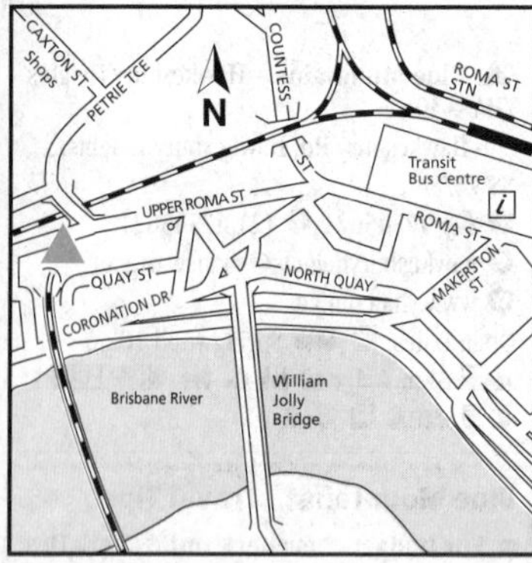

Brisbane... Travel Tips

- **For budget eats check out...** Fortitude Valley, The Windmill Pizza, Caxton Street, South Bank Parklands, Queen Street Mall
- **For great nightlife try...** Fortitude Valley, Caxton Street, South Bank, City Centre
- **Don't miss...** Brisbane River by bike or City Cat, Free Markets (South Bank, Brunswick St, Riverside), South Bank Parklands, Day trip to Stradbroke and Moreton Islands, Story Bridge Adventure Climb, Lone Pine Koala Sanctuary, Roma Street Parklands, Arts & Cultural Centre, XXXX Brewery Tour, Mt Coot-tha Lookout

▲ **Broken Hill YHA** – The Tourist Lodge – 3048
100 Argent St, Broken Hill, NSW 2880.
(8) 80882086 (8) 80879511
brokenhill@yhansw.org.au
www.yha.com.au
Open Dates: Daily flights from Sydney and Adelaide 5km Daily services to/from Sydney 1km 50m x 77

▲ **Broome** – Kimberley Klub YHA – 3049
62 Frederick Street, Broome, WA 6725.
(8) 91923233 (8) 91923530
info@kimberleyklub.com
www.yha.com.au
Open Dates: 200m Courtesy pick up from all Greyhound arrivals 1km x 160

▲ **Bunbury** – Dolphin Retreat YHA – 3171
14 Wellington Street Bunbury WA 6230
(8) 97924690 (8) 97925724
dolphinretreatbunburyyha@iinet.net.au
www.yha.com.au
Open Dates: Bunbury 5km Southwest Coachlines and TransWA 300m x 26

▲ **Bundanoon** – Bundanoon YHA – 3052
Railway Avenue, Bundanoon, NSW 2578.
(2) 48836010 (2) 48837470
bundanoon@yhansw.org.au
www.yha.com.au
Open Dates: Daily services to/from Sydney and Canberra 1km From Sydney with Priors Scenic Express, change at Bowral 1km x 37

Byron Bay – Byron Bay YHA – 3054
7 Carlyle St, Byron Bay, NSW 2481.
(2) 66858853; (Freecall 1800 678195)
(2) 66856766
byronbay@yhansw.org.au
www.yha.com.au
Open Dates: Open Times: 08.00-21.00hrs
Beds: 94 - 8x2 5x4 10x5
Price Range: from $22
Directions: Ballina 34km Daily XPT service from/to Sydney and Brisbane 250m Daily 150m x 1 300m

Byron Bay – Byron Bay YHA

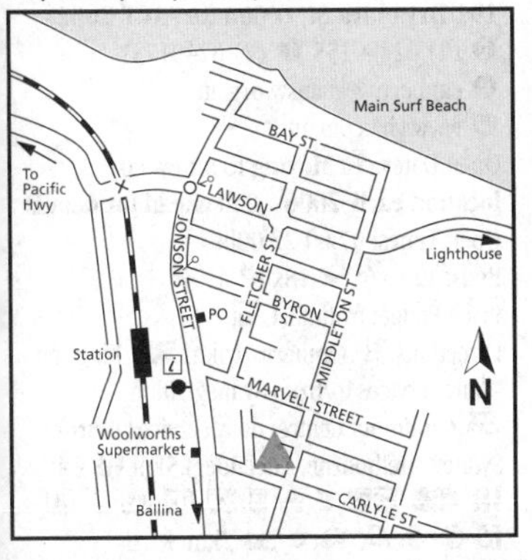

Byron Bay – Cape Byron YHA – 3053
Cnr Byron & Middleton St, Byron Bay, NSW 2481.
(2) 66858788; (Freecall 1800 652627)
(2) 66858814
capebyron@yhansw.org.au
www.yha.com.au
Open Dates: Open Times: 06.45-22.00hrs
Beds: 129 - 6x2 23x5
Price Range: from $25
Directions: Ballina 34km Daily XPT to/from Sydney and Brisbane 200m
200m R CC TV 8 P 100m

Byron Bay – Cape Byron YHA

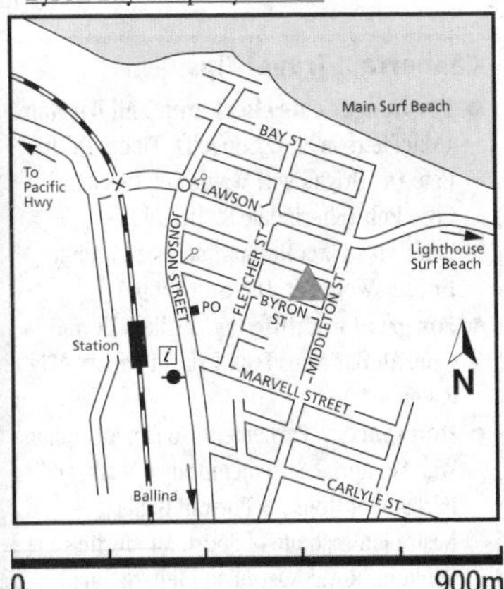

Byron Bay... Travel Tips

- **For budget eats check out...** Bay Kebabs, Cheeky Monkey's, Earth and Sea Pizza, Thai Lucy, Byron Bay RSL
- **For great nightlife try...** Beach Hotel, Cocomangas, Cheeky Monkey's, Great Northern Hotel, Railway Friendly Bar
- **Don't miss...** Byron Bay Lighthouse, Byron Bay Main Beach, Nimbin, World Heritage Rainforest, Broken Head Nature Reserve, Dolphin/Whale watching, Blues & Roots Music Festival, Byron Bay Alternative Markets, Byron Bay Arts & Crafts, Most easterly point of Australia

Cairns – Cairns Central YHA 3016
20-26 McLeod St, Cairns, QLD 4870.
(7) 40510772 (7) 40313158
cairns_central@yhaqld.org
www.yha.com.au
Open Dates: Open Times: 06.30-23.00hrs
(access to rooms)
Beds: 235 - 28x2 8x4 12x6
Price Range: from $23
Directions: Cairns International 12km
A Direct to hostel 100m
500m R CC
TV 8 P

Cairns – Cairns Central YHA

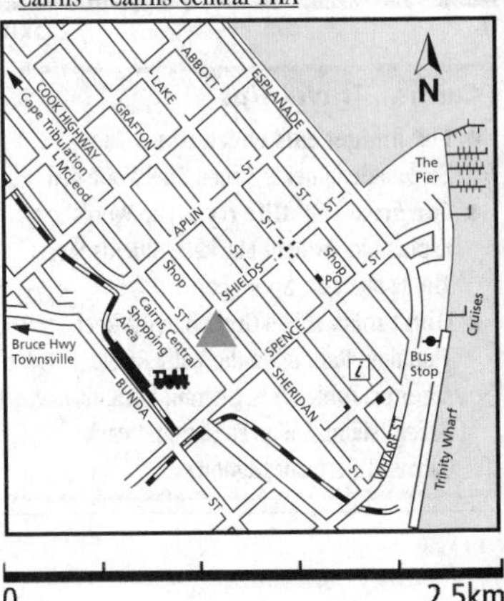

Cairns – Cairns Esplanade YHA – 3055
93 The Esplanade, Cairns, QLD 4870.
(7) 40311919 (7) 40314381
cairnsesplanade@yhaqld.org
www.yha.com.au
Open Dates: Open Times: 07.00-22.00hrs
(access to rooms)
Beds: 68 - 10x2 8x6
Price Range: from $20
Directions: Cairns International 8km
A Direct to hostel 800m
800m

Cairns – Cairns Esplanade YHA

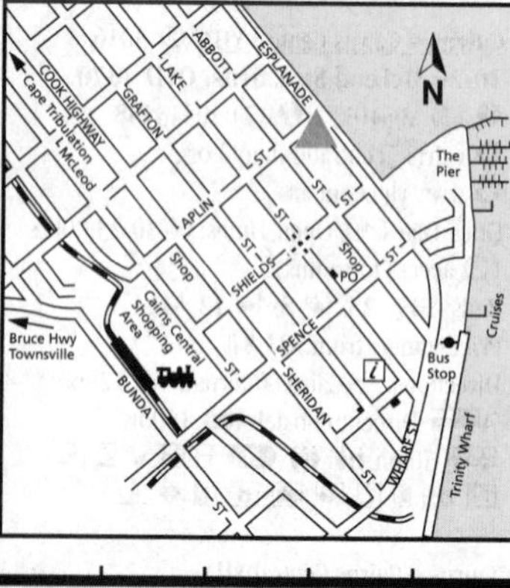

Cairns... Travel Tips

- **For budget eats check out...** The Esplanade, Shields Street, The Woolshed
- **For great nightlife try...** The Woolshed, Esplanade Twilight Markets, Shields Street, The Esplanade, Sportsbar
- **Don't miss...** The Great Barrier Reef, Tjapukai, Rafting on the Tully River, Atherton Tablelands, Skyrail, Kuranda, Green Island, Daintree National Park, Cairns Waterfront Lagoon

Canberra – Canberra YHA 3012
191 Dryandra St, O'Connor, ACT 2602.
(2) 62489155 (2) 62491731
canberra@yhansw.org.au
www.yha.com.au
Open Dates: **Moving to a new city location early 2006 - Call ahead for details**
Open Times: 07.00-22.00hrs
Beds: 124 - 6x2 18x4 4x6
Price Range: from $21
Directions: Canberra 14km Kingston -daily services to/from Sydney 10km
Jolimont Centre, daily services to/from Sydney, Melbourne, Adelaide 3.5km x 4
2km

Canberra – Canberra YHA

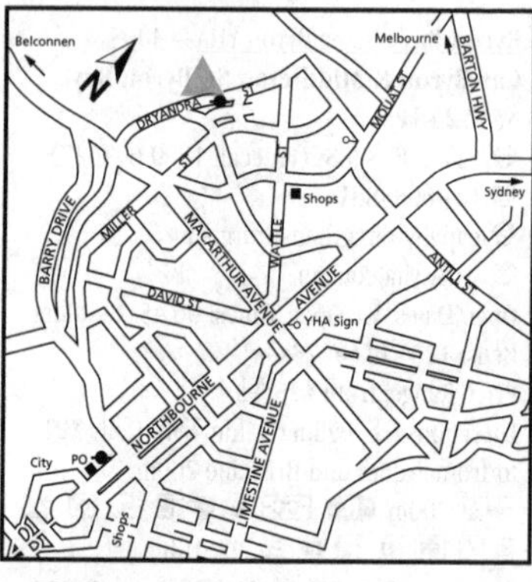

Canberra... Travel Tips

- **For budget eats check out...** All Bar Nun (MacPherson St. O'Connell), Tilleys Devine Café (nr Brigalow & Wattle Sts, Lyneham), Civic Pub (Sherindale St, Braddon), Zeffirelli's Pizza Restaurant, Asian Noodle House (Wolley St, Dickson Shops)
- **For great nightlife try...** Tilleys Devine Café, All Bar Nun, Trinity Bar, Phoenix, Wig & Pen
- **Don't miss...** Parliament House, Australian War Memorial & Remembrance Walk, Old Parliament House & Portrait Gallery, Australian Institute of Sport, Mt Ainslie Lookout, Royal Australian Mint, National Gallery of Australia, National Museum of Australia, National Archives, Tidbinbilla Nature Reserve

▲ **Cape Tribulation** – Crocodylus Village YHA – 3056
Lot 5, Buchanan Creek Rd, Cow Bay, QLD 4873.
(7) 40989166 (7) 40989131
crocodylus@austarnet.com.au
www.yha.com.au
Open Dates: Cow Bay 2km 150km
x 92

▲ **Cardwell** – Hinchinbrook YHA – 3057
175 Bruce Hwy, Cardwell,QLD 4849.
(7) 40668648 (7) 40668910
admin@kookaburraholidaypark.com.au
www.yha.com.au
Open Dates: 1km 800m
x 72

Coffs Harbour – Coffs Harbour YHA Backpackers Resort – 3058
51 Collingwood St, Coffs Harbour, NSW 2450.
(2) 66526462 (2) 66518629
coffsharbour@yhansw.org.au
www.yha.com.au
Open Dates: Open Times: 07.00-23.00hrs; 08.00-22.00hrs (Winter)
Beds: 92 - 7x2 7x4 5x6
Price Range: from $23
Directions: Coffs Harbour 3km Daily services to/from Sydney and Brisbane 500m Daily services to/from Sydney, Brisbane, Tamworth 1km x 5

Coffs Harbour – Coffs Harbour YHA

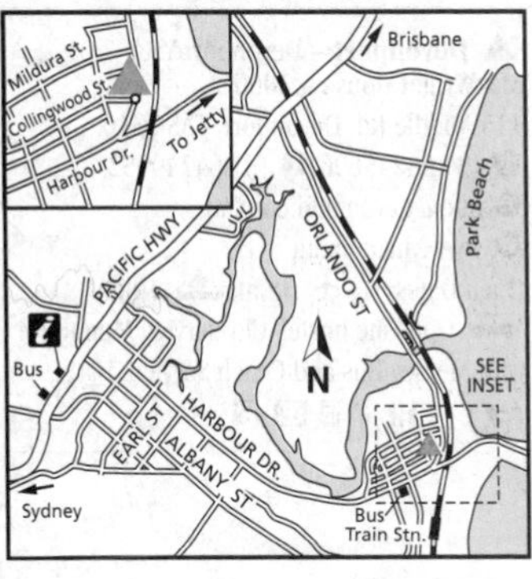

Coffs Harbour... Travel Tips

- **For budget eats check out...** Coffs Harbour Hotel, Plantation Hotel, Coffs Catholic Club, Coffs Yacht Club, Foreshores Café
- **For great nightlife try...** Plantation Hotel, Coffs Harbour Hotel, Hoey Moey Pub, Coffs RSL Club, Heat Nightclub
- **Don't miss...** North Coast Botanic Gardens, Coffs Creek Habitat Walk, Mutton Bird Island, Solitary Islands Marine Park, Coffs Zoo, Big Banana

---

△ ***Coles Bay** – Coles Bay YHA – 3059*
Coles Bay, Freycinet National Park, TAS 7215.
(3) 62349617 (3) 62347422
yhatas@yhatas.org.au
www.yha.com.au
Open Dates: 7km - Bicheno Coach Service will drop off at walking tracks car park (1km from hostel) on request
x 10

▲ **Coles Bay** – Iluka Backpackers YHA – 3060
Esplanade, Coles Bay, TAS 7215.
(3) 62570115 (3) 62570384
ilukaholidaycentre@bigpond.com.au
www.yha.com.au
Open Dates: Bicheno Coach Services meets Redline Coaches or Tassie Link Coaches from Hobart or Launceston x 32

▲ **Cooktown** – Pam's Place YHA – 3061
Cnr Boundary & Charlotte Streets, Cooktown, QLD 4871.
(7) 40695166 (7) 40695964
info@cooktownhostel.com
www.yha.com.au
Open Dates: Local airport with daily flights from Cairns 1km Countryroad Coachlines direct to YH from Cairns x 66

Darwin – Darwin International YHA 3013
69 Mitchell St, Darwin, NT 0800.
(8) 89813995 (8) 89816674
darwinyha@yhant.org.au
www.yha.com.au
Open Dates: Open Times: ; Reception 06.00-24.00hrs
Beds: 324 - 23x2 67x4 2x6
Price Range: from $17
Directions: Darwin International 15km A free Airport Shuttle if reservation is made before arrival Local Bus Depot, Greyhound/McCafferty's terminal located next door

Darwin – Darwin International YHA

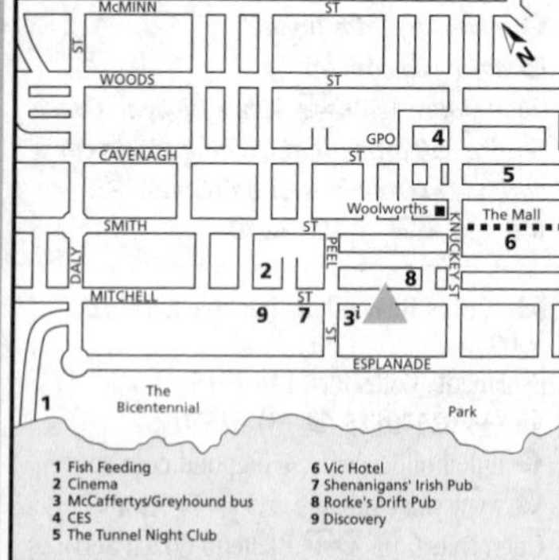

Darwin... Travel Tips

- **For budget eats check out...** Shennanigans Irish Pub, Parap Markets, Mindil Beach Markets, Stokes Hill Wharf, Rendezvous Café
- **For great nightlife try...** The Vic Hotel, Shennanigans Irish Pub, Discovery, Rorke's Drift, Ducks Nuts
- **Don't miss...** Litchfield Park, Kakadu National Park, Crocodylus Park, Botanical Gardens, Sunset Harbour Cruise, Deck Chair Cinema, Northern Territory Museum & Art Gallery, Territory Wildlife Park, Mindil Beach Sunset Markets, Adelaide River Jumping Crocodile Cruise

▲ **Daylesford** – Wildwood YHA – 3063
42 Main Rd, Hepburn Springs VIC 3461.
(3) 53484435 (3) 53483555
daylesford@yhavic.org.au
www.yha.com.au
Open Dates: 2km 3 services each day to/from Melbourne 2km 3N x 21

▲ **Deloraine** – Highview Lodge YHA – 3064
8 Blake St, Deloraine, TAS 7304.
(3) 63622996
bodach@microtech.com.au
www.yha.com.au
Open Dates: Devonport 50km Devonport 50km Regular Red Line and Tassie Link buses 1km x 30

▲ **Denham** – Bay Lodge YHA – 3065
113 Knight Terrace, Denham, WA 6537.
(8) 99481278 (8) 99481031
baylodge@wn.com.au
www.yha.com.au
Open Dates: 7km YH x 62

▲ **Denmark** – Blue Wren Travellers Rest YHA – 3159
17 Price Street Denmark WA 6333.
(8) 98483300
blue.wren@bigpond.com
www.yha.com.au
Open Dates: 50m x 20

▲ **Devonport** – Devonport YHA - MacWright House – 3066
115 Middle Rd, Devonport, TAS 7310.
(3) 64245696 (3) 64249952
info@devonfield.com.au
www.yha.com.au
Open Dates: 10km 10km Opposite hostel. City service Mon to Fri with Mersey Bus and Coach Service 3SW x 45

▲ **Dubbo** – Dubbo Backpackers YHA – 3067
87 Brisbane St (off Newell Highway), Dubbo, NSW 2830.
(2) 68820922 (2) 68820922
dubbo@yhansw.org.au
www.yha.com.au
Open Dates: 5km Daily services to/from Sydney, Katoomba, Broken Hill 500m Daily services to/from Sydney, Melbourne, Brisbane, Newcastle 1km x 24

▲ **Dunsborough** – Dunsborough Beachouse YHA – 3068
201-205 Geographe Bay Rd, Quindalup, WA 6281.
(8) 97553107 (8) 97553028
dunsborough@yhawa.com.au
www.yha.com.au
Open Dates: Train to Bunbury 7 days a week with connecting bus service to Dunsborough. Daily services with Southwest coachlines and TransWA Bus 200m ap request Quindalup x 61

▲ **Echuca** – Echuca Gardens YHA – 3069
103 Mitchell St, Echuca, VIC 3564.
(3) 54806522 echuca@yhavic.org.au
www.yha.com.au
Open Dates: Melbourne 200km Special weekend return service from Melbourne via Bendigo Daily service, courtesy pick up 700m 0.8E x 10

▲ **Esperance** – Blue Waters Lodge YHA – 3070
299 Goldfields Rd, Esperance, WA 6450. (720km SE of Perth).
(8) 90711040 (8) 90711040
yhaesperance@hotmail.com
www.yha.com.au
Open Dates: 20km A Shuttle service available Regular coach services. Phone ahead for free pick up. 2km 1NE x 114

▲ **Exmouth** – Excape Backpackers YHA – 3175
Murat Road, Exmouth WA 6707
(8) 99491200 (8) 99491486
potshotresort@bigpond.com
www.yha.com.au
Open Dates: Learmonth Airport, shuttle bus available $18 38km A Geyhound bus stop at Exmouth Visitors Centre, short walk North along Murat Rd 1km x 82

▲ **Flinders Rangers** – Rawnsky Park Station YHA – 3177
Rawnsky Park Station Wilpena Road, Hawker SA 5434
(8) 8648 0008 (8) 8648 0050
caravanpark@rawnsleypark.com.au
www.yha.com.au
Open Dates: x 20

▲ **Forster** – Dolphin Lodge YHA – 3072
43 Head St, Forster, NSW 2428.
(2) 65558155 (2) 65558155
forster@yhansw.org.au
www.yha.com.au
Open Dates: Taree 35km A 3 x daily to Forster 500m Taree, connecting bus to Forster 30km Daily services from Sydney 500m x 78

▲ **Foster** – Prom Coast Backpackers YHA – 3180
40 Station Road, Foster, VIC 3960.
(3) 56822171; (42) 7875735
foster@yhavic.org.au www.yha.com.au
Open Dates: Melbourne 200km A V-Line Coach Station 200m x 10

▲ **Fremantle** – Backpackers Inn Freo YHA – 3073
11 Pakenham St, Fremantle, WA 6160.
(8) 94317065 (8) 93367106
bpinnfreo@yahoo.com.au
www.yha.com.au
Open Dates: Rottnest Ferry 4 minutes walk 2 minutes walk to Station 2 minutes walk to bus terminal x 140

▲ **Gerringong** – Gerringong YHA - Nestor House – 3078
Fern St, Gerringong, NSW 2534.
(2) 42341249 (2) 42341249 after 16.00hrs gerringong@yhansw.org.au
www.yha.com.au
Open Dates: 1km x 24

△ ***Girvan*** – *Girvan YHA – 3079*
'Canberra', 36 Greys Lane, Girvan, via Stroud, NSW 2425.
(2) 49976639 www.yha.com.au
Open Dates: Bus from Newcastle Station Bulahdelah Coach Lines 25m x 8

▲ **Gold Coast** – Coolangatta YHA – 3080
230 Coolangatta Rd, Bilinga, QLD 4225.
(7) 55367644 (7) 55995436
booking@coolangattayha.com
www.yha.com.au
Open Dates: 1km A courtesy pick up available Courtesy pick up available 2.5km x 82 (B)

▲ **Great Keppel Island** – Great Keppel Island Holiday Village YHA – 3081
Great Keppel Island, QLD 4700.
(7) 49398655; (Freecall 1800 180235)
(7) 49398755
gkiholidays@ozemail.com.au
www.yha.com.au
Open Dates: Ferry to Great Keppel Island daily x 50

Halls Gap – Grampians YHA Eco-Hostel – 3082
Corner Buckler Street and Grampians Rd, Halls Gap, VIC 3381.
(3) 53564544 (3) 53564543
grampians@yhavic.org.au
www.yha.com.au
Open Dates: Open Times:
Beds: 60 - 10x2 10x4
Price Range: from $24
Directions: Daily train from Melbourne to Ballarat, change to coach service to Stawell, then to Halls Gap 26km ap Bus stop at hostel

---

Halls Gap – Grampians YHA Eco-Hostel

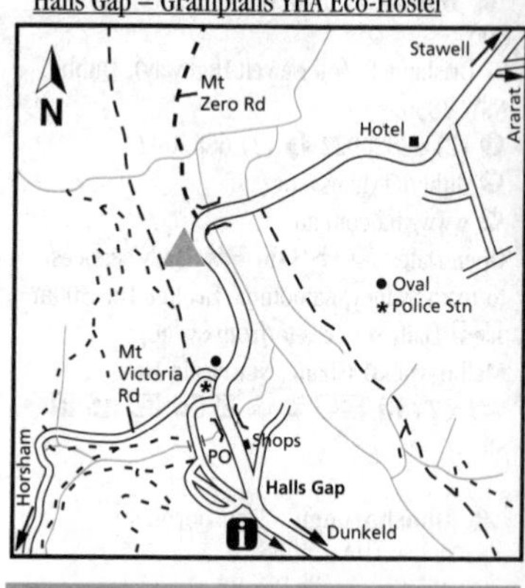

Halls Gap... Travel Tips

- **For budget eats check out...** Halls Gap Hotel, Flying Emu Café, Kookaburra Restaurant
- **For great nightlife try...** Mountain View Hotel, Halls Gap Hotel
- **Don't miss...** Grampians National Park, Aboriginal Rock Art, Waterfalls, Abseiling, Rock climbing, Guided nature walks, Mountain bike riding, Jazz Festival (February), Vineyards, Bush walking

---

▲ **Hervey Bay** – Colonial Cabins Resort YHA – 3083
820 Boat Harbour Drive, Hervey Bay, QLD 4655.
(7) 41251844; (Freecall 1800 818280)
(7) 41253161
herveybay@bigpond.com
www.yha.com.au
Open Dates: 3km Local bus from station to hostel 30km Courtesy pick up available 7km x 125

Hobart – Adelphi Court YHA – 3084
17 Stoke St, New Town, TAS 7008.
(3) 62284829 (3) 62782047
adelphi@yhatas.org.au
www.yha.com.au
Open Dates: Open Times: 07.30-10.30hrs; 16.00-21.00hrs (16.12-15.03); 08.00-10hrs; 16.00-19.00hrs (16.03-15.12)
Beds: 115 - 16x2 5x3 8x4 1x6
Price Range: from $20
Directions: 2N from city centre
Hobart 18km A Shuttle service departs 10-15 minutes after each domestic arrival 300km 25-42, 100, 105-128 depart from stop E Metro City Bus Terminus outside GPO in Elizabeth Street ap Stop 13, 15-16 departs from Argyle Street ap Stop 8A x 12 R CC (B) 2 x 1km

Hobart – Adelphi Court YHA

▲ **Hobart** – Montgomery's YHA Backpackers – 3085
9 Argyle St, Hobart, TAS 7000.
(3) 62312660 (3) 62314817
montys@southcom.com.au
www.yha.com.au
Open Dates: Hobart 18km
A Shuttle service departs airport 10-15 minutes after each domestic arrival
100m x 112 R CC

Hobart... Travel Tips

- **For budget eats check out...** A Taste of Asia, Ball & Chain Grill, Black Buffalo Hotel, Customs House Hotel, Thai Garden Restaurant
- **For great nightlife try...** Salamanca Place, Isobar, Republic Bar & Café, Wrest Point Hotel Casino, Saint Ives
- **Don't miss...** Battery Point Historic Village, Mount Wellington, Mount Nelson Signal Station & Lookout, Richmond Historic Village, Cadburys Chocolate Factory, Cascade Brewery, Tasmanian Museum & Art Gallery, Royal Tasmanian Botanical Gardens, Maritime Museum of Tasmania, Derwent River Cruise

▲ **Hunter Valley** – Hunter Valley YHA – 3179
100 Wine Country Drive, Nulkaba NSW 2325.
(2) 49913278 (2) 49913278
huntervalley@yhansw.org.au
www.yha.com.au
Open Dates: Newcastle 40km
A Cessnock 2km Maitland 40km
x 46

▲ **Jabiru** – Kakadu National Park/Jabiru – 3172
Lakeview Park YHA Lakeview Drive Jabiru, Northern Territory 0886.
(8) 89793144 (8) 89792176
info@lakeviewkakadu.com.au
www.yha.com.au
Open Dates: ap 500m - 24hrs notice for pick up x 95

▲ **Kadina** – Iron Horse Junction YHA – 3162
7 Francis Terrace, Kadina SA 5554.
(8) 88213886 (8) 88213886
ironhorse@yp-connect.net
www.yha.com.au
Open Dates: Premier Stateliner twice a day from Adelaide 100m ap YH x 24

△ ***Kakadu National Park*** *– Gagudju Lodge YHA – 3086*
off Kakadu Hwy, Kakadu National Park, NT 0886.
(8) 89790145 (8) 89790148
reservations@gagudjulodgecooinda.com.au www.yha.com.au
Open Dates: At reception ap YH
0.2W x 44 R CC

Kalbarri – Kalbarri Backpackers YHA – 3088
51 Mortimer Street, Kalbarri, WA 6536.
(8) 99371430 (8) 99371563
kalbarribackpackers@wn.com.au
www.yha.com.au
Open Dates: TransWA & Greyhound Services 400m x 48

Kalgoorlie – Golddust Backpackers YHA – 3089
192 Hay St, Kalgoorlie, WA 6430.
(8) 9091 3737 (8) 90913737
golddust@westnet.com.au
www.yha.com.au
Open Dates: 4km Daily from/to Perth 1km 1km x 53

Kangaroo Island – Kangaroo Island YHA – 3090
33 Middle Tce, Penneshaw, Kangaroo Island, SA 5222.
(8) 85531344 (8) 85531278
kangarooisland@yhasa.org.au
www.yha.com.au
Open Dates: Open Times:
Beds: 48
Price Range: from $23
Directions: 110S from city centre
60km 100m 100m Twice daily service from Adelaide to Cape Jervis, connecting with ferry to Kangaroo Island

Kangaroo Island – Kangaroo Island YHA

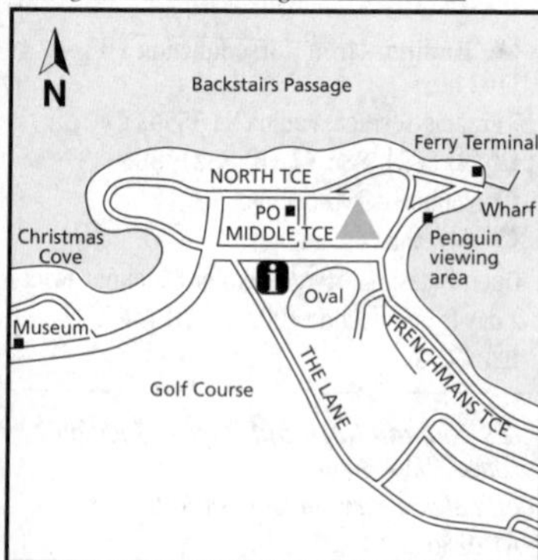

Katherine – Kookaburra Backpackers YHA – 3091
Corner Lindsay and Third Streets, Katherine, NT 0850.
(8) 89710257; Free call 1800808211
(8) 89721567
kookaburrabackpacker@bigpond.com
www.yha.com.au
Open Dates: Greyhound service daily 500m x 60

Katoomba ☛ **Blue Mountains**

Kings Canyon – Kings Canyon YHA – 3092
Ernest Giles Rd, Watarrka National Park, Kings Canyon, NT 0872.
(8) 89567442 (8) 89567410
reservations@voyages.com.au
www.yha.com.au
Open Dates: ap YH x 96

Kroombit – Kroombit YHA – 3093
"Lochenbar Station", Valentine Plains, Biloela, QLD 4715.
(7) 49922186 (7) 49924186
lochenbar@kroombit.com.au
www.yha.com.au
Open Dates: 40km 35km 35E x 142

Kununurra – Kimberley Croc YHA – 3094
Cnr Konkerberry Drive & Tristania St, Kununurra, WA 6743.
(8) 91682702; 1300136702
(8) 91693122
kimberley.croc@westnet.com.au
www.yha.com.au
Open Dates: 4km Courtesy bus to/from hostel. 600m x 49

Lakes Entrance – Riviera Backpackers YHA – 3095
669-671 Esplanade, Lakes Entrance, VIC 3909.
(3) 51552444 (3) 51554558
lakesentrance@yhavic.org.au
www.yha.com.au
Open Dates:
Premier/V-Line/Sapphire Coast buses stop at hostel 1NE x 56

Lancelin – Lancelin Lodge YHA – 3096
10 Hopkins St, Lancelin, WA 6044.
(8) 96552020 (8) 96552021
accom@lancelinlodge.com.au
www.yha.com.au
Open Dates: 130km Buses from Perth directly to hostel every Mon, Wed and Fri. R (08) 9655 2020. x 40 CC 200m

Launceston – The Devils Playground YHA – 3097
10 Morris Street Prospect TAS 7250
(3) 6343 3119 (3) 6344 7917
info@thedevilsplayground.com.au
www.yha.com.au
Open Dates: 0.1W x 99 R CC TV

Lennox Head – Lennox Head Beach House YHA – 3098
3 Ross St, Lennox Head, NSW 2478.
(2) 66877636
lennoxhead@yhansw.org.au
www.yha.com.au
Open Dates: Ballina 13km Country Link 600m Premier Coaches stop 800m Other coach stop 12km x 46 R CC TV

Lorne – Great Ocean Road Backpackers YHA – 3099
10 Erskine Avenue, Lorne, VIC 3232.
(3) 52891809 (3) 52892508
lorne@yhavic.org.au www.yha.com.au
Open Dates: Melbourne 100km Train to Geelong then V/Line bus to Lorne. 100m ap Erskine River, walk up Erskine Avenue to hostel x 36 CC

▲ **Mackay** – Larrikin Lodge YHA – 3100
32 Peel St, Mackay, QLD 4740.
(7) 49513728 (7) 49514660
larrikin@mackay.net.au
www.yha.com.au
Open Dates: 4km 4km 700m x 28

▲ **Magnetic Island** – Bungalow Bay Resort YHA – 3101
40 Horseshoe Bay Rd, Magnetic Island, QLD 4819.
(7) 47785577 (7) 47785781
info@bungalowbay.com.au
www.yha.com.au
Open Dates: Sunferries operate ferry service between Townsville and Magnetic Island x 105 200m

▲ **Margaret River** – Margaret River Lodge YHA – 3103
220 Railway Terrace, Margaret River, WA 6285.
(8) 97579532 (8) 97572532
stay@mrlodge.com.au
www.yha.com.au
Open Dates: Daily bus services. Free pick up from bus stop by prior arrangement 1.5km x 111

▲ **Maroochydore** – Maroochydore YHA Backpackers – 3104
24 Schirrmann Drive, Maroochydore, QLD 4558.
(7) 54433151; (Freecall 1800 302855)
(7) 54793156
mail@yhabackpackers.com
www.yha.com.au
Open Dates: 6km A Airport shuttle bus direct to and from hostel Local (Sunbus 2) service between Nambour and hostel 15km Courtesy pick up available 2km x 48

▲ **Mary River Park** – Mary River YHA – 3105
Arnhem Hwy, Mary River NT.
(8) 89788877 (8) 89788899
general@maryriverpark.com.au
www.yha.com.au
Open Dates: Greyhound buses stop at the hostel x 11 R

Melbourne – Melbourne Metro YHA
3002
78 Howard St, North Melbourne, VIC 3051.
(3) 93298599 (3) 93268427
melbmetro@yhavic.org.au
www.yha.com.au
Open Dates: Open Times:
Beds: 348 - 15x1 20x2 40x4 1x6 6x6+
Price Range: from $26
Directions: 1.4N from city centre
Melbourne 26km A Skybus operates 24 hours to/from Spencer St Station, also operates specific hours to hostel Station Pier 3.25km Spencer Street 1.4km 1km to Franklin St 55 from William St, 200m up Queensberry St 8 1km

Melbourne – Melbourne Metro YHA

Melbourne – Melbourne Oasis YHA – 3106
76 Chapman St, North Melbourne, VIC 3051.
(3) 93283595 (3) 93297863
oasis@yhavic.org.au www.yha.com.au
Open Dates: Open Times:
Beds: 120 - 44x² 3x³ 3x⁴
Price Range: from $27
Directions: 2SW from city centre
Melbourne 26km A Skybus operates 24 hours to/from Spencer St station, also operates specific hours directly to the hostel 50m Station Pier 4.25km Spencer Street 2.5km 2.5km to Franklin and Spencer Street 57 or 59 from Elizabeth St, travel N to Stop 18, Abbotsford St
U Melbourne Central 1.25km
2km

Melbourne – Melbourne Oasis YHA

Melbourne... Travel Tips

- **For budget eats check out...** Warwick Thai (Sydney Road), Thresherman's Bakehouse (Faraday Street), Pellegrinis (Bourke Street), Town Hall Hotel (Errol Street), Chocolate Buddha (Federation Square)
- **For great nightlife try...** Brunswick St., Cookie Bar (Swanston Street), Pug Mahones (Hardware Lane), Young & Jacksons Pub (Swanston Street), Manchester Lane
- **Don't miss...** The Zoo, Melbourne Museum, Aquarium, Botanical Gardens, Rialto, St Kilda Esplanade, Victoria Market, Southbank, M.C.G. (Melbourne Cricket Ground), Old Melbourne Gaol

Merimbula – Wandarrah Lodge YHA – 3107
8 Marine Parade, Merimbula, NSW 2548.
(2) 64953503 (2) 64953163
merimbula@yhansw.org.au
www.yha.com.au
Open Dates: Merimbula 2km
Daily services to/from Sydney, Melbourne, Canberra. Free pick up on request 400m x 49 R CC

Mission Beach – Treehouse YHA – 3108
Frizelle Rd via Bingil Bay Rd, Mission Beach, QLD 4852.
(7) 40687137 (7) 40687028
treehouse@qld.chariot.net.au
www.yha.com.au
Open Dates: Open Times: 07.15-20.30hrs
Beds: 56
Price Range: from $20
Directions: 25km Courtesy bus meets all coaches 08.00-20.15hrs 7km CC

Mission Beach – Treehouse YHA

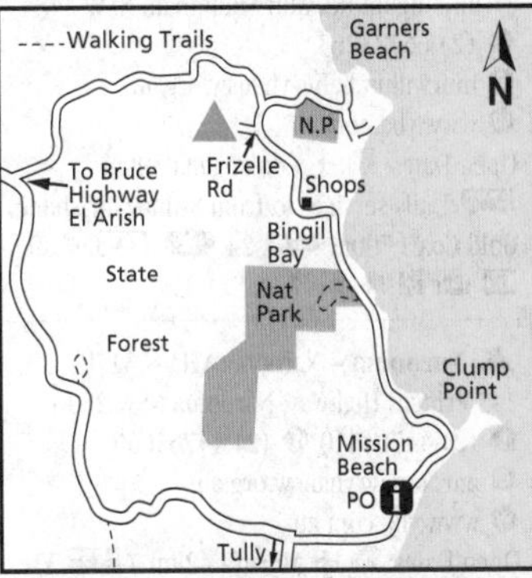

Mission Beach... Travel Tips

- **For budget eats check out...** Fish Bites, Café Coconutz, Munchie Mart, Look What's Cooking, Oceania Bar & Grill
- **For great nightlife try...** Rafter's, Coconutz, Shrubbery, Oceania
- **Don't miss...** White Water Rafting, Skydiving on the Beach, Snorkelling on the River, Crocodile Spotting, Scuba Diving, Dunk Island, Rainforest Walks, Kayaking, Jet Ski, Cassowary spotting

▲ **Monkey Mia/Shark Bay** – Monkey Mia Dolphin Resort YHA – 3109
Monkey Mia Rd, Monkey Mia, Shark Bay, WA 6537.
(8) 99481320; 1800 653 611
(8) 99481034
reservations@monkeymia.com.au
www.yha.com.au
Open Dates: 11km A Shuttle bus available Daily service. Pick up and drop off at hostel x 113

▲ **Mount Buller** – YHA Lodge – 3110
The Avenue, Mt Buller, VIC 3723.
(3) 57776181 (3) 57776691
mountbuller@yhavic.org.au
www.yha.com.au
Open Dates: Ski season Jun-Oct V/Line bus connects with Mansfield Mt Buller Buslines (Winter only) x 46

▲ **Mount Warning/Murwillumbah** – Murwillumbah YHA - Riverside Backpackers – 3113
1 Tumbulgum Rd, Murwillumbah, NSW 2484.
(2) 66723763
murwillumbah@yhansw.org.au
www.yha.com.au
Open Dates: Coolangatta 30km
Daily services to/from Sydney, Brisbane, Gold Coast 700m x 24

▲ **Narooma** – Narooma YHA – 3178
243 Princes Highway, Narooma NSW 2546.
(2) 44764440 (2) 44765660
narooma@yhansw.org.au
www.yha.com.au
Open Dates: Moruya 42km A YH x 31

Newcastle – Newcastle Beach YHA – 3116
30 Pacific St (Corner King Street), Newcastle, NSW 2300.
(2) 49253544 (2) 49253944
newcastle@yhansw.org.au
www.yha.com.au
Open Dates: Open Times: 07.00-22.30hrs
Beds: 100 - 2x1 9x2 10x4 3x6+
Price Range: from $25
Directions: Williamtown 15km
Hourly service to/from Sydney 150m
150m x 4

Newcastle – Newcastle Beach YHA

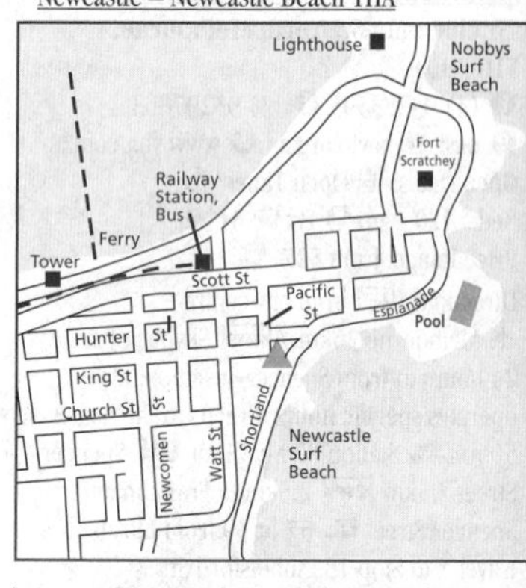

Newcastle... Travel Tips

- **For budget eats check out...** M J Finnegans, The Last Drop, San Marco on the Park, Keith's Kitchen Westminster Café
- **For great nightlife try...** M J Finnegans Irish Pub, The Great Northern, Hotel Delany, The Brewery, The Crown & Anchor Hotel
- **Don't miss...** Beaches, Newcastle Regional Museum, Newcastle Regional Art Gallery, Blackbutt Reserve, The Wetlands Centre, Hunter Valley Wineries

---

▲ **Nimbin** – Nimbin Rox YHA – 3117
74 Thorburn Street, Nimbin, NSW 2480.
(2) 6689 0022 (2) 66890022
nimbinrox@yhansw.org.au
www.yha.com.au
Open Dates: Lismore 32km
Lismore 32km Nimbin-Byron Shuttle 1km x 28

▲ **Noosa Heads** – Halse Lodge Guesthouse YHA – 3118
2 Halse Lane, Noosa Heads, QLD 4567.
(7) 54473377; (Freecall 1800 242567)
(7) 54472929
backpackers@halselodge.com.au
www.yha.com.au
Open Dates: Maroochydore 28km
Nambour 34km 50m x 92
200m

Rockhampton... Travel Tips

- **For budget eats check out...** Victoria Hotel, Post Office Hotel, Criterion Hotel, Great Western Hotel
- **For great nightlife try...** Great Western Hotel, East Street, William Street
- **Don't miss...** Great Keppel Island, Great Western Rodeo, Rockhampton Botanical Gardens, Capricorn Daves Beef 'n' Reef Adventures, Capricorn Caves, Crocodile Farm, Myella Farm Stay Day Tours, Kroombit Farm Stay, Dreamtime Cultural Centre, Gemstone Fossicking

▲ **Rottnest Island** – Rottnest Island YHA – 3134
Kingstown Barracks, Rottnest Island, WA 6161.
(8) 94329111; (Freecall 1800 111111)
(8) 94329315
reservations@rottnestisland.com
www.yha.com.au
Open Dates: 1.5km Several ferries daily from Fremantle. 20 mins walk from Ferry Jetty or free shuttle bus from Accommodation Office near Jetty. 1.5km Free shuttle bus from the main bus stop to Kingstown 27W x 54

▲ **Sorrento** – Sorrento Beach House YHA – 3137
3 Miranda St, Sorrento, VIC 3943.
(3) 59844323 (3) 59842430
sorrento@yhavic.org.au
www.yha.com.au
Open Dates: Melbourne to Frankston 788 from Frankston Station to Stop 18 x 29

▲ **St Helens** – St Helens YHA – 3139
5 Cameron St, St Helens, TAS 7216.
(3) 63761661; (4) 28140958
(3) 63761661 yhatas@yhatas.org.au
www.yha.com.au
Open Dates: Daily except Sat 100m x 20

▲ **Stanley** – Stanley YHA – 3140
Wharf Rd, Stanley, TAS 7331.
(3) 64581266 (3) 64581255
enquiries@stanleycabinpark.com.au
www.yha.com.au
Open Dates: Burnie-Wynyard 61km Mon-Fri Hobart to Stanley, Tasmanian Redline Coaches 50m x 24

△ ***Stradbroke Island*** – *Manta Lodge & Scuba Centre YHA – 3158*
1 Eastcoast Rd, Point Lookout 4183.
(7) 3409 8888 (7) 3409 8588
stay@mantalodge.com.au
www.yha.com.au
Open Dates: 20km Catch train to Cleveland for connecting to island x 62

▲ **Surfers Paradise/Gold Coast** – British Arms International Backpackers Resort YHA – 3142
Mariners Cove, 70 Seaworld Drive, Main Beach, Surfers Paradise, QLD 4217.
(7) 55711776 (Freecall 1800 680269 reservations only) (7) 55711747
info@britisharms.com.au
www.yha.com.au
Open Dates: Coolangatta 20km Free pick up available from hostel 4km 4N x 112

Sydney – Bondi Beachouse YHA – 3143
Cnr Fletcher and Dellview Street, Bondi Beach, NSW 2027.
(2) 93652088 (2) 93652177
bondi@yhansw.org.au
www.yha.com.au
Open Dates: Open Times: 07.00-22.00hrs
Beds: 95 - 16x1 11x2 6x4 2x6
Price Range: from $22
Directions: 10E from city centre
Sydney Airport - phone on arrival for pick up 15km Bondi Junction Station, take bus 381 3km 381 50m x 5

Sydney – Bondi Beachouse YHA

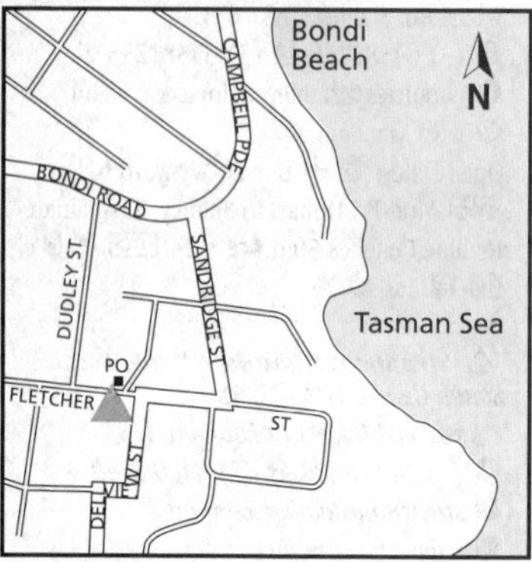

▲ **Sydney** – Cronulla Beach YHA 3028
Level 1, 40-42 Kingsway, Cronulla, NSW 2230.
(2) 95277772 (2) 95270533
cronulla@yhansw.org.au
www.yha.com.au
Open Dates: Train to Wolli Creek. From there Illawara Line to Cronulla Station 15km Cronulla Station - walk north to YHA 300m 30km x 70

▲ **Sydney** – Dulwich Hill YHA 3144
407 Marrickville Road, Dulwich Hill, NSW 2203.
(2) 95500054 (2) 95500570
dulwichhill@yhansw.org.au
www.yha.com.au
Open Dates: Sydney Airport 5km Dulwich Hill station 500m 426, 428 ap YH x 170

△ ***Sydney*** *– Garie Beach YHA – 3074*
Royal National Park, NSW 2508.
(2) 92611111 (2) 92611969
bookings@yhansw.org.au
www.yha.com.au
Open Dates: Ferry from Cronulla to Bundeena - 15km walk 15km Otford - walk 10km to YHA 10km x 12

Sydney – Glebe Point YHA 3003
262-264 Glebe Point Rd, Glebe, NSW 2037.
(2) 96928418 (2) 96600431
glebe@yhansw.org.au
www.yha.com.au
Open Dates: Open Times: 07.00-19.30hrs; 20.00-23.00hrs
Beds: 147 - 17x2 6x3 19x4 3x5
Price Range: from $25
Directions: Sydney 16km A Airport private shuttle to Central then bus to Glebe 16km Central 2.5km, take bus or light rail to YHA 431, 432, 433, 434 depart along George St and Railway Square 2.5km - YH 10m Jubilee Park Station 500m U Central Station 2.5km 2km

Sydney – Glebe Point YHA

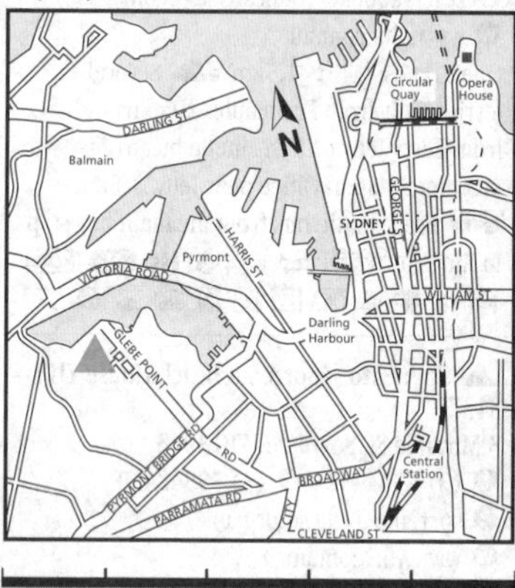

▲ **Sydney** – Pittwater YHA – 3145
Via Halls Wharf, Morning Bay via Church Point, NSW 2105. (30km N of Sydney - Kur-ring-gai National Park). Call to discuss arrival details.
(2) 99995748 (2) 99995749
pittwater@yhansw.org.au
www.yha.com.au
Open Dates: Ferry or water taxi to Halls Wharf from Church Point 1 hour bus from Sydney City to Church Point x 32

Sydney – Railway Square YHA 3160
8-10 Lee Street, Sydney NSW 2000.
(2) 92819666 (2) 92819688
railway@yhansw.org.au
www.yha.com.au
Open Dates: Open Times:
Beds: 280 - 10x2 40x4 6x6 8x6+
Price Range: from $28
Directions: Sydney Airport 10km
A Take Airport private shuttle to YHA or train from Airport Follow Railway Square signs to YHA 50m 150m to Coach Terminal

Sydney – Railway Square YHA

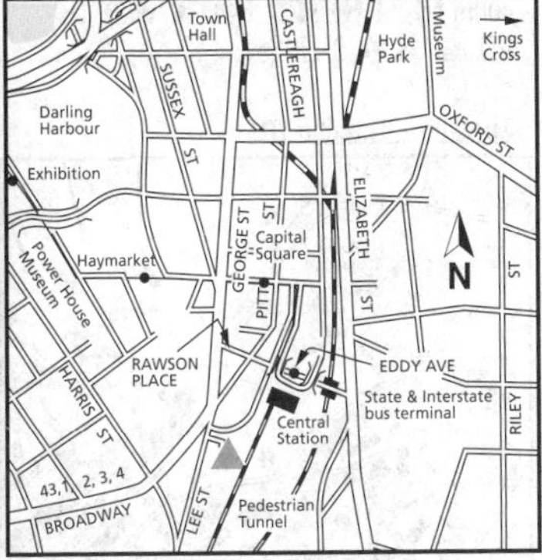

Sydney – Sydney Beachouse YHA - Collaroy 3027
4 Collaroy St, Collaroy Beach, NSW 2097.
(2) 99811177 (2) 99811114
collaroy@yhansw.org.au
www.yha.com.au
Open Dates: Open Times: 08.00-21.00hrs
Beds: 212 - 13x2 24x4 10x6
Price Range: from $20
Directions: Sydney 30km A Direct shuttle bus service from Sydney to Collaroy (must be booked) L90, L88 from Railway Square 50m x 9

Sydney – Sydney Beachouse YHA - Collaroy

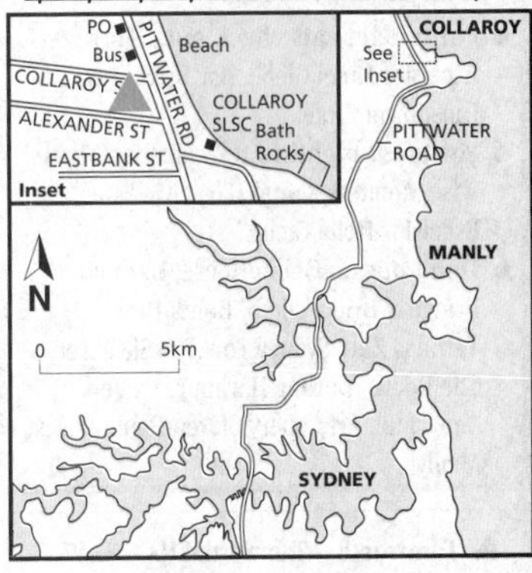

Sydney – Sydney Central YHA 3014
Sydney Central YHA, 11 Rawson Place. (cnr Pitt St and Rawson Place opposite Central Railway Station) NSW 2000.
(2) 92189000 (2) 92189099
sydcentral@yhansw.org.au
www.yha.com.au
Open Dates: Open Times:
Beds: 556 - 54x2 70x4 24x6 3x6+
Price Range: from $29
Directions: Sydney 10km A Airport private shuttle stops at YHA 100m
Central Railway Station opposite YHA 100m All buses stop at Railway Square 100m ap Central Station (BL)

Sydney – Sydney Central YHA

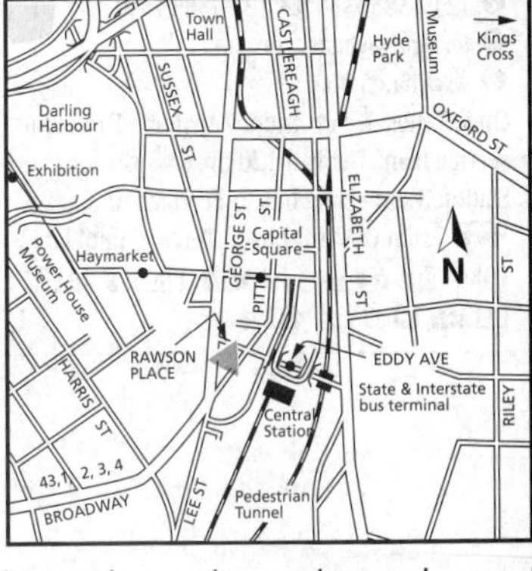

0 5km

Sydney... Travel Tips

- **For budget eats check out...** Forresters, Excelsior Hotel Glebe, Bar Broadway, Lansdowne Hotel
- **For great nightlife try...** Scubar, Three Wise Monkeys, Cargo Bar, Civic Hotel, Excelsior Hotel Glebe
- **Don't miss...** Opera House, Harbour Bridge & Bridgeclimb, Bondi Beach, Taronga Zoo, Sydney Tower & Skytower, The Rocks, Darling Harbour, Sydney Aquarium, Art Gallery of New South Wales, Manly

▲ **Tamworth** – Tamworth YHA – 3147
169 Marius St, Tamworth, NSW 2340.
(2) 67612600 (2) 67612002
tamworth@yhansw.org.au
www.yha.com.au
Open Dates: 12 Tamworth 8km 100m To/from Sydney and Brisbane 1km 0.2N x 43 R

▲ **Tennant Creek** – Safari Backpackers YHA – 3148
12 Davidson St, Tennant Creek, NT 0860.
(8) 89622207 (8) 89623188
safari@swtch.com.au www.yha.com.au
Open Dates: 12 1km 250m x 25 CC TV P

▲ **Terrigal** – Terrigal Beach Lodge YHA – 3149
12 Campbell Crescent, Terrigal, NSW 2260.
(2) 43853330 (2) 43853330
terrigal@yhansw.org.au
ww.yha.com.au
Open Dates: 12 Sydney Airport - Direct bus service from Terrigal 120km Gosford Station. Connecting bus to Terrigal 10km From Gosford bus to Terrigal until late 10km 0.1N x 32 R CC TV P

Thredbo – Thredbo YHA – 3150
8 Jack Adams Pathway,
Thredbo Alpine Village, NSW 2625.
(2) 64576376 (2) 64576043
thredbo@yhansw.org.au
www.yha.com.au
Open Dates: 12 Open Times: 07.00-10.00hrs; 16.30-21.00hrs (June-Sept); 08.00-10.00hrs; 15.00-20.00hrs (Oct-May)
Beds: 52 - 3x2 9x4 1x6
Price Range: from $24 - winter rates vary and cannot be booked online
Directions: Winter: Murrays & Greyhound buses offer daily service to/from Sydney. Summer: Transborder Express runs daily year-round between Canberra & Thredbo 400m x 1 R CC TV

Thredbo – Thredbo YHA

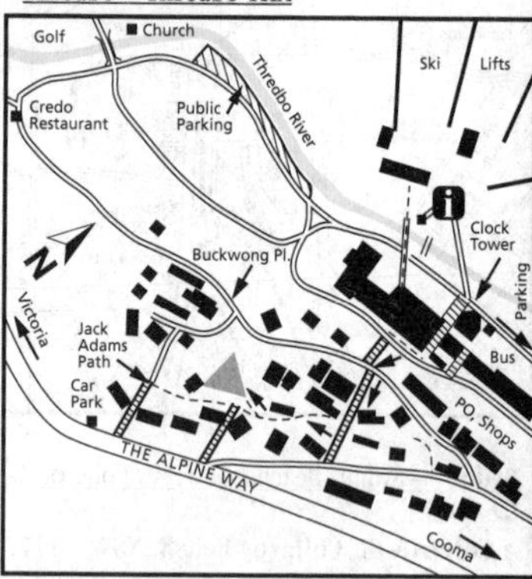

Thredbo... Travel Tips

- **For budget eats check out...** Alfresco Pizza, Kebabz, Alpine Hotel's Bistro & Bar, Bernti's Café, Avalanche Café
- **For great nightlife try...** Schuss Bar, Keller Bar, Lounge Bar, Ullr Bar and Grill
- **Don't miss...** Mt Kosciuszko, Ski Slopes, The Kosciuszko National Park, Snowy River Winery, Yarrangobilly Caves, Raw NRG Mountain Biking, Blues & Jazz Music Festivals, Alpine Leisure Centre, Horseriding, Snowy Mountains Scheme

▲ **Undara Volcanic National Park** – Undara Experience YHA – 3153
Undara Volcanic National Park,
Savannah Way via Mt Surprise QLD 4871
(7) 40971900; (Freecall 1800 990992)
(7) 40971955 res@undara.com.au
www.yha.com.au
Open Dates: The Savannahlander operates once a week from Cairns
Scheduled coach service operates from Cairns x 117

▲ **Walpole** – Tingle All Over YHA – 3154
60 Nockolds St, Walpole, WA 6398.
(8) 98401041 (8) 98401041
tingleallover2000@yahoo.com.au
www.yha.com.au
Open Dates: Daily TransWA bus service from Perth and Albany. For free pick up from Walpole bus terminal call hostel. 100m x 21
600m 600m

▲ **Wollongong** – Wollongong YHA – 3161
75-79 Keira Street, Wollongong NSW 2500.
(2) 42291132
wollongong@yhansw.org.au
www.yha.com.au
Open Dates: Sydney Airport 80km
Wollongong Station 1km 100m
x 42

Austria

Ⓥ Österreichischer Jugendherbergsverband, Hauptverband, 1010 Wien, Schottenring 28, Austria.

Ⓣ (43) (1) 5335353; 5335354
Ⓕ (43) (1) 5350861
Ⓔ oejhv-zentrale@oejhv.or.at
Ⓦ www.oejhv.or.at; www.jugendherberge.at; www.youthhostel.at

Office Hours: Office Hours: Mon-Thurs 09.00-17.00hrs; Fri 09.00-15.00hrs; Fri (Summer) 09.00-17.00hrs

Travel Service, GmbH: Österreichischer Jugendherbergsverband, Gonzagagasse 22, 1010 Wien, Austria.

Ⓣ (43) (1) 5321660
Ⓕ (43) (1) 5350861
Ⓔ oejhv-travelservice@oejhv.or.at
Ⓦ www.oejhv.or.at

Office Hours: Office Hours: Mon-Thurs 09.00-17.00hrs; Fri 09.00-15.00hrs; Fri (Summer) 09.00-17.00hrs

Ⓦ Österreichisches Jugendherbergswerk, Junge Hotels Austria Helferstorferstraße 4, 1010 Wien, Austria.

Ⓣ (43) (1) 5331833
Ⓕ (43) (1) 5331833 Ext 84 or 85
Ⓔ office@jungehotels.at
Ⓦ www.jungehotels.at

Office Hours: Mon-Fri 09.30-18.00hrs

Travel Section: Supertramp, Helferstorferstraße 4, 1010 Wien, Austria.

Ⓣ (43) (1) 5335137
Ⓕ (43) (1) 5331833 Ext 84
Ⓔ travel@supertramp.at
Ⓦ www.supertramp.at

Office Hours: Mon-Fri 09.30-18.00hrs

A copy of the Hostel Directory for Ⓥ & Ⓦ can be obtained from: Hauptverband, 1010 Wien, Schottenring 28, Austria. and ÖJHW, 1010 Wien, Helferstorferstraße 4, Austria.

National Tourist Authority/Board:	www.austria-tourism.at
Capital:	Vienna
Language:	German
Currency:	€ Euro
Population:	8,025,000
Size:	83,849 sq km
Telephone Country Code:	43
eKit Access Number:	0800-677-664

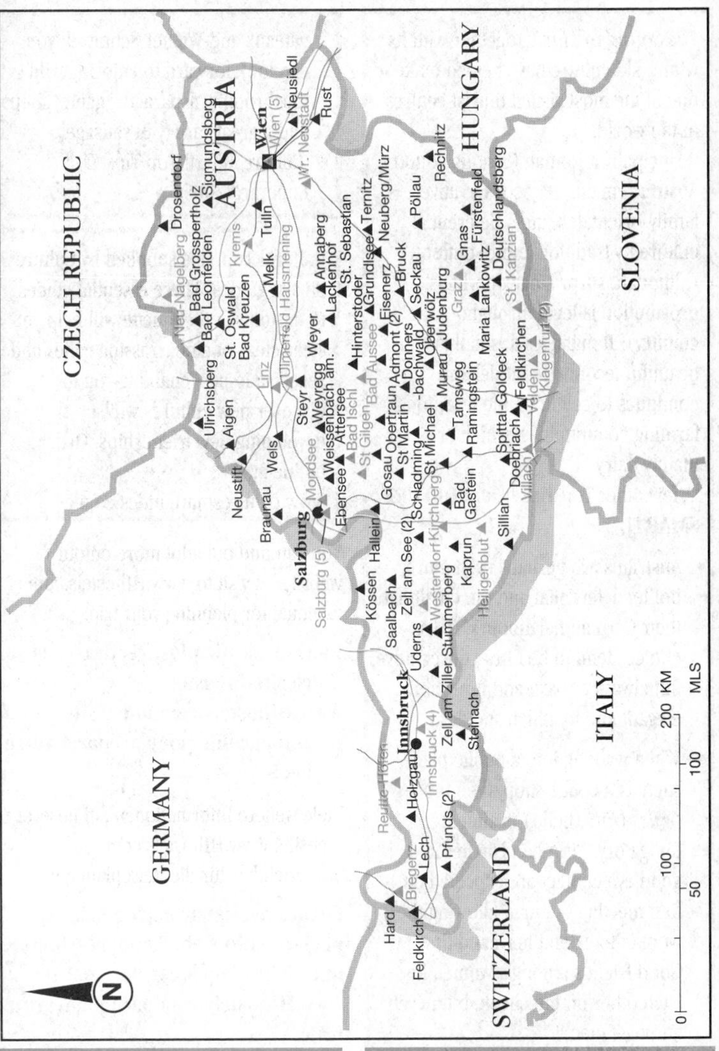

It may be hard to believe that this small, landlocked Alpine country, bordering eight other states (Germany, Switzerland, Liechtenstein, Italy, Slovenia, Hungary, Slovakia and the Czech Republic) was once the hub of the great Habsburg Empire that endured for more than 600 years up until the First World War. The Alps – the great wall of mountains that runs through the centre – dominates the country's economy, way of life and of course the majestic scenery that seems to go on forever.

Austria is today a country of some 8 million people, 'perpetually neutral' following the settlements after the Second World War, a key member of the European Union and the headquarters or regional centre of many international organizations including the UN. It is also the country of edelweiss and leather breeches (lederhosen), chocolate cakes and in recent times the birthplace of Arnold Schwarzenegger. Julie Andrews and

The Sound of Music together with its winter ski culture have helped make it one of the most visited tourist centres in the world.

Principally a Roman Catholic country, Austria remains very conservative, family-orientated and a deferential culture by tradition and in outlook (although, surprisingly, perhaps, prostitution is legal throughout the country). It manages a 'small is beautiful' economic model and continues to celebrate the traditional farming communities, which are mainly dairy.

A few other Top Tips from **CULTURE SMART!:**

- Austrians are perhaps even more polite, deferential and punctual than their German neighbours. Dress choices tend to be ultra conservative, but always correct and invariably elegant and to a high standard.
- When walking into a public place, such as a coffee shop, the phrase *Grüss Gott* (hello) is almost obligatory. Firm handshakes and good eye contact are expected on first meeting – a man allowing the woman to extend her hand first. Good friends amongst women kiss each other on the cheek, but never amongst men.
- Always remember that in Austria there is a 'right' way to do things in this very civil society: there are protocols for every aspect of social life; thus, a quiet, observant but deferential approach will be noticed and appreciated and much will flow from that.
- Though not known for their spontaneous humour, Austrians do enjoy irony in conversation. They also enjoy their food, which is much more than the traditional chocolate gateaux and Wiener Schnitzel: you can look forward to enjoying wild mushrooms, asparagus, game, soups and a great variety of sausages.

Culture Smart! Top Tips © Kuperard 2005

Cultural Top Tips supplied by Culture Smart! guides. These essential guides to customs and etiquette will help you steer clear of embarrassing gaffes and sensitive issues, enabling you to discover new cultures whilst developing new friendships. Order online at www.culturesmartguides.co.uk

You can find out a lot more on our website - a visit to www.HIhostels.com is essential for planning your trip!

Pour en savoir plus, rendez-vous sur notre site Internet, www.HIhostels.com une visite incontournable pour préparer votre voyage!

Viele weitere Informationen auf unserer Website: www.HIhostels.com - unverzichtbar für die Reiseplanung!

Puedes averiguar mucho más en nuestro sitio web. Es imprescindible que visites la página www.HIhostels.com para planear tu viaje.

▲ **Admont** Ⓥ – Jugend-und Familiengästehaus Admont – 4086
A-8911 Admont, Schulstr. 446, Steiermark.
(3613) 2432 (3613) 2432-4
admont@jfgh.at; bookingcenter@jfgh.at
www.jfgh.at
Open Dates: Graz-Thalerhof 110km
Admont 200m x 70 R

▲ **Admont** Ⓥ – Jugend-und Familiengästehaus Schloss Röthelstein – 4093
A-8911 Admont, Steiermark.
(3613) 2432 (3613) 2795-83
admont@jfgh.at; bookingcenter@jfgh.at
www.jfgh.at
Open Dates: Opening 01.07.2005
Graz-Thalerhof 110km Admont 2km x 100 1 x

▲ **Aigen** Ⓥ – 4050
A-4160 Aigen im Mühlkreis, Adalbert-Stifter-Landesjugendherberge, Oberösterreich.
(7281) 6283 (7281) 6283-4
ljh-aigen.post@ooe.gv.at
www.land-oberoesterreich.gv.at
Open Dates: 01.01-31.08; 23.09-31.12
x 80

▲ **Annaberg** Ⓦ – 5021
3222 Annaberg, Annarotte 77, Niederösterreich.
(2728) 8496 (2728) 8496-4
annaberg@noejhw.at
http://annaberg.noejhw.at
Open Dates: Annaberg/Reith 12km
x 108 3 x

▲ **Bad Aussee** Ⓥ – Jugend-und Familiengästehaus Bad Aussee Ⓗ 4010
A-8990 Bad Aussee, Jugendherbergsstraße 148, Steiermark.
(3622) 52238 (3622) 52238-88
badaussee@jfgh.at; bookingcenter@jfgh.at www.jfgh.at
Open Dates: Salzburg-Amadeus 85km
Bad Aussee 2.4km x 158 4 x

Bad Gastein Ⓦ – 5016
5640 Bad Gastein, Ederplatz 2, Salzburg.
(6434) 2080 (6434) 50688
hostel.badgastein@salzburg.co.at
www.hostel-badgastein.at
Open Dates: Open Times: 08.00-14.00hrs; 16.00-22.00hrs
Beds: 180 - 10x2 44x4
Price Range: € 14-21 BB inc
Directions: Salzburg-Amadeus 80km
Bad Gastein 400m x 53 (BD) 2 x 40m

Bad Gastein Ⓦ

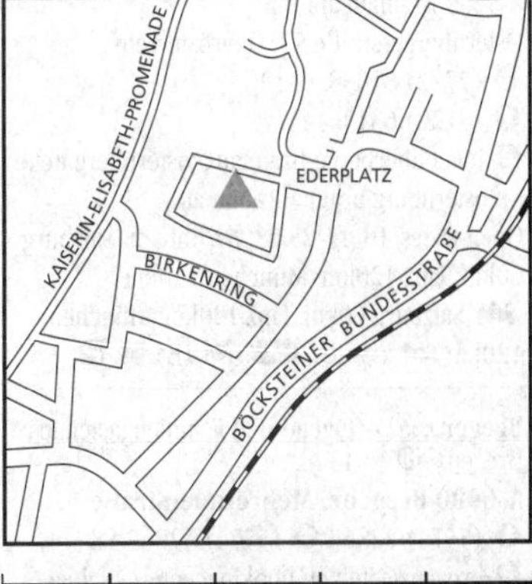

Bad Gastein... Travel Tips

- **For budget eats check out...** Town centre
- **For great nightlife try...** Town centre (around station & am Wasserfall)
- **Don't miss...** Coal and steel museum (Böckstein), Gasteiner Heilstollen, Panning for gold in Böckstein, Entrische Kirche (natural cave), Liechtenstein gorge (St Johann im Pongau), Krimml Waterfalls, Eisriesenwelt (world of ice, Werfen), Hallein salt mine, Hohe Tavern National Park

---

▲ **Bad Großpertholz** Ⓦ – 5022
3972 Bad Großpertholz, Bad Großpertholz 177, Niederösterreich.
(2857) 2965 (2857) 25227
badgrosspertholz@noejhw.at
http://badgrosspertholz.noejhw.at
Open Dates: 01.04-15.11 Gmünd 20km
Bus direct to hostel from train station
x 55

▲ **Bad Ischl** Ⓥ – JGH Bad Ischl Ⓗ 4018
JGH A-4820 Bad Ischl, Am Rechensteg 5, Oberösterreich.
(6132) 26577 (6132) 26577 Ext 75
jgh.badischl@oejhv.or.at
www.jugendherbergsverband.at
Open Dates: 01.01-07.12; 27-31.12 ( )
Salzburg or Hörsching 70km A 500m
Gmunden 18km 300m 400m
x 116 1 x

▲ **Braunau** Ⓥ – 4051
A-5280 Braunau am Inn,
Osternbergerstraße 57, Oberösterreich.
(7722) 81638; 63136
(7722) 6313614
jugendherberge-braunau@osternberg.net; int.osternberg.braunau@aon.at
Open Dates: 01.11-28.02 only Salzburg 60km; Linz 120km; München 110km
Salzburg 60km; Linz 120km; München 120km x 54 (B)

Bregenz Ⓥ – Jugend-und Familiengästehaus Bregenz 4015
A-6900 Bregenz, Mehrerauerstraße 5.
(5574) 42867 (5574) 42867-88
bregenz@jfgh.at; bookingcenter@jfgh.at
www.jfgh.at
Open Dates: Open Times: 07.00-22.00hrs
Beds: 165
Price Range: € 16.90-21.70 BBinc
Directions: Altenrhein (CH) 20km
A 20m 300m
3 x 200m 300m

Bregenz Ⓥ – Jugend-und Familiengästehaus

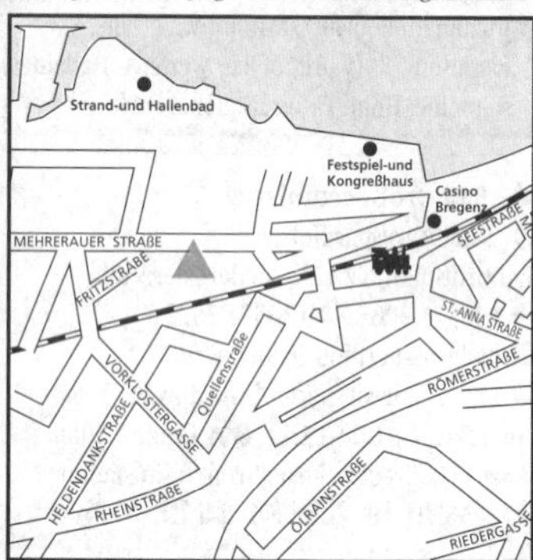

Bregenz... Travel Tips

- **For budget eats check out...** Wirtshaus am See, König Kebap, Toscana, Ikarus, Gösser
- **For great nightlife try...** Wunderbar, Kuba, Flexibel, Kanzlei, Berg Isel
- **Don't miss...** Pfänder (mountain), Cruise on Lake Constance, Lindau (Island on lake), Affenberg (monkey mountain), Summer Tobbogan Bizau, Rappenloch Canyon

---

▲ **Bruck an der Mur** Ⓥ – Jugend-und Familiengästehaus Bruck/Weitental – 4053
A-8600 Bruck/Mur, Stadtwaldstraße 1, Steiermark.
(3862) 58448 (3862) 58448-88
bruck@jfgh.at; bookingcenter@jfgh.at
www.jfgh.at
Open Dates: Graz-Thalerhof 50km
Bruck/Mur 2km Citybus from hostel to city x 147
5 x

▲ **Deutschlandsberg** Ⓥ – Jugend-und Familiengästehaus Deutschlandsberg – 4054
A-8530 Deutschlandsberg, Burgstraße 5, Steiermark.
(3462) 22000 (3462) 22000-88
deutschlandsberg@jfgh.at; bookingcenter@jfgh.at www.jfgh.at
Open Dates: Graz-Thalerhof 40km
Deutschlandsberg 500m x 152
3 x

△ ***Doebriach am Millstaetter See*** Ⓥ – *Ernestos - Jugend, Kinder und Familiengästehaus – 4052*
A-9873 Doebriach, Glanzerstraße 44, Kärnten.
(4246) 7595 (4246) 7595-16
office@ernestos.at
Open Dates: 01.05-31.10 Klagenfurt 100km Spittal 15km 0.2SW x 47

▲ **Donnersbachwald** Ⓥ – Jugend-und Familiengästehaus Donnersbachwald – 4095
A-8953 Donnersbachwald 190, Steiermark.
(662) 842984 (662) 841101
bookingcenter@jfgh.at www.jfgh.at
Open Dates: Opening July 2006
1 x

▲ **Drosendorf** Ⓦ – 5025
2095 Drosendorf an der Thaya, Badstraße 25.
(2915) 2257 (2915) 2257
drosendorf@noejhw.at
http://drosendorf.noejhw.at
Open Dates: 01.04-15.11 x 62

△ ***Ebensee*** Ⓦ *– 5008*
4802 Ebensee, Rindbachstraße 27, Oberösterreich.
(6133) 6698 (6133) 669885
ebensee@jutel.at www.jutel.at
Open Dates: 01.05-31.10 Linz 81km 1.5km 1.5km x 80 1 x

▲ **Eisenerz** Ⓥ – Jugend-und Familiengästehaus Eisenerz – 4055
A-8790 Eisenerz, Ramsau 1, Steiermark.
(3848) 60560 (3848) 60560 ext 88
eisenerz@jfgh.at; bookingcenter@jfgh.at
www.jfgh.at
Open Dates: Graz-Thalerhof 80km
Leoben 30km x 138 2 x

▲ **Feldkirch** Ⓦ – 5027
6805 Feldkirch-Levis, Reichstraße 111, Vorarlberg.
(5522) 73181 (5522) 79399
jugendherberge.fk@cable.vol.at
Open Dates: x 80

△ ***Feldkirchen*** Ⓥ *– Feriendorf Maltschacher See – 4056*
9560 Feldkirchen, Briefelsdorf 7, Kärnten.
(4277) 2644 (4277) 2644-51
info@maltschach.at
www.maltschach.at
Open Dates: 30.04-15.10 Klagenfurt 20km A Klagenfurt 20km Feldkirchen 8km Feldkirchen 8km x 38

▲ **Fürstenfeld** Ⓥ – Jugend-und Familiengästehaus Thermenland/Fürstenfeld – 4057
Burgenlandstraße 15, A-8280 Fürstenfeld, Steiermark.
(3382) 52152 (3382) 52152-88
fuerstenfeld@jfgh.at; bookingcenter@jfgh.at www.jfgh.at
Open Dates: Graz-Thalerhof 55km
10 min walk 50m 0.5E x 166 6 x

▲ **Gnas** Ⓥ – Jugend-und Familiengästehaus Gnas Sport & Erlebniswelt – 4084
A-8342 Gnas 194, Steiermark.
(3151) 51472 (3151) 51472-88
gnas@jfgh.at; bookingcenter@jfgh.at
www.jfgh.at
Open Dates: Graz-Thalerhof 60km
Gnas 500m x 172 1 x

△ ***Gosau*** Ⓦ *– 5051*
4824 Gosau 168, Oberösterreich
(6136) 8352 (6136) 83524
gosau@jutel.at www.jutel.at
Open Dates: Linz 126km; Salzburg 68km 13km 1km x 72

Graz Ⓥ – Jugend-und Familiengästehaus und Jugendhotel Graz 4006
A-8020 Graz, Idlhofgasse 74, Steiermark.
(316) 7083-50 (316) 7083-55
graz@jfgh.at; bookingcenter@jfgh.at
www.jfgh.at
Open Dates: Open Times: 07.00-23.00hrs
Beds: 194 - 11x2 16x4 2x6
Price Range: € 17-24.50 BBinc
Directions: 2SW from city centre
Graz-Thalerhof 7km A 500m
Hauptbahnhof Graz 500m 50 150m
300m 8 x 3km

Graz Ⓥ – Jugend-und Familiengästehaus

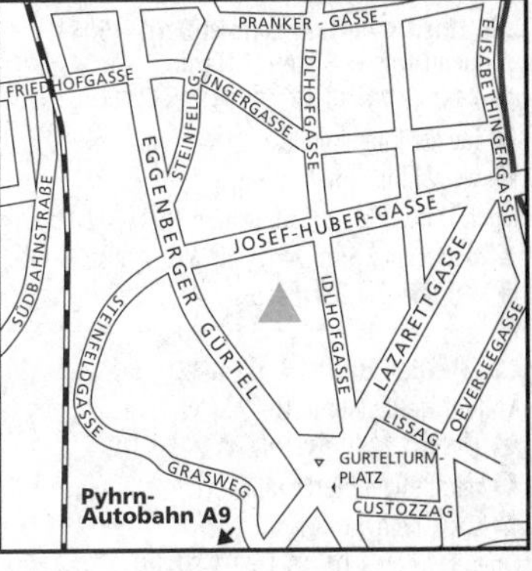

Graz... Travel Tips

- **For budget eats check out...** Alt Steirische Schmankerlstube, 3 Goldene Kugeln, Da Vinci, Gambrinus Keller, Leudplatzl
- **For great nightlife try...** Arcadium, Parkhouse, Kulturhauskeller, Stern, Three Monkeys
- **Don't miss...** The Provincial Armoury, Schlossbergbahn, Cathedral & mausoleum, Eggenberg Castle, Palm House, Open Air Museum Stübing

▲ **Grundlsee** – Jugend-und Familiengästehaus Grundlsee – 4087
A-8993 Grundlsee, Gössl 149, Steiermark.
(3622) 8629 (3622) 8629-4
grundlsee@jfgh.at; bookingcenter@jfgh.at
www.jfgh.at
Open Dates: Salzburg-Amadeus 85km Bad Aussee 5km x 85

▲ **Hallein** – Jugendherberge Schloss-Wispach/Hallein – 4058
A-5400 Hallein, Schloss Wispach-Esterhazy, Salzburg.
(6245) 80397 (6245) 80397 Ext 3
hallein@jfgh.at; bookingcenter@jfgh.at
www.jfgh.at
Open Dates: 01.05-30.09
Salzburg-Amadeus 15km Hallein 500m 200m x 104 50m

▲ **Hard** – Junges Hotel Hard – 5054
Allmendstrasse. 87, 6971 Hard.
(5574) 73435 (5574) 73435 4
hard@jungehotels.at
www.jungehotels.at/hard
Open Dates: Altenrhein (CH) Bregenz 5km ap YH x 76

▲ **Heiligenblut** 4022
A-9844 Heiligenblut, Hof 36, Kärnten.
(4824) 2259 (4824) 2259-19
jgh.heiligenblut@oejhv.or.at
www.oejhv.or.at
Open Dates: 01.01-15.10; 01-31.12
Klagenfurt 160km Mallnitz 40km ap near the hostel x 100

▲ **Hinterstoder** – 5017
4573 Hinterstoder 33, Oberösterreich.
(7564) 5227 (7564) 522711
hinterstoder@jutel.at www.jutel.at
Open Dates: Linz 79km 11km 250m x 87 1 x

▲ **Holzgau** – Holzgauerhof – 5028
6654 Holzgau 66.
(5633) 5250 (5633) 20031
holzgauer-hof@aon.at
Open Dates: 15.12-15.05; 15.06-01.11
x 53

▲ **Innsbruck** – 4060
6020 Innsbruck, Volkshaus, Radetzkystraße 47.
(512) 395882; (664) 2667004
(512) 341086
jgh.volkshaus-ibk@aon.at
www.volkshaus.at
Open Dates: x 52

▲ **Innsbruck** – "Fritz Prior - Schwedenhaus" – 5029
6020 Innsbruck, Rennweg 17b, Tirol.
(512) 585814 (512) 585814-14
youth.hostel@tirol.com
www.tirol.com/youth-hostel
Open Dates: 06.07-05.09; 26.12-05.01 2NE
x 100

Innsbruck – Jugendherberge Innsbruck
5003
6020 Innsbruck, Reichenauerstraße 147, Tirol.
(512) 346179; (512) 346180
(512) 346179 Ext 12
info@youth-hostel-innsbruck.at
www.youth-hostel-innsbruck.at
Open Dates: 01.01-15.12; 27-31.12
Open Times: 07.00-10.00hrs; 17.00-23.00hrs
Beds: 178 - 5x1 5x2 6x4 24x6+
Price Range: € 15.00-24.00 BBinc
Directions: 2NE from city centre
Innsbruck 5km Innsbruck Hauptbahnhof 2km Bus O, 2km ap König Laurinstraße (B) 1 x 1km

Innsbruck Ⓦ – Jugendherberge Innsbruck

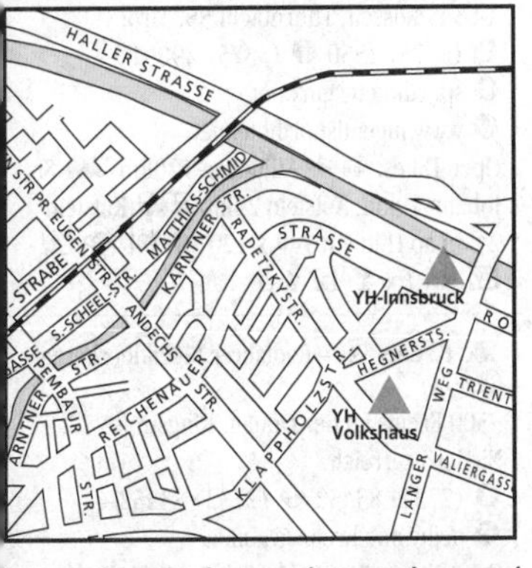

▲ **Innsbruck** Ⓦ – Studentenheim – 5030
Reichenauerstraße 147, 6020 Innsbruck.
Ⓣ (512) 346179; 346180
Ⓕ (512) 346179-12
Ⓔ info@youth-hostel-innsbruck.at
Ⓦ www.youth-hostel-innsbruck.at
Open Dates: 06.07-05.09 ✈ Innsbruck 5km
Innsbruck Hauptbahnhof 2km Bus O 2km ap König Laurinstrasse x 112

Innsbruck... Travel Tips

- **For budget eats check out...** Milano, Sandwirt, Waldorf, Jimmy's, Crocodiles
- **For great nightlife try...** Nachtschicht, Cinema Complex, Theresien bräu, Plateau, Couch
- **Don't miss...** Goldenes Dachl, Alpen Zoo, Nordkette, Ambras Castle, Swarovski World of Crystal, Hofburg (Imperial Palace), Hofkirche (Royal Church), Ferdinandeum, Hof Garten (Royal Gardens), Bergisel - Ski Jump

▲ **Judenburg** Ⓥ – Jugend-und Familiengästehaus Judenburg – 4009
8750 Judenburg, Kaserngasse 22, Steiermark.
Ⓣ (3572) 87355 Ⓕ (3572) 87355-88
Ⓔ judenburg@jfgh.at;
bookingcenter@jfgh.at Ⓦ www.jfgh.at
Open Dates: ✈ Graz-Thalerhof 80km
Judenburg 1km x 102 2 x

Kaprun Ⓥ – Jugend-und Familiengästehaus Kaprun – 4061
A-5710 Kaprun,
Nikolaus Gassnerstraße 448, Salzburg.
Ⓣ (6547) 8507 Ⓕ (6547) 8507 Ext 3
Ⓔ kaprun@jfgh.at; bookingcenter@jfgh.at
Ⓦ www.jfgh.at
Open Dates: Open Times: 08.00-20.00hrs
Beds: 150 - 2x1 4x2 4x3 9x4 13x6 2x6+
Price Range: € 17.00-25.30 BBinc
Directions: ✈ Salzburg-Amadeus 100km
Zell am See 6km 100m
3 x
700m

Kaprun Ⓥ – Jugend-und Familiengästehaus

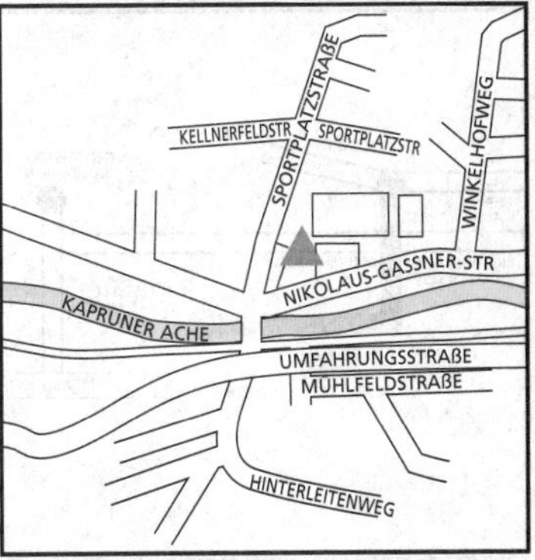

Kaprun... Travel Tips

- **For budget eats check out...** Gasthof zur Mühle, Gasthof Mitteregger, SB-Restaurant Metzgerstube, Guggenbichel
- **For great nightlife try...** Baum Bar, Kitsch & Bitter, Pavillon
- **Don't miss...** Reservoir Lakes Kaprun, Alpine Mountain Road to Grossglockner, Krimml Waterfalls, Fortress and Icecaves at Werfen, Rafting

△ ***Kirchberg bei Kitzbühel*** Ⓥ *– Club Habitat* Ⓗ *4094*
A-6365 Kirchberg bei Kitzbühel, Tirol, Kohlgrub 9.
Ⓣ *(5357) 2254* Ⓕ *(5357) 2254*
Ⓔ *info@clubhabitat.at*
Open Dates: 01.05-30.11 x 46

Klagenfurt Ⓥ – Jugendgästehaus Ⓗ 4007
A-9020 Klagenfurt, Universitätsviertel, Neckheimg. 6, Kärnten.
(463) 230020 (463) 230020 Ext: 20
jgh.klagenfurt@oejhv.or.at
www.oejhv.or.at
Open Dates: Open Times: 07.00-10.00hrs; 17.00-23.00hrs
Beds: 146 - 3x2 35x4
Price Range: € 18.40 BBinc
Directions: Klagenfurt-Wörthersee 8km Klagenfurt 4km #10 or #12 200m x 35 (LD) 6 x 1km 1km

Klagenfurt Ⓥ – Jugendgästehaus

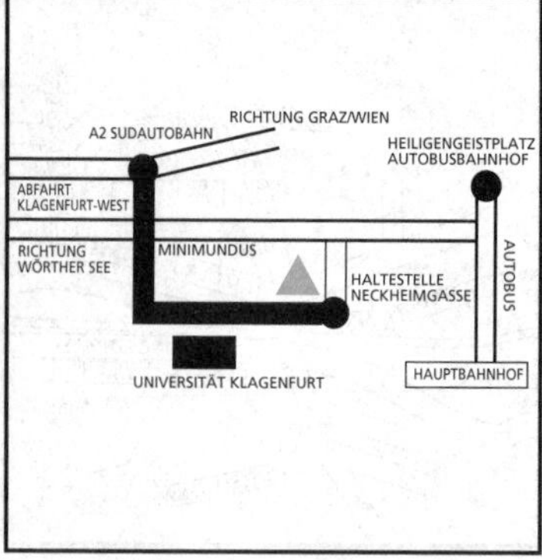

△ ***Klagenfurt*** Ⓦ – *Kolping JGH – 5031*
9020 Klagenfurt, Enzenbergstraße 26, Kärnten.
(463) 56965 (463) 56965-632
Open Dates: 15.07-15.09 x 200

Klagenfurt... Travel Tips

- **For budget eats check out...** Youth Hostel, Uni-Pizzeria, Uni-Wirt, Vier Jahreszeiten (Chinese), UniCafé Karner
- **For great nightlife try...** Cinema Complex, Municipal Theatre, Bermudadreieck (Herzengasse/Alter Platz)
- **Don't miss...** Minimundus, Reptile zoo, Wörther See - boat trip, Hochosterwitz mountain, Wallfahrts Church (Maria Wörth), Wild Animal Park (Rosegg), Landskon castle ruins & falconry show, Old Town & Wappensaal country house, Musil Museum

▲ **Kössen** Ⓥ – 4088
A-6345 Kössen, Thurnbichl 55, Tirol.
(5375) 2550 (5375) 29001
sporthotel@gmx.net
www.jugendsporthotel.net
Open Dates: München 120km St. Johann 19km; Kufstein 24km Kufstein 24km ap Hüttwirt x 120 1 x

▲ **Krems** Ⓥ – Radfahrer Jugendherberge Ⓗ 4024
3500 Krems an der Donau, Ringstraße 77, Niederösterreich.
(2732) 83452 (2732) 83452-4
oejhv.noe.krems@aon.at
Open Dates: 01.04-31.10 (01.11-31.03 with 20 or more only) Wien-Schwechat 95km Krems 500m 1415, 1451, 1453, 1455, 2047, 2061, 2068, 2075 150m ap Stadtpark x 52

▲ **Lackenhof** Ⓦ – 5033
3295 Lackenhof am Ötscher, Ötscherweg 3, Niederösterreich.
(7480) 5251 (7480) 5338
lackenhof@noejhw.at
http://lackenhof.noejhw.at
Open Dates: Kiemberg 14km x 128

△ ***Lech-Stubenbach*** Ⓦ *– 5034*
Jugendheim Lech-Stubenbach, A-6764 Lech am Arlberg, Stubenbach 244.
(5583) 2419 (5583) 24194
lech@jungehotels.at
www.members.aon.at/jbl
Open Dates: 05.12-23.04; 01.07-02.09
x 64

Linz Ⓥ – Stanglhofweg Ⓗ 4019
A-4020 Linz, Stanglhofweg 3, Oberösterreich: (near the stadium, 1km to centre).
❶ (732) 664434 ❻ (732) 664434 Ext. 75
❺ jgh.linz@oejhv.or.at
Ⓦ www.jugendherbergsverband.at
Open Dates: 09.01-23.12
Open Times: 07.00-15.00hrs (Mon-Fri); 17.00-21.00hrs (daily)
Beds: 208 - 6x2 4x3 46x4
Price Range: € 14.75-29.25 BBinc
Directions: Linz 10km Linz-Schiffsanlegestelle 4km Linz 2km #17, #19, #45 500m ap Leondingerstr #1, #3, #2 2km ap Goethekreuzung x 28 4 x 3km

Linz Ⓥ – Stanglhofweg

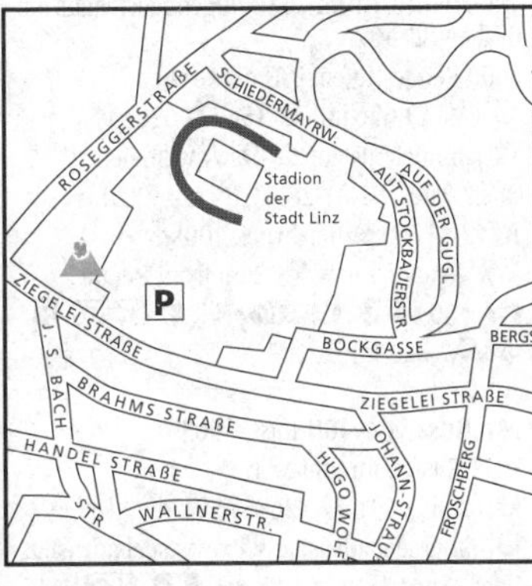

Linz... Travel Tips

- **For budget eats check out...** Café am Froschberg, Stadiongrill, Wienerwald
- **For great nightlife try...** Remembar, Nachtschicht, Josef, Old Town, Empire
- **Don't miss...** ARS-Electronica Centre, Old Town, Hauptplatz (main square), Pöstlingberg, New art gallery, New Cathedral, Lentos Art Museum, Brucknerhaus, Regional Theatre, Botanical Gardens

▲ **Maria Lankowitz** Ⓥ – Jugend-und Familiengästehaus Maria Lankowitz – 4011
A-8591 Maria Lankowitz, Am See 2, Steiermark.
❶ (3144) 71700 ❻ (3144) 71700-88
❺ marialankowitz@jfgh.at; bookingcenter@jfgh.at Ⓦ www.jfgh.at
Open Dates: Graz-Thalerhof 30km Köflach 2km 500m x 124 1 x

▲ **Melk** Ⓦ – 5035
3390 Melk an der Donau, Abt-Karl-Straße 42, Niederösterreich.
❶ (2752) 52681 ❻ (2752) 52681-5
❺ melk@noejhw.at Ⓦ http://melk.noejhw.at
Open Dates: 01.03-15.11 Melk 800m x 104

▲ **Mondsee** Ⓥ – "JGH Mondsee" Ⓗ 4020
A-5310 Mondsee, Krankenhausstraße 9, Oberösterreich.
❶ (6232) 2418 ❻ (6232) 2418 Ext 75
❺ jgh.mondsee@oejhv.or.at
Ⓦ www.jugendherbergsverband.at
Open Dates: 01-15.01; 20.02-31.12
Salzburg 30km Mondsee 800m Salzburg 27km 3010 to Salzburg 900m x 80 1 x

▲ **Murau** Ⓥ – Jugend-und Familiengästehaus Murau – 4096
A-8850 Murau, St. Leonhardsplatz 4, Steiermark.
❶ (3532) 2395 ❻ (3532) 2395-88
❺ murau@jfgh.at; bookingcenter@jfgh.at
Ⓦ www.jfgh.at
Open Dates: x 190

△ ***Neuberg*** Ⓥ – *Jugend-und Familiengästehaus Neuberg – 4065*
A-8692 Neuberg an der Mürz, Kaplanweg 8, Steiermark.
❶ *(3857) 8495* ❻ *(3857) 8495-88*
❺ *bookingcenter@jfgh.at* Ⓦ *www.jfgh.at*
Open Dates: Graz-Thalerhof 90km A 500m Murzzuschlag 12km x 50

▲ **Neu-Nagelberg** – "Hans Czettel JH" 4025
3871 Neu-Nagelberg 114.
(2859) 7476 (2859) 7476
oejhv-noe@oejhv.or.at
Open Dates: 11.01-23.12 Wien-Schwechat 157km Gmünd 8km Neu-Nagelberg 200m x 37 R 1 x

▲ **Neusiedl** – 5036
7100 Neusiedl am See, Herbergsgasse 1, Burgenland.
(2167) 2252 (2167) 2252
neusiedl@jungehotels.at
www.jungehotels.at/neuisedl
Open Dates: 01.03-30.11 x 86 R

▲ **Obertraun** – 5012
4831 Obertraun, Winkl 26, Oberösterreich.
(6131) 360 (6131) 3604
obertraun@jutel.at www.jutel.at
Open Dates: Linz 122km; Salzburg 82km 1km ap directly in front of the hostel x 138 R 1 x

▲ **Oberwölz** – Jugend-und Familiengästehaus Oberwölz – 4089
A-8832 Oberwölz, Hauptplatz, Steiermark.
(3581) 76919 (3581) 76919-88
oberwoelz@jfgh.at; bookingcenter@jfgh.at
www.jfgh.at
Open Dates: Graz-Thalerhof 120km Niederwölz 10km x 95 R

▲ **Pfunds** – Jugendgästehaus Hirschen – 4068
A-6542 Pfunds 92, Tirol.
(5474) 5711 (5474) 5711-34
post.pfunds@netway.at
Open Dates: 15.05-20.10; 15.12-08.01 120km A 100km 30km x 54 R

▲ **Pfunds** – Jugend-und Familiengästehaus Dangl – 4067
JGH Dangl, A-6542 Pfunds 347, Tirol.
(5474) 5244 (5474) 5244-4
www.pfunds.at/pensiondangl
Open Dates: x 50 R

▲ **Pöllau** – Jugend-und Familiengästehaus Pöllau – 4090
A-8225 Pöllau, Marktstraße 603.
(3335) 30011 (3335) 30011-88
poellau@jfgh.at; bookingcenter@jfgh.at
www.jfgh.at
Open Dates: Graz-Thalerhof 80km Hartberg 14km x 130 R CC 1 x 200m

▲ **Rechnitz** – 4070
Burgenland, 7471 Rechnitz, Hochstraße 1.
(3363) 79245; (664) 5347892
(3363) 79245-12
ev.pfarr-u.gaestehaus-rechnitz@aon.at
www.geschriebenstein.at/jugendgaestehaus
Open Dates: Wien 140km; Graz 110km von Oberwart Rechnitz x 58

▲ **Reutte-Höfen** – Jugendgästehaus am Graben 4071
6600 Reutte-Höfen, JGH am Graben 1.
(5672) 626440 (5672) 626444
jgh-hoefen@aon.at www.hoefen.at
Open Dates: 01.01-28.03; 29.04-30.10; 16.12-31.12 Innsbruck 100km Reutte 2km 2km from Reutte x 50 R 2km

▲ **Rust** – JGH Rust – 5039
7071 Rust, Conradplatz 1.
(2685) 591 (2685) 591-4
info@seebadrust.at www.seebadrust.at
Open Dates: x 85 R CC

▲ **Saalbach** – Jugend-und Familiengästehaus Saalbach/Hinterglemm – 4091
5753 Saalbach 60, Salzburg.
(662) 842984 (Booking Centre)
(662) 841101 (Booking Centre)
saalbach@jfgh.at; bookingcenter@jfgh.at
www.jfgh.at
Open Dates: Opening December 2006 München 220km; Innsbruck 180km; Salzburg 95km 680 x 120 R CC 8

▲ **Salzburg** Ⓦ – Aigner Straße – 5040
5026 Salzburg, Aigner Straße 34.
(662) 623248 (662) 623248-4
hostel.aigen@salzburg.co.at
www.lbsh-aigen.at
Open Dates: 12 2NW x 45

Salzburg Ⓦ – Eduard Heinrich Haus
5001
5020 Salzburg-Josefiau,
Eduard-Heinrich Straße 2.
(662) 625976 (662) 627980
hostel.eduard-heinrich@salzburg.co.at
www.hostel-ehh.at
Open Dates: 12 Open Times: 07.00-10.00hrs; 17.00-24.00hrs
Beds: 114 - 3x2 3x4 14x6
Price Range: € 14-20 BBinc
Directions: 3SW from city centre
Salzburg-Amadeus 6km Salzburg 4km 500m ap Bundespolizeidirektion 1km x 21 R CC (BD) TV 2 x 2km

Salzburg Ⓦ – Eduard Heinrich Haus

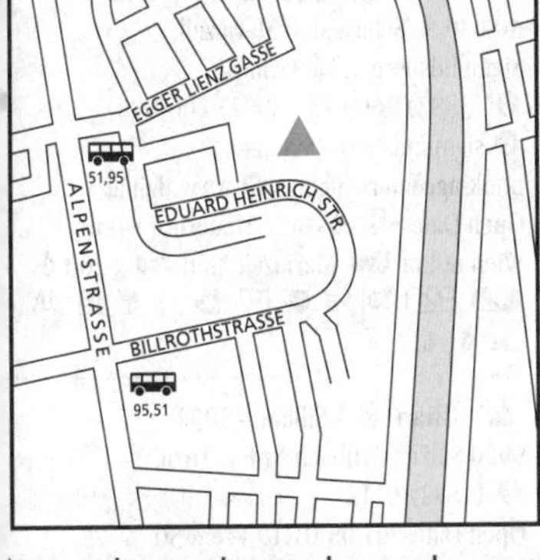

▲ **Salzburg** Ⓦ – Haunspergstraße – 5041
5020 Salzburg, Haunspergstraße 27.
(662) 875030 (662) 883477
haunspergstrasse@jungehotels.at
www.lbsh-haunspergstrasse.at
Open Dates: 01.07-26.08 x 89 R

Salzburg Ⓥ – Jugend-und Familiengästehaus Salzburg 4001
A-5020 Salzburg Nonntal,
Josef-Preis Allee 18, Salzburg.
(662) 842670 (662) 841101
salzburg@jfgh.at; bookingcenter@jfgh.at
www.jfgh.at
Open Dates: 12 Open Times: 07.00-04.00hrs (Reception 07.00-01.00hrs)
Beds: 396 - 30x2 5x3 19x4 4x5 31x6+
Price Range: € 14.30 (8 Bed/room); 4 € 18.40; 2 € 24.40 + € 2.50 for 1 night BBinc
Directions: 1SW from city centre
Salzburg-Amadeus 5km A #2 to station, #5 to Justizgebäude Salzburg 3km #5, #25 ap Justizgebäude #5 150m R CC TV 5 x 8 1.5km

Salzburg Ⓥ – Jugend-und Familiengästehaus

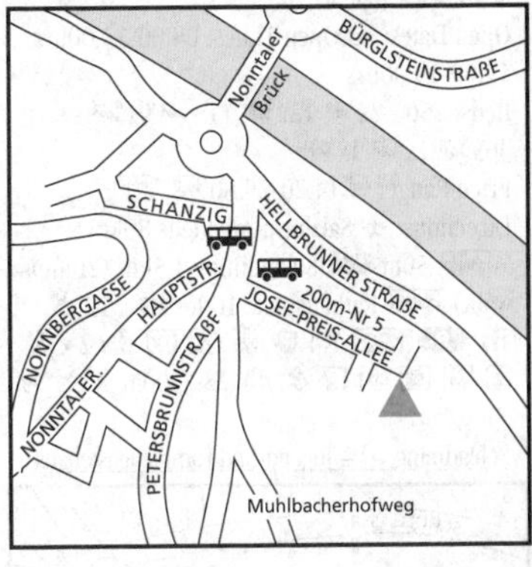

▲ **Salzburg** Ⓦ – Walserfeld – 5042
5071 Salzburg-Walserfeld, Schulstraße 18.
(662) 851377 (662) 853301
heimleitung@lbsh-walserfeld.at
www.lbsh-walserfeld.at
Open Dates: 01.07-26.08 x 156

AUSTRIA – AUTRICHE – ÖSTERREICH – AUSTRIA

Salzburg... Travel Tips

- **For budget eats check out...** Lemon & Chilli, Arge Beisl, Gösser Stüberl, Wilder Mann, Lin's Garden (Chinese)
- **For great nightlife try...** Old Town centre - Rudolfskai, Cineplex, Das Kino, Rockhouse, Republic
- **Don't miss...** Getreidegasse (cathedral), Mozart's birth place & living house, Hohensalzburg castle, Mirabell Gardens, Mönchsberg (mountain), Hellbrunn Castle (water games & zoo), Saltmines (Hallein), Kehlsteinhaus - Eagles Nest (Berchtesgaden), Ice caves (Werfen), Sound of music tour

Schladming Ⓥ – Jugend-und Familiengästehaus Schladming – 4012
A-8970 Schladming, Coburgstraße 253, Steiermark.
(3687) 24531 (3687) 24531-88
schladming@jfgh.at; bookingcenter@jfgh.at www.jfgh.at
Open Dates: 12 Open Times: 08.00-13.00hrs; 17.00-19.00hrs
Beds: 256 - 2x1 12x2 11x3 9x4 30x5 1x6 1x6+
Price Range: € 14.20-25.80 BBinc
Directions: Salzburg-Amadeus 89km A 50m Schladming 1.5km (20mins walk) Rathausplatz 100m x 12 R CC 2 x 500m

Schladming Ⓥ – Jugend-und Familiengästehaus

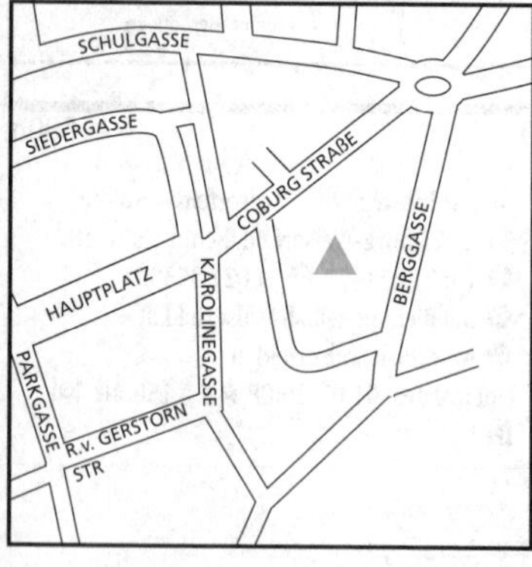

Schladming... Travel Tips

- **For budget eats check out...** Youth and Family Hostel Schladming, Guest House Brunner, Um's Eck, Va Bene Pizzeria, Fleischhauerei Wanke
- **For great nightlife try...** Siglu, X-Small, La Porta, Beisl
- **Don't miss...** Skiing Area - Planai-Hochwurzen, Rafting, Erlebnisbad Schladming, Dachsteinhòhlen Obertraun, Hallein Saltmines, Mountain bike downhill from the "Planai", Paragliding, Summer skiing, Summer Toboggan Track

▲ **Seckau** Ⓥ – Jugend-und Familiengästehaus Seckau – 4092
A-8732 Seckau, Nr 2.
(662) 842984 (662) 841101
seckau@jfgh.at; bookingcenter@jfgh.at
www.jfgh.at
Open Dates: 12 Graz-Thalerhof 75km St. Lorenzen 10km x 65 R 1 x 2km

▲ **Sigmundsberg** Ⓥ – Jugend-und Familiengästehaus Mariazellerland/Sigmundsberg – 4072
A-8630 St. Sebastian b.Mariazell, Sigmundsberg 1, Steiermark.
(3882) 2669 (3882) 2669-88
sigmundsberg@jfgh.at; bookingcenter@jfgh.at www.jfgh.at
Open Dates: 12 Graz-Thalerhof 80km; Wien 80km Mariazell 3km x 200 R CC 8 x

▲ **Sillian** Ⓦ – Sillian – 5052
9920 Sillian, Arnbach Nr 84, Tirol.
(4842) 6112
Open Dates: 01.05-01.10 x 36

△ ***Spittal/Goldeck*** Ⓦ *– 5043*
9800 Spittal/Goldeck, Kärnten.
(4762) 2701 goldeck@gmx.at; goldeck@jungehotels.at
www.jungehotels.at/goldeck
Open Dates: 26.12-01.04; 25.06-15.09
x 45 R

▲ **St. Gilgen** Ⓥ – JGH Schafbergblick
Ⓗ 4021
A-5340 St. Gilgen, Mondseerstr. 7, Salzburg.
ⓣ (6227) 2365 ⓕ (6227) 2365 Ext 75
ⓔ jgh.stgilgen@oejhv.or.at
ⓦ www.jugendherbergsverband.at
Open Dates: 01-07.01; 23.01-17.12; 27-31.12
✈ Salzburg 40km ⛴ St. Gilgen 500m
🚂 Salzburg 30km 🛏 x 128 R CC 2 x 8 P

▲ **St. Kanzian, Unterburg** Ⓥ – Klopeiner See Ⓗ 4023
A-9122 St. Kanzian, Lerchenweg 2, Kärnten.
ⓣ (4239) 40160 ⓕ (4239) 40160-20
ⓔ jgh.klopeinersee@oejhv.or.at
ⓦ www.oejhv.or.at
Open Dates: 01.03-31.10 ✈ Klagenfurt 30km
🚂 Volkermarkt 4km 🚌 ap directly near the hostel 2.3E 🛏 x 72 R TV P

▲ **St. Martin am Tennengebirge** Ⓥ – Jugend-und Familiengästehaus St. Martin/Tennengebirdge – 4075
JH Sonnrain, A-5522 St. Martin Nr 100, Salzburg.
ⓣ (6463) 7318 ⓕ (6463) 7318 Ext 3
ⓔ stmartin@jfgh.at; bookingcenter@jfgh.at
ⓦ www.jfgh.at
Open Dates: 12 ✈ Salzburg-Amadeus 60km
🚂 Eben I. Pongau 10km 🚌 1.5km 4SE
🛏 x 136 P

▲ **St. Michael im Lungau** Ⓥ – Jugend-und Familiengästehaus St. Michael – 4076
A-5582 St. Michael Herbergsgasse 348, Salzburg.
ⓣ (6477) 8630 ⓕ (6477) 8630-3
ⓔ stmichael@jfgh.at; bookingcenter@jfgh.at
ⓦ www.jfgh.at
Open Dates: 12 ✈ Salzburg-Amadeus 100km
🚂 Radstadt 50km 🚌 200m 4SE
🛏 x 205 R P

AUSTRIA – AUTRICHE – ÖSTERREICH – AUSTRIA

▲ **St. Oswald** Ⓦ – 5053
4271 St. Oswald/Freistadt, Markt 22.
(7945) 7218 (7945) 72188
gasthof@trenda.at www.trenda.at
Open Dates: x 135 R
1 x

▲ **St. Sebastian/Mariazell** Ⓥ – Jugend-und Familiengästehaus Mariazellerland/St. Sebastian – 4077
A-8630 St. Sebastian/ Mariazell, Erlaufseestraße 49, Steiermark.
(3882) 34543 (3882) 34543-88
stsebastian@jfgh.at; bookingcenter@jfgh.at www.jfgh.at
Open Dates: Graz-Thalerhof 110km Mariazell - 10mins walk Mariazell - 10mins walk ap In winter ap YH x 140 CC 2 x

▲ **Steinach** Ⓥ – Jugend-und Familiengästehaus Steinach – 4097
A-6150 Steinach, Tirol.
(662) 842984 (662) 841101
bookingcenter@jfgh.at www.jfgh.at
Open Dates: Opening December 2006
x 250 TV 1 x

△ ***Steyr*** Ⓥ *– 4074*
4400 Steyr, Josef Hafnerstrasse 14, Oberösterreich.
(7252) 45580 (7252) 52733
jugend@steyr.gv.at www.steyr.at
Open Dates: 05.01-23.12 Linz 40km Steyr 1km Line 3 1km ap Bus Station x 74 R TV 3.5km

▲ **Stummerberg** Ⓦ – 5044
6272 Kaltenbach/Stumm, Zillertal, Stummerberg 68, Tirol.
(5283) 3577
Open Dates: x 40

▲ **Tamsweg** Ⓦ – "Haus Hatheyerbühel" – 5045
5580 Tamsweg, Hatheyergasse 512.
(6474) 2199 (6474) 2194
jugendherbergswerk.twg@sbg.at
www.lbsh-tamsweg.at
Open Dates: 01.07-31.08 x 44 R

△ ***Ternitz*** Ⓥ *– 4078*
2630 Ternitz, Straße des 12. Februar 38.
(2630) 38483; (650) 3848300
(2630) 38483-4
office@jugendherberge-ternitz.at
www.jugendherberge-ternitz.at
Open Dates: 01-31.01; 15.02-15.10; 15.11-31.12 x 32

Tulln Ⓦ – 5018
Marc Aurel Park 1c, 3430 Tulln.
(2272) 65165 (2272) 65165-4
tulln@noejhw.at http://tulln.noejhw.at
Open Dates: Open Times:
Beds: 126
Directions: 800m R CC TV 5 x

Tulln Ⓦ

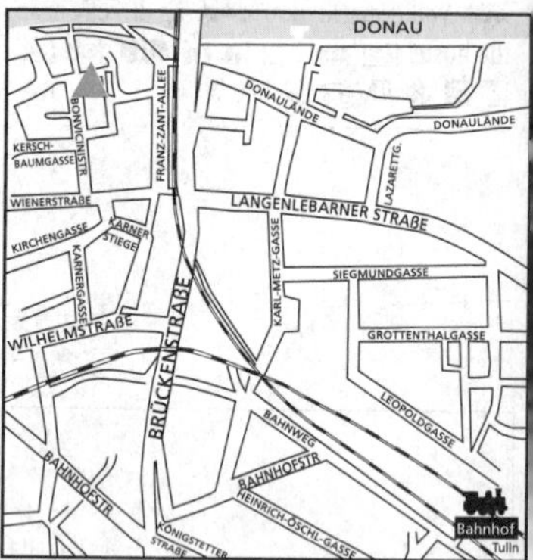

Tulln... Travel Tips

- **For budget eats check out...** Café Lime, Konditorei Köstlbauer, Restaurants Pfundl, Segafredo Espresso, Steinkeller
- **For great nightlife try...** Kinocenter Tulln, Disco Mythos, Café Winzig, Pliff - Bierpub, Snack & Co
- **Don't miss...** Minoritenkloster, Stadtmuseum, Tulln unter der Erde, Aubad, Österreichischers Zuchermuseum, Egon Schiele Museum, Tullner Karner, Donaulände, Römerturm, Stadtplarrkirche

▲ **Uderns** Ⓥ – Finsingerhof – 4079
6271 Uderns, Finsing 73, YGH , Finsingerhof.
(5288) 62010; (6644) 109514
(5288) 62866 tirol@finsingerhof.at
www.finsingerhof.at
Open Dates: 50km BHF Uderns 400m Uderns 400m x 89 R

▲ Ulmerfeld-Hausmening Ⓥ – "JH Schlosz Ulmerfeld" Ⓗ 4026
3363 Ulmerfeld-Hausmening Burgweg 1.
(7475) 54080 (7475) 54080-4
oejhv-noe@oejhv.or.at
Open Dates: 01.04-31.10 (01.11-31.03 with 20 or more only) Wien-Schwechat 160km x 62 R
1 x

▲ Ulrichsberg Ⓦ – 5047
4161 Ulrichsberg, Falkensteinstraße 1.
(7288) 7046 (7288) 7046-20
jgh@alom.at www.alom.at/jgh
Open Dates: x 34 R

▲ Velden Ⓥ – Cap Wörth Ⓗ 4028
A-9220 Velden, Seecorso 37-39, Kärnten.
(4274) 2646 (4274) 2646-20
jgh.capwoerth@oejhv.or.at
www.oejhv.or.at
Open Dates: Klagenfurt 30km
Velden 3km Velden 3km 0.8E
x 231 R CC

Vienna/Vienne/Viena ☛ **Wien**

Vienna/Vienne/Viena ☛ Wien

Villach Ⓥ – **Jugendgästehaus** Ⓗ 4008
A-9500 Villach, St Martin, Dinzlweg 34, Kärnten.
(4242) 56368 (4242) 56368-20
jgh.villach@oejhv.or.at
www.oejhv.or.at
Open Dates: Open Times: 07.00-10.00hrs; 17.00-22.00hrs
Beds: 144 - 2x2 28x5
Price Range: € 17.40 BBinc
Directions: Klagenfurt-Wörthersee 45km
Villach 1.5km St. Martin 300m
x 28 R CC
3 x 2.5km
2.5km

Villach Ⓥ – Jugendgästehaus

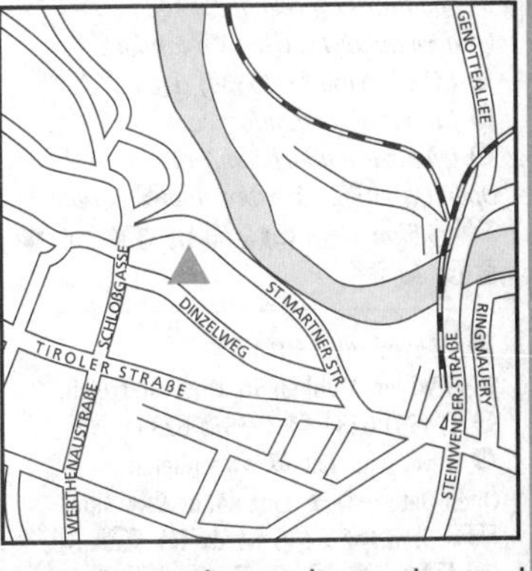

Villach... Travel Tips

- **For budget eats check out...** Youth Hostel, Lounge Mauer (Chinese), Gasthof Kramer, Brauhof, VAS Stüberl
- **For great nightlife try...** Cinema Complex, Night Life (disco), Holly Gods (disco), Malzamt (pub), Jungle Jim (pub, music)
- **Don't miss...** Castle ruins & falconry exhibitions, Boat trip, Wild Animal Park (Rosegg), Wallfahrts Church (Maria Wörth), Look out tower, Terra Mystika (mystical earth & mountain world), Porsche Car Museum (Gmund), Raggra Gorge (Mölltal), Bell Ringer (Hochalpenstr.), Hohe Tauern National Park

▲ Weissenbach am Attersee Ⓥ – Europacamp – 4081
Franz von Schönthanallee 42,
4854 Weissenbach, Oberösterreich.
(7663) 8905 (7663) 8905-14
office@europacamp.at
www.europacamp.at
Open Dates: 15.05-10.09 x 178

▲ Wels Ⓥ – 4082
4600 Wels, Dragonerstraße 22.
(7242) 67284; 2357570
(7242) 2357560
jugendherberge@wels.at
Open Dates: 07.01-23.12 Linz 16km
Wels x 50 CC

△ ***Westendorf*** ⓥ *– Funpark Westendorf/Burgweghof* Ⓗ *4083*
Vorderwindau 15, 6363 Westendorf.
Ⓣ *(5334) 6460* Ⓕ *(5334) 6460*
Ⓔ *funpark@westendorf.com*
Ⓦ *www.westendorf.com/funpark*
Open Dates: 12 *80km* A *2.5km*
3.5km 2.5SW x 60 R

▲ **Weyer** Ⓦ – 5013
3335 Weyer, Mühlein 56, Oberösterreich.
Ⓣ (7355) 6284 Ⓕ (7355) 62844
Ⓔ weyer@jutel.at Ⓦ www.jutel.at
Open Dates: 12 Linz 84km 3km
3km x 136 R
TV 1 x P

▲ **Weyregg/Attersee** Ⓦ – 5048
4852 Weyregg/Attersee Kirchendorf 7, Oberösterreich.
Ⓣ (7664) 2780 Ⓕ (7664) 27804
Ⓔ weyregg@jutel.at Ⓦ www.jutel.at
Open Dates: 01.05-31.10 Linz 76km
22km 150m x 42 R
TV P 2km

Wien ⓥ – Brigittenau Ⓗ 4003
1200 Wien, Friedrich Engelsplatz 24.
Ⓣ (1) 3328294-0 Ⓕ (1) 3308379
Ⓔ jgh.1200wien@chello.at
Ⓦ www.oejhv.or.at; www.youthhostel.at
Open Dates: 01-07.01; 23.01-31.12
Open Times:
Beds: 410 - 103x² 12x³ 36x⁴ 4x⁶
Price Range: € 15.50-19.50 BB inc
Directions: 4NW from city centre
Wien-Schwechat 20km
Wien-Reichsbrücke 2.5km W 6km
U6, S 7km, S1, S2 or S3 ap Handelskai 500m
11A, 5A ap Friedrich Engelsplatz 50m
N, 31, 33 ap Friedrich Engelsplatz 50m
U U6 Handelskai 500m x 155
R CC TV 4 x
8 1km 1.5km

Wien ⓥ – Brigittenau

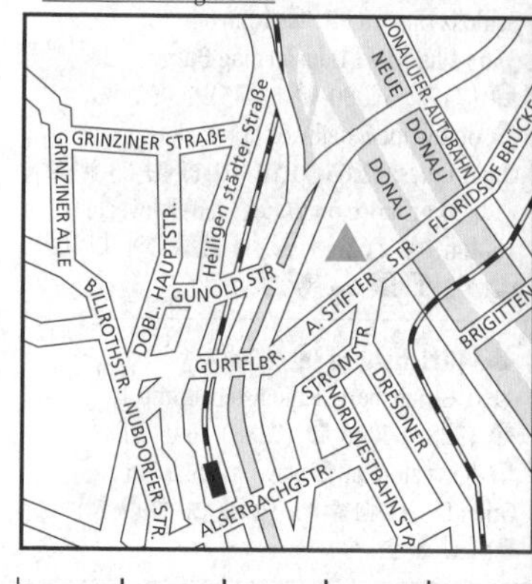

Wien ⓥ – Hostel Hütteldorf Ⓗ 4014 FNM
1130 Wien, Schlossberggasse 8.
Ⓣ (1) 8771501; 8770263
Ⓕ (1) 8770263 Ext 2 Ⓔ jgh@hostel.at
Ⓦ www.hostel.at
Open Dates: 12 Open Times: 07.00-00.00hrs
Beds: 295 - 4x¹ 11x² 2x³ 11x⁴ 1x⁵ 24x⁶ 7x⁶⁺
Price Range: € 12.50-17.60 BB inc
Directions: 10W from city centre
Vienna International 30km A Hilton Air Terminal, then U4 to Hütteldorf Wien Hütteldorf 500m 53B 20m U U4 Hütteldorf 500m x 25 R CC
(BD) TV i 8 P
1km

Wien ⓥ – Hostel Hütteldorf

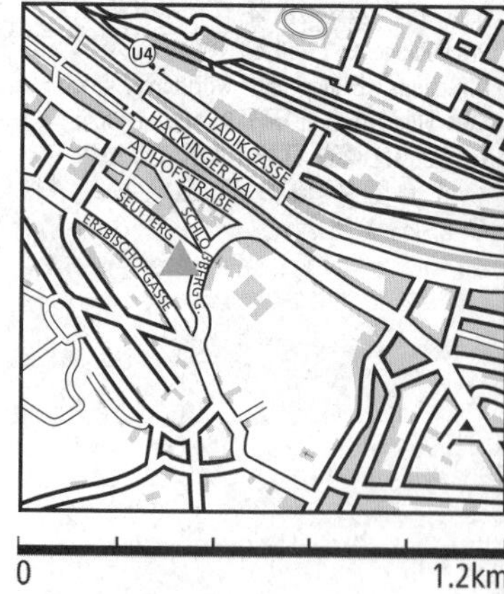

Wien Ⓦ **– Myrthengasse** Ⓗ 5014
1070 Wien, Myrthengasse 7.
Ⓣ (1) 52363160 Ⓕ (1) 5235849
Ⓔ hostel@chello.at
Ⓦ www.oejhv.or.at; www.youthhostel.at
Open Dates: 12 Open Times: 24
Beds: 260 - 17x2 1x3 41x4 1x5 9x6
Price Range: € 15.50-19.50 BBinc
Directions: 2W from city centre
✈ Wien-Schwechat 20km A Vienna ✈ lines ap Westbahnhof 20km
Westbahnhof 3km, Südbahnhof 8km
#48A 500m; #13A 500m U U2, U3 Volkstheater; U6 Burggasse x 41
R CC 1 x i

Wien Ⓦ – Myrthengasse

▲ **Wien** Ⓥ – Hostel Schlossherberge (Palace Hostel) Ⓗ 4013
Schloßherberge am Wilhelminenberg, 1160 Wien, Savoyenstraße 2.
Ⓣ (1) 4858503700 Ⓕ (1) 4858503702
Ⓔ shb@hostel.at Ⓦ www.hostel.at
Open Dates: 12 ✈ Schwechat 24km
Westbahnhof 6km 46B, 146B
U U3 Ottakring 10W x 164 R
CC
500m

Wien... Travel Tips

- **For budget eats check out...** Café Schwarzenberg, Mensa of the Vienna University, Naschmarkt (Schwarzenbergplatz 16), Schnitzelwirt (Neubaugasse 52), Café Einstein (Rathausplatz 4)
- **For great nightlife try...** Pubs in the 1st District/Bermuda Triangle, Pubs along Gürtel/Chelsea, Grinzing - famous wine village, Opera, Theatre, Musicals, Events
- **Don't miss...** Stephansdom (Cathedral), Oper, Kärntnerstrasse, Graben, Hofburg, Imperial Palace, Spanish Riding School, Ringstrasse, Belvedere Palace, Schloss Schönbrunn, Museums quarter

▲ **Wiener Neustadt** Ⓥ – "Europahaus" Ⓗ 4027
2700 Wiener Neustadt, Promenade 1, Niederösterreich. (50km SE of Wien).
Ⓣ (2622) 29695 Ⓕ (2622) 29695
Ⓔ oejhv-noe@oejhv.or.at
Open Dates: 11.01-23.12 ✈ Wien-Schwechat 72km Hauptbahnhof Wr. Neustadt 900m
100m ap Grazerstrasse x 34
R P

Zell am See Ⓦ – 5050
5700 Zell am See, Haus der Jugend, Seespitzstraße 13, Salzburg.
Ⓣ (6542) 57185 Ⓕ (6542) 571854
Ⓔ hostel.zell-see@salzburg.co.at
Ⓦ www.hostel-zell.at
Open Dates: 12 Open Times: 07.00-10.00hrs; 16.00-22.00hrs
Beds: 106 - 7x2 17x4 4x6+
Price Range: € 12.80-17.40 BBinc
Directions: ✈ Salzburg-Amadeus 100km
Zell am See 2km x 28 R CC
i P
2km

AUSTRIA – AUTRICHE – ÖSTERREICH – AUSTRIA

Zell am See Ⓦ

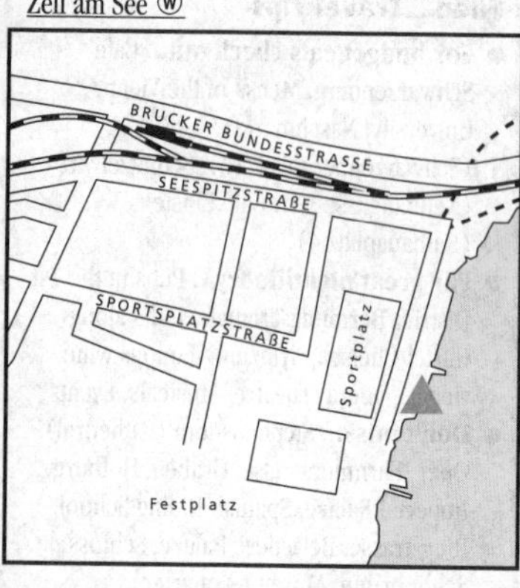

▲ Zell am See Ⓦ – 5019
Schmittenstraße 27, 5700 Zell am See.
(6542) 47036 (6542) 47036
schueler@sbg.at
Open Dates: 01.07-31.08; 25.12-07.01
x 33

Zell am See... Travel Tips

- **For budget eats check out...** McDonalds, Kupferkessel, Mini-Golf Stüberl, Antonia (pizzeria), 5 Planets (Chinese)
- **For great nightlife try...** Crazy Daisy, Viva, Diele, Piccadilly, Bierstadl
- **Don't miss...** Großglockner Hochalpenstraße, Krimml Waterfalls, Kitzsteinhorn Glacier, Schmittenhöhe (mountain peak), Kaprun reservoir & power station, Ferleiten Game Reserve, Kitzloch Gorge (Taxenbach), Eisreisenwelt (world of ice, Werfen), Liechtenstein Gorge (St Johann im Pongau), Leoganger exhibition mine

▲ Zell am Ziller Ⓥ – Jeunesse Hotel Tirolerhof – 4098
A-6280 Zell am Ziller, Tirol, Dorfplatz 8.
(5282) 55075 (5282) 55075-5
jeunessehotel.tirolerhof@aon.at
Open Dates: x 32

YOUTH HOSTEL ACCOMMODATION OUTSIDE THE ASSURED STANDARDS SCHEME

Bad Kreuzen Ⓦ – 5023
Oberösterreich, 4362 Bad Kreuzen, Neuaigen 14, Burg.
(7266) 6686 (7266) 6686
Open Dates: 01.05-31.10 x 68

Bad Leonfelden Ⓦ – 5024
Passauer Straße 3, 4190 Bad Leonfelden.
(7213) 8357
Open Dates: x 44

Neustift Ⓦ – 5037
4143 Neustift im Mühlkreis 71, Rannahof, Oberösterreich.
(7284) 8196 (7284) 8196-4
jugendherberge.neustift@resi.at
www.jugendherberge-neustift.com
Open Dates: x 100 1 x

Ramingstein Ⓥ – Burg Finstergrün – 4069
5591 Ramingstein, Wald 65.
(06475) 228 (06475) 228-4
info@burg-finstergruen.at
www.burg-finstergruen.at
Open Dates: 01.05-15.10 Salzburg 130km
Ramingstein Haltestelle 500m
Ramingstein Bräuwirt 500m x 165

Wien Ⓦ – Turmherberge Don Bosco – 5049
1030 Wien, Lechnerstraße 12.
(1) 7131494
Open Dates: 01.03-30.11 Wien-Schwechat 20km Sud Bahnhof 1.5km 77A or 79A 50m 18 200m U3 Kardinal-Nagl-Platz 150m 3SE x 53

Bahrain

Bahrain Youth Hostels Society (Head Office),
Building 1105, Road 4225, Block 342,
PO Box 2455, Manama, Bahrain.

t (973) 17727170
f (973) 17729919
e byhs@batelco.com.bh; mabul@byhs.org.bh
w www.byhs.org.bh

Office Hours: 08.00-24.00hrs

A copy of the Hostel Directory for this Country can be obtained from: The National Office

Capital:	Manama
Language:	Arabic/English
Currency:	BD (Dinar)
Population:	677,886
Size:	665 sq km
Telephone Country Code:	973
eKit Access Number:	Check www.hi.ekit.com for up to date Access Numbers

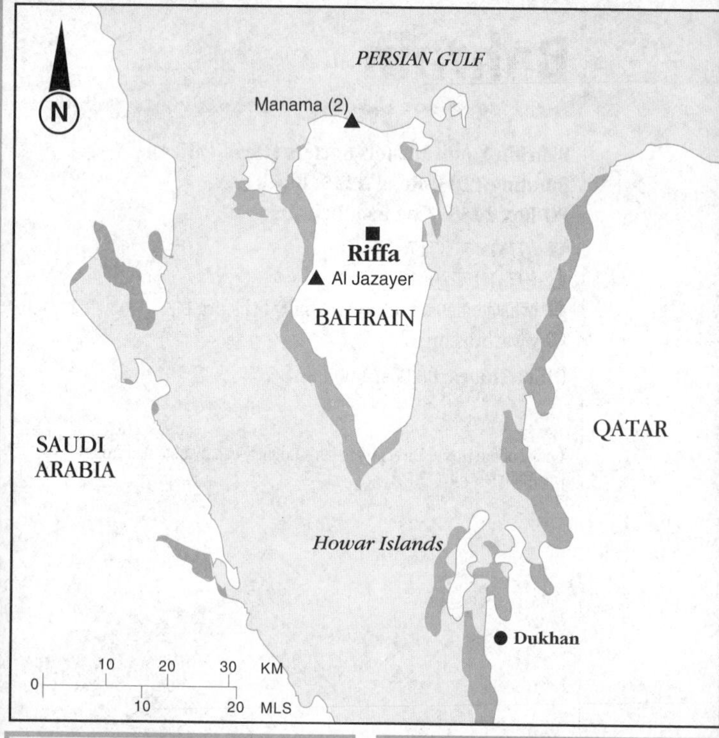

HI Suggests...

Bahrain, a group of 33 islands, with an area of 620 square kilometres, is situated in the Arabian Gulf, off the east coast of Saudi Arabia. The local time is GMT + 3 hours.

The state takes its name from the largest island Bahrain, which is 586.5 square kilometres. The state is linked to Muharraq (international airport) and Sitra (industrial area and tank-farm) by causeways. There are numerous other tiny islands, but they are mainly uninhabited and are best known for the variety of migrating birds, which pass through in spring and autumn.

Arabic is the official language, although English is widely understood and is used mostly in the business context.

Islam is the religion of Bahrain and is practised by a large majority. There are other places of faith and worship on the island.

The climate is hot in the summer and mild in the winter. From November to April the weather is pleasant, with temperatures from 15 to 24°C. Temperatures are at their coolest between December and March when northerly winds prevail. During July to September the temperatures average 36°C with high humidity.

Bahrain is rich in history and international archaeologists have only recently discovered ancient civilisations. It is believed that for tens of thousands of years, nomads travelled over Bahrain's desert and primitive flint tolls found, testify to this history. Recent finds have evidence that Bahrain was indeed the site of the lost civilisation of Dilmun dating from the third millennium BC, often referred to as the fabled Garden of

Eden and described as 'paradise' in the Epic of Gilgamesh.
No visit to Bahrain would be completed without a trip to the Soukh with its profusion of colours, sounds and aromas. All wares are sold, from cloth of many colours and textures to gold and jewellery as well as the traditional array of spices and local produce. Bartering is expected and indeed turns the whole experience of shopping into a challenge to see who can obtain the best price.

You can find out a lot more on our website - a visit to www.HIhostels.com is essential for planning your trip!

Pour en savoir plus, rendez-vous sur notre site Internet, www.HIhostels.com une visite incontournable pour préparer votre voyage!

Viele weitere Informationen auf unserer Website: www.HIhostels.com - unverzichtbar für die Reiseplanung!

Puedes averiguar mucho más en nuestro sitio web. Es imprescindible que visites la página www.HIhostels.com para planear tu viaje.

▲ **Al Jazayer Youth Hostel** – 6003
Al Jazayer Beach, Zallak.
t 17727170 f 17729919
e mabul@byhs.org.bh w www.byhs.org.bh
Open Dates: 12 x 52

▲ **Juffair Youth Hostel** – 6001
Al-Juffair YH, Building 1105, Rd 4225,
Block 342, PO Box 2455, Manama.
t 17727170; 17725177 f 17729919
e mabul@byhs.org.bh w www.byhs.org.bh
Open Dates: 12 5km 800m 3N
x 120 TV i P 4km

▲ **Seef Youth Hostel** – 6004
Bldg 162, Road 16, Block 408,
Dhahiyat Al Seef, Manama, Bahrain.
t 17725177; 17556962 f 17729919
e mabul@byhs.org.bh w www.byhs.org.bh
Open Dates: 12 Bahrain International 7km
3NE x 36 (B) TV i P

Belgium

Ⓥ Vlaamse Jeugdherbergen,
Van Stralenstraat 40,
B-2060 Antwerp, Belgium.
Ⓣ (32) 03 2327218
Ⓕ (32) 03 2318126
Ⓔ info@vjh.be
Ⓦ www.vjh.be
Office Hours: Monday-Friday 09.00-18.00hrs

Ⓛ Les Auberges de Jeunesse,
Rue de la Sablonnière 28,
B-1000 Brussels, Belgium.
Ⓣ (32) 02 2195676
Ⓕ (32) 02 2191451
Ⓔ info@laj.be
Ⓦ www.laj.be
Office Hours: Monday-Friday 09.00-12.30hrs; 13.30-16.30hrs

A copy of the Hostel Directory for this Country can be obtained from:
The National Office

Capital:	Brussels
Language:	Dutch, French, German
Currency:	€ Euro
Population:	10,000,100
Size:	30,515 sq km
Telephone Country Code:	32
eKit Access Number:	0800-49943

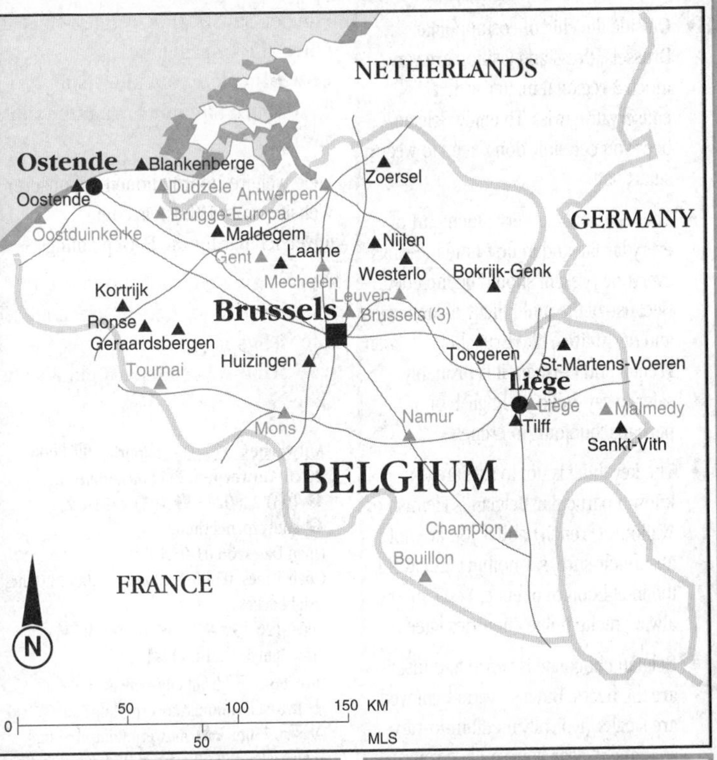

Once the battleground or 'Cockpit' of Europe because of the battles that were fought there, including the Battle of the Bulge in WWII, today Belgium is the centre of the European Union with the capital, Brussels, being the Union's administrative hub. Today a federal state of some 10 million, Belgium is something of a curiosity – an invention of the early nineteenth century following a revolution in the then larger kingdom of The Netherlands, when for religious (Catholic) reasons two incompatible groups – the French-speakers (Wallons) in the south and the Flemish-speakers (who speak a form of Dutch) in the north formed two provinces to create the new country. Initially, they even had to import a king from Germany, Leopold I, to establish their own monarchy. Today, the Belgian monarchy continues to flourish and especially remembers the much-loved King Boudouin.

The 'compromise' and 'fudge' that originally created the state seems to have become part of the national character, hence, some would say, it is perfectly placed for the European Union bureaucracy to flourish. It is well known that in a Belgian café or restaurant 'chips' (fries) are (mostly!) served with everything; but equally true is that it is home to the widest selection of beers in Europe.

Belgium is part of the 'Low Countries' (along with The Netherlands and Luxembourg), and so-called because its landscape is just that –flat. Yet, for all the flatness and jokes about boring, stoical Belgians, there is a wonderful competitive mix of cultures and lifestyles to be enjoyed, including shopping!

A few other Top Tips from **CULTURE SMART!:**

- Outside the chic of cosmopolitan Brussels, dress and fashion are very much a regional matter with a conservative twist. To enjoy Belgian beer you certainly don't need to wear a smart hat!
- The handshake is very much part of everyday life and in first-time meetings, everyone present should be included. Because of the multiplicity of languages and derivatives, like Bruxellois, Belgian French and German, it is probably safer to say 'hello' in English or perhaps 'bonjour' in French.
- The key thing is not to assume you know a particular Belgian is Flemish or Walloon (French) and if you are not absolutely sure, say nothing and avoid the likelihood of offence. You can always make polite enquiries later.
- Belgian chocolate is world famous, as are the beers. But also widely enjoyed are steaks (typically medium-to-rare, so make it clear how you like yours cooked), seafood (especially mussels) and endives, a white-green lettuce-type vegetable that the whole nation seems to enjoy – not to mention chips, of course!

Culture Smart! Top Tips © Kuperard 2005

Cultural Top Tips supplied by Culture Smart! guides. These essential guides to customs and etiquette will help you steer clear of embarrassing gaffes and sensitive issues, enabling you to discover new cultures whilst developing new friendships. Order online at www.culturesmartguides.co.uk

You can find out a lot more on our website - a visit to www.HIhostels.com is essential for planning your trip!

Pour en savoir plus, rendez-vous sur notre site Internet, www.HIhostels.com une visite incontournable pour préparer votre voyage!

Viele weitere Informationen auf unserer Website: www.HIhostels.com - unverzichtbar für die Reiseplanung!

Puedes averiguar mucho más en nuestro sitio web. Es imprescindible que visites la página www.HIhostels.com para planear tu viaje.

Antwerpen Ⓥ – Op Sinjoorke Ⓗ 8006
2020 Antwerpen, Eric Sasselaan 2.
Ⓣ (03) 2380273 Ⓕ (03) 2481932
Ⓔ antwerpen@vjh.be
Open Dates: 06.01-05.12
Open Times: 07.00-10.00hrs; 15.00-23.00hrs (Night access)
Beds: 126 - 5x2 8x4 10x6 3x6+
Price Range: € 14.50 BBinc
Directions: 4S from city centre
Brussels 45km; Antwerp 5km
A 750m Antwerp Central 5km; Antwerp South 500m 27 Central Station, 25 Groenplaats (direction Antwerp Expo) 100m 2 U Central Station (direction Hoboken U direction Antwerp Expo) 100m
x 8 CC TV
2 x 8 P 500m

Antwerpen Ⓥ – Op Sinjoorke

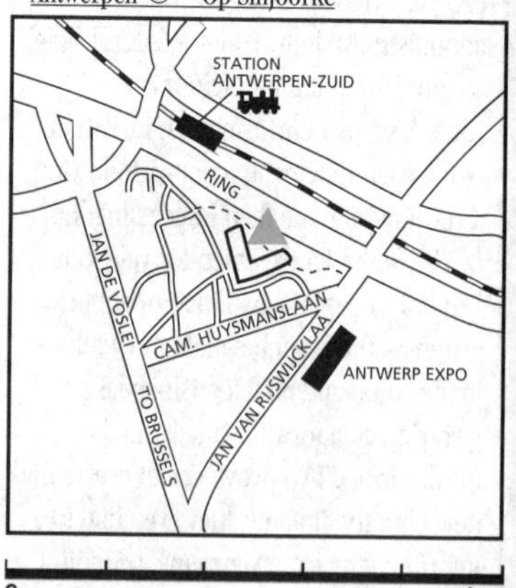

Antwerpen... Travel Tips

- **For budget eats check out...** Zuiderpershuis, Elixir (Vegetarian), Finjan (Pita Bar), Dikke Mee (500m from YH), Soups and Salads (1km from YH)
- **For great nightlife try...** Café D'Anvers, De Vagant, Bierland, Several bars near Grote Markt
- **Don't miss...** Cathedral/Market Square area, Rubens House (Museum), Museum of Modern Art, Harbour, Museum of Fine Arts, Bourla Theatre, Museum Mayer van den Bergh, National Maritime Museum, Rockoxhuis, Diamond Museum

▲ **Blankenberge** Ⓥ – De Wullok – 8013
8370 Blankenberge, Ruitersstraat 9.
(050) 415307 (050) 426014
blankenberge@vjh.be
Open Dates: 12 Oostende 25km Zeebrugge 5km Blankenberge 2km 50m ap St. Amandus Church 2N
x 79 R CC

▲ **Bokrijk/Genk** Ⓥ – De Roerdomp – 8014
3600 Bokrijk/Genk, Boekrakelaan 30.
(089) 356220 (089) 303980
bokrijk@vjh.be
Open Dates: 01.03-10.11 5km
300m ap Zonhoven x 105
1 x P

▲ **Bouillon** Ⓛ – Sur La Hauteur 7011
Route du Christ 16, 6830 Bouillon.
(061) 468137 (061) 467818
bouillon@laj.be
Open Dates: 01-08.01; 10.02-12.11; 17.11-31.12 (R 10.02-31.03; 01.11-31.12) Zaventem Libramont 35km 8 ap Rempart - Depôt TEC 0.75NW
x 132 R CC
TV i P

Brugge Ⓥ – Europa 8001
8310 Brugge 4/Assebroek, Baron Ruzettelaan 143.
(050) 352679 (050) 353732
brugge@vjh.be
Open Dates: 17.01-25.12
Open Times: 07.30-10.30hrs; 13.30-23.00hrs (Night access)
Beds: 212 - 4x1 22x4 20x6
Price Range: € 14.50-16.60 BB inc
Directions: 2SE from city centre
Brussels 85km Brugge 1.5km
2 300m; 749 100m x 22 R
CC TV 2 x P

Brugge Ⓥ – Europa

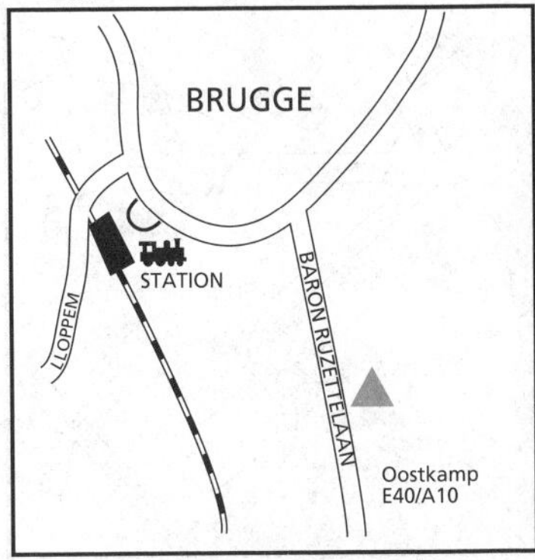

Brugge... Travel Tips

- **For great nightlife try...** Market Area, Zand Area
- **Don't miss...** Groeninge Museum, Gruuthuse Museum, St John's Hospital, Gothic Hall & City Wall, Belfry, Bruges Diamond Museum, Basilica of the Holy Blood, Beguinage, Lace Centre, Lake of Love

Brussels ⓥ – Bruegel – 8007
1000 Brussel, Heilig Geeststraat 2. (Corner: Keizerslaan-Kapellekerk/ Eglise de la Chapelle).
(02) 5110436 (02) 5120711
brussel@vjh.be www.vjh.be
Open Dates: Open Times: 07.00-01.00hrs
Beds: 135 - 4x1 22x2 1x3 21x4
Price Range: € 17.60-30.00 BBinc
Directions: 1S from city centre
Brussels 15km Central 300m
20 Midi Station 50m ap Chapelle
U Central Station 300m x 31
R CC 3 x
300m

Brussels ⓥ – Bruegel

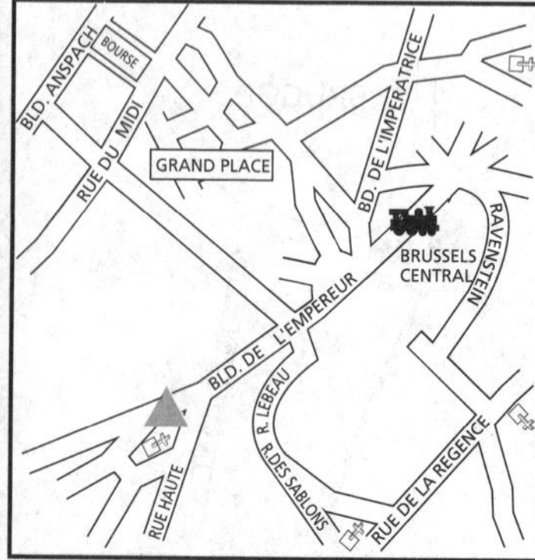

Brussels ⓛ – Génération Europe Ⓗ 7002
4 Rue de l'Eléphant, 1080 Bruxelles.
(02) 4103858 (02) 4103905
brussels.europe@laj.be
Open Dates: 21.01-12.11; 17.11-31.12
Open Times: 07.30-24.00hrs (Night access)
Beds: 162 - 8x2 22x4 2x5 3x6 4x6+
Price Range: € 17.60 BBinc
Directions: 1.5NW from city centre
Zaventem 15km Zeebrugge 125km
South Station 2km 18 500m
ap Porte de Flandre U Comte de Flandre
300m x 26 R CC
4 x P

Brussels ⓛ – Génération Europe

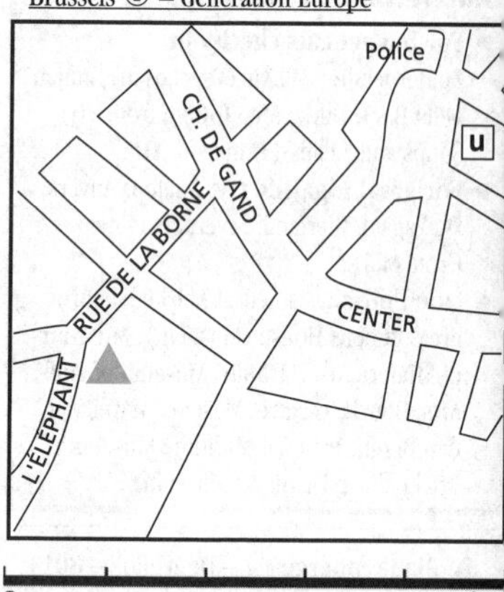

Brussels ⓛ – Jacques Brel Ⓗ 7009
Rue de la Sablonnière 30, 1000 Bruxelles.
(02) 2180187 (02) 2172005
brussels.brel@laj.be
Open Dates: 02.01-17.12 Brussels 20km
A BH, BZ 200m Zeebrugge 125km
North 2km 61, 65, 66, 29, 63
200m ap Presse, Congres, Madou 92, 93, 94 200m ap Botanique U Madou 200m;
Botanique 200m 1NE x 173
CC 4 x

Brussels... Travel Tips

- **For budget eats check out...** Pablo's - Tex Mex (Rue de Namur 51), Chez Yasmina (near the Grand Place - Rue Marché au Fromage), Chez Léon (Petite Rue des bouchers 18), Skievelat (Rue J Stevens 16-18), Big Mama (near Bruegel Hostel, cosy and cheap)
- **For great nightlife try...** Porte Noire - Special Beers (Rue des Alexiens 65), Archiduc - Jazz Bar (Rue A. Dansaert 6), St Goriks Square (many bars), O'Reilly's - Irish Pub (Place de La Bourse 1), Sphinx - Cocktail Bar (Rue Marché au Fromage)
- **Don't miss...** Grand Place, St Michael's Cathedral, Modern & Ancient Art Museum, Brewery Museum, Middle Africa Museum in Tervuren, Atomium, Comic Strip Museum, Horta Museum - Art Nouveau Buildings, Museums around Parc du Cinquantenaire, Mini Europe

▲ **Champlon** Ⓛ – Barrière de Champlon Ⓗ 7012
Rue de la Gendarmerie 5, 6971 Champlon.
(084) 455294 (084) 457045
champlon@laj.be
Open Dates: 01-08.01; 10.02-12.11; 17.11-31.12 (R 10.02-31.03; 01.11-31.12) Zaventem Marloie 20km Line 1 300m x 74 R CC 2 x 12km

▲ **Dudzele** Ⓥ – "Herdersbrug" Ⓗ 8015
8380 Brugge/Dudzele, Louis Coiseaukaai 46.
(050) 599321 (050) 599349
brugge.dudzele@vjh.be
Open Dates: 15.01-15.12 7km 41 or 42 700m x 112 CC

Gent Ⓥ – De Draecke Ⓗ 8005
9000 Gent, St Widostraat 11.
(09) 2337050 (09) 2338001
gent@vjh.be www.ghent-hostel.com
Open Dates: 01.01-30.12
Open Times: 07.00-23.00hrs (Night access)
Beds: 106 - 6x2 3x3 10x4 3x5 5x6
Price Range: € 16.60-21.00 BBinc
Directions: Brussels 65km Oostende 55km Gent St Pieters 4km 1 200m ap Gravensteen (Castle) x 27 R CC 1 x

Gent Ⓥ – De Draecke

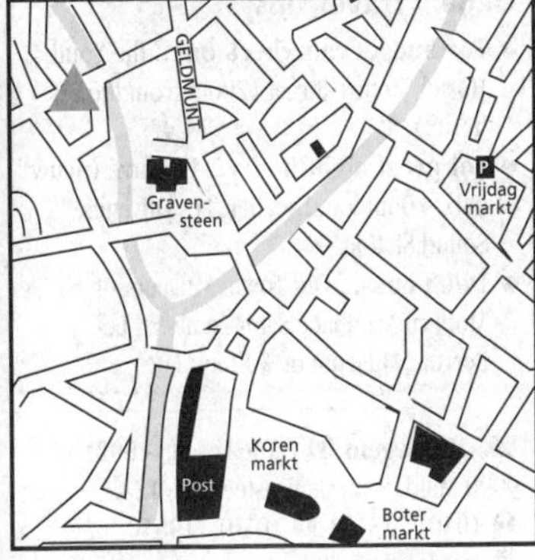

Gent... Travel Tips

- **For budget eats check out...** Pizza Faki (Turkish), Turkish Area, University Area, De Lieve, Korenmarkt Square
- **For great nightlife try...** Hotsy Totsy, Korenmarkt Area, University Area, Vlasmarkt, 'T Floere Foefken
- **Don't miss...** Gravensteen Castle, St Baafs Cathedral, Belfry, Museum of Modern Art (Smak), Museum of Fine Arts, Museum of Decorative Arts and Design, M.I.A.T. (Museum for Industrial Archaeology and Textiles), City Centre, Gent Festival mid July (Music & Theatre)

▲ **Geraardsbergen** Ⓥ – 't Schipken – 8017
9500 Geraardsbergen, Kampstraat 59. (Recreatiedomein 'De Gavers').
(054) 416189 (054) 419461
geraardsbergen@vjh.be
Open Dates: 24.02-31.03 (weekends only); 31.03-05.11 Brussels 40km Schendelbeke 500m x 104 R

▲ **Huizingen** Ⓥ – 't Golvende Brabant – 8018
1654 Huizingen, Prov Domein.
(02) 3830026 (02) 3830026
Open Dates: 01.02-30.11 25km 1.5km 200m x 58 R 100m

▲ **Kortrijk** Ⓥ – Groeninghe – 8019
8500 Kortrijk, Passionistenlaan 1A.
(056) 201442 (056) 204663
kortrijk@vjh.be
Open Dates: 16.01-15.12 Kortrijk 1km 1 250m ap St. Antonius Church x 96

▲ **Laarne** Ⓥ – De Valk – 8031
9270 Laarne, Mellestraat 18A.
(09) 2320075 (09) 2301274
laarne@vjh.be www.infrafos.be
Open Dates: 15.01-15.12 Wetteren 4km 34 1km x 77 R

Leuven Ⓥ – De Blauwput Ⓗ 8020
Martelarenlaan 11A, 3010 Leuven.
(016) 639062 (016) 639064
leuven@vjh.be www.leuven-hostel.com
Open Dates: 16.01-22.12
Open Times: 07.00-23.00hrs
Beds: 116
Directions: 1E from city centre
Brussels-National (Zaventem) 25km
Leuven - stop Kessel-Lo 50m
Central Bus Station 50m
3 x

Leuven Ⓥ – De Blauwput

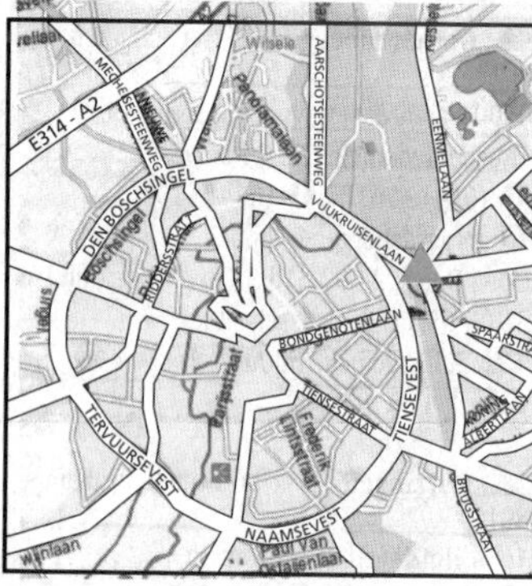

Leuven... Travel Tips

- **For budget eats check out...** De Werf, Wereld Café COOP, Bar Del Sol, Metropole, Carlisse
- **For great nightlife try...** The Old Market - Leuven's medieval square with over 50 pubs, Disco Rumba, Café Manget, Libertad, Kaminsky
- **Don't miss...** Leuven's medieval buildings and squares, The great beguinage, The abbey of Park, STUK (Cultural Centre), Plenty of marked and mapped cycle tours, Relaxing walk in the Meerdaalforest and Zoete Waters, Local breweries (Domus), The botanical garden, Visits to Brussel and Antwerpen

Liège Ⓛ – Georges Simenon Ⓗ 7007
Rue Georges Simenon 2, 4020 Liège.
(04) 3445689 (04) 3445687
liege@laj.be
Open Dates: 01-08.01; 04.02-12.11; 17.11-31.12 Open Times: 07.30-01.00hrs (Night access)
Beds: 204 - 16x4 12x5 4x6 8x6+
Price Range: € 16.60-29.00 BB inc
Directions: 0.5SE from city centre
Zaventem 100km Palais 1km; Liège Guillemins 2km No. 4 300m ap Constitution/Congrès x 40 CC
4 x
500m

Liège Ⓛ – Georges Simenon

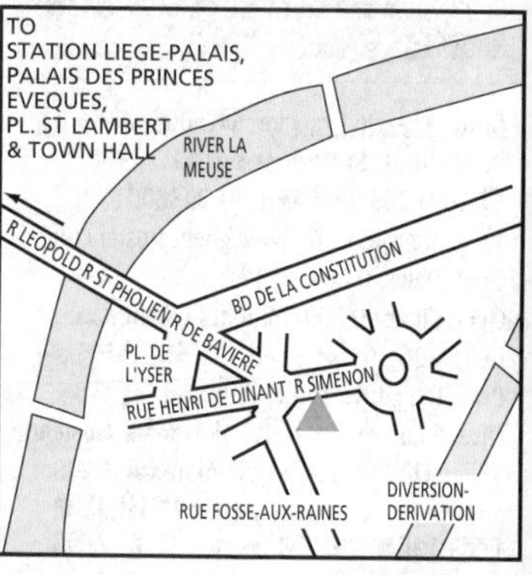

Liège... Travel Tips

- **For budget eats check out...** the Youth Hostel, Roture Street (200m from the hostel)
- **For great nightlife try...** Le Carré (many bars), Bouldou, Escalier, Les Olivettes, Sound Station
- **Don't miss...** Old Town, Museum of Modern Art, Place Saint-Lambert, Le Perron, Museum of Walloon Life

▲ **Maldegem** Ⓥ – Die Loyale – 8021
9990 Maldegem, Gentsesteenweg 124.
(050) 713121 (050) 719070
maldegem@vjh.be
Open Dates: 15.02-15.11 Eeklo 9km
58 5m ap Ommeloper x 74
2 x

▲ **Malmedy** Ⓛ – Hautes Fagnes Ⓗ 7013
Bévercé, route d'Eupen 36, 4960 Malmedy.
(080) 338386 (080) 770504
malmedy@laj.be
Open Dates: 01-08.01; 16.01-24.08; 04.09-11.11; 24.11-31.12 Trois-Ponts; Verviers 35km from Trois-Ponts 45A; from Verviers 395; from Malmedy 397 2.5N
x 178 4 x 700m

▲ **Mechelen** Ⓥ – De Zandpoort Ⓗ 8009
Zandpoortvest 70, 2800 Mechelen.
(015) 278539 (015) 278540
mechelen@vjh.be
Open Dates: 16.01-15.12 Brussels 18km
Mechelen Central 600m 100m
x 112 2 x

Mons Ⓛ – Auberge du Beffroi Ⓗ 7010
Rampe du Château 2, 7000 Mons.
(065) 875570 (065) 875571
mons@laj.be
Open Dates: 03.01-08.01; 03.02-12.11; 17.11-31.12 (12)
Open Times: 07.30-24.00hrs (Night access)
Beds: 115 - 3x3 25x4 1x6
Price Range: € 16.60-29.00 BBinc
Directions: 0.1N from city centre
Zaventem 45km Mons 700m
Free Shuttle Service 3 x

Mons Ⓛ – Auberge du Beffroi

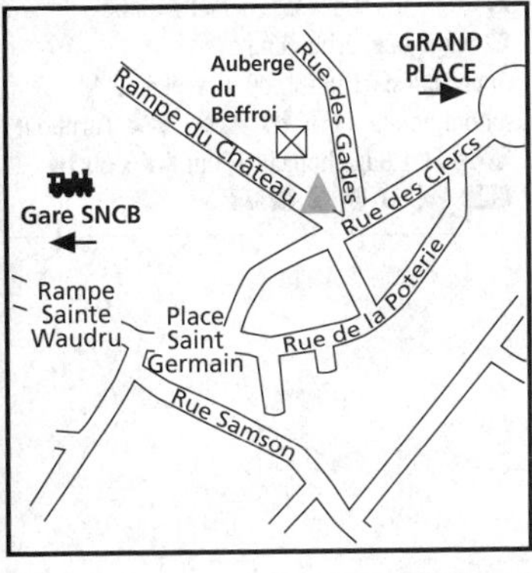

Mons... Travel Tips

- **For budget eats check out...** Buffet de la Gare, Chez Ferdinand, Chez Henri, La Petite Couscoussière, La Grillade
- **For great nightlife try...** Imagimons (Cinema), Le Plaza Art (Cinema), Marché aux Herbes Area
- **Don't miss...** Grand Place, Van Gogh Museum, Town Hall, Collegial Church of Sainte-Waudru, Pass Park, Paradisio Park, The Inclined Plan of Ronquieres, The Lifts of Strepy-Thieu

Namur Ⓛ – Félicien Rops Ⓗ 7008
Av. Félicien Rops 8, 5000 Namur.
(081) 223688 (081) 224412
namur@laj.be
Open Dates: 01.01-12.11; 17.11-31.12 (01.01-15.03; 15.10-31.12)
Open Times: 08.00-23.00hrs (Night access)
Beds: 100 - 2x2 12x4 6x5 3x6
Price Range: € 14.50 BBinc
Directions: 2.5S from city centre
Namur 3km 3, 4 300m 4 x 2km

Namur Ⓛ – Félicien Rops

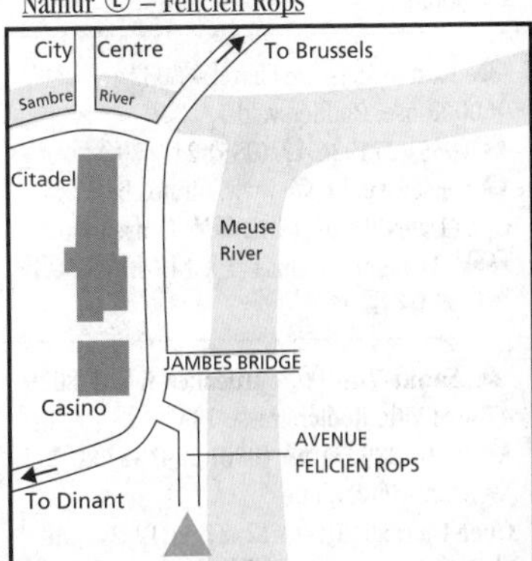

Namur... Travel Tips

- **For budget eats check out...** Hot's, Phenix
- **For great nightlife try...** Le Temps d'Ivresse (Bar), Theatre, Place du Vieux Marché, Piano Bar
- **Don't miss...** La Citadelle de Namur, Old City Centre, Ravel (hiking & cycling), Museum of Beer, Museum Félicien Rops

▲ Nijlen Ⓥ – 't Pannenhuis – 8022
2560 Nijlen, Wijngaardberg 42.
(03) 4110733 (03) 4110725
nijlen@vjh.be
Open Dates: 15.02-15.11 1km
1km x 64

▲ Oostduinkerke Ⓥ –
De Peerdevisser 8023
8670 Oostduinkerke, Duinparklaan 41.
(058) 512649 (058) 522880
oostduinkerke@vjh.be
www.peerdevisser.be
Open Dates: 01.02-15.12 Oostende 30km
Oostende 30km Koksijde 4km
500m ap Oostduinkerke - Midden
500m ap Duinpark x 135
3 x 500m

▲ Oostende Ⓥ – De Ploate – 8024
8400 Oostende, Langestraat 82.
(059) 805297 (059) 809274
oostende@vjh.be www.deploate.com
Open Dates: 01.01-08.01; 06.02-23.12
Oostende 5km A Line 6 Airport 5km
Oostende 1km Oostende 1km
x 106
3 x 300m
300m

▲ Ronse Ⓥ – De Fiertel – 8032
9600 Ronse, Ruddersveld 7.
(055) 211926 (055) 217870
ronse@vjh.be www.infrafos.be
Open Dates: 15.01-15.12 Ronse 4km
21 Belbus 100m x 146

▲ Sankt-Vith Ⓥ – Ardennen-Eifel – 8025
4780 St Vith, Rodterstrasse 13A.
(080) 229331 (080) 229332
sankt-vith@vjh.be
Open Dates: 01.01-23.12; 27-31.12
Liege-Bierset 80km Verviers 45km;
Gouwy 20km 395 500m; 48B 500m
x 100 2 x

▲ Tilff Ⓛ – Ferme du Château – 7014
4130 Tilff, Esplanade de l'Abeille 9.
(04) 3445689 (04) 3445687
tilff@laj.be
Open Dates: 01-08.01; 04.02-12.11;
17.11-31.12 (1 only) Brussels 100km
Gare de Tilff 800m 377
(Liège-Comblain au pont) x 34
1 x

▲ Tongeren Ⓥ – Begeinhof – 8026
3700 Tongeren, St Ursulastraat 1.
(012) 391370 (012) 391348
tongeren@vjh.be
Open Dates: x 82

▲ Tournai Ⓛ 7015
7500 Tournai, Rue Saint-Martin 64.
(069) 216136 (069) 216140
tournai@laj.be
Open Dates: 01-08.01; 10.02-12.11;
17.11-31.12 (24.02-31.03;
01.11-31.12) Zaventem 100km
Tournai 1.5km 400m 0.5SW
x 100
2 x

▲ Voeren Ⓥ – De Veurs – 8027
3790 St Martens Voeren, Comberg 29B.
(04) 3811110 (04) 3811313
voeren@vjh.be
Open Dates: 24.02-12.11 Visé 8km;
Maastricht 25km 39B ap
Voeren-Tongeren; 39C ap St.-Martens Voeren
(Gendarmerie) x 90 2 x

▲ Westerlo Ⓥ – Boswachtershuis – 8028
2260 Westerlo, Papedreef 1.
(014) 547938 (014) 547938
westerlo@vjh.be
Open Dates: 01.03-13.11 (01.03-23.12)
15km 500m x 82

▲ Zoersel Ⓥ – Gagelhof – 8029
2980 Zoersel, Gagelhoflaan 18.
(03) 3851642 zoersel@vjh.be
www.jeugherbergen.be
Open Dates: 01.06-30.09 + weekends &
school holidays ( ) Turnhout
41.1 Gagelhoflaan 150m x 60

Brazil

Federação Brasileira dos Albergues da Juventude,
Rua General Dionísio, 63-Botafogo - Rio de Janeiro
CEP: 22271-050, Brasil.

t (55) (21) 22860303
f (55) (21) 22865652
e info@hostel.org.br
w www.hostel.org.br

A copy of the Hostel Directory for this Country can be obtained from:
The National Office

Capital:	Brasilia
Language:	Portuguese
Currency:	R$ (Real)
Population:	184,000,000
Size:	8,511,865 sq km
Telephone Country Code:	55
eKit Access Number:	0800-891-5825

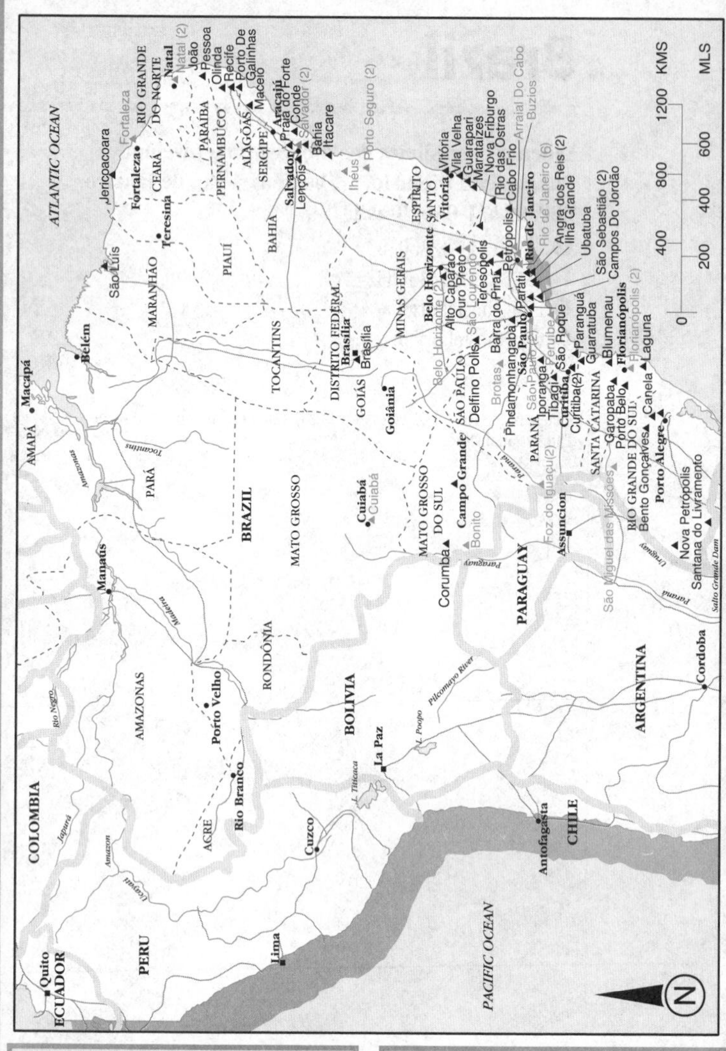

Colonized by the Portuguese in the sixteenth century, Brazil (Federal Republic) is not only the largest country geographically and by population in South America (184 million) it is the only one to speak Portuguese. It is almost unimaginably vast, from huge, primordial rain forests of the Amazon basin in the north, to huge, empty deserts, wild highlands and lush savannahs in the centre and south. Not surprisingly, most of the population lives on or near the sea. Its two largest cities are São Paulo (16 million) and Rio de Janeiro, (11 million), famous for its carnival and Copacabana and Ipanema beaches. It also has a futuristic city and federal state known as Brasilia, built in the middle of nowhere in the middle of the country.

There is still a lot of coffee in Brazil and it is still one of the most welcoming places on earth where sport, above all football, is king (the 'king of kings' being Pelé), with motor racing following a close second.

A rich mixture of cultures, including the indigenous American Indians and the largest Japanese population outside Japan, Brazil is also full of paradoxes, especially the enormous gap between rich and poor which has created many different urban sub-cultures, including the street urchins.

A few other Top Tips from **CULTURE SMART!**:

- Brazilian fashion reflects where you live – whether in the sprawling urban cities or the beautiful coastline. European and US fashion tends to dominate city life, but with a distinctly Brazilian twist; whereas in coastal areas Brazilian swimwear fashion is trendsetter to the world!
- Greetings with handshakes is the norm, and with hugs when it is close friends. If it is a group, on arriving, everyone should be greeted with a handshake as well as on leaving. Women tend to kiss each other on alternating cheeks.
- An 'OK' sign formed by touching the thumb and index finger is a positive sign in the US, Italy and other countries; but in Brazil it is obscene. Whistling to attract someone's attention is also taboo.
- Food is very much determined by region, but is essentially a variation of traditional Portuguese, American Indian, Afro-Bahian and European. A knife and fork are always used and Brazilians tend not to eat 'on the hoof', i.e. while riding the bus or subway. Sunday family lunch is highly regarded.

You can find out a lot more on our website - a visit to www.HIhostels.com is essential for planning your trip!

Pour en savoir plus, rendez-vous sur notre site Internet, www.HIhostels.com une visite incontournable pour préparer votre voyage!

Viele weitere Informationen auf unserer Website: www.HIhostels.com - unverzichtbar für die Reiseplanung!

Puedes averiguar mucho más en nuestro sitio web. Es imprescindible que visites la página www.HIhostels.com para planear tu viaje.

△ ***Alto Caparaó*** *– Querência – 9026*
Av. Pico Da Bandeira, 1061 - Centro
Alto Caparaó-MG. CEP: 36836-000.
(32) 37472566 *(32) 37472566*
turismoquerencia@uol.com.br
www.picodabandeiratur.hpg.com.br
Open Dates: x 24

△ ***Angra Dos Reis*** *– Bracuí – 9112*
Estrada Santa Rita, 04-KM 505.
(24) 33631234 *aj@riobracui.com.br*
www.riobracui.com.br
Open Dates: 01.01-30.03; 01-30.07 x 35

△ ***Angra dos Reis*** *– Angra Hostel – 9027*
Praça Da Matriz, 152 - Sobrado -
Angra dos Reis - RJ CEP: 23900-00.
(24) 33644759 *(24) 33644759*
aj@riobracui.com.br
www.riobracui.com.br
Open Dates: x 20

Arraial D'Ajuda – Arraial D'Ajuda – 9103
Rua do Campo,
94 - Centro CEP:45816.000-Bahia.
(73) 35751192 (73) 35751636
arraial@arraialdajudahostel.com.br
www.arraialdajudahostel.com.br
Open Dates: x 60

Arraial do Cabo – Marina dos Anjos 9090
Rua Bernardo Lens, 145, Praia dos Anjos,
Arraial do Cabo - RJ - CEP: 28930-000.
(22) 26224060 (22) 26224060
marinadosanjos@arraialweb.com.br
www.marinadosanjos.com.br
Open Dates: x 22

Barra do Piraí – Na Toca – 9029
Estrada Municipal Rui Pio Davi Gomes,
1876 Dorândia, Barra do Piraí,
Rio de Janeiro State. CEP: 27160-000.
(24) 24331234
pousadanatoca@uol.com.br
www.natocahostel.com.br
Open Dates: x 49

Belo Horizonte – *Chalé Mineiro – 9030*
Rua Santa Luzia 288,
30260-120 Belo Horizonte, MG.
(31) 34671576 (31) 34671576
chalemineiro@ig.com.br
www.chalemineirohostel.com.br
Open Dates: Confirns x 54

Belo Horizonte – Sossego da Pampulha 9031
Av. Coronel José Dias Bicalho,
1258 - Belo Horizonte - MG - CEP: 31275050.
(31) 34918020 (31) 34270990
sossegodapampulha@hotmail.com
www.sossegodapampulha.com.br
Open Dates: Pampulha or Confins
x 60 1 x

Bento Gonçalves – Casa Mia – 9032
Travessa Niterói 71,
95700-000 Bento Gonçalves, RS.
(54) 4511215
atendimento@pousadacasamia.com.br
www.pousadacasamia.com.br
Open Dates: x 47

Blumenau – *Grun Garten – 9033*
Rua São Paulo, 2457.
(47) 3234332 (47) 3234332
grungarten@grungarten.com.br
www.grungarten.com.br
Open Dates: x 50

Bonito – Bonito 9006
Rua Lucio Borralho,
716 - Bonito - MS. CEP: 79290-000.
(67) 2551022; 2551462
(67) 2552646 ajbonito@terra.com.br
www.ajbonito.com.br
Open Dates: x 86

Brasilia – Brasilia – 9034
SRPN-QD02, Lote:02 ASA Norte,
CEP: 70800-200.
(61) 33430531 (61) 33449191
hibsb@opendf.com.br
Open Dates: x 120
1 x

Brotas – Canto do Sol 9035
Av. Lorival Jaubert da Silva Braga,
1.750. Brotas-SP. CEP: 17380 000.
/ (14) 36538081; 36534403;
36530330 hi@cantodosol.com.br
www.cantodosol.com.br
Open Dates: x 84
1 x

Búzios 9036
Rua Marisol, 35, CEP: 28950-000-RJ.
(22) 26236024; 88066024
(22) 26236177
reservas@buzioshostel.com.br
www.buzioshostel.com.br
Open Dates: x 34 (L)

Cabo Frio – Peró Hostel – 9091
Rua Coutrim, 13, Peró,
Cabo Frio - RJ - CEP: 28924-170.
(22) 26443123 (22) 26477605
info@perohostel.com.br
www.perohostel.com.br
Open Dates: x 96

△ ***Campo Grande*** *– Campo Grande – 9038*
Rua Juaquim Nabuco, 185-Centro-Campo Grande-MS. CEP: 79008-340.
(67) 3210505 (67) 3210505
ajcampogrande@hotmail.com
Open Dates: x 60

△ ***Campos Do Jordão*** *– Campos Do Jordão – 9104*
Rua Pereira Barreto, 22 Vila Abernesia, CEP: 12460-000-SP.
(12) 36622341 (12) 36641707
info@camposdojordaohostel.com.br
www.camposdojordaohostel.com.br
Open Dates: x 18

▲ **Canela** – Viajante – 9039
Rua Ernesto Urbani 132, 95680-000 Canela, RS.
(54) 2822017
www.albergues.com.br
Open Dates: x 67

△ ***Conde*** *– Onze Praias – 9108*
Praia De Carapibus, Jacumã, s/n CEP: 58322-000-PB.
(83) 32901434
feliz@onzepraias.com.br
www.onzepraias.com.br
Open Dates: x 40

▲ **Corumbá** – Corumbá – 9121
Rua Colombo, 1419.
(067) 2311005 (067) 2311005
corumbahostel@corumbahostel.com.br
www.corumbahostel.com.br
Open Dates: x 37

▲ **Cuiabá** – Portal Do Pantanal HI 9025
Av. Isaac Póvoas, 665-Centro Cuiabá-MT. UP: 78005-560.
(65) 6248999 (65) 6248999
albergue@vsp.com.br
www.portaldopantanal.com.br
Open Dates: x 54

▲ **Curitiba** – Curitiba Eco Hostel – 9120
Rua Luiz Tramontin, 1693.
(41) 32747979 (41) 30291693
info@curitibaecohostel.com.br
www.curitibaecohostel.com.br
Open Dates: x 52

△ ***Curitiba*** *– Roma – 9111*
Rua Barão Do Rio Branco, 805 CEP: 80010. 180 PR.
(41) 32242117 (41) 33222838
info@hostelroma.com.br
www.hostelroma.com.br
Open Dates: x 110

▲ **Delfinó Polis** – Rio Grande – 9123
Rua Torquato Jose de Almeida, 790.
(35) 35251073 (35) 25251124
reservas@pousadariogrande.com.br
www.pousadariogrande.com.br
Open Dates: x 40

▲ **Extrema** – Eco Hostel Village Natureza – 9068
Rodovia Fernaõ Dias, Km 927 Minas Gerais - CEP: 37640000.
(35) 34352398 (35) 34352398
viajens2005-reservas@yahoo.com.br
http://ecohostel.multiply.com
Open Dates: x 20

▲ **Florianópolis** – Canasvieiras – 9041
Rua Dr. João de Oliveira, 517 Florianópolis - SC - 88054-120.
(48) 2254515 (48) 2662036
alberguesfloripa@uol.com.br
www.alberguedajuventudefpolis.com.br
Open Dates: 15.12-15.03 x 130

▲ **Florianópolis** – Ilha de Santa Catarina HI 9013
Rua Duarte Schutel 227. 88015-640 Florianópolis, SC.
(48) 2253781 (48) 2254515
alberguesfloripa@uol.com.br
www.alberguedajuventudefpolis.com.br
Open Dates: x 60

▲ **Fortáleza** – Pousada Atalaia HI 9042
Av. Beiramar, 814-Praia de Iracema - Fortáleza - CE CEP: 60165-121.
(85) 32190755 (85) 32190658
contato@alberguedajuventudeatalaia.com.br
www.alberguedajuventudeatalaia.com.br
Open Dates: x 72

▲ **Foz do Iguaçú** – Paudimar HI 9043
Rodovia das Cataratas, KM 12, 5,
Remanso Grande, Foz do Iguaçú,
PR CEP: 85830-000.
t (45) 35296061 f (45) 35296061
e info@paudimar.com.br
w www.paudimar.com.br
Open Dates: x 140

△ ***Foz do Iguaçú** – Paudimar Falls – 9119*
Rua Antonio Raposo, 820-Centro.
t (045) 30285503 f (045) 30285503
e paudimar_falls@hotmail.com
w www.paudimar.com.br
Open Dates: x 46 R CC

△ ***Garopaba** – Praia Do Ferrugem – 9044*
Rua Das Bromélias,
35 Garopaba - SC - 88495-000.
t (48) 2540035 f (48) 2540035
e ajferrugem@bol.com.br
w www.hostelferrugem.hpg.com.br
Open Dates: 01.01-31.03 x 40 R
P

▲ **Gramado** – Gramado – 9045
Av. Das Hortensias, 3880, CEP 95670-000.
t (54) 2951020 f (54) 2951020
e ajig@terra.com.br
w www.gramadohostel.com.br
Open Dates: x 50

▲ **Guarapari** – Guaralbergue – 9046
Av. Antônio Guimarães, Quadra 40,
Itapebussu, 29200-000 Guarapari, ES.
t (27) 32610475 f (27) 32625210
w www.guaratur.com.br/guaralbergue
Open Dates: 0.8S x 100 R
1 x P

▲ **Guaratuba** – Cabana Suíça – 9110
Av. Curitiba, 1445 - CEP: 83280-000-PR.
t (41) 34431066
e cabanasuissa@lol.com.br
w www.cabanasuica.com.br
Open Dates: x 90 R P

▲ **Ilha do Mel** – Zorro – 9115
Ilha do Mel,
Praia da Encantadas CEP: 83203-970-PR.
t (41) 34269052 f (41) 34269050
e zorro@zorro.com.br
w www.hostelzorro.com.br
Open Dates: x 70 R

△ ***Ilha Grande - Angra Dos Reis** – Holandês – 9047*
Rua da Assembléia, s/no- Vila do
Abraão - Ilha Grande - CEP: 23900-000.
t (24) 33615034
e pousadaholandes@bol.com.br
w www.holandeshostel.com.br
Open Dates: 80N x 25 R

▲ **Ilhéus** – Fazenda Tororomba HI 9016
Rua Luiz Eduardo Magalhaēs,
175 - Centro - Olivença. CEP: 45668-000.
t (73) 91414372
e info@fazendatororomba.com.br
w www.fazendatororomba.com.br
Open Dates: 5S x 100 R
P

△ ***Iporanga** – Capitaõ Caverna – 9048*
Rua Joaõ Evilásio Nunes,
160-Iporanga - SP - CEP: 18330000.
t (15) 35561125 f (15) 35561125
e info@ajcapitaocaverna.com.br
w www.ajcapitaocaverna.com.br
Open Dates: x 40 R

▲ **Itacare** – Itacare – 9122
Rua Londõnio Almeida, 120.
t (073) 91414372
e itacarehostel@yahoo.com.br
w www.itacarehostel.com.br
Open Dates: x 30 R CC

△ ***Jericoacara** – Jericoacara – 9050*
Rua São Francisco,
202 - Jericoacara - CE - CEP: 62598000.
t (88) 36692006 f (88) 36692006
e jericoacoarahostel@uol.com.br
w www.jericoacoarahostel.com.br
Open Dates: x 22 R

▲ João Pessoa – Manaíra – 9109
Rua Major Ciraulo, 380 - CEP: 58038-290-PB.
(83) 32471962
manairahostel@hotmail.com
www.manairahostel.br2.net
Open Dates: x 46

*△ **Laguna** – Laguna – 9116*
Av. Auretio Rotolo, 497,
Praia do Mar Grosso.
(48) 6470675 (48) 6470675
laguna.hostel@terra.com.br
www.schostel.com.br
Open Dates: x 25

*△ **Lençóis** – Chapada – 9092*
Rua Boa Vista, 121 - Chapada
Diamantina - Lençóis - BA- CEP: 46960-000.
(75) 33341497
reserevas@hostelchapada.com.br
www.hostelchapada.com.br
Open Dates: x 25

*△ **Maceió** – Alagamar – 9051*
Rua Prefeito Abdon Arroxelas, 327,
Ponta Verde, 57035-380 Maceió, AL.
(82) 32312246
a.j.alagamar@ofm.com.br
Open Dates: x 75

▲ Marataízes – Art Final – 9052
Av. Simão Soares ,
s/nº - Barra Marataízes - ES - 29334-000.
(28) 35322481 (28) 35322481
Open Dates: x 115

▲ Natal – Lua Cheia 9020
Rua Dr Manoel Augusto Bezerra de Araújo,
500 Ponta Negra, Natal, RN, CP: 59090-430.
(84) 32363696 (84) 32364747
luacheia@lucheia.com.br
www.luacheia.com.br
Open Dates: x 70

▲ Natal – Verdes Mares – 9053
Rua Das Algas, 2166-Praia De Ponta
Negra. CEP 59090-410.
(84) 32362872 (84) 32362872
albergue@hostelverdesmares.com.br
www.hostelverdesmares.com.br
Open Dates: x 28

*△ **Nova Friburgo** – Ale Friburgo – 9113*
R. Ernesto Bizzotto Filho, 02 Braunes,
CEP: 28611-200-RJ.
(22) 25220540 (22) 25220540
ajfriburgo@yahoo.com.br
www.hiale.com
Open Dates: x 20 (L)

*△ **Nova Petrópolis** – Bom Pastor – 9054*
Estrada RS 235,
KM 14 - Linha Brasil - Nova Petrópolis-RS. C
EP: 95150-970.
(54) 2988066 (54) 2988066
administracao@escolabompastor.com.br
www.escolabompastor.com.br
Open Dates: x 60

▲ Olinda – Olinda – 9055
Rua do Sol,
233-Olinda - Pernambuco CEP: 53120-010.
(81) 34291592 (81) 34391913
alberguedeolinda@alberguedeolinda.com.
br www.alberguedeolinda.com.br
Open Dates: x 70

*△ **Ouro Preto** – Brumas – 9056*
Ladeira São Francisco de Paula,
68 - Centro CEP: 35400-000.
(31) 35512944
brumasonline@hotmail.com
www.brumasonline.hpg.com.br
Open Dates: x 45 (L)

*△ **Paranaguá** – Continente – 9118*
Rua General Carneiro, 300.
(41) 34233224 (41) 34233224
hostelcontinente@hotmail.com
Open Dates: x 76

*△ **Paraty** – Casa do Rio – 9058*
Rua Antônio de Oliveira Vidal,
120 - CEP:23970-000.
(24) 33712223
casadorio@paratyhostel.com
www.paratyhostel.com
Open Dates: x 45

△ ***Peruíbe*** *– Peruíbe-Juréia 9061*
Rua Prudente de Morais,
106-Peruíbe - SP - CEP: 11750000.
(13) 34535573 (13) 34535573
ajperuibejureia@hotmail.com
www.ajperuibejureia.hpg.com.br
Open Dates: x 42

▲ **Petrópolis** – Quitandinha – 9062
Rua Uruguai,
570-Petrópolis-RJ CEP: 25650-130.
(24) 22914483; 22479165
info@alberguequitandinha.com.br
www.alberguequitandinha.com.br
Open Dates: x 65

▲ **Porto Belo** – Porto Belo – 9064
Rua José Amancio,
246 Porto Belo - SC. CEP: 88210.000.
(47) 3694295 (47) 3694483
claudio@portobelohostel.com
www.portobelohostel.com
Open Dates: 01.01-31.03 x 40

▲ **Porto De Galinhas** – A Casa Branca – 9114
Praça 18, Lote: S CEP: 55590-000-PE.
(81) 35521808 (81) 35521808
contato@pousadaacasabranca.com.br
www.pousadaacasabranca.com.br
Open Dates: x 56

▲ **Porto Seguro** – Maracaia 9019
Rodovia Porto Seguro - Km 77.5 - CEP: 45.820-0
00 Coroa Vermelha, Santa Cruz de Cabrália, BA.
(73) 36721155 (73) 36721156
reservas@maracaiahostel.com.br
www.maracaiahostel.com.br
Open Dates: 15N x 180

▲ **Porto Seguro** – Porto Seguro – 9065
R. Cova da Moça,
720 - Porto Seguro - BA. CEP: 45810-000.
(73) 32881742 (73) 32881742
reservas@portosegurohostel.com.br
www.portosegurohostel.com.br
Open Dates: 01.10-30.04; 01-31.07 x 80

▲ **Praia do Forte** – Praia do Forte – 9066
Rua da Aurora No. 3,
Praia do Forte/BA. CEP: 48280-000.
(71) 36761094 (71) 36761094
praiadoforte@albergue.com.br
www.albergue.com.br
Open Dates: 0.2S x 62

△ ***Recife*** *– Boa Viagem – 9107*
Rua Aviador Severiano Lins,
455 - CEP: 51111-050-PE.
(81) 33269572 (81) 33269572
hostel@hostelboaviagem.com.br
www.hostelboaviagem.com.br
Open Dates: x 40

△ ***Rio das Ostras*** *– Pousada Entrada do Coqueiro – 9067*
Av. Roberto Silveira,
1088 - Rio das Ostras - RJ - CEP: 28890000.
(22) 27600165
riodasostras_hostel@hotmail.com
www.riodasostrashostel.com.br
Open Dates: x 27

▲ **Rio de Janeiro** – Adventure – 9124
Rua Vinicius De Moraes, 174-Ipanema.
(21) 38132726 (21) 38133320
hostel@adventurehostel.com.br
www.adventurehostel.com.br
Open Dates: x 40 CC

▲ **Rio de Janeiro** – Che Lagarto – 9099
Rua Anita Garibaldi, 87 - CEP:22041080, Copacabana.
(21) 22562776; 22562778
(21) 22562777
copacabana@chelagarto.com
www.chelagarto.com
Open Dates: x 62

▲ **Rio de Janeiro** – Che Lagarto - Hostel Ipanema – 9125
Rua Paul Redfern, 48-Ipanema.
(21) 22582777 (21) 22562777
Ipanema@chelagarto.com
Open Dates: x 60 CC

Rio de Janeiro – Rio Hostel 9003
Rua General Dionísio 63, Botafogo, 22271-050 Rio de Janeiro, RJ.
(21) 22860303 (21) 22865652
riohostel@riohostel.com.br
www.riohostel.com.br
Open Dates: Open Times:
Beds: 70 - 1x² 3x⁴ 6x⁶ 2x⁶⁺
Price Range: $10-12
Directions: 8S from city centre
Internacional 20km Do RJ 11km
172, 176, 409 500m Botafogo 1.5km (B) 1 x 8 3km

Rio de Janeiro – Rio Hostel

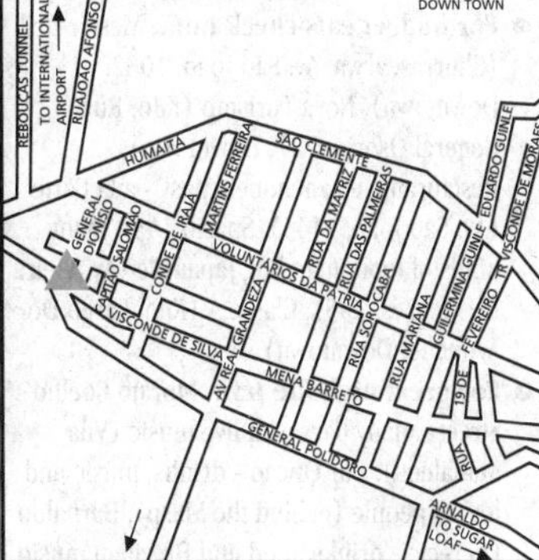

▲ **Rio de Janeiro** – Shenkin – 9100
Rua Santa Clara, 304-Copa Cabana.
(21) 22573133 (21) 22562777
info@shenkinhostel.com
www.shenkinhostel.com
Open Dates: x 56

▲ **Rio de Janeiro** – Tijuca – 9106
Rua Araújo Pena, 58 - CEP: 20260-230.
(21) 22045059 (21) 22045059
reservas@riotijucahostel.com.br
www.riotijucahostel.com.br
Open Dates: x 43

Rio de Janeiro... Travel Tips

- **For budget eats check out...** Area around hostel, Cobal, All hostel neighbourhood, Visconde de Caravelas Street
- **For great nightlife try...** Clubs near the hostel, Lago'as huts (typical food & music), Beach clubs & bars, Theatres, Rodrigo De Freitas Lagoon
- **Don't miss...** Corcovado (Christ), Sugar Loaf, Botanic Garden, Rodrigo de Freitas Lagoon, Copacabana Beach, Ipanema Beach, Maracanã Stadium, Barra da Tijuca Beach, Tijuca Forest, Favela tours

▲ **Salvador** – Barra – 9069
Rua Dr. Artur Neiva,
04 Barra. CEP 40140-210.
(71) 32452600 (71) 32452600
reservas@alberguebarra.com.br
www.alberguebarra.com.br
Open Dates: x 58

▲ **Salvador** – Do Porto 9028
Rua Barão do Sergy 197, Barra-Salvador, Bahia. CEP: 40140-040.
(71) 32646600; 32646452
(71) 32644006
hosteldoporto@hotmail.com
www.alberguedoporto.com.br
Open Dates: Antonio Carlos Magalhães International 5N x 50

▲ **Salvador** – Laranjeiras 9070
Rua da Ordem Terceira,
13-Pelourinho-Salvador-BA. CEP: 40030-020.
(71) 33211366 (71) 33212816
hi@laranjeirashostel.com.br
www.laranjeirashostel.com.br
Open Dates: x 60

▲ **São Lourenço** – Recanto Dos Carvalhos 9072
Br 460 - Km78, CEP: 37470-000.
(35) 33327900; 33316886; 33332790
(35) 33328799
hostel@recantodoscarvalhos.com.br
www.recantodoscarvalhos.com.br
Open Dates: x 70

△ ***São Luis*** *– Solar Das Pedras – 9073*
Rua Da Palma,
127-Centro-São Luiz Ma. CEP: 65010-440.
(98) 32326694 (98) 32326694
aj.solardaspedras.ma@bol.com.br
www.solardaspedras.com.br
Open Dates: x 40 R CC

▲ **São Miguel Das Missoẽs** – Missoẽs
HI 9010
Rua São Nicolau, 601-São Miguel Das Missoẽs-RS. CEP: 98865-000.
(55) 33811202 (55) 33811030
pousada.missoes@terra.com.br
www.rotamissoes.com.br/pousada
Open Dates: x 100 R CC

▲ **São Paulo** – Praça Da Árvore HI 9007
Rua Pageú, 266 - Saúde - São Paulo - SP. CEP: 04139-000.
(11) 50715148; 55845319
(11) 50715148; 55845319
info@spalbergue.com.br
www.spalbergue.com.br
Open Dates: 0.5NE x 40 R
CC

São Paulo – São Paulo Hostel – 9093
Rua Barão de Campinas,
94 Centro - SP - CEP: 01201-000
(11) 33330844; 33381414
(11) 32250623 info@hostel.com.br
www.hostel.com.br
Open Dates: Open Times:
Beds: 120 - 15x² 10x³ 10x⁴
Price Range: US$10-12 BBinc
Directions: Cumbica International 15km
A 2km x 5 R CC

São Paulo – São Paulo Hostel

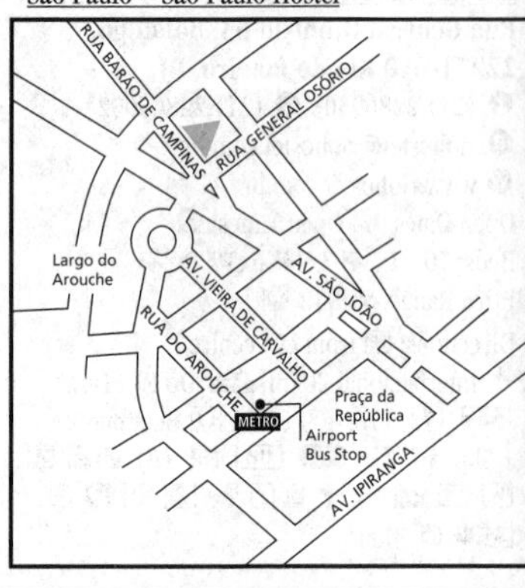

São Paulo... Travel Tips

- **For budget eats check out...** Mester Grill (Churrascarwa, Av. Sao Joao, 1032, Downtown), Nova Turismo (Kilo, Rua General Osorio, 727, Downtown), Restaurante e Lanchonete pasv - a la Carte (Av. Sao Joao, 1145), Spazio 145 - many kinds of food including Japanese (Av. Vieira De Moraes, 145), Classe A (Kilo, Largo Do Arouche, Downtown)
- **For great nightlife try...** Morato Coelho Street - many bars with live music (Vila Madalena), Bar Opcao - drinks, music and lots of people (behind the Masp), Barnaldo Lucrecia - drinks, food and Brazilian music (Rua Airton Senna), Piranha - Dancing venue with many types of music (Lapa), Romanina - pizza and Brazilian music (Caramuru Street on the corner of Orissanga)
- **Don't miss...** Ibirapuera Park - green, beautiful and tranquil with a free concert some Sundays, Pinacoteca Do Estado - art museum, park and coffee, Praca da Republica on Sunday - Brazilian art and food market, Terraco Italia - the ancient highest building in the city, Museu do Ipiranga - historical Brazilian museum with beautiful garden, Masp - museum art of Sao Paulo - interesting modern architecture, Zoo and botanic garden - lots of different animals and plants including orchids, Butanta Institute - snakes, spiders and scorpions and a science museum, Liberdade - the Japanese Neighbourhood with food and art on Sundays, Vila Madalena - the nightlife area - more than one hundred places to eat and dance

Canada

Hostelling International - Canada (National Office),
205 Catherine St, Suite 400, Ottawa,
Ontario K2P 1C3 Canada.

t (1) (613) 2377884
f (1) (613) 2377868
e info@hihostels.ca
w www.hihostels.ca

A copy of the Hostel Directory for this Country can be obtained from:
The National Office

Capital:	Ottawa
Language:	English, French
Currency:	$ (Canadian dollar)
Population:	31,752,842
Size:	9,984,670 sq km
Telephone Country Code:	1
eKit Access Number:	1866-626-9724

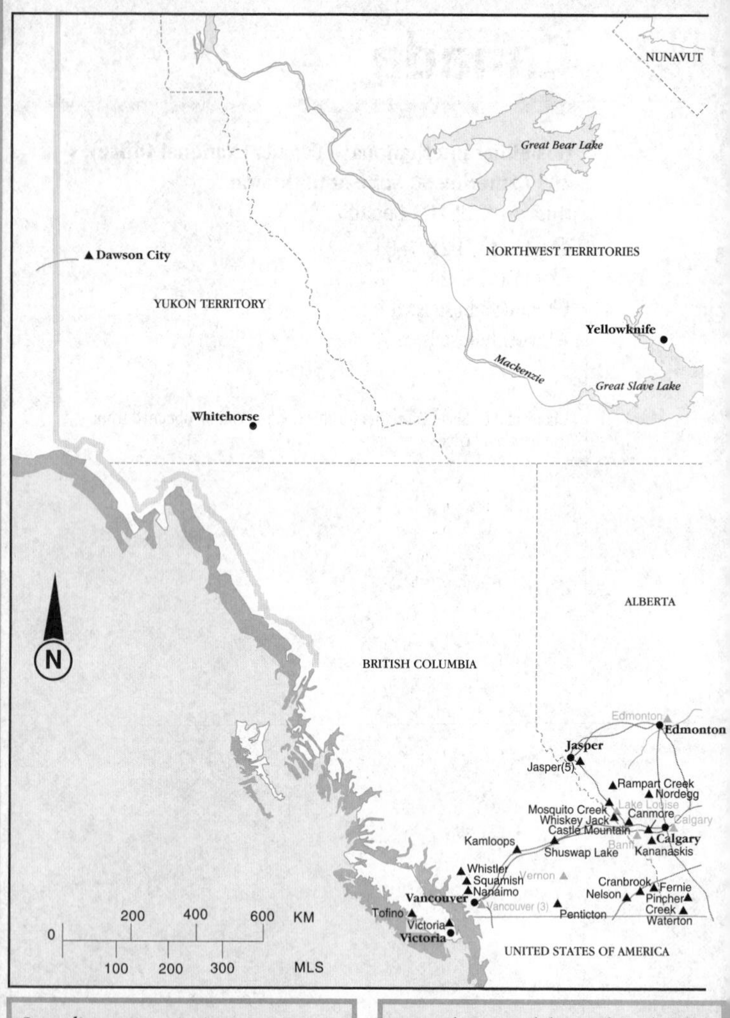

Sprawling across six time zones, Canada is the second largest country in the world. Its sheer size, natural wonders and extremes of temperature, from the warm 'Southern European' climate of Victoria on the Pacific, to the rigours of -60° weather in the Arctic north, make it a land of force and grandeur. The fact that most of the country is uninhabited (with a population of 32 million, there are just over three people per square km) and that it takes nearly five days to cross between Pacific to Atlantic coasts by train means that it is a dream for nature lovers and those who relish the outdoors. Add the Rockies in the west, the Arctic Ocean in the north, and the Great Lakes in the east and prepare to be amazed!

Even more significant is the fact that Canada has well over a million streams, rivers and lakes, which combined account for a quarter of the world's fresh water supply. Canada is also home to perhaps the world's most famous police force: the Mounties, formed in the 1870s to check frontier lawlessness and famously involved in dealing with the Klondike Gold Rush in

the Yukon Territory in the 1890s.

Nature's challenges are to some extent mirrored in the country's history and culture and the ongoing - to some irreconcilable - differences between francophone Canada, centred on the province of Quebec, and the rest of the country. The Quebecois have a very distinct culture, language, civil law, architecture, and way of life, enshrined in the Quebec Act of 1714.

Furthermore, the divide between francophone and anglo culture means that Canada as a whole is bilingual and that official publications and government throughout the country are available in both English and French.

A few other Top Tips from **CULTURE SMART!**:

- Most of the population lives in the east, close to the US border. The major cities are Quebec, Montreal, Toronto, Kingston, and the federal capital of Ottawa (with Vancouver and Victoria in the west). Fashion and manners are influenced by French, British and American culture, but tempered by the values

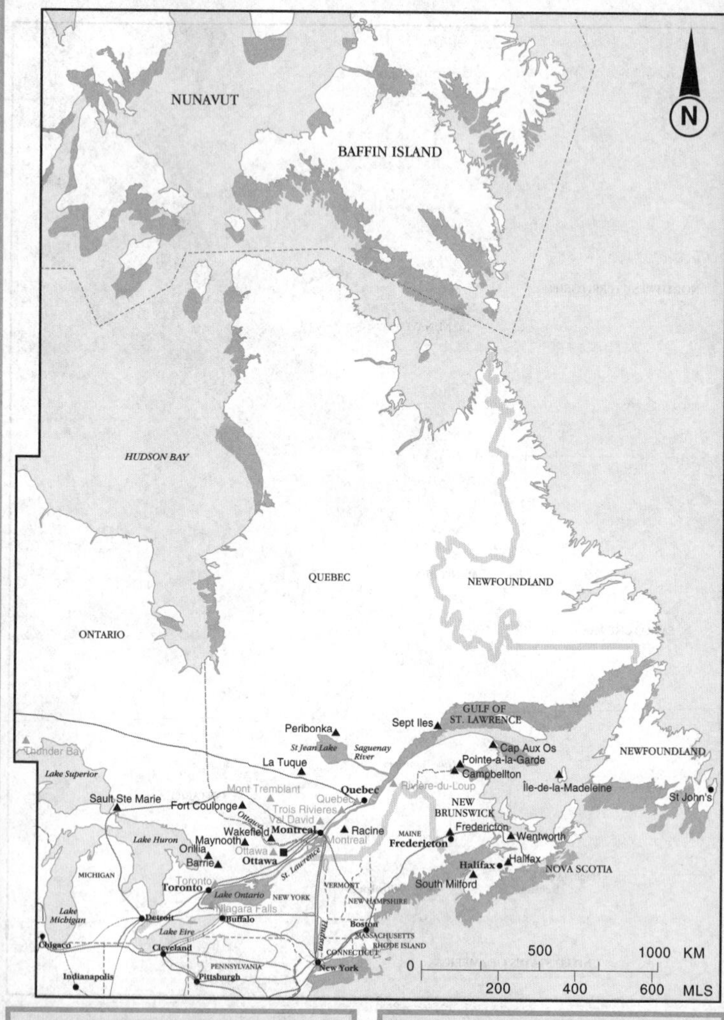

of traditional farm-life; these values still have a strong influence on the way Canadians see themselves.

- The politics of national identity are a Canadian preoccupation. Many Canadians endeavour to resist the 'Americanization' of their country and strongly deny any notions of dependency, although the facts of the connections between the two countries are inescapable. Visitors should be sensitive to this issue and to the possibility of confusing American and Canadian accents; as well, discussions of French/English value systems are best avoided.
- A strong sense of community and a strong belief in the importance of duty and respect continues to be important in both family and public life, helping to make Canada a safe and welcoming society.
- Canada is not known for its *haute cuisine*, but immigration from the rest of the world has brought considerable diversity to dining in the major cities. There are some traditional delicacies too, from

Atlantic salmon to French Canadian pea soup and *poutine* to maple syrup.
Culture Smart! Top Tips © Kuperard 2005

Cultural Top Tips supplied by Culture Smart! guides. These essential guides to customs and etiquette will help you steer clear of embarrassing gaffes and sensitive issues, enabling you to discover new cultures whilst developing new friendships. Order online at www.culturesmartguides.co.uk

You can find out a lot more on our website - a visit to www.HIhostels.com is essential for planning your trip!

Pour en savoir plus, rendez-vous sur notre site Internet, www.HIhostels.com une visite incontournable pour préparer votre voyage!

Viele weitere Informationen auf unserer Website: www.HIhostels.com - unverzichtbar für die Reiseplanung!

Puedes averiguar mucho más en nuestro sitio web. Es imprescindible que visites la página www.HIhostels.com para planear tu viaje.

Banff – HI-Banff Alpine Centre 11001
PO Box 1358, 801 Hidden Ridge Way, Banff, Alberta, T0L 1B3.
(403) 6707580 (R)
(403) 2836503 cr.banff@hihostels.ca
www.hihostels.ca
Open Dates: Open Times:
Beds: 221 - 5x 33x 14x
Price Range: from $23-35 (dorm); $71-133 (private)
Directions: 150W from city centre
Calgary International 160km
A Brewster/Greyhound 3km x 7

Banff – HI-Banff Alpine Centre

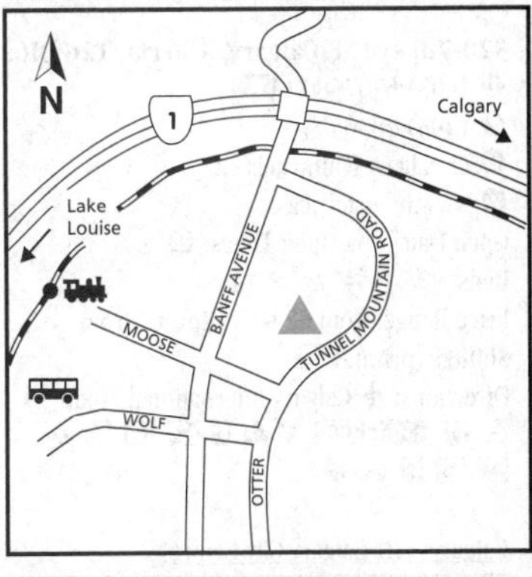

Banff... Travel Tips

- **For budget eats check out...** Cougar Pete's Kitchen & Lookout, The Storm Cellar, Aardvark Pizza & Sub, Magpie & Stump, Evelyn's Café
- **For great nightlife try...** The Storm Cellar, Cougar Pete's Kitchen and Lookout, Pump & Tap, St James Gate, Rose & Crown
- **Don't miss...** Canadian Rockies Hot Springs, Banff Gondola, Whyte Museum of the Canadian Rockies, Johnston Canyon, Sunshine Village, Tunnel Mountain Hoodoos, Cave & Basin, Bow Falls, Lake Minnewanka, Johnson Lake, Banff Film Festival

Barrie – Barrie Summer Hostel – 11039
140 Bell Farm Rd, Barrie, ON, L4M 5K5.
(705) 7350772 (705) 7398615
georgian.green@hihostels.ca
www.hihostels.ca
Open Dates: 01.05-17.08 Pearson International (Toronto) 77km 1, 2 5km ap Bell Farm Road 5NE x 160
5km 5km

Calgary – HI-Calgary City Centre 11012

520-7th Ave SE Calgary, Alberta, T2G 0J6.
(403) 6707580 (R)
(403) 2836503
cr.calgary@hihostels.ca
www.hihostels.ca
Open Dates: Open Times:
Beds: 92 - 1x2 2x3 14x6
Price Range: from $24-33 (dorm); from $60-83 (private)
Directions: Calgary International 20km

Calgary – HI-Calgary City Centre

Calgary... Travel Tips

- **For budget eats check out...** The Arden, Nellie's, Original Joe's, Wicked Wedge Pizza, Oriental Phoenix
- **For great nightlife try...** Aussie Rules Foodhouse & Bar, Jubilations Dinner Theatre, Cowboy's Night Club, Yuk Yuk's, Uptown 17th Avenue
- **Don't miss...** Calgary Zoo, Glenbow Museum, Calgary Tower, Heritage Park Historical Village, Calgary Science Centre, Canada Olympic Park, IMAX Theatre at Eau Claire, Calgary Stampede, Fort Calgary, Calaway Park

Campbellton – Campbellton Lighthouse Youth Hostel – 11040
1 Ritchie St, PO Box 100, Campbellton, New Brunswick, E3N 3G1.
(506) 7597044 (506) 7597403
hihostels@campbellton.org
www.hihostels.ca/campbellton
Open Dates: 12.06-20.08 Via Rail 1.5km SMT Eastern Ltd. 500m x 20
200m 8km

Canmore – HI-Canmore Clubhouse – 11041
Box 8040, Indian Flats Road, Canmore, AB T1W 2T8.
(403) 6783200 (403) 6783224
info@alpineclubofcanada.ca
www.hihostels.ca
Open Dates: Calgary International 140km x 46
1 x

Cap-Aux-Os, Gaspé – Auberge Internationale Forillon – 11042
2095 Boul Grande-Grève,
Cap-Aux-Os Québec G4X 6L7
(418) 8925153 (418) 8925292
aujecao@globetrotter.net
www.gaspesie.net/aj-gaspe/
Open Dates: 01.05-31.10 (R)
Gaspé 30km Cap-Aux-Os 10m
x 54
1km

Castle Mountain *– HI-Castle Mountain Wilderness Hostel – 11043*
Box 1358, Banff, AB, T1L 1B3
(Banff National Park) (on Hwy #1A, 1.5km E of the junction with Hwy #1 & #93 S).
(403) 6707580 (R)
(403) 2836503
centralres.sa@hihostels.ca
www.hihostels.ca
Open Dates: Occasionally closed. Check when open. Calgary International 185km x 28

▲ **Cranbrook** – HI Cranbook - Purcell House – 11044
College of the Rockies, Bag 9000, 2700 College Way, Cranbrook, BC, V1C 5L7.
(250) 4898282; Toll Free: 1 (877) 4892687 (250) 4898240
cranbrook@hihostels.ca
www.hihostels.ca
Open Dates: 01.05-30.08 2NE x 42

△ ***Dawson City** – HI Dawson City River Hostel – 11045*
PO Box 32, Dawson City, Yukon, Y0B 1G0.
(867) 9936823 dawson@hihostels.ca
www.hihostels.ca
Open Dates: 15.05-30.09 Dawson City 20km Yukon Ferry Landing 200m
x 39 8

Edmonton – HI-Edmonton 11010
10647-81 Ave Edmonton, AB, T6E 1Y1.
(780) 9886836; Toll Free in NA 1 (877) 4 678336 (780) 9888698
edmonton@hihostels.ca
www.hihostels.ca/edmonton
Open Dates: 12 Open Times:
Beds: 88 - 8x2 9x3 1x4 3x5 1x6 3x6+
Price Range: $19-$24
Directions: 3.5S from city centre
Edmonton International 26km A Sky Shuttle 26km Via Rail Station 12 Kingsway, 9 Southgate 10km 7, 9 from 101 St & 104 Ave ap 109 St & 82 (Whyte) Ave
x 3 1 x 8 1.5km

Edmonton – HI-Edmonton

82 AVE (WHYTE AVE.)
Bus Stop
81 AVE
80 AVE
N
109 ST
108 ST
107 ST
106 ST
0
600m

Edmonton... Travel Tips

- **For budget eats check out...** Dadeo (Cajun), Café Mosaics (Vegetarian), Sam Wok (Chinese), China Town, Subway
- **For great nightlife try...** Whyte Avenue (Pubs & Clubs), Princess & Garneau movie theatres, Metro Cinema, Downtown Clubs (Halo & Decadence), Red's (Dining, dancing, bowling, billiard, games etc)
- **Don't miss...** West Edmonton Mall, the world's largest indoor mall, Odyssium (Science Centre), Provincial Museum of Alberta, Alberta Legislature Building, Fort Edmonton Park, Summer Festivals (Fringe, Jazz City, Folk Festival, Street Performers), Muttart Conservatory, Elk Island Park, Ukrainian Cultural Heritage Village

▲ **Fernie** – HI Fernie - Raging Elk Hostel – 11046
PO Box 160, 892 6th Ave, Fernie, BC, V0B 1M0.
(250) 4236811; Toll Free: 1 (877) 4236811 (250) 4236812
fernie@hihostels.ca www.hihostels.ca
Open Dates: 01.06-30.04 0.2N x 90 (B)

▲ **Fort Coulonge** – Auberge Esprit – 11047
3, Chemin Esprit, Davidson, Québec, J0X 1R0.
(819) 6833241; 1 (800) 5967238
(819) 6833641
info@espritrafting.com
www.espritrafting.com
Open Dates: 01.05-30.10 Ottawa International 125km Ottawa 125km Davidson 2km 3W x 34
(B)
1 x

▲ **Fredericton** – International Hostel (Rosary Hall) – 11048
621 Churchill Row, Fredericton, New Brunswick, E3B 1M3.
(506) 4504417 (506) 4629692
www.hihostels.ca/fredericton
Open Dates: 12 Fredericton Junction 40km SMT Eastern Ltd. 500m 1E
x 40
1km 4km

Halifax – Heritage House Hostel – 11008
1253 Barrington St, Halifax, Nova Scotia, B3J 1Y3.
(902) 4223863 (902) 4220116
halifax@hihostels.ca www.hihostels.ca
Open Dates: 12 Open Times: 08.00-23.00hrs
Beds: 73 - 2x2 5x4 5x6 2x6+
Price Range: $19-25
Directions: Halifax International 32km A Airport Shuttle 500m Halifax Harbour 500m Via Rail 500m Acadian Bus Depot 500m x 4

Halifax – Heritage House Hostel

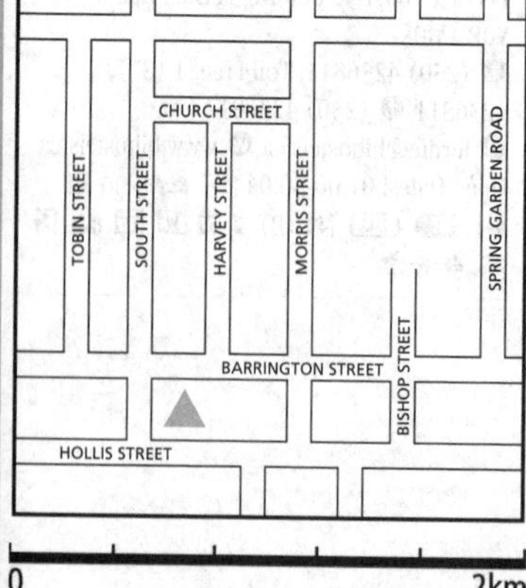

Halifax... Travel Tips
- **For budget eats check out...** C'est Ce Bon (breakfast), Deli Green, Granite Brewery (pub style), The Apple Barrell, Economy Shoe Shop
- **For great nightlife try...** Lower Deck, Split Crow, Old Triangle, The Marqui, The Idiot
- **Don't miss...** Salty Bear Adventure Travel, South Shore, Cape Breton - Pleasant Bay, Point Pleasant Park - Public gardens, Buskers Festival (August), Hostel activities - games, BBQ, pub crawl, Nova Scotia Tattoo, Peggy's Cove Tour, Halifax Waterfront, Pier 21

▲ **Iles-de-la-Madeleine** – Auberge Internationale des Iles-de-la Madeleine – 11050
74 chemin du Camping, L'Étang-du-Nord, Iles-de-la-Madeleine, Québec G4T 3P2
(418) 9864505; 1 (800) 9864505
(418) 9864523
parcdegroscap@sympatico.ca
www.parcdegroscap.ca
Open Dates: 01.05-30.09 (12 R)
15km 3km x 30
(B)

△ ***Jasper National Park*** *– HI-Athabasca Falls – 11051*
Box 387, Jasper, Alberta, T0E 1E0.
(32km S of Jasper on Hwy 93, 200m past Athabasca Falls on east side, turn off).
(780) 8523215; Toll Free in NA 1 (877) 8520781 (780) 8525560
jasper@hihostels.ca
www.hihostels.ca/athabascafalls
Open Dates: 01.12-31.10 Via Rail ap Jasper 32km Brewster & Greyhound 32km ap Jasper 32S x 40

△ ***Jasper National Park*** *– HI-Beauty Creek – 11052*
Box 387, Jasper, Alberta, T0E 1E0.
(87km S of Jasper & 17km N of Columbia Icefield Centre on W side of Hwy #93).
(780) 8523215; Toll Free in NA 1 (877) 8520781 (780) 8525560
jasper@hihostels.ca
www.hihostels.ca/beautycreek
Open Dates: 15.05-30.09 (only 01.10-14.05) Via Rail ap Jasper 87km Brewster & Greyhound 87km ap Jasper 87S x 22

▲ Jasper National Park – HI-Jasper – 11011 (FNM)
Box 387, Jasper, Alberta, T0E 1E0
(travel 4km S of Jasper on Hwy 93, turn right on Skytram Rd for 3km).
t (780) 8523215; Toll Free in NA 1 (877) 8520781 f (780) 8525560
e jasper@hihostels.ca
w www.hihostels.ca/jasper
Open Dates: 12 Via Rail ap Jasper 7km Greyhound & Brewster 7km ap Jasper 7SW x 80 R CC

△ ***Jasper National Park*** – *HI-Maligne Canyon – 11053*
Box 387, Jasper, Alberta, T0E 1E0.
(11km E of Jasper on Maligne Lake Rd, NE from Hwy #16).
t (780) 8523215; Toll Free in NA 1 (877) 8520781 f (780) 8525560
e jasper@hihostels.ca
w www.hihostels.ca/malignecanyon
Open Dates: 12 Via Rail ap Jasper 11km Greyhound & Brewster 11km ap Jasper 11E x 24 R CC

△ ***Jasper National Park*** – *HI-Mount Edith Cavell – 11054*
Box 387, Jasper, Alberta, T0E 1E0.
(27km from Jasper townsite: 7km S on Hwy 93, turn right on Hwy 93A for 8km to Mt. Edith Cavell. Turn off, follow road 12km).
t (780) 8523215; Toll Free in NA 1 (877) 8520781 f (780) 8525560
e jasper@hihostels.ca
w www.hihostels.ca
Open Dates: 15.06-15.10 Via Rail ap Jasper 27km Brewster & Greyhound 27km ap Jasper 32SW x 32 R CC

▲ Kamloops – HI Kamloops – 11055
7 West Seymour St, Kamloops, BC, V2C 1E4.
t (250) 8287991; Toll Free: 1 (866) STAY KAM f (250) 8282442
e kamloops@hihostels.ca
w www.hihostels.ca
Open Dates: 12 Kamloops 11km 17km 3km 0.1E x 72 R CC 200m 200m

▲ Kananaskis – HI-Kananaskis Wilderness Hostel – 11056
Box 1358, Banff, AB, T1L 1B3
(70km W of Calgary on Trans Canada Hwy at Kananaskis turn off (Hwy #40 S) follow signs to Ribbon Creek).
t (403) 6707580 (R)
f (403) 2836503
e centralres.sa@hihostels.ca
w www.hihostels.ca
Open Dates: Occasionally closed. Check when open. Calgary International 180km x 41 R CC

▲ La Tuque – Auberge la Residence – 11058
352, Ave Brown, La Tuque, Québec, G9X 2W4
t (819) 5239267 f (819) 5233678
e aubergellaresidence@hb.sympatico.ca
w www.hihostels.ca
Open Dates: 12 La Tuque 800m La Tuque Terminal 800m x 41 R CC TV 800m 800m

▲ Lake Louise – HI-Lake Louise Alpine Centre HI 11028 (FNM)
Village Rd, Box 115, Lake Louise, Alberta, T0L 1E0.
t (403) 6707580 (R)
f (403) 2836503
e cr.lakelouise@hihostel.ca
w www.hihostels.ca
Open Dates: 12 Calgary International 200km A Airporter 500m Greyhound 200W x 140 R CC TV 1 x

▲ Maynooth – HI-South Algonquin Backpackers Hostel – 11086
Box 233, Maynooth, ON K0L 2S0.
t (613) 3382080; (1) 800 5958064
f (613) 3382080
e south.algonquin@hihostels.ca
w www.hihostels.ca
Open Dates: 12 Pearson International (Toronto) 260km, Ottawa International 240km Greyhound ap YH x 24 R CC TV

CANADA – CANADA – KANADA – CANADÁ

Montréal – Auberge de Montréal 11002
1030, Rue Mackay, Montréal, Québec, H3G 2H1
(514) 843 3317; 1(866) 8433317
(514) 9343251
info@hostellingmontreal.com
www.hostellingmontreal.com
Open Dates: Open Times:
Beds: 235 - 15x 3x 22x 8x 6x
Price Range: $24.75-28.75 (dorm) $65-75 (private)
Directions: Dorval 12km A Shuttle to hostel Central 500m Terminal 3km Lucien L'Allier 200m (BD)

Montréal – Auberge de Montréal

Montréal... Travel Tips

- **For budget eats check out...** Faubourg Ste-Catherine, Aromate d'Asie, E1 Zazium, La Binerie Mont-Royal, Juste Nouilles
- **For great nightlife try...** Brutopia, Diable Vert, L'Amère à Boire, St. Sulpice, Café-Campus
- **Don't miss...** International Firework Festival, Tam Tam, Ile Ste-Hélène, Old Port, Just for Laughs Festival, Pointe-à-Callière (museum of archaeology & history), Montreal International Jazz Festival, Montreal Biodome, Montreal Botanic Garden, Francofolies French Festival

▲ **Mont-Tremblant Village** – Auberge Internationale du Mont-Tremblant 11026
2213, Chemin du Village, Mont-Tremblant, Québec J8E 1K4
(819) 4256008; 1 (866) 4256008
(819) 4253760
info@hostellingtremblant.com
www.hostellingtremblant.com
Open Dates: 130km
Mont-Tremblant Village 500m 0.5NE
x 70 (B) 1 x

△ ***Mosquito Creek** – HI-Mosquito Creek Wilderness Hostel – 11060*
Banff National Park, Box 1358, Banff, AB T1L 1B3. (27 km N of Lake Louise on Hwy #93, 211km S of Jasper).
(403) 6707580 ( )
(403) 2836503
centralres.sa@hihostels.ca
www.hihostels.ca
Open Dates: Occasionally closed. Check when open. Calgary International 225km x 32

▲ **Nanaimo** – HI-Nanaimo, Painted Turtle Guesthouse – 11089
121 Bastion Street, Nanaimo BC V9R 3A2.
(250) 7534432; Toll Free: 1 (866) 3094432 (250) 7534434
nanaimo@hihostels.ca
www.hihostels.ca
Open Dates: Nanaimo Airport 18km
A Shuttle to hostel ($17) Bay Ferry Terminal 2.5km Nanaimo x 45

▲ **Nelson** – HI Nelson - Dancing Bear Inn – 11061
171 Baker St., Nelson, BC, V1L 4H1.
(250) 3527573; Toll Free: 1 (877) 3527573 (250) 3529818
nelson@hihostels.ca www.hihostels.ca
Open Dates: Castlegar 35km
Greyhound Bus 1.5km ap YH 50m
x 43

Niagara Falls – HI-Niagara Falls Rainbow Hostel 11017
4549 Cataract Ave, Niagara Falls, Ontario, L2E 3M2.
(905) 3570770; Toll Free: 1 (888) 7490058 (905) 3577673
niagara.falls@hihostels.ca
www.hihostels.ca
Open Dates: Open Times:
Beds: 88 - 6x2 16x4 2x6
Price Range: from $18
Directions: 0.1NE from city centre
Pearson International (Toronto) 140km
A Niagara Airbus 160km 200m
Niagara 200m x 1 R CC
(B)
P

Niagara Falls – HI-Niagara Falls Rainbow Hostel

Niagara Falls... Travel Tips

- **For budget eats check out...** Niagara Cumpir Fast Food, Jade Gardens (Chinese), Dad's Diner (Canadian & American Cuisine), Paesano Italian Restaurant, Xin Vego Café (Vegetarian)
- **For great nightlife try...** Daily Planet (Tap & Eatery), Blue Lagoon, Pumps Nightclub & Patio, Rumours
- **Don't miss...** Canadian Horseshoe Falls, Casino Niagara, IMAX Theatre, Skylon Tower, Niagara Parks Botanical Gardens, Niagara Parks Butterfly Conservatory, Niagara on the Lake, Wineries & Vineyards, Maid of The Mist, Great Gorge Adventure, Table Rock Complex

▲ **Nordegg** – HI-Shunda Creek – 11062
Box 54, Nordegg, Alberta, T0M 2H0. (Located 3km N of Hwy 11 on the Shunda Creek Recreation Area Rd, 87km E of Banff National Park and 94km W of Rocky Mountain House).
(403) 7212140 (403) 7212140
shunda@hihostels.ca
www.hihostels.ca/shundacreek
Open Dates: Greyhound - Rocky Mountain House 94km 3N x 48
R CC 8 P

▲ **Orillia** – Orillia Home Hostel – 11063
198 Borland St East, Orillia, Ontario, L3V 2C3.
(705) 3250970 (705) 3259826
www.hihostels.ca
Open Dates: Orillia 22km
Orillia 1.5km x 9 R
8 P 500m 500m

Ottawa – HI Ottawa Jail 11004 FNM
75 Nicholas St, Ottawa, Ontario, K1N 7B9.
(613) 2352595 (613) 2359202
ottawa.jail@hihostels.ca
www.hihostels.ca
Open Dates: Open Times: 07.00-01.00hrs (01.10-30.04); (01.05-30.09)
Beds: 154 - 1x2 2x3 11x4 4x5 11x6 2x6+
Price Range: $21-25 (dorm) $53-57 (private)
Directions: 0.1E from city centre
Ottawa International 25km A to Novotel Hotel 50m Via Rail - city bus 95 to MacKenzie King 3.2km Ottawa Bus Central Station - city bus 4 to Rideau Centre 1.2km ap Rideau Centre 100m x 5
R CC
8 P 2km 10km

Ottawa – HI Ottawa Jail

Ottawa... Travel Tips

- **For budget eats check out...** Pita Pit, Nickels, Mexicali Rosa's, Alfie's Pub, Tucker's Market Place Buffet
- **For great nightlife try...** The Highlander Pub, Yuk Yuk's Comedy Club, Mavericks, Zaphods, Great Canadian Cabin
- **Don't miss...** The Original Walking Tour, Haunted Walks of Ottawa, Museum of Civilization, National Art Gallery, Canadian Museum of Nature, Greyline Bus Tours, Paul's Boat Cruise, Sparks Street & Rideau Centre (Shopping Centres), Byward Market & Parliament Hill, Great Canadian Bungee

▲ **Penticton** – HI Penticton – 11064

464 Ellis St, Penticton, BC, V2A 4M2.

(250) 4923992;

Toll Free: 1 (866) STAY PEN

(250) 4928755

penticton@hihostels.ca

www.hihostels.ca

Open Dates: Penticton (Taxi to hostel ~$15) 7km Greyhound bus depot 200m 0.2E x 47 1km 1km

▲ **Péribonka** – Auberge Ile-du-Repos – 11065

105, route Ile-du-Repos, Péribonka, Québec, G0W 2G0

(418) 3475649 (418) 3474810

iledurepos@bellnet.ca

www.iledurepos.com

Open Dates: Héberville 60km Alma 40km 5E x 58 1 x

▲ **Pincher Creek** – HI-Pincher Creek - Parkway Motel – 11087

1070 Waterton Ave, PO Box 130, Pincher Creek, Alberta, T0K 1W0.

(403) 6707580 (403) 2836503

centralres.sa@hihostels.ca

www.hihostels.ca

Open Dates: x 15 8

▲ **Pointe-à-la-Garde** – Auberge Château Bahia – 11067

152 Boul. Perron, Pointe-à-la-Garde, Québec, G0C 2M0

(418) 7882048 (418) 7882048

aubchaba@globetrotter.net

www.hihostels.ca

Open Dates: 18km 100m 3E x 48 3km 3km

Québec – Auberge internationale de Québec

11013

19 rue Ste Ursule, Québec, G1R 4E1

(418) 6940755 (418) 6942278

reservation@hostellingquebec.com

www.aubergeinternationaledequebec.com

Open Dates: Open Times:

Beds: 278 - 10x2 8x3 16x4 6x5 8x6 11x6+

Price Range: $21.50-30 (dorm) $67-134 (private)

Directions: Québec City International 15km Québec - Levis Ferry 2km Gare du Palais 1km 25, 800 from Z and M 200m ap Terminus Place d'Youville, walking distance 2 x 8

Québec – Auberge internationale de Québec

Québec... Travel Tips

- **For budget eats check out...** Le Café - Bistrot de l'auberge, Le Petit Coin Latin, La Rotisserie Ste-Angèle, Le Commensal (vegetarian), Le Chanteauteil
- **For great nightlife try...** Le Fou Bar, Bar Chez Son Père, La Barberie, Le Dagobert, L'Inox
- **Don't miss...** Old Québec City & Fortifications, Artillery Park, Battlefields Park & visitor centre, Petit Champlain district, Museum of Civilization, Québec Museum, Chute Montmorency Park, Canyon Sainte-Anne, Citadelle, Jacques-Cartier Park

▲ **Racine** – Auberge de la Grande Ligne – 11068
318 Chemin de la Grande Ligne, Racine, Québec, J0E 1Y0
(450) 5323177 (450) 5324082
auberge.grande.ligne@videotron.ca
www.geocities.com/auberge_grande_ligne
Open Dates: 12 ✈ 125km 20km
Magog/Sherbrooke 30km x 25

△ ***Rampart Creek** – HI-Rampart Creek Wilderness Hostel – 11069*
Banff National Park, Box 1358, Banff, AB, T1L 1B3. (95km N of Lake Louise & 34km S of the Columbia Icefield Centre on Hwy #93).
(403) 6707580 (R)
(403) 2836503
centralres.sa@hihostels.ca
www.hihostels.ca
Open Dates: Occasionally closed. Check when open. ✈ *Calgary International 260km* x 24

▲ **Regina** – Turgeon International Hostel – 11070
2310 McIntyre St, Regina, Saskatchewan, S4P 2S2.
(306) 7918165 (306) 7212667
regina@hihostels.ca www.hihostels.ca
Open Dates: 01.02-23.12 ✈ Regina (Taxi to Hostel $9) 4km 10 500m 1SW x 28
1km

▲ **Rivière-du-Loup** – Auberge internationale de Rivière-du-Loup 11023
46 Hotel-de-Ville, Rivière-du-Loup, Québec, G5R 1L5 (200km to Québec City)
(418) 8627566 (418) 8621843
info@aubergeriviere-du-loup.qc.ca
www.aubergerdl.ca
Open Dates: 15.04-10.01 4km
1.5km 2km x 65

▲ **Sault Ste Marie** – The Algonquin Hotel – 11073
864 Queen St East, Sault Ste Marie, Ontario, P6A 2B4.
(705) 2532311; Toll Free: 1 (888) 2697728 (705) 9420269
algonquin.hotel@hihostels.ca
www.hihostels.ca
Open Dates: 12 ✈ Sault Ste Marie 24km
Sault Ste Marie 1km x 30

▲ **Sept-Iles** – Auberge Internationale Le Tangon – 11074
555, rue Cartier, Sept-Îles, Québec, G4R 2T8
(418) 9628180 (418) 9612965
tangon@aubergeletangon.com
www.aubergeletangon.com
Open Dates: 1.5km 1km
x 43 10km

▲ **Shuswap Lake** – HI Shuswap Lake - Squilax General Store and Hostel – 11085
Hostel address: #229 Trans Canada Hwy #1 (10km east of Chase) Squilax, BC,
Mailing address: Rural Route #2, S2-C11, Chase, BC, Canada V0E 1MO.
(250) 6752977; Toll Free 1 (888) 6752977 (250) 6752977
shuswap@hihostels.ca
www.hihostels.ca
Open Dates: x 24

△ ***South Milford*** *– Raven Haven Hostel – 11075*
PO Box 100, Annapolis Royal, Nova Scotia, B0S 1A0.
(902) 5327320 (902) 5322096
www.hihostels.ca
Open Dates: 15.06-01.09 x 5

▲ **Thunder Bay** – Confederation College-Sibley Hall Residence 11030
960 William St, Thunder Bay, Ontario, P7C 4W1.
(807) 4756381 (807) 6259596
confederation.college@hihostels.ca
www.hihostels.ca
Open Dates: 15.05-15.08 Thunder Bay International 5km Thunder Bay 10km
x 100 5km
5km

▲ **Tofino** – HI Tofino - Whalers on the Point Guesthouse – 11076
Box 296, 81 West St, Tofino BC, V0R 2Z0.
(250) 7253443 (250) 7253463
tofino@hihostels.ca www.hihostels.ca
Open Dates: 12km 400m 0.2W
x 56

Toronto – HI Toronto 11006
76 Church St, Toronto, Ontario, M5C 2G1.
(416) 9714440; Toll Free: 1 (877) 8488737
(416) 9714088 toronto@hihostels.ca
www.hihostels.ca
Open Dates: Open Times:
Beds: 170 - 8x2 9x4 12x6 5x6+
Price Range: from $23.80
Directions: Pearson International 30km A from all terminals 500m Union (Amtrak) 500m Bay Street 1km ap King 250m x 5 5km

---

Toronto – HI Toronto

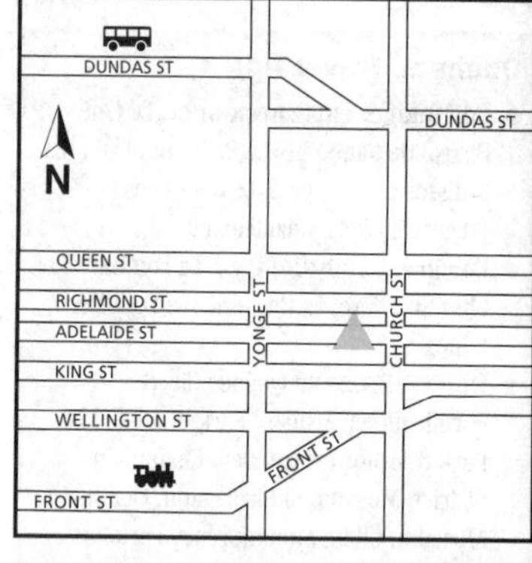

Toronto... Travel Tips

- **For budget eats check out...** Down One Lounge, Country Style Café, Old Spaghetti Factory, Young Thailand, Natcho's
- **For great nightlife try...** Down One Lounge, The Beer Market, Hard Rock Café (Yonge St.), The Joker, Warehouse
- **Don't miss...** CN Tower, Queen Street West, St Lawrence Market, Eaton Centre, Hockey Hall of Fame, Art Gallery of Ontario, Royal Ontario Museum, Harbour Front Centre, Distillery District

▲ Trois-Rivières – Auberge internationale de Trois-Rivières Ⓗ 11036

497, rue Radisson, Trois-Rivières, Québec, G9A 2C7

ⓣ (819) 3788010 ⓕ (819) 3784334

ⓔ trois-rivieres@auberge-hi.ca

ⓦ www.hihostels.ca

Open Dates: 01.03-01.10 2km 2km x 55 R CC (B) TV i 8 P

▲ Val-David – Le Chalet Beaumont Ⓗ 11034

1451, rue Beaumont, Val-David, Québec, J0T 2N0

ⓣ (819) 3221972 ⓕ (819) 3223793

ⓔ info@chaletbeaumont.com

ⓦ www.chaletbeaumont.com

Open Dates: 12 2km 2W x 72 R CC 1 x 8 P 4km 4km

Vancouver – HI Vancouver Central

Ⓗ 11031 FNM

1025 Granville St, Vancouver BC, V62 1L4.

ⓣ (604) 6855335; Toll Free: 1 (888) 2038333

ⓕ (604) 6855351

ⓔ vancouver.central@hihostels.ca

ⓦ www.hihostels.ca

Open Dates: 12 Open Times:

Beds: 226 - 33x² 13x³ 30x⁴

Price Range: $22-28 (dorm) $52-90 (private) BB inc

Directions: Vancouver International 15km A Holiday Inn Howe St Tsawwassen 32km Pacific Central 2km 8 Granville ap Granville & Nelson U Granville 750m R CC (B) TV i 8 1km

Vancouver – HI Vancouver Central

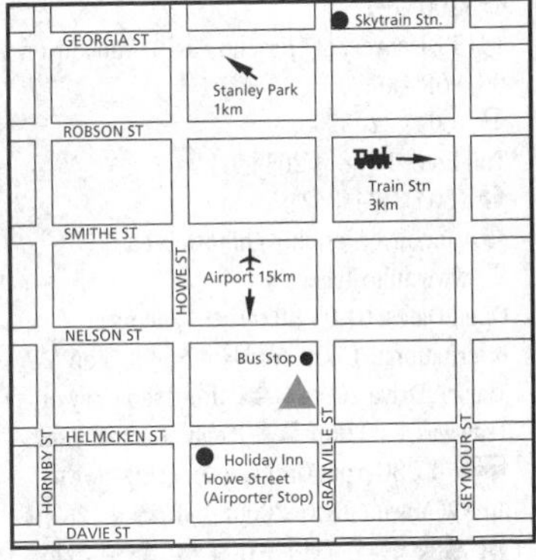

Vancouver – HI Vancouver Downtown

Ⓗ 11016 FNM

1114 Burnaby St, Vancouver, BC, V6E 1P1.

ⓣ (604) 6844565; Toll Free: 1 (888) 2034302 ⓕ (604) 6844540

ⓔ vancouver.downtown@hihostels.ca

ⓦ www.hihostels.ca

Open Dates: 12 Open Times:

Beds: 223 - 7x² 16x³ 44x⁴

Price Range: $22-28 (dorm) $53-74 (private) BB inc

Directions: Vancouver International 15km A Airporter Shuttle to Sandman Suites 200m Tsawwassen 32km Pacific Central 2.5km 6 Davie 1km ap Thurlow & Davie U Granville 1.5km x 23 R CC (B) TV 1 x i 8 P 50m

Vancouver – HI Vancouver Downtown

▲ **Vancouver** – HI Vancouver Jericho Beach
HI 11003 FNM
1515 Discovery St (Jericho Park), Vancouver, BC, V6R 4K5.
t (604) 2243208;
Toll Free: 1 (888) 2034303
f (604) 2244852
e vancouver.jericho@hihostels.ca
w www.hihostels.ca
Open Dates: 01.05-30.09 ✈ Vancouver International 15km A 424, 98, 4 ap NW Marine Drive 200m Horseshoe Bay or Tsawwassen 22km Pacific Central 9km 4 UBC from Granville St. (Downtown) ap NW Marine Drive 200m 5SW x 286 R CC (BD) TV i 8 P

Vancouver... Travel Tips

- **For budget eats check out...** The Dish, Thai Away Home, Ho-Ho's, DV8 Lounge, The Naam
- **For great nightlife try...** Morrissey Pub, Disco Night at the Commodore, Jupiter Lounge, The Vancouver Playhouse, Arts Club Theatre
- **Don't miss...** Stanley Park, Grouse Mountain, English Bay, Granville Island, Robson Street, Chinatown Night Market, Gastown, Kits Beach, Lighthouse Park, Museum of Anthropology

▲ **Vernon** – HI-Vernon Lodged Inn
HI 11077
3201 Pleasant Valley Rd, Vernon, British Columbia, V1T 4L4.
t (250) 5493742;
Toll Free: 1 (888) 7379427
f (250) 5493748 e vernon@hihostels.ca
w www.hihostels.ca
Open Dates: 01.12-31.10 ✈ 48km A 500m 500m 0.5E x 40 R CC TV i P 2km

HI-Canada National Discounts

At HI-Canada we not only say you will save money, we deliver. Your HI-Canada/YHA membership will get you access to over 450 different discounts across this great country. To get a full list of all the 450 discounts in Canada visit **www.hihostels.ca/discounts**

HI-C Travel Shops and Boutiques

10% discount on all travel gear and accessories!

Greyhound Canada

Members get 10% off regular fares.

Moose Travel Network

Members get 5% off tours and transportation.

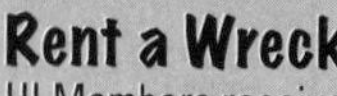

Rent a Wreck

HI Members receive $25 off weekly rental rates.

Global TESOL

HI members receive a $50 discount.

True North Tours

Save between $10 and $60 on True North Tours when booked directly. *Not valid with any other discounts.

Victoria – HI Victoria – 11078
516 Yates St, Victoria, BC, V8W 1K8.
(250) 3854511; Toll Free: 1 (888) 88300 99; R 1 (403) 6707580
(250) 3853232 victoria@hihostels.ca
www.hihostels.ca
Open Dates: Open Times:
Beds: 110 - 2x 1x 1x 4x
Price Range: $17-24 (dorm)
Directions: Victoria 28km A Shuttle to hostel Swartz Bay 32km, Victoria 700m E+N Via 200m 70 280m ap Yates & Douglas x 2 R CC
1.5km

Victoria – HI Victoria

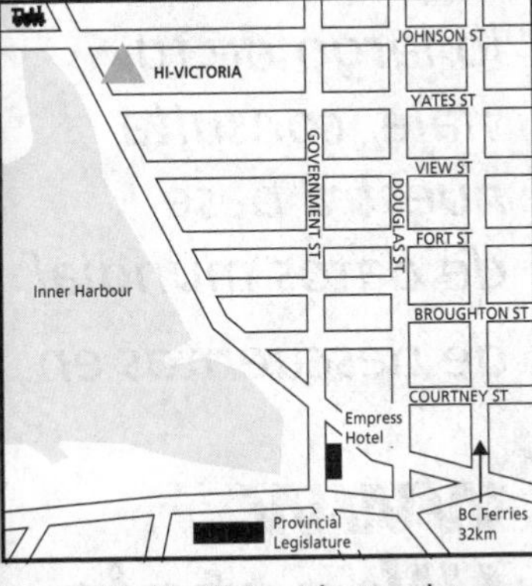

Victoria... Travel Tips

- **For budget eats check out...** China Town, Ferri's Oyster Burger Bar, Sour Pickel Café, Maharaja Restaurant, Pita Pit
- **For great nightlife try...** Steamers, Sugar, Legends, Darcy McGee's, Causeway Inner Harbour
- **Don't miss...** Royal British Columbia Museum, Art Gallery of Greater Victoria, Butchart Gardens, Beacon Hill Park, Legislative Building, Inner Harbour/Causeway, Craigdarroch Castle, Empress Hotel, Fishermans Wharf, Market Square

▲ **Waterton Lakes National Park** – HI-Waterton Alpine Centre – 11080
Waterton Lakes Lodge, Corner of Cameron Falls Drive & Windflower Ave, in Waterton townsite.
(403) 8592150; 8592151
(403) 8592229
info@watertonlakeslodge.com
www.hihostels.ca
Open Dates: Occasionally closed. Check when open. 118km A 48km x 22 R CC

▲ **Wentworth** – International Hostel – 11081
RR #1, Wentworth, Nova Scotia, B0M 1Z0. (Route 4 (Trans-Canada) to Wentworth Valley, exit on Valley Rd - follow signs to YH).
(902) 5482379 (902) 5482389
wentworthhostel@ns.sympatico.ca
www.hihostels.ca
Open Dates: Halifax International 110km Acadia Bus Lines 3km x 24 R CC 5km

△ ***Whiskey Jack** – HI-Whiskey Jack Wilderness Hostel, Yoho National Park – 11082*
Yoho National Park, BC. (near Alberta border, 27km W of Lake Louise on Hwy #1 (Trans-Canada), 13km W along Yoho Valley Rd from Kicking Horse Camp Ground).
(403) 6707580 (R)
(403) 2836503
centralres.sa@hihostels.ca
www.hihostels.ca
Open Dates: 20.06-01.10 x 27 R CC

▲ **Whistler** – HI Whistler – 11083
5678 Alta Lake Rd, Whistler, BC, V0N 1B5. (121km N of Vancouver on Hwy 99, turn off on Alta Lake Rd, continue 5km).
(604) 9325492 (604) 9324687
whistler@hihostels.ca
www.hihostels.ca
Open Dates: Vancouver International 130km A Perimeter Bus to Whistler Village 130km 4SW x 32 R CC

▲ **Winnipeg** – HI-Winnipeg Ivey House Hostel 11084
210 Maryland St, Winnipeg, Manitoba, R3G 1L6.
(204) 772-3022 (204) 784-1133
winnipeg@hihostels.ca
www.hihostels.ca/winnipeg
Open Dates: Winnipeg International 7km CN, VIA (Winnipeg) 2km 29 Sherbrook ap Maryland and Broadway 15m
2SW x 43

YOUTH HOSTEL ACCOMMODATION OUTSIDE THE ASSURED STANDARDS SCHEME

Wakefield – Auberge international Parc de la Gatineau – 11079
66 Chemin Carman, Chelsea, Québec J9B 2K3
(819) 4593180 (819) 4592113
carman@magma.ca
www.magma.ca/~carman
Open Dates: 50km Touristic Steam Train 6km 500m 15W x 56 1 x 1km

Chile

Asociación Chilena de Albergues Turísticos Juveniles,
Hernando de Aguirre 201 of 602,
Providencia,
Santiago, Chile

t (56) (2) 4112050
f (56) (2) 2332555
e reservas@hostelling.cl
e hostelling@hostelling.cl
w www.hostelling.cl

Travel Section:
Gts Travel
Cienfuegos 151,
Santiago, Chile

t (56) (2) 6997892
f (56) (2) 6997893
e info@gtstravel.cl

Student Flight Center
Hernando de Aguirre 201 of 401,
Providencia,
Santiago, Chile

t (56) (2) 4112000
f (56) (2) 3350394
e sfc@sertur.cl
w www.sertur.cl

A copy of the Hostel Directory for this Country can be obtained from:
The National Office

National Tourist Authority/Board:	www.minrel.cl; www.sernatur.cl
Capital:	Santiago
Language:	Spanish
Currency:	$ peso
Population:	15,000,000
Size:	56,945 sq km
Telephone Country Code:	56
eKit Access Number:	800-800-014

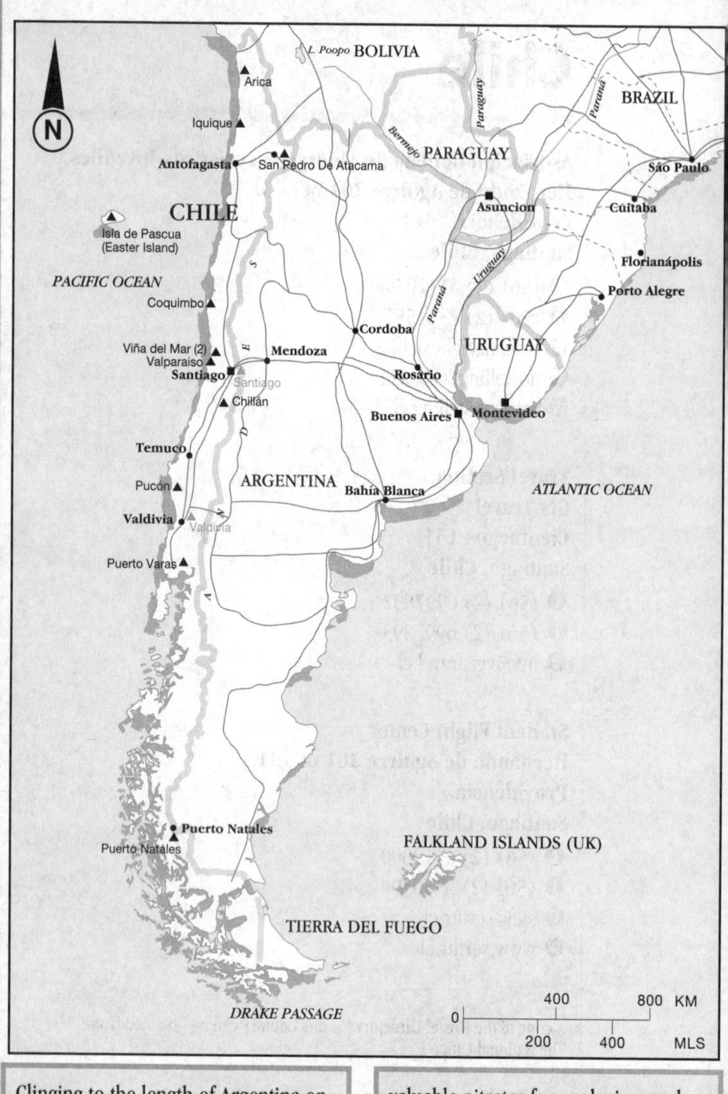

Clinging to the length of Argentina on the other side of the Andes, Chile with a population of some 16 million, is like a long backbone of pre-history, stretching along the Pacific coast for over 2600 miles, with nowhere over 250 miles and most places barely over 100 miles from the sea. Yet, its length envelopes every type of climate with deserts in the north, fertile valleys in the centre and forests, fjords and glaciers in the south. The deserts, however, are not barren, yielding up valuable nitrates for explosives and fertilizers, which were a major source of wealth well into the twentieth century, and also the world's largest reserves of copper, which today is Chile's leading export.

The coastal seas are teamimg with salmon, which supports a major canning industry, while the central area, from Valparaiso to Conception, is Chile's heartland, with a mild Mediterranean climate, similar to southern California, and today famous for producing excellent wine at affordable prices. It is where the capital Santiago is located.

Like much of South America, a heartland of the Roman Catholic Church, which remains fundamental to its way of life, Chile's past, is dominated by a kaleidoscope of exploitation, good and bad regimes and civil war. After the end of Pinochet era (16 years), Chile finally in 1990 voted for a democratic government and is today highly regarded for turning its fortunes around and the new 'young Chile' is set to keep it that way.

A few other Top Tips from **CULTURE SMART!**:

- Chile's population is largely European, principally Spanish, but also has a significant German population in the south as a result of forestry opportunities in the nineteenth century. Indigenous Mapuche Indian blood is extensive throughout the population.
- Chileans are not flashy in manner or in dress. Dress tends to be conservative. Modern Chile has a growing middle class (over forty per cent). Family is always an important topic of conversation.
- In addition to their birthdays Chileans also celebrate their Saint's Day, though it is less common among the young. Celebrations generally call for dressing up, including going out for dinner. So, even if you are told 'informal' make sure you know exactly what that means!
- Handshakes among men are the norm while Chilean women will kiss each other once on the right cheek. Always include everyone in your group. And remember, Latin Americans are notorious for turning up late: Chileans are no exception!
- In a country where fish is so plentiful it is worth noting that beef is also a major component of Chilean cuisine. Equally, there is a huge range of 'local' food based on fresh corn and other vegetables.

Culture Smart! Top Tips © Kuperard 2005

Cultural Top Tips supplied by Culture Smart! guides. These essential guides to customs and etiquette will help you steer clear of embarrassing gaffes and sensitive issues, enabling you to discover new cultures whilst developing new friendships. Order online at www.culturesmartguides.co.uk

You can find out a lot more on our website - a visit to www.HIhostels.com is essential for planning your trip!

Pour en savoir plus, rendez-vous sur notre site Internet, www.HIhostels.com une visite incontournable pour préparer votre voyage!

Viele weitere Informationen auf unserer Website: www.HIhostels.com - unverzichtbar für die Reiseplanung!

Puedes averiguar mucho más en nuestro sitio web. Es imprescindible que visites la página www.HIhostels.com para planear tu viaje.

▲ **Arica** – Doña Inés – 12018 (FNM)
Manuel Rojas #2864.
(58) 226372; 248108
hiarica@hostelling.cl
www.hostelling.cl
Open Dates: 12 ✈ Chacalluta 15km
2.5km 2.5km 1.5km 2S
x 35

▲ **Chillán** – Complejo Turístico "Las Trancas" – 12004
Km 73.5 Camino a las Termas de Chillán, Chillán.
(42) 243211 (42) 243211
hilastrancas@hostelling.cl
Open Dates: Chillán 75.5km Terminal Constitución 73.5km 73.3SE x 40

▲ **Coquimbo** – Hostal Nomade – 12019
Regimiento Coquimbo 5, Barrio Inglés Coquimbo.
(51) 315665
hicoquimbo@hostelling.cl
www.hostalnomade.cl
Open Dates: Aeropuerto La Florida 25km 3km 4km 0.1SW x 30 (B)

▲ **Iquique** – 12020
Amunategui 2075 Iquique.
(57) 320223 hiiquique@hostelling.cl
www.hosteliquique.cl
Open Dates: Diego Aracena 25km 1km 1km 0.7S x 29 (B)

▲ **Isla de Pascua** – Residencial Kona Tau – 12006
Avaripua S/N.
(12332) 100321 (12332) 100321
hieasterisland@hostelling.cl
www.hostelling.cl
Open Dates: Mataveri 300m 0.5SE x 16

▲ **Pucón** – Refugio Peninsula – 12021
Clemente Holzapfell 11 Pucón
(45) 443398; (09) 8205893
hipucon@hostelling.cl
www.refugiopeninsula.cl
Open Dates: Pucón (open during summer) 2km, Manquehue -Temuco (open all year) 105Km Temuco 108km 700m 0.4S x 30 (B)

△ ***Puerto Natales*** *– Path@gone – 12009*
Eberhard 595, Puerto Natales.
(61) 413291 (61) 413290
hipatagonia@hostelling.cl
www.chileaustral.com/pathgone
Open Dates: 01.09-30.05 Presidente Ibañez (Punta Arenas) 256km A Buses Fernández 300m Puerto Natales 700m 0.15W x 22 (B)

▲ **Puerto Varas** – Hospedaje Patiperros – 12022
Mirador 135 Puerto Varas
(65) 235050 hipvaras@hostelling.cl
www.jardinsa.cl
Open Dates: El Tepual (Puerto Montt) 30km 300m 0.1E x 46 (B)

△ ***San Pedro De Atacama*** *– HI San Pedro De Atacama – 12016*
Caracoles 360, San Pedro.
(55) 851426
hiatacama@hostelling.cl
www.hostellingatacama.com
Open Dates: El Loa (Calama) 100km A 100m Antofagasta 345km 150m 0.06SE x 33

__Santiago – Hostelling International__
HI 12002
Cienfuegos 151, Santiago de Chile.
(2) 6718532 (2) 6728880
reservas@hostelling.cl
www.hisantiago.cl
Open Dates: Open Times:
Beds: 120 - 2x[2] 20x[4] 6x[6]
Directions: 1.5NE from city centre
Arturo Merino Benitez 21km
A Centropuerto 500m, Tour Express 500m Valparaíso 120km Estacion Central 1km Estacion Central 1km
U 1, 2: Los Héroes Station 300m, 2: Santa Ana Station 400m

Santiago – Hostelling International

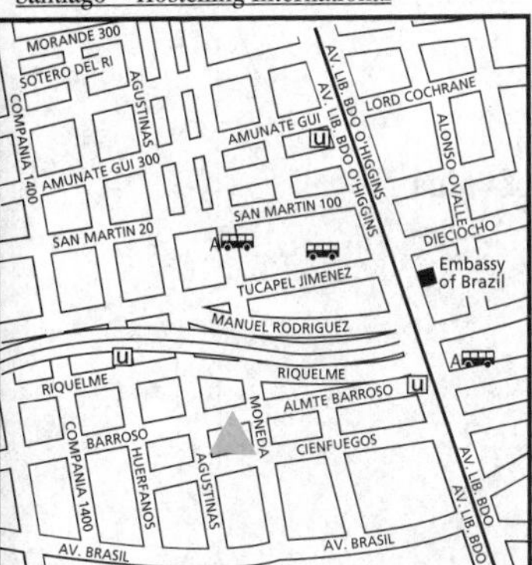

Santiago... Travel Tips

- **For budget eats check out...** Liguria (Av. Providencia 1373), Galindo (Darignac 098), Bar Nacional (Bandera 317), El Toro (Loreto 33), El Parron (Av. Providencia 1184)
- **For great nightlife try...** Barrio Bellavista (Bellavista District), Plaza Brazil, Plaza Ñuñoa, Lastarria, Pasaje Orrego Luco
- **Don't miss...** San Cristobal Hill, Visit to vineyards, Ski resorts, Civic District, Parque Forestal (Forest Park area), Santa Lucía Hill, Central Market & Mapocho Station, Pueblito de Los Dominicos (The Dominicans' Little Village), Pablo Neruda Museum "La Chascona", Cajòn del Maipo (Maipo's Ravine)

△ ***Valdivia*** *– Aires Buenos Hostel HI 12017 FNM*

General Lagos 1036, Valdivia.
(63) 206304 (63) 206304
hivaldivia@hostelling.cl
www.airesbuenos.cl
Open Dates: 12 Pichoy 30km
A 1km Corral 16km 1.5km
0.4SE x 48 R CC (B)

▲ **Valparaiso** – Villa Maria Antonieta – 12023 FNM

Bernardo Vera 542 Cerro San Juan de Dios.
(32) 734336 (32)493033
hivalpo@hostelling.cl
www.hivalparaiso.cl
Open Dates: 12 Arturo Marino Benitez 140km Valparaiso 1km 300m
1km 0.5NW x 42 R CC
(B) i 8

▲ **Viña del Mar** – Hotel Asturias – 12014 FNM

Av. Valparaíso 299, Viña del Mar, Viña del Mar.
(32) 711565 (32) 711590
hivinaasturias@hostelling.cl
Open Dates: 12 Arturo Merino Benitez 140km Valparaíso 10km Estación Miramar 200m 700m 0.4W x 50
R i
8

△ ***Viña del Mar*** *– Hotel Capric – 12015 FNM*

Von Schroeders 39, Viña del Mar.
(32) 978295 (32) 978295
hivinacapric@hostelling.cl
Open Dates: 12 Arturo Merino Benitez 140km Valparaíso 10km
Miramar 300m 1km 0.7W
x 20 R CC (B)
i 8 P

China

Guangdong Youth Hostels Association of China
18C Ming Yue Ge Building (Moon Tower),
No. 20 Ming Yue Yi Road,
Wu Yang Xin Cheng,
Guangzhou, 510600
China.

t (86) (20) 87345080
f (86) (20) 87345428
e yhachina@yahoo.com.cn
w www.yhachina.com

Capital:	Beijing
Language:	Mandarin, Cantonese
Currency:	Yuan (Renminbi)
Population:	1,270,000,000
Size:	9,596,960 sq km
Telephone Country Code:	86
eKit Access Number:	10800-180-0072

Hong Kong (Special Administrative Region - SAR)
Hong Kong Youth Hostels Association,
Room 225, Block 19,
Shek Kip Mei Estate,
Sham Shui Po,
Kowloon,
Hong Kong.

t (852) 27881638
f (852) 27883105
e info@yha.org.hk
w www.yha.org.hk

Capital:	Hong Kong
Language:	Cantonese, English, Mandarin
Currency:	HK$
Population:	7,000,000
Size:	1,097 sq km
Telephone Country Code:	852
eKit Access Number:	800-967-389

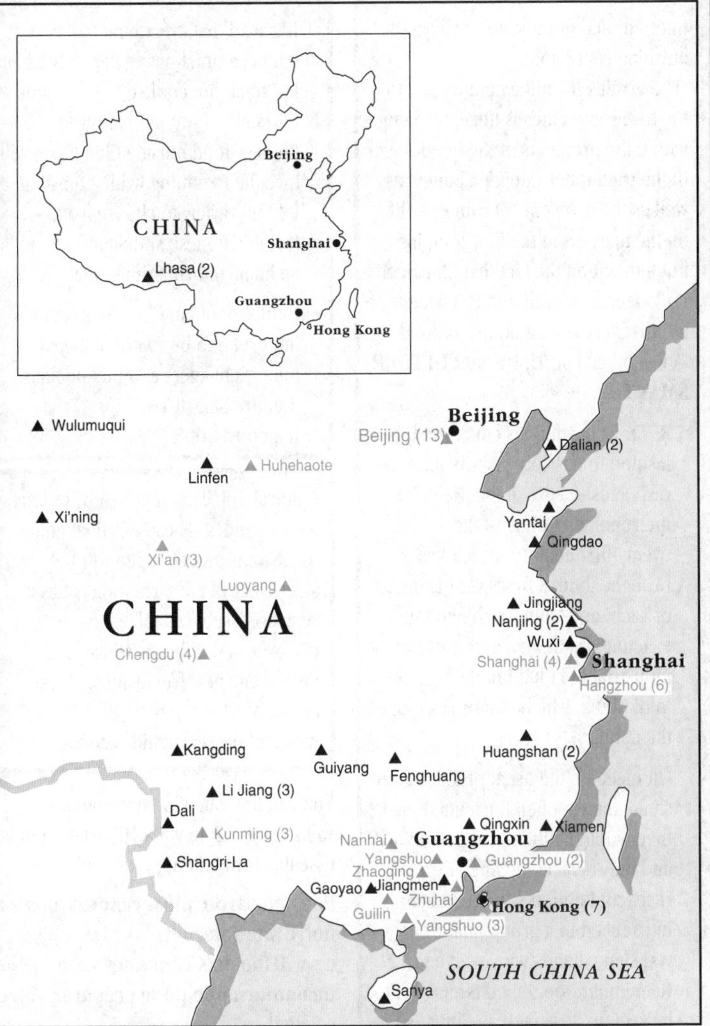

Whatever images we may have of China of recent times past, the fact is that this amazing country of over 1.2 billion people is literally and metaphorically 'on the move'. What used to be everyman's dream of owning a bicycle has given way to owning a car, whole cities are being refurbished and reinvigorated by the drive to modernize and realize visions of a better life. The decision to hold the 2008 Olympics in Beijing has acted as a magnet on the entire country, energizing the nation to participate in some way in the project, which, say their leaders, will be completed ahead of time.

Whole cities like Shanghai and Beijing have become a world metropolis for investors and entrepreneurs, bristling with skyscrapers and a brand-new infrastructure, where blue-suited 'robots' of the Mao era have been replaced by a dynamic, individualistic new generation sporting designer jeans, eager to identify with top international brands, and believing anything is possible.

The exodus from the countryside to the towns and cities is huge, bringing with it the problems of the breakdown of the traditional extended family, as well as the problems of living city life on the margins in the new 'Utopias', not to mention the fact that China can no longer feed itself and is having to import increasing amounts of food.

A few other Top Tips from **CULTURE SMART!:**

- As far as anything is concerned, from fashion to passion, visitors have to distinguish between the 'New, New metropolitan China' of the twenty-first century, which has brought about a first-ever generation of 'rich' and 'super rich', and the exacting, traditional agrarian and industrial life found in the rest of 'old' China, which comprises most of the country!
- On meeting, the usual practice is to shake hands, often for much longer than would be the norm in the West and may be accompanied by a respectful nod. If you are being introduced to a group, make sure you shake hands with everyone. Remember, too, that it is vital not to be seen to 'lose face' in China, so avoid any situation where embarrassment might occur and which might be camouflaged with laughter.
- Even with the great leaps, in modernisation, in the PRC (People's Republic of China) bureaucracy still reigns supreme and there continues to be an enormous amount of red tape everywhere you go and for everything you do. The key is to avoid showing impatience, raising your voice or worse, showing anger.
- It is said that everything that is edible, animal or vegetable, is eaten in China, but cooked to perfection. Certainly, if you have enjoyed Chinese food outside China, you will love the real thing, with almost an infinite variety to choose from – from Cantonese and Shandong, to Sichuan and Huaiyang food.
- In metropolitan China it is vitally important to be aware of illegal money changers and pickpockets.

Cultural Top Tips supplied by Culture Smart! guides. These essential guides to customs and etiquette will help you steer clear of embarrassing gaffes and sensitive issues, enabling you to discover new cultures whilst developing new friendships. Order online at www.culturesmartguides.co.uk

You can find out a lot more on our website - a visit to www.HIhostels.com is essential for planning your trip!

Pour en savoir plus, rendez-vous sur notre site Internet, www.HIhostels.com une visite incontournable pour préparer votre voyage!

Viele weitere Informationen auf unserer Website: www.HIhostels.com - unverzichtbar für die Reiseplanung!

Puedes averiguar mucho más en nuestro sitio web. Es imprescindible que visites la página www.HIhostels.com para planear tu viaje.

▲ **Beijing** – Beijing City Central Youth Hostel – 24616
No. 1 Beijingzhangqianjie, Dongcheng District, Beijing, 10005.
(10) 65258066 (10) 85114861
bjyha@byecity.com
www.yhachina.com
Open Dates: Beijing 28km A Airport Bus Beijing 50m 1, 4, 24, 10, 54, 22 ap Beijing Station x 364 1 x

▲ **Beijing** – Beijing Far East Youth Hostel 24525
No. 113 Tieshuxiejie, Xuanwu District, Beijing, 100050 China.
(10) 63018811 (10) 63018233
yhachina@yahoo.com.cn
www.yhachina.com
Open Dates: Beijing International 35km A Airport Bus to Xidan Aviation Building and change to No. 14 ap Liulichang Tanggu, Tianjin Beijing 4km; Beijing West 6km 6, 7, 14, 15, 25, 50 ap Liulichang 102, 105 ap Liulichang, Hufargqiao U Hepingmen x 202 R 8 P 1km

▲ **Beijing** – Beijing Feiying YH 24543
No.10, Xida Street, Xuanwumen, Beijing, 100053 China.
(10) 63171116-4010 (10) 63151165
yhachina@yahoo.com.cn
www.yhachina.com
Open Dates: Beijing International 35km A to International Hotel then contact the reception of the Hotel Tanggu Tianjin Beijing 4km; Beijing West 2km 9, 48, 337, 848 ap Changchunjie 105, Xuanwuman Station U Changchunjie 100m x 148 P

▲ **Beijing** – Beijing Fenglong Youth Hostel – 24519
No. 5 You'anmen Dongjie, Xuanwu District, Beijing, 100054 China.
(10) 63545836 (10) 63536415
bjyha@bycity.com www.yhachina.com
Open Dates: Beijing International 35km A to Xidan Aviation Building then change to No. 103 ap Youyongchi Beijing West 10km; Beijing 10km 14, 20, 40, 72, 102, 122, 603, 613, 800 ap Beijing Nanzhan, Taoranting 102, 106 ap Youyongchi, Taoranting U Hepingmen 8km x 350 P

▲ **Beijing** – Beijing Gongti Youth Hostel – 24553
No.9 Tai, Worker's Stadium (Gongrentiyuchang), Chaoyang District, Beijing 100027.
(10) 65524800 (10) 65524860
yhachina@yahoo.com.cn
www.yhachina.com
Open Dates: Beijing International 23km A Airport Bus "C" to the East Gate of the stadium (Gongtidongmen) Tanggu, Tianjin Beijing 4km; Beijing West 14km 110, 120, 403, 703, 813 ap Gongtidonglu; 113, 701, 823, 834 ap Gongtibeilu 15, 118 ap Gongti U Line 2 ap Dongshisitiao x 100 1 x 8 P 100m

▲ **Beijing** – Beijing Hongdu Sunshine Youth Hostel – 24605
No. 23 West of Xi bahe, Chaoyang District, Beijing.
(10) 64213461 (10) 64200755
hdsunshine@126.com
Open Dates: Beijing Capital 18km Beijing 8km 300, 302, 606, 830, 730, 974, 731 ap Xibeihe, Qisheng Road x 200 1 x P

Beijing – Beijing Jade Youth Hostel – 24601
No. 5, North Zhide Alley, Beiheyan Street, Dongcheng District, Beijing, 100006.
(10) 65228036 (10) 65226224
bjyha@byecity.com
Open Dates: Open Times:
Beds: 265
Directions: Beijing 28km A Airport Bus Tanggu, Tianjin Beijing 1.5km 8, 60, 819, 8, 2 ap Fuchan Hospital, Dengshixikou 103, 104 ap Fuchan Hospital, Dengshixikou U 1 to Tian'an Men, East. Then 2 ap Fuchan Hospital, Dengshixikou
1 x

Beijing – Beijing Jade Youth Hostel

▲ **Beijing** – Beijing Saga Youth Hostel – 24527
No. 9 Shijia Hutong, Dongcheng District, South Street, Beijing, 100010 China.
(10) 65272773 (10) 65249098
yhachina@yahoo.com.cn
www.yhachina.com
Open Dates: Beijing International 32km A Beijing International Hotel or Beijing Railway Station Tanggu, Tianjin Beijing 1.5km; Beijing West 10km 24, 713 ap Lumikang 103, 104, 106 ap Dengshikou U Line 1 ap Beijing Railway Station or Jianguomen 1km x 90

▲ **Beijing** – Beijing Zhaolong International Youth Hostel 24508
2 Worker's Stadium Rd (N), Chaoyang District, Beijing, 100027 China.
(10) 65972299-6111 (10) 65972288
yhachina@yahoo.com.cn
www.yhachina.com
Open Dates: Beijing International 25km A Beijing Kunlun Hotel Tanggu, Tianjin Beijing 5km; Beijing West 15km 113, 120, 403, 701, 703, 801 ap Tuanjie Lake; Zhaolong Hotel 115 ap Zhaolong Hotel U at Dongshisitiao Station change to 115 ap Zhaolong Hotel
x 160

▲ **Beijing** – Lvsongyuan Youth Hostel – 24614
22, Kuaijiebanchang Lane, Dongcheng District, Beijing.
(10) 64040436 (10) 64030418
gdyha@yahoo.com.cn
www.yhachina.com
Open Dates: 24km 7km 2, 5, 13, 803 ap Lvsongyuan Hotel 104, 108 ap Lvsongyuan Hotel U 2km x 22
1 x

▲ **Beijing** – Ruihaimu International Youth Hostel – 24554
No.30, Xidaqiao Road, Miyun County, Beijing, 101500.
(10) 89098888-8818 (10) 69026666
yhachina@yahoo.com.cn
www.yhachina.com
Open Dates: Beijing International 55km A to Dongzhimen, change to Dongmi bus to the Resort ap Xidaqiao Beijing West 80km; Miyun 2km P70, P80 ap Xidaqiao
x 210 1 x
3km

▲ **Beijing** – Simatai Great Wall Youth Hostel – 24612
Simatai, Great Wall Scenic Area, Miyun County, Beijing, 101508.
(10) 69035311 (10) 69035655
bjyha@byecity.com www.yhachina.com
Open Dates: Beijing International 4hrs by Bus Simatai YH is far away from the city centre. It's located near Simaitai Great Wall. Other hostels in Beijing can arrange transportation and tours to Simatai YH. Contact YH's in Beijing for information
x 120 1 x

▲ **Beijing** – Xindadu International Youth Hostel – 24604
21, Chegongzhuang Dajie, Xicheng District, Beijing 100044.
(10) 68319988-180, 185
(10) 88373701 gdyha@yahoo.com.cn
www.yhachina.com
Open Dates: Beijing International Airport bus to Chegongzhuang, then change 320, 727 to Zrligouxikou 392, 701, 748 to Hejiawan, 320, 707 to Baiwanzhuang 102, 103, to Baiwanzhuang, 118 to Hejiawan U Line 1, 2 to Chegongzhuang, then change to 26, 701, 748, 118 to Hejiawan x 208

Beijing... Travel Tips

- **For budget eats check out...** Wang Fu Jing Mian Dian Wang (King of Pastry in Wang Fu Jing Str.), Dong Fang Yi Yuan Roast Duck Restaurant, Jiu Tou Niao Interlock Restaurant (Hubei cuisine), Jin Ding Restaurant (Guangdong cuisine), Yuan Tai Zu Mongolia Barbecue (buffet)
- **For great nightlife try...** Dong Hua Men Night Market, Lao She Teahouse, San Li Tun/ Chao Yang Park Bar Street, Li Yuan Theatre in Qian Men Hotel (Beijing Opera), Chao Yang Theatre (Acrobatics)
- **Don't miss...** Forbidden City, The Great Wall, Summer Palace, Tian Au Men Square, Temple of Heaven, Yong He Palace/ La Ma Temple, Old Beijing Hutong Tour, Bei Hai Park, Xiang Shan Park, The Ming Tombs

▲ **Chengdu** – Chengdu Dragon Town Youth Hostel – 24555
No. 27 Kuanxiangzi Street, Chengdu, 610014 China.
(28) 86648408 (28) 86245901
yhachina@yahoo.com.cn
www.yhachina.com
Open Dates: Chengdu Shuangliu International 18km A to Minshan Hotel, then 78 to Tongrenlukou Chengdu North 4km 4, 64, 78 ap Tongrenlukou x 84 2km

▲ **Chengdu** – Chengdu Dreams Travel Youth Hostel – 24556
242 Wuhouci Road, Chengdu, Sichuan, 610041.
(28) 85570315; 85570322
(28) 85570321 gdyha@yahoo.com.cn
www.yhachina.com
Open Dates: Chengdu Shuangliu International 10km A to Renminnan, then 301 ap Wuhouci Chengdu North 10km 1, 8, 10, 27, 53, 57, 59, 82, 109, 110, 212, 213, 301, 302 ap Wuhouci x 100 300m

▲ **Chengdu** – Chengdu Forest Youth Hostel HI 24529
No. 6 Renminbeiluyiduan, Chengdu City, Sichuan Province, 610081 China.
(28) 83416580 (28) 83364547
yhachina@yahoo.com.cn
www.yhachina.com
Open Dates: Chengdu Shuangliu International 15km A Wanfuqiao Chengdu North 2km 55, 47, 54, 99 ap Jinghua Street x 31

▲ **Chengdu** – Chengdu Traffic Youth Hostel – 24594
No. 6 Linjiangzhong Rd, Chengdu, Sichuan, 610041.
(28) 85451017 (28) 85440977
yhachina@yahoo.com.cn
www.yhachina.com
Open Dates: Chengdu Shuangliu 12km Chengdu North 5km 55, 28, 8, 16 ap Xin Nanmen 500m x 230 1 x

▲ **Dali** – Old Dali Youth Hostel – 24615
No. 55, Bo'ai Rd, Dali Old Town, 671003.
(872) 2670382; 2663925
(872) 2670382 sijinn@hotmail.com
www.sijinn.com
Open Dates: Dali 75km Dali 12km Dali 17km 4 ap Honglongjing x 73

▲ **Dalian** – Dalian Huanan Youth Hostel – 24532
No. 1 Yingchun Rd, Xigang District, Dalian City, Liaoning Province, 116013 China.
(411) 82496830 (411) 84954946
yhachina@yahoo.com.cn
www.yhachina.com
Open Dates: Dalian Zhoushuizi International 6km A Renmin Guangchang, 702, 4, 17 ap Nanshidaojie Dalian Harbour 5km Dalian 3km 4, 17, 407, 525, 526, 702, 715 ap Nanshidaojie x 197 2 x 2km

△ ***Dalian*** *– Dalian Sea Rhyme Youth Hostel – 24531*
104 Warship, No. 667, Zhongshan District, Dalian City, Liaoning Province, 116018, China.
(411) 82394400; 85852224
(411) 82394400
yhachina@yahoo.com.cn
www.yhachina.com
Open Dates: 01.04-31.10 Dalian Zhousuizi International 15km A Airport Bus to , then 2 ap Laohutan Daliangang Harbour 6km Dalian 10km 708 from Harbour to Sanba Plaza, then 402 ap Laohutan; 2 from x 98

△ ***Fenghuang*** *– Fenghuang International Youth Hostel – 24597*
No. 11 Shawan, Tuojiang, Fenghuang Xiangxi, Hunan 416200.
(743) 3260546 (743) 3260546
yhachina@yahoo.com.cn
www.yhachina.com
Open Dates: Zhangjiajie International 140km; Guizhou Tongren 24km Huaihua 92km; Jishou 52km x 42

▲ **Gaoyao** – Gaoyao Guangxin Youth Hostel – 24533
Lüyindadao Baitu Town, Gaoyao City, Guangdong Province, 526109 China.
(758) 8162228 (758) 8162753
yhachina@yahoo.com.cn
www.yhachina.com
Open Dates: Zhuhai International 95km; Guangzhou Baiyun 100km A Zhaoqing Zhaoqing 18km Guangzhou Liuhua to Zhaoqing Qiaoxi, then 315 ap Guangxin Nongye Shengtaiyuan x 250

Guangzhou – Guangzhou Binjiang Youth Hostel 24557
No.405 Yanjiangdong Road, Guangzhou, 510100 China.
(20) 83834110 (20) 83831017
gdyha@yahoo.com.cn
www.yhachina.com
Open Dates: Open Times:
Beds: 98
Directions: Guangzhou Baiyun 36km A to Quanqiutong Hotel, and then take a taxi to the hostel (about 2km) Guangzhou 2km; Guangzhou East 3km 7, 12, 18, 36, 44, 45, 57, 61, 80, 89, 125, 128, 131, 182, 184, 192, 208, 277, 287 ap Dashatou 101, 104 ap Dashatou U Line 1 ap Lieshilingyuan; Line 2 ap Haizhuguang-chang 1 x 400m

Guangzhou – Guangzhou Binjiang Youth Hostel

▲ Guangzhou – Guangzhou City Youth Hostel HI 24501
179, Huanshi Xi Rd, Guangzhou, Guangdong, 510010 China.
(20) 86666889 Ext 3813
(20) 86679787
yhachina@yahoo.com.cn
www.yhachina.com
Open Dates: (Except 13-30.04; 13-30.10)
Baiyun 34km A to Nanhang Ticket Center Zhoutouzui 20km
Guangzhou 200m 7, 30, 31, 33, 52, 203, 210, 211, 228, 234, 242, 254, 257, 261, 269, 272, 274, 275, 350, 523, 529, 550, 552, 803, 805, 807, 813, 823, 862 ap Guangzhou Railway Station U Line 2 - Guangzhou Railway Station x 90
R CC
8 P 1km

Guangzhou... Travel Tips

- **For budget eats check out...** Banxi (famous in Guangdong Dimsam), Guangzhou (located in Old Town), Greenery Café (best cooking in west food), Tian He Porridge, Dong Bei Ren Interlock (north-east cuisine)
- **For great nightlife try...** Pan Yu Chang Long Night Zoo - Circus Show (every evening), Beijing Road shopping street (downtown), Shang Xia Jiu Road shopping street (downtown), Tao Jin Bei Road disco & bar street, Night cruise on Pearl River
- **Don't miss...** The Chen Clan Temple, The memorial hall of Doctor Sun Yi Shen, Pan Yu Xiang Jiang River Wildlife World, The Southern Yue Mausoleum Museum, Bai Yun Hill, Yue Xiu Park (The Five Goats statue on the Yue Xiu Hill is the symbol of Guangzhou City), Guangzhou Art Museum, Bao Mo Yuan Ganden, Sha Mian Island, Beijing Road & Shang Xia Jiu Road (Old Town)

▲ Guilin – Guilin Flowers Youth Hostel – 24560
Block 2, No. 6, Shangzhi Lane, Zhongshan Nan Road, Guilin City, Guangxi Province 541002.
(773) 3839625; 3845275
(773) 3845275
yhachina@yahoo.com.cn
www.yhachina.com
Open Dates: Guilin Liangjiang 30km A to Railway Station 100m 1, 3, 4, 8, 9, 12, 15, 19, 51 ap Guilin Station x 100 1 x 8

▲ Guiyang – Yidu Youth Hostel – 24598
No. 63 Wenchangnan Road, Guiyang 550001, Guizhou, China.
(851)8649777 (851) 8631799
www.yhachina.com
Open Dates: Longdongbao 2km A Huguolukou 100m (20min by Taxi) Guiyang 2km 1, 2, 40 ap Laodongmen 100m x 142
1 x 8 P

▲ Hangzhou – Hangzhou Jiangnanyi International Youth Hostel HI 24558
No.32, Xiamanjuelong Road, Xihu District, Hangzhou City, Zhejiang Province, 310008.
(571) 87153419; 87153273
(571) 87153419
yhachina@yahoo.com.cn
www.yhachina.com
Open Dates: Hangzhou Xiaoshan International 27km A to Wulinmen, change bus "Jiari No.1" ap Zoo (Dongwuyuan) Hangzhou Wulinmen Pier 9km Hangzhou 7.5km, bus "Jiari 5; Hangzhou East 7km, bus "You 7" ap Zoo Jiari 1, 9,16, K4, 315, 514/K514, K 504, K5045, K514, K808, You 3, You 7 ap Zoo (Dongwuyuan) x 48
TV 1 x 8 P
4km

CHINA – CHINE – CHINA – CHINA

▲ **Hangzhou** – Hangzhou Sailor Youth Hostel – 24613
Xinyifang Shangjie, Gongshu District, Hangzhou 310005.
(571) 88236392 (571) 88236392
gdyha@yahoo.com.cn
www.yhachina.com
Open Dates: Xiaoshan 35km
A Airport bus to Wulinmen, change to 155 to Yuhangtangshangzhan Station then take a taxi (about RMB 10) to hostel
Huochedong 6.5km; Huochecheng 8.5km K516 from Huochedong Railway Station ap Congjinxincun; 151 from Huochecheng Railway Station ap Cangjixincun; K188, 333, K204, 155, K11, Y8, 85, 845, 23, K67, 67, K70, 70, K15, 15, K555 ap Yuhangtangshangzhan; 813, K251 ap Cangjinxincunzhan x 99 1 x

▲ **Hangzhou** – Hangzhou Xinyu Youth Hostel – 24559
No. 21, 1 Qingchun Rd, Hangzhou City, Zhejiang Province, 310009.
(571) 87244888 (571) 87238088
www.yhachina.com
Open Dates: Hangzhou Xiaoshan International 37km A to Wulinmen, change to bus No.14, 32, 858 ap Daxuelubeikou Hangzhou East 4km; Hangzhou City 2km 14, 18, 31, 32, 40, 59, 156, 528, 834, 836 ap Daxuelubeikou, Qingchunmen x 94 1 x

▲ **Hangzhou** – Hangzhou Youth Hostel
HI 24561
No. 101, Nanshan Rd, Hangzhou, 310002.
(571) 87918948; 87087891-8098
(571) 87087891-8000
yhachina.@yahoo.com.cn
www.yhachina.com
Open Dates: Hangzhou Xiaoshan International 37km A to Wulinmen, change to bus No.30/K30 ap Qianwangci
Hangzhou Pier (the end of Grand Canal) 3km Hangzhou City 2km; Hangzhou East 2.5km 30/K30, 12/K12, K4 ap Qianwangci x 88

▲ **Hangzhou** – Lake View Youth Hostel – 24606
No. 17, Jinshagang (North of Yaggong, besides the former residence of Gaijiaotian).
yhachina@yahoo.com.cn
www.yhachina.com
Open Dates: Hangzhou Xiaoshan 35km
A Wulinmen, change to Y5 ap Huapu;
A to Wulinguangchangm change Y1 ap Yuemiao Hangzhou Wulinmen 5km; Y1 from the Harbour ap Yuemiao
Hangzhoucheng 5.5km; Y2 to Huapu, 7 to Yuemiao. Hangzhou East 18km; Y5 to Huapu Y1, Y2, Y5, Y9, J1, J16, 527 ap Hangzhouhuapu 200m; Y3, J6, 81, K81, K7, 27, K27, K850 ap Yuemiao 500m; No. Y4, Y6, 28, K28, 82, K82, K807, 15, K15, K7 ap Yuquan 500m x 80 1km

▲ **Hangzhou** – Tonglu Barbizon Youth Hostel – 24587
Daqishan National Forest Park, Tonglu, Hangzhou, Zhejiang 311500.
(571) 64241960 (571) 64241666
yhachina@yahoo.com.cn
www.yhachina.com
Open Dates: Xiaoshan International 120km A Airport Bus to Hangzhou then change to Kuaike Bus to Tonglu
Hangzhou/Hangzhou East 90km 6 200m ap Xinhengji Station x 100 1 x

▲ **Huangshan** – Huangshan Hotspring Youth Hostel – 24591
Hotspring Senic Zone, Huangshan, Anhui 242709.
(559) 5585660; 5585003
(559) 5585003
yhachina@yahoo.com.cn
www.yhachina.com
Open Dates: Huangshan 60km
A ap Wenguan Huangshan 67km
x 250 1 x

▲ **Huangshan** – Huangshan International Youth Hostel – 24592
58, Beihai Rd, Tunxi District, Huangshan City, Anhui Province, 245000.
t (559) 2114522 f (559) 2114523
e yhachina@yahoo.com.cn
w www.yhachina.com
Open Dates: ✈ Huangshan International 6km Huangshan 100m x 52

▲ **Huhehaote** – Binyue International Youth Hostel 24562
Middle of Zhaowuda Road, Saihan District, Huhehaote City, Inner Mongolia, 010050.
t (471) 6605666 f (471) 4310808
w www.yhachina.com
Open Dates: ✈ Huhehaote Baita 10km 3km 21, 34, 36, 50 ap Binyue Hotel x 153 1 x 100m

▲ **Jiangmen** – Jiangmen Youth Hostel – 24534
No. 86 Ti Zhong Road, Jiangmen City, Guangdong Province, 529000 China.
t (750) 3683908 f (750) 3681908
e yhachina@yahoo.com.cn
w www.yhachina.com
Open Dates: ✈ Guangzhou Baiyun 150km Jiangmen 8km 1, 9, 10 ap Chang'anlu x 62 1 x 2km

▲ **Kangding** – Kangding Gaxiba – 24610
Kang Ding Xian, The Zangs Autonomous Prefecture, Gan Zhi, Sichuan.
t (836) 2811570; 8887721
f (836) 2811791 e kdxh@sina.com
Open Dates: Circular Bus from south to north through the Kangding City ap YH x 75 1 x

▲ **Kunming** – Kunming Camellia Youth Hostel 24535
No. 96 Dongfengdong Road, Kunming City, Yunnan Province, 650041 China.
t (871) 3163000 f (871) 3147033
e yhachina@yahoo.com.cn
w www.yhachina.com
Open Dates: ✈ Kunming International 6km A 103 ap Dongjiawan (walk westward for 3 mins) Kunming 3km 103 from the Airport ap Dongjiawan; 5, 63, 78, 89 ap Shengtiyuguan x 164 100m

Kunming – Kunming Cloudland Youth Hostel – 24602
23 Zhuan Tang Road, Kunming.
t (871) 4103777 f (871) 4103777
w www.yhachina.com
Open Dates: Open Times:
Beds: 49
Directions: ✈ Kunming International 8km A 52 to Haotang Station, 103 to Kunyifuyiynan Station then walk Kunming 4km 64 ap Yunnamribaashe Station

Kunming – Kunming Cloudland Youth Hostel

▲ **Kunming** – Kunming Youth Hostel 24511
1st Floor, Building C, Zhengxie Hotel, No. 96, Cuihunan Rd, Kunming, Yunnan.
t (871) 5175395; 5167131
f (871) 5167131
e yhachina@yahoo.com.cn
w www.yhachina.com
Open Dates: ✈ Kunming International 7km A 52 ap Xiaoximen 5km 2, 5, 52 ap Xiaoximen x 56 18km 20km

▲ **Lhasa** – Lhasa Zhengchang Dongcu International Youth Hostel – 24603
No. 10, Beijing East Rd, Lhasa, Tibet, 850000.
(891) 6330683 (891) 6330683
kittynchen@hotmail.com
Open Dates: Gongge 70km x 200

▲ **Lhasa** – Tibet Sunlight International Youth Hostel – 24588
27 Linju Road, Lhasa, Tibet, 850000 China.
(891) 6334321 (891) 6330175
beast@eyou.com www.hostel.tibet.cn
Open Dates: Gongga 97km A take a taxi (about RMB 10) from the airport
x 150

▲ **Lijiang** – Lijiang Old Town Youth Hostel – 24512
No. 44 Mishi Xiang, Xinyi Str. Dayan Town, Lijiang, Yunnan, 674100 China.
(888) 5105403; 5180124
yhachina@yahoo.com.cn
www.yhachina.com
Open Dates: Lijiang 27km A to Lijiang New Town, then walk or take a taxi to Gucheng Lijiang Express Bus Terminal (2km), walk or take 8 ap Baixinshangchang x 96

▲ **Lijiang** – Old Town Laojie Youth Hostel – 24564
No.61, Shuangshiduan, Xinhua Street, Dayan Town, Lijiang, Yunnan, 674100.
(888) 5188611 (888) 5188611
yhachina@yahoo.com.cn
www.yhachina.com
Open Dates: Lijiang 27km A to Minhang Hotel 1, 8 ap Baihuodalou (walk for 26mins) x 28

▲ **Lijiang** – Old Town Tingyuan Youth Hostel – 24565
46, Zhongyi Lane, Guangyi Street, Dayan Town, Lijiang County, Yunnan, 674100.
(888) 5102339 www.yhachina.com
Open Dates: Lijiang 25km
A Airport Bus to new town, change to 3 ap Zhongyishichang 3 ap Zhongyishichang x 32

▲ **Linfen** – Linfen Honglou International Youth Hostel – 24584
No. 7 Gongyuan Street, Linfen, Shanxi, 041000 China.
(357) 2082222 (357) 2082200
yhachina@yahoo.com.cn
www.yhachina.com
Open Dates: Taiyuan Wusu 200km Linfen 3km 1, 2, 3 ap Shanxi Shifandaxue x 38 1 x

▲ **Luoyang** – Luoyang Mingyuan Youth Hostel HI 24536
No. 20 Jiefanglu, Xigong District, Luoyang City, Henan Province, 471000
(379) 3192297; 3194668
(379) 3194668
yhachina@yahoo.com.cn
www.yhachina.com
Open Dates: Luoyang 10km
A Luoyang Railway Station 500m
Luoyang 500m 41, 55, 81 ap Gongchedaxiuchang x 60 1 x 1km

▲ **Nanhai** – Mt. Xiqiao Youth Hostel HI 24505
Yunyingqionglou, Xiqiao Mountain, Nanhai City, Guangdong, 528211.
(757) 86886799 Ext 8188
(757) 86889689
yhachina@yahoo.com.cn
www.yhachina.com
Open Dates: Guangzhou Baiyun 65km; Guangzhou Foshan 50km Guangzhou 65km; Foshan 50km Bus from Guangzhou Liuhua Station, Guangdong Province Bus Terminal or Guangzhou Bus Terminal, Guangzhou Fangcun Kengkou Subway Station to Xiqiao Bus Terminal ap Xiqiao Shan 60SW x 135 R CC 1 x 300m

▲ **Nanjing** – Nanjing Fuzimiao International Youth Hostel – 24566
No.38, Dashiba Street, Fuzimiao Nanjing, (by the side of Pingjiang Bridge, Qinghuai River).
(25) 86625133; 86624133
(25) 86624133
yhachina@yahoo.com.cn
www.yhachina.com
Open Dates: Nanjing Lukou International 20km A to Fuzimiao Zhongshan Pier 8km Nanjing 6km 1, 4, 7, 30, 31, 36, 44, 49, 301, 303, 305, 306, Y2, You 4/Tourist Bus No.4 ap Fuzimiao x 80 2 x 2km

▲ **Nanjing** – Zhongshanling Youth Hostel – 24537
No. 7 Shixianglu, Nanjing City, Jiangsu Province, 210000.
(25) 84446688; 84432615
(25) 84446688; 84432615
yhachina@yahoo.com.cn
www.yhachina.com
Open Dates: Nanjing Lukou International 60km A to Ruijinlu, then take 4 ap Jiefanglu, then take 9 ap Sifangcheng Xiaguan Harbour 31km Nanjing 18km Y1, 9 ap Sifangcheng x 43 1 x

▲ **Qingdao** – Kai Yue International Hostelling – 24609
Ji Ling Road, 31#, Qing Dao City, Shangdong.
(136) 78859848
Open Dates: Lin Ting International 30km A Airport bus to Xin Guido Hotel, then change 228 to Huang Dao Road Qing Dao-Huang Dao Harbour, take taxi to hostel (RMN 7) Qing Dao Station, (walk to hostel - 15min) 405, 223, 302, 2, 5, 320, 301 ap from Airport to Nanmen Station x 86 1 x

▲ **Qingxin** – Guangdong Sports Youth Hostel – 24568
Qingxin Hot Spring Tourism & Holiday Resort, Sankeng Town, Qingxin County, Qingyuan City, Guangdong Province, 511855.
(763) 5862622; 5862611
(763) 5862090
yhachina@yahoo.com.cn
www.yhachina.com
Open Dates: Guangzhou Baiyun 70km A to Guangzhou Provincial Bus Terminal, change bus to the Qingxin Hot Spring Holiday Resort Qingyuan Yuantan 60km Shuttle Bus every half an hour from Qingyuan Railway Station to hostel ap Qingxin Hot Spring Tourism Holiday Resort x 789 1 x

▲ **Sanya** – Sanya Blue Sky Youth Hostel – 24586
20 Dadonghai New Village, Sanya, Hainan
(898) 88182320 (898) 88211770
yhachina@yahoo.com.cn
www.yhachina.com
Open Dates: Sanya Fenghuang International 20km A to Diyi Shichang then take 202 or 2 ap Chengshijiudian 202 to Ruihai Shopping Park ap Sanya 3km x 47

▲ **Shanghai** – Hiker Youth Hostel – 24607
No. 450 Jiangxi Zhong Road, Huang pu District, Shanghai (Beijingdong Lukou).
(21) 63297889
yhachina@yahoo.com.cn
www.yhachina.com
Open Dates: Pudong 30km; Hongqiao 15km A Airport bus 3, 7 from Pudong Airport to Longyang Rd, change to U 2 ap Henanzhonglu; 925 to Renminguangchang, change to 145, 934 ap Jiangxizhonglu Waihongqiao Shanghai 8km, take 64 to Jiangxizhonglu or U to Henanzhonglu; Meilong 15km, take U to Hananzhonglu 939, 934, 921, 330, 316, 145, 64, 21, 20 ap Jiangxizhonglu 600m U 2, ap Henanzhonglu 1.2km x 120 1km

▲ **Shanghai** – Shanghai Captain Youth Hostel 24539
No. 37 Fuzhou Rd, Shanghai City, 200002.
(21) 63235053 (21) 63219331
yhachina@yahoo.com.cn
www.yhachina.com
Open Dates: Hongqiao International 15km; Pudong International 30km A from Pudong Airport ap Xincheng Hotel Waihongqiao Port 2km Shanghai 7km 928 from Hongqiao to Renmin Guangchang, then change to 71 ap Waitan; 64. From ap Jiangxi Rd; 37, 55, 65 ap Waitan 20 ap Jiangxilu 1 ap Renmin Guangchang; Line 2 ap Henanlu x 120

Shanghai – Shanghai Easy Tour Youth Hostel 24600
57 Jiangyin Road, Huangpu District, Shanghai.
(21) 63277766 (21) 63277766
wolf_chau@126.com
www.easy-tour.cn
Open Dates: Open Times:
Beds: 164
Directions: Pu Dong International 38km; Hongqiao 17km A 5 to Renmin Guangxhang, Airport to Renmin Guangchang Shanghai Internation 3km Shanghai 3km 3, 6, 37, 46, 145 ap Remnin Guangchang 1, 2 ap Remin Guangchang

Shanghai – Shanghai Easy Tour Youth Hostel

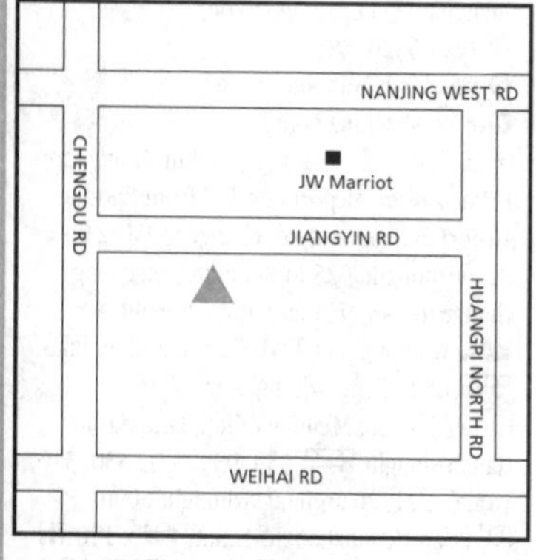

▲ **Shanghai** – Shanghai Pujiang Youth Hostel 24513
No. 15 Huang Pu Rd, Shanghai 200080.
(21) 63246388 (21) 63243179
yhachina@yahoo.com.cn
www.yhachina.com
Open Dates: Pudong International 50km; Hongqiao International 18km A Wai Tan or Shanghaidasa Wai Hongqiao 1km 5km 930, 910, 55, 61, 65, 123, 950, 928 ap Waibaiduqiao; Shanghaidasha 22, 37 ap Waibaiduqiao Line 2; ap Henanlu or Nanjingdonglu 1km x 260

Shanghai... Travel Tips

- **For budget eats check out...** Huang He Road Snack Street, Zha Pu Road Snack Street, Yunnan Road (South) Snack Street, Cheng Huang Miao Snack, Xu Jia Hui Snack
- **For great nightlife try...** Coffer Club (chain club), Rojie Disco Club, Mao Ming (South) Road Bar Street, The Bund & Nanjing Road Down Town, Heng Shan Road Bar & Club Street, Xintiandi Bar
- **Don't miss...** Yu Yuan Garden, Dong Fang Pearl (TV Tower), Jade Buddhist Temple, The Bund, Nanjing Road Down Town (shopping street), Shanghai Wild Animal Zoo, Huaihai Road Shopping Centre, Pu Dong Century Street & Century Park, Shanghai Museum, Doctor Sun Ye Sen's former residence, Evening tour on Pujiang River, Shanghai Art Museum

▲ **Shangri-La** – Diqing Tibetan Area Youth Hostel – 24569
No.98, Heping Road, Shangri-la County, Yunnan, 674400.
(887) 8228671 (887) 8228451
yhachina@yahoo.com.cn
www.yhachina.com
Open Dates: Diqing 5km A take a taxi (about 10 Yuan) from the Airport 1, 3, 5 ap Hepinglukou x 98 10km

Shangri-La – Shangri-La International Youth Hostel – 24567
North of Jiantand Dong Road, Shangri-La, Yunnan Provice 674400.
(887) 8226948 (887) 8226949
yhachina@yahoo.com.cn
www.yhachina.com
Open Dates: Shangri-la 5km, take a taxi (about RMB 20) 2 x 88 1 x

---

Wulumuqi – Xinjiang Sliver Bircbes International Youth Hostel – 24608
28#, Nanhu Road, Wulumuqi City, Xinjiang.
(991) 4881428 (991) 4881428
syb-2000@sohu.com; yhaxinjiang@hotmail.com
www.yhaxinjiang.com
Open Dates: Wulumuqi International 7km A Airport Bus to Hongshan Station, than take taxi to hostel (RMB 35) Wulumuqi Station 6km, then 62 to Dianxing Gongsi Station 26, 32, 46, 59, 61, 62, 104, 105, 152, 153 ap Dianxin Gongsi Station x 54

Wuxi – Wuxi International Youth Hostel – 24593
No. 49 Renminzhong Rd, Wuxi, Jiangsu, 214002.
(510) 2755990; 2756990
(510) 2735427
yhachina@yahoo.com.cn
www.yhachina.com
Open Dates: Wuxi Shuofang 10km Wuxi Hubin 3km Wuxi Hubin 1km 10, 25, 30, 35, 89 ap Dongmen x 46 8km

---

Xiamen – Xiamen International Youth hostel – 24599
No.41 Nanhua Road, Siming District, Xiamen City, Fujian Province 361005.
(592) 2082345 (592) 2199876
yhachina@yahoo.com.cn
www.yhachina.com
Open Dates: Xiamen Gaoqi International 18km A 1, 17, 21, 48 to Railway Station then change 37, 98 Helping Harbour 3km; Xiagu Harbour 3km Xiamen 6km 1, 17, 21, 48 from the railway station; 2, 71, 531 from Lundu Harbour ap 15, 45 x 47 1 x 300m 1.2km

---

Xi'an – Xi'an Bell Tower Youth Hostel – 24585
No. 1 Beida Street, Xi'an, Shaanxi, 710003.
(29) 87231203; 87233005
(29) 87233005
yhachina@yahoo.com.cn
www.yhachina.com
Open Dates: Xianyang International 45km A Airport Bus to Meilun Hotel, through Zhonglou Tunnel to Beidajiedongkou Xi'an 2.5km 611, 603, 201 ap Zhonglou x 160 2km

---

Xi'an – Xi'an Fenghe Youth Hostel – 24540
No. 11 Fenghe Rd, Xi'an City, Shaanxi Province, 710014.
(29) 86240349 (29) 86240349
yhachina@yahoo.com.cn
www.yhachina.com
Open Dates: Shaanxi Xianyang International 43km A Fenghelu 200m Xi'an 3km 9, 21, 202, 705 ap Fenghelu; 501 ap Gongyu x 170

Xi'an – Xi'an Shuyuan Youth Hostel
HI 24522
No. 2 Shuncheng Xi-Xiang (Lane), Inside South Gate, Xi'an City, Shaanxi Province, 71000.
(29) 87287721; 87287720
(29) 87287720
yhachina@yahoo.com.cn
www.yhachina.com
Open Dates: Shaanxi Xianyang 50km A to Zhonglou (walk south to the City Wall) 3km 603 from ; 29, 402, 600, 605, 608, 707 ap Nanmen x 96 1 x 1km

---

Xining – Qinghai Sangzhu Youth Hostel – 24595
No. 94 Huzhuzhong Rd, Xi'ning, Qinghai, 810001.
(971) 7134066; 7134077
(971) 7134068
yhachina@yahoo.com.cn
www.yhachina.com
Open Dates: Xi'ning Caojiabao 26km Xi'ning 4.2km 5, 32 ap Roulianchanglengku x 34 2.5km

▲ **Yangshuo** – Yangshuo Guihuaxiang Youth Hostel – 24596
No. 60, Guihuanan Xiang,
Weststreet Yangshuo Guilin 541900.
(773) 8820933 (773) 8820988
backstreet_hostel@hotmail.com
www.yhachina.com
Open Dates: Guilin Liangjiang International 100km Waishi 50m; Neibin 600m Guilin, (10min by bus) ap Yangshuo Bus Terminal 1km
x 29

▲ **Yangshuo** – Yangshuo Youth Hostel
HI 24515
No. 102 West Str Yangshuo, Guilin City,
Guangxi Province, 541900.
(773) 8820933 (773) 8820988
yhachina@yahoo.com.cn
www.yhachina.com
Open Dates: Guilin 120km Panshan Harbour 800m Guilin 66km from Guilin Express Bus Terminal to Yangshuo Express Bus Terminal x 72
R 600m

▲ **Yantai** – Yantai International Youth Hostel – 24589
Building 2, No. 18 Taishan Road, Yantai,
264006.
(535) 6936988 (535) 6373171
yhachina@yahoo.com.cn
www.yhachina.com
Open Dates: Yantai Huashan 32km A 21 to Pesheng Shopping Center (walk to the north for 500m) Yantai 15km Yantai 12km 21, 28, 23 ap Desheng Shangcheng, Kaifaju Yiyuan
x 137
1 x 8 P

▲ **Zhaoqing** – Mt. Dinghu International Youth Hostel HI 24502
Mt. Dinghu, Zhaoqing City,
Guangdong Province, 526040.
(758) 2621668 (758) 2621665
yhachina@yahoo.com.cn
www.yhachina.com
Open Dates: Guangzhou Baijun 80km Zhaoqing Harbour 18km Zhaoqing 18km Shuttle Bus from Guangzhou Yuexiunan Bus Terminal or No. 21 from Zhaoqing Paifang ap Dinghu Shan 18NE
x 96 R
1 x 8 P

△ ***Zhuhai** – Zhuhai Youth Hostel*
HI 24503
Zhuhai Holiday Resort, Shihua Shan,
Zhuhai S.E.Z. Guangdong, 519015.
(756) 3332038; 3333838
(756) 3333311
yhachina@yahoo.com.cn
www.yhachina.com
Open Dates: Zhuhai International 50km Jiuzhou Harbour 1km 4 from Xiangzhou stop; 26 from Jiuzhou Harbour ap Dujiacun x 20
R CC P

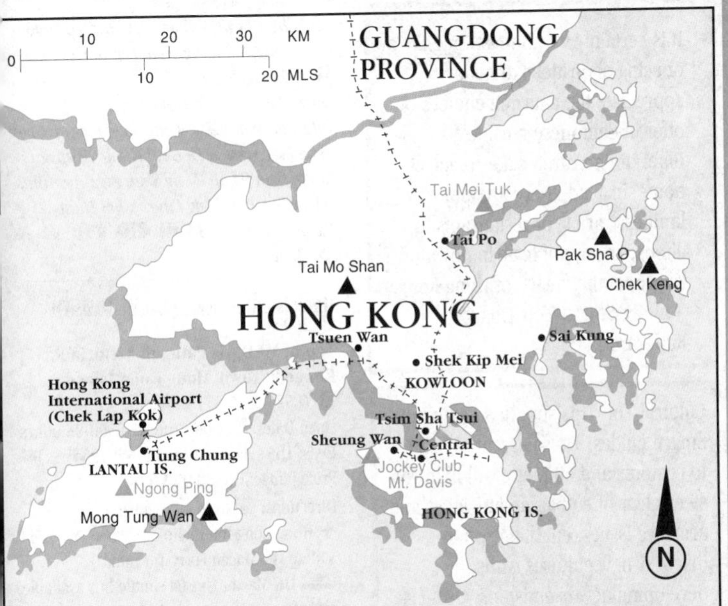

Once it was a British colony and a showcase of Western capitalism, but since 1997 when it was returned to China, it has become a special status but vital show-case of the Chinese economy, although still coming to terms with its Western democratic heritage in the context of its new status within the People's Republic. Yet the sense of urgency, industry and inventiveness of the Hong Kong industrial and economic culture continue at a pace; competition is almost a way of life in this non-stop corner of the world of only some 400 square miles.

Indeed, flying into Hong Kong, brings this so-called 'Asian Tiger' economy into clear focus as its three great assets are revealed – its magnificent harbour, its position to the world's great trading routes of the Pacific and the remarkable and in some senses, notorious, work ethic of its people. (Some people used to say that flying into the old Kaitak airport, in the middle of the city, was a miracle in itself!) And though political life may be different, the historic traditions and values continue to thrive.

A few other Top Tips from **CULTURE SMART!**:

- The people of Hong Kong speak Cantonese rather than the Mandarin of Mainland China, but it remains largely a bi-lingual country, with English the second language. Remember that when introduced, according to Chinese custom, the family name is given first.
- The handshake is universal for both men and women, as is the traditional slight bow, which accompanies it.
- Lucky symbols and 'auspicious' moments for determining dates such as a marriage or the opening of a new business are prevalent throughout China and very much in evidence in Hong Kong. Red, for example, is considered a lucky colour, as it represents happiness; so cash gifts given at New Year are always presented in red envelopes.

- It is certainly worth mastering the art of using chopsticks to better appreciate the amazing choices on offer in Cantonese cuisine. Entertaining rarely takes place at home, instead, there are almost a limitless variety of restaurants to choose from, not least in downtown Kowloon, the 'heart' of Hong Kong.
 Culture Smart! Top Tips © Kuperard 2005

Cultural Top Tips supplied by Culture Smart! guides. These essential guides to customs and etiquette will help you steer clear of embarrassing gaffes and sensitive issues, enabling you to discover new cultures whilst developing new friendships. Order online at www.culturesmartguides.co.uk

You can find out a lot more on our website - a visit to www.HIhostels.com is essential for planning your trip!

Pour en savoir plus, rendez-vous sur notre site Internet, www.HIhostels.com une visite incontournable pour préparer votre voyage!

Viele weitere Informationen auf unserer Website: www.HIhostels.com - unverzichtbar für die Reiseplanung!

Puedes averiguar mucho más en nuestro sitio web. Es imprescindible que visites la página www.HIhostels.com para planear tu viaje.

△ ***Chek Keng** – Bradbury Hall – 24006*
Chek Keng, Sai Kung, New Territories.
(852) 2328 2458
Open Dates: 12 Hong Kong International Wong Shek Pier ap Chek Keng Pier MTR Choi Hung 92 ap Sai Kung, then 94 ap Wong Shek Pier Terminus U MTR Kwun Tong Line - Choi Hung Station x 90 R 8

Hong Kong – Jockey Club Mt. Davis YH
24002
Top of Mt Davis Path, off Victoria Rd, Kennedy Town, Hong Kong Island.
(852) 2817 5715
Open Dates: 12 Open Times: 07.00-23.00hrs
Beds: 165 - 4x2 1x3 11x4 1x6 5x6+
Price Range: HK$80-90
Directions: 4W from city centre
Hong Kong International A A11, E11, N11 ap HK-Macau Ferry Terminal
HK-Macau (hostel shuttle bus available)
Airport Express Train to Central Station (walk 10mins to HK-Macau Ferry Terminal)
U Sheung Wan Station (HK-Macau Ferry Terminal exit) x 17 R TV 8

Hong Kong – Jockey Club Mt. Davis YH

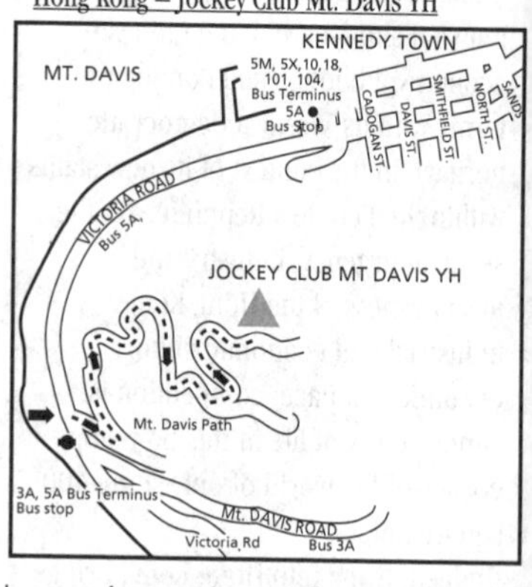

Hong Kong... Travel Tips

- **For budget eats check out...** Kennedy Town & Western District, Wan Chai District, Mong Kok District, Tsuen Wan District, Sha Tin District
- **For great nightlife try...** Lan Kwai Fong - Central District, Causeway Bay District, Wan Chai District, Tsim Sha Tsui District, Mong Kok District
- **Don't miss...** The Peak, Ocean Park, Aberdeen, Stanley, Wong Tai Sin Temple, Tsim Sha Tsui East Promenade, Po Lin Monastery & Buddha Statue, Tai O Fishing Village, Cheung Chau, Cat Street, Temple Street
- **Tourist Authority:** www.bta.org.uk

△ ***Mong Tung Wan*** *– Jockey Club Mong Tung Wan Hostel – 24007*
Mong Tung Wan, Lantau Island.
(852) 2984 1389
Open Dates: 12 Hong Kong International A S1 ap Tung Chung Terminus, A35 ap Mui Wo 7P from Mui Wo Ferry Pier x 88 R 8

▲ **Ngong Ping** – S G Davis YH HI 24005
Ngong Ping, Lantau Island.
(852) 2985 5610
Open Dates: 12 Hong Kong International A S1 ap Tung Chung Terminus 23 from Tung Chung Terminus ap Ngong Ping Terminus (walk 8 mins YH) 28SW x 46 R TV 8

△ ***Pak Sha O*** *– Pak Sha O YH – 24008*
Hoi Ha Rd, Pak Sha O, Sai Kung, New Territories.
(852) 2328 2327
Open Dates: 12 Hong Kong International 92 from MTR Choi Hung Station ap Sai Kung Town Centre, then 94 ap Ko Tong Village (1hr walk to YH along Pak Tam Rd and Hoi Ha Rd) U MTR Kwun Tong Line - Choi Hung Station x 112 R 8

▲ **Tai Mei Tuk** – Bradbury Lodge
HI 24003
66 Tai Mei Tuk Rd, Tai Mei Tuk, Tai Po, New Territories.
(852) 2662 5123
Open Dates: 12 Hong Kong International A A21 ap KCR Hung Hom KCR to Tai Po Market KMB 75K (daily), 275R (Sun & Public Holidays) ap Tai Mei Tuk Terminus (walk 4 mins with sea on right towards Water Sports Centre and YH) 16NE x 96 R TV 1 x 8

△ ***Tai Mo Shan*** *– Sze Lok Yuen – 24009*
Off Tai Mo Shan Rd, Tsuen Wan, New Territories.
(852) 2488 8188
Open Dates: 12 Hong Kong International 51 from MTR Tsuen Wan Station ap junction of Tai Mo Shan Rd & Route Twisk (walk up Tai Mo Shan Rd for 1hr to reach YH) U MTR Tsuen Wan Line - Tsuen Wan Station x 88 R 8

Costa Rica

Asociacion Red Costarricense de Albergues Juveniles,
PO Box 1355-1002, Paseo de los Estudiantes
Avenida Central, Calles 29 y 31
San José, Costa Rica.

t (506) 2348186
f (506) 2244085
e recajhi@racsa.co.cr
w www.hicr.org; www.toruma.com

A copy of the Hostel Directory for this Country can be obtained from:
The National Office

Capital:	San José
Language:	Spanish
Currency:	colón
Population:	4,500,000
Size:	50,900 sq km
Telephone Country Code:	506
eKit Access Number:	Check www.hi.ekit.com for up to date Access Numbers

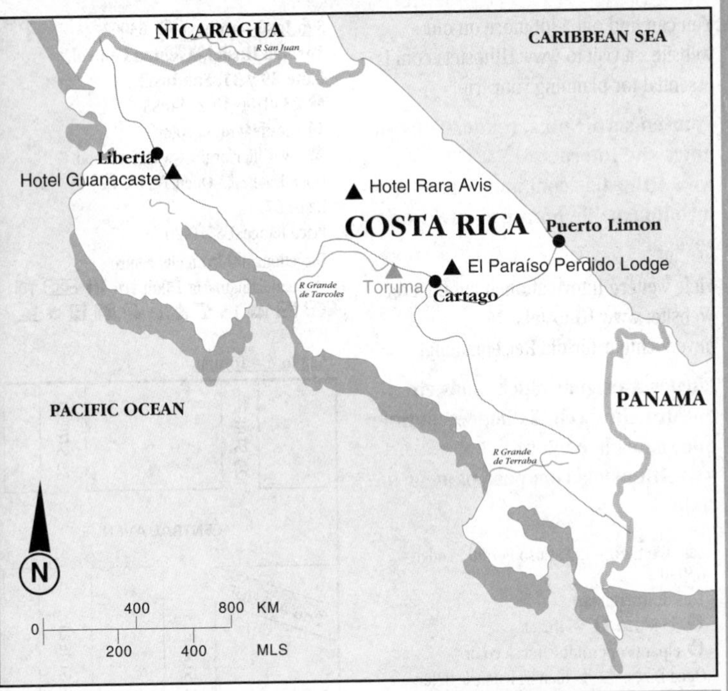

HI Suggests...

If you're looking for paradise, welcome to Costa Rica!

Situated in an area of almost 50,900 square kilometres, with no more than a five hour drive from the Pacific to the Atlantic; through national parks, biological reserves and environmental protected areas. This makes Costa Rica the main eco-tourism spot in the Americas.

Rain-forest tracks, rafting, volcano climbing, diving and mountain biking are only a few of the different activities to experience in this country, which has 5% of the world's biodiversity.

However, if you're just looking for a deserted beach to relax in the sun, Costa Rica's coast has a lot to offer as well. With a variety of waves, nature and culture there are beaches for all tastes and budgets. On the Pacific Coast, you will find the best waves while on the Caribbean Coast you will find the best diving spots and several national parks.

The weather is mild most of the year and during the high tourist season from December to April it is usually dry.

The people in Costa Rica are warm, welcoming and fully aware of the importance of tourism for the economy of the country. The "Ticos", as Costa Ricans are more commonly known, take pride on their democracy and on the importance of education.

A good suggestion would be to start your trip from the capital city of San José. The city has excellent cafés (Costa Rican coffee is among the best in the world) and restaurants where you can find excellent food at a fair price.

The Toruma Hostel in San José has a travel agency with special deals for members of Hostelling International. Packages for several destinations in Costa Rica and reservations for all the hostels in the country are available.

You can find out a lot more on our website - a visit to www.HIhostels.com is essential for planning your trip!

Pour en savoir plus, rendez-vous sur notre site Internet, www.HIhostels.com une visite incontournable pour préparer votre voyage!

Viele weitere Informationen auf unserer Website: www.HIhostels.com - unverzichtbar für die Reiseplanung!

Puedes averiguar mucho más en nuestro sitio web. Es imprescindible que visites la página www.HIhostels.com para planear tu viaje.

▲ **Cartago** – El Paraíso Perdido Lodge – 63030
Tuis de Turrialba.
T 5548026 F 5548221
E elparaisoperdido@racsa.co.cr
Open Dates: 12 ✈ Juan Santamaría 82km
x 20

▲ **Guanacaste** – Hotel Guanacaste – 63009
Liberia, Guanacaste.
T 6660085; 6664285 F 6662287
E htlguana@sol.racsa.co.cr W www.hicr.org
Open Dates: 12 ✈ Daniel Oduber (LIR) 10km
0.5W x 68 R CC

▲ **Horquetas Sarapiqui** – Rara Avis – 63012
Take a bus from San José to Horquetas de Sarapiquí. There you must be met and transported by tractor to the hostel, 15km over difficult terrain.
T 7643131; 2530575; 7644187; 2530844
F 7644187 E raraavis@racsa.co.cr
W www.rara-avis.com
Open Dates: 12 ✈ Juan Santamaría 90km 15W
x 51 R CC

San José – Toruma HI 63002
Toruma Hostel, Avenida Central, Calle 29 y 31, San José.
T 2348186 F 2244085
E recajhi@racsa.co.cr
W www.hicr.org; www.toruma.com
Open Dates: 12 Open Times:
Beds: 87
Price Range: US$10-20
Directions: 2E from city centre
✈ Juan Santamaría 15km CC TV 1 x

San José – Toruma

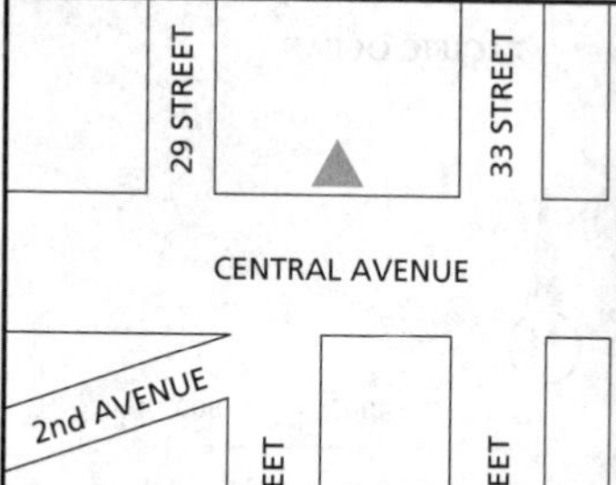

San José... Travel Tips

- **For budget eats check out...** Chaplin, Mall San Pedro, Antojitos, Spoon, Rustico
- **For great nightlife try...** Teatro Qira Tablas, El Pueblo, El Cuartel, Rio, Las Orquideas
- **Don't miss...** Sky Trek, Sky Walk, Aerial Tram, Poas Volcano, Irazu Volcano, Rafting, Sarapiqui River, Lankester Gardens, Grecia and Sarchi, Carara Biological Reserve

Croatia

Hrvatski Ferijalni i Hostelski Savez (Croatian Youth Hostel Association), Savska cesta 5/1 10000 Zagreb, Croatia.

t (385) (1) 4829294
f (385) (1) 4829296
e info@hfhs.hr
w www.hfhs.hr

Office Hours: Monday-Friday 08.00-16.00hrs

Travel Section: HFHS Travel Section, Dežmanova 9, 10000 Zagreb, Croatia.

t (385) (1) 4847474
f (385) (1) 4847472
e travelsection@hfhs.hr

Office Hours: Monday-Friday 08.00-16.00hrs

A copy of the Hostel Directory for this Country can be obtained from: The National Office

National Tourist Authority/Board:	www.croatia.hr
Capital:	Zagreb
Language:	Croatian
Currency:	Kuna (Kn)
Population:	4,784,265
Size:	56,538 sq km
Telephone Country Code:	385
eKit Access Number:	Check www.hi.ekit.com for up to date Access Numbers

HI Suggests...

"The gods wanted to crown their creation and on the last day they turned tears, stars and the sea breeze into the isles of Kornati" (George Bernard Shaw)

Croatia is indeed unique, not only for its crystal clear, clean blue sea, but also for a thousand years of different cultures that have replaced each other and sometimes assimilated in these areas. The Adriatic Sea got its name from an ancient port of the same name and is not only a deep gulf in the Mediterranean, cut into the Continent of Europe, thereby, creating the most economical trade route between Europe and the East, it is also the cradle of ancient civilizations.

Side by side in Croatia there are phenomena's, which are usually many miles apart. Within a hundred kilometres you will find the sea, densely wooded mountains and fertile plains.

Tourists will find thousands of reasons to visit Croatia. Some because they simply want to experience a pleasant holiday; others to explore its cultural and historical monuments; some visit for relaxation, sailing and to enjoy nature at its most pristine. This is a unique area in Europe for cruising with motorboats, speedboats, or sailboats, but also for enjoying the underwater world. From north to south, from the east to the west of Croatia, there are lots of bike paths as well as mountain bike tracks. The Croatian coast, abundant in natural harbours, with its countless bays, beaches, ports and marinas are a real heaven.

Croatia is also one of the few European countries, which can pride itself on its clean environment and rich flora and fauna.

Croatian cuisine is heterogeneous, and is therefore known as "the cuisine of regions". The white fish and crab of the Adriatic is the best in the world. A tantalising choice of gourmets!

- **Capital:** Zagreb (779.145 inhabitants – the administrative, cultural, academic and communication centre of the country).
- **Length of coast:** 5,835 km – including 4,058 km of island, islet and reef coastline.
- **Number of islands, islets and reefs:** 1,185. The largest islands are those of Krk and Cres. There are 67 inhabited islands.
- **Population:** The majority of the population are Croats. National minorities include Serbs, Moslems, Slovenes, Italians, Hungarians, Czechs, Slovaks, and others.
- **Official language and alphabet:** Croatian language and Latin alphabet.
- **Religions:** The majority of the population are Roman Catholics; in addition there are a number of those of Orthodox faith.

You can find out a lot more on our website - a visit to www.HIhostels.com is essential for planning your trip!

Pour en savoir plus, rendez-vous sur notre site Internet, www.HIhostels.com une visite incontournable pour préparer votre voyage!

Viele weitere Informationen auf unserer Website: www.HIhostels.com - unverzichtbar für die Reiseplanung!

Puedes averiguar mucho más en nuestro sitio web. Es imprescindible que visites la página www.HIhostels.com para planear tu viaje.

Dubrovnik HI 21004
Vinka Sagrestana 3, 20000 Dubrovnik.
T (20) 423241 F (20) 412592
e dubrovnik@hfhs.hr W www.hfhs.hr
Open Dates: 12 Open Times:
Beds: 82 - 1x2 14x4 4x6
Price Range: Kunas 75-175 € 10-23.35 BB inc

Directions: Dubrovnik 10km A Gruž Station 500m Gruž-Luka 1km #4 & 5 100m ap Montovijerna x 2 R 1 x 250m

Dubrovnik

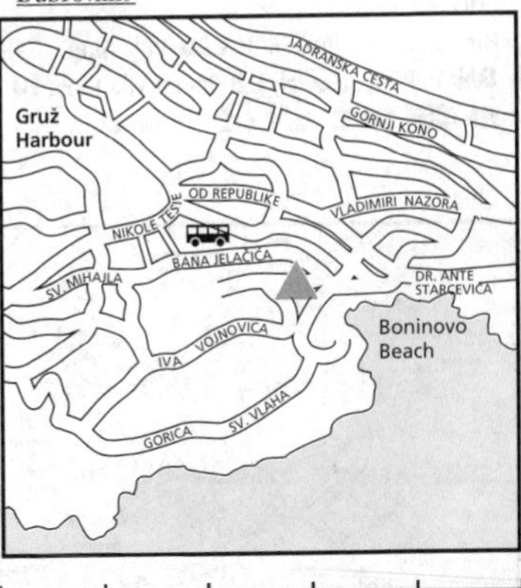

Dubrovnik... Travel Tips

- **For budget eats check out...** "Kamenice" (Old City), "Jadran" (Old City), "Mama Mia" Pizzeria (Bana Jelačića), Konoba "Amore" (Old City), "Ragusea" (Bana Jelačića)
- **For great nightlife try...** Divinae Folie Disco Club (Babin Kuk), Bana Jelačića, Old City - Stradun (Main Street), Café Bars "Trubadur" & "Be Bop" (live music & jazz), Dubrovnik Summer Festival (performances around the whole old city)
- **Don't miss...** Main street in Old Town "Placa" or "Stradun", Old City Walls/towers, Monasteries/St Blaise Church, Clock Tower & Orlando Column, Island of Mljet (National Park), Elaphite Islands, Island of Lokrum, Cavtat, Dubrovnik Summer Festival (10.07-25.08), Aquarium in St John Fort

▲ **KRK** – 21005
Dr. Vinka Vitezica 32, 51500 KRK.
(51) 220212 (51) 220212
www.hfhs.hr
Open Dates: KRK 30km 400m ap KRK x 60 R

Pula 21003
Zaljev Valsaline 4, 52 100 Pula.
(52) 391124; 391133 (52) 391106
pula@hfhs.hr www.hfhs.hr
Open Dates: Open Times:
Beds: 180
Price Range: BB inc
Directions: Pula 5km Pula 3km Pula 3km 2 200m ap Vila Idola R 1 x

Pula

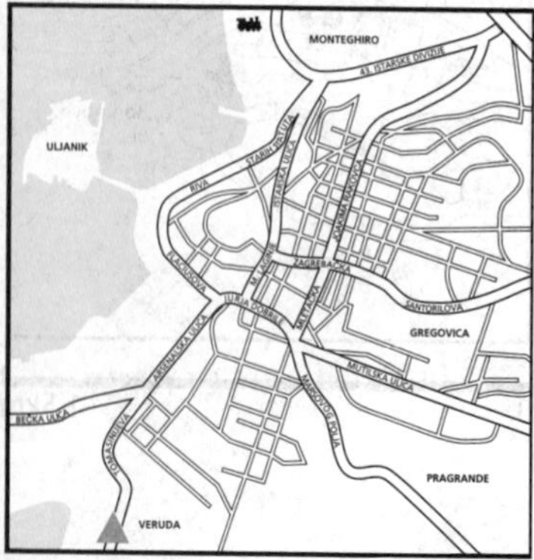

Pula... Travel Tips

- **For budget eats check out...** Restaurant Biska, Kolioba Veruda, Vodnjanka
- **For great nightlife try...** Uljanik (Disco Club), Fort Bourghignoli, Molite Serpente, Oasis Disco Club, Rock Caffe
- **Don't miss...** Amphitheater, City Walls, Kaštel (Castle), National Park Brijuni, Hesactium - Pre Roman Old City ruins, Kamenjak, City of Vodnjan (5km from Pula), Recommended to visit cities of Rovinj and Motovun, Excursions to some fortresses (information at hostel)

▲ **Punat, Island KRK** – Halugica – 21006
Novi Put 8, 51521 Punat.
(51) 854037 www.hfhs.hr
Open Dates: 01.05-30.09 KRK 40km 500m ap Punat x 90 R

▲ **Veli Lošinj** – Zlatokrila – 21007
Kaciol 26, 51551 Veli Lošinj.
(51) 236312 (51) 236312
www.hfhs.hr
Open Dates: 01.05-30.09 Mali Lošinj 10km Veli Lošinj 300m x 60 R

▲ **Zadar** 21002
Obala Kneza Trpimira 76, 23 000 Zadar.
(23) 331145 (23) 331190
zadar@hfhs.hr www.hfhs.hr
Open Dates: Zemunik 20km Zadar 4km Zadar 7km 5 100m ap Puntamika x 300 R 1 x

YOUTH HOSTEL ACCOMMODATION OUTSIDE THE ASSURED STANDARDS SCHEME

Zagreb – 21008
Petrinjska 77, 10 000 Zagreb.
(1) 4841261 (1) 4841269
zagreb@hfhs.hr www.hfhs.hr
Open Dates: Zagreb 20km Zagreb - Gl. Koloavor 300m 600m ap Zagreb x 210 R

Denmark

DANHOSTEL Danmarks Vandrerhjem
Vesterbrogade 39, DK-1620 Copenhagen V,
Denmark.

(t) (45) 33313612
(f) (45) 33313626
(e) ldv@danhostel.dk
(w) www.danhostel.dk

Office Hours: Monday-Thursday 09.00-16.00hrs;
Friday 09.00-15.00hrs

A copy of the Hostel Directory for this Country can be obtained from: The National Office, all hostels and Tourist Informations.

National Tourist Authority/Board:	www.visitdenmark.com
Capital:	Copenhagen
Language:	Danish
Currency:	kr (1 Krone = 100 øre)
Population:	5,170,000
Size:	43,069 sq km
Telephone Country Code:	45
eKit Access Number:	8088-1909

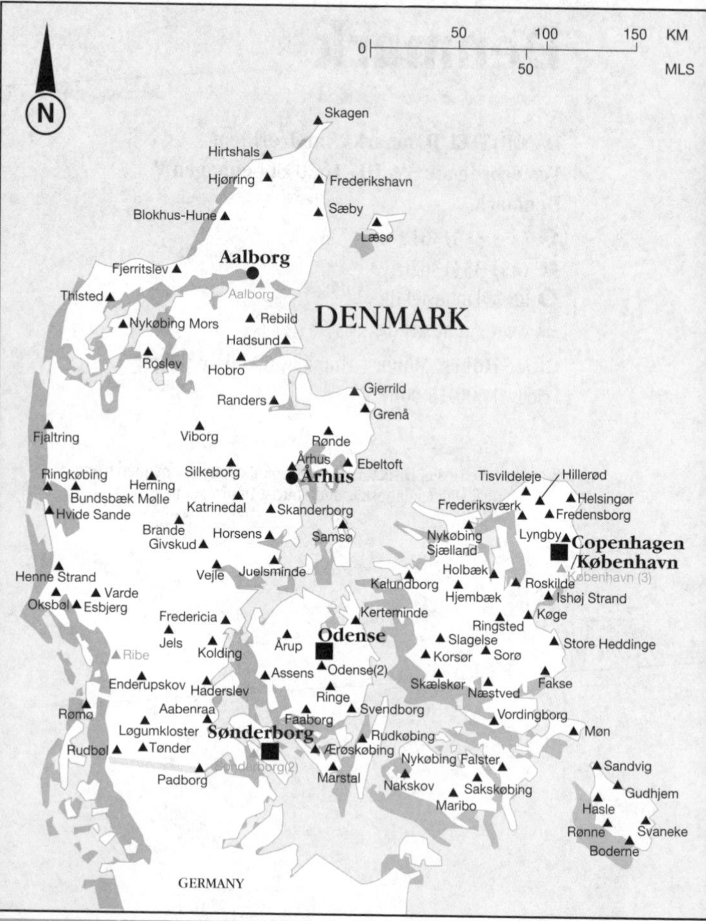

Home of the Vikings, Hans Christian Andersen and Lego it may be, but modern Denmark is a model of a polite, caring society in the twenty-first century still rejoicing in so-called old-fashioned values and being very family orientated; yet also at the forefront of design and innovation, fully engaged with new technologies. It also happens to have the highest taxes in the world. Although a member of the European Union, it has chosen to remain separate in some respects, not adopting the Euro currency, keeping the Danish Krone.

Denmark is an 'island' country, the biggest being Zealand (facing Sweden) where the capital Copenhagen is located and where about two of the five million population live, with most of the rest living on the Jutland peninsular which connects the country to the European mainland (Germany). The international airport is on yet another island nearby called Amager Island. There are nearly 500 other small islands, of which some seventy or so have small populations.

Like the rest of Scandinavia, Danes are mostly bi-lingual with English as their second 'working' language, and govern themselves through a constitutional monarchy, which continues to matter to them. Their natural resources of oil, natural gas, fish, salt and limestone enable them to develop one of the highest standards of living in Europe, with a social welfare programme second to none.

A few other Top Tips from **CULTURE SMART!:**

- Denmark is a very homogeneous place and although church-going has diminished, and divorce is increasing, almost a hundred per cent of the population belong to the state-sponsored Lutheran Church, which has helped underpin the principles of conformity and coherence as well as non-competitiveness; in turn, this can be seen in the conservative approach to dress and fashion statements generally, although the young have their own views about this and challenge what is sometimes known as the Danish 'equality complex'.
- Danes are known for being reserved and do not readily engage in small talk, which could include giving directions in the street. But once the barriers are down, you will be as welcome as any others in their circle.
- Whenever there is an excuse for a party, from christenings to what are called the 'round' anniversaries (20,30,40 etc), or other occasions, the Danes do like to make these moments memorable and apply themselves with vigour in planning and execution. Their grasp of detail is ever present and worth remembering in whatever context, and of course, they are never late!
- World famous is the Danish Smorgasbord, often seen at party-time, which includes many varieties of meat and fish, eaten with rye bread. Marinated fish, beer and snaps (40% proof and not everyone's favourite liquor!) are also widely consumed. Otherwise, French, Italian and Chinese restaurants tend to offer most of the other choices.

Cultural Top Tips supplied by Culture Smart! guides. These essential guides to customs and etiquette will help you steer clear of embarrassing gaffes and sensitive issues, enabling you to discover new cultures whilst developing new friendships. Order online at www.culturesmartguides.co.uk

You can find out a lot more on our website - a visit to www.HIhostels.com is essential for planning your trip!

Pour en savoir plus, rendez-vous sur notre site Internet, www.HIhostels.com une visite incontournable pour préparer votre voyage!

Viele weitere Informationen auf unserer Website: www.HIhostels.com - unverzichtbar für die Reiseplanung!

Puedes averiguar mucho más en nuestro sitio web. Es imprescindible que visites la página www.HIhostels.com para planear tu viaje.

▲ **Aabenraa** – DANHOSTEL Aabenraa – 16020
Sønderskovvej 100, 6200 Aabenraa.
74622699 74622939
mail@fjordlyst.dk www.fjordlyst.dk
Open Dates: 01.03-31.10 (12) Billund 100km Aabenraa 2km Rødekro 10km 3 100m x 86 R
CC (B)
400m 400m

Aalborg – DANHOSTEL Aalborg 16021
Skydebanevej 50, 9000 Aalborg.
98116044 98124711
aalborg@danhostel.dk www.bbbb.dk
Open Dates: 12 Open Times: 08.00-21.00hrs; Sun 08.00-21.00hrs
Beds: 140 - 35x4
Price Range: DKK 125 (Rooms DKK 275-600) € 16.80 (rooms € 37.16-80.64)
Directions: Aalborg 10km A 4km 60km Aalborg 3km 13, 16 500m ap railroad station x 35 R
CC (B)
4 x 500m

Aalborg – DANHOSTEL Aalborg

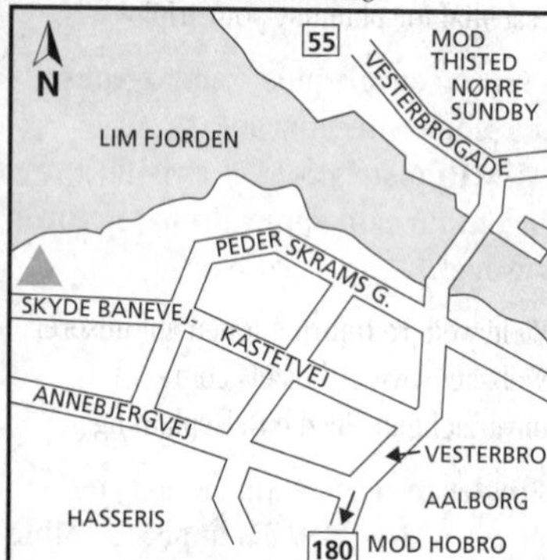

Aalborg... Travel Tips

- **For budget eats check out...** Many small restaurants in Jomfru Ane Gade, Pizzaria, 8 min walk from the hostel, More than 10 people - order food at the hostel
- **For great nightlife try...** Aalborg Congress and Culture Centre, Jomfru Ane Gade, Skraaen - music place, Aalborg Stadium, Gigantium
- **Don't miss...** Aalborg Zoo, Aalborg Museum of Modern Art, Tivoliland, Aalborg Historical Museum, Aalborg Tower, Jens Bang's Stone House from 1624, The Helligånd Monastery, Carnival in Aalborg, Aalborg Marine Museum, Aalborg Garnisons Museum

---

▲ **Aarup** – DANHOSTEL Aarup – 16022
Skolegade 3, 5560 Aarup.
64431328 64432034
aarup@danhostel.dk
www.danhostel.dk/aarup
Open Dates: 15.01-15.12 15km A 500m 35km 500m x 50 15km

▲ **Ærøskøbing** – DANHOSTEL Ærøskøbing – 16023
Smedevejen 15, 5970 Ærøskøbing.
62521044 62521644
aeroeskoebing@danhostel.dk
www.danhostel.dk/aeroeskoebing
Open Dates: 01.04-30.09 0.5S x 87
1 x

Århus – DANHOSTEL Århus – 16024
Marienlundsvej 10, 8240 Risskov.
86167298 86105560
info@aarhus-danhostel.dk
www.aarhus-danhostel.dk
Open Dates: 27.01-17.12
Open Times: 08.00-12.00hrs; 16.00-20.00hrs
Beds: 146 - 20x4 2x5 9x6
Price Range: DKK 115 (Rooms DKK 432-660)
Directions: 3N from city centre
Tirstrup-Århus 30km Århus 3km 1, 6, 8, 9, 16, 56, 58 to Marienlund 300m x 20 R CC (B)
8
500m 500m

Århus – DANHOSTEL Århus

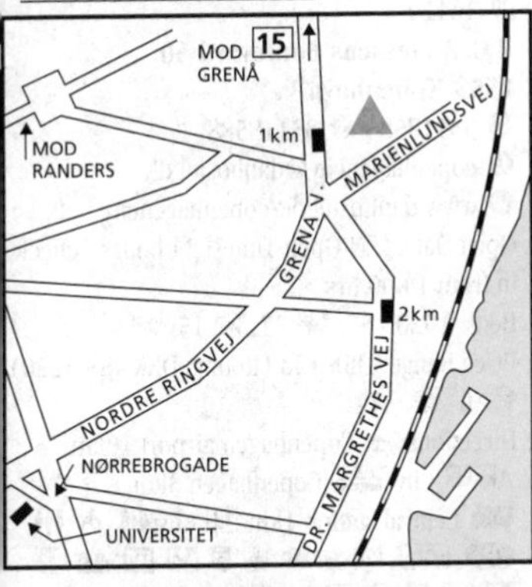

0 2km

Århus... Travel Tips

- **For budget eats check out...** Please check www.visitaarhus.dk
- **For great nightlife try...** Please check www.visitaarhus.dk
- **Don't miss...** Please check www.visitaarhus.dk

▲ **Assens** – DANHOSTEL Assens – 16025
Adelgade 26, 5610 Assens.
64711357 64715657
assensvandrerhjem@post.tele.dk
www.danhostel.dk/assens
Open Dates: 01.03-29.10 (01.02-15.12)
x 54 (B)
14km 500m

▲ **Blokhus-Hune** – DANHOSTEL Blokhus-Hune – 16026
Kirkevej 26, 9492 Blokhus.
98249180 98209005
blokhus@danhostel.dk
www.danhostel.dk/blokhus
Open Dates: 01.03-01.11 Aalborg 30km
Hirtshals 50km Brønderslev 20km
200 300m x 100
5km 2km

▲ **Boderne** – DANHOSTEL Boderne – 16027
Bodernevej 28, 3720 Aakirkeby.
56974950 56974948
boderne@danhostel.dk
www.rosengaarden.dk
Open Dates: 15.01-15.12 Bornholms Lufthavn 15km Rønne 17km 7 10m x 86
(BD) 1 x
1km 1km

▲ **Brande** – DANHOSTEL Brande – 16028
Dr. Arendsvej 2, 7330 Brande.
97182197 97182109
brande@danhostel.dk
www.danhostel.dk/brande
Open Dates: 01.03-30.11 (01.01-20.12)
800m 100m x 54

▲ **Bundsbæk Mølle** – DANHOSTEL Bundsbæk Mølle – 16096
Bundsbækvej 25, 6900 Skjern.
97362343 97362480
museum@skjern-egvad-museum.dk
www.skjern-egvad-museum.dk
Open Dates: 01.03-30.11 Billund 60km
Esbjerg 60km Skjern 9km
26 800m x 52
(B) 3 x
9km 35km

Copenhagen – DANHOSTEL Copenhagen Amager 16001
Vejlands Allé 200, 2300 København S.
32522908 32522708
copenhagen@danhostel.dk
www.copenhagenyouthhostel.dk; www.danhostel.dk/copenhagen
Open Dates: 02.01-15.12 Open Times: - check in from 14.00hrs
Beds: 524 - 72x2 76x5
Price Range: DKK 100 (Rooms DKK 325-525)
Directions: 4SE from city centre
Copenhagen 4km A 30 + 250S
Copenhagen 4km Copenhagen Central 5km 30 - direct 05.30-22.00, 4A U Metro Bella Center 10 mins walk
x 148 (B)
2km

Copenhagen – Copenhagen Amager

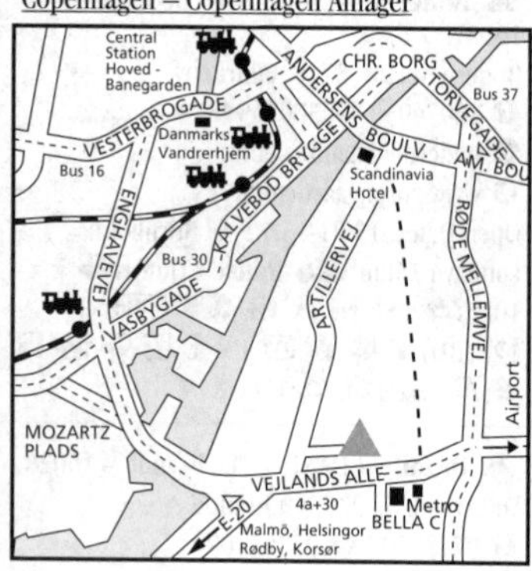

Copenhagen – DANHOSTEL Copenhagen Bellahøj 16003

Herbergvejen 8, 2700 Brønshøj.

38289715 38890210

bellahoej@danhostel.dk

www.youth-hostel.dk

Open Dates: 01.02-20.12 Open Times: 07.00 am to 10.00 pm.

Beds: 248 - 7x4 9x6 25x6+

Price Range: DKK 100 (Rooms DKK 325-700)

Directions: 5NW from city centre

Kastrup-Copenhagen 15km A 2A 200m Copenhagen 5km

Copenhagen Central 4km 2A to Tingbjerg 200m U Grøndal 500m x 7

R CC 3 x

150m

Copenhagen – Copenhagen Bellahøj

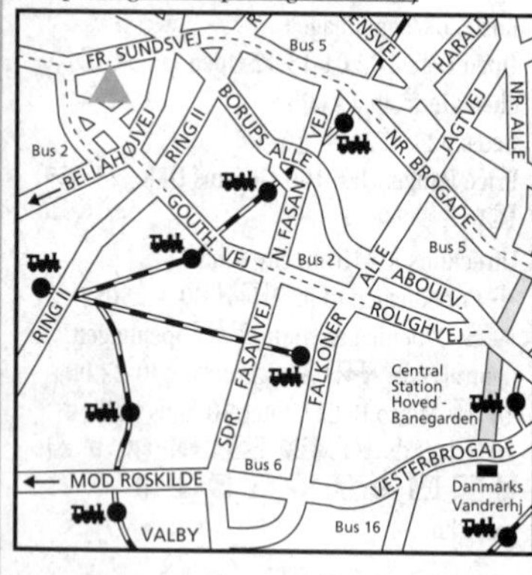

Copenhagen – DANHOSTEL Copenhagen City 16119

H.C. Andersens Boulevard 50, 1553 København V.

33118585 33118588

copenhagencity@danhostel.dk

www.danhostel.dk/copenhagencity

Open Dates: 12 Open Times: 24 hours - check in from 14.00 hrs

Beds: 1020 - 87x4 87x6 15x6+

Price Range: DKK 122 (Rooms DKK 488-1220) € 16

Directions: Copenhagen airport 10km A City Copenhagen 3km

Central station 1km U City

R CC

500m 5km

Copenhagen – Copenhagen City

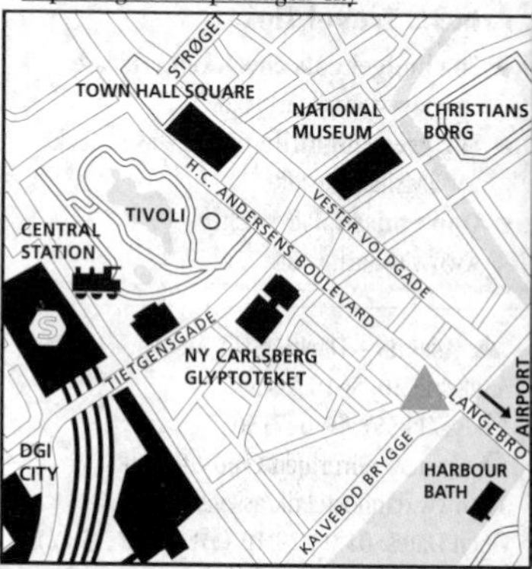

Copenhagen... Travel Tips

- **For budget eats check out...** Please check www.visitcopenhagen.dk
- **For great nightlife try...** Please check www.visitcopenhagen.dk
- **Don't miss...** Please check www.visitcopenhagen.dk

▲ **Ebeltoft** – DANHOSTEL Ebeltoft – 16029

Søndergade 43, 8400 Ebeltoft.

86342053 86342077

ebeltoft@danhostel.dk

www.danhostel.dk/ebeltoft

Open Dates: 01.02-30.11 Aarhus Airpot 15km Ebeltoft Færgehavn 5km

Aarhus 50km 123 1km x 72

R

▲ **Enderupskov** – DANHOSTEL Enderupskov – 16030
Ribe Landevej 30, Enderupskov, 6510 Gram.
t 74821711 f 74820782
e info@enderupskov.dk
w www.enderupskov.dk
Open Dates: 12 x 50 P

▲ **Esbjerg** – DANHOSTEL Esbjerg – 16031
Gl. Vardevej 80, 6700 Esbjerg.
t 75124258 f 75136833
e esbjerg@danhostel.dk
w www.esbjerg-danhostel.dk
Open Dates: 01.02-15.12 Esbjerg Airport 12km A 2.5km Esbjerg 2.5km 4 100m x 132 CC TV 3 x 8 P 200m 6km

▲ **Faaborg** – DANHOSTEL Faaborg – 16032
Grønnegade 71-72, 5600 Faaborg.
t 62611203 f 62613508
e faaborg@danhostel.dk
w www.danhostel.dk/faaborg
Open Dates: 01.04-01.11 (12) x 69 TV 1 x

▲ **Fakse** – DANHOSTEL Fakse – 16033
Østervej 4, 4640 Fakse.
t 56714181 f 56715492
e fvh@faksevandrerhjem.stam.dk
Open Dates: 08.01-20.12 Fakse Syd 2km Fakse Bystation 0.1S x 70 R CC (BD) TV 2 x 8 P 2km 600km

▲ **Fjaltring** – DANHOSTEL Fjaltring – 16034
Vestermøllevej 7, Fjaltring, 7620 Lemvig.
t 97887700 f 97887122
e fjaltring@danhostel.dk
w www.danhostel.dk/fjaltring
Open Dates: 12 Karup 60km A Lemvig 17km Thyborøn 30km Ramme 6km 491 300m x 34 R (B) TV 1 x i P 12km 500m

▲ **Fjerritslev** – DANHOSTEL Fjerritslev – 16035
Brøndumvej 14-16, 9690 Fjerritslev.
t 98211190 f 98212522
e hhf@post10.tele.dk
w www.danhostelnord.dk/fjerritslev
Open Dates: 05.01-20.12 50km A 200m 50km x 216 R CC TV 3 x i 8 P 5km

▲ **Fredensborg** – DANHOSTEL Fredensborg – 16036
Østrupvej 3, 3480 Fredensborg.
t 48480315 f 48481656
e danhostel@mail.dk
w www.fredensborghostel.dk
Open Dates: 05.01-15.12 (05.01-31.12) Copenhagen 50km Helsingør 15km Fredensborg 800m 336, 384, 733 150m U Metro in copenhagen 45km 45N x 112 R CC (BL) TV 2 x i P 600m 600m

▲ **Fredericia** – DANHOSTEL Fredericia – 16037
Vestre Ringvej 98, 7000 Fredericia.
t 75921287 f 75932905
e fredericia@danhostel.dk
w www.fredericia-danhostel.dk
Open Dates: 02.01-10.12 Billund 60km A Fredericia-Billund 2.5km Fredericia 2.5km Fredericia 2km 6 500m 2SE x 150 R CC TV 2 x 8 P 500m 2km

▲ **Frederikshavn** – DANHOSTEL Frederikshavn – 16038
Buhlsvej 6, 9900 Frederikshavn.
t 98421475 f 98426522
e frederikshavn@danhostel.dk
w www.danhostel.dk/frederikshavn
Open Dates: 01.02-20.12 Ålborg 65km A Air Taxa 2km Frederikshavn 3km Frederikshavn 1km 1NW x 130 R TV P 100km 3km

Frederiksværk – DANHOSTEL Frederiksværk – 16039
Strandgade 30, 3300 Frederiksværk.
47770725 47720766
post@strandbo.dk www.strandbo.dk
Open Dates: 01.02-30.11 Kastrup 60km Helsingør 40km Frederiksværk 500m x 75 2 x 3km 6km

Givskud – DANHOSTEL Givskud – 16040
Løveparkvej 2b, Givskud, 7323 Give.
75730500 75730530
givskud@danhostel.dk
www.danhostel-givskud.dk
Open Dates: 15.01-01.12 25km A 200m Jelling 8km 211, 117 200m x 136 (BD) 20km 20km

Gjerrild – DANHOSTEL Gjerrild – 16041
Dyrehavevej 9, Gjerrild, 8500 Grenå.
86384199 86384302
djursvold@post.tele.dk
www.danhostel-gjerrild.dk
Open Dates: 01.04-30.09 (02.01-22.12) Århus 35km Grenå 15km Grenå 12km 352 200m ap Grenå x 92 (BD) 2 x 3.6km 3.6km

Grenå – DANHOSTEL Grenå – 16042
Ydesvej 4, 8500 Grenå.
86326622 86321248
danhostel-grenaa-vandrerhjem@worldonline.dk www.danhostel.dk/grenaa
Open Dates: 09.01-20.12 Århus 20km A Grenå Busstation 2km Grenå Havn 2km Grenå Station 2km x 108 6 x 2km 2km

Gudhjem – DANHOSTEL Gudhjem – 16043
Ejner Mikkelsens Vej 14, 3760 Gudhjem.
56485035 56485635
dgh@mail.tele.dk
www.danhostel-gudhjem.dk
Open Dates: (01.04-01.11) Bornholm 24km Rønne 24km Copenhagen Central Station 150km Gudhjem 3 ap Gudhjem Harbour x 220 1km 1km

Haderslev – DANHOSTEL Haderslev – 16044
Erlevvej 34, 6100 Haderslev.
74521347 74521364
haderslev@danhostel.dk
www.danhostel.dk/haderslev
Open Dates: 01.02-30.11 Vojens 15km Haderslev centrum 2km x 120 2km 10km

Hadsund – DANHOSTEL Hadsund – 16045
Stadionvej 33, 9560 Hadsund.
98574345 98574356
hadsund@danhostel.dk
www.danhostel.dk/hadsund
Open Dates: 01.04.-31.10 (01.03-31.10) 48km A 1.5km Hobro 24km Hobro-Hadsund 1km x 48 1km

Hasle – DANHOSTEL Hasle – 16046
Fælledvej 28, 3790 Hasle.
56964175 56964145
info@dh-hasle.dk www.dh-hasle.dk
Open Dates: 01.06-01.09 (01.04-01.10) 15km Rønne 12km x 92 (B)

Helsingør – DANHOSTEL Helsingør – 16004
Ndr Strandvej 24, 3000 Helsingør.
49211640 49211399
helsingor@danhostel.dk
www.helsingorhostel.dk
Open Dates: 01.02-30.11
Open Times: 08.00-12.00hrs; 15.00-21.00hrs (01.05-30.09); 08.00-12.00hrs; 15.00-18.00hrs (01.02-30.04 & 01.10-30.04)
Beds: 180 - 3x2 2x3 19x4 7x5 3x6 6x6+
Price Range: DKK 120 (Rooms DKK 350-650)
Directions: 1.5NW from city centre
Copenhagen 60km
Helsingborg-Helsingør 2km
Helsingør 2km 340 200m ap Højstrup 200m
Helsingør-Hornbaek-Gillelejebanen 200m ap Højstrup x 38 R CC (B) TV 3 x

Helsingør – DANHOSTEL Helsingør

Helsingør... Travel Tips

- **For budget eats check out...** Café Olai, Sommariva, Kronborg Havbad, Italia, Rendez Vous
- **For great nightlife try...** Buddy Holly, Café Manhattan, Rådmand Davids Hus, Club Retro
- **Don't miss...** Kronborg Castle, Bakken Amusement Park, Louisiana Museum of Modern Art, Frederiksborg Castle, North Sealand Summerpark, Fredensborg Castle, Copenhagen (Tivoli, Amalienborg etc.)

△ ***Henne Strand*** *– DANHOSTEL Henne Strand – 16047*
Strandvejen 458, 6854 Henne Strand.
75255075 75255074
hennestrand@danhostel.dk
www.danhostel.dk/hennestrand
Open Dates: 01.06-01.09 (15.04-15.10)
Esbjerg 40km Esbjerg 45km
Henne 9km Henne Strand 300m
x 44 R (B) 300m 300m

▲ **Herning** – DANHOSTEL Herning – 16048
Holingknuden 2, Holing, 7400 Herning.
97123144 97216169
danhostel.herning@email.dk
www.danhostel.dk/herning
Open Dates: 12 Karup 25km
Herning 3km 1 100m 3NW
x 112 R CC (B) TV 3 x 500m 500m

▲ **Hillerød** – DANHOSTEL Hillerød – 16120
Lejrskolevej 4, 3400 Hillerød
48261986 48269786
info@hillerodhostel.dk
www.hillerodhostel.dk
Open Dates: 12 Copenhagen 40km
Helsingør 25km Hillerød 2km
702, 701 150m U Metro in Copenhagen 40N x 104 R CC TV 5 x 2km

▲ **Hirtshals** – DANHOSTEL Hirtshals – 16049
Kystvejen 53, 9850 Hirtshals.
98941248 98945655
danhostel.hirtshals@mail.dk
www.danhostelnord.dk/hirtshals
Open Dates: 01.03-31.10 Aalborg 60km
A Hirtshals Bus station 800m
Hirtshals - Norway 1km Hirtshals station 800m Hirtshals Bus station 800m x 73 R CC (BD) TV 8 100m 100m

▲ **Hjembæk** – DANHOSTEL Hjembæk – 16050
Tornbrinken 2, Hjembæk, 4450 Jyderup.
59268181 59216656
vandrerhjem@svp.dk
www.danhostel.dk/hjembaek
Open Dates: 12 25km 7km
x 50 R CC
7km

▲ **Hjørring** – DANHOSTEL Hjørring – 16051
Thomas Morildsvej, 9800 Hjørring.
98926700 98901550
danhostel.hjoerring@adr.dk
www.danhostelnord.dk/hjoerring
Open Dates: 01.03-01.10 Aalborg Airport (AAL) 45km Hirtshals 40km
Hjørring 2km Hjørring 2km 2E
x 140 R CC
TV 2 x i P
13km

▲ **Hobro** – DANHOSTEL Hobro – 16052
Amerikavej 24, 9500 Hobro.
98521847 98511847
danhostel.hobro@adr.dk
www.danhostelnord.dk/hobro
Open Dates: 06.01-15.12 x 106
CC TV 2 x i 8 P

▲ **Holbæk** – DANHOSTEL Holbæk – 16053
Ahlgade 1B, 4300 Holbæk.
59442919 59439485
vandrerhjem@sidesporet.dk
www.sidesporet.dk/vandrerhjem
Open Dates: 05.01-20.12 Kastrup 65km
Oroe Havn 200m Holbaek 500m
Holbaek station 500m ap Holbaek station x 76 R CC
TV 3 x i P
500m

▲ **Horsens** – DANHOSTEL Horsens – 16054
Flintebakken 150, 8700 Horsens.
75616777 75610871
horsens@danhostel.dk
www.danhostelhorsens.dk
Open Dates: 15.01-15.12 Billund 70km
Horsens 2.5km Local bus for the station 150m x 114 CC
(B) TV 2 x P
700m 1.5km

▲ **Hvide Sande** – DANHOSTEL Hvide Sande – 16055
Numitvej 5, 6960 Hvide Sande.
97312105 97312196
danhostel@hvidesande.dk
www.hvidesande.dk/danhostel
Open Dates: 20.01-20.12 (12) Billund 100km Ringkøbing 22km 58
x 88 (B) TV
P 100m 1km

<u>Ishøj – DANHOSTEL Ishøj Strand</u> – 16056
Ishøj Strandvej 13, 2635 Ishøj.
43535015 43535045
ishoj@danhostel.dk
www.danhostel.dk/ishoj
Open Dates: 03.01-20.12
Open Times: 08.00 -12.00 and 14.00 - 18.00
Beds: 229
Price Range: DKK 118 (Rooms DKK 460)
Directions: 0.8W from city centre
Copenhagen 20km A 500m
Copenhagen 20km Ishøj 1km
300S, 121, 174E, 94N 50m x 40
R CC (B) TV 3 x
8 P 800m 800m

<u>Ishøj – DANHOSTEL Ishøj Strand</u>

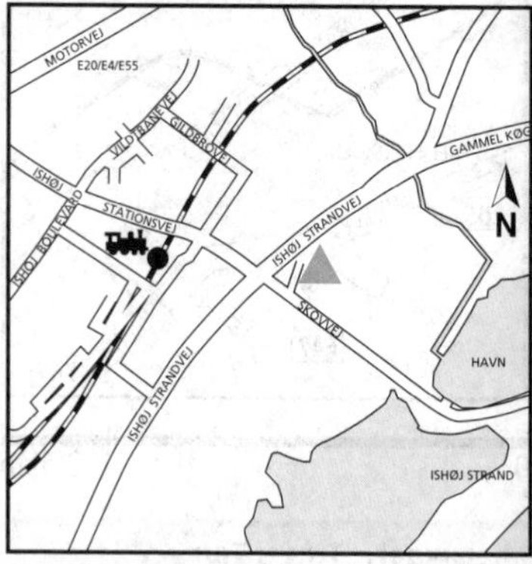

Ishøj... Travel Tips

- **For budget eats check out...** Café L'amore, Kabyssen, McDonalds, Hummeren
- **For great nightlife try...** Ishøj Bio, Copenhagen Central, Portalen (Hundige Bycenter), Ritz (Køge), Gordon Bleu (Ishøj Bycenter)
- **Don't miss...** Arken - Museum for Modern Art, Ishøj Yacht Harbour, Ishøj Beach, 37km cycle path network, Viking Museum (Roskilde), Copenhagen (Tivoli, Little Mermaid etc.)

Jels – DANHOSTEL Jels – 16058
Ørstedvej 10, Jels, 6630 Rødding.
74552869 74553107 info@jicv.dk
jicv.dk
Open Dates: 03.01-22.12 Billund 45km
Vamdrup 10km 47, 55, 38
x 88
3 x

Juelsminde – DANHOSTEL Juelsminde – 16059
Rousthøjs Allé 1, 7130 Juelsminde.
75693066 75693957; 75693130
jlc@juelsminde.dk
www.danhostel.dk/juelsminde
Open Dates: 01.05-30.09 (31.10-30.04)
Billund 60km Århus 70km
Horsens 25km 102, 103, 105
x 68 (B)
1 x 200m
200m

Kalundborg – DANHOSTEL Kalundborg – 16060
Stadion Alle 5, 4400 Kalundborg.
59561366 59564626
kalundborg@danhostel.dk
www.fridage.dk
Open Dates: Kalundborg 1km
Kalundborg 1km 202 50m 1W
x 118
3 x
300m 500m

Katrinedal – DANHOSTEL Katrinedal – 16061
Vellingvej 53, Katrinedal, 8654 Bryrup.
75756146 75757810
mail@katrinedal-vandrerhjem.dk
www.katrinedal-vandrerhjem.dk
Open Dates: 01.06-01.09 (01.03-01.12)
215 200m x 64

Kerteminde – DANHOSTEL Kerteminde – 16062
Skovvej 46, 5300 Kerteminde.
65323929 65323924
info@dkhostel.dk www.dkhostel.dk
Open Dates: 03.01-16.12 (03.01-16.12)
Odense 20km 890 1km x 90
3 x
500m 500m

Køge – DANHOSTEL Køge – 16064
Vamdrupvej 1, 4600 Køge.
56676650 56660869
koegedanhostel@koegekom.dk
www.danhostel.dk/koege
Open Dates: 01.03-01.12 (01.01-15.12)
Copenhagen 38km Køge Køge, Ølby 210 300m 2.5W x 74
2 x
3km 3km

Kolding – DANHOSTEL Kolding – 16063
Ørnsborgvej 10, 6000 Kolding.
75509140 75509151
kolding@danhostel.dk
www.danhostel.dk/kolding
Open Dates: 01.02-30-11 Billund 37km
A Kolding 1km Kolding 1.9km
Kolding 300m x 117
1km 3km

Korsør – DANHOSTEL Korsør – 16065
Svenstrup Strandvej 3, 4220 Korsør.
58380502 58381509
korsoer@danhostel.dk
www.svenstrupgaard.dk
Open Dates: Copenhagen 100km
Korsør 2.8km 35 400m 3.5NE
x 65
8 40m
400m

Læsø – DANHOSTEL Læsø – 16067
Lærkevej 6, Vesterø Havn, 9940 Læsø.
98499195 98499160
ts@laesoe-vandrerhjem.dk
www.laesoe-vandrerhjem.dk
Open Dates: 01.05-30.09 10km
A 100m 200m x 94
(B)

Løgumkloster – DANHOSTEL Løgumkloster – 16068
Vænget 28, 6240 Løgumkloster.
74743618 74743518
www.danhostel.dk/loegumkloster
Open Dates: 12.02-12.12 x 42

▲ **Lyngby** – DANHOSTEL Lyngby – 16066
Rådvad 1, 2800 Lyngby.
45803074 45803032
lyngby@danhostel.dk
www.lyngbyhostel.dk
Open Dates: 01.04-17.10 (31.01-15.12)
30km A 5km Lyngby Station
182-183 x 94
2 x 3km
3km

▲ **Maribo** – DANHOSTEL Maribo – 16069
Sdr Boulevard 82B, 4930 Maribo.
54783314 54783265
maribo@danhostel.dk
www.danhostel.dk/maribo
Open Dates: 01.02-19.12 150km
Rødby - Puttgarden 15km Maribo 2km 2 x 96
(BL)
12km

▲ **Marstal** – DANHOSTEL Marstal – 16070
Færgestræde 29, 5960 Marstal.
63526358 63526359
danhostel@marstal.dk
www.danhostel.dk/marstal
Open Dates: 01.04-21.10 (01.04-21.10)
Marstal 500m 0.5S x 82
(B) 1km
700m

▲ **Møn** – DANHOSTEL Møn – 16071
Langebjergvej 1, 4791 Borre.
55812030 55812818
moen@danhostel.dk
www.danhostel.dk/moen
Open Dates: 01.05-15.09 Copenhagen 130km Rødby 90km Vordingborg 45km Magleby 2.5km x 105
(B) 5km

▲ **Næstved** – DANHOSTEL Næstved – 16076
Præstøvej 65, 4700 Næstved.
55722091 55725645
naestved@danhostel.dk
www.danhostelnaestved.dk
Open Dates: 15.01-15.12 Copenhagen 87km A Copenhagen 87km
Næstved 1km Næstved 1km
4 200m x 147
4 x
1km 10km

▲ **Nakskov** – DANHOSTEL Nakskov – 16072
Branderslevvej 11, 4900 Nakskov.
54922434 54923367
nakskov@danhostel.dk
www.danhostel.dk/nakskov
Open Dates: 12 Nakskov 4km 800 100m x 60
40 x
4km 6km

▲ **Nykøbing Falster (Falster)** – DANHOSTEL Nykøbing Falster – 16073
Østre Alle 110, 4800 Nykøbing Falster.
54856699 54823242
nyk.f@danhostel.dk
www.danhostel.dk/nykoebingfalster
Open Dates: 15.01-15.12 108km
A 1km 25km 1km
10m x 94 (B)
500m 10km

▲ **Nykøbing Mors (Jutland)** – DANHOSTEL Nykøbing Mors – 16074
Øroddevej 15, 7900 Nykøbing Mors.
97720617 97720776
danhostel.nyk.mors@adr.dk
www.danhostelnord.dk/mors
Open Dates: 01.03-30.11 Skive or Thisted 30km 40, 96 2km x 141
2 x 8

▲ **Nykøbing Sjælland (Sealand)** – DANHOSTEL Nykøbing Sjælland – 16075
Egebjergvej 162, 4500 Nykøbing Sj.
59930062 59930162
vandrerhjem@odsherred-naturskole.dk
Open Dates: 01.02-05.12 Kastrup 120km
Rørvig 11km, Odden Færgehavn 27km
Nykøbing Sj. 3.5km 66 50m
x 48 (B)
50 x 500m
500m

Odense – DANHOSTEL Odense City – 16014
Østre Stationvej 31, 5000 Odense.
☎ 63110425 ℻ 63113520
W www.cityhostel.dk
Open Dates: 15.01-30.11
Open Times: 08.00-12.00hrs; 16.00-20.00hrs (Summer 21.00hrs)
Beds: 140
Price Range: DKK 122 (Rooms DKK 488-732)
Directions: 0.1W from city centre
✈ Billund 75km A 🚌 200m 🚆 Odense 100m (R) (CC) (BL)
2km 17km

Odense – DANHOSTEL Odense City

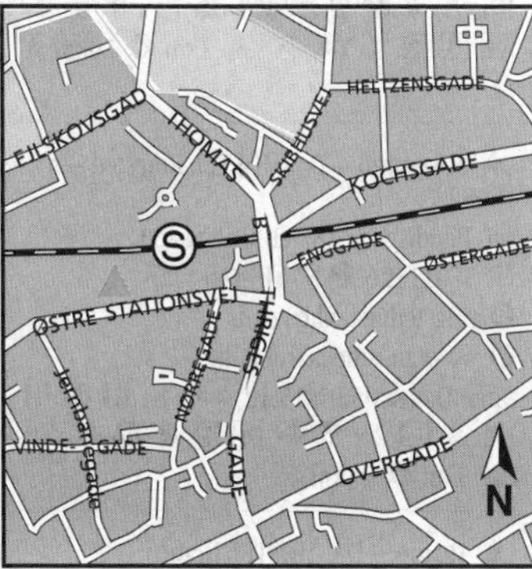

▲ **Odense** – DANHOSTEL Odense Kragsbjerggaard – 16011
Kragsbjergvej 121, 5230 Odense M.
☎ 66130425 ℻ 65912863
e odense@danhostel.dk
W www.odense-danhostel.dk
Open Dates: 01.03-30.11 (15.01-30.11)
✈ Billund 75km A 🚌 from railway station also train to Copenhagen 75 min. 2.5km
🚆 Odense 2.5km 🚌 61, 62 200m ap Munkebjerg Plads (Vandrerhjemmet) 2SE
x 170 (R) (CC) (B)
3 x
2km 17km

Odense... Travel Tips

- **For budget eats check out...** Railway Station restaurants, Froggy, Café Oscar (Mexican), Restaurant Djengis Khan, The Cinema Café
- **For great nightlife try...** Music house "City Arkaden", Rytmeposten, Music-house Oscar, Jazz-house Dexter, Ryans Pub
- **Don't miss...** Odense Zoo, Egeskov Renaissance Castle, The H.C. Andersen Museum, Fyrtøjet culture-house (for children), Den fynske landsby open-air museum (Funen), The Danish Railway Museum, The Fjord & Belt-centre, Kunsthallen Brandts Klædefabrik Art Museum, Odense small river cruise, Sydfyn Bird and Nature Park

▲ **Oksbøl** – DANHOSTEL Oksbøl – 16077
Præstegårdsvej 21, 6840 Oksbøl.
☎ 75271877 ℻ 75272544
e oksboel@danhostel.dk
W www.danhostel.dk/oksboel
Open Dates: 15.01-31.12 ✈ Billund 80km
⛴ Esbjerg 25km 🚆 Oksbøl 1km 🚌 ap Oksbøl x 107 (R) (CC)
2 x
500m 10km

▲ **Padborg** – DANHOSTEL Padborg – 16116
Lyren 2, 6330 Padborg.
☎ 74670003 ℻ 74673967
e padborg@danhostel.dk
W www.danhostel.dk/padborg
Open Dates: ✈ 35km 🚆 3.5km
🚌 2km x 48 (CC)
2.1km 6km

▲ **Randers** – DANHOSTEL Randers – 16078
Gethersvej 1, 8900 Randers.
☎ 86425044 ℻ 86419854
e randers.danhostel@adr.dk
W www.bbbb.dk
Open Dates: ✈ Aarhus (Tirstrup) 35km
A 🚌 Randers 1km ⛴ Ebeltoft - Odden 42km 🚆 Randers 600m 🚌 4, 5 300m ap Værket 0.5NW x 136 (R) (CC)
(B) 4 x
3.5km 35km

Rebild – DANHOSTEL Rebild – 16079
Rebildvej 23, Rebild, 9520 Skørping.
98391340 98392740
rebild@danhostel.dk
www.danhostel.dk/rebild
Open Dates: 01.02-30.11 Aalborg 30km
Skørping 1.8km 104 200m
x 91 (B)
1 x 5km 15km

Ribe – DANHOSTEL Ribe 16008
Sct. Pedersgade 16, 6760 Ribe.
75420620 75424288
ribe@danhostel.dk
www.danhostel-ribe.dk
Open Dates: 01.02-30.11
Open Times: 08.00-12.00hrs; 16.00-18.00hrs
Beds: 170 - 10x2 18x4 12x5
Price Range: DKK 122 (Rooms DKK 320-580) € 16.82 (Rooms 44.14-80.00)
Directions: Billund 55km Esbjerg 35km Ribe 500m Ribe 500m ap Ribe Bus Station x 40
(B) 4 x
1km

Ribe – DANHOSTEL Ribe

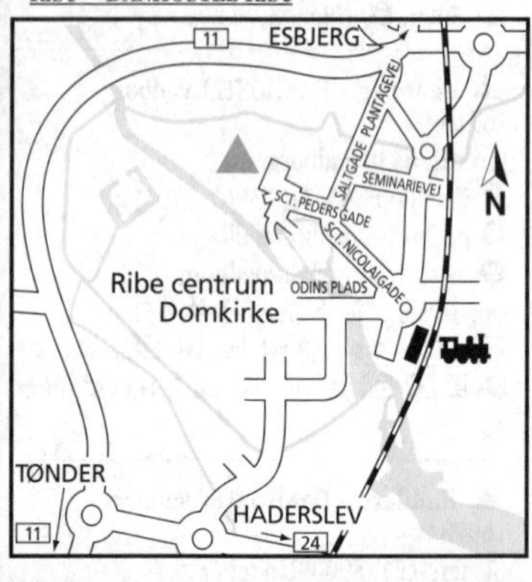

Ribe... Travel Tips

- **For budget eats check out...** Ask for the list at the reception
- **For great nightlife try...** Ask for the list at the reception
- **Don't miss...** Ribe Cathedral, The Ribe Viking Centre, Ribe Old Town, Guided tours with the watchman at 10pm (01.05-15.09), Ribe Art Museum, The Wadden Sea Museum (01.02-30.11)

Ringe – DANHOSTEL Ringe – 16080
Søvej 34, 5750 Ringe.
62622151 62622154
mfc@midtfyns-fritidscenter.dk
www.midtfyns-fritidscenter.dk
Open Dates: 05.01-16.12 25km
500m 500m x 46

Ringkøbing – DANHOSTEL Ringkøbing – 16081
Kirkevej 28, 6950 Ringkøbing.
97322455 97324959 rofi@rofi.dk
www.rofi.dk
Open Dates: Billund or Karup 60km
Ringkøbing 2km Ringkøbing 2km
1.5SW x 132
(B) 12 x
2km 10km

Ringsted – DANHOSTEL Ringsted – 16082
Sct. Bendtsgade 18, 4100 Ringsted.
57611526 57613426
ringsted@danhostel.dk
www.amtstuegaarden.dk
Open Dates: 05.01-15.12 x 84
2 x
5km 25km

Rømø – DANHOSTEL Rømø Vandrerhjem – 16088
Lyngvejen 7, 6792 Rømø.
74755188 74755187
romo@danhostel.dk
www.danhostel.dk/romo
Open Dates: 15.03-01.11 Billund 100km
Rømø Havn (Daily several connections tol Sylt, Germany) 1km Skærbæk Station 15km Sydbus rute 29 300m
ap Skærbæk Station x 92
1 x
2km 2km

Rønde – DANHOSTEL Rønde – 16089
Grenåvej 10B, 8410 Rønde.
86371108 86371128
roende@danhostel.dk
www.danhostel.dk/roende
Open Dates: 10km Nappedam 3km Mørke 10km 1km x 70
3km 3km

▲ **Rønne** – DANHOSTEL Rønne – 16090
Arsenalvej 12, 3700 Rønne.
Ⓣ 56951340 Ⓕ 56950132
Ⓔ roenne@danhostel.dk
Ⓦ www.danhostel-roenne.dk
Open Dates: 01.04-23.10 ✈ Rønne 4km
⛴ Rønne 1.5km [1S] x 140
(B)
200m

Roskilde – DANHOSTEL Roskilde – 16083
Vindeboder 7, 4000 Roskilde.
Ⓣ 46352184 Ⓕ 46326690
Ⓔ roskilde@danhostel.dk Ⓦ www.rova.dk
Open Dates: [12] Open Times: 07.00-22.00hrs (20.00hrs in winter)
Beds: 168 - 16x3 8x4 8x5 8x6
Price Range: DKK 120 (Rooms DKK 400-690) € 16 (Rooms € 50-92)
Directions: [1N] from city centre
✈ Copenhagen 35km, Roskilde 7km
A Airport train (direct connection) 1.5km Roskilde 1.5km 100m
x 40 CC
1 x 2.5km 4km

Roskilde – DANHOSTEL Roskilde

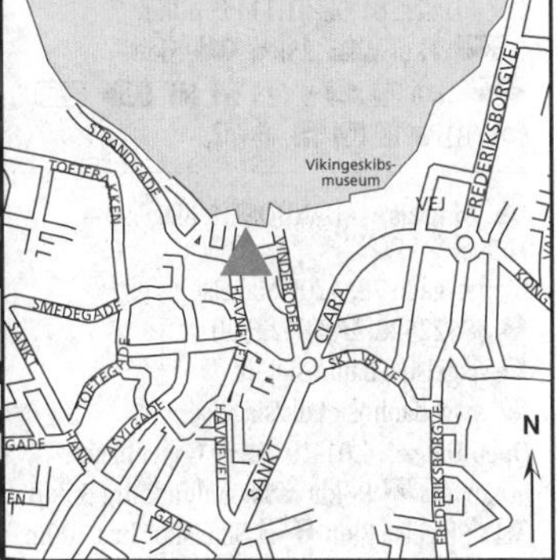

Roskilde... Travel Tips

- **For budget eats check out...** Snekken, Jensens Bøfhus, Rådhuskælderen, Philis (Turkish), Bryggergaarden
- **For great nightlife try...** Lots of pubs, clubs, cafés in town centre, Gimle café (centre)
- **Don't miss...** The Cathedral & Sepulchral Church, Viking Ship Museum & Museum Island with workshop & sailing trips, Lejre Research Centre - living past (Iron age village and more), Roskilde Festival (Rock Festival end of June every year), Ledreborg Palace & Park with giant maze, Roskilde Museum, Old Grocers shops with sale of delicacies, Hedeland Veteran Railway & mini railway, Tramway Museum, Tadre Water Mill

▲ **Roslev** – DANHOSTEL Roslev – 16084
Viumvej 8, 7870 Roslev.
Ⓣ 97571385 Ⓕ 97572052
Ⓔ roslev@danhostel.dk
Ⓦ www.danhostelnord.dk/roslev - www.danhostel.dk/roslev
Open Dates: [12] ([12]) Skive 17km
Roslev 200m x 107
(BD) 3 x
4km 4km

▲ **Rudbøl** – DANHOSTEL Rudbøl – 16085
Rudbølvej 19-21, Rudbøl, 6280 Højer.
Ⓣ 74738298 Ⓕ 74738035
Ⓔ danhostelrudb@mail.tele.dk
Ⓦ www.danhostel.dk/rudboel; www.rudboel-danhostel.dk
Open Dates: 01.03-31.10 (01.02-01.12)
✈ Hamburg (D), Billund(DK) 200km
⛴ Esbjerg (DK) 80 km, Hamburg (D) 230km Klanxbüll (D), Tønder (DK) 10km x 54
5km 40km

▲ **Rudkøbing** – DANHOSTEL Rudkøbing – 16086
Engdraget 11, 5900 Rudkøbing.
Ⓣ 62511830 Ⓕ 97542376
Ⓔ rudkobing@danhostel.dk
Ⓦ www.rudkoebingvandrerhjem.dk
Open Dates: 01.04-31.10 ([12])
⛴ Spodsbjerg 8km Svendborg 20km
800, 910 800m x 64
1 x
500m 500m

▲ **Sæby** – DANHOSTEL Sæby – 16104
Sæbygaardsvej 32, 9300 Sæby.
t 98463650 f 98467630
e sabyfri@internord.dk
w www.saebyfritidscenter.dk
Open Dates: 02.01-23.12 (group) ✈ Aalborg 50km A bus Sæby Bus Station 1km ferry Frederikshavn: Stena Line, Color Line, Læsø 12km train Frederikshavn 12km bus 73 200m 0.8NW bed x 166 R 2 x 12km 1.5km

▲ **Sakskøbing** – DANHOSTEL Sakskøbing – 16091
Saxe's alle 10, 4990 Sakskøbing.
t 54706045 f 54706041
e danhostel@sakskoebing-vandrerhjem.dk
w www.sakskoebing-vandrerhjem.dk
Open Dates: 20.01-19.12 bed x 78 R CC (BD) 1 x

▲ **Samsø** – DANHOSTEL Samsø – 16092
Klintevej 8, Ballen, 8305 Samsø.
t 86592044 f 86592343
e samsoe@danhostel.dk
w www.danhostel.dk/samsoe
Open Dates: 01.04-01.11
ferry Kalundborg-Kolby Kås, Hou-Sælvig 8km bus 300m bed x 108 (BL) 10m

▲ **Sandvig** – DANHOSTEL Sandvig – 16093
Hammershusvej 94, 3770 Allinge.
t 56480362 f 56481862
e sandvig@danhostel.dk
w www.danhostel.dk/sandvig
Open Dates: 01.05-01.09 (group 12) bed x 100

▲ **Silkeborg** – DANHOSTEL Silkeborg – 16094
Åhavevej 55, 8600 Silkeborg.
t 86823642 f 86812777
e silkeborg@danhostel.dk
w www.danhostel.dk/silkeborg
Open Dates: 01.03-01.12 ✈ Billund 63km train Silkeborg 500m bus Silkeborg 500m bed x 113 R CC 3 x 2km

▲ **Skælskør** – DANHOSTEL Skælskør – 16097
Slagelsevej 48, 4230 Skælskør.
t 58160980 f 58160989
e vandrerhjem@lystskoven.dk
w www.lystskoven.dk
Open Dates: 16.01-15.12 ✈ Copenhagen 105km train Slagelse, Korsør 18km bus 87 to Slagelse, 59 to Korsør 200m bed x 100 R CC (B) 2 x 15km 2km

▲ **Skagen** – DANHOSTEL Skagen – 16095
Rolighedsvej 2, 9990 Skagen.
t 98442200 f 98442255
e danhostel.skagen@adr.dk
w www.skagenvandrerhjem.dk
Open Dates: 15.02-30.11 ✈ 100km A bus 40km ferry 40km train 200m bus 200m bed x 128 R (B) 1 x 800m 800m

▲ **Skanderborg** – DANHOSTEL Skanderborg – 16017
Dyrehaven 9, 8660 Skanderborg.
t 86511966 f 86511334
e skanderborg@danhostel.dk
w www.skanderborg-danhostel.dk
Open Dates: 01.02-01.11 ✈ 40km A bus 1km ferry 25km train 3km bus 1km 3N bed x 128 R CC (B)

▲ **Slagelse** – DANHOSTEL Slagelse – 16098
Bjergbygade 78, 4200 Slagelse.
t 58522528 f 58522540
e slagelse@danhostel.dk
w www.danhostel.dk/slagelse
Open Dates: 15.01-10.12 ✈ Copenhagen 90km A bus 90km ferry Kalundborg 35km train Slagelse 2km bus Skælskør bus 100m bed x 125 R CC 3 x 500m 8km

▲ **Sønderborg** – DANHOSTEL Sønderborg City – 16106
Kærvej 70, 6400 Sønderborg.
74423112 74425631
sonderborg@danhostel.dk
www.sonderborgdanhostel.dk
Open Dates: 03.01-15.12 (03.01-15.12)
Sønderborg 5km A 1km
Fynshav 14km Sønderborg 2km
1 1.5NW x 200 R
CC 6 x
500m 1km

▲ **Sønderborg-Vollerup** – DANHOSTEL Sønderborg-Vollerup 16105
Mommarkvej, 17+22, 6400 Sønderborg.
74423990 74425290
vollerup@post1.tele.dk
www.visit-sonderborg.dk
Open Dates: Sønderborg 6km
Mommark, Fynshav 12km
Sønderborg 6km 11, 14,13 1E
x 150 R CC
3 x
1km 1km

▲ **Sorø** – DANHOSTEL Sorø – 16099
Skælskørvej 34, 4180 Sorø.
57849200 57849201
info@kkfg.dk
www.kongskildefriluftsgaard.dk
Open Dates: 01.04-31.10 (01.01-30.11)
x 77 CC

▲ **Store Heddinge** – DANHOSTEL Store Heddinge – 16100
Ved Munkevænget 1, 4660 Store Heddinge.
56502022 56502022
hak@stevns.dk www.visitdanhostel.dk
Open Dates: 01.04-01.10 ()
Copenhagen 60km A Store Heddinge 600m Store Heddinge 600m x 63
R 1 x
7km

▲ **Svaneke** – DANHOSTEL Svaneke – 16102
Reberbanevej 9, 3740 Svaneke.
56496242 56497383
info@danhostel-svaneke.dk
www.danhostel-svaneke.dk
Open Dates: 01.04-01.11 Bornholms 30km A DANHOSTEL Svaneke
Rønne 30km 4, 5 200m
x 152 R CC (B)
200m
200m

▲ **Svendborg** – DANHOSTEL Svendborg – 16103
Vestergade 45, 5700 Svendborg.
62216699 62202939
dk@danhostel-svendborg.dk
www.danhostel-svendborg.dk
Open Dates: Copenhagen International 180km A Odense 43km
Svendborg 500m Svendborg 500m
Svendborg 500m x 284
R CC 5 x
8 1.5km
2km

▲ **Thisted** – DANHOSTEL Thisted – 16107
Kongemøllevej 8, 7700 Thisted.
97925042 97925150
thisted@danhostel.dk
www.danhostelnord.dk/thisted
Open Dates: 01.03-31.10 Thisted airport 4km A 20m Hanstholm - Norvay 16km 4km 20m 4N x 88
CC 4km 4km

▲ **Tisvildeleje** – DANHOSTEL Tisvildeleje – 16108
Bygmarken 30, 3220 Tisvildeleje.
48709850 48709897
info@helene.dk www.helene.dk
Open Dates: () Copenhagen 70km Helsingør 35km Tisvildeleje 500m x 160 R CC
8 x
9km 500m

▲ **Tønder** – DANHOSTEL Tønder – 16109
Sønderport 4, 6270 Tønder.
74723500 74722797
toender@danhostel.dk
www.tonder-net.dk/danhostel
Open Dates: 15.02-15.12 50km
A 1km 80km 1km x 130

DENMARK – DANEMARK – DÄNEMARK – DINAMARCA

▲ **Varde** – DANHOSTEL Varde – 16110
Pramstedvej 10, 6800 Varde.
75221091 75223338
varde@danhostel.dk
www.danhostel.dk/varde
Open Dates: 15.03-01.10 ( ) 60km
A 800m 22km 800m
800m x 48
2km 15km

Vejle – DANHOSTEL Vejle – 16111
Gl. Landevej 80, 7100 Vejle.
75825188 75831783
info@vejle-danhostel.dk
www.vejle-danhostel.dk
Open Dates: 01.02-11.12
Open Times: 08.00-12.00hrs;
16.00-20.00hrs01.06.-01.09 08.00-10.00 hrs
16.00-18.00 hrs 01.09-01.06
Beds: 120 - 7x[4] 4x[5] 12x[6]
Price Range: DKK 115 (Rooms DKK 240-560)
Directions: 3.5SE from city centre
Billund 30km A 3km Esbjerg 80km Vejle 3km 2 500m ap Hesselbjerg x 23 (B) 1 x 4km 3km

Vejle – DANHOSTEL Vejle

Vejle... Travel Tips

- **For budget eats check out...** Jensens Befhus, Bones, Il Teatia Pizzaria, Conrad, Fetex Bistro
- **For great nightlife try...** Seven Oaks, Crazy Daisy, Casino Munkebjerg, Roast 'n' beers, Please check www.visitvejle.com
- **Don't miss...** Legoland, Madsbyparken, Vejle Ådal, Egtvedpigen, Bathing, Bowling, Casino Munkebjerg, The Lion Park - Givskud, The Concert Hall, Vintage Train from Vejle to Jelling

---

▲ **Viborg** – DANHOSTEL Viborg – 16112
Vinkelvej 36, 8800 Viborg.
86671781 86671788
viborg@danhostel.dk
www.danhostel.dk/viborg
Open Dates: 31.01-01.12 Viborg Station 3km 5 100m 2SE x 112 (B) 1 x

---

△ ***Vordingborg*** – *DANHOSTEL Vordingborg – 16113*
Præstegaardsvej 16, 4760 Vordingborg.
55360800 *55360801*
vandrerhjem@vordingborg.dk
Open Dates: 2.5SW x 112

FAROE ISLANDS HOSTELS

All the hostels listed here are Simple Standard

W www.farhostel.fo

W www.visit-faroeislands.com

Prices for members from DKK 135-170. No dorms, but rooms for 2-8 persons.
Discount is given to schools and groups.
See the web pages for further information.

Ferðamannaheimið á - Giljanesi
FO-360 Sandavágur
t (298) 333465
f (298) 332901
e giljanes@post.olivant.fo
w www.giljanes.fo
Open Dates: 12 x 30

Gjáargarður
FO-476 Gjógv
t (298) 211590
f (298) 423505
e info@gjaarhostel.com
w www.gjaarhostel.com
Open Dates: 15.06-15.08 x 80

Áargarður
FO-827 Øravik
t (298) 371302
f (298) 372057
e oeravik@post.olivant.fo
Open Dates: 12 x 28

Bládýpi
Dr. Jakobsensgøta 14-16
FO-100 Tórshavn
t (298) 311951
f (298) 319451
e bladypi@bladypi.fo
w www.bladypi.fo
Open Dates: 12 x 60

Scout Centre Selatrað
FO-497 Selatraõ
t (298) 212940
t (298) 448950
f (298) 310775
e kjartand@post.olivant.fo
w kfum.scout.fo
Check our booking calendar at our website: kfum.scout.fo.
Booking recommended.
Open Dates: 15.06-15.08 x 64

Vallaraheimð Tórshavn
Viō Oyggjarvegin
FO-100 Tórshavn
t (298) 318900
f (298) 315707
Open Dates 01.05-15.09 x 98

Ecuador

Fundación Hostelling del Ecuador,
Junín 203 y Panamá, Piso 2 oficina 4,
Guayaquil, Ecuador.

t (593) (4) 2564488
f (593) (4) 2566939
e info@hihostels.com.ec
w www.hihostels.com.ec

A copy of the Hostel Directory for this Country can be obtained from: The Hostel

National Tourist Authority/Board:	**www.vivecuador.com**
Capital:	**Quito**
Language:	**Spanish/Quichua**
Currency:	**US Dollar**
Population:	**12,200,000**
Size:	**270,000 sq km**
Telephone Country Code:	**593**
eKit Access Number:	**Check www.hi.ekit.com for up to date Access Numbers**

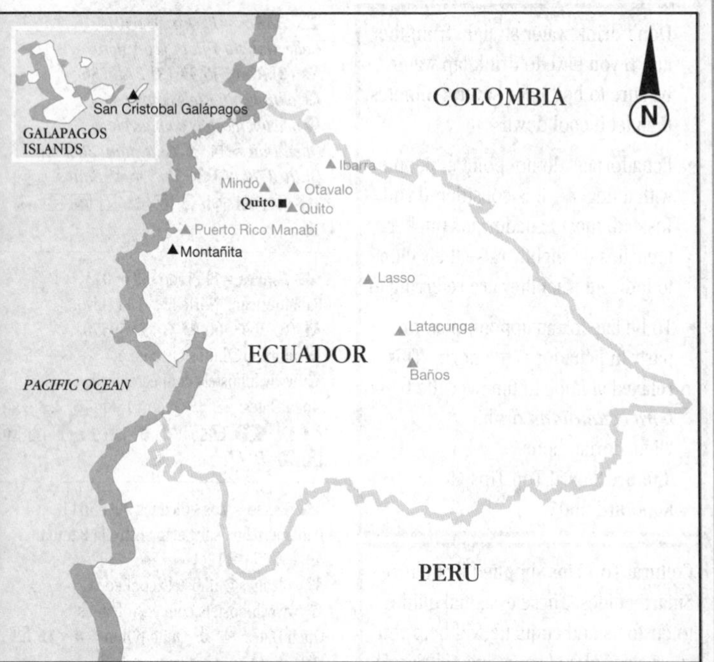

Located in the northwest of South America, Ecuador is a small country that has an incredibly rich landscape; with glaciers, rainforests and mangroves in close proximity to each other. The country is made up of four geographical zones, known as the Costa, the Sierra, the Oriente and the Galápagos Islands, or the Archipiélago de Colón. Costa is the agricultural centre of Ecuador, producing crops of bananas, cacao, rice, sugar, coffee and toquilla palm. The Sierra is the main mountainous area, which slopes down to the jungle region of the Oriente. The Galapagos Islands are a protected marine reserve inhabited by sharks, giant turtles, seals and whales.

Ecuador's history is thought to date back to around 5,000 years ago, when various tribes settled in the Sierra and the Amazonian forest. In the twelfth century the Incas came, introducing taxes, the Incan faith and the Quechua language. Bridges and roads were established; llamas were the main form of transport; and runners were used to relay messages. Ecuador's society today is based on a class structure, dating back to colonial times, in which the whiteness of one's skin determines the class to which one belongs.

A few other Top Tips from **CULTURE SMART!**:

- Judging someone by his or her clothing is common practice. Ecuadorians are very much aware of class divisions, and their attire reflects this. An upper class Ecuadorian, for example, would not be seen wearing a Panama hat. Designer labels are also very popular, Polo and Tommy Hilfiger being favourites.
- In a café or restaurant, ask for bottled water (*agua pura* or *agua con gas*), and make sure that the bottle is opened in front of you.

Don't drink water straight from the tap. If you have to drink tap water, be sure to boil it for several minutes, then let it cool down.

- Ecuadorians do not point at people with a finger – it is considered rude. Instead, most Ecuadorians pucker their lips or slightly raise their chin to indicate what they are referring to.
- To be late for an appointment or a party in Ecuador is the norm. This relaxed attitude to time is called *hora ecuatoiana* or the "Ecuadorian hour."

Culture Smart! Top Tips © Kuperard 2005

Cultural Top Tips supplied by Culture Smart! guides. These essential guides to customs and etiquette will help you steer clear of embarrassing gaffes and sensitive issues, enabling you to discover new cultures whilst developing new friendships. Order online at www.culturesmartguides.co.uk

You can find out a lot more on our website - a visit to www.HIhostels.com is essential for planning your trip!

Pour en savoir plus, rendez-vous sur notre site Internet, www.HIhostels.com une visite incontournable pour préparer votre voyage!

Viele weitere Informationen auf unserer Website: www.HIhostels.com - unverzichtbar für die Reiseplanung!

Puedes averiguar mucho más en nuestro sitio web. Es imprescindible que visites la página www.HIhostels.com para planear tu viaje.

△ ***Baños*** *– El Oro 65014*
Calle Ambato Y Juan Leon Mera.
(3) 2740736 (3) 2740736
eloro@hihostels.com.ec
www.hihostels.com.ec/eloro
Open Dates: Guayaquil 288km; Quito 178km 5km Baños 0.5NW x 41

▲ **Ibarra** – El Prado 65013
Panamericana Norte KM. 1 El Olivo.
(6) 2643460 (6) 2959570
elprado@hihostels.com.ec
www.hihostels.com.ec/elprado
Open Dates: Quito 115km 1N x 80 1 x

▲ **Lasso** – Los Volcanes 65011
Panamericana sur Sector Estrella Pamba.
(3) 2719112
volcanes@hihostels.com.ec
www.hihostels.com.ec/volcanes
Open Dates: Quito 60km x 16

▲ **Latacunga** – Rosim 65010
Calle Quito 16-49 Y Padre Salcedo.
(3) 2802172 (3) 2802172
rosim@hihostels.com.ec
www.hihostels.com.ec/rosim
Open Dates: Quito 89km Latacunga 2km ap Palacio Municipal x 30

△ ***Mindo*** *– Los Colibries 65012*
700m Via al Carmelo.
(2) 2568890
mindo@hihostels.com.ec
www.hihostels.com.ec/mindo
Open Dates: Quito 130km ap Mindo 130NW x 13

△ ***Montañita*** *– La Casa del Sol – 65006*
Punta Montañita lote no 5, Cel 099321210 Ramon Rocal.
(4) 2901302 (4) 2901302
casasol@hihostels.com.ec
www.hihostels.com.ec/casasol
Open Dates: CLP - Santa Elena 5min ap Montañita 0.2SE x 46

▲ **Otavalo** – HI Otavalo Ⓗ 65015
Roca 504 Y Juan Montalvo.
Ⓣ (6) 2923712
Ⓔ otavalo@hihostels.com.ec
Ⓦ www.hihostels.com.ec/otavalo
Open Dates: 12 ✈ Quito 95km x 46

▲ **Puerto Rico Manabí** – Hostería La Barquita Ⓗ 65008
Ciudadela 12 de Octubre frente al mar.
Ⓣ (4) 780051 Ⓕ (4) 780051
Ⓔ labarquita@hihostels.com.ec
Ⓦ www.hihostels.com.ec/labarquita
Open Dates: 12 x 12 R
10m 10m

Quito – IYHF Quito International Hostel Ⓗ 65001
Joaquin Pinto 325 y Reina Victoria.
Ⓣ (2) 2543995 Ⓕ (2) 2508221
Ⓔ quito@hihostels.com.ec
Ⓦ www.hihostels.com.ec
Open Dates: 12 Open Times:
Beds: 71 - 4x2 5x3 9x4 2x6
Price Range: $8-13 BBinc
Directions: 1SE from city centre
✈ Mariscal Sucre 5km A Aguila Dorada (20 mins) 1, 2 300m ap Av. Amazonas
10 500m ap de agosto x 3 R
CC (B) TV i

Quito – IYHF Quito International Hostel

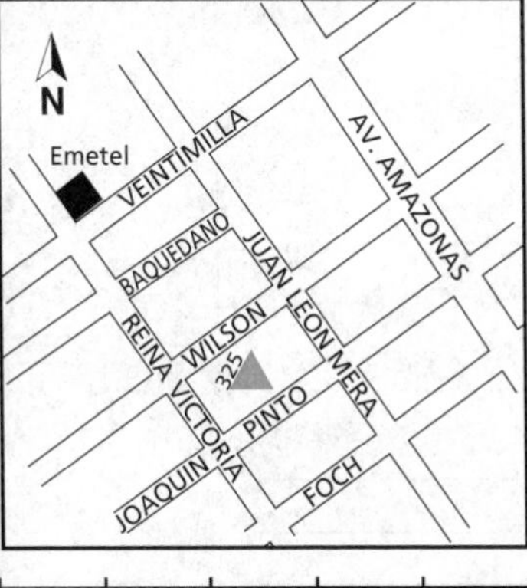

Quito... Travel Tips

- **For budget eats check out...** Zocalo (Juan León Mera y Calama), Posada del Maple (Vegetarian - Juan León Mera y Calama), Papaya Net Cyber Café & Restaurant (Juan León Mera y Calama), Lemon (Café-bar - Calama y Juan León Mera), Cyber Pizza Net (Calama y Juan León Mera)
- **For great nightlife try...** No Bar (J. Mera y Calama), Tijuana Bar (Reina Victoria y Santa Maria), Papillon Bar (Reina Victoria y Santa Maria), Cali Salsoteca (Colon y 9 de Octubre), La Bodeguita de Cuba (R. Victoria y la Pinta)
- **Don't miss...** La Mitad del Mundo (monument), Pasochoa Private Reserve, Historic City Centre, Guayasamin Museum, El Panecillo (panoramic views), Pululahua, La Carolina Park, Las Ruinas de Cochasqui, Museo Inti Raimi, Parque Metropolitano

---

▲ **San Cristobal (Galápagos)** – Galahost – 65009
Playa de Oro y Malecón sin número.
Ⓣ (4) 312697; 303698 Ⓕ (4) 566575
Ⓔ galapagos@hihostels.com.ec
Ⓦ www.hihostels.com.ec/galapagos
Open Dates: 12 1N x 30 R CC

Egypt

Egyptian Youth Hostels Association,
1 El-Ibrahimy Street, Garden City,
Cairo, Egypt.

(t) (20) (2) 7961448; 7940527
(f) (20) (2) 7950329
(e) eyha@link.net

Office Hours: Saturday-Thursday 08.30-18.30hrs

Travel Section: Camping and Travel Department,
7 Dr Abdel Hamid St, Maarouf,
Cairo, Egypt.

(t) (20) (2) 7926175

Office Hours: Saturday-Thursday 08.30-18.30hrs

A copy of the Hostel Directory for this Country can be obtained from:
The National Office

National Tourist Authority/Board:	www.egypttourism.org
Capital:	Cairo
Language:	Arabic
Currency:	LE (Egyptian £) = 100 piastres
Population:	69,213,274
Size:	1,001,449 sq km
Telephone Country Code:	20
eKit Access Number:	Check www.hi.ekit.com for up to date Access Numbers

In 3050 BC the first Pharaoh united Upper and Lower Egypt, creating a country whose legacy is unrivalled by any other nation in the world. Egypt identifies itself as an Arab nation, and the vast majority of the population are Muslim. The introduction of Islam occurred in 640 AD, when the Arabs invaded.

Egypt's long and wonderfully rich history has left the country a wealth of treasures, including elaborately painted tombs, great pyramids, and vast temples built to honour a pantheon of deities. The history of the ancient Egyptians is quite literally etched in stone, as can be seen from the hieroglyphs that detail everything from the lives of the gods to the work of the lowest slaves.

Geographically, the country is a gigantic desert expanse, broken by the oasis of the Nile River valley; the Nile is dammed to form a huge expanse of water near Aswan. The capital city, Cairo, or *al-Qahirah*, lies at the head of the Nile delta. The visitor will experience a dramatic contrast of modern and ancient life in this busy, twenty-four-hour city.

A few other Top Tips from **CULTURE SMART!**:

- In conversation, Egyptians frequently use blessings to demonstrate that they do not feel any animosity or jealousy towards the other person. "*Ma'a ssalama*," meaning "Go with safety," and "*Allah yisallimak*," "May God make you safe," are often used when leaving someone's company.
- Most Egyptians dress in Western fashion. Tourists in Egypt already wear as they wish but it is advisable to wear a reserved clothing "specially for women" to suit both the Egyptian reserved traditions and to avoid the strong heat of sun especially in summer.
- At meal times, Egyptians are always keen to prepare enough amount of food to ensure that all their guests are well fed and also to be ready to feed any incoming visitor. This generosity should be appreciated and enjoyed.
- Foreign men should avoid talking to Egyptian women if they have not been introduced, except in a modern business situation. This would be seen as disrespectful, and could compromise a woman's reputation.

Cultural Top Tips supplied by Culture Smart! guides. These essential guides to customs and etiquette will help you steer clear of embarrassing gaffes and sensitive issues, enabling you to discover new cultures whilst developing new friendships. Order online at www.culturesmartguides.co.uk

You can find out a lot more on our website - a visit to www.HIhostels.com is essential for planning your trip!

Pour en savoir plus, rendez-vous sur notre site Internet, www.HIhostels.com une visite incontournable pour préparer votre voyage!

Viele weitere Informationen auf unserer Website: www.HIhostels.com - unverzichtbar für die Reiseplanung!

Puedes averiguar mucho más en nuestro sitio web. Es imprescindible que visites la página www.HIhostels.com para planear tu viaje.

▲ **Alexandria** – El Shatbi Y.H – 96078
32 Port Said St, Shatbi, Raml, Alexandria.
(3) 5925459 (3) 5914759
Open Dates: 6km 3km 2km
2km x 202
30m

△ ***Assyout*** *– 96079*
Lux Housing El Walidia, Bldg 503.
(88) 2324846 (88) 2324846
Open Dates: 45km 4km
4km x 43

▲ **Cairo** – Cairo International Youth Hostel – 96081
135 Abdel Aziz Al Saoud St, El Manial, Kobri El Gamaa (University Bridge), Cairo.
(2) 3640729; 3624593 (2) 3684107
Open Dates: 32km 4.5km
100m x 180

△ ***Damanhour*** *– 96082*
9 Madrasset El-Rahebat St., Damanhour.
(45) 314056
Open Dates: 5km 500m
x 30

△ ***El Fayoum*** *– 96083*
Lux Housing Block of Flats, Hadaka, Block 7, Flat No 7, 8 Fayoum.
(84) 310005
Open Dates: 2km 3km
x 46

England & Wales

YHA (England & Wales) Limited,
Trevelyan House,
Dimple Road,
Matlock, Derbyshire DE4 3YH, England.
t Customer Services (44) 870 7708868
t International Enquiries (44) 1629 592700
f (44) 870 7706127; (44) 1629 592627
e customerservices@yha.org.uk
w www.yha.org.uk

Office Hours: Monday-Friday 08.00-20.00hrs
Saturday 09.00-13.00hrs

A copy of the Hostel Directory for this Country can be obtained from:
The National Office

National Tourist Authority/Board:	www.visitbritain.com www.uktheguide.com
Capital:	London
Language:	English
Currency:	£ Sterling (Pound)
Population:	52,211,175
Size:	151,207 sq km
Telephone Country Code:	44
eKit Access Number:	0800-032-6297

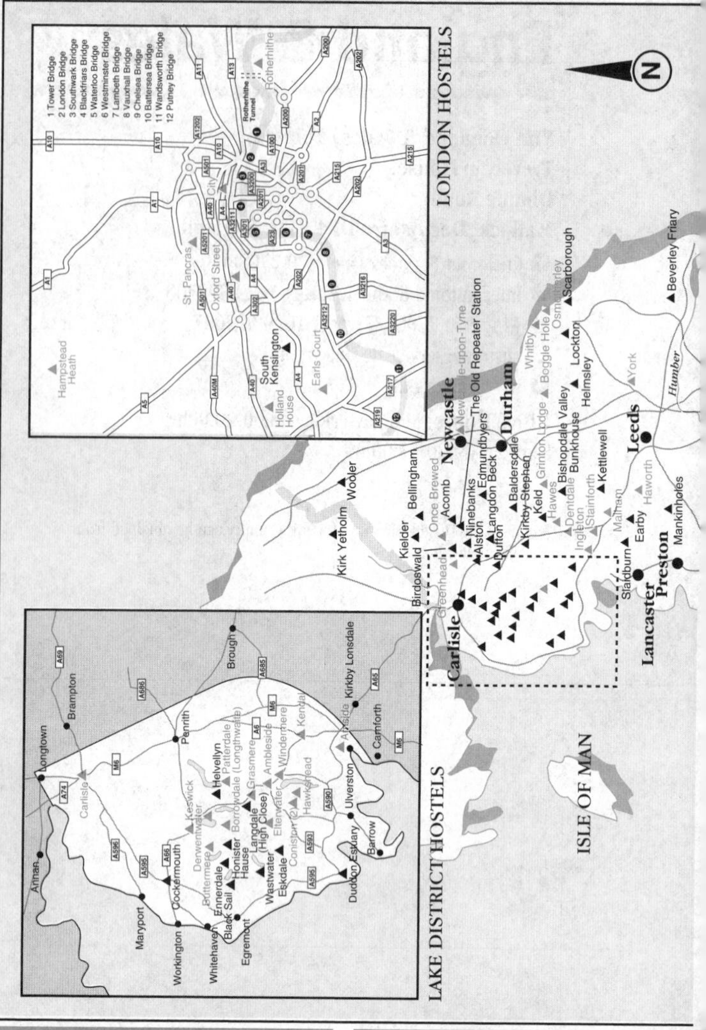

Visitors will welcome the fact that Keat's vision of England as 'this green and pleasant land' is very much a reality and continues to survive, thrive and prosper even at a time of great social change as the country gradually adjusts to the reality of its new post-war, multi-ethnic structure, the modernization of its infrastructure and industry and even its politics, including its ambivalent relationship with Europe and its new post-Empire place in the world.

Indeed, the old stereotypes that are associated with "Englishness", including cricket, country gardens, 'warm' beer, 'stiff upper lip', class structure, 'traditional English gentleman' and monarchy are actually very much alive and well, although now to be experienced in their more modernized versions.

At another level, English individualism, refinement, sense of fair play and common sense juxtaposed to English humour, coarseness, anarchic

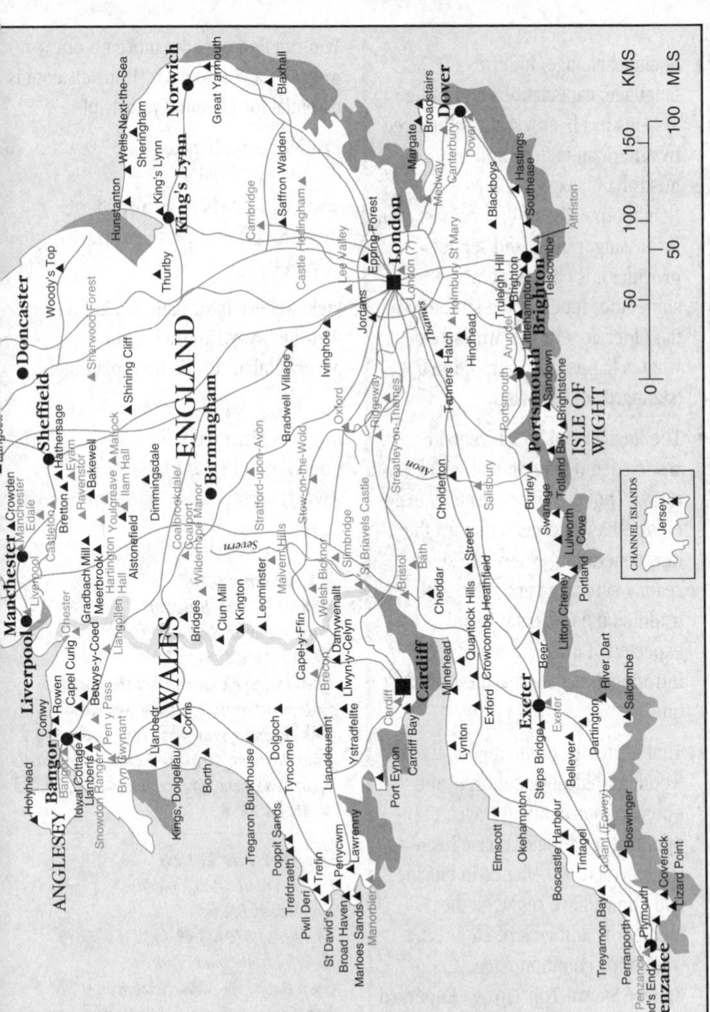

tendencies and manifestations of creative genius continue to fascinate the outside world.

Wales, however, though forever part of England's 'domain' since Henry VIII's Act of Union (1536) has its own very different persona and culture and no Welshman would wish it otherwise. Visitors will note in particular that the Welsh language is widely used (on all road signs and public notices) and increasingly widely spoken and used in schools, as well as on radio and TV.

A few other Top Tips from **CULTURE SMART!**:

- Once England was a 'bowler-hat' society – very staid and very correct. This has been replaced with a free, fashion-is-for-everyone culture, where the preference is to 'dress down', except for the main professions, such as banking, the civil service and national institutions. In some respects this is true of Wales also, although by nature it is a more conservative society.

- Social exchange, in terms of language, expectations and value systems has been greatly influenced by American culture and by Australian 'soaps' such as Neighbours. Use of first names, even by passing traders and service providers, is commonplace – sometimes much to the irritation of the older generation, who wonder what is happening to traditional 'standards of behaviour'.
- The English and Welsh remain reserved and take time to get to know. Though a more 'touchy-feely' culture has emerged amongst the new generation, where the sexes readily embrace each other, the traditional handshake is still expected in most contexts when introductions take place for the first time.
- Thanks in part to the media, the new 'youth and lifestyle cultures' and the boom in international travel; the options for eating out have been transformed. Excellence in cuisine and choice have replaced the mediocrity and lack of choice that were once commonplace.
  Culture Smart! Top Tips © Kuperard 2005

Cultural Top Tips supplied by Culture Smart! guides. These essential guides to customs and etiquette will help you steer clear of embarrassing gaffes and sensitive issues, enabling you to discover new cultures whilst developing new friendships. Order online at www.culturesmartguides.co.uk

You can find out a lot more on our website - a visit to www.HIhostels.com is essential for planning your trip!

Pour en savoir plus, rendez-vous sur notre site Internet, www.HIhostels.com une visite incontournable pour préparer votre voyage!

Viele weitere Informationen auf unserer Website: www.HIhostels.com - unverzichtbar für die Reiseplanung!

Puedes averiguar mucho más en nuestro sitio web. Es imprescindible que visites la página www.HIhostels.com para planear tu viaje.

△ ***Acomb*** *– 18107*
Main St, Acomb, Hexham, Northumberland NE46 4PL.
(1434) 602864
Open Dates: Please contact the hostel for further information Newcastle Hexham 3km Tyne Valley 880-2 from Hexham, Arriva 685 Carlise-Newcastle Upon Tyne 4km ap Hexham x 26

△ ***Alfriston*** *18087*
Frog Firle, Alfriston, Polegate, East Sussex BN26 5TT.
(1323) 870423 (1323) 870615
alfriston@yha.org.uk
Open Dates: Newhaven 9.5km Seaford, Berwick 4.8km Renown 126 Seaford-Alfriston-Eastbourne, RDH 125 from Lewes 800m x 66

▲ **Alston** – 18108
The Firs, Alston, Cumbria CA9 3RW.
(1434) 381509 (1434) 382401
alston@yha.org.uk
Open Dates: Please contact the hostel for further information Langwathby, Haltwhistle, Penrith 24km Wrights 681 from Haltwhistle, 888 from Penrith, Highfield 680 from Carlisle x 30

▲ Alstonefield – 18091

Gypsy Lane, Alstonefield, near Ashbourne, Derbyshire DE6 2FZ.
(1335) 310206 (1335) 310206
ilam@yha.org.uk
Open Dates: Cromford, Buxton 21km Postbus from Leek, Warrington 441 from Ashbourne (Thurs & Sat only) x 20

Ambleside – Waterhead 18015

Ambleside, Cumbria LA22 0EU.
(15394) 32304 (15394) 34408
ambleside@yha.org.uk
Open Dates: Open Times:
Beds: 257 - 22x2 17x3 9x4 9x5 5x6 4x6+
Price Range: £19.00
Directions: 1.5S from city centre
Manchester 145km Stranraer/Belfast 97km Windermere 6.5km 555 50m ap Waterhead Pier x 47 R CC 2 x 4km

Ambleside – Waterhead

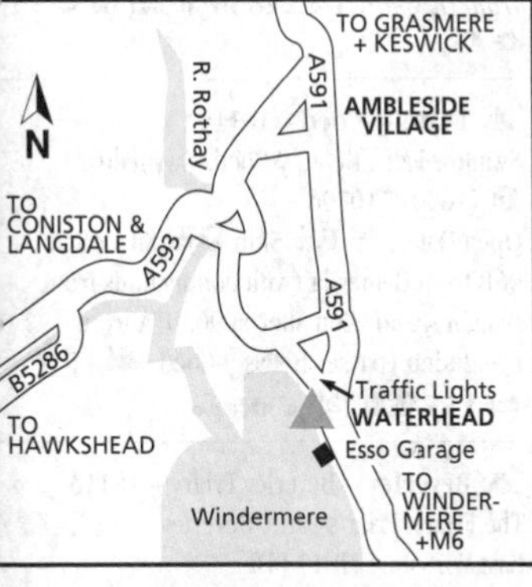

Ambleside... Travel Tips

- **For budget eats check out...** YHA Ambleside, Pippins, Lucy's, Daisy's, The Jumble Room (Grasmere)
- **For great nightlife try...** Wide choice of friendly pubs & restaurants
- **Don't miss...** Windermere Steamers, Lakeland Aquarium, Lakeside Railway, Hill Top (Beatrix Potter's House), Dove Cottage (Wordsworth's House), The Beatrix Potter Experience, The Rheged Centre, The Steamboat Museum, Fell Foot Park, Muncaster Castle and World Owl Centre

▲ Arnside 18106

Oakfield Lodge, Redhills Rd, Arnside, Carnforth, Lancashire LA5 0AT.
(1524) 761781 (1524) 762589
arnside@yha.org.uk
Open Dates: Please contact the hostel for further information Heysham-Isle of Man 24km Arnside 1km Stagecoach in Cumbria 552 from Kendal x 72 R CC 1 x

---

▲ Arundel 18058

Warningcamp, Arundel, West Sussex BN18 9QY.
(1903) 882204 (1903) 882776
arundel@yha.org.uk
Open Dates: Portsmouth to Le Havre, Caen, Cherbourg, St Malo 44km Arundel 1.6km Stagecoach Coastline 702 from Brighton ap Arundel Station x 65 R CC

▲ Bakewell – 18110

Fly Hill, Bakewell, Derbyshire DE45 1DN.
(1629) 812313 (1629) 812313
bakewell@yha.org.uk
Open Dates: Please contact the hostel for further information Manchester 59.1km Matlock 13km Frequent from surrounding areas x 28 CC

▲ Baldersdale – 18111

Blackton, Baldersdale, Barnard Castle, Co Durham DL12 9UP.
(1833) 650629 (1833) 650513
Open Dates: Please contact the hostel for further information Darlington 44km Arriva North East 95/96 from Barnard Castle 10km ap Cotherstone or Romaldkirk x 37 R CC

▲ Bangor 18033

Tan-y-Bryn, Bangor, Gwynedd, Wales LL57 1PZ.
(1248) 353516 (1248) 371176
bangor@yha.org.uk
Open Dates: Please contact the hostel for further information Holyhead to Dublin (Ireland) 27km Bangor 2km Frequent from surrounding areas x 70 CC 1 x

Bath 18010
Bathwick Hill Bath BA2 6JZ
(1225) 465674 (1225) 482947
bath@yha.org.uk
Open Dates: Please contact the hostel for further information Open Times:
Beds: 122 - 5x2 12x4 2x5 3x6 3x6+
Price Range: £11.00
Directions: 1E from city centre
Bristol 30km Bath Spa 1.5km
First Badgerline 18 1.5km ap YH
R CC
1km

Bath

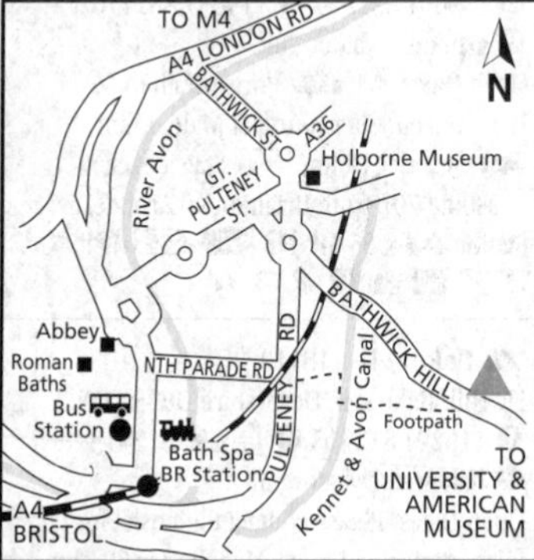

Bath... Travel Tips

- **For budget eats check out...** YHA Bath, Café Retro, Porter Bar (specialises in vegetarian meals), Jazz Café, Bengal Brassiere
- **For great nightlife try...** Loads of pubs, many with free live music, Various nightclubs, Plenty of Café Bars, 3 Cinemas, 3 Excellent Theatres
- **Don't miss...** Roman Baths Museum & Pump Room, Costume Museum & Assembly Rooms, Jane Austen Centre, The American Museum, Bath Abbey & Heritage Vaults, Royal Crescent & Circus, Victoria Art Gallery, Botanical Gardens, Pulteney Bridge & Weir, Prior Park & Landscaped Gardens

▲ **Beer** – 18112
Bovey Combe, Townsend, Beer, Seaton, Devon EX12 3LL.
(1297) 20296 (1297) 23690
beer@yha.org.uk
Open Dates: 12 Axminster 11km
Axe Valley from Seaton, X53 Weymouth-Exeter ap Beer Village x 40
R CC

△ ***Bellever** – 18113*
Postbridge, Yelverton, Devon PL20 6TU.
(1822) 880227 (1822) 880302
bellever@yha.org.uk
Open Dates: 12 Plymouth 40km
Plymouth 37km First Western National 98 from Tavistock ap YH x 38
R CC

△ ***Bellingham** – 18114*
Woodburn Rd, Bellingham, Hexham, Northumberland NE48 2ED.
(1434) 220313 (1434) 220313
Open Dates: Please contact the hostel for further information Newcastle
Hexham 26km Tyne Valley 880 from Hexham x 28

▲ **Betws-y-Coed** – 18115
Swallow Falls, Betws-y-Coed, Gwynedd.
(1690) 710796
Open Dates: 5km Silver Star 96B from Bethesda (with connections from Bangor), Snowdon Sherpa 96, 97A from Llandudno (passes Betws-y-Coed) 1.5N
x 53 R

▲ **Beverley** – Beverley Friary – 18116
The Friary, Friar's Lane, Beverley, East Yorkshire HU17 0DF.
(1482) 881751 (1482) 880118
beverleyfriary@yha.org.uk
Open Dates: Hull to Zeebrugge, Rotterdam 19km Beverley 500m
Frequent from surrounding areas
x 34 R CC
1 x

△ ***Black Sail** – 18117*
Black Sail Hut, Ennerdale, Cleator, Cumbria CA23 3AY.
(7711) 108450 (7711) 159472
Open Dates: Please contact the hostel for further information Whitehaven 32km, Penrith 72km X4/ X5/X50 Penrith to Keswick and 77/77a Keswick to Conister 4km ap Honister x 16
500m

△ ***Blackboys** – 18118*
Uckfield, East Sussex TN22 5HU.
(1825) 890607 (1825) 890104
Open Dates: Newhaven 35km Buxted 4km Stagecoach in East Sussex 728 500m ap Blackboys x 29

▲ **Blaxhall** – 18120
Heath Walk, Blaxhall, Woodbridge, Suffolk IP12 2EA.
(1728) 688206 (1728) 689191
blaxhall@yha.org.uk
Open Dates: Harwich Wickham Market 4.8km First Eastern Counties 81 Ipswich-Aldeburgh x 40
1 x

▲ **Boggle Hole** 18060
Mill Beck, Fylingthorpe, Whitby, North Yorkshire YO22 4UQ.
(1947) 880352 (1947) 880987
bogglehole@yha.org.uk
Open Dates: Hull to Zeebrugge, Rotterdam 80km Whitby (not Sun except June-Sept) 11km Arriva North East 93A Scarborough-Whitby 1.5km ap Robin Hood's Bay x 80

▲ **Borrowdale (Longthwaite)** 18071
Longthwaite, Borrowdale, Keswick, Cumbria CA12 5XE.
(17687) 77257 (17687) 77393
borrowdale@yha.org.uk
Open Dates: Workington 40km Stagecoach in Cumbria 79 from Keswick x 88

▲ **Borth** – 18121
Morlais, Borth, Ceredigion, Wales SY24 5JS.
(1970) 871498 (1970) 871827
borth@yha.org.uk
Open Dates: Fishguard-Rosslare (Ireland) 88.5km Borth 1km Aberystwyth 8.2km, Arriva Cymru 520/4 from Aberystwyth x 60
8

△ ***Boscastle Harbour** – 18122*
Palace Stables, Boscastle, Cornwall PL35 0HD.
(1840) 250287 (1840) 250615
Open Dates: Please contact the hostel for further information Bodmin Parkway 38.5km Please check before travelling x 25

▲ **Boswinger** – 18123
Gorran, St. Austell, Cornwall PL26 6LL.
(1726) 844527 (1726) 844527
boswinger@yha.org.uk
Open Dates: Please contact the hostel for further information Plymouth St. Austell 16km First Western Greyhound 526 - St Austell-Gorran Churchtown 1.5km x 40 (B)

▲ **Bradwell Village** – 18125
Vicarage Rd, Bradwell, Milton Keynes, Buckinghamshire MK13 9AG.
(1908) 227477 (1908) 227477
bradwellvillage@yha.org.uk
Open Dates: Luton 40km Milton Keynes Central 1km Frequent from surrounding areas 2NW x 37
(B)

▲ **Brecon** 18082
Groesffordd, Brecon, Powys, Wales LD3 7SW.
(1874) 665270 (1874) 665278
brecon@yha.org.uk
Open Dates: Abervagenny 30.5km 39 from Abervagenny 800m x 54

ENGLAND & WALES – ANGLETERRE & PAYS DE GALLES – ENGLAND & WALES – INGLATERRA Y GALES

△ ***Bretton*** *– 18126*
Bretton, nr Eyam, Hope Valley, Sheffield S32 5QD.
(1433) 639864 bretton@yha.org.uk
Open Dates: Please contact the hostel for further information Grindleford, Hathersage 6km Services from Sheffield, Buxton and Chesterfield ap Foolow x 18

▲ **Bridges Long Mynd** – 18127
Ratlinghope, Shrewsbury, Shropshire SY5 0SP.
(1588) 650656 (1588) 650531
Open Dates: Church Stretton 8km Boultons 551 ap Shrewsbury (Tues only) x 37

△ ***Brighstone (Isle of Wight)*** *– 18262*
Please direct all enquiries for YHA Brighstone through YHA Totland Bay.
(1983) 752165 (1983) 756443
totland@yha.org.uk
Open Dates: Please contact the hostel for further information Yarmouth 16km, Fishbourne 27km, Ryde 32km. 500m ap Three Bishops Pub x 12 1.6km

---

▲ **Brighton** – 18029
Patcham Place, London Rd, Brighton, Sussex BN1 8YD.
(1273) 556196 (1273) 509366
brighton@yha.org.uk
Open Dates: Preston Park 3km 5a ap Patcham Co-op 6NW x 56

△ ***Bristol*** *18011*
International YHA, Hayman House, 14 Narrow Quay, Bristol BS1 4QA.
(117) 9221659 (117) 9273789
bristol@yha.org.uk
Open Dates: Bristol 15km Bristol Temple Meads 1km Frequent from surrounding areas 1SW x 92 (B) 1 x

---

▲ **Broad Haven** – 18128
Broad Haven, Haverfordwest, Pembrokeshire, Wales SA62 3JH.
(1437) 781688 (1437) 781100
broadhaven@yha.org.uk
Open Dates: Please contact the hostel for further information Pembroke Dock 16km Haverfordwest 11km First Cymru/Silcox 311 ap Haverfordwest x 77 1 x

---

▲ **Broadstairs** – 18129
3 Osborne Rd, Broadstairs, Kent CT10 2AE.
(1843) 604121 (1843) 604121
broadstairs@yha.org.uk
Open Dates: Please contact the hostel for further information London (Manston) 5km Dover (30km), Ramsgate (4km) Broadstairs 100m From Ramsgate, Canterbury and surrounding areas 0.5W x 25 1km

---

▲ **Bryn Gwynant** 18072
Nantgwynant, Caernarfon, Gwynedd, Wales LL55 4NP.
(1766) 890251 (1766) 890479
bryngwynant@yha.org.uk
Open Dates: Holyhead 56km Betws-y-Coed 21km 97A ap Snowdon Sherpa x 77

▲ **Burley** – 18130
Cott Lane, Burley, Ringwood, Hampshire BH24 4BB.
(1425) 403233 (1425) 403233
Open Dates: Please contact the hostel for further information Sway 9km Wilts & Dorset X34/5 Bournemouth-Southampton ap Durmast Corner x 36

▲ **Buttermere** 18057
King George VI Memorial Hostel, Buttermere, Cockermouth, Cumbria CA13 9XA.
(17687) 70245 (17687) 70231
buttermere@yha.org.uk
Open Dates: Workington 29km Stagecoach in Cumbria 77A from Keswick (Apr-Oct only) x 70

Cambridge 18012
97 Tenison Rd, Cambridge CB1 2DN.
(1223) 354601 (1223) 312780
cambridge@yha.org.uk
Open Dates: Open Times:
Beds: 100 - 10x² 1x³ 8x⁴ 6x⁶⁺
Price Range: £16
Directions: 2SE from city centre
Stansted 32km A Cambridge 1.6km
Cambridge 400m C1, C3 400m
ap Cambridge 800m

Cambridge

Cambridge... Travel Tips

- **For budget eats check out...** YHA Cambridge, McDonalds, Burger King, Pizza Hut, Various Takeaways on Mill Road
- **For great nightlife try...** The Junction, The Boat Race, 5th Avenue, The Locomotive, Corn Exchange
- **Don't miss...** Cambridge Colleges & Museums, Punting on the River Cam, Cycling around Cambridge & The Fens, Duxford Imperial War Museum, Grantchester, Ely Cathedral, Anglesey Abbey, Botanic Gardens, Wicken Fen, Linton Zoo

Canterbury 18016
54 New Dover Rd, Canterbury, Kent CT1 3DT.
(1227) 462911 (1227) 470752
canterbury@yha.org.uk
Open Dates: Gatwick 107.2km
Dover 22.4km Canterbury East 1km, Canterbury West 2km 1SE x 68 (B) 2km 10km

Capel Curig – 18132
Plas Curig, Capel Curig, Betws-y-Coed, Wales LL24 0EL.
(1690) 720225 (1690) 720270
capelcurig@yha.org.uk
Open Dates: Betws-y-Coed 8km
Silver Star 96B ap Bethesda (with connections from Bangor) x 52

Capel-y-Ffin – 18133
Castle Farm, Capel-y-Ffin, Llanthony, near Abervagenny, Wales NP7 7NP.
(1873) 890650
capel-y-ffinyha@amserve.com
Open Dates: Please contact the hostel for further information Bristol or Cardiff
Abervagenny 26km Canyon 40 Hereford-Brecon (passes close to Hereford) 13km ap Hay-on-Wye x 42

Cardiff 18017
2 Wedal Rd, Roath Park, Cardiff, Wales CF14 3QX.
(2920) 462303 (2920) 464571
cardiff@yha.org.uk
Open Dates: Swansea 80km
Heath High or Low Level 1.2km
Cardiff Bus 28, 29 ap Cardiff Central x 66 (B)

Carlisle 18090
The University of Northumbria, The Old Brewery Residences, Bridge Lane, Caldewgate, Carlisle, Cumbria CA2 5SR.
(1228) 597352 (1228) 597352
dee.carruthers@unn.ac.uk
Open Dates: Please contact the hostel for further information Carlisle 3.2km
Stagecoach in Cumbria 62 ap Town Hall - St Ann's Hill x 56

▲ Castle Hedingham 18105
7 Falcon Square, Castle Hedingham, Halstead, Essex CO9 3BU.
(1787) 460799 (1787) 461302
castlehed@yha.org.uk
Open Dates: Please contact the hostel for further information Harwich 40km Sudbury (not Sun except May-Sept) 11km, Braintree 12km Hedingham Omnibuses 89 (not sun) (passes near Braintree) x 50

▲ Castleton 18085
Castleton Hall, Castleton, Hope Valley S33 8WG.
(1433) 620235 (1433) 621767
castleton@yha.org.uk
Open Dates: Hull to Zeebrugge, Rotterdam 96km Hope 4.8km Mainline/Stagecoach East Midland 272/4 from Sheffield (passes Hope) x 135

▲ Cheddar – 18135
Hillfield, Cheddar, Somerset BS27 3HN.
(1934) 742494 (1934) 744724
cheddar@yha.org.uk
Open Dates: Please contact the hostel for further information Weston-Super-Mare 17.7km First Badgerline 126, 826 Weston Super Mare-Wells (passes close to Weston Milton & Weston Super Mare) x 45

▲ Chester 18023
Hough Green House, 40 Hough Green, Chester CH4 8JD.
(1244) 680056 (1244) 681204
chester@yha.org.uk
Open Dates: Please contact the hostel for further information Chester 2.4km Frequent from surrounding areas 2SW x 117

▲ Cholderton (Stonehenge) – 18266
Cholderton Rare Breeds Farm, Amesbury Road, Cholderton, Wiltshire SP4 0EW
(1980) 629438 (1980) 629594
cholderton@yha.org.uk
Open Dates: Southampton 40km Grateley 6km, Salisbury 12km, Andover 14km Cholderton Village 800m x 60 (BD)

△ *Clun Mill – 18136*
The Mill, Clun, near Craven Arms, Shropshire SY7 8NY.
(1588) 640582 (1588) 640582
Open Dates: Please contact the hostel for further information Broome, Hopton 11.2km Whittlebus 743/5 from Ludlow & Craven Arms (passes close Ludlow and Craven Arms) 400m ap Clun
x 24

▲ Coalbrookdale – Ironbridge – 18137
C/O High St, Coalport, Telford, Shropshire TF8 7HT
(1952) 588755 (1952) 588722
ironbridge@yha.org.uk
Open Dates: Please contact the hostel for further information Telford Central 8km Telford Link Wellington-Telford x 80

▲ Coalport – Ironbridge 18068
High St, Coalport, Telford, Shropshire TF8 7HT.
(1952) 588755 (1952) 588722
ironbridge@yha.org.uk
Open Dates: Please contact the hostel for further information Telford Central 8km Telford Link Wellington-Telford x 85 1 x

△ *Cockermouth – 18138*
Double Mills, Cockermouth, Cumbria CA13 0DS.
(1900) 822561 (1900) 822561
cockermouth@yha.org.uk
Open Dates: Please contact the hostel for further information Workington 13km Stagecoach in Cumbria X4/5
x 26

▲ **Coniston (Holly How)** 18073
Holly How, Far End, Coniston,
Cumbria LA21 8DD.
(15394) 41323 (15394) 41803
conistonhh@yha.org.uk
Open Dates: Ulverston 21km
Stagecoach in Cumbria 505/6 from Ambleside, X12/512 from Ulverston 0.4N
x 60
1 x

△ ***Coniston Coppermines** – 18139*
Coppermines House, Coniston,
Cumbria LA21 8HP.
(15394) 41261 (15394) 41571
coppermines@yha.org.uk
Open Dates: Please contact the hostel for further information Ulverston 22.5km
Stagecoach 505/6 from Ambleside 1km x 26

▲ **Conwy** – 18140
Larkhill, Sychnant Pass Rd, Conwy,
Wales LL32 8AJ.
(1492) 593571 (1492) 593580
conwy@yha.org.uk
Open Dates: Holyhead to Dun Laoghaire (Ireland) 51km Conwy 400m
Frequent from surrounding areas
x 80

▲ **Corris** – 18142
Old School, Old Rd, Corris, Machynlleth,
Powys SY20 9QT.
(1654) 761686 (1654) 761686
corrishostel@canolfrancorris.com
Open Dates: Machynlleth 10km
Arriva Cymru 28, 30, 32, 34, 35 Aberystwyth-Dolgellau (passes Machynlleth), Trawscambria 701 x 48

▲ **Coverack** – 18143
Parc Behan, School Hill, Coverack, Helston,
Cornwall TR12 6SA.
(1326) 280687 (1326) 280119
coverack@yha.org.uk
Open Dates: Please contact the hostel for further information Penzance to Scilly Isles Redruth 29km Truronian T2
x 35

▲ **Crowcombe Heathfield** – 18144
Denzel House, Crowcombe Heathfield,
Taunton, Somerset TA4 4BT.
(1984) 667249 (1984) 667249
crowcombe@yha.org.uk
Open Dates: Taunton 16km
First Southern National 28/C 928 1.2km ap Red Post x 47

▲ **Crowden-in-Longdendale** – 18145
Peak National Park Hostel, Crowden, Glossop,
Derbyshire SK13 1HZ.
(1457) 852135 (1457) 852135
Open Dates: Please contact the hostel for further information Hadfield 8km
National Express 350 Sheffield-Manchester x 38

▲ **Danywenallt** – 18269
Talybont-on-Usk, Brecon, Powys, LD3 7YS
(1874) 676677 (0870) 7706137
danywenallt@yha.org.uk
Open Dates: Cardiff International 84km
Pembroke Dock 129km
Abergavenny 19km X43 from Brecon or Abergavenny ap Post Office in Talybont 3km from hostel x 36

△ ***Dartington** – 18147*
Lownard, Dartington, Totnes,
Devon TQ9 6JJ.
(1803) 862303 (1803) 865171
Open Dates: Please contact the hostel for further information Totnes 3km
First Western X80 800m ap Shinner's Bridge x 30

▲ **Dentdale** 18097
Cowgill, Dent, Sedbergh, Cumbria LA10 5RN.
(15396) 25251 (15396) 25068
dentdale@yha.org.uk
Open Dates: Please contact the hostel for further information Dent 3km
Limited Sevice - Please check with hostel x 41

▲ Derwentwater Ⓗ 18061
Barrow House, Borrowdale, Keswick, Cumbria CA12 5UR.
(17687) 77246 (17687) 77396
derwentwater@yha.org.uk
Open Dates: Penrith 32km Stagecoach in Cumbria 79 x 88

△ Dimmingsdale – 18148
Little Ranger, Dimmingsdale, Oakamoor, Stoke-on-Trent, Staffordshire ST10 3AS.
(1538) 702304 (1538) 702304
dimmingsdale@yha.org.uk
Open Dates: Please contact the hostel for further information Blythe Bridge 10km First PMT 238 3km ap Oakamoor
x 20

△ Dolgoch – 18149
Tregaron, Ceredigion SY25 6NR.
(1974) 298680 (1629) 592627
reservations @yha.org.uk
Open Dates: Fishguard-Rosslare (Ireland) 70km Llanwrtyd Wells 16km Arriva Cymru 516, James 589
x 22

▲ Dover Ⓗ 18018
306 London Rd, Dover, Kent CT17 0SY.
(1304) 201314 (1304) 202236
dover@yha.org.uk
Open Dates: Dover 2km Dover Priory 1km Frequent from surrounding areas 0.5NW x 127 1km 1km

▲ Duddon Estuary – 18150
Borwick Rails, Millom, Cumbria LA18 4JU.
(1229) 773937 (1229) 773937
duddon@yha.org.uk
Open Dates: Millom (not Sun) 2km X6, X7, Stagecoach 511 1.6km ap Millom x 18 1km

▲ Dufton – 18151
'Redstones', Dufton, Appleby, Cumbria CA16 6DB.
(17683) 51236 (17683) 53798
dufton@yha.org.uk
Open Dates: Please contact the hostel for further information Appleby 5.5km
x 39

▲ Earby – 18152
9-11 Birch Hall Lane, Earby, Barnoldswick, Lancashire BB18 6JX.
(1282) 842349 (1282) 842349
earby@yha.org.uk
Open Dates: Please contact the hostel for further information Colne 8km Services from Burnley and Skipton 800m ap Earby x 22

▲ Edale Ⓗ 18074
Hostel and Activity Centre, Rowland Cote, Edale, Hope Valley S33 7ZH.
(1433) 670302 (1433) 670243
edale@yha.org.uk
Open Dates: Edale 3km No service x 143

▲ Edmundbyers – 18154
Low House, Edmundbyers, Consett, Co Durham DH8 9NL.
(1207) 255651 (1207) 255651
edmundbyers@yha.org.uk
Open Dates: Please contact the hostel for further information Newcastle 30km A YH Newcastle 40km Hexham 21km 45, 46, 770 Newcastle-Consett, 773 Stanley Taxis connections on Go Northern 719, 765 8km ap Consett x 29

△ Elmscott – 18156
Hartland, Bideford, Devon EX39 6ES.
(1237) 441367 (1237) 441910
reservations@yha.org.uk
Open Dates: Please contact the hostel for further information Barnstaple 40km First Red Bus 119 5.5km ap Hartland
x 32

▲ Elterwater – Langdale Ⓗ 18086
Ambleside, Cumbria LA22 9HX.
(15394) 37245 (15394) 37120
elterwater@yha.org.uk
Open Dates: Windermere 12.8km Stagecoach in Cumbria 516 x 43

*△ **Ennerdale (Gillerthwaite)** – 18158*
Cat Crag, Ennerdale, Cleator, Cumbria CA23 3AX.
(1946) 861237 (1946) 861237
ennerdale@yha.org.uk
Open Dates: Please contact the hostel for further information Whitehaven 24km Stagecoach in Cumbria 77A from Keswick (Apr-Oct only) ap Buttermere x 24

▲ Epping Forest – 18159
Wellington Hill, High Beach, Loughton, Essex IG10 4AG.
(20) 85085971 (20) 85085161
epping@yha.org.uk
Open Dates: Please contact the hostel for further information Chingford 5.6km Arriva The Shires & Essex 240, 250 from Waltham Cross , Loughton ap Volunteer Inn Loughton 3.2km x 36 (B)

▲ Eskdale – 18160
Boot, Holmrook, Cumbria CA19 1TH.
(19467) 23219 (19467) 23163
eskdale@yha.org.uk
Open Dates: Please contact the hostel for further information Eskdale (Ravenglass & Eskdale Railway) 2.4km x 50 1 x

▲ Exeter 18030
Mount Wear House, 47 Countess Wear Rd, Exeter, Devon EX2 6LR.
(1392) 873329 (1392) 876939
exeter@yha.org.uk
Open Dates: Exeter Central 3km 57, 85 from station; K, T from High Street (close to Exeter Central) ap Countess Wear Post Office 3SE x 66

▲ Exford – 18161
Exe Mead, Exford, Minehead, Somerset TA24 7PU.
(1643) 831288 (1643) 831650
Open Dates: Minehead (West Somerset Rly) 20.9km Exmoor Buses 178, 285, Southern National 38 ap Porlock x 51

▲ Eyam 18075
Hawkhill Rd, Eyam, Hope Valley S32 5QP.
(1433) 630335 (1433) 639202
eyam@yha.org.uk
Open Dates: Please contact the hostel for further information Grindleford 5.6km Services from Sheffield, Buxton and Chesterfield x 60

▲ Gilsland – Birdoswald – 18275
Birdoswald Roman Fort, Gilsland, Carlisle, CA6 7DD.
(773) 9085676 (16977) 47884
birdoswald@yha.org.uk
Open Dates: Please contact the hostel for further information Haltwhistle 9.7km, Brampton 9.7km AD122 Hadrian's Chariot (24/5 - 14/9) x 36 (BL)

▲ Golant 18054
Penquite House, Golant, Fowey, Cornwall PL23 1LA.
(1726) 833507 (1726) 832947
golant@yha.org.uk
Open Dates: Plymouth 64km Par 4.8km First Western National 24, St Austell-Fowey (passes Par) ap Castle Dore Crossroads x 94

▲ Gradbach Mill – 18162
Gradbach, Quarnford, Buxton, Derbyshire SK17 0SU.
(1260) 227625 (1260) 227334
gradbach@yha.org.uk
Open Dates: Buxton 11.2km First PMT X18 Sheffield-Keele ap Flash Bar Stores x 93

▲ Grasmere – Butterlip How/Thorney How 18050
Easedale Rd, Grasmere, Cumbria LA22 9QG.
(15394) 35316 (15394) 35798
grasmere@yha.org.uk
Open Dates: Please contact the hostel for further information Windermere 13.6km Stagecoach in Cumbria 555/6/9 Lancaster-Keswick, 599 from Windermere ap Grasmere x 82

▲ **Great Yarmouth** – 18163
2 Sandown Rd, Great Yarmouth,
Norfolk NR30 1EY.
(1493) 843991 (1493) 856600
gtyarmouth@yha.org.uk
Open Dates: Please contact the hostel for further information Harwich 96.5km Great Yarmouth 1.2km Frequent from surrounding areas x 40

▲ **Greenhead** 18164
Station Rd, Greenhead, Brampton,
Cumbria CA8 7HG.
(16977) 47401 (16977) 47884
greenhead@yha.org.uk
Open Dates: Please contact the hostel for further information Haltwhistle 4.8km Arriva Northumbria 685 Carlisle-Newcastle Upon Tyne (passes Haltwhistle) x 40

▲ **Grinton Lodge** 18059
Grinton Lodge, Grinton, Richmond,
North Yorkshire DL11 6HS.
(1748) 884206 (1748) 884876
grinton@yha.org.uk
Open Dates: Kirby Stephen 38.6km Arriva 30/6 Richmond-Keld (infrequent) passes Darlington ap Grinton x 69

▲ **Hartington** 18076
Hartington Hall, Hartington, Buxton,
Derbyshire SK17 0AT.
(1298) 84223 (1298) 84415
hartington@yha.org.uk
Open Dates: Buxton 19.3km Bowers 442 from Buxton and Ashbourne Bus Station x 131 1 x

▲ **Hastings** – 18165
Guestling Hall, Rye Rd, Guestling, Hastings,
East Sussex TN35 4LP.
(1424) 812373 (1424) 814273
hastings@yha.org.uk
Open Dates: Please contact the hostel for further information Hastings 8km Stagecoach South Coast 711 Eastbourne-Dover (passes close to Hastings & Rye) x 52

▲ **Hathersage** – 18166
Castleton Rd, Hathersage,
Hope Valley S32 1EH.
(1433) 650493 (1433) 650493
hathersage@yha.org.uk
Open Dates: Please contact the hostel for further information Hathersage 800m First Mainline 214 from Hathersage-Matlock & 272 Sheffield x 40

▲ **Hawes** 18096
Lancaster Terrace, Hawes,
North Yorkshire DL8 3LQ.
(1969) 667368 (1969) 667723
hawes@yha.org.uk
Open Dates: Garsdale 9.6km R Harrington from Garsdale , Dales & District 156/7 from Bedale x 54

▲ **Hawkshead** 18051
Esthwaite Lodge, Hawkshead, Ambleside,
Cumbria LA22 0QD.
(15394) 36293 (15394) 36720
hawkshead@yha.org.uk
Open Dates: Windermere 11.2km Stagecoach in Cumbria 505/6 from Ambleside ap Hawkshead x 109

▲ **Haworth** 18095
Longlands Hall, Longlands Drive, Lees Lane,
Haworth, Keighley, West Yorkshire BD22 8RT.
(1535) 642234 (1535) 643023
haworth@yha.org.uk
Open Dates: Haworth (Worth Valley Railway) 800m Keighley & District 663, 664, 665, M2-4 from Keighley x 92 1 x

▲ **Haydon Bridge** – The Old Repeater Station – 18273
Old Repeater Station, Military Road, Grinton,
near Haydon Bridge, NE47 6NQ.
(1434) 688668 (1434) 688668
les.gibson@tiscali.co.uk
Open Dates: Newcastle 35.4km Tynemouth 56km Haydon Bridge on Newcastle-Carlisle line 6km Hadrian's Wall Bus AD 122 x 12

▲ **Helmsley** – 18167
Carlton Lane, Helmsley, York YO62 5HB.
(1439) 770433 (1439) 770433
helmsley@yha.org.uk
Open Dates: Hull to Zeebrugge, Rotterdam 96.5km Thirsk 24km Stephensons from York , Scarborough and District 128 from Scarborough x 35 R CC

▲ **Helvellyn** – 18168
Greenside, Glenridding, Penrith, Cumbria CA11 0QR.
(17684) 82269 (17684) 82009
helvellyn@yha.org.uk
Open Dates: Please contact the hostel for further information Penrith 22.5km Stagecoach in Cumbria 108 from Penrith ap Glenridding x 60 CC P

High Close ☛ **Langdale**

△ ***Hindhead** – 18169*
Devils Punchbowl, off Portsmouth Rd, Thursley, near Godalming, Surrey GU8 6NS.
(1428) 604285 (1428) 604285
reservations@yha.org.uk
Open Dates: Haslemere 4km Stagecoach in Hants & Surrey 18/9 Aldershot-Haslemere ap Hindhead Area x 12 R CC P

▲ **Holmbury St Mary** 18067
Radnor Lane, Holmbury St Mary, near Dorking, Surrey RH5 6NW.
(1306) 730777 (1306) 730933
holmbury@yha.org.uk
Open Dates: Gomshall 4.8km Arriva Surrey & W Sussex 21, 31 Guildford-Dorking x 52 R CC P

▲ **Honister Hause** – 18171
Seatoller, Keswick, Cumbria CA12 5XN.
(17687) 77267 honister@yha.org.uk
Open Dates: Please contact the hostel for further information Workington 37km 77, 77A (late Easter-October), 79 Keswick-Seatoller 2.4km ap YH x 26 CC P

▲ **Hunstanton** – 18172
15 Avenue Rd, Hunstanton, Norfolk PE36 5BW.
(1485) 532061 (1485) 532632
hunstanton@yha.org.uk
Open Dates: Please contact the hostel for further information Harwich 44km King's Lynn 26km First Eastern Counties 411, 412, 413, 36 ap YH 250m x 45 CC TV P

▲ **Idwal Cottage** – 18173
Nant Ffrancon, Bethesda, Bangor, Gwynedd, Wales LL57 3LZ.
(1248) 600225 (1248) 602952
idwal@yha.org.uk
Open Dates: Please contact the hostel for further information Bangor 18km 6, 7, 66, 67 6km ap Bethesda x 37 R CC P

▲ **Ilam** 18069
Ilam Hall, Ashbourne, Derbyshire DE6 2AZ.
(1335) 350212 (1335) 350350
ilam@yha.org.uk
Open Dates: Please contact the hostel for further information Matlock 22.5km x 135 R CC TV 1 x P

▲ **Ingleton** 18053
Greta Tower, Sammy Lane, Ingleton, Carnforth, Lancashire LA6 3EG.
(15242) 41444 (15242) 41854
ingleton@yha.org.uk
Open Dates: Keighley 6km Keighley & District 663, 664, 665, M2-4 from Keighley x 66 R CC TV P

Ironbridge ☛ **Coalport/Coalbrookdale**

▲ **Ivinghoe** – 18176
The Old Brewery House, High St, Ivinghoe, Leighton Buzzard, Buckinghamshire LU7 9EP.
(1296) 668251 (1296) 662903
ivinghoe@yha.org.uk
Open Dates: Cheddington 4km Arriva The Shires 61 x 48 R CC TV P

▲ **Jersey** – 18264
Haut de la Garenne,
La Rue de la Pouclee des Quatre Chemins,
St Martin, Jersey JE3 6DU.
(1534) 840 100 (1534) 840 119
Jersey@yha.org.uk
Open Dates: 6km 3a St Helier (1 to Gorey after 17.45hrs) 800m x 110
1 x

▲ **Jordans** – 18177
Welders Lane, Jordans, Beaconsfield,
Buckinghamshire HP9 2SN.
(1494) 873135 (1494) 875907
jordans@yha.org.uk
Open Dates: Heathrow 24.14km Seer Green 1km Arriva The Shires 305 1.2km ap Sheer Green x 22
1km

▲ **Keld** – 18178
Keld Lodge, Upper Swaledale, Keld,
Richmond, North Yorkshire DL11 6LL.
(1748) 886259 (1748) 886013
keld@yha.org.uk
Open Dates: Please contact the hostel for further information Kirby Stephen 18km Arriva North East 30/6 from Richmond
x 38

▲ **Kendal** 18066
118 Highgate, Kendal, Cumbria LA9 4HE.
(1539) 724066 (1539) 724906
kendal@yha.org.uk
Open Dates: Please contact the hostel for further information Kendal 1.2km Frequent from surrounding areas
x 54

▲ **Keswick** 18049
Station Rd, Keswick, Cumbria CA12 5LH.
(17687) 72484 (17687) 74129
keswick@yha.org.uk
Open Dates: Penrith 26km Stagecoach in Cumbria X4/5, 555/6
x 91

▲ **Kettlewell** – 18180
Whernside House, Kettlewell, Skipton,
North Yorkshire BD23 5QU.
(1756) 760232 (1756) 760402
kettlewell@yha.org.uk
Open Dates: Skipton 26km Pride of the Dales 74 ap Kettlewell
x 43

▲ **Kielder** – 18181
Kielder, Hexham, Northumberland,
NE48 1HQ.
(1434) 250195 (1434) 250195
kielder@yha.org.uk
Open Dates: Please contact the hostel for further information Hexham 53km Snaith's 814, Postbus 815 x 40

▲ **King's Lynn** – 18182
Thoresby College, College Lane, King's Lynn,
Norfolk PE30 1JB.
(1553) 772461 (1553) 764312
kingslynn@yha.org.uk
Open Dates: Please contact the hostel for further information King's Lynn 1km Frequent from surrounding areas
x 35

▲ **Kings, Dolgellau** – 18183
Kings, Penmaenpool, Dolgellau, Gwynedd,
Wales LL40 1TB.
(1341) 422392 (1341) 422477
kings@yha.org.uk
Open Dates: Please contact the hostel for further information Morfa Mawddach 8km Arriva Cymru 28 4km ap West of Penmaenpool 6SW x 42 (B)

▲ **Kington** – 18263
Victoria Road, Kington, Herefordshire,
HR5 3BX.
(1544) 232745 (1544) 231285
kington@yha.org.uk
Open Dates: Please contact the hostel for further information Leominster 22.5km Kington Mill Street (Rural service)
x 31

Kirk Yetholm ☛ Scotland

▲ **Kirkby Stephen** – 18184
Fletcher Hill, Market St, Kirkby Stephen, Cumbria CA17 4QQ.
(17683) 71793 (17683) 72236
kirkbystephen@yha.org.uk
Open Dates: Please contact the hostel for further information Kirby Stephen 2.5km Various services x 40 CC

▲ **Land's End** – 18185
Letcha Vean, St Just in Penwith, Penzance, Cornwall TR19 7NT. (7km N of Land's End).
(1736) 788437 (1736) 787337
Open Dates: Please contact the hostel for further information Penzance 13km First Western 10 A/B, 11A from Penzance 1km ap St Just x 37 CC

▲ **Langdale** – 18186
High Close, Loughrigg, Ambleside, Cumbria LA22 9HJ.
(15394) 32304 (15394) 34408
langdale@yha.org.uk
Open Dates: 12 Windermere 16km (Any service to Grasmere) Stagecoach in Cumbria S16 from Ambleside 1.2km ap SE of Elterwater x 96 R CC TV

▲ **Langdon Beck** – 18187
Forest-in-Teesdale, Barnard Castle, Co Durham DL12 0XN.
(1833) 622228 (1833) 622372
langdonbeck@yha.org.uk
Open Dates: Please contact the hostel for further information Darlington 53km Arriva North East 95/6 ap High Force x 34 R CC

△ *Langsett – 18188*
Stockbridge, Sheffield S36 4GY.
(1629) 592707 (1226) 761548
reservations@yha.org.uk
Open Dates: 12 Peniston 8km Yorkshire Traction 23, 23a, 24, 24a from Barnsley x 27 R

▲ **Lawrenny** – 18189
Millenium YH, Lawrenny, Kilgetty, Pembrokeshire, Wales SA68 0PN.
(1646) 651270 (1646) 651856
Open Dates: Please contact the hostel for further information Pembroke Dock 19km Kilgetty 13km x 23

▲ **Lee Valley** 18190
Windmill Lane, Cheshunt, Hertfordshire, EN8 9AJ.
(1992) 628392 (1992) 643984
leevalley@yha.org.uk
Open Dates: 12 Stanstead 47km Cheshunt 200m Frequent from surrounding areas 800m 1E x 114 R CC TV 1 x 8

▲ **Leominster** – Leominster Priory – 18191
The Old Priory, Leominster, Herefordshire HR6 8EQ.
(1568) 620517 (1568) 620517
Open Dates: Please contact the hostel for further information Leominster 400m Frequent from surrounding areas 0.2NE x 30 CC

▲ **Littlehampton** – 18194
Littlehampton, West Sussex.
(1903) 882204 (1903) 882776
littlehampton@yha.org.uk
Open Dates: Please contact the hostel for further information Portsmouth, Newhaven Littlehampton 800m 700, 702 (not Suns) x 32 TV

▲ **Litton Cheney** – 18195
Dorchester, Dorset DT2 9AT.
(1308) 482340 (1308) 482636
reservations@yha.org.uk
Open Dates: Please contact the hostel for further information Dorchester South or West 16km First Southern National 31 2.5km ap Whiteway x 22 CC

Liverpool 18039
25 Tabley St (off Wapping), Liverpool L1 8EE.
(151) 7098888 (151) 7090417
liverpool@yha.org.uk
Open Dates: Open Times:
Beds: 108 - 2x3 12x4 1x5 6x6
Price Range: £20.50 BB inc
Directions: 1SW from city centre
Liverpool 8km, Manchester 44km
A 500m Liverpool 1km Lime Street 1.5km U James Street 60m
R CC 3 x
8 P

Liverpool

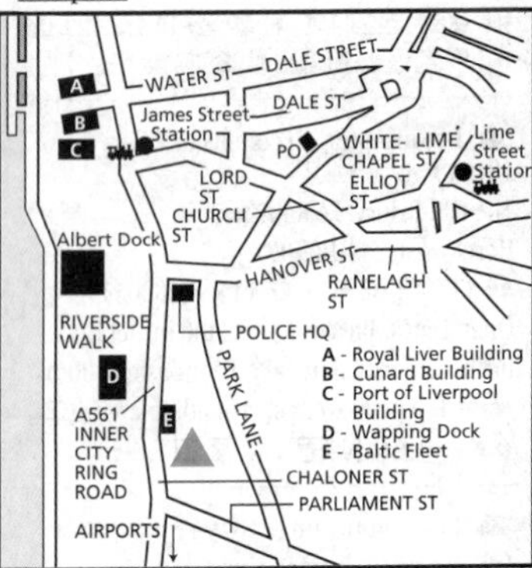

Liverpool... Travel Tips

- **For budget eats check out...** Baltic Fleet, Casa Italia, Yums, Passage to India, China Town
- **For great nightlife try...** Concert Square, Mathew St (including The Cavern), Slater St Area, Empire/Philharmonic/Everyman Theatres, Albert Dock
- **Don't miss...** World Heritage City and European Capital of Culture 2008, Albert Dock, Tate and Walker Art Galleries, Beatles Story, Cavern Quarter and Mathew St., Everton and Liverpool Football Clubs, Anglican and Catholic Cathedrals, FACT Centre and Cinemas, World and Maritime Museums, Numerous Theatres

▲ **Lizard Point** – 18235
Lizard Point Youth Hostel, Lizard, Cornwall, TR12 7NT.
(1326) 291145 (1326) 291238
lizard@yha.org.uk
Open Dates: Please contact the hostel for further information Penzance to Scilly Isles 40km Redruth, Truro 30km
Truronian T1 from Helston x 30
R CC 1 x P
2km

▲ **Llanbedr** – 18196
Plas Newydd, Llanbedr, Barmouth, Gwynedd, Wales LL45 2LE.
(1341) 241287 (1341) 241389
llanbedr@yha.org.uk
Open Dates: Please contact the hostel for further information Llanbedr 800m
Arriva Cymru 38 x 42 CC
P

▲ **Llanberis** – 18197
Llwyn Celyn, Llanberis, Caernarfon, Gwynedd, Wales LL55 4SR.
(1286) 870280 (1286) 870936
llanberis@yha.org.uk
Open Dates: Bangor 18km
Arriva Cymru 94, Bryn Melyn X5, GHA 5 2.5km ap Llangollen x 60 R CC
TV 8 P

▲ **Llanddeusant** – 18198
The Old Red Lion, Llanddeusant, Llangadog, Carmarthenshire, Wales SA19 6UL.
(1550) 740218 (1550) 740218
llanddeusant@yha.org.uk
Open Dates: R Llanagadog 11km
x 26 CC P

▲ **Llangollen** 18077
Tyndwr Hall, Tyndwr Rd, Llangollen, Denbighshire, Wales LL20 8AR.
(1978) 860330 (1978) 861709
llangollen@yha.org.uk
Open Dates: Chirk, Ruabon 8km
Arriva Cymru 94, Bryn Melyn X5, GHA 5
x 134 R CC
P

▲ **Llwyn y Celyn** – 18199
Libanus, Brecon, Powys, Wales LD3 8NH.
(1874) 624261 (1874) 625916
llwynycelyn@yha.org.uk
Open Dates: Merthyr Tydfil 24km
'Sixty-Sixty' 43 x 40 R CC

▲ **Lockton** – 18200
The Old School, Lockton, Pickering, North Yorkshire YO18 7PY.
(1751) 460376 (1751) 460376
Open Dates: Malton 22.5km
Yorkshire Coastliner 840 x 22 R CC

London – City of London 18001
36 Carter Lane, London EC4V 5AB.
(20) 72364965 (20) 72367681
city@yha.org.uk www.yha.org.uk
Open Dates: Open Times:
Beds: 190 - 3x^{1} 6x^{2} 7x^{3} 8x^{4} 8x^{5} 7x^{6} 7x^{6+}
Price Range: £17.20 BB inc
Directions: 2NE from city centre
Heathrow 27km, Gatwick 43km, Luton 52km, Stansted 55km, City 12km Dover 125km Blackfriars 300m, St Pauls 50m
Frequent LT services ap St. Pauls 500m
U Blackfriars 300m, St Pauls 20m x 5
R CC 1 x 1km

London – City of London

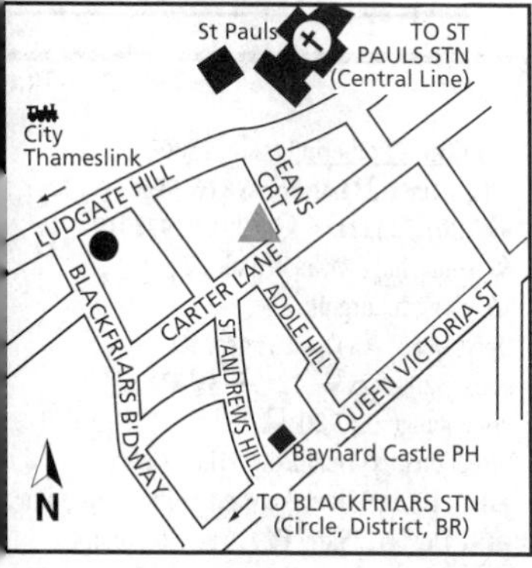

London – Earls Court 18002
38 Bolton Gardens, London SW5 0AQ.
(20) 73737083 (20) 78352034
earlscourt@yha.org.uk
www.yha.org.uk
Open Dates: Open Times:
Beds: 180 - 7x^{2} 2x^{3} 19x^{4} 7x^{6} 6x^{6+}
Price Range: £17.20
Directions: 6SW from city centre
Heathrow 19.5km, Gatwick 40km, Luton 51km, Stansted 60.5km, City 19km
Victoria 2.5km, Waterloo 3.5km, West Brompton 700m C1, 74, N74. N97, Heathrow Airport Express 412 100m
U Earl's Court 300m R CC (B)
1km

London – Earls Court

London – Hampstead Heath 18005
4 Wellgarth Rd, Golders Green, London NW11 7HR.
(20) 84589054 (20) 82090546
hampstead@yha.org.uk
www.yha.org.uk
Open Dates: Open Times:
Beds: 199 - 16x^{2} 9x^{3} 17x^{4} 9x^{5} 2x^{6} 2x^{6+}
Price Range: £17.20 BB inc
Directions: 9NW from city centre
Heathrow 25km, Gatwick 51km, Luton 44km, Stansted 58km, City 21.5km
Kings Cross/St. Pancras 8km 210, 268 400m ap North End Road U Northern, Golder's Green 750m x 36 R CC

London – Hampstead Heath

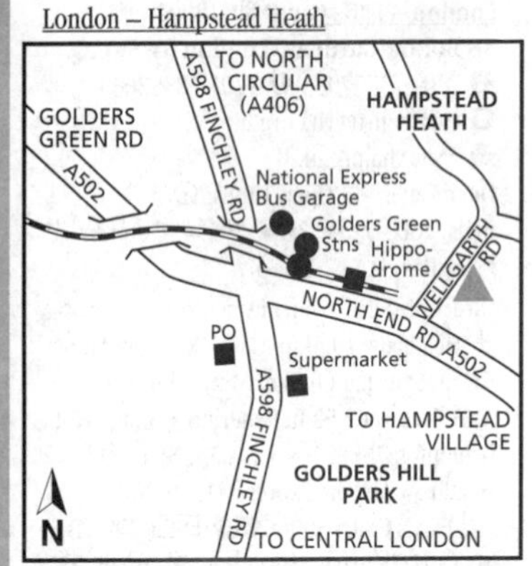

London – Holland House 18004
Holland House, Holland Walk, Kensington, London W8 7QU.
(20) 79370748 (20) 73760667
hollandhouse@yha.org.uk
www.yha.org.uk
Open Dates: Open Times:
Beds: 200 - 1x1 1x2 1x3 1x4 1x6 13x6+
Price Range: £17.20 BBinc
Directions: 6SW from city centre
Heathrow 19.5km, Gatwick 42km, Luton 49km, Stansted 62km, City 19km
A Airbus Paddington 3.2km, Waterloo 14.4km 9, 10 50m ap Kensington High Street U Holland Park, Circle Line 400m, High Street, Kensington 400m R CC
1 x

London – Holland House

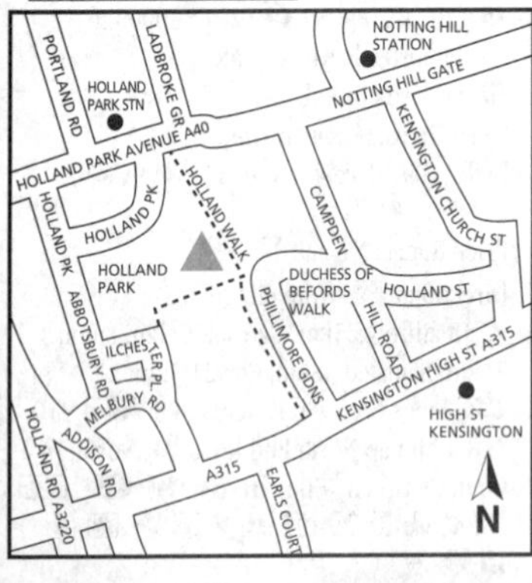

London – Oxford Street 18007
14 Noel St, London W1F 8GJ.
(20) 77341618 (20) 77341657
oxfordst@yha.org.uk www.yha.org.uk
Open Dates: Open Times:
Beds: 75 - 24x2 5x3 3x4
Price Range: £17.20
Directions: Heathrow 25km, Gatwick 44km, Luton 50km, Stansted 56km, City 15km
A A2 Kings Cross & Marble Arch 1.5km
Victoria 3km, Waterloo 3km, Kings Cross 1.5km 10, 8, 73, 25, 55, 176 200m, 6, 12, 13, 15, 23, 94, 139, 113 40m ap Oxford Street, Regent Street U Central, Bakerloo and Victoria Lines to Oxford Circus 400m, or Northern and Central Lines to Tottenham Court Road 500m R CC

London – Oxford Street

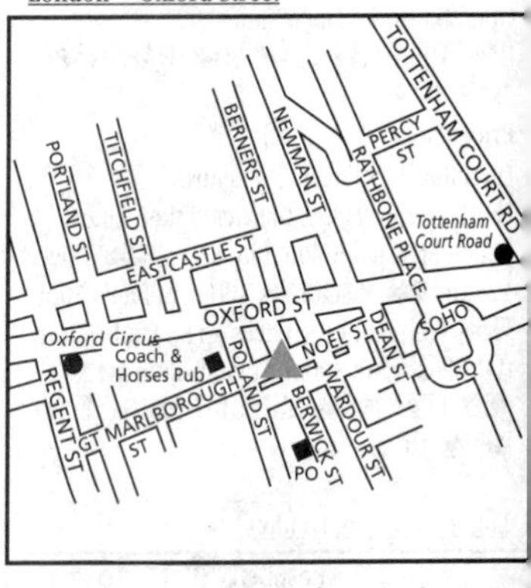

London – Rotherhithe 18003
20 Salter Rd, London SE16 5PR.
(20) 72322114 (20) 72372919
rotherhithe@yha.org.uk
www.yha.org.uk
Open Dates: Open Times:
Beds: 320 - 22x2 12x4 3x6+
Price Range: £17.20 BBinc
Directions: Heathrow 31km, Gatwick 44km, Luton 57km, Stansted 56km, City 10km
Dover 125km Waterloo 6km
381, N381 ap YH U Rotherhithe 400m
R CC
3 x
2km

London – Rotherhithe

RIVER THAMES
ROTHERHITHE STREET
SALTER ROAD
SWAN RD
BRUNEL ROAD
Surrey Water
Canal
Rotherhithe Station (East London Line)
Rotherhithe Tunnel Approach
To Canada Water Station (Jubilee Line)
N
500m

London – St Pancras 18025
79-81 Euston Rd, London NW1 2QS.
(20) 73889998 (20) 73886766
stpancras@yha.org.uk
www.yha.org.uk
Open Dates: Open Times:
Beds: 152 - 10x2 1x3 18x4 3x5 7x6
Price Range: £17.20 BBinc
Directions: Heathrow 25.5km, Gatwick 45km, Luton 49.5km, Stansted 54km, City 15km A Airbus 48km Kings Cross 200m, Euston 200m 73 100m U Kings Cross 200m, Euston 200m R CC (BD)

London – St Pancras

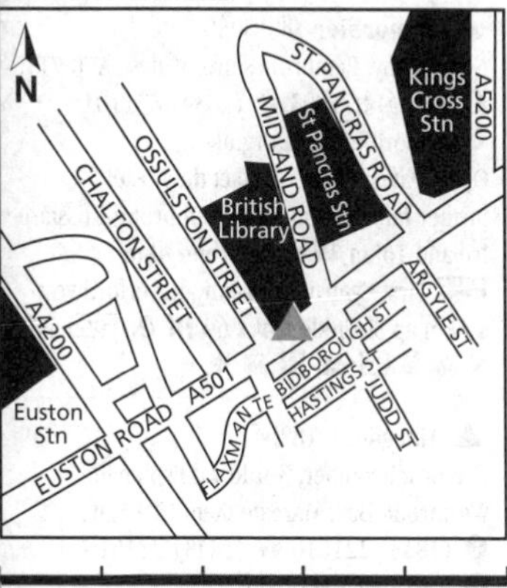

▲ **London** – YHA South Kensington – 18265
65-67 Queensgate, London SW7 5JS
(20) 75847031 (20) 75906902
bph.hostel@scout.org.uk
Open Dates: Paddington 4.8km
74, 70 ap YH x 180

London... Travel Tips

- **For budget eats check out...** London YHA hostels (5), Chinatown, Troubador Coffee House (2 mins from Earls Court), Noodle Zone (Hampstead Heath), Wagamamas (Holland House)
- **For great nightlife try...** Covent Garden, Leicester Square, Camden Markets, Trafalgar Square, Bagleys Studio
- **Don't miss...** London Eye, Tate Modern, Madame Tussauds, London Zoo, Tower Bridge & The Tower of London, British Museum, Imperial War Museum, Science Museum, Planetarium, National Gallery, YHA Explorer Packages including London History Explorer, London City Sights Explorer and London Groups Explorer - For more information visit the YHA website: www.yha.org.uk under "Stay at YHA"

Longthwaite ☛ **Borrowdale**

▲ **Lulworth Cove** – 18201
School Lane, West Lulworth, Wareham, Dorset BH20 5SA.
(1929) 400564 (1929) 400640
lulworth@yha.org.uk
Open Dates: Please contact the hostel for further information Wool 8km
First Southern National 103 x 34
CC

▲ **Lynton** – 18202
Lynbridge, Lynton, Devon EX35 6AZ.
(1598) 753237 (1598) 753305
lynton@yha.org.uk
Open Dates: Barnstaple 32km
First Red Bus 309, 310, 300 x 36
R CC

▲ Malham 18063
John Dower Memorial Hostel, Malham, Skipton, North Yorkshire BD23 4DE.
(1729) 830321 (1729) 830551
malham@yha.org.uk
Open Dates: Settle 11km
Postbus, Pennine 210 from Skipton, Dales Bus from West Yorkshire x 82

▲ Malvern Hills 18088
18 Peachfield Rd, Malvern Wells, Malvern, Worcestershire WR14 4AP.
(1684) 569131 (1684) 565205
malvern@yha.org.uk
Open Dates: Please contact the hostel for further information Great Malvern 1.6km
Frequent from surrounding areas
x 58

Manchester 18021
Potato Wharf, Castlefield, Manchester M3 4NB.
(161) 8399960 (161) 8352054
manchester@yha.org.uk
Open Dates: Open Times:
Beds: 144 - 30x4 4x6
Price Range: £20.50 BB inc
Directions: 0.5SW from city centre
Manchester 16km A 380 or 325
Liverpool 44km Manchester Piccadilly 1.5km 33 50m ap Liverpool Road GMEX 300m ap GMEX
3 x
100m

Manchester

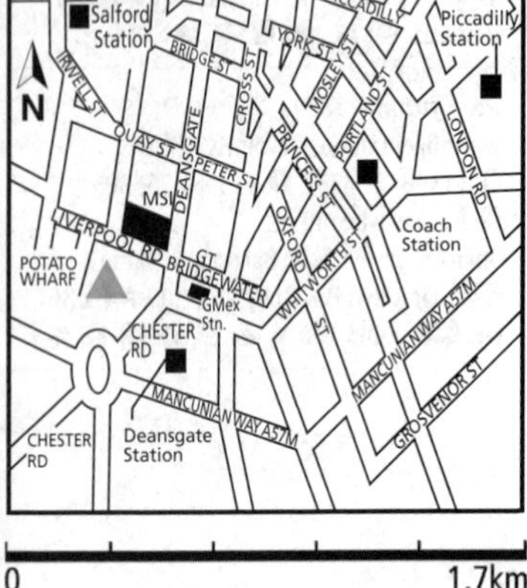

Manchester... Travel Tips
- **For budget eats check out...** Dimitri's Tapas Bar (Castlefield), Rusholmes Curry Mile, The Eighth Day Vegetarian Café, Buy The Slice Pizza, The Oxnoble Hotel just round corner from the YHA
- **For great nightlife try...** The Comedy Store, Paradise Factory (legendary Gay Nightclubs), Manto's, The Venue (full of Smiths & Stone Roses Fan's), Havana Bar (free Salsa lessons some nights)
- **Don't miss...** Industrial Revolutionary Action at the Museum of Science & Industry, Imperial War Museum North, URBIS (Exploring cultural differences in cities around the world), Manchester United Football Stadium & Tour, The Lowry - National Landmark Millennium Project for the Arts, Whitworth Art Gallery, Textile & Design Exhibitions, Peoples Museum (dedicated exhibition of ordinary people), Waterways River Trips (experience travel on the canal), Manchester Jewish Museum, The Trafford Centre (indoor shopping)

▲ Mankinholes – 18203
Todmorden, Lancashire OL14 6HR.
(1706) 812340 (1706) 812340
mankinholes@yha.org.uk
Open Dates: Please contact the hostel for further information Todmorden 5km
First CalderlineT6, T8 from Todmorden ap YH 5SE x 32

▲ Manorbier 18056
Near Tenby, Pembrokeshire, Wales SA70 7TT.
(1834) 871803 (1834) 871101
manorbier@yha.org.uk
Open Dates: Please contact the hostel for further information Pembroke-Rosslare Ireland 16km Manorbier 4km
First Cymru 349 Tenby-Haverfordwest 1.6km ap Skrinkle x 69

▲ Margate – 18204
The Beachcomber, 3-4 Royal Esplanade, Westbrook Bay, Margate, Kent CT9 5DL.
(1843) 221616 (1843) 221616
margate@yha.org.uk
Open Dates: London (Manston) 5km
Dover 30.5km Margate 500m
Ramsgate, Canterbury & surrounding areas
0.7W x 55

▲ **Marloes Sands** – 18205
Runwayskiln, Marloes, Haverfordwest, Pembrokeshire, Wales SA62 3BH.
(1646) 636667 (1646) 636667
reservations@yha.org.uk
Open Dates: Please contact the hostel for further information Pembroke-Rosslare Ireland 11km Milford Haven 18km Haverfordwest or Milford Haven (infrequent - not daily) 1.6km ap Marloes x 26

▲ **Matlock** 18064
40 Bank Rd, Matlock, Derbyshire DE4 3NF.
(1629) 582983 (1629) 583484
matlock@yha.org.uk
Open Dates: Matlock 400m Frequent from surrounding areas x 52 R CC

▲ **Medway** 18065
Capstone Farm, Capstone Rd, Gillingham, Kent ME7 3JE.
(1634) 400788 (1634) 400794
medway@yha.org.uk
Open Dates: Please contact the hostel for further information Dover, Ramsgate, Folkestone 64km Chatham 3km Nu-venture 114 200m ap Luton Rec Ground x 40 CC

▲ **Meerbrook** – 18207
Old School, Meerbrook, Leek, Staffordshire ST13 8SJ.
(1538) 702304 (1538) 702304
dimmingsdale@yha.org.uk
Open Dates: Please contact the hostel for further information Stoke-on-Trent 24km First PMT X18 Sheffield-Keele 3km ap Blackshaw Moor x 22 CC

Milton Keynes ☛ **Bradwell Village**

▲ **Minehead** – 18208
Alcombe Combe, Minehead, Somerset TA24 6EW.
(1643) 702595 (1643) 703016
minehead@yha.org.uk
Open Dates: Minehead, Dunster 3km First Southern National 28, 928 Taunton-Minehead 1.2km ap Alcombe x 35 R CC

▲ **Newcastle upon Tyne** 18024
107 Jesmond Rd, Newcastle upon Tyne NE2 1NJ.
(191) 2812570 (191) 2818779
newcastle@yha.org.uk
Open Dates: Newcastle 11km Jesmond 400m Frequent from surrounding areas x 50 R CC

▲ **Ninebanks** – 18210
Orchard House, Mohope, Ninebanks, Hexham, Northumberland NE47 8DO.
(1434) 345288 (1434) 345414
ninebanks@yha.org.uk
www.yha.ninebanks.co.uk
Open Dates: Newcastle 61km Haydon Bridge 17.7km Wrights 889 Hexham-Alston (Tue, Fri only) otherwise 888 Keswick-Newcastle ap Ouston x 26 CC

▲ **Okehampton** – 18211
Klondyke Rd, Okehampton, Devon EX20 1EW.
(1837) 53916 (1837) 53965
okehampton@yha.org.uk
Open Dates: Okehampton First Western X9/10 Exeter-Bude (Exeter St David's) ap Okehampton 0.5SW x 102 R CC

▲ **Once Brewed** 18104
Military Rd, Bardon Mill, Hexham, Northumberland NE47 7AN.
(1434) 344360 (1434) 344045
oncebrewed@yha.org.uk
Open Dates: Bardon Mill 4km White Star 185 from Carlisle ap Housesteads x 90 R CC

▲ **Osmotherley** 18103
Cote Ghyll, Osmotherley, Northallerton, North Yorkshire DL6 3AH.
(1609) 883575 (1609) 883715
osmotherley@yha.org.uk
Open Dates: Newcastle 80km Northallerton 13km Arriva 80/89 Northallerton-Stokesley ap Osmotherley x 72 R CC

Oxford 18019
2a Botley Rd, Oxford OX2 0AB.
(1865) 727275 (1865) 251182
oxford@yha.org.uk www.yha.org.uk
Open Dates: Open Times:
Beds: 184 - 8x² 12x⁴ 20x⁶
Price Range: 18.00 BB inc
Directions: 0.5W from city centre
Heathrow 80km, Gatwick 176km
A Regular bus from Gatwick & Heathrow 100m Portsmouth 136km Oxford 50m Frequent from surrounding areas
x 20 R CC
1 x

Oxford

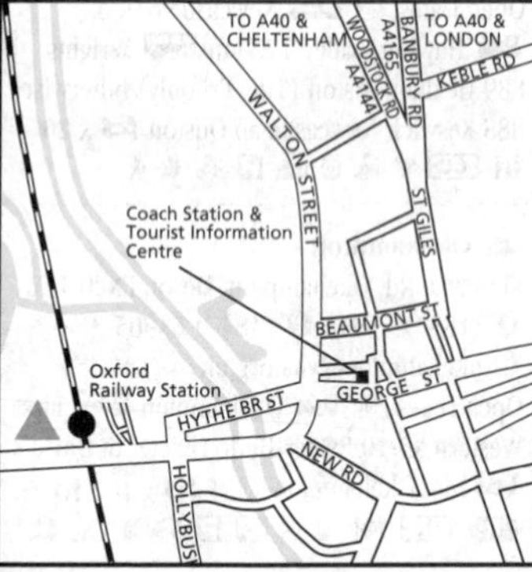

Oxford... Travel Tips

- **For budget eats check out...** YHA Oxford, Local Pubs - Wheatsheaf (High St), White House Pub (next door to YHA), Emayl (Park End St, nr YHA), The Nose Bag (off Cornmarket)
- **For great nightlife try...** Eagle and Child Pub (St. Giles), The Zodiac, Kazbar (Mediterranean Bar/Restaurant, Cowley Road), Po Na Na Souk Bar, Phoenix Independent Cinema (Jericho)
- **Don't miss...** University Botanic Gardens, Oxford Covered Market, Carfax Tower, Apollo Theatre, Museum of Modern Art, Christchurch & Picture Gallery, Blenheim Palace, The Ashmolean Museum, Pitt Rivers Museum, Boating on The Thames

▲ **Patterdale** 18055
Goldrill House, Patterdale, Penrith, Cumbria CA11 0NW.
(17684) 82394 (17684) 82034
patterdale@yha.org.uk
Open Dates: Ullswater Steamer (Mar-Oct) 1.6km Penrith 24km
Stagecoach Cumberland/Postbus 108 from Penrith x 82 R CC

▲ **Penycwm (Solva)** – 18212
Solva, Whitehouse, Penycwm, near Solva, Haverfordwest, Pembrokeshire, Wales SA62 6LA.
(1437) 721940 (1437) 720959
penycwm@yha.org.uk
Open Dates: Fishguard-Rosslare (Ireland) 19km Fishguard Harbour 32km Richards 411 ap Penycwm 4SE
x 26 R

▲ **Pen-y-Pass** 18078
Nantgwynant, Caernarfon, Gwynedd, Wales LL55 4NY.
(1286) 870428 (1286) 872434
penypass@yha.org.uk
Open Dates: Please contact the hostel for further information Bangor 29km
Snowdon Sherpa 96A from Llanberis, 96, 97A from Lladudno Pass, 97A from Porthmadog x 84 CC

▲ **Penzance** 18032
Castle Horneck, Alverton, Penzance, Cornwall TR20 8TF.
(1736) 362666 (1736) 362663
penzance@yha.org.uk
Open Dates: Isles of Scilly 2km Penzance 2km First 5, 6, from Penzance 1W x 80 R CC

▲ **Perranporth** – 18213
Droskyn Point, Perranporth, Cornwall TR6 0GS.
(1872) 573812 (1872) 573812
Open Dates: Please contact the hostel for further information Truro 14.4km
First Western National 57 St Ives-Newquay, 87A/B/C Truro-Newquay
x 26 CC

▲ **Poppit Sands** – 18214
'Sea View', Poppit, Cardigan, Pembrokeshire, Wales SA43 3LP.
(1239) 612936 (1239) 612936
poppit@yha.org.uk
Open Dates: Please contact the hostel for further information Fishguard-Rosslare (Ireland) 32km Fishguard Harbour 32km Richards 407/9 from Cardigan, Poppit Rocket from Fishguard to Poppit Sands x 34

▲ **Port Eynon** – 18215
The Old Lifeboat House, Port Eynon, Swansea, Wales SA3 1NN.
(1792) 391794 (1792) 391623
porteynon@yha.org.uk
Open Dates: Swansea (ferries to Ireland) 25km Swansea 25.7km 18A from Swansea centre x 28 R CC

▲ **Portland** – 18216
Hardy House, Castle Rd, Portland, Dorset DT5 1AU.
(1305) 861368 (1305) 861568
portland@yha.org.uk
Open Dates: White Boat Services from Weymouth Quay to Portland Castle (May-Oct), Condor Ferries to Channel Islands (Mar-Oct) Weymouth 8.8km Sureline 1X, X10 Weymouth seafront, FirstBus 1 Debenhams Store x 28 R CC

▲ **Portsmouth** 18035
Wymering Manor, Old Wymering Lane, Cosham, Portsmouth, Hampshire PO6 3NL.
(23) 92375661 (23) 92214177
portsmouth@yha.org.uk
Open Dates: Portsmouth to Caen, Cherbourg, St Malo, Le Havre, Santander, Bilbao. Also Isle of Wight Cosham 800m Frequent from surrounding areas 6NE x 50 R CC

▲ **Pwll Deri** – 18217
Castell Mawr, Tref Asser, Goodwick, Pembrokeshire, Wales SA64 0LR.
(1348) 891385 (1348) 891385
Open Dates: Please contact the hostel for further information Fishguard-Rosslare (Ireland) 7.2km Fishguard Harbour 7.2km Richards 410 Fishguard - Goodwick (connections from Haverfordwest) ap Goodwick x 30 CC

△ ***Quantock Hills** – 18218*
Sevenacres, Holford, Bridgewater, Somerset TA5 1SQ.
(1278) 741224 (1278) 741224
reservations@yha.org.uk
Open Dates: Bridgewater 20.9km First Southern National 15, 915, 927 Bridgewater-Minehead x 24 R CC

▲ **Ravenstor** 18092
Millers Dale, Buxton, Derbyshire SK17 8SS.
(1298) 871826 (1298) 871275
ravenstor@yha.org.uk
Open Dates: Please contact the hostel for further information Buxton 12.8km From Sheffield, Buxton (passes close Sheffield & Buxton) x 83 R CC TV 1 x

▲ **Ridgeway** 18052
Ridgeway Centre, Courthill, Wantage, Oxfordshire OX12 9NE.
(12357) 60253 (12357) 68865
ridgeway@yha.org.uk
Open Dates: Please contact the hostel for further information Didcot Parkway 16km 32a/b, X35, 36 3km ap Wantage x 59 CC TV

▲ **River Dart** – 18206
Maypool House, Galmpton, Brixham, Devon TQ5 0ET.
(1803) 842444 (1803) 845939
maypool@yha.org.uk
Open Dates: Please contact the hostel for further information Plymouth-Rosscoff 58km Paignton 8km Stagecoach Devon 12 3km ap Churston Grammar School x 65 CC TV

▲ Rowen – 18219
Rhiw Farm, Rowen, Conwy, Wales LL32 8YW.
(1492) 650089 (1492) 593580
Open Dates: Please contact the hostel for further information Tal-y-Cafn 4.8km Arriva Cymru 19 Llandudno-Llanwrst ap Rowen PO x 24 TV P

▲ Saffron Walden – 18220
1 Myddylton Place, Saffron Walden, Essex CB10 1BB.
(1799) 523117 (1799) 520840
saffron@yha.org.uk
Open Dates: Please contact the hostel for further information Audley End 4km Frequent local services (including link with Audley End and Stanstead Airport) x 40 CC P

▲ Salcombe – 18221
'Overbecks', Sharpitor, Salcombe, Devon TQ8 8LW.
(1548) 842856 (1548) 843865
Open Dates: Please contact the hostel for further information Totnes 32km Tally Ho! from Kingsbridge (connects from Plymouth, Dartmouth and for connections from Totnes) ap South Sands. (10mins walk up the hill to 'Overbecks') x 51 CC TV P

▲ Salisbury HI 18022
Milford Hill House, Milford Hill, Salisbury, Wiltshire SP1 2QW.
(1722) 327572 (1722) 330446
salisbury@yha.org.uk
Open Dates: 12 Portsmouth to Caen, Cherbourg, St Malo, Le Havre, Santander Salisbury 1.6km Frequent from surrounding areas x 70 CC (BL) TV i 8 P

▲ Sandown – 18222
The Firs, Fitzroy St, Sandown, Isle of Wight PO36 8JH.
(1983) 402651 (1983) 403565
sandown@yha.org.uk
Open Dates: Please contact the hostel for further information Ryde Pierhead (Wightlink) 9.6km Sandown 800m Frequent from surrounding areas x 47 CC TV P

▲ Scarborough – 18223
The White House, Burniston Rd, Scarborough, North Yorkshire YO13 0DA.
(1723) 361176 (1723) 500054
scarborough@yha.org.uk
Open Dates: 12 Hull to Zeebrugge, Rotterdam 72km Scarborough 3km Frequent from surrounding areas 3N x 48 R CC P

▲ Sheringham – 18224
1 Cremer's Drift, Sheringham, Norfolk NR26 8HX.
(1263) 823215 (1263) 824679
sheringham@yha.org.uk
Open Dates: Please contact the hostel for further information Sheringham 400m First Eastern Counties/Sanders 50, 50A, X98 Kings Lynn-Cromer x 100 R CC TV P

▲ Sherwood Forest HI 18034
Forest Corner, Edwinstowe, Nottinghamshire, NG21 9RN.
(1623) 825794 (1623) 825796
sherwood@yha.org.uk
Open Dates: 12 Mansfield Woodhouse 13km Stagecoach 10, 100/13, 33, 233 x 39 R CC P

△ Shining Cliff – 18225
Shining Cliff Woods, Jackass Lane, near Ambergate, Derbyshire DE56 2RE.
(7788) 725938 (1629) 592627
reservations@yha.org.uk
Open Dates: Please contact the hostel for further information Ambergate 2.4km TP from Derby 2.4km ap Hurt Arms - Ambergate x 18 P

▲ Slaidburn – 18228
King's House, Slaidburn, Clitheroe, Lancashire BB7 3ER.
(1200) 446656
slaidburn@yha.org.uk
Open Dates: Please contact the hostel for further information Clitheroe 13km 110/1 x 30 CC P

▲ Slimbridge Ⓗ 18099
Shepherd's Patch, Slimbridge, Gloucestershire GL2 7BP.
(1453) 890275 (1453) 890625
slimbridge@yha.org.uk
Open Dates: Please contact the hostel for further information Cam & Dursley 5km Stagecoach 20, 91 2.4km ap Slimbridge roundabout x 56 R CC

▲ Snowdon Ranger Ⓗ 18079
Rhyd Ddu, Caernarfon, Gwynedd, Wales LL54 7YS.
(1286) 650391 (1286) 650093
snowdon@yha.org.uk
Open Dates: 12 Holyhead to Dun Laoghaire (Ireland) 48km Bangor 25km Snowdon Sherpa 95/S4 x 59 R CC

Solva ☛ Penycwm

▲ St Briavels Castle Ⓗ 18062
The Castle, St Briavels, Lydney, Gloucestershire GL15 6RG.
(1594) 530272 (1594) 530849
stbriavels@yha.org.uk
Open Dates: Please contact the hostel for further information Chepstow 11km Frequent from surrounding areas x 70 R CC

△ ***St David's** – 18229*
Llaethdy, St David's, Haverfordwest, Pembrokeshire, Wales SA62 6PR.
(1437) 720345 (1437) 721831
stdavids@yha.org.uk
Open Dates: Please contact the hostel for further information Fishguard Rosslare (Ireland) 24km Fishguard Harbour, Haverfordwest 24km Richards 411 3km ap St David's x 40 CC

▲ Stainforth Ⓗ 18080
Taitlands, Stainforth, Settle, North Yorkshire BD24 9PA.
(1729) 823577 (1729) 825404
stainforth@yha.org.uk
Open Dates: 12 Settle 4km Bibby's/ Kirkby Lonsdale Coaches x 47 R CC 8

△ ***Steps Bridge** – 18230*
Dunsford, Exeter, Devon EX6 7EQ.
(1647) 252435 (1647) 252948
bellever@yha.org.uk
Open Dates: Please contact the hostel for further information Exeter Central/Exeter St David's 14.5km Stagecoach 359 x 24 CC

▲ Stow-on-the-Wold Ⓗ 18081
The Square, Stow-on-the-Wold, The Cotswolds, Gloucestershire GL54 1AF.
(1451) 830497 (1451) 870102
stow@yha.org.uk
Open Dates: Please contact the hostel for further information Moreton-in-Marsh, Kingham 6km Pulhams PI, Stagecoach 55 x 48 R CC TV 8

▲ Stratford-upon-Avon Ⓗ 18008
Alveston, Stratford-upon-Avon, Warwickshire CV37 7RG.
(1789) 297093 (1789) 205513
stratford@yha.org.uk
Open Dates: 12 Birmingham 32km
A National Express 3.5km
Stratford-upon-Avon 4.5km X18 or 77 ap YH x 132 R CC TV 1 x i 8

▲ Streatley-on-Thames Ⓗ 18070
Hill House, Reading Rd, Streatley, Reading, Berkshire RG8 9JJ.
(1491) 872278 (1491) 873056
streatley@yha.org.uk
Open Dates: 12 Goring & Streatley 1.6km Thames Travel 132 x 49 R CC TV

▲ Street – 18231
The Chalet, Ivythorn Hill, Street, Somerset BA16 0TZ.
(1458) 442961 (1458) 442738
street@yha.org.uk
Open Dates: 12 Castle Cary 18km 376, 676, 976/7 500m ap Marshalls Elm x 28 R CC

▲ **Swanage** – 18232
Cluny, Cluny Crescent, Swanage,
Dorset BH19 2BS.
(1929) 422113 (1929) 426327
swanage@yha.org.uk
Open Dates: Please contact the hostel for further information Cherbourg/Poole 24km Wareham 16km Wilts & Dorest 150, 142-4 400m ap Swanage x 100 (B)

△ ***Tanners Hatch*** *– 18233*
Off Ranmore Rd, Polesden Lacey, Dorking, Surrey RH5 6BE.
(1306) 877964 (1306) 877964
tanners@yha.org.uk
Open Dates: Gatwick 32km Box Hill & Westhumble 2.8km 465 3.6km ap West Humble x 25

▲ **Telscombe** – 18234
Bank Cottages, Telscombe, Lewes,
East Sussex BN7 3HZ.
(1273) 301357 (1273) 301357
reservations@yha.org.uk
Open Dates: Please contact the hostel for further information Newhaven 8km Southease 4km 14a 1.2km ap Telcombe Rd, Peacehaven x 22

△ ***Thoralby*** *– Bishopdale Valley Bunkhouse – 18274*
The Old School Bunkhouse, Bishopdale Valley, Thoralby, Leybun, North Yorkshire, DL8 3TB
(1629) 592700 (1629) 592627
reservations@yha.org.uk
Open Dates: Please contact the hostel for further information Garsdale 25.7km, Northallerton 38.6km, Skipton 45km Service 156 (Leyburn-Hawes) and Post Bus to Thoralby x 20

▲ **Thurlby** – 18236
16 High St, Thurlby, Bourne,
Lincolnshire PE10 0EE.
(1778) 425588 (1778) 425588
thurlby@yha.org.uk
Open Dates: Peterborough 24km Delaine's service from Peterborough x 24

△ ***Tintagel*** *– 18237*
Dunderhole Point, Tintagel, Cornwall PL34 0DW.
(1840) 770334 (1840) 770733
reservations@yha.org.uk
Open Dates: Please contact the hostel for further information Bodmin Parkway 32km Please check before travelling 1.2km ap Tintagel x 22

▲ **Totland Bay** – 18238
Hurst Hill, Totland Bay,
Isle of Wight PO39 0HD.
(1983) 752165 (1983) 756443
totland@yha.org.uk
Open Dates: Yarmouth 5km 7a/b, 42 400m ap Totland War Memorial x 56

▲ **Trefdraeth** – Newport – 18209
Lower St Mary St, Newport, Pembrokeshire, Wales SA42 0TS.
(1239) 820080 (1239) 820080
reservations@yha.org.uk
Open Dates: Please contact the hostel for further information Fishguard-Rosslare (Ireland) 14.5km Fishguard Harbour 14.5km Richards 412 x 28

▲ **Trefin** – Trevine – 18239
Fford-yr-Afon Trevine, Haverfordwest, Pembrokeshire, Wales SA62 5AU.
(1348) 831414 (1348) 831414
reservations@yha.org.uk
Open Dates: Please contact the hostel for further information Fishguard-Rosslare (Ireland) 19km Fishguard Harbour 19km 411 x 26

△ ***Tregaron Bunkhouse*** *– 18119*
Tregaron, Ceredigion, Wales SY25 6HL.
(1974) 298953
reservations@yha.org.uk
Open Dates: Aberystwyth 32km Arriva Cymru 516, James 589 3km ap Tregaron x 16

▲ **Treyarnon Bay** – 18240
Tregonnan, Treyarnon, Padstow, Cornwall PL28 8JR.
(1841) 520322 (1841) 521457
treyanon@yha.org.uk
Open Dates: Newquay (not Sun except Jun-Sept) 16km First Western National 55 7km ap Padstow x 41

▲ **Truleigh Hill** – 18241
Tottington Barn, Truleigh Hill, Shoreham-by-Sea, West Sussex BN43 5FB.
(1903) 813419 (1903) 812016
truleighhill@yha.org.uk
Open Dates: Shoreham-by-Sea 6.4km Compass 100 BR Pulborough-Henfield ap Junction of the Edburton Rd x 56

△ ***Tyncornel** – 18242*
Llanddewi-Brefi, Tregaron, Ceredigion, Wales SY25 6PH.
(1629) 592708 (1629) 592627
reservations@yha.org.uk
Open Dates: Aberystwyth 45km Arriva Cymru 516, James 589 Aberystwyth-Tregaron, some calling, some with connections on James 588 to Llanddewi-Brefi ap Tregaron x 16

▲ **Wastwater** – 18243
Wasdale Hall, Wasdale, Seascale, Cumbria CA20 1ET.
(19467) 26222 (19467) 26056
wastwater@yha.org.uk
Open Dates: Irton Road (Ravenglass & Eskdale Railway) 8.8km Stagecoach In Cumbria 6, X 6, Whitehaven-Seascale and Gosforth x 50

▲ **Wells-Next-The-Sea** – 18244
Church Plain, Wells-Next-The-Sea, Norfolk NR23 1EQ.
(1328) 711748 (1328) 711748
wellsnorfolk@yha.org.uk
Open Dates: Please contact the hostel for further information Sheringham 29km Coastliner (hourly) & Fakenham 0.5S x 32

▲ **Welsh Bicknor** 18100
The Rectory, Welsh Bicknor, near Goodrich, Ross-on-Wye, Herefordshire HR9 6JJ.
(1594) 860300 (1594) 861276
welshbicknor@yha.org.uk
Open Dates: Please contact the hostel for further information Lydney 19km Stagecoach in Wye & Dean 34 ap Goodrich x 76

▲ **Whitby** 18102
East Cliff, Whitby, North Yorkshire YO22 4JT.
(1947) 602878 (1947) 825146
whitby@yha.org.uk
Open Dates: Whitby 800m Frequent from surrounding areas x 58 8

Wight, Isle of ☛ **Sandown and Totland**

▲ **Wilderhope Manor** 18101
The John Cadbury Memorial Hostel, Longville in the Dale, Much Wenlock, Shropshire TF13 6EG.
(1694) 771363 (1694) 771520
wilderhope@yha.org.uk
Open Dates: Please contact the hostel for further information Church Stretton 12.8km Choice Travel 712 from Ludlow x 70

▲ **Windermere** 18048
Bridge Lane, Troutbeck, Windermere, Cumbria LA23 1LA.
(15394) 43543 (15394) 47165
windermere@yha.org.uk
Open Dates: Windermere (YHA operate a free Shuttle Bus transfer to the hostel Easter-Oct) 3km Frequent from surrounding areas ap Troutbeck Bridge x 69

▲ **Woody's Top** – 18246
Ruckland, near Louth, Lincolnshire LN11 8RQ.
(1507) 533323 (1507) 533323
woodystop@yha.org.uk
Open Dates: Please contact the hostel for further information Hull to Zeebrugge, Rotterdam 72km Thorpe Culvert 29km Post Bus from Louth, Translinc 6C x 22

▲ **Wooler** – Cheviot – 18247
30 Cheviot St, Wooler,
Northumberland NE71 6LW.
(1668) 281365 (1668) 282368
wooler@yha.org.uk
Open Dates: Please contact the hostel for further information
Berwick-upon-Tweed 25km Arriva Northumbria/Travelsure 464, Border Village 267 from Berwick Upon Tweed, Travelsure 470/3 from Alnwick x 46

York 18009
York International, Water End, Clifton, York, North Yorkshire YO30 6LP.
(1904) 653147 (1904) 651230
york@yha.org.uk
Open Dates: Open Times:
Beds: 150 - 1x1 7x2 1x3 21x4 4x6 3x6+
Price Range: £19 BBinc
Directions: 1.5NW from city centre
Leeds-Bradford 40km Hull to Zeebrugge, Rotterdam 80km York 2km FirstYork 2, 17 50m ap Clifton Green
x 21 1 x 2km

York

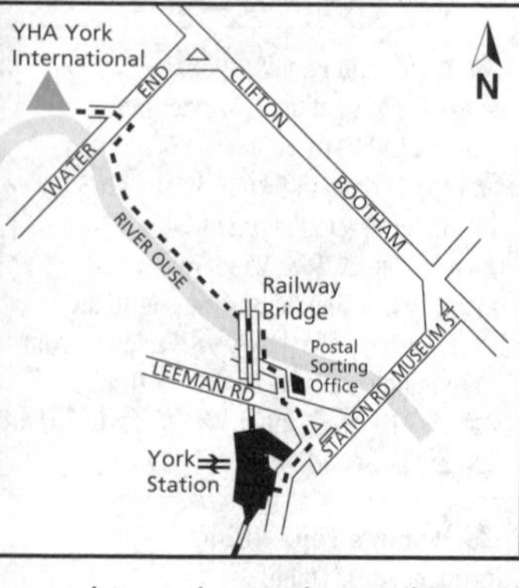

York... Travel Tips

- **For budget eats check out...** YHA York, La Piazza, Lendal Cellars, Fiesta Mehicana, La Romantica
- **For great nightlife try...** Theatre Royal, Grand Opera House, Floodlit Cruise, The Gallery, The Micklegate Run
- **Don't miss...** Jorvik Viking Centre, York Minster, City Walls, National Railway Museum, York Dungeon, City Sightseeing, Clifford's Tower, The Ghost Trail, York Boat, Castle Howard

---

▲ **Youlgreave** 18093
Fountain Square, Youlgreave, Bakewell, Derbyshire DE45 1UR.
(1629) 636518 (1629) 636518
youlgreave@yha.org.uk
Open Dates: R Matlock 16km Hulleys 170/1 from Bakewell (with connections from Chesterfield & Matlock) x 42

▲ **Ystradfellte** – 18248
Tai'r Heol, Ystradfellte, Aberdare, Wales CF44 9JF.
(1639) 720301 (1639) 720301
ystradfellte@yha.org.uk
Open Dates: Please contact the hostel for further information Aberdare 16km First Cymru X5, 160/1 Swansea-Glynneath ap Penderyn x 28

Finland

**Suomen Retkeilymajajärjestö-SRM ry,
Yrjönkatu 38 B 15, FI-00100 Helsinki,
Finland.**

t (358) (9) 5657150
f (358) (9) 56571510
e info@srm.inet.fi
w www.srmnet.org

Office Hours: Monday-Friday 09.00-16.00hrs

A copy of the Hostel Directory for this Country can be obtained from:
The National Office

National Tourist Authority/Board:	www.visitfinland.com
Capital:	Helsinki
Language:	Finnish and Swedish
Currency:	€ Euro
Population:	5,200,000
Size:	338,145 sq km
Telephone Country Code:	358
eKit Access Number:	0800-112-010

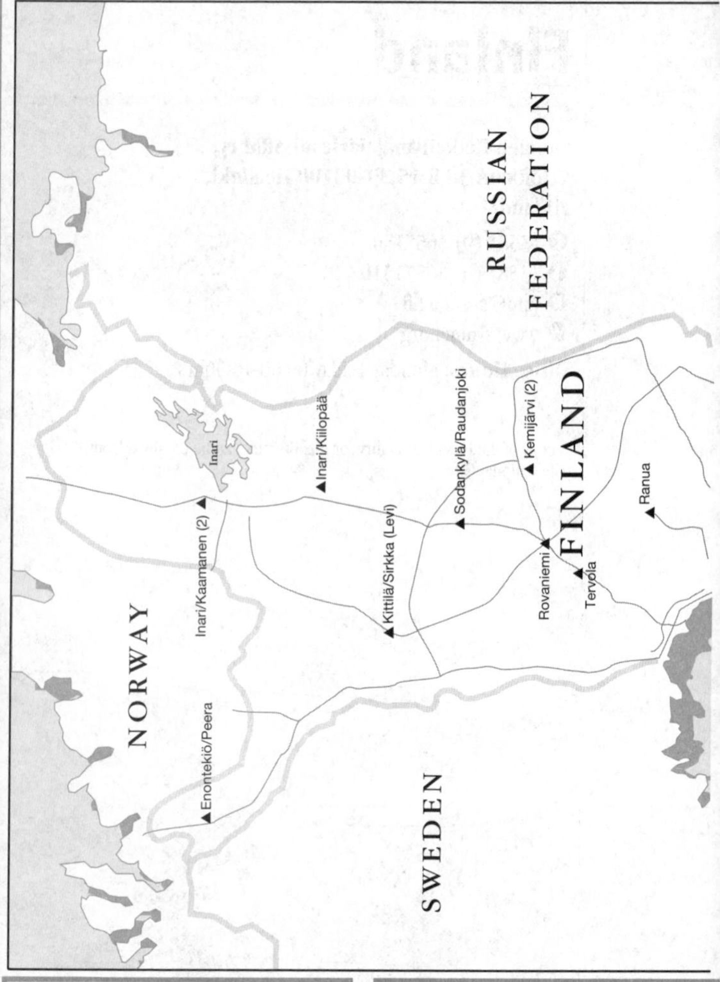

This vast and majestic frontier country of forests and lakes, the inspiration for Sibelius's wonderful 'Finlandia' music, sits as one of the newer members of the European Union at the northern edges of Europe 'between east and west' – very much aware of its earlier history when it was once part of Sweden and more recently part of Russia. Its language also marks it out as a distinct and separate place, being related to Estonian, but bearing no resemblance to any other European tongue.

The fifth largest country in Europe, but with one of the smallest populations (5.2 million), the geography is almost unimaginable: nearly 200,000 lakes, slightly fewer islands and forests that cover over two-thirds of the country. Not surprisingly, timber and paper are among its principal exports; but perhaps more surprisingly is that Finland has embraced the new information and electronics technologies so successfully so quickly. And from being a closed 'fortress Finland' in the Communist era, it has quickly become an open

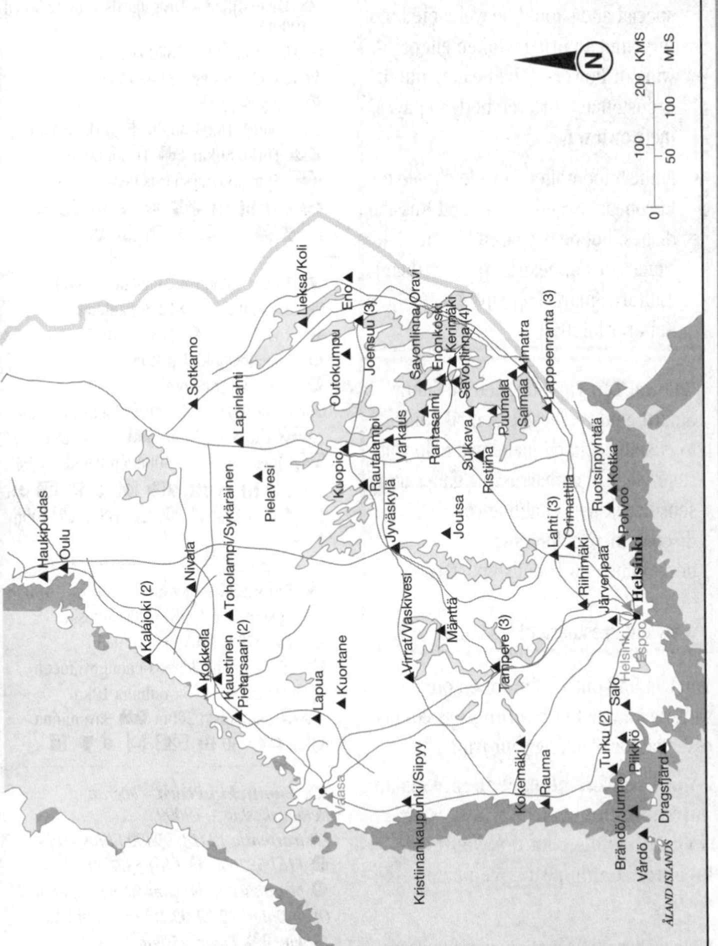

and free market economy, with visitors always welcome. It is as if Finland's Arctic Circle daylight, (when the sun is always above the horizon for two months between end of May and end of July) has symbolically illuminated and liberated the whole country from its closed past.

A few other Top Tips from **CULTURE SMART!**:

- Being a large country with a sparse population, it is perhaps unsurprising that the Finns cherish their personal space. Small talk does not come readily and there is no great desire for constant socializing, although the advent of the mobile phone has been a boon in a country where distances are so great.
- Finns are extremely hard working and very committed once decisions are taken; they are also known for their integrity and open dealing.
- Understandably, dress for everyone is casual with jeans and jumpers essential for the climate most of the time; suits make rare appearances!
- When hospitality is extended to a Finnish home it would be something

special and should be welcomed, not forgetting to bring a token gift of wine or flowers. When eating out, it is customary for everybody to pay their own way.

- Finnish food offers a wide choice of European, Scandinavian and Russian dishes: but be prepared for the rich sauces that appear in many of them!

Culture Smart! Top Tips © Kuperard 2005

Cultural Top Tips supplied by Culture Smart! guides. These essential guides to customs and etiquette will help you steer clear of embarrassing gaffes and sensitive issues, enabling you to discover new cultures whilst developing new friendships. Order online at www.culturesmartguides.co.uk

You can find out a lot more on our website - a visit to www.HIhostels.com is essential for planning your trip!

Pour en savoir plus, rendez-vous sur notre site Internet, www.HIhostels.com une visite incontournable pour préparer votre voyage!

Viele weitere Informationen auf unserer Website: www.HIhostels.com - unverzichtbar für die Reiseplanung!

Puedes averiguar mucho más en nuestro sitio web. Es imprescindible que visites la página www.HIhostels.com para planear tu viaje.

▲ **Dragsfjärd** – Dragsfjärds Vandrarhotell – 19006
Pensionatvägen 6, 25870 Dragsfjärd.
(2) 424553 (2) 424553
panget@pp.inet.fi
Open Dates: 15.05-30.09 Turku 80km Turku 80km Turku 80km 50m ap Dragsfjärds Pensionat 1N x 41 R 2 x 8 P

▲ **Eno** – Jokipirtin Majatalo – 19007
Uimaharjuntie 751, 81270 Paukkaja.
(13) 774607 (13) 774607
majatalo@jokipirtti.com
www.jokipirtti.com
Open Dates: 01.04-30.09 Joensuu 50km A Paukkaja 500m Uimaharju 7km Joensuu-Lieksa 500m ap Paukkaja 8N x 40 R TV 1 x i P 100m 100m

▲ **Enonkoski** – Kievari Enonhovi – 19008
Urheilukentäntie 1, 58175 Enonkoski.
(15) 479431 (15) 479435
raili.polonen@kievari-enonhovi.inet.fi
Open Dates: 12 Savonlinna 19km A Enonkoski 200m Savonlinna 33km x 30 CC P

△ ***Enontekiö/Peera*** – *Peeran Retkeilykeskus – 19009*
Käsivarrentie 12413, 99490 Kilpisjärvi.
(16) 532659 (16) 532659
peeran@luukku.com www.peera.fi
Open Dates: 19.02-02.10 Enontekiö 130km Kolari 250km Rovaniemi-Kilpisjärvi 300m ap Peera 90NW x 43 R CC TV i P 1km

▲ **Espoo** – Budget Hotel Matinlahti
HI 19010
Rantamäki 3, 02230 Espoo.
(9) 88761 (9) 8032664
hotelli.matinlahti-reception@sodexho.fi
www.sodexho.fi/hotellimatinlahti
Open Dates: 01.01-23.12 Helsinki-Vantaa 30km Helsinki 12km Helsinki 14km 132 200m ap Matinlahti 14W x 104 CC (B) TV 17 x i 8 P 100m 100m

▲ **Haukipudas** – Hostel Virpiniemi – 19015
Hiihtomajantie 27, 90820 Kello.
(8) 5614200 (8) 5614224
virpiniemi@mail.suomi.net
www.virpiniemenliikuntaopisto.com
Open Dates: 12 Oulu 33km A 5km Oulu 23km 1, 10, 24, 31 5km ap Kiviniementie 12SW x 101 3 x 1km

---

Helsinki – Eurohostel 19001
Linnankatu 9, 00160 Helsinki.
(9) 6220470 (9) 655044
eurohostel@eurohostel.fi
www.eurohostel.fi
Open Dates: 12 Open Times:
Beds: 365 - 25x1 100x2 8x4 2x6
Price Range: € 20.70-41.30
Directions: 2SE from city centre
Helsinki-Vantaa 20km A 615 2km Viking Line & Finnjet Terminal / Katajanokka Terminal 500m Central Station Helsinki 2km Central Station Helsinki 2km #4, #2 100m ap Vyökatu U Railway Station 2km x 110

Helsinki – Eurohostel

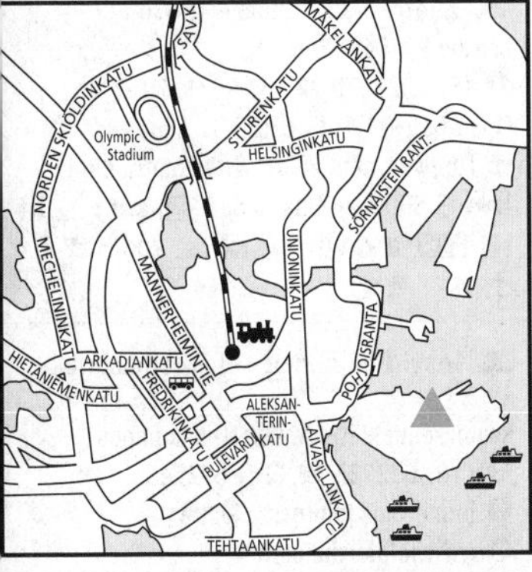

▲ **Helsinki** – Hostel Academica 19018
Hietaniemenkatu 14, 00100 Helsinki.
(9) 13114334 (9) 441201
hostel.academica@hyy.fi
www.hostelacademica.fi
Open Dates: 01.06-01.09 Helsinki-Vantaa 18km A 615 1.5km West Terminal 1.5km Helsinki 1.5km 800m ap Bus station 3T, 3B, 8 100m ap Kauppakorkeakoulu 0.5 km (3T), Perhonkatu 0.1 km (8) U Kamppi 500m 1W x 66 (B) 500m

---

▲ **Helsinki** – Hostel Erottajanpuisto – 19019
Uudenmaankatu 9, 00120 Helsinki.
(9) 642169 (9) 6802757
booking@erottajanpuisto.com
www.erottajanpuisto.com
Open Dates: 12 Helsinki-Vantaa 25km A 615, 617 800m Olympic Terminal 600m Helsinki 800m 17 100m ap Erottaja 3T, 6 100m ap Erottaja U Railway Station 800m x 54 (B) 8 300m 2km

---

▲ **Helsinki** – Hostel Lönnrot – 19107
Lönnrotinkatu 16 D, 00120 Helsinki.
(9) 6932590 (9) 6932482
hostel@saunalahti.fi
www.hostellonnrot.com
Open Dates: 12 Helsinki-Vantaa 25km A 615, Finnair bus 1km Länsisatama/West Harbour 1.5km Main Railway Station 1km 6, 3B 100m U Kamppi 500m x 50 (B) 8 300m 1km

▲ **Helsinki** – Hostel Satakuntatalo
HI 19021
Lapinrinne 1 A, 00180 Helsinki.
(9) 69585232 (9) 6854245
ravintola.satakunta@sodexho.fi
www.sodexho.fi
Open Dates: 01.06-31.08 Helsinki-Vantaa 25km A 615, 617, Finnair bus 1km West Terminal 1km, Olympic Terminal 3 km Helsinki 1km 55, 65A, 66A 100m ap Lapinlahdenkatu/Lapinrinne 8, 3B, 3T, 10, 4, 7A, 7B ap Maria Hospital 0.2 km; Mannerheimintie 0.4 km U Kamppi 100m 1SW x 160 R CC (B) 4 x i 8 P 800m 800m

▲ **Helsinki** – Hostel Suomenlinna – 19022
Suomenlinna C 9, 00190 Helsinki.
(Note: the hostel is situated on an island)
(9) 6847471 (9) 6847471
leirikoulu@pp.inet.fi
www.leirikoulut.com
Open Dates: 01.01-20.12 Helsinki-Vantaa 20km A Finnair bus 3km Olympic Terminal 1km Helsinki 3km 16, 13, change to ferry (15 min.) ap Kauppatori 3T, 1, 4, change to ferry (15 min.) ap Kauppatori U Kaisaniemi 3km 3S x 40 R CC (B) TV 1 x i 8 1km 1km

Helsinki – Stadion Hostel HI 19004
Olympic Stadium - northern curve. Pohjoinen Stadiontie 3 B, 00250 Helsinki.
(9) 4778480 (9) 47784811
info@stadionhostel.com
www.stadionhostel.com
Open Dates: 01.01-24.12; 27-31.12
Open Times: Winter: 07.00-02.00hrs; Summer: 07.00-03.00hrs; (dormitories closed 12.00-16.00hrs).
Beds: 162 - 5x1 5x2 1x3 3x4 3x5 13x6+
Price Range: € 16.00-32.00
Directions: 1N from city centre
Helsinki-Vantaa 15km A Finnair bus 500m Helsinki harbours 3km Helsinki 1km 500m ap Olympic Stadium 7A, 3T 300m ap Aurora Hospital - Auroran sairaala U Central Railway Station 1.5km x 9 R CC (B) TV i 8 P 500m

Helsinki – Stadion Hostel

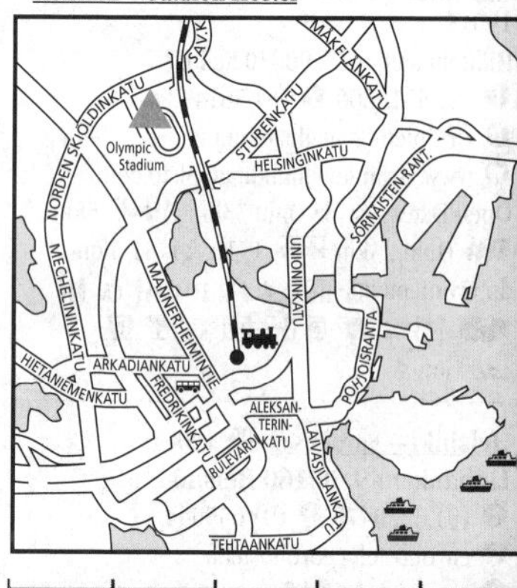

Helsinki... Travel Tips

- **For budget eats check out...** Café Esplanad, Hessburger, UniCafe, Golden RAX Pizza Buffet, Katajanmarja (at Eurohostel)
- **For great nightlife try...** Helsinki Club, Botta, Kaarle XII, Baker's, Molly Malone's
- **Don't miss...** Suomenlinna, Korkeasaari Zoo, Linnanmäki Amusement Park, Finnish National Gallery, Senate Square & Cathedral, Finlandia Hall, Finnish National Opera, Ateneum, Olympic Stadium, Sea Life

▲ **Imatra** – Ukonlinna – 19026
Leiritie 8, 55420 Imatra.
(5) 4321270 (5) 4321270
Open Dates: 1.1-23.12;27-31.12
Lappeenranta 40km Imatra 4km 3 500m ap Imatra Spa 6NW x 22 CC TV i P 500m

▲ **Inari/Kaamanen** – Hostel Jokitörmä – 19027
Kaamasentie 2709 A, 99910 Kaamanen.
(16) 672725 (16) 672745
lomakyla@jokitorma.inet.fi
www.jokitorma.com
Open Dates: 12 Ivalo 68km Rovaniemi 350km Eskelisen Lapin Linjat/Gold Line 100m 27N x 50 R CC (B) P

▲ **Inari/Kaamanen** – Kaamasen Kievari – 19028
99910 Kaamanen.
(16) 672713 (16) 672786
info@kaamasenkievari.fi
www.kaamasenkievari.fi
Open Dates: Ivalo 70km A All buses stop at the hostel Rovaniemi 360km ap Hostel Kaamasen Kievari 28N x 97

▲ **Inari/Kiilopää** – Hostel Ahopää – 19029
Fell Resort Kiilopää, 99830 Saariselkä.
(16) 6700700 (16) 667121
kiilopaa@suomenlatu.fi
www.kiilopaa.com
Open Dates: 01.01-30.04; 07.06-30.09; 07.11-31.12 Ivalo 45km
A Saariselkä-Kiilopää Rovaniemi 240km ap Kiilopää 45S x 36 2 x 8 100m

---

▲ **Joensuu** – Finnhostel Joensuu – 19031
The Eastern Finland Sport Institute, Kalevankatu 8, 80110 Joensuu.
(13) 2675076; (13) 2675083
(13) 2675075 finnhostel@islo.jns.fi
www.islo.jns.fi
Open Dates: Joensuu 10km
Joensuu 1.5km 5 50m ap Kirkonmäki 0.5W x 84 3 x 500m 500m

▲ **Joensuu** – Kesähotelli Joensuun Elli – 19032
Länsikatu 18, 80110 Joensuu.
(13) 225927 (13) 225763
info@summerhotelelli.fi
www.summerhotelelli.fi
Open Dates: 01.06-31.08 Joensuu 6km
A 500m Joensuu 2km 1W x 40 1 x 500m 500m

△ ***Joensuu*** – *Partiotalo – 19033*
Vanamokatu 25, 80130 Joensuu.
(13) 123381
partiotalo@youthhostel-joensuu.net; sale@youthhostel-joensuu.net
www.youthhostel-joensuu.net
Open Dates: 01.06-31.08
Joensuu-Onttola 12km Joensuu 2km 1N x 44 1.7km 2.3km

▲ **Joutsa** – Vaihelan Tila – 19034
Vaihelantie 24, 19920 Pappinen.
(14) 889107 vaihelan.tila@co.inet.fi
www.vaihela.com
Open Dates: Jyväskylä-Tikkakoski 85km Jyväskylä 65km 1km ap Pappinen 16NW x 14 (B) 1 x 700m 700m

---

Jyväskylä – Finnhostel Laajari – 19002
Laajavuorentie 15, 40740 Jyväskylä.
(14) 624885 (14) 624888
finnhostel@jkl.fi www.laajavuori.com
Open Dates: 01.01-23.12; 26-31.12
Open Times: Mon-Fri: 06.30-22.00hrs; Sat 07.00-22.00hrs; Sun 07.00-21.00hrs
Beds: 78 - 19x2 10x4
Price Range: € 24-36 BBinc
Directions: 4W from city centre
Tikkakoski 16km Jyväskylä 4km 25 50m ap Laajavuori x 10 (B) 500m

Jyväskylä – Finnhostel Laajari

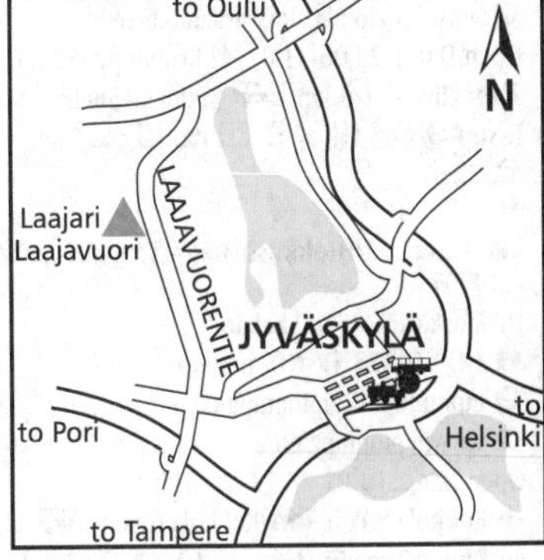

Jyväskylä... Travel Tips

- **For budget eats check out...** Salsa Orkidea, Rosso, Memphis, Golden Rax Pizza Buffet, Ali Baba
- **For great nightlife try...** Elohuvi, Jyväshovi (dancing restaurant for adults), Finnkino (cinema centre), Coffee House, m/s Rhea (restaurant ship, cruises on Lake Päijänne)
- **Don't miss...** Jyväskylä ridge and observation tower, Laajavuori (mountain car centre, summer theatre, skiing centre), Harbour (boats from the 19th century), Neste Rally Finland (in August), Viherlandia (garden centre, Iittala factory shop), Alvar Aalto (many buildings designed by architect Alvar Aalto), Sippulanniemi (golf course), Viherlaakso (land of fantasy and adventure for the children), The centre of Jyväskylä (pedestrian precinct: shops, cafes, restaurants etc)

▲ **Järvenpää** – Järvenpään Matkailukeskus – 19030
Stålhanentie, 04400 Järvenpää.
(9) 74255200 (9) 74255250
matkailukeskus@msn.com
www.matkailukeskus.com
Open Dates: 20.01-22.12 Helsinki-Vantaa 30km Järvenpää 3km 2.5S x 19 R CC 1 x P 500m 500m

▲ **Kalajoki** – Hostel Retkeilijä – 19036
Opintie 2, 85100 Kalajoki.
(500) 510303 (8) 463431
retkeilymaja@kam.fi
www.kalajokikeskusvaraamo.fi/retku
Open Dates: 22.06-31.07 Kruunupyy 82km Ylivieska 40km 300m ap Shell, Esso x 43 P 7km 7km

▲ **Kalajoki/Hiekkasärkät** – Tapion Tupa – 19037
Hiekkasärkät, 85100 Kalajoki.
(8) 466622 (8) 466699
tapiontupa@tapiontupa.com
www.tapiontupa.com
Open Dates: 01.01-23.12; 26-31.12
Kokkola 80km Kokkola 60km ap Tapion Tupa 4S x 36 CC 3 x P 1km 1km

▲ **Kaustinen** – Koskelan Lomatalo – 19040
Känsäläntie 123, 69600 Kaustinen.
(6) 8611338
koskelan.lomatalo@kaustinen.fi
Open Dates: 12 Kruunupyy 45km Kokkola 45km 5km ap Kaustinen 5W x 31 1 x P 10km

▲ **Kemijärvi** – Hostel Kemijärvi – 19041
Lohelankatu 1, 98100 Kemijärvi.
(16) 813253 (16) 813342
lohelanrantamokit@pp.inet.fi
Open Dates: 12 Rovaniemi 79km A 2 500m Kemijärvi 1km 500m ap Särkimäki 0.3W x 35 R (B) 1 x i P 100m 100m

△ *Kemijärvi – Matkatupa – 19042*
Luusuantie 2661, 98230 Luusua.
(16) 888517 (16) 3420465
matkatupa@pp.nic.fi
Open Dates: 01.05-31.10 Rovaniemi 80km Kemijärvi 28km 100m ap Matkatupa 26S x 74 1 x i P 50m 50m

▲ **Kerimäki** – Korkeamäen Majatalo – 19043
Ruokolahdentie 545, 58200 Kerimäki.
(15) 544827; (440) 544827
ritva_kraftkekki@hotmail.com
www.korkeamaenmajatalo.fi
Open Dates: 15.05-31.08 Savonlinna 28km Retretti 9km Bus company Linja-Kosonen (green bus) ap Korkeamäen Majatalo 6S x 38 R (B) P 200m 200m

▲ **Kittilä/Sirkka (Levi)** – Hullu Poro – 19111
99130 Levi.
(16) 6510100 (16) 641568
hullu.poro@levi.fi www.hulluporo.fi
Open Dates: 01.05-30.11 Kittilä 15km A Hullu Poro 100m Kolari 80km 500m x 44 R CC 5 x i P 8km

Kokemäki – Kesähotelli Tyrni – 19044
Kauvatsantie 189, 32800 Kokemäki.
(50) 3946817; (2) 5604711
(2) 5604703
luonnonvara@huittinen.fi
www.huittinen.fi/hayo
Open Dates: 01.06-31.07 (only 01.08-31.05)
Pori 40km Turku 112km
Kokemäki 7km ap Kokemäki 1.9N
x 88 R 5 x
50m 8km

Kokkola – Hostel Tankkari – 19045
Vanhansatamanlahti, 67100 Kokkola.
(6) 8314006
vastaanotto@suntinsuu.inet.fi
www.kokkolacamping.com
Open Dates: 01.06-31.08 Kruunupyy 17km
Kokkola 3km 3km ap Kokkola
2.5N x 23 R CC (LD)

Kotka (Sunila) – Asuntohotelli Aallon Maja – 19122
Valliniemenkatu 2, 48900 Sunila (Kotka).
(5) 3444310 (5) 3444300
varaukset@aallonmaja.com
www.aallonmaja.com
Open Dates: Helsinki-Vantaa 130km
Kymi 6km 5B, 6B 100m ap Aallon Maja 12E x 50 R CC
(B) 3 x
2km 2km

Kristiinankaupunki/Siipyy – Hostel Kilstrand/Kiilinranta – 19047
Kiilintie 90, 64490 Siipyy.
(6) 2225611 (6) 2225615
kilen@kiili.inet.fi
www.edu.krs.fi/museo
Open Dates: Pori 80km A 15km
Pori 80km 100m ap Kiili 40S
x 60 R 1 x
100m 100m

Kuopio – Puijon Maja – 19049
Puijo, 70300 Kuopio.
(17) 2555250; 2555253
(17) 2555266 puijo@sakky.fi
www.puijo.com
Open Dates: Kuopio 15km
A Finnair bus, Kuopio 2km
Helsinki 390km Kuopio 2km
2km ap Kuopio 2NW x 48
R CC 1 x
2.5km 2.5km

Kuortane – Finnhostel Virtaniemen Lomatila – 19099
Virtala (Virtaniementie 35), 63100 Kuortane.
(40) 5936588 info@virtaniemi.net
www.virtaniemi.net
Open Dates: Seinäjoki 55km
Seinäjoki 45km 14SE x 70
R CC 3 x

Lahti – Lahden Kansanopisto – 19051
Harjukatu 46, 15100 Lahti.
(3) 8781181 (3) 8781234
lahden.kansanopisto@lahdenkansanopisto.fi www.lahdenkansanopisto.fi
Open Dates: 30.05-14.08 Helsinki-Vantaa 100km A 400m Helsinki 120km
Lahti 400m 300m ap Kansanopisto
0.5E x 72 R CC (B)
10 x
700m 700m

Lahti – Matkakoti Patria – 19109
Vesijärvenkatu 3, 15100 Lahti.
(3) 7823783 (3) 7823793
http://koti.mbnet.fi/patria
Open Dates: Helsinki-Vantaa 120km
A 50m Lahti 100m 1km
x 22 R CC (B)
1km 3km

Lahti – Mukkulan Kesähotelli – 19052
Ritaniemenkatu 10, 15240 Lahti.
(3) 8823602 (3) 8823603
info@mukkulankesahotelli.fi
www.mukkulankesahotelli.fi
Open Dates: 01.06-15.08 Helsinki-Vantaa 90km Helsinki 100km Lahti 4km
30 ap Mukkulan Kesähotelli 3N
x 40 R CC (B)
1 x

Lapinlahti – Hostel Portaanpää – 19053
Portaanpääntie 63, 73100 Lapinlahti.
(17) 2720900 (17) 2720901
toimisto@portaanpaa.fi
www.portaanpaa.fi
Open Dates: 01-31.07 Rissala 50km
A 1km Lapinlahti 1km 2S
x 100 R (BL)
3 x 200m

FINLAND - FINLANDE - FINNLAND - FINLANDIA

Lappeenranta – Finnhostel Lappeenranta – 19054
Kuusimäenkatu 18, 53810 Lappeenranta.
(5) 4515555 (5) 4515558
huhtiniemi@loma-oksa.inet.fi
www.huhtiniemi.com
Open Dates: 15.01-15.12 Lappeenranta 3km Lappeenranta 4km 5, 6 100m ap Camping 2W x 80

Lappeenranta – Huhtiniemi – 19055
Kuusimäenkatu 18, 53810 Lappeenranta.
(5) 4515555 (5) 4515558
huhtiniemi@loma-oksa.inet.fi
www.huhtiniemi.com
Open Dates: 01.06-15.08 Lappeenranta 3km Lappeenranta 4km 5, 6 ap Camping 2W x 24

Lappeenranta – Karelia Park – 19056
Korpraalinkuja 1, 53810 Lappeenranta.
(5) 4530405 (5) 4528454
kari.nalli@armpa.inet.fi
www.karelia-park.fi
Open Dates: 01.06-31.08 Lappeenranta 2.5km Lappeenranta 2.5km 1, 3, 5 200m ap Kornetinkatu 2W x 48 800m 800m

Lapua – Wanha Karhunmäki – 19057
Karhunmäentie 923, 62100 Lapua.
(6) 4377757 (6) 4388912
karhunmaki@wanhakarhunmaki.net
www.wanhakarhunmaki.net
Open Dates: 12 Seinäjoki 30km Vaasa 80km Lapua 10km 10W x 150 7 x 2km

Lieksa/Koli – Kolin Retkeilymaja – 19058
Niinilahdentie 47, 83960 Koli.
(13) 673131 (13) 673131
kolihostel@hotmail.com
www.kolinretkeilymaja.net
Open Dates: 12 Joensuu 85km Joensuu 85km 6km ap Koli 85S x 47 (B) 1 x 2km 2km

Mänttä – Mänttä Hostel – 19059
Koulukatu 6, 35800 Mänttä.
(3) 4886841; (50) 3705246
(3) 4886847 matkailu@mantta.fi
www.mantta.fi/kaupunki/matkailu/rmaja.htm
Open Dates: 01.06-14.08 Tampere-Pirkkala 90km Vilppula 7km 0.5SW x 53 1 x 500m 500m

Nivala – Hostel Nivala – 19061
Maliskyläntie 2, 85500 Nivala.
(8) 443171 (8) 442555
Open Dates: 01-31.07 (05-30.06 on request) 100km Nivala 1.5km 1km ap Nivala 1E x 112 (B)

Orimattila – Orimattila-instituutti – 19120
Heinämaantie 35, 16300 Orimattila.
(50) 5265970 (3) 8284035
orihostel@salpaus.fi www.salpaus.fi/oi
Open Dates: 12 (Mon-Fri) Helsinki-Vantaa 95km Helsinki 110km Lahti 23km 50m 2.5NE x 94 2 x 2.5km

Oulu – Kesähotelli Oppimestari – 19117
Nahkatehtaankatu 3, 90100 Oulu.
(8) 8848527 (8) 8848772
oppimestari@merikoski.fi
www.merikoski.fi/oppimestari
Open Dates: 01.06-31.07 Oulunsalo 12km 1km 7 200m 1N x 120 (B) 300m 300m

Outokumpu – Kesähotelli Vanha Kaivos – 19118
Mikonkatu 2 a, 83500 Outokumpu.
(Check-in/out: Vanha Kaivos Info, Kummunkatu 21)
(13) 554990 (13) 554996
toimisto@vanhakaivos.fi
www.vanhakaivos.fi
Open Dates: 12.06-06.08 Joensuu 40km Joensuu 45km 1.5NE x 60 (B) 1km

Pielavesi – Pielavesi Hostelli – 19064
Laurinpurontie 23 A-C, 72400 Pielavesi.
(17) 862970 (17) 861031
asiakaspalvelu@monitaitoset.inet.fi
www.monitaitoset.cjb.net
Open Dates: 06.06-06.08 Kuopio 70km
Iisalmi 54km 500m ap Pielavesi
0.5E x 29
500m 500m

Pietarsaari – Hostel Lilja – 19065
Isokatu 6, 68600 Pietarsaari.
(6) 7816500 (6) 7816533
hostel.lilja@aftereight.fi
www.aftereight.fi
Open Dates: 02.01-20.12 Kokkola 30km
A 200m Pännäinen 10km
ap Market Square 0.15S x 28
(BL)
3 x
1.5km

Pietarsaari – Svanen/Joutsen – 19066
Luodontie 50, 68660 Pietarsaari.
(6) 7230660 (6) 7810008
svanen@cop.fi www.multi.fi/svanen
Open Dates: 01.06-31.08 Kruunupyy 25km
A Kruunupyy-Pietarsaari 4km
Vaasa 100km Pännäinen 16km
Kokkola-Pietarsaari 500m
ap Furuholmen 4N x 20
5km 100m

Piikkiö – Hostel Tuorla – 19067
Country College of South West Finland,
Tuorlantie 1, 21500 Piikkiö.
(2) 4726625; (50) 3039803
(2) 2334399
myynti@tuorlanmajatalo.fi
www.tuorlanmajatalo.fi
Open Dates: 12 Turku 25km
A 13km Turku 15km Turku
13km 111 100m ap Tuorla 4W x 50
3 x
2km 2km

Porvoo – Porvoon Retkeilymaja-Porvoo Hostel – 19068
Linnankoskenkatu 1-3, 06100 Porvoo.
(19) 5230012 (19) 5230012
porvoohostel@co.inet.fi
www.porvoohostel.cjb.net
Open Dates: 02.01-20.12 Helsinki-Vantaa
50km Helsinki 50km Helsinki
50km 1km ap Porvoo x 33
2km

Puumala – Hostel Reissumaja – 19069
Koskenseläntie 98, 52200 Puumala.
(15) 4681119 (15) 4681809
info@koskenselka.fi
www.koskenselka.fi
Open Dates: 12 Mikkeli 75km
Mikkeli 75km 2km ap Puumala
2NW x 16

Rantasalmi – Country Hotel SaimaanSydän – 19112
Ohitustie 5, 58900 Rantasalmi.
(15) 440761 (15) 440722
country.hotel@saimaaholiday.net
www.saimaaholiday.net/Rantasalmi
Open Dates: 12 Savonlinna 50km; Helsinki
320km Varkaus/Savonlinna 50km
500m ap Rantasalmi 0.5E x 62
2 x
500m 500m

Ranua – Pikku Ilves – 19070
Keskustie 10, 97700 Ranua.
(16) 3551201 (16) 3551284
info@hotelliilveslinna.fi
www.hotelliilveslinna.fi
Open Dates: 12 Rovaniemi 90km
Rovaniemi 80km 100m ap Ranua
x 36
2 x
100m 100m

Rauma – Hostel Poroholma – 19071
Camping Site, 26100 Rauma.
(2) 83882500 (2) 83882400
poroholma@kalliohovi.fi
Open Dates: 15.05-31.08 Pori 50km
Turku 100km Kokemäki 30km 2N
x 38 (B)

Rautalampi – Korholan Kartano – 19073
Korholantie 111, 77700 Rautalampi.
(17) 530320
info@korholankartano.com
www.korholankartano.com
Open Dates: 01.01-21.12; 26-31.12
Rissala 90km Suonenjoki 17km
2km ap Bus station 2N x 50
(B) 2 x

▲ **Riihimäki** – Kesähotelli Taru – 19110
Merkuriuksenkatu 7, 11130 Riihimäki.
(40) 589 2929 tarulife@hotmail.com
Open Dates: 01.06-15.08 Helsinki-Vantaa 60km Riihimäki 500m 0.5E x 60 (B) 1km

▲ **Ristiina** – Löydön Kartano – 19075
Kartanontie 151, 52300 Ristiina.
(15) 664101 (15) 664109
loydonkartano@co.inet.fi
http://personal.inet.fi/yritys/kartano
Open Dates: 01.01-22.12 Mikkeli 18km Mikkeli 15km Ristiina via Löytö 300m ap Kartanontie, Vitsiälä school 6N x 58 (B) 2 x 500m 500m

▲ **Rovaniemi** – Hostel Rudolf – 19076
Koskikatu 41, 96200 Rovaniemi.
(Check-in/out: Clarion Hotel Santa Claus, Korkalonkatu 29)
(16) 321321 (16) 3213225
sales@rudolf.fi www.rudolf.fi
Open Dates: Rovaniemi 8km A Airport taxi 500m Rovaniemi 2km ap Koskikatu 41 x 88 CC (B) 1 x 8 1km 1km

▲ **Ruotsinpyhtää** – Finnhostel Krouvinmäki – 19077
Ruotsinpyhtään Ruukkialue Oy, Puistokuja 19, 07970 Ruotsinpyhtää.
(19) 618474 (19) 618475
ruotsinpyhtaan.ruukkialue@co.inet.fi
www.ruotsinpyhtaa.fi
Open Dates: Helsinki-Vantaa 130km Helsinki 130km Kouvola 55km 100m ap Ruukki x 18 1 x 500m

▲ **Salo** – Laurin Koulu – 19078
Venemestarinkatu 37, 24240 Salo.
(2) 7784409 (2) 7784810
maku@salo.fi www.salo.fi
Open Dates: 05.06-09.08 Turku 60km Turku 60km Salo 500m ap Salo x 42 2km 4km

▲ **Savonlinna** – Malakias – 19079
Pihlajavedenkuja 6, 57170 Savonlinna.
(15) 73950; 533283 (15) 272524; 533283 myynti@spahotelcasino.fi
www.spahotelcasino.fi
Open Dates: 29.06-31.07 Savonlinna 17km Savonlinna 1.5km 2, 3, 4 200m ap Hernemäki 2W x 30 CC 1km

▲ **Savonlinna** – SKO Hostel – 19119
Opistokatu 1, 57600 Savonlinna.
(15) 572 910 (15) 572 9121
info@sko.fi www.sko.fi
Open Dates: (Mon-Fri) Savonlinna 25km Savonlinna 6km 3 400m 6E x 88

▲ **Savonlinna** – Vuorilinna – 19080
Kylpylaitoksentie, 57130 Savonlinna.
(15) 7395430; 73950 (15) 272524
myynti@spahotelcasino.fi
www.spahotelcasino.fi
Open Dates: 01.06-27.08 Savonlinna 15km Savonlinna, Kauppatori 200m 0.3E x 30 CC 200m 200m

▲ **Savonlinna** – WillaNuttu – 19114
Juvolantie 1353, 57310 Savonlinna.
(44) 5715890 (15) 649239
willanuttu@verkkosaari.net
www.verkkosaari.net
Open Dates: Savonlinna 10km Savonlinna 23km 400m ap Varparanta 23N x 50 (B) 4 x 8 900m 900m

▲ **Savonlinna/Oravi** – Hostel Oravin Melontakeskus – 19101
Kiramontie 11, 58130 Oravi.
(15) 647290 (15) 647292
oravi@saimaaholiday.net
www.saimaaholiday.net/wild
Open Dates: 01.06-31.08; 01.09-31.05 on request Savonlinna 35km Savonlinna 42km 200m ap Oravi 40NW x 20 CC 1 x

▲ **Sodankylä/Raudanjoki** – Hostel Visatupa – 19082
Seipäjärventie 409, 99510 Raudanjoki.
(16) 634133 (16) 634101
visatupa@visatupa.fi www.visatupa.fi
Open Dates: Rovaniemi 79km
Rovaniemi 86km Sodankylä/Ivalo - Rovaniemi 4km ap Raudanjoki 56S x 45
1 x

▲ **Sotkamo** – Hostel Tikkanen – 19083
Kainuuntie 31, 88600 Sotkamo.
(8) 6660541 (8) 6660541
tuula.hattunen@luukku.com
http://personal.inet.fi/yritys/matkakoti.tikkanen
Open Dates: Kajaani 40km
A 300m Kajaani 40km 50m
x 32 (B)
1 x 300m
300m

▲ **Sulkava/Kaartilankoski** – Partalansaaren Lomakoti – 19084
Hirviniementie 5, 58720 Kaartilankoski.
(15) 478850; (50) 5817460
(15) 478850
arjaschenkwein@partalansaarenlomakoti.com www.partalansaarenlomakoti.com
Open Dates: Savonlinna 70km
Savonlinna 60km 16km
ap Sulkava 16S x 50 R
1 x
200m 200m

▲ **Tampere** – Hostel Tampere YWCA – 19087
Tuomiokirkonkatu 12 A, 33100 Tampere.
(3) 2544020 (3) 2544022
tnnky@tnnky.fi www.tnnky.fi
Open Dates: 01.06-25.08 Pirkkala 10km
A 61 500m Tampere 500m
5, 3, 20 500m 0.5NE x 61
R 8
1.5km

Tampere – Hostel Uimahallin Maja – 19088
Pirkankatu 10-12, 33230 Tampere.
(3) 2229460 (3) 2229940
sales@hosteltampere.com
www.hosteltampere.com
Open Dates: 01.01-23.06; 26.06-22.12; 27-31.12 Open Times: 06.30-22.30hrs (23.30hrs) (Reception will close on winter Suns at 14.30hrs and on summer Suns at 21.30hrs)
Beds: 107 - 30x1 5x2 10x4 3x5 2x6
Price Range: € 20.00-41.50
Directions: Tampere-Pirkkala 17km
A 61 100m Tampere 1.5km
1, 2, 13, 16, 22, 25, 26, 28 50m
ap Pyynikintori x 15 R
1.3km 1.3km

Tampere – Hostel Uimahallin Maja

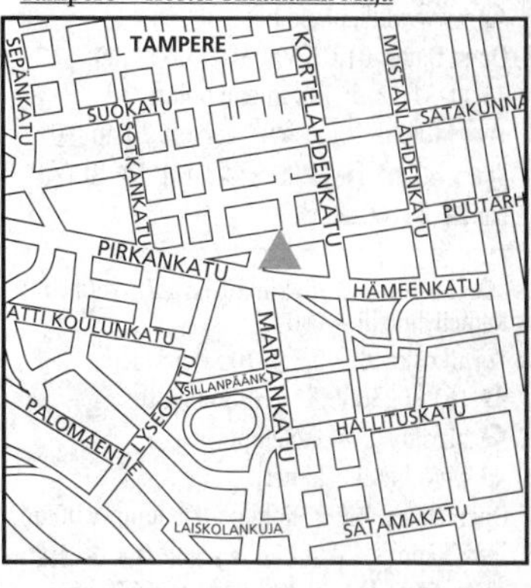

▲ **Tampere** – Summer Hotel Härmälä – 19089
Nuolialantie 50, 33900 Tampere.
(3) 2651355; (9) 61383210
(9) 713713
myyntipalvelu@lomaliitto.fi
www.lomaliitto.fi/harmala
Open Dates: 01.06-28.08.05 (please enquire about the opening dates before planning your stay) Pirkkala 5km Tampere 4km
100m 4S x 35 CC
200m 200m

Tampere... Travel Tips

- **For budget eats check out...** Golden RAX megabuffet, Grill, Katupoika, Harald, Henriks (Finnish cuisine)
- **For great nightlife try...** Ilves Bar & Night, Doris, Night Life, Emma, Nite Train
- **Don't miss...** Vapriikki Museum Centre, Finlayson Site, The Main Library METSO, Moominvalley Museum, Amuri Museum of Workers' Housing, Särkänniemi Adventure Park, Näsinneula Observation Tower, Pispala residential area, Kauppahalli indoor market place, Tampere Hall, Kehräsaari

▲ **Tervola** – Wild Lapland – 19090
Kätkävaara, 95300 Tervola.
(16) 439148 (16) 439150
info@wildlapland.net
www.wildlapland.net
Open Dates: 01.01-30.04; 01.06-30.09; 15.11-31.12 Rovaniemi 60km
A Loue 10km Tervola 20km 20N
x 40

▲ **Toholampi/Sykäräinen** – Hirvikoski Retkeilyhotelli – 19091
Tornikoskentie 50, 69410 Sykäräinen.
(6) 8623086 (6) 8623080
hirvikoski@toholampi.fi
www.hirvikoski.net
Open Dates: Kokkola-Kruunupyy 90km
Kannus 45km 24W x 84
3 x

Turku – Hostel Turku – 19093
Linnankatu 39, 20100 Turku.
(2) 2627680 (2) 2627675
hostel@turku.fi
www.turku.fi/hostelturku
Open Dates: 01.01-22.12; 27-31.12
Open Times: 06.00-10.00hrs; 15.00-24.00hrs
Beds: 100 - 2x 16x 4x 1x
Price Range: € 14.30-43.00
Directions: 2S from city centre
Turku 10km Turku 2km Turku 2km 1 100m ap Boren Puisto x 16
(B)

Turku – Hostel Turku

▲ **Turku** – Linnasmäki – 19115
Lustokatu 7, 20380 Turku.
(2) 4123500 (2) 4123600
info.tko@tk-opisto.fi
www.linnasmaki.fi
Open Dates: 15-23.06; 27.06-15.09 Turku 6km Turku 7km Turku, Kupittaa 4km 14, 15, 55, 22, 221 300m ap Hamaronkatu x 90
(B) 22 x

Turku... Travel Tips

- **For budget eats check out...** Italian Garden, Blanko, Market Hall, Golden RAX Pizza Buffet, Svarte Rudolf
- **For great nightlife try...** Giggling Marlin, Prima, Cosmic Comic Café, Mocca, Börs
- **Don't miss...** The Turku Castle, The Cathedral, The Banks of River Aura, Ruissalo Island, Aboa Vetus & Ars Nova-museums, Luostarinmäki Handicrafts Museum, Forum Marinum (maritime museum), Naantali's Moominworld (open in the summer), Caribia Spa, The Pharmacy Museum

▲ **Vaasa** – Hostel Vaasa 19102
Niemeläntie, 65170 Vaasa.
(6) 3241555 (6) 3241501
info@hostelvaasa.com
www.hostelvaasa.com
Open Dates: 12 Vaasa 10km Vaasa 1.5km Vaasa 2km 10A, 5 1km 2W
x 80 (BD)
2 x
1km 500m

▲ **Varkaus** – Varkauden Retkeilymaja – 19094
Kuparisepänkatu 5, 78870 Varkaus.
(17) 5795700 (17) 5795700
retkeilymaja@varkaus.fi
www.varkaus.fi/retkeilymaja
Open Dates: 01.06-12.08 Varkaus 16km
Varkaus 2km 50m ap Jäppiläntie
2W x 73 (B)
1.2km 1.2km

▲ **Virrat/Vaskivesi** – Finnhostel Haapamäki – 19096
34710 Vaskivesi.
(3) 4758845; (400) 627854
(3) 4758811
timo@matkailutilahaapamaki.com
www.matkailutilahaapamaki.com
Open Dates: 01.05-30.09 Tampere 90km
Tampere 85km 1.5km 20S
x 100
200m 200m

△ ***Åland Islands/Brändö*** – *Jurmo Vandrarhem - Jurmo Hostel – 19121*
22950 Jurmo.
(40) 5064777
jurmo.vandrarhem@aland.net
www.jurmo.net
Open Dates: 12 *Turku 80km*
Jurmo 100m *Turku 80km*
x 16 (B)

▲ **Åland Islands/Vårdö** – Bomans Gästhem B&B/Hostel – 19103
Vårdöbyväg 75, 22550 Vårdö.
(18) 47821; (457) 3421821; (457) 5244260 (18) 47885
bomans.gasthem@aland.net
www.GoAland.net/bomansgasthem
Open Dates: 01.05-15.09 (at other times by agreement) Maarianhamina 45km
Hummelvik 5km 4 2km ap Church of Vårdö 45NE x 56
(B) 1 x
1.5km

HOSTELLING
INTERNATIONAL

France

Federal Centre,
Fédération Unie des Auberges de Jeunesse (FUAJ),
27, rue Pajol, 75018 Paris, France.
t (33) (0) 1 44898727
f (33) (0) 1 44898710
e fuaj@fuaj.org
w www.fuaj.org

Individuals and Groups Travel Section,
Fédération Unie des Auberges de Jeunesse,
27, rue Pajol, 75018 Paris, France.
t (33) (0) 1 44898727
f (33) (0) 1 44898749

Office Hours for Individuals: Tuesday-Friday 10.00-18.00hrs; Saturday 10.00-17.00hrs

A copy of the Hostel Directory for this Country can be obtained from:
The National Office

Capital:	Paris
Language:	French
Currency:	€ Euro
Population:	61,684,291
Size:	550,000 sq km
Telephone Country Code:	33
eKit Access Number:	0805-113-721

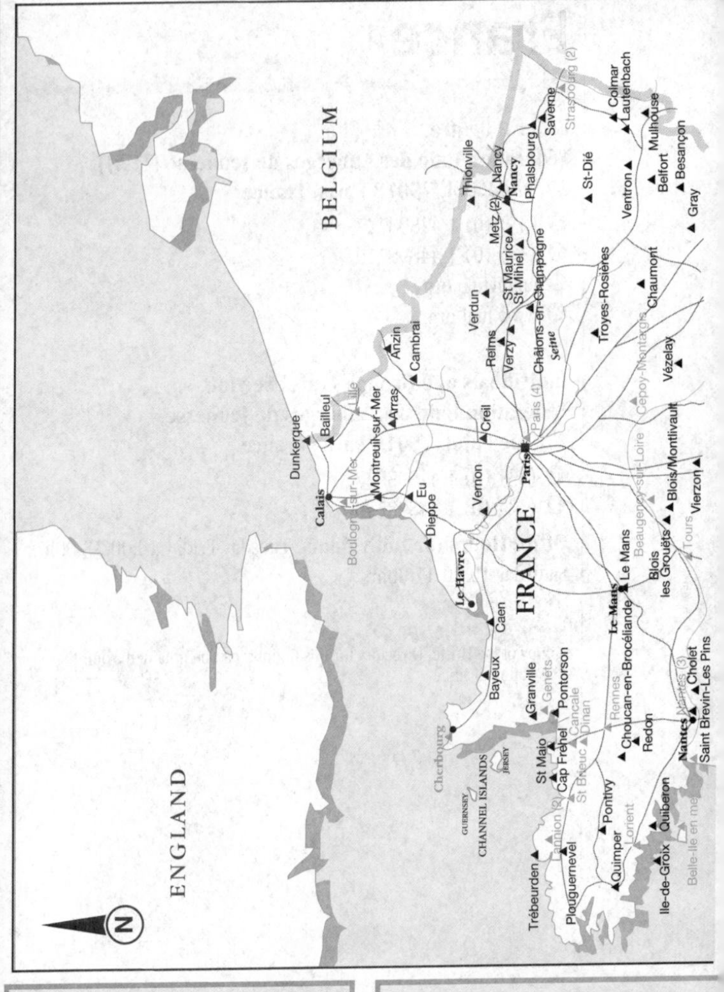

France is Europe's largest country (including Corsica), though one of the least densely populated. It is divided into 26 regions and 100 *départements*, which were introduced after the French Revolution of 1789. The variety in terms of cuisine, customs and ways of life is enormous, as is the landscape. Yet, there continues to be a wonderful singularity about the French and how they see themselves, summed up in the expressions *'Vive la France. Vive la difference!'* ('Long live France. Celebrate the difference' – in relation to other countries).

Not surprisingly, therefore, the French tend to be 'non-compliers' – they choose to be different and to have a different view of life generally, rejoicing in the cliché that they live to eat, not the other way round, and the fact that theirs is a 'high' culture, informed by the finer things of life, from the arts to *haute couture*, from literature to philosophy and will debate any subject any time, any place.

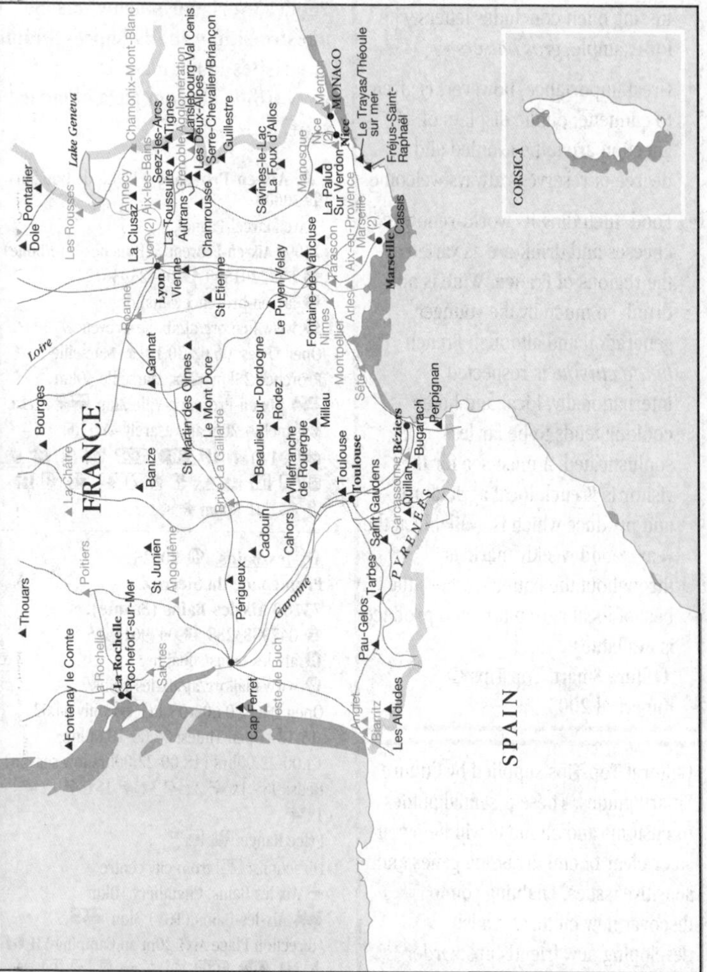

As Latinos (Gallo-Romans), the French are also very demonstrative and physical; they routinely embrace each other and figuratively will embrace any visitor who loves France and the French ways.

A few other Top Tips from **CULTURE SMART!**:

- Although there are big differences in cultural norms and standards of behaviour between metropolitan France, and the regions, the French love style, and dress accordingly. You certainly cannot be overdressed for a French social occasion, where casual dress would be taboo.
- Greetings in France are actually more formal than might be expected. Shake hands on meeting, and if it is a group be sure to include everyone. Shake hands also on leaving. The French shake hands whenever they meet, including at the start of a new working day. Kissing among close friends and relatives is also commonplace – two, three, or four times, depending on the region, and

kissing often concludes letters with, for example, *gros baisers*.

- Great importance, however, is given to etiquette: public displays of affection are to be avoided and a degree of reserve is always welcome.
- Food, including its world-renowned cheeses and drink are as varied as the regions of France. Wine is not drunk so much by the younger generation and although French *haute cuisine* is respected internationally, local and home cooking tends to be far less sophisticated. A must-see for the visitor is French local agriculture and produce which is available at the year-round weekly markets throughout the country, where the best of local agriculture and produce is available.

Culture Smart! Top Tips © Kuperard 2005

Cultural Top Tips supplied by Culture Smart! guides. These essential guides to customs and etiquette will help you steer clear of embarrassing gaffes and sensitive issues, enabling you to discover new cultures whilst developing new friendships. Order online at www.culturesmartguides.co.uk

You can find out a lot more on our website - a visit to www.HIhostels.com is essential for planning your trip!

Pour en savoir plus, rendez-vous sur notre site Internet, www.HIhostels.com une visite incontournable pour préparer votre voyage!

Viele weitere Informationen auf unserer Website: www.HIhostels.com - unverzichtbar für die Reiseplanung!

Puedes averiguar mucho más en nuestro sitio web. Es imprescindible que visites la página www.HIhostels.com para planear tu viaje.

▲ **Aix-en-Provence** – Le Jas de Bouffan
HI 20006
3 Ave Marcel-Pagnol,
13090 Aix-en-Provence (Bouches-du-Rhône).
T 0442201599 F 0442593612
e aix-en-provence@fuaj.org
W www.fuaj.org/aj/aix-en-provence/
Open Dates: 06.02-20.12 ✈ Marseille Provence 25km ⛴ Marseille 30km
🚂 Aix-en-Provence-Ville 2km 🚌 4 (La Mayanelle) 20m ap Vasarely - YH 2W
x 140 R CC (B) 2 x 500m

Aix-les-Bains HI 20025
Promenade du Sierroz,
73100 Aix-les-Bains (Savoie).
T 0479883288 F 0479611405
e aix-les-bains@fuaj.org
W www.fuaj.org/aj/aix-les-bains/
Open Dates: 04.02-05.11 (only 04.02 -15.12) Open Times: 07.00-10.00hrs; 14.00-22.00hrs (18.00-22.00hrs low season)
Beds: 96 - 1x[1] 2x[2] 3x[3] 18x[4] 1x[5] 1x[6]
Price Range: BB inc
Directions: 3NW from city centre
✈ Aix les Bains, Chambéry 10km
🚂 Aix-les-Bains (TGV) 3km 🚌 2 (direction Plage Aix) 20m ap Camping YH
R CC 1 x 1km 400m

Aix-les-Bains

Aix-les-Bains... Travel Tips

- **For budget eats check out...** Les Platanes (nice restaurant & jazz nights)
- **For great nightlife try...** Skill, Pub 31, Nurphy Pub
- **Don't miss...** Hautecombe Abbaye, Faure Museum, Diane's Temple, "Belle Epoque" Palace, Golf, Maison du lac du Bourget

▲ Anglet – Gazte Etxea 20029
19 Route des Vignes,
64600 Anglet (Pyrénées Atlantiques).
0559587000 0559587007
anglet@fuaj.org
www.fuaj.org/aj/anglet/
Open Dates: 01.04-06.11 Biarritz (Parme) 5km Bayonne 3km Bayonne 5km 7.1, 7.2 ap Les Sables 2E x 85 (BD) 3km 500m

▲ Angoulême 20036
Ile de Bourgines,
16000 Angoulême (Charente).
0545924580 0545922750
angouleme@fuaj.org
www.fuaj.org/aj/angouleme/
Open Dates: 03.01-22.12 Bordeaux 120km Bordeaux 120km Angouleme 1km 7, 9 200m ap Port de l'Houmeau 1N x 85 (B) 3 x 2km 2km

Annecy 20020
4 Route du Semnoz,
74000 Annecy (Haute-Savoie).
0450453319 0450527752
annecy@fuaj.org
www.fuaj.org/aj/annecy/
Open Dates: 15.01-30.11 (01.12-15.01 on request - 50 people min)
Open Times: 07.00-12.00hrs; 15.00-22.00hrs
Beds: 117 - 1x1 2x2 2x3 19x4 6x5
Price Range: BBinc
Directions: 1.5W from city centre
Genève 40km Annecy 2km 6 direction Les Marquisats 1km ap Hôtel de Police, YH 2 x 500m 500m

Annecy

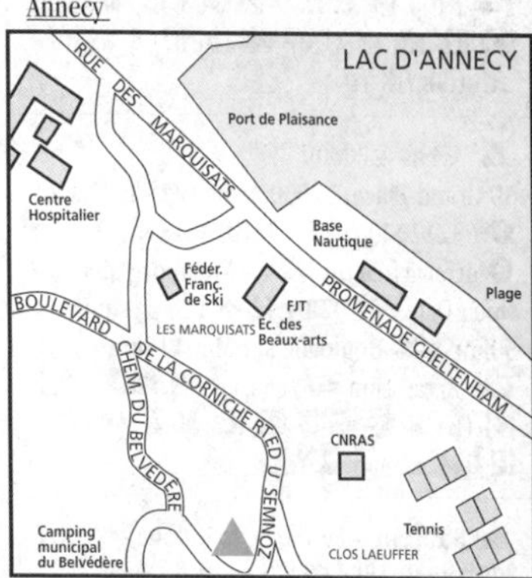

Annecy... Travel Tips

- **For budget eats check out...** Information available from the Hostel, L'Estraminet, Le Pétrin, Le Freti (Restaurant Savoyard), La Brasserie de Bonlieu (Restaurant Savoyard)
- **For great nightlife try...** Information available from the Hostel, Le Café des Arts, Red Zed, Le Bull, Le Brise Glace (Concert Hall)
- **Don't miss...** Old Town, Lake, Mountains, International Animated Film Festival (1st week in June), Fête du lac (August), Carnaval d'Annecy (end of February), Carnaval Vénitien (March), Fête de la Musique (21 June), Marathon du lac (Mid-April)

△ ***Anzin (Assoc)*** *– Auberge du Parc Mathieu – 20062*
43 rue des Martyrs, 59410 Anzin (Nord).
0327347892 0327347892
www.fuaj.org/aj/anzin/
Open Dates: 06.01-31.07; 01.09-23.12
Lesquin 50km Dunkerque 180km Valenciennes 3km 4 500m ap Place d'Anzin 0.5N x 40 R 8 4km

▲ **Arles** 20034
20 Ave Foch, 13200 Arles (Bouches-du-Rhône).
0490961825 0490963126
arles@fuaj.org www.fuaj.org/aj/arles/
Open Dates: 05.02-15.12 Nîmes 30km Marseille 100km Arles 2km 2, 3 ap Imbert (2), Clémenceau (3) 1S x 109 R CC (BD) 8 100m

▲ **Arras** – 20009
59 Grand-Place, 62000 Arras (Pas-de-Calais).
0321227002 0321074615
arras@fuaj.org www.fuaj.org/aj/arras/
Open Dates: 01.02-01.12 Lille-Lesquin 50km Boulogne sur Mer 115km Arras 1km x 54 R CC (B) 3km

▲ **Bailleul** – Ferme de la Hulotte – 20064
278, rue de Lille, 59270 Bailleul (Nord).
0328500010 0328500011
bailleul@fuaj.org
www.fuaj.org/aj/bailleul/
Open Dates: 12 Lille-Lesquin 37km Dunkerque 52km Bailleul 1km x 44 R (B) 1 x 1km

△ ***Banize (Assoc)*** *– Lou Pélélé – 20065*
23120 Banize (Creuse).
0555665228 0555665228
www.fuaj.org/aj/banize/
Open Dates: 12 Limoges 80km Aubusson 15km Felletin-Limoges 3km ap Cadet x 26 R

▲ **Bayeux (Assoc)** – Family Home – 20066
39 Rue Général de Dais, 14400 Bayeux (Calvados).
0231921522 0231925572
www.fuaj.org/aj/bayeux/
Open Dates: 12 Caen 25km Caen 25km Bayeux 1km Bus Vert 300m ap Place Charles de Gaulle x 150 R (B) 2 x 500m 9km

▲ **Beaugency-sur-Loire** 20053
152 route de Châteaudun,
45190 Beaugency (Loiret).
0238446131 0238441473
beaugency@fuaj.org
www.fuaj.org/aj/beaugency/
Open Dates: 01.02-30.11 Paris 150km Beaugency 2km 2S x 116 R CC (B) 1 x 2km

▲ **Beaulieu-sur-Dordogne** – La Riviera Limousine – 20067
Place du Monturuc,
19120 Beaulieu-sur-Dordogne (Corrèze).
0555911382 0555912606
beaulieu@fuaj.org
www.fuaj.org/aj/beaulieu/
Open Dates: 01.04-06.11 (12 on request) Toulouse 150km Bretenoux-Biars 7km 23 to Brive 500m ap Beaulieu 0.3NE x 28 R 400m 400m

▲ **Belfort (Assoc)** – FJT, Résidence Madrid – 20068
6 rue de Madrid,
90000 Belfort (Territoire de Belfort).
0384213916 0384285895
fjt.belfort@wanadoo.fr
www.fuaj.org/aj/belfort/
Open Dates: 12 Bâle Mulhouse 65km Belfort 500m 1 100m ap Madrid 0.8NW x 20 R CC 1 x

▲ **Belle-Ile en Mer** – Haute Boulogne 20058
Belle Ile, 56360 Le Palais (Morbihan).
0297318133 0297315838
belle-ile@fuaj.org
www.fuaj.org/aj/belle-ile/
Open Dates: 03.01-30.09; 02.11-24.12 (only 15.03-30.09) Lorient 80km Le Palais (on the island), Quiberon 1.5km
Quiberon 15km 1.5NW x 96
(BD)
2 x 500m

▲ **Besançon (Assoc)** – FMJT - "Les Oiseaux" – 20069
48 rue des Cras, 25000 Besançon (Doubs).
0381403200 0381403201
fjtlesoiseaux@yahoo.fr
www.fuaj.org/aj/besancon/
Open Dates: Mulhouse 150km
Viotte-Besançon 2km 7 to Orchamps 500m ap Les Oiseaux 3E x 20
3km

Biarritz – Aintziko Gazte Etxea 20043
8 Rue Chiquito de Cambo,
64200 Biarritz (Pyrénées-Atlantiques).
0559417600 0559417607
biarritz@fuaj.org
www.fuaj.org/aj/biarritz/
Open Dates: 03.01-23.12
Open Times: 08.30-11.30hrs (12.30hrs high season); 18.00hrs-midnight
Beds: 96 - 6x2 6x3 18x4
Price Range: BBinc
Directions: 3S from city centre
Biarritz Parme 2km A 2, 6 500m
Bayonne 6km Biarritz 800m
2, 9, B 500m ap Bois de Boulogne
(BD)
3 x 3km
1.5km

Biarritz – Aintziko Gazte Etxea

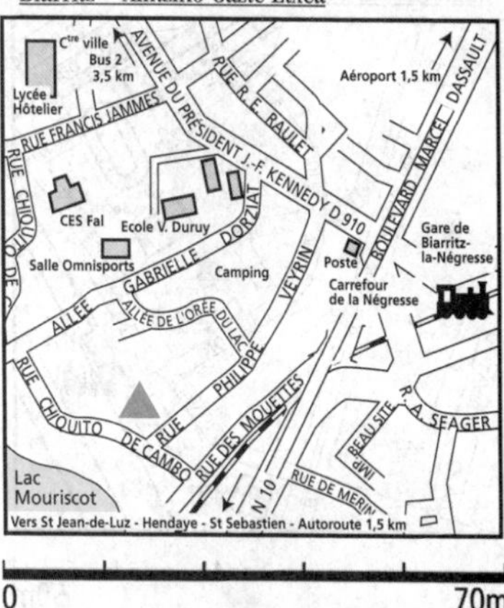

Biarritz... Travel Tips

- **For budget eats check out...** Youth Hostel
- **For great nightlife try...** Hostel Bar, Discos, Casino, Jorkiball & Cinema, Karting
- **Don't miss...** Surf, Maritime Museum, Basque Museum (Bayonne), Chocolate Museum, La Rhune (Mountain), Arnaga à Cambo (Edmond Rostand's house), Sare Caves, Typical Villages (Espelette, Sarc, Ainhoa), Beach, Basque Ecological Museum

---

Boulogne-sur-Mer 20008
Place Rouget de Lisle,
62200 Boulogne-sur-Mer (Pas-de-Calais).
0321991530 0321991539
boulogne-sur-mer@fuaj.org
www.fuaj.org/aj/boulogne/
Open Dates: 01.02-22.12 (12)
Open Times: 09.00-23.00hrs (Summer: 08.00-24.00hrs)
Beds: 137 - 5x2 13x3 22x4
Price Range: BBinc
Directions: 0.5S from city centre
Lille Lesquin 120km Boulogne, Calais 35km Boulogne 100m 6, 7, 10, 11, 15, 19, 20 100m ap Gare SNCF
(BD)
1 x
2km 2km

Boulogne-sur-Mer

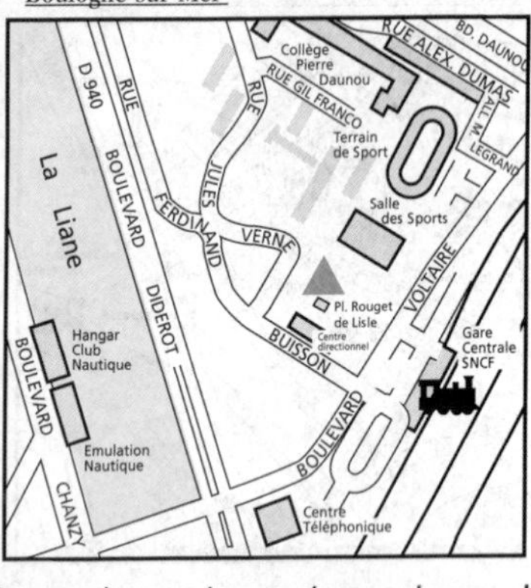

Boulogne-sur-Mer... Travel Tips

- **For budget eats check out...** La Nauiuia, Thalassa, Chuck Wagon (Bar TexMex), Poulet d'Enfer, Marivaux
- **For great nightlife try...** Bowling , Irish Pub, Casino, Santo Domingo
- **Don't miss...** Nausicaa (marine aquarium), Bagatelle, Becasuc, Cap Blanc-Nez, Cap Gris-Nez, Beurière Museum, Castle Museum, Harbour, Beussent Chocolate, Aqualud

▲ **Bourges** – AJ-Jacques Coeur – 20072
22 rue Henri Sellier, 18000 Bourges (Cher).
0248245809 0248655146
bourges@fuaj.org
www.fuaj.org/aj/bourges/
Open Dates: 06.01-15.12 Bourges 3km
1, 2 500m ap Conde (1), Val d'Auron (2) 1SW x 58 (B) 1 x
1.5km

▲ **Brive-La-Gaillarde** 20026
56 Av Maréchal Bugeaud,
19100 Brive-La-Gaillarde (Corrèze).
0555243400 0555848280
brive@fuaj.org www.fuaj.org/aj/brive/
Open Dates: 15.01-15.12 (12)
Limoges 100km Brive 1.5km 2, 4 (Tujac/Gaubre-Les Bordes/Palisse) 100m ap Centre Nautique 0.4E x 78 CC (BD)
1 x
100m

▲ **Bugarach (Assoc)** – Maison de la Nature et de la Randonnée – 20179
Centre d'hébergement 11190 Bugarach (Aude)
0468698388 0468698163 (mairie)
mairie.bugarach@ataraxie.fr
Open Dates: 12 Linoux 35km x 34

Cadouin – 20073
Abbaye de Cadouin,
24480 Cadouin (Dordogne).
0553732878 0553732879
cadouin@fuaj.org
www.fuaj.org/aj/cadouin/
Open Dates: 01.02-10.12
Open Times: 08.00-12.00hrs; 17.00-22.00hrs; (01.07-31.08: 08.00-23.00hrs)
Beds: 80 - 6x^{2} 1x^{3} 9x^{5} 1x^{6} 2x^{6+}
Price Range: BB inc
Directions: Bergerac 35km
Bordeaux 120km Le Buisson 5km
1 x
15km

Cadouin

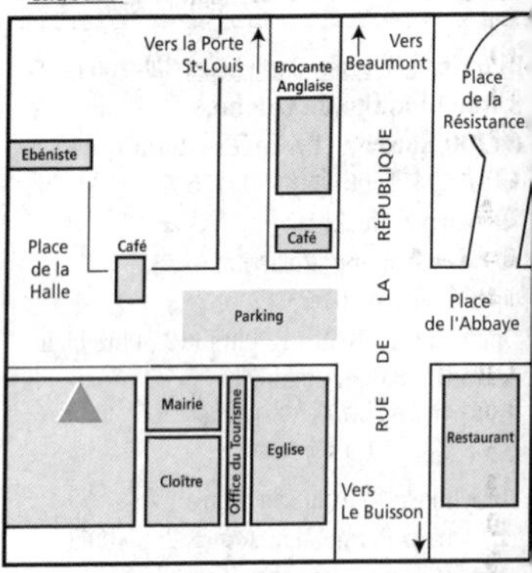

Cadouin... Travel Tips

- **For budget eats check out...** Restaurant de l'Abbaye, Auberge de la Salvetat, L'Assiette Gourmande
- **For great nightlife try...** Sarlat, Perigueux, Montpazier, Cadouin, Bergerac
- **Don't miss...** Sarlat, Begnac Castle, Biron Castle, Prehistoric Museum (les Eyzies), Lascaux Caves, Caves of 100 Mammoths, Cadouin Abbey, Bastille de Montpazier (fortress)

▲ **Caen (Assoc)** – FJT - "Robert Rême" – 20074
68 rue Eustache Restout,
14000 Caen (Calvados).
0231521996 0231842949
www.fuaj.org/aj/caen/
Open Dates: 01.06-30.09 Caen-Carpiquet 12km Ouistreham 25km Caen 2km 5, 14, 7 Grâce de Dieu 100m ap Lycée Fresnel B line 3S x 52 (B) 1 x 500m

---

△ ***Cabors (Assoc)*** *– FJT Frédéric Suisse – 20075*
20 Rue Frédéric Suisse, 46000 Cabors (Lot).
0565356471 0565359592
fjt46@wanadoo.fr
www.fuaj.org/aj/cabors/
Open Dates: Blagnac-Toulouse 120km Cabors 500m x 50 1 x 2km

▲ **Cambrai (Assoc)** – "Etape" – 20183
Sentier de l'Eglise, 59400 Cambrai (Nord).
0327378080 0327378081
educrotois@l-etape.asso.fr
www.fuaj.org/aj/cambrai/
Open Dates: Lille Lesquin 80km Calais 140km Cambrai 3km 3SE x 82 (B) 1 x 2km

---

Cancale 20045
Port Picain,
35260 Cancale (Ille-et-Vilaine).
0299896262 0299897879
cancale@fuaj.org
www.fuaj.org/aj/cancale/
Open Dates: 05.02-01.12 (05.02-23.12)
Open Times: May-Sep: 08.00-12.00hrs; 17.00-22.00hrs; Oct-Apr:09.00-12.00hrs; 18.00-20.00hrs
Beds: 72 - 1x1 13x2 1x3 6x4 2x5 1x6+
Price Range:
Directions: 3N from city centre
Rennes or Dinard (20 km) 70km
St-Malo 15km St-Malo 15km
St-Malo - Cancale 500m ap Port Picain
(BD) 2 x 15km 100m

Cancale

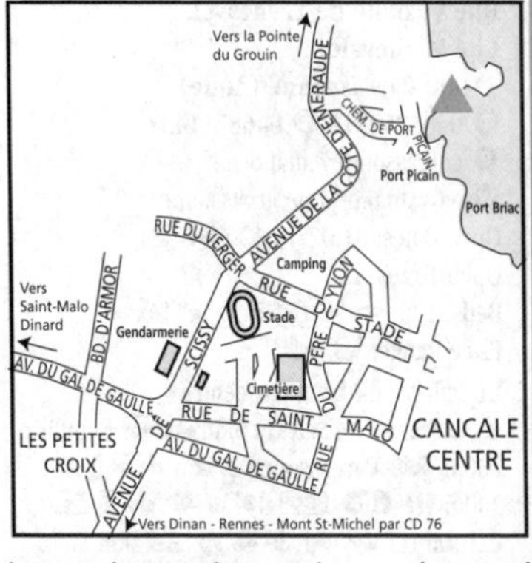

Cancale... Travel Tips

- **For budget eats check out...** Crêperie du Port, Le Piccolo, Bar de la Plage, Le Rocher de Cancale, Belle de Villaine
- **For great nightlife try...** Le Gallion, Le Tap'cul, Le Tangon
- **Don't miss...** La Houle (harbour, beaches & oyster museum), St-Malo, Mont St-Michel, Dinan (medieval city), Pointe du Grouin, Water sports, Gastronomy & sea food discovery, Sea Trips, Le Cap Fréhel (headland), beaches

---

Cannes ☛ **Le Trayas**

△ ***Cap Fréhel*** *– 20077*
la ville Hardrieux,
22240 Plevenon (Côtes-d'Armor).
0296414898 0296414898
capfrebel@fuaj.org
www.fuaj.org/aj/cap-frebel/
Open Dates: 01.04-30.09 Saint-Brieuc 45km Saint-Malo 45km Lamballe 30km 2 7km ap Croisement Plevenon (1.07 -31.08) 2NE x 44 3km

Carcassonne 20010
Rue Vicomte de Trencavel,
Cité Médiévale,
11000 Carcassonne (Aude).
0468252316 0468711484
carcassonne@fuaj.org
www.fuaj.org/aj/carcassonne/
Open Dates: 01.02-15.12
Open Times:
Beds: 120 - 2x 6x 2x 14x
Price Range: BB inc
Directions: 1E from city centre
Carcassonne Salvaza 5km A Shuttle 200m Carcassonne 2.5km 2, 4 200m 2km

Carcassonne

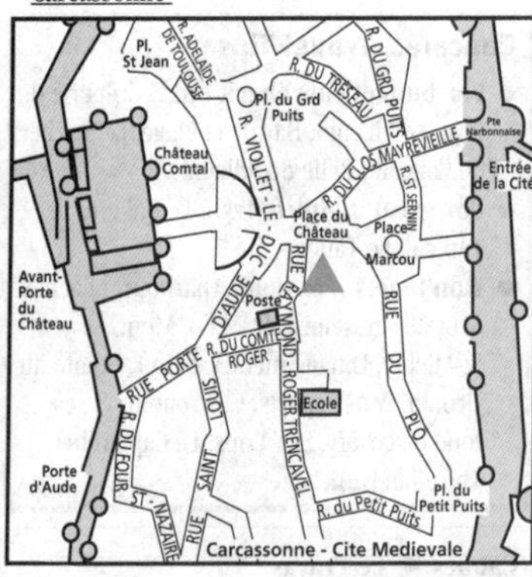

Carcassonne... Travel Tips

- **For budget eats check out...** Le Saint Jean, Les Buissonnets (Cité Mediévale), La Bastide de St Louis, La Taverne du Château (Cité Médiévale), Le Cathare
- **For great nightlife try...** Le Bar à Vin, La place Marcou (Cité Mediévale), Le Bar et le Conti (Bastide St Louis), La Fiesta Bodéga (Route de Montréal), L'Astronaute (Le Viguier)
- **Don't miss...** Medieval City, St-Nazaire Basilica, Canal du Midi, Bastide St-Louis (fortified town), Herb Market, Feu d'artifice (14 July) - unique spectical, Montolieu (The Book Village), Lac de la Cavayere, Gouffre de Cabrespine (chasm), Les Aigles de la Cité

△ ***Cassis – 20078***
AJ - La Fontasse,
13260 Cassis (Bouches-du-Rhône).
0442010272 www.fuaj.org/aj/cassis/
Open Dates: 15.03-31.12
Marseille-Marignane 50km
A Marseille, St Charles's Station 25km
Marseille 25km Cassis 7km 4W
x 60
2km

▲ **Cepoy-Montargis** 20056
AJ - 25 Quai du Port, 45120 Cepoy (Loiret).
0238932545 0238931925
cepoy@fuaj.org
www.fuaj.org/aj/cepoy/
Open Dates: 01.02-20.12 (only 05.01-20.12) Paris 150km Montargis 6km 2 500m ap St Loup 0.5N x 112 (BD) 3 x 3km 3km

Chamonix/Mont-Blanc 20011
127 Montée J Balmat,
Les Pélerins d'en Haut, 74400
Chamonix Mont-Blanc (Haute-Savoie).
0450531452 0450559234
chamonix@fuaj.org
www.fuaj.org/aj/chamonix/
Open Dates: 01.12-05.05; 20.05-01.10
Open Times: 08.00-12.00hrs; 17.00-22.00hrs
Beds: 120 - 12x 15x 6x
Price Range: BB inc
Directions: 2S from city centre
Genève, Annecy 90km A SAT Chamonix Station 2.5km Les Pélerins 700m Chamonix-Les Pélerins d'en Haut 300m ap Pélerins Ecole 4 x 3km

Chamonix/Mont-Blanc

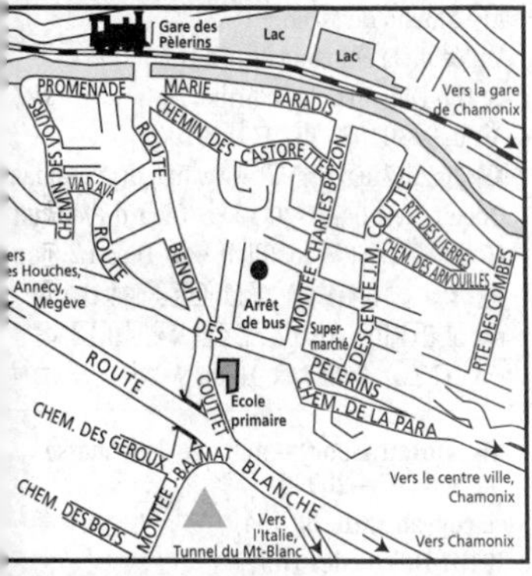

Chamonix/Mont-Blanc... Travel Tips

- **For budget eats check out...** Youth Hostel Restaurant, Le Dru, L'Omeletterie, Le Pitz, Le Bartavel
- **For great nightlife try...** Le Piano Bar, Le Gasaf, Le Chouca (Night Bar)
- **Don't miss...** La Mer de Glace (glacier), L'Aiguille du Midi (rock spire), Parc des Accros de la Branche, luge d'été, Le Lac Blanc

---

▲ Chamrousse – 20081

AJ - Le Recoin, 38410 Chamrousse (Isère).
0476899131 0476899666
chamrousse@fuaj.org
www.fuaj.org/aj/chamrousse/
Open Dates: 01.12-28.04; 10.06-19.09
Grenoble 30km Grenoble 30km
VFD 0.4SW x 64 R CC
TV 2 x

▲ Chaumont (Assoc) – 20082

FJT - 1 rue de Carcassonne,
52000 Chaumont (Haute Marne).
0325032277 0325021181
www.fuaj.org/aj/chaumont/
Open Dates: 12 Chaumont 1.2km
2 300m ap La Suize 1SW x 12
R TV 3 x
500m

Cherbourg/Octeville 20044

55 Rue de L'Abbaye,
50100 Cherbourg (Manche).
0233781515 0233781516
cherbourg@fuaj.org
www.fuaj.org/aj/cherbourg/
Open Dates: 31.01-21.12 (12)
Open Times: 08.00-12.00hrs; 18.00-23.00hrs
Beds: 99 - 3x2 3x3 16x4 4x5
Price Range: BBinc
Directions: Maupertus 10km
Cherbourg 3km Cherbourg 3km
3, 5 100m ap Chantier R
CC (BD) TV
3 x 300m 3km

Cherbourg/Octeville

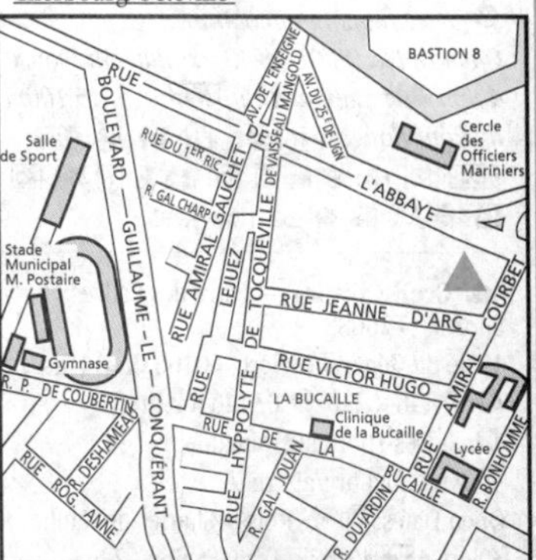

Cherbourg/Octeville... Travel Tips

- **For budget eats check out...** Le Commerce, La Cendrée, La Ciboulette
- **For great nightlife try...** Les 4 Eléments (café, live music), Le Crabe Tambour (disco), Casino, Freedom Café
- **Don't miss...** City of the sea, Regional National Park of the Contentin & Bessin Marshes, Harbour boat trip, Maritime Museum & Ile de Tatihou, Jacques Prévert House (Omonville La Petite), Regional Cider Museum (Valognes), Milk Museum (Montebourg), Nez de Jobourg, Ferme aux 5 saisons (farm, Flamanville), Station nautique de Cherbourg-Hague

▲ Cholet – Association "Les Pâquerettes" (Assoc) – 20084
5 rue de la Casse, BP 316,
49303 Cholet Cedex (Maine et Loire).
0241713636 0241626222
contact@lespaquerettes.fr
www.fuaj.org/aj/cholet-paquerettes/
Open Dates: 01.07-31.08 & school holidays Area A (call the hostel) Nantes 65km Cholet 500m 1 300m ap St Pierre 0.8E x 12 1 x 2km

*△ **Colmar (Assoc)** – AJ - "Mittelhart" – 20087*
2 Rue Pasteur, 68000 Colmar (Haut-Rhin).
0389805739 0389807616
www.fuaj.org/aj/colmar/
Open Dates: 23.01-18.12 Bâle-Mulhouse 40km Colmar 1km 4, 5, 15 100m ap Pont Rouge 1W x 110 (B) 1km

▲ Creil (Assoc) – Centre des Cadres Sportifs – 20088
1 rue du Général Leclerc, 60100 Creil (Oise).
0344646220 0344646229
cadres-sportifs@wanadoo.fr
www.fuaj.org/aj/creil/
Open Dates: Roissy-Charles de Gaulle 30km A Creil (Train Station) 2km Creil 2km 1 2km ap Roger Salengro 1S x 138 1 x 1km

*△ **Dieppe** – 20089*
AJ - 48 Rue Louis Fromager,
Quartier Janval de Dieppe,
76550 Saint Aubin/Scie (the Youth Hostel is in Dieppe) (Seine-Maritime).
0235848573 0235848962
dieppe@fuaj.org
www.fuaj.org/aj/dieppe/
Open Dates: 01.05-30.09 Dieppe 4km 3km 2 (direction Val Druel) 300m ap Château Michel 3S x 42 (B) 8 500m 4km

▲ Dinan 20051
AJ - Moulin de Méen,
Vallée de la Fontaine des Eaux,
22100 Dinan (Côtes d'Armor).
0296391083 0296391062
dinan@fuaj.org www.fuaj.org/aj/dinan
Open Dates: 04.01-20.12 Dinard-Pleurtuit 17km St Malo 28km Dinan 2.5km 2NE x 70 (B) 1 x 500m 18km

▲ Dole (Assoc) – Auberge de Jeunesse "Le St Jean" – 20090
Place Jean XXIII, BP 164,
39101 Dole Cedex (Jura).
0384823674 0384791769
lestjean@wanadoo.fr
www.fuaj.org/aj/dole/
Open Dates: Lyon 200km Dôle 2km 1, 2 ap Beau Regard, Les Paters 1S x 60 4 x 500m 5km

▲ Dunkerque – 20091
Place Paul Asseman,
59140 Dunkerque (Nord).
0328633634 0328632454
www.fuaj.org/aj/dunkerque/
Open Dates: 03.01-17.12 Lille-Lesquin 75km Dunkerque 3km Dunkerque 3km 3 500m ap Piscine 3NW x 96 300m 100m

▲ Eu-Le Tréport (Assoc) – Centre des Fontaines – 20092
rue des Fontaines, BP 123,
76260 Eu Cedex (Seine Maritime).
0235860503 0235864512
centre-des-fontaines@wanadoo.fr
www.fuaj.org/aj/eu/
Open Dates: 06.01-19.12 Dieppe 30km Eu (just a stop) 1km Trois Villes 500m ap Place Guillaume le Conquérant x 64 (B) 3km 3km

△ ***Fontaine-de-Vaucluse** – 20094*
AJ - Chemin de la Vignasse,
84800 Fontaine-de-Vaucluse (Vaucluse).
0490203165 0490202620
fontaine@fuaj.org
www.fuaj.org/aj/fontaine/
Open Dates: 01.02-15.11 Avignon 35km Isles sur la Sorgue 7km Autocars Arnaud 800m ap Fontaine-de-Vaucluse 0.8S x 50 (B) 1km

▲ **Fontenay-le-Comte (Assoc)** – FJT – 20095
16 Rue des Gravants, BP 347,
85206 Fontenay le Comte Cedex (Vendée).
0251691344 0251690423
les-trois-portes@wanadoo.fr
www.fuaj.org/aj/fontenay/
Open Dates: 01.06-30.09 Fontenay 500m 0.5E x 50 1 x 500m

▲ **Fréjus/St-Raphaël** – 20096
Chemin du Counillier, 83600 Fréjus (Var).
0494531875 0494532586
frejus-st-raphael@fuaj.org
www.fuaj.org/aj/frejus/
Open Dates: 01.03-14.11 (on request) Nice 60km Fréjus 1.7km St Raphaël and Frejus 1.5km 10 (6.45 pm), 7 (8.40 am) ap Youth Hostel 1.7NE x 106 (BD) 1 x 2km 3.5km

▲ **Gannat (Assoc)** – Maison des Cultures et Traditions – 20097
Route de St Priest, 03800 Gannat (Allier).
0470901267 0470906636
cultures-traditions@wanadoo.fr
www.fuaj.org/aj/gannat/
Open Dates: only on request Aulnat 50km Gannat 1.5km 1W x 52 2 x 3km

▲ **Genêts** 20060
28, rue de l'Ortillon, 50530 Genêts (Manche).
0233584016 0233584238
genets@fuaj.org
www.fuaj.org/aj/genets/
Open Dates: 01.03-15.11 Rennes or Caen 100km Granville 25km Avranches 14km 12 Granville/Avranches 300m ap Genêts 0.3NE x 51 (BD) 1 x 14km 5km

▲ **Granville (Assoc)** – Centre Régional de Nautisme – 20098
Bd des Amiraux, 50400 Granville (Manche).
0233912262 0233505199
crng50@wanadoo.fr
www.fuaj.org/aj/granville/
Open Dates: 05.01-20.12 Rennes or Caen 100km Granville Granville 800m 0.2S x 160 2 x 3km

▲ **Gray (Assoc)** – 20099
FJT AJ "Le Foyer" - 2 Rue André Maginot, 70100 Gray (Haute Saône).
0384649920 0384649929
le-foyer@wanadoo.fr
www.fuaj.org/aj/gray/
Open Dates: Dijon 45km x 10 2 x 1km

Grenoble-Agglomération 20012
10 Avenue du Grésivaudan,
38130 Echirolles (Isère).
0476093352 0476093899
grenoble@fuaj.org
www.fuaj.org/aj/grenoble/
Open Dates: Open Times: 07.30-23.00hrs
Beds: 130 - 11x² 20x⁴ 2x⁶ 2x⁶⁺
Price Range: BB inc
Directions: 5SW from city centre
Grenoble 40km, Lyon 80km A Gare routière 5km Grenoble 5km 1 20m ap La Quinzaine A 500m ap La Rampe 3 x 400m

FRANCE – FRANCE – FRANKREICH – FRANCIA

Grenoble-Agglomération

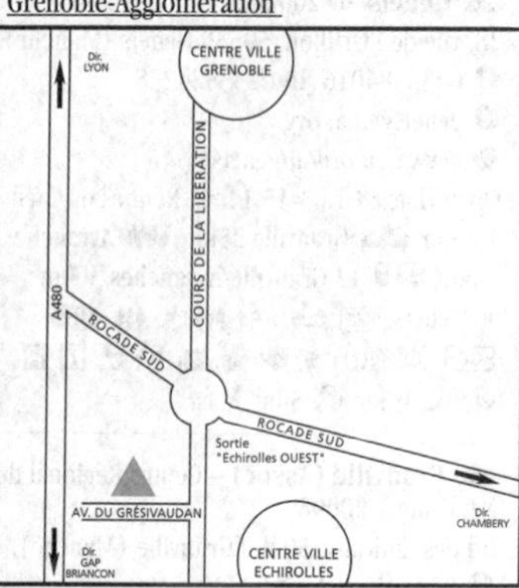

Grenoble-Agglomération... Travel Tips

- **For budget eats check out...** Fast Food, Cafeteria Self
- **For great nightlife try...** Cinemas at 15min walking distance, Bowling & Disco, Irish Pub
- **Don't miss...** La Bastille in Grenoble

▲ **Guillestre (Assoc)** – 20100
les Quatre Vents, "La Rochette", 05600 Guillestre (Hautes Alpes).
0492450432 0492450432
aj.guillestre@free.fr
www.fuaj.org/aj/guillestre/
Open Dates: 26.12-31.10 (01.12-31.10) Montdauphin 5km 1.5SW x 84 2 x 500m

▲ **Guyana** – Awala Yalimapo – 20178
Auberge de Jeunesse de Simili - Zone de Simili - 97319 Awala Yalimapo (Guyana).
0594341625 0594341625
awalayalimapo@fuaj.org
Open Dates: Cayenne 200km Cayenne 200km 4W x 24 1 x 500m

△ ***Ile-de-Groix*** *– 20101*
AJ - Fort du Méné, 56590 Ile-de-Groix (Morbihan).
0297868138 0297865243
www.fuaj.org/aj/ile-de-groix/
Open Dates: 01.04-15.10 Lorient (but then access by boat compulsory) 14km Lorient (compulsory) 14km Lorient (but then access by boat compulsory) 14km Primiture Line (July & August) ap Le Méné 1.2NE x 72 (B) 200m

▲ **La Châtre** 20177
Auberge de Jeunesse 10 rue du Moulin Borgnon, 36400 La Châtre (Indre).
0254060055 0254481703
lachatre@fuaj.org
www.fuaj.org/aj/la.chatre/
Open Dates: 01.03-01.10 (weekends on request) Tours 155km Châteauroux 36km Châteauroux to La Châtre ap Champs de Foire x 58 (B)

▲ **La Clusaz** – 20103
AJ - Route du Col de Croix Fry, Les Etages, BP47, 74220 La Clusaz (Haute-Savoie).
0450024173 0450026585
la-clusaz@fuaj.org
www.fuaj.org/aj/la-clusaz/
Open Dates: 18.12-15.04; 04.06-17.09 (on request) Genève 40km Aravis Voyages: 0609471074 (taxi-bus) Annecy 30km Annecy to La Clusaz ap La Clusaz 3SE x 79 3km 18km

▲ **La Foux d'Allos** – AJ - Neige et soleil – 20104
04260 La Foux d'Allos (Alpes-de-Haute-Provence).
0492838108 0492838370
la-foux-allos@fuaj.org
www.fuaj.org/aj/la-foux/
Open Dates: 04.12-23.04 Nice 127km only in winter (free) Nice 127km Digne-les-Bains 89km Verdon voyages 30m 0.2N x 72 4km

△ ***La Palud-sur-Verdon*** *– 20105*
"L'immense Botte de Paille",
Départementale 23, 04120 La Palud-sur-Verdon (Alpes-de-Haute-Provence).
0492773872 0492773872
www.fuaj.org/aj/la-palud/
Open Dates: Call the FUAJ National Center: 0144898727 Marignane 150km Manosque 65km Marseille - Castelane 500m ap La Palud City 0.5S
x 68 R (B)
20km

▲ **La Rochelle** 20106
Ave des Minimes, BP 3045, 17031 La Rochelle Cedex (Charente-Maritime).
0546444311 0546454148
larochelle@fuaj.org
www.fuaj.org/aj/la-rochelle/
Open Dates: 05.01-22.12 La Rochelle-Laleu 7km A Shuttle bus from the train station 2km La Rochelle 7km La Rochelle 2km 10, 19, 42 A (weekends: only 42 A) 500m ap La Sole 2SW
x 235 R CC TV 4 x 8
4km 500m

▲ **La Teste de Buch** – Dune du Pyla – 20180
Plaine des Sports - 33260 La Teste-de-Buch (Gironde).
0557525481 0557525482
centrebonneval@wanadoo.fr
Open Dates: 10.04-12.11 (01.01-22.12 on request) Bordeaux Mérignac 60km Arcachon 5km La Teste de Buch 2km 2S x 150 R TV 1 x 300m
5km

▲ **La Toussuire** – 20107
AJ - La Toussuire - Foncouverte,
73300 St Jean de Maurienne (Savoie).
0479567204 0479830093
la-toussuire@fuaj.org
www.fuaj.org/aj/la-toussuire/
Open Dates: 11.12-01.04 Lyon St Exupéry, Chambéry et Grenoble (60 km) 170km St Jean-de-Maurienne 18km Trans-Alpes from St Jean de Maurienne 100m ap YH or Poste de secours x 72 R CC TV 200m

---

△ ***Lannion*** *– Beg Leguer – 20108*
Plage du Goalagorn, Beg Leguer,
22300 Lannion (Côtes d'Armor).
0296472486 (0296379128 low season)
0296370206
www.fuaj.org/aj/lannion-beg/
Open Dates: 16.04-15.09 (12) Lannion-Trégor 6km Roscoff or St Malo 100km Lannion Trégor 8km 50m ap Beg Leguer 8W x 15
R (B)
50m

▲ **Lannion** – Les Korrigans 20021
Rive Gauche - 6, Rue du 73e Territorial,
22300 Lannion (Côtes d'Armor).
0296379128 0296370206
lannion@fuaj.org
www.fuaj.org/aj/lannion/
Open Dates: 12 Lannion-Trégor 2km A 300m Roscoff or St Malo 100km Lannion-Trégor 300m 300m ap Monastère Ste Anne 0.3SW
x 66 R 2 x 1km
6km

▲ **Lanslebourg/Val Cenis** – 20109
AJ - Hameau des Champs,
73480 Lanslebourg/Mont-Cenis (Savoie).
0479059096 0479058252
val-cenis@fuaj.org
www.fuaj.org/aj/lanslebourg/
Open Dates: 17.12-22.04; 15.06-30.09 (15.05-15.06 on request) Lyon (220 km), Chambéry (125 km), Turin (Italy, 90 km) Modane 25km Modane/Val-Cenis 200m ap Hameau des Champs, Lanslevillard Télécabine 1E x 76 R CC TV 1km

---

▲ **Le Mans (Assoc)** – 20111
FJT - le Flore, 23 rue Maupertuis,
72000 le Mans (Sarthe).
0243812755 0243810610
florefjt@noos.fr
www.fuaj.org/aj/le-mans/
Open Dates: 03.01-23.12 (only 01.05-30.08 and weekends) Paris-Orly 160km Le Mans 1km 4, 12 100m ap Erpell 0.2NE x 28 R TV 8 3km

▲ **Le Mont-Dore** – AJ - "Chalet Le Grand Volcan" – 20032
Route de Sancy 63240 Le Mont-Dore (Puy-de-Dome).
0473650353 0473652639
le-mont-dore@fuaj.org
www.fuaj.org/aj/le-mont-dore/
Open Dates: 01.01-06.11; 09.12-31.12 ( ) Clermont-Ferrand 45km
Mont-Dore 4km Shuttle Mont Dore-Sancy at specific hours in winter and summer 50m ap Les Chomets 4S x 87
R CC 1 x 8km
15km

△ ***Le Puy-en-Velay (Assoc)*** *– 20112*
Centre Pierre Cardinal, 9 Rue Jules Vallès, 43000 Le Puy en Velay (Haute Loire).
0471055240 0471056124
auberge.jeunesse@mairie-le-puy-en-velay.fr
www.fuaj.org/aj/le-puy-en-velay/
Open Dates: contact the youth hostel
Lyon-Saint-Exupéry 160km Le Puy-en-Velay 500m 0.2SE x 70
R CC (B)
8 P 800m

▲ **Le Trayas/Théoule-sur-Mer** – 20113
AJ - 9 Av de la Véronèse, Le Trayas, 06590 Théoule-sur-Mer (Alpes-Maritimes).
0493754023 0493754345
le-trayas@wanadoo.fr
www.fuaj.org/aj/le-trayas/
Open Dates: 01.04-30.09 (01.04-30.09)
Nice 45km Port de la Figuerette 2km
Le Trayas 2km Cannes to St Raphaël 2km ap YH 8W x 100
R (BD)
P 2km

▲ **Les Aldudes** – Erreka Gorri – 20114
Route d'Urepel,
64430 Les Aldudes (Pyrénées-Atlantiques)
0559375658 0559375525
erreka.gorri@tiscali.fr
Open Dates: 01.04-01.11 Biarritz 60km
Bayonne 60km
Saint-Jean-Pied-de-Port 30km x 80
R 1 x
P

▲ **Les Deux Alpes** – AJ - "Les Brûleurs de Loups" – 20115
34, Avenue de la Muzelle
38860 Les Deux Alpes (Isère).
0476792280 0476792615
les-deux-alpes@fuaj.org
www.fuaj.org/aj/les-deux-alpes/
Open Dates: 22.10-01.11; 26.11-29.04; 17.06-26.08 Grenoble-St-Geoirs 100km
A VFD Grenoble Grenoble 70km
Bus VFD Line Grenoble- Les Deux Alpes 200m ap Information Point 0.15S x 57
R CC
P 300m

▲ **Les Rousses** 20047
AJ - 2400 Le Bief de la Chaille,
39220 Les Rousses (Jura).
0384600280 0384600967
les-rousses@fuaj.org
www.fuaj.org/aj/les-rousses/
Open Dates: 22.12-26.03; 15.05-24.09 ( ) Genève 40km A Train Nyon-La Cure 2km Morez 12km 150 3km ap La Cure 3.5S x 45 R
(BD) 8 P

▲ **Lille** 20037
12 Rue Malpart, 59800 Lille (Nord).
0320570894 0320639893
lille@fuaj.org www.fuaj.org/aj/lille/
Open Dates: 31.01-23.12 Lille-Lesquin 10km Lille - Flandres 500m 13 200m ap Hôtel de Ville U 1 (République-Beaux-Arts) et 2 300m 0.5SW
x 165 R CC (B)
1 x P
1.5km

Lorient 20049
AJ - 41 rue Victor Schoelcher, 56100 Lorient (Morbihan).
0297371165 0297879549
lorient@fuaj.org
www.fuaj.org/aj/lorient/
Open Dates: 02.01-22.12
Open Times: 08.30-12.00hrs; 17.30-22.00hrs
Beds: 104 - 4x3 6x4 12x5
Price Range:
Directions: 4SW from city centre
Lan-Bihoué 3km A B2 200m
Lorient 4km Lorient 4km B2 - C1 200m ap YH R CC
2 x
8 P 1km 4km

Lorient

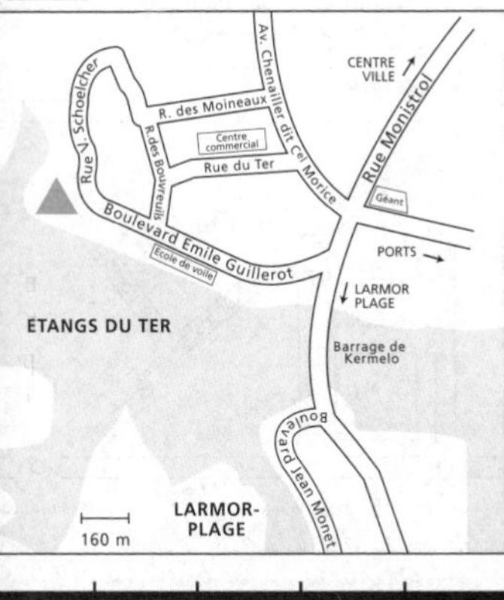

0 160m

Lyon – AJ du Vieux Lyon

0 500m

Lorient... Travel Tips

- **For budget eats check out...** In town centre: Crêperies, Kebabs, Pizzeria
- **For great nightlife try...** Theme Bars (tapas, Cuban, Irish pub), Ice-skating ring, Karting, Bowling
- **Don't miss...** Beaches from Larmor to Guidel (20km of creeks), Vauban's Citadelle at Port Louis, Museum ships, The underwater base & le pôle "Course Rumer", Megaliths and the Gulf of Morbihan

Lyon... Travel Tips

- **For budget eats check out...** Les Lyonnais, Les Ventres Jaunes, Rue Mercier
- **For great nightlife try...** Bar Café, Disco, Pubs, Irish Bars
- **Don't miss...** Fourvière Theatre, Fourvière Basilica (11th century), St Jean Cathedral (14th Century), St Jean District, La Croix Rousse District, Opera House, St Pierre Museum, Museum of Gallo-Roman Civilisation, Museum of Contemporary Art

Lyon – AJ du Vieux Lyon (H) 20042
41-45 Montée du Chemin Neuf,
69005 Lyon (Rhône).
(T) 0478150550 (F) 0478150551
(E) lyon@fuaj.org (W) www.fuaj.org/aj/lyon/
Open Dates: 12 (Call the youth hostel for Dec)
Open Times: 07.00-13.00hrs; 14.00-21.00hrs; 22.00-01.00hrs
Beds: 180 - 2x2 10x4 3x5 16x6 2x6+
Price Range: BB inc
Directions: Lyon-St-Exupery 25km A Airport shuttle 2km Part-Dieu, Perrache 3km 28, 31, Funiculaire St Jean to St Just ap Les Minimes U Saint-Jean 200m R CC (B) 3km

*△ **Lyon-Sud** (H) 20013*
AJ - 51 rue Roger Salengro,
69200 Vénissieux (Rhône).
(T) 0478763923 (F) 0478775111
(E) lyon-sud@fuaj.org
(W) www.fuaj.org/aj/lyon-venissieux/
Open Dates: 15.01-19.12 Lyon St Exupéry 22km Lyon Part Dieu 4km 36, 35 200m ap J. Curie-AJ (36), G. Lévy-AJ (35) U Parilly ap 1,5 km - Vénissieux Station ap 2.5 km 5SE x 72 (B) 2 x 8 1.5km

△ ***Manosque*** Ⓗ *20116*
AJ - Parc de la Rochette,
04100 Manosque (Alpes de Haute-Provence).
0492875744 0492724391
manosque@fuaj.org
www.fuaj.org/aj/manosque/
Open Dates: 01.03-30.11 Marseille 90km
Shuttle from the train station of Manosque 4km Marseille 90km Manosque 4km 1 30m ap La Rochette 1N x 57 (B)
1 x
50m

△ ***Marseille*** –
AJ - "Château de Bois-Luzy" – 20117
Allée des Primevères,
13012 Marseille (Bouches-du-Rhône).
0491490618 0491490618
www.fuaj.org/aj/marseille/
Open Dates: 03.01-18.12 Marignane 55km Marseille-Joliette 5km St Charles 4km 6 at 200 m, 8 at 400 m ap Marius Richard-Py (6), Bois Luzy (8)
4NE x 92 R (B) 200m
4km

Marseille – Bonneveine Ⓗ 20014
(Impasse du Dr Bonfils) Av J. Vidal,
13008 Marseille (Bouches-du-Rhône).
0491176330 0491739723
marseille-bonneveine@fuaj.org
www.fuaj.org/aj/marseille-bonneveine/
Open Dates: 17.01-17.12
Open Times: 07.00-24.00hrs
Beds: 150
Directions: 5SE from city centre
Marseille Provence 35km 44 or metro line 2 to then shuttle bus
Marseille 5km St Charles 5km
44 200m ap Bonnefon Line 2 ap Rond-point Prado 1km R CC
8
550m 200m

Marseille – Bonneveine

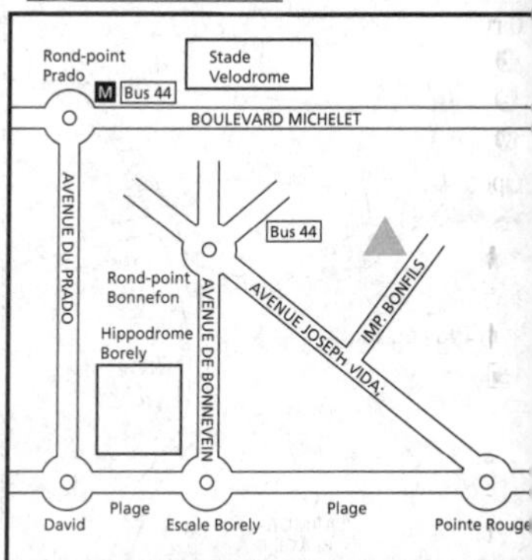

Marseille... Travel Tips
- **For budget eats check out...** Chez Jeaunot (Vallon de Auffes), Escale Borelly
- **For great nightlife try...** Escale Borelly
- **Don't miss...** Les Calanques, Notie - Dauie de la Garde, Le Vieux Port, Le Quartier du Panier/La Vieille Charité - visit by foot

△ ***Martinique*** *– Morne Rouge – 20118*
AJ - Av Jean Jaurès, Hauts du Bourg,
97260 Morne Rouge (Martinique).
0596523981 0596523981
www.fuaj.org/aj/martinique/
Open Dates: 12 Fort de France 35km
Urban Service Line ap Mespont 1N
x 40 R
1 x 7km

▲ **Menton** Ⓗ 20027
AJ - Plateau St-Michel,
06500 Menton (Alpes-Maritimes).
0493359314 0493359307
menton@fuaj.org
www.fuaj.org/aj/menton/
Open Dates: 01.02-31.10 Nice 35km
Nice-Monaco-Menton 1.5km
Nice 25km Menton 1.5km 6 600m ap Camping St Michel 1.5NW x 80
R (BD)
2km 1.5km

▲ Metz (Assoc) – Carrefour – 20119
6 rue Marchant, 57000 Metz (Moselle).
0387750726 0387367144
ascarrefour@wanadoo.fr
www.fuaj.org/aj/metz-carrefour/
Open Dates: 01.01-23.12; 26-30.12
Metz-Nancy Lorraine 30km A Shuttle
Metz Ville 1km 3, 11 200m
ap Saint-Georges x 60
3 x
1km

*△ **Metz (Assoc)** – Plage – 20120*
AJ - 1 Allée de Metz Plage,
57000 Metz (Moselle).
0387304402 0387331980
aubjeumetz@aol.com
www.fuaj.org/aj/metz-plage/
Open Dates: Metz-Nancy 15km
Metz 1.5km 3, 11 10m
ap Pontiffroy 0.3N x 62
2 x
200m

Montargis ☛ Cepoy

*△ **Montpellier** 20015*
AJ - Rue des Ecoles Laïques (Impasse Petite Corraterie), 34000 Montpellier (Hérault).
0467603222 0467603230
montpellier@fuaj.org
www.fuaj.org/aj/montpellier/
Open Dates: 09.01-10.12 Montpellier 10km A Shuttle near the train station 1km Marseille 200km
Montpellier 1km 100m ap Louis Blanc Line direction "Mosson" 100m ap Louis Blanc x 92
(B) 1 x
1km 10km

▲ Mulhouse – 20125
AJ - 37 Rue de l'Illberg,
68200 Mulhouse (Haut-Rhin).
0389426328 0389597495
mulhouse@fuaj.org
www.fuaj.org/aj/mulhouse/
Open Dates: 16.01-23.12 Bâle-Mulhouse 35km A Railway station Mulhouse 1.5km 2 ap Salle des Sports 2W
x 100
1 x
200m

▲ Nancy (Assoc) – 20126
"Château de Rémicourt", 149,
Rue de Vandoeuvre,
54600 Villers les Nancy (Meurthe et Moselle).
0383277367 0383414135
aubergeremicourt@mairie-nancy.fr
www.fuaj.org/aj/nancy/
Open Dates: 02.01-22.12 Nancy Metz 30km Nancy 4km 126,134, 135 400m ap St Fiacre, Lycée Stanislas Line I 1km ap Le reclus 5SW x 60
4 x
500m

▲ Nantes – La Manu 20039
2 Place de la Manu,
44000 Nantes (Loire-Atlantique).
0240292920 0251124842
nanteslamanu@fuaj.org
www.fuaj.org/aj/nantes-manu/
Open Dates: 09.01-22.12 Nantes Atlantique 8km A Commerces (tramway) Nantes Nord 300m 12 100m ap Manufacture 1 100m ap Manufacture 2E x 122
(B) 1 x
2km

▲ Nantes – FJT - Port Beaulieu (Assoc) – 20127
9 Bd Vincent Gâche,
44200 Nantes (Loire Atlantique).
0240122400 0251820005
fjt.beaulieu@anfjt.asso.fr
www.fuaj.org/aj/nantes-gache/
Open Dates: 01.07-31.08 Nantes 2km Saint-Nazaire 40km Nantes Sud 2km 24, 26, 28, 29 500m 1 100m ap Vincent Gâche 3S x 60
(B) 1 x
1km

▲ Nantes – FJT - Porte Neuve (Assoc) – 20128
1 place Ste Elisabeth,
44042 Nantes Cedex (Loire Atlantique).
0240206363 0240206379
fjt.porteneuve@anfjt.asso.fr
www.fuaj.org/aj/nantes-ste-elisabeth/
Open Dates: 01.07-31.08 Nantes 2km Saint-Nazaire 40km Nantes 2km 1, 3 100m ap Marchix 0.5NW x 35
(B)
1km

Nice – Les Camélias HI 20173
3, rue Spitalieri,
06000 Nice (Alpes-Maritimes).
T 0493621554 F 0493804296
E nice-camelias@fuaj.org
W www.fuaj.org/aj/nice-camelias/
Open Dates: 12 Open Times:
Beds: 135 - 1x3 10x4 4x6 9x6+
Price Range: BB inc
Directions: Nice Côte d'Azur 3km
A 98 from the Gare Routière 100m
Nice 500m Nice Central 500m
(B)
1km
500m

Nice – Les Camélias

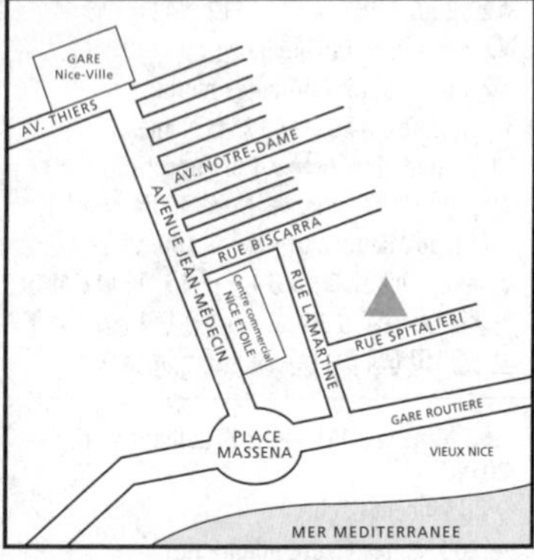

▲ **Nice** – Mont-Boron HI 20023
AJ - Route Forestière du Mont Alban,
06300 Nice (Alpes-Maritimes).
T 0493892364 F 0492040310
E nice@fuaj.org
W www.fuaj.org/aj/nice-boron/
Open Dates: 01.02-31.10 Nice 10km
A 98 3km 2km Nice Town
4km 17 to Jean Medecin-Gioffredo; then
14 to Mont-Boron direction ap YH 4E
x 56 (B)
3km
3km

Nice... Travel Tips

- **For budget eats check out...** Many restaurants in the old city (cuisine nicoise and provençale)
- **For great nightlife try...** Many pubs (Old Nice and Rues Pietounes á Côté de l'Auberge)
- **Don't miss...** Site romain de Cimiez, Le Vieux Nice, La cathédrale russe, La Promenade des Anglais

Nîmes – La Cigale HI 20031
257 Chemin de l'Auberge de Jeunesse,
30900 Nîmes (Gard).
T 0466680320 F 0466680321
E nimes@fuaj.org
W www.fuaj.org/aj/nimes/
Open Dates: 12 Open Times:
Beds: 80
Price Range:
Directions: 2NW from city centre
Nîmes-Camargue 15km A after 8.00 pm ask the bus driver to stop at the hostel 500m Nimes 4km 1 (Alès or Villeverte direction) 400m ap Stade
1 x
4km 15km

Nîmes – La Cigale

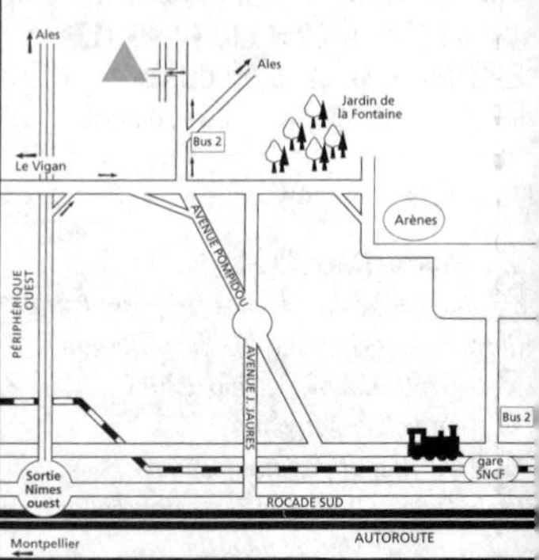

Nîmes... Travel Tips

- **For budget eats check out...** Youth Hostel, Pizzeria Croquignole, Saladerie Tati Agùes
- **For great nightlife try...** Marché du Jeudi Soir, O'Flahertys Pub, Queens Beer, La Cantina (Bar Tapas), Cinema Semaphore (Film V.O.)
- **Don't miss...** Le Pont du Gard (Roman aqueduct), Roman amphitheatre, temples & monuments, La Camargue (horses, bulls, pink flamingoes), beach (30km), Uzes (Provencal market), Perrier (spring, factory & bottling), Les Cévennes

▲ **Nouméa** – 20129
City Hostel, 51 bis rue Pasteur Marcel Ariège, BP 767, 98845 Nouméa Cedex (New Caledonia).
00/687/275879 00/687/254817
yha.noumea@lagoon.nc
www.fuaj.org/aj/noumea/
Open Dates: Tontouta 50km Noumea 200m 100m x 96 3km

▲ **Paris** – Cité des Sciences 20017
24, Rue des Sept Arpents, 1 rue Jean-Baptiste Clément, 93310 Le Pré-St-Gervais (Seine-Saint-Denis).
0148432411 0148432682
paris.cite-des-sciences@fuaj.org
www.fuaj.org/aj/paris-cite/
Open Dates: 01.01-09.11; 01.12-31.12 (only 01.01-30.06; 01.09 -09.11; 01.12-21.12) Roissy-Charles de Gaulle 25km A RER B + underground line 5 Gare du Nord PC - 75 300m ap Porte de Pantin U 5 Bobigny ap Hoche 200m 3NE x 184 (B) 2km

▲ **Paris** – Jules Ferry – 20131
8 Boulevard Jules Ferry, 75011 Paris.
0143575560 0143148209
paris.julesferry@fuaj.org
www.fuaj.org/aj/paris-jules/
Open Dates: Orly 15km, Roissy 30km 30km Gare du Nord, Gare de l'Est 5km 46, 54, 56, 65, 75, 96 300m ap République or Jules Ferry U 3, 5, 8, 9, 11 ap République 200m x 99 (B) 3km

Paris – Le d'Artagnan 20001
80 rue Vitruve, 75020 Paris.
0140323456 0140323455
paris.le-dartagnan@fuaj.org
www.fuaj.org/aj/paris-dartagnan/
Open Dates: Open Times: 08.00-13.00hrs
Beds: 435 - 38x2 42x3 35x4 5x5 7x6+
Price Range: BB inc
Directions: 5E from city centre
Roissy-Charles de Gaulle 25km
A Porte de Bagnolet 351 300m
Gare du Nord, Gare de l'Est 5km
26, 57, PC2, 351, 76 ap Vitruve (57, PC2), Porte de Bagnolet (351), Bagnolet-Pelleport (76) U 3 ap Porte de Bagnolet 800m 3 x

Paris – Le d'Artagnan

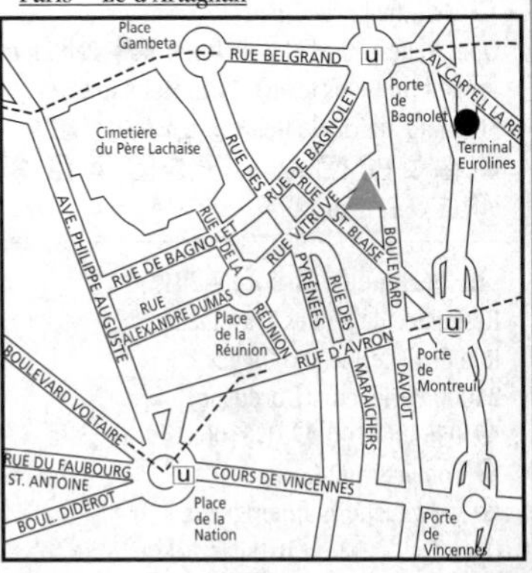

Paris... Travel Tips

- **For budget eats check out...** Youth Hostel Restaurant, Exotic little restaurants, Le Nacabaue (Saint-Blaise), La Gondole (Saint-Blaise), Le Nandariu (Saint-Blaise)
- **For great nightlife try...** Le Zetore, Théâtre de la Colline, La Goguelte (Saint-Blaise), Lo Loco (Pigalle), Le Gibus (République)
- **Don't miss...** Cimetière du Père Lachaise, Puces de Montreuil, nearby the hostel and all the very famous places to visit, Open Tour (Bus touristique à République), Quartier Saint-Naur/Oberkaupf

▲ **Paris Clichy** – Auberge "Léo Lagrange" 20024
107 Rue Martre, 92110 Clichy (Hauts-de-Seine).
0141272690 0142705263
paris.clichy@fuaj.org
www.fuaj.org/aj/paris-clichy/
Open Dates: Charles-de-Gaulle 20km St Lazare Station & all the stations in Paris at less than 30' 3km 54, night bus C 200m 13, Mairie de Clichy ap 200m 2NW x 338 R CC (B) 1 x 500m

▲ **Pau-Gelos (Assoc)** – FJT - Logis Gaston Marsan – 20132
Base de Plein Air,
64110 Gelos (Pyrénées-Atlantiques).
0559350999; 0559110505
0559350998; 0559110520
logis.des.jeunes@ldjpau.org
www.fuaj.org/aj/pau/
Open Dates: Uzein 10km Pau 2km 1 (in Gelos town), 7 (in Hounau town) 300m ap Mairie de Gelos 3SE x 12 R 1 x 2km

▲ **Périgueux (Assoc)** – 20133
Residence de Jeunes Travailleurs,
Rue des Thermes Prolongés,
24000 Périgueux (Dordogne).
0553068140 0553068149
contact@fjt24.com
www.fuaj.org/aj/perigueux/
Open Dates: Bassilac 12km Périgueux 2km 6 500m x 16 R CC 200m

△ ***Perpignan** – 20134*
AJ - Allée Marc Pierre, Parc de la Pépinière, Av de la Grande-Bretagne, 66000 Perpignan (Pyrénées-Orientales).
0468346332 0468511602
perpignan@fuaj.org
www.fuaj.org/aj/perpignan/
Open Dates: 01.03-15.11 Perpignan 10km A Shuttle (Gare routière) Perpignan 600m x 49 R (B) 4km 13km

△ ***Plouguernevel (Assoc)** – Village Vacances de Kermarc'h – 20136*
22110 Plouguernevel (Côtes d' Armor).
0296291095 / 0673556031
www.fuaj.org/aj/plouguernevel/
Open Dates: Saint-Brieuc 70km Saint-Brieuc 70km Carhaix 25km In Rostrenen village 2km ap Rostrenen 3N x 25 R

▲ **Poitiers** 20016
AJ - 1 Allée Roger Tagault,
86000 Poitiers (Vienne).
0549300970 0549300979
poitiers@fuaj.org
www.fuaj.org/aj/poitiers/
Open Dates: 02.01-24.12 Biard 3km Poitiers 3km 7 100m ap Cap Sud 3SW x 140 R CC 2 x 10m

▲ **Pontarlier** – 20137
AJ - 2 rue Jouffroy, 25300 Pontarlier (Doubs).
0381390657 0381390657
pontarlier@fuaj.org
www.fuaj.org/aj/pontarlier/
Open Dates: 20.12-10.11 ( ) Genève 70km Pontarlier 300m from Besançon 100m ap Mont Jura 0.2N x 72 R 2 x 1km 6km

▲ **Pontivy** – 20138
AJ - Ile des Récollets,
56300 Pontivy (Morbihan).
0297255827 0297257648
www.fuaj.org/aj/pontivy/
Open Dates: (R for low season weekends; on request) Lorient 50km Lorient 50km Pontivy 1.5km Gare routière 500m ap La Plaine x 65 R (B) 2 x 3km

△ ***Pontorson (Assoc)*** – *Centre Duguesclin – 20139*
21 bd Patton, 50170 Pontorson (Manche).
0233601865 0233602581
aj@ville-pontorson.fr
www.fuaj.org/aj/pontorson/
Open Dates: 30.04-30.09 Rennes 60km St Malo, Granville 40km Pontorson 700m Les Courriers Bretons 700m 0.5NW x 57 (B) 1 x 22km 30km

---

▲ **Quillan (Assoc)** – La Forge de Quillan – 20181
Route de Perpignan - 11500 Quillan (Aude).
0468202379 0468201364
laforge.quillan@wanadoo.fr
Open Dates: 01.04-15.09 (12 on request) Carcassonne 50km Quillan 1km SNCF/Tessier 1km 0.6S x 70 1 x 600m

---

△ ***Quimper*** – *20142*
Auberge de Jeunesse, 6 ave des Oiseaux, 29000 Quimper (Finistère).
0298649797 0298553837
quimper@fuaj.org
www.fuaj.org/aj/quimper/
Open Dates: 01.04-30.09 Quimper 3km 1 (Kermoysan direction) 1km ap Lycée Chaptal 2W x 54 (B) 500m 15km

---

▲ **Redon (Assoc)** – FJT - "Mapar" – 20143
1, rue du Plessis, BP 10317,
35603 Redon Cedex (Ille-et-Vilaine).
0299721439 0299721653
mapar-redon@wanadoo.fr
www.fuaj.org/aj/redon/
Open Dates: 01.06-31.08 Nantes 70km Redon 500m 0.5N x 10 1km

▲ **Reims (Assoc)** – Centre International de Séjour – 20144
Chaussée Bocquaine, Parc Léo Lagrange, 51100 Reims (Marne).
0326405260 0326473570
info@cis-reims.com
www.fuaj.org/aj/reims/
Open Dates: 12 Reims 1km H, K, N 500m ap Comédie, Pont de Gaulle 0.5SW x 217 2 x 500m 10km

---

Reims ☛ Verzy

▲ **Rennes** HI 20002
AJ - 10-12 Canal Saint-Martin, 35700 Rennes (Ille-et-Vilaine).
0299332233 0299590621
rennes@fuaj.org
www.fuaj.org/aj/rennes/
Open Dates: 02.01-22.12 St Jacques 12km A Line 57 1.5km Rennes 2km 18 100m ap Auberge de Jeunesse U Place Sainte-Anne 500m 1.5N x 96 (B) 2 x 2km

---

▲ **Roanne** HI 20057
AJ - 4 Rue Fontenille, 42300 Roanne (Loire).
0477725211 0477706628
roanne@fuaj.org
www.fuaj.org/aj/roanne/
Open Dates: 12 Saint-Etienne 60km Roanne 1.5km 3, 2, 7 200m ap Clémenceau 0.5N x 57 (BL) 1 x 5km

---

△ ***Rochefort-sur-Mer*** – *Logis Etape – 20145*
20 rue de la République, 17300 Rochefort-sur-Mer (Charente-Maritime).
0546997462 (every day June till August otherwise Mon, Tues, Thurs and Fri)
0546997462 rochefort@fuaj.org
www.fuaj.org/aj/rochefort/
Open Dates: 03.01-16.12 La Rochelle-Laleu 35km A 400m Rochefort 2km Rochefort 800m Down Town 200m x 44 (BD) 2km 12km

Rodez (Assoc) – "Les Quatre Saisons" – 20146
26 bd des Capucines,BP 3408 Onet le Château 12034 Rodez Cedex 9 (Aveyron).
0565775105 0565673797
fjt-aj-rodez@wanadoo.fr
www.fuaj.org/aj/rodez/
Open Dates: Rodez-Marcillac 10km
A find out from the Youth Hostel
Rodez 2km 1, 3 50m ap Les Marguerites 3N x 60 R CC 6 x TV 300m

Saint-Brévin-les-Pins – AJ - "La Pinède" – 20038
1 Allée de la Jeunesse,
44250 St-Brévin-Les-Pins (Loire- Atlantique).
0240272527 0240272502
saint-brevin@fuaj.org
www.fuaj.org/aj/st-brevin/
Open Dates: 23.01-06.10; 23.10-23.12 (low season, call the youth hostel to confirm)
Nantes 60km St-Nazaire or Pornic 15km St-Nazaire 15km 18, 19 (weekends) 200m ap La Courance 1W x 59 R TV 800m 300m

Saint-Brieuc 20052
Manoir de la Ville Guyomard,
Les Villages,
22000 St-Brieuc (Côtes-d'Armor).
0296787070 0296782747
saint-brieuc@fuaj.org
www.fuaj.org/aj/st-brieuc/
Open Dates: Open Times: 08.00-22.00hrs
Beds: 125 - 2x 3x 10x 15x 1x 1x 2x
Price Range: BB inc
Directions: 3W from city centre
Trémilson 8km St-Malo, Roskof 110km St-Brieuc 3km 3, 2 300m ap Centre commercial-Les Villages or Centre Jacques Cartier R CC (B) TV 3 x 2km 6km

Saint-Brieuc

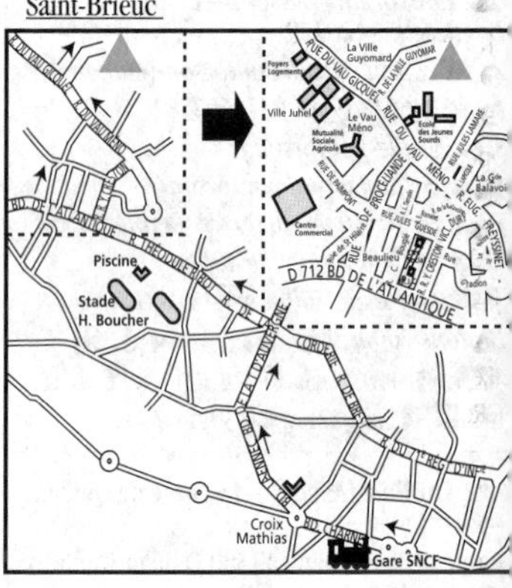

Saint-Brieuc... Travel Tips
- **For budget eats check out...** La Grille district (Rue des Trois Frères Legoff), Tex-Mex, Le Capri (Pizzeria), La Proue (Pizzeria)
- **For great nightlife try...** La Grille district (nightclubs-eg Le Chat Noir, Le Calibo), Le O'Kenny - pub, Le Piano Bleu
- **Don't miss...** Mussel farming, Ethnographic Museum, Museum of Nature & the Coast, Walk along the custom officers footpath, Historic Town, Swimming pool & water sports, Beaches, La Briguelterie

Saint-Dié (Assoc) – FJT Cap Jeunes – 20182
Cap jeunes, 1 rue Ernest Colin,
88100 Saint-Dié-des-Vosges (Vosges).
0329516550 0329516556
ftj.saint-die@wanadoo.fr
Open Dates: Strasbourg 80km
Saint-Dié 500m 1 10m ap 4 Frère Mougeotte 0.5E x 22 R (L) TV 500m

Saintes 20048
AJ - 2 Place Geoffroy Martel,
17100 Saintes (Charente-Maritime).
0546921492 0546929782
saintes@fuaj.org
www.fuaj.org/aj/saintes/
Open Dates: 03.01-18.12 Bordeaux 100km La Rochelle 70km Saintes 800m 1 200m ap Abbaye x 88 R CC TV 2 x 1km

▲ **Saint-Etienne Les Echandes** – 20174
AJ, Le Pertuiset, 42240 Unieux (Loire)
0477357203 0477357818
les-echandes@fuaj.org
Open Dates: Firminy 10km
Saint-Etienne-Firminy ap Le Pertuiset
x 97 R
1 x 3km

▲ **Saint-Gaudens (Assoc)** – FJT - "Le Vénasque" – 20147
3 Rue de la Résidence, BP 158,
31804 Saint-Gaudens Cedex (Haute-Garonne).
0561947273 0561947274
residencevenasque@wanadoo.fr
www.fuaj.org/aj/st-gaudens/
Open Dates: 02.01-31.12
Toulouse-Blagnac 95km
Saint-Gaudens 1.5km 1W x 24
2km

▲ **Saint-Junien** – Auberge de Jeunesse de l'Abbaye de St. Amand – 20149
13 rue de St. Amand,
87200 St-Junien (Haute-Vienne).
0555022279 0555022279
www.fuaj.org/aj/st-junien/
Open Dates: Limoges Bellegarde 19km
St-Junien 1.5km St-Junien - Limoges 1km ap Comodoliac 1NW x 54
R 2 x
1km 6km

▲ **Saint-Malo (Assoc)** – Centre Patrick Varangot – 20150
37 av du RP Umbricht, BP 108,
35407 St-Malo Cedex (Ille-et- Vilaine).
0299402980 0299402902
info@centrevarangot.com
www.fuaj.org/aj/st-malo/
Open Dates: Dinard-Pleurtuit 12km
A Tourist Information Office/Airport Line St-Malo 2km St-Malo 1.5km
2, 5 100m ap YH 1.5NE x 242
R CC
4 x 8
2km 200m

△ ***Saint-Martin-des-Olmes (Assoc)*** – *Auberge de Saint-Martin – 20151*
Le Bourg, St-Martin-des-Olmes
63600 Ambert (Puy-de-Dome).
0473820138 0473820138
aj.stmartin@free.fr
www.fuaj.org/aj/st-martin/
Open Dates: 15.02-15.11 (on request) Andrézieux-Bouthéon 50km
Ambert 6km Shuttel on request. Call YH x 36 R (BD)
1 x 6km

▲ **Saint-Maurice-Sous-les-Côtes** – Maison de la Croueé – 20186
40, Rue de L'Eglise,
55210 Saint-Maurice-Sous-les-Côtes (Neuse).
0329893895 0329893895
toyer-ruralcrouee@wanadoo.fr
Open Dates: Nancy-Metz 60km
Verdum 30km; Metz 60km x 37
1 x
10km

△ ***Saint-Mibiel*** *– 20152*
AJ - 12 rue sur Meuse,
55300 St-Mibiel (Meuse).
0329891506 0329891506
www.fuaj.org/aj/st-mibiel/
Open Dates: 01.04-30.11 (on request) Commercy 18km
Nancy - Verdun Line 50m x 52
1 x
2km

Saint-Raphaël ☛ Fréjus

▲ **Saverne** – 20154
AJ - Château des Rohan,
67700 Saverne (Bas-Rhin).
0388911484 0388711597
saverne@fuaj.org
www.fuaj.org/aj/saverne/
Open Dates: 01.02-24.12
Strasbourg-Entzheim 35km Saverne 500m x 87 R CC (B)
1 x
500m

▲ ***Savines-le-Lac*** *– AJ - "Les Chaumettes" – 20155*
05160 Savines-le-Lac (Hautes-Alpes).
0492442016 0492442454
savines@fuaj.org
www.fuaj.org/aj/savines/
Open Dates: 15.06-01.09 Marseille 220km Marseille 220km Embrun or Chorges & Gap junction at 30 km 10km Marseille-Gap-Briançon Line 300m ap Savines 0.8SW x 50 R (B) 4km 500m

---

▲ **Seez-Les-Arcs** – La Verdache – 20156
AJ - 73700 Seez (Savoie).
0479410193 0479410336
seez-les-arcs@fuaj.org
www.fuaj.org/aj/seez/
Open Dates: 01.01-08.05; 23.05-19.09; 17.12-31.12 (12 R only)
Chambéry 110km Bourg-St-Maurice 4km Martin Bus (Tignes direction) 200m ap Longefoy 1.5E x 80 R CC 2 x 3km

---

▲ **Sète** – AJ - "Villa Salis" 20035
rue du Général Revest, 34200 Sète (Hérault).
0467534668 0467513401
sete@fuaj.org www.fuaj.org/aj/sete/
Open Dates: 01.02-15.12 (15.01-15.12)
Montpellier 25km Sète 500m
Sète 1km 1, 2, 4 300m ap Caraussane (1), Paul Valery (2) x 92 R CC (B) 2km 2km

---

Strasbourg – 2 Rives (Parc du Rhin)
20004
Rue des Cavaliers, BP 58,
67017 Strasbourg Cedex (Bas-Rhin).
0388455420 0388455421
strasbourg.2rives@fuaj.org
www.fuaj.org/aj/strasbourg-rhin/
Open Dates: 05.01-31.10 Open Times:
Beds: 246 - 18x3 43x4 4x5
Price Range: BB inc
Directions: 5SE from city centre
Entzheim 25km A 6km Khel (Germany) 2km 21, 2 1km ap Parc du Rhin R CC 3 x 8 3km

---

Strasbourg – 2 Rives (Parc du Rhin)

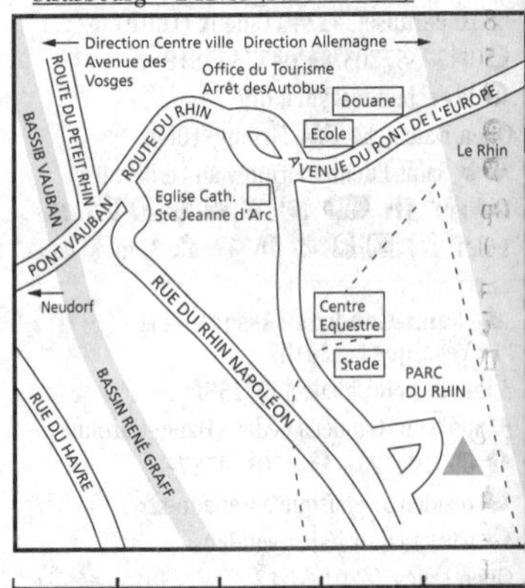

▲ **Strasbourg** – René Cassin 20003
9 rue de l'Auberge de Jeunesse,
67200 Strasbourg (Bas-Rhin).
0388302646 0388303516
strasbourg.rene-cassin@fuaj.org
www.fuaj.org/aj/strasbourg-cassin/
Open Dates: 12 Entzheim 12km
Strasbourg 2.5km 2 200m ap YH
C 500m ap Montagne Verte 2W x 264 R CC 2 x 4km

Strasbourg... Travel Tips

- **For budget eats check out...** Youth Hostel Restaurant, Le Baeckeoffe d'Alsace, Au Pont Saint Martin, Le Flam's, L'Aucieune Douane
- **For great nightlife try...** Information available from the youth hostel, Quartier derrière la Cathèdrale (Pubs), Le bowling de l'Orangerie, Patinoire
- **Don't miss...** La Petite France, La Route de Vins, Cathèdrale d' Strasbourg, Bâteau Nouche, Le Parc de Orangerie, Le Vaisseau, L'éco museé d'Alsace

---

▲ **Tarascon** 20050
AJ - 31 Boulevard Gambetta,
13150 Tarascon (Bouches-du-Rhône).
0490910408 0490915417
tarascon@fuaj.org
www.fuaj.org/aj/tarascon/
Open Dates: 10.03-15.12 Nîmes 20km
Tarascon 1km 0.5NE x 65 R (B) 2km

▲ **Tarbes (Assoc)** – Atrium - FJT – 20158
88 Rue Alsace Lorraine,
65000 Tarbes (Hautes-Pyrénées).
0562389120 0562376981
aj.tarbes@wanadoo.fr
www.fuaj.org/aj/tarbes/
Open Dates: Tarbes-Ossun-Lourdes 10km Tarbes 2km 1 ap FJT x 58 1 x 1km

Théoule-sur-Mer ☛ **Le Trayas**

▲ **Thionville (Assoc)** – Salvador Allende – 20159
3 Place de la Gare,
57100 Thionville (Moselle).
0382563214 0382561606
aubergejeunesse@aj-thionville.com
www.fuaj.org/aj/thionville/
Open Dates: Luxembourg 30km Thionville 200m x 60 1km

△ ***Thouars (Assoc)*** *– AJ - "Hector Etoubleau" – 20160*
5 Boulevard du 8 Mai,
79102 Thouars (Deux-Sèvres).
0549662240 0549661074
fjt-aj-thouars@wanadoo.fr
www.fuaj.org/aj/thouars/
Open Dates: Poitiers 60km Thouars 600m x 38 1 x 50m

▲ **Tignes** – AJ - "Les Clarines" – 20161
73320 Tignes (Savoie).
0479410193 0479410336
tignes@fuaj.org
www.fuaj.org/aj/tignes/
Open Dates: 01.01-08.05; 19.06-31-07; 01.10-31.12 (on request) Chambéry 130km Bourg-St-Maurice 25km Cars Martin 100m ap Tignes-les-Boisses x 66

▲ **Toulouse** – Résidence Jolinont – 20185
2, Avenue Yves Brunaud
31500 Toulouse (Haute Garonne).
0534304280 0534301967
dfresidence-jolimont@wanadoo.fr
Open Dates: Toulose - Blagnac 10km Toulouse - Natabiau 50m 39 ap Jolinont x 90 2 x 1km

Tours – AJ du Vieux Tours – 20028
5, rue Bretonneau 37000 Tours.
0247378158 0247379611
tours@fuaj.org www.fuaj.org/aj/tours/
Open Dates: Open Times: 08.00-12.00hrs; 18.00-23.00hrs
Beds: 181 - 96x¹ 31x² 5x³ 2x⁴
Price Range: BB inc
Directions: Tours 10km Tours 1km 4 (from the Central Post Office) ap Vieux Tours (B) 2km

Tours – AJ du Vieux Tours

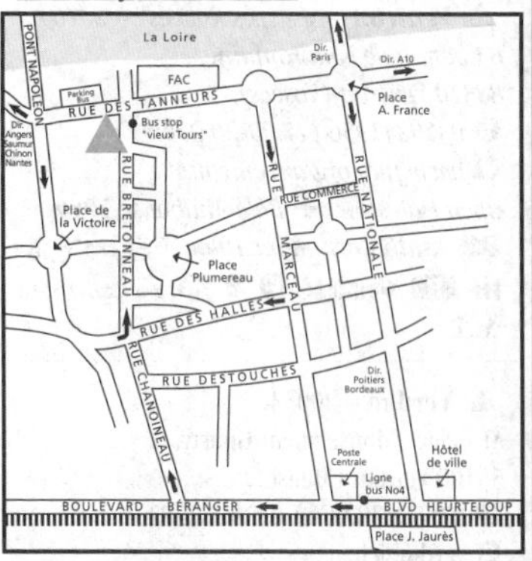

Tours... Travel Tips

- **For budget eats check out...** Place Plumereau
- **For great nightlife try...** Place Plumereau (cyber-cafés)
- **Don't miss...** Small tourist train (not on rails), which takes in the main sights of the town, Horse-drawn carriage rides, Guided tours of the town, Bus tours of the Loire Valley Castles, Special well known architecture from the Loire Region & especially from Tours (Middle Age)

△ ***Trébeurden** – AJ - Le Toëno – 20162*
60 Route de la Corniche, 22560 Trébeurden (Côtes-d'Armor).
0296235222 0296154434
trebeurden@fuaj.org
www.fuaj.org/aj/trebeurden/
Open Dates: 01.03-30.09 (on request) Lannion 11km Lannion 11km 15 200m ap Auberge de Jeunesse 1N x 55 (B) 200m

▲ **Troyes-Rosières** – 20163
AJ - Chemin Ste Scholastique 10430, Rosières (Aube).
0325820065 0325729378
troyes-rosieres@fuaj.org
www.fuaj.org/aj/troyes/
Open Dates: Vatry 55km Troyes 5km 6, 8 100m ap Liberté 0.2S x 104 2 x 3km 20km

Vénissieux ☛ Lyon-Sud

△ ***Ventron** – AJ - "Les Roches" – 20164*
8 Chemin de Fondronfaing, 88310 Ventron (Vosges).
0329241956 (17.00-20.00hrs)
www.fuaj.org/aj/ventron/
Open Dates: Bâle-Mulhouse 70km Kruth/Cornimont 10km 2.5S x 36 15km

▲ **Verdun** – 20033
AJ - Place Monseigneur Ginisty, 55100 Verdun (Meuse).
0329862828 0329862882
verdun@fuaj.org
www.fuaj.org/aj/verdun/
Open Dates: 15.02-20.12 Nancy-Metz 80km Verdun 1km x 80 1 x 1km 500m

△ ***Vernon (Assoc)** – 20165*
Auberge de Jeunesse, 28 Av de l'Ile-de-France, 27200 Vernon (Eure).
0232516648 0232212341
aj-vernon@cape27.fr
www.fuaj.org/aj/vernon/
Open Dates: 01.04-30.09 Roissy-Charles de Gaulle 90km Vernon 3km C 50m ap Folenrue 1.5W x 24 (B)

△ ***Verzy** – 20166*
AJ - 16 Rue du Bassin, 51380 Verzy (Marne).
0326979010 0326979010
www.fuaj.org/aj/verzy/
Open Dates: Reims 20km Beaumont-sur-Vesle 3km 0.25W x 51

▲ **Vienne (Assoc)** – M.J.C. – 20167
11 Quai Riondet, 38200 Vienne (Isère).
0474532197 0474319893
mjcvienne.auberge@laposte.net
www.fuaj.org/aj/vienne/
Open Dates: except Sat-Sun 15.09-15.06 Lyon-St Exupéry 35km Vienne 500m 1, 2, 3, 4, 5 200m ap Tourist Information Centre 0.2S x 54 (B) 2km

△ ***Vierzon** – 20168*
AJ - 1, place François Mitterrand, 18100 Vierzon (Cher).
0248753062 0248711903
vierzon@fuaj.org
www.fuaj.org/aj/vierzon/
Open Dates: 27.02-11.02 (on request) Vierzon 500m Forum République Line 100m ap Pierre Debournou 0.2W x 84 (B) 1 x 1km

△ ***Villefranche-de-Rouergue (Assoc)** – FJT - du Rouergue – 20169*
23 rue Lapeyrade, Cour de La Gare, 12200 Villefranche-de-Rouergue (Aveyron).
0565450968 0565458282
www.fuaj.org/aj/villefranche/
Open Dates: Rodez 55km Villefranche-de-Rouergue 20m 0.5S x 13 2km

YOUTH HOSTEL ACCOMMODATION OUTSIDE THE ASSURED STANDARDS SCHEME

Autrans – Les Hirondelles – 20063
Les Gaillards, 38880 Autrans (Isère).
0476947715 0476947789
autrans@fuaj.org
www.fuaj.org/aj/autrans/
Open Dates: 01.12-31.03; 01.06-31.08
Grenoble St Geais 60km Grenoble 35km VFD ap Ask the driver 0.2S x 55 500m

Blois – Les Grouëts – 20070
18 rue de l'Hôtel Pasquier, Les Grouëts, 41000 Blois (Loir-et-Cher).
0254782721 0254782721
blois@fuaj.org
www.fuaj.org/aj/blois-les-grouets/
Open Dates: 01.03-15.11 Paris 170km Blois 5km 4 100m 5W x 48 (B) 5km

Blois – Montlivault – 20071
AJ - Levée de la Loire, Cedex 181, Montlivault, 41350 Vineuil Cedex (Loir-et-Cher). (réservatio ns : AJ - Les Grouëts - 18, rue de l'Hôtel Pasquier - 41000 Blois)
0254782721 0254782721
blois@fuaj.org
www.fuaj.org/aj/blois-montlivault/
Open Dates: 01.07-31.08 Blois 10km 1 500m 1SW x 30 10km

Cap-Ferret – 20076
AJ - 87 Ave de Bordeaux, 33970 Cap-Ferret (Gironde).
0556606462 (July & Aug.) or Anglet Youth hostel: 0559587000 0556606462
www.fuaj.org/aj/cap-ferret/
Open Dates: 01.07-31.08 (no) Bordeaux 50km Bordeaux 50km Arcachon (by boat) Citram buses 0.5E x 60 100m

Châlons-en-Champagne – 20080
AJ - L'Embellie, Square Antral, rue Kellermann, 51000 Châlons-en-Champagne (Marne).
0326681356 0326681356
aj.chalons@gnu-rox.org
www.fuaj.org/aj/chalons/
Open Dates: on request Châlons 3km Bus 100m ap Doulcet 1E x 40 250m

Choucan-en-Brocéliande – Choucan – 20085
Paimpont, 35380 Plélan-le-Grand (Ille-et-Vilaine).
0297227675 (0299332233 low season)
0299590621 (AJ Rennes)
www.fuaj.org/aj/choucan/
Open Dates: 12.06-03.09 (01.05-31.10) Rennes 45km Rennes 45km Rennes-Paimpont 6km 2NW x 20

Lautenbach – AJ "Dynamo" – 20110
La Schellimatt, 68610 Lautenbach (Haut-Rhin).
0389742681
www.fuaj.org/aj/lautenbach/
Open Dates: Weekends & School holidays Mulhouse 30km Kunegel 5km ap La Scierie x 30

Montreuil-sur-Mer (Assoc) – AJ "La Hulotte" – 20123
Citadelle rue Carnot, 62170 Montreuil-Sur-Mer (Pas de Calais).
0321061083 0321061083
www.fuaj.org/aj/montreuil/
Open Dates: 01.03-30.10 Lille-Lesquin 128km Boulogne-sur-Mer 40km (Calais at 72 km is further but better) 40km Montreuil-sur-Mer 1km Montreuil-Berck Line 500m ap Grand Place 0.2W x 35 3km 20km

Phalsbourg (Assoc) – Centre Européen de Rencontres – 20135
6 Rue du Général Rottembourg, 57370 Phalsbourg (Moselle).
0387243737 0387241356
aubergejeunesse@aol.com
www.fuaj.org/aj/phalsbourg/
Open Dates: 12 Entzheim 60km Lutzelbourg 7km 153 (Rémy Bentz) 500m ap Rue de la Gare 0.5SE x 76 2 x 15km 15km

Quiberon – AJ - "Les Filets Bleus" – 20141
45 rue du Roch Priol,
56170 Quiberon (Morbihan).
0297501554 quiberon@fuaj.org
www.fuaj.org/aj/quiberon/
Open Dates: 01.04-30.09 Lorient 70km
A 1km Auray 30km 1E x 28
R (B)
500m

Serre-Chevalier/Briançon – 20157
AJ - Le Bez, BP2,
05240 Serre-Chevalier 1400 (Hautes-Alpes).
0492247454 0492248339
serre-chevalier@fuaj.org
www.fuaj.org/aj/serre-chevalier/
Open Dates: 18.12-22.04; 15.06-04.09 (12 on request) Turin (Italy) 100km
Briançon 8km Monetier-les-Bains 500m ap Villeneuve-Pré Long 0.5NW x 130
R CC TV
3 x
800m 500m

Vézelay (Assoc) – 20175
Route de l'Etang, 89450 Vézelay (Yonne).
0386332418 0386332418
www.fuaj.org/aj/vezelay/
Open Dates: 01.04-31.10 (12 on resquest)
Sermizelles-Vézelay 10km Shuttle on request 0.6SW x 22 R CC
1 x

Germany

**Deutsches Jugendherbergswerk,
Hauptverband für Jugendwandern
und Jugendherbergen e.V.,
Im Gilde-Park,
Leonardo-da-Vinci-Weg 1,
D-32760 Detmold, Germany.**

t (49) (5231) 9936-0
f (49) (5231) 9936-66
e hauptverband@djh.org
w www.jugendherberge.de

Office Hours: Monday-Thursday 08.00-16.30hrs;
Friday 08.00-14.30hrs

**Travel Section:
Bismarckstraße 8,
DJH Service GmbH
D-32756 Detmold, Germany.**

t (49) (5231) 7401-0
f (49) (5231) 7401-49
e service@djh.de
w www.jugendherberge.de

Office Hours: Monday-Friday 08.00-16.30hrs

National Tourist Authority/Board:	www.germany-tourism.de
Capital:	Berlin
Language:	German
Currency:	€ Euro
Population:	82,431,000
Size:	357,021 sq km
Telephone Country Code:	49
eKit Access Number:	0800-100-6492

Western Europe's largest country (population 82 million) and one of the economic drivers of the European Union, Germany is still preoccupied with the challenges of reconciling the parallel cultures, economies and traditions of the former communist East with its vastly more prosperous Western 'host'. It is still 'early days' in this regard, although much has already been done due to the sheer determination of the German people, and visitors need to be aware of all the sensitivities surrounding this issue wherever they go.

Germany remains very much a respect culture, where traditional morality and value systems, based on Lutheran and Catholic teachings that are deeply embedded in the German psyche, continue to matter in everyday life, including the matriarchal family structure and extended family, the work-place and the main professions. It is no surprise that the Green movement is so strong in Germany.

The backdrop to all of this are the sixteen semi-autonomous Länder (states) of the Federal Republic with their varied cultures and cuisines, histories and rivalries and amazing natural beauty; from the lowland plains in the north, the uplands in the centre and the mountainous region in the south. The country's main artery and a symbol of its identity is the River Rhine.

A few other Top Tips from **CULTURE SMART!**:

- The German's passion for protocol, which determines that there is a right time and place for everything, is particularly noticeable in terms of dress and forms of greeting. Dress, especially in a business context, continues to be very formal. There is no such thing as 'dressing down on Friday', as there is in the UK and the US.
- German, like the Latin languages, but unlike English, distinguishes between the personal *(du)* and

impersonal *(Sie)* form of 'you'. It is essential; therefore, that the visitor does not take anything for granted and uses the impersonal *(Sie)* form unless told otherwise.

- Handshaking on arrival and departure is the norm and in a business or professional context, it is most important to recognize the correct title of the person, who may be 'Herr Professor Dr Dr Schmidt' because he is a Professor with two doctorates.

- German food is known for its variety of sausages and its main meat, pork, and the fact that it is invariably well prepared and well served, including snacks and so-called 'fast food'. German beer, of course, is legendary (there are over 1500 breweries, over half of them in Bavaria) and especially celebrated annually at *Oktober Fest*, centred on Munich.

Cultural Top Tips supplied by Culture Smart! guides. These essential guides to customs and etiquette will help you steer clear of embarrassing gaffes and sensitive issues, enabling you to discover new cultures whilst developing new friendships. Order online at www.culturesmartguides.co.uk

You can find out a lot more on our website - a visit to www.HIhostels.com is essential for planning your trip!

Youth hostels are mainly intended for young people. For this reason, it is the policy of the Bavarian youth hostels to accord secondary priority to individuals over the age of 26. This age limit does not apply to group leaders or families with at least one minor.

Price for hostelling in Germany: from €13 including bed, breakfast and linen.

Pour en savoir plus, rendez-vous sur notre site Internet, www.HIhostels.com une visite

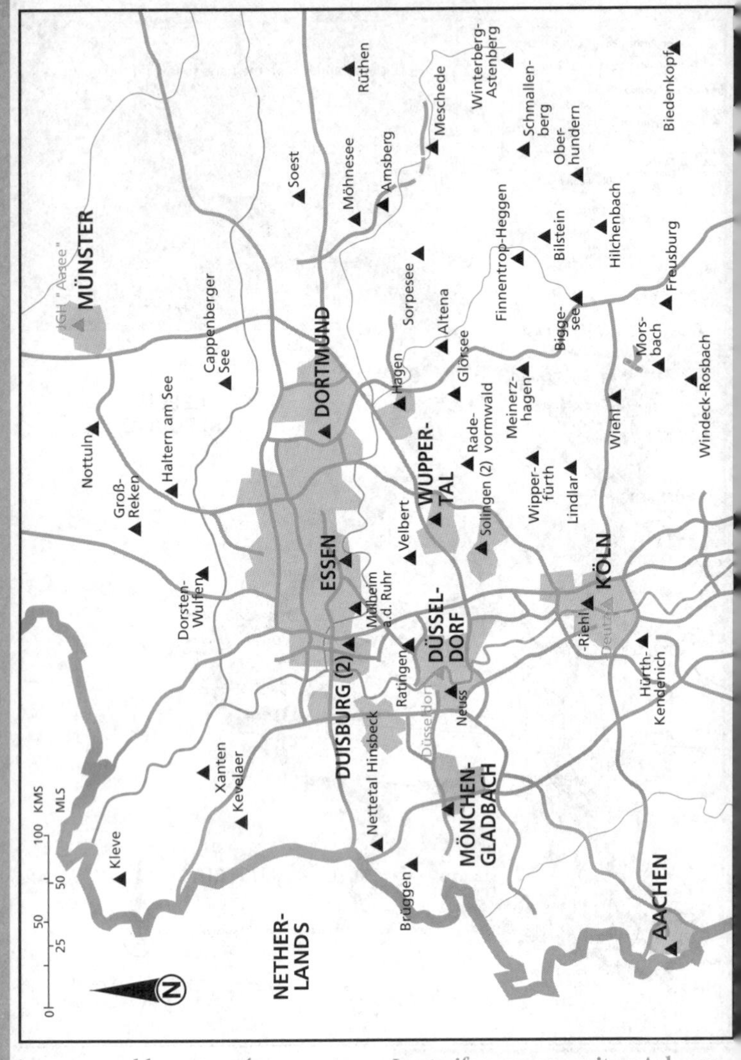

incontournable pour préparer votre voyage!

Les Auberges de Jeunesse s'adressent principalement aux jeunes. C'est pour cette raison que dans les Auberges de Jeunesse bavaroises, les ajistes individuels de plus de 26 ans ont seconde priorité. Cette limite d'âge ne s'applique pas aux accompagnateurs de groupe ni aux familles séjournant avec au moins un mineur.

Les tarifs pour une nuit en Auberge de Jeunesse en Allemagne commencent à 13€, petit-déjeuner et draps compris.

Viele weitere Informationen auf unserer Website: www.HIhostels.com - unverzichtbar für die Reiseplanung!

Jugendherbergen sind in erster Linie ein Angebot für junge Menschen. Deshalb werden in bayerischen Jugendherbergen Einzelgäste ab dem 27. Lebensjahr nachrangig aufgenommen. Diese Altersbeschränkung gilt

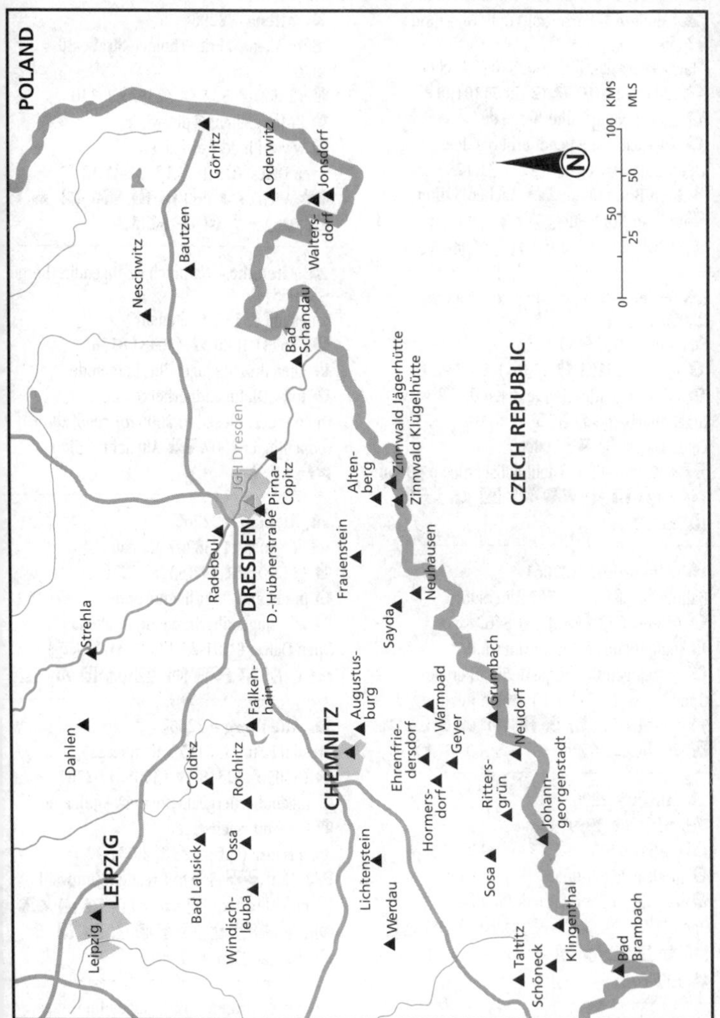

selbstverständlich nicht für Gruppenleiter sowie Familien mit mindestens einem minderjährigen Kind.

Übernachtungspreis in deutschen Jugendherbergen einschließlich Frühstück und Bettwäsche ab 13 €.

Puedes averiguar mucho más en nuestro sitio web. Es imprescindible que visites la página www.HIhostels.com para planear tu viaje.

Los albergues juveniles están fundamentalmente dirigidos a la gente joven. Por este motivo, según la política de los albergues juveniles bávaros se concede prioridad secundaria a los huéspedes individuos mayores de 26 años. Este límite de edad no se aplica a los responsables acompañantes de grupos ni a las familias con al menos un menor.

Tarifa de albergues de Alemania: desde 13 €, incluye alojamiento, desayuno y sábanas.

▲ **Aachen** – European Youth Guesthouse – 22059
Maria-Theresia-Allee 260, 52074 Aachen
(241) 711010 (241) 7110120
aachen@jugendherberge.de
www.aachen.jugendherberge.de
Open Dates: 01.01-23.12; 27-31.12
Köln/Bonn 68km Aachen 3.4km
2 ap Ronheide 5SW x 180 R 11 x

▲ **Aalen** – Schubart-Jugendherberge – 22060
Stadionweg 8, 73430 Aalen.
(7361) 49203 (7361) 44682
info@jugendherberge-aalen.de www.jugendherberge-aalen.de
Open Dates: Aalen
Waldfriedhof, Fachhochschule ap 500 m
x 123 R 3 x

▲ **Albersdorf** – 22061
Bahnhofstraße 19, 25767 Albersdorf.
(4835) 642 (4835) 8462
jhalbersdorf@djh-nordmark.de
www.jugendherberge.de/jh/albersdorf
Open Dates: 14.04-31.10 Albersdorf 500m x 114 600m

▲ **Alfsee** – 22062
Westerfeldstr., 49597 Rieste.
(5464) 9208-0 (5464) 9208-55
jh-alfsee@djh-unterweser-ems.de
www.jugendherberge.de/jh/alfsee
Open Dates: 2E x 152 CC 100m
100m

▲ **Alpirsbach** – 22063
Reinerzauer Steige 80, 72275 Alpirsbach.
(7444) 2477 (7444) 1304
info@jugendherberge-alpirsbach.de
www.jugendherberge-alpirsbach.de
Open Dates: Alpirsbach 2km
x 122 R 4 x

▲ **Altena** – 22064
"Burg Altena", Fritz-Thomée-Straße 80, 58762 Altena.
(2352) 23522 (2352) 26330
jh-burg.altena@djh-wl.de
www.djh.de/westfalen
Open Dates: 01.01-23.12; 27-31.12
Altena x 60 R 3 x

▲ **Altenahr** – Naturschutz-Jugendherberge – 22065
Langfigtal 8, 53505 Altenahr.
(2643) 1880 (2643) 8136
altenahr@diejugendherbergen.de
www.DieJugendherbergen.de
Open Dates: Closed in 2006 for renovation, reopening in 2007 Altenahr 1.5km
x 98

▲ **Altenau** – 22066
Auf der Rose 11, 38707 Altenau.
(5328) 361 (5328) 8276
jh-altenau@djh-hannover.de
www.jugendherberge.de/jh/altenau
Open Dates: 01.01-23.12; 27-31.12 0.5SE
x 164 CC

▲ **Altenberg** – 22067
Dresdner Str 70, 01773 Altenberg.
(35056) 32318 (35056) 32707
jugendherbergealtenberg@t-online.de
www.djh-sachsen.de
Open Dates: 01.01-22.12; 27-31.12
1km 360 to Dresden-Zinnwald 1km ap Altenberg 1W x 115 R 2 x 1km

▲ **Altleiningen** – Burg-Jugendherberge, Jugendgästehaus – 22068
Burg, 67317 Altleiningen.
(6356) 1580 (6356) 6364
altleiningen@diejugendherbergen.de
www.diejugendherbergen.de
Open Dates: 01.01-23.12; 27-31.12
Grünstadt 8km Grünstadt 8km
x 160 R CC 6 x

▲ Arnsberg – 22071
Rumbecker Höhe 1, 59821 Arnsberg.
(2931) 10627 (2931) 13589
jh-arnsberg@djh-wl.de
www.djh.de/westfalen
Open Dates: 01.01-23.12; 27-31.12
Dortmund 60km Arnsberg/Westfalen 2km 371 2km ap Wolfschlucht x 122 R 3 x 8km

▲ Aschaffenburg – 22072
Beckerstraße 47,
63739 Aschaffenburg (Bavaria).
(6021) 930763 (6021) 970694
jhaschaffenburg@djh-bayern.de
www.aschaffenburg.jugendherberge.de
Open Dates: Temporarily closed Frankfurt am Main 45km Aschaffenburg Central 3km 15 Kneippstraße 500m 2SE x 110 CC 3 x 4km

▲ Ascheffel-Aschberg – 22073
24358 Ascheffel.
(4353) 307 (4353) 815
jheckernfoerde@djh-nordmark.de
www.jugendherberge.de/jh/aschberg
Open Dates: 01.04-31.10 1km x 36

▲ Augsburg – 22074
Beim Pfaffenkeller 3, 86152 Augsburg (Bavaria), from May 2006: Unterer Graben 6, 86152 Augsburg (Bavaria).
(821) 33909 (821) 151149
info@augsburg-jugendherberge.de
www.augsburg.jugendherberge.de
Open Dates: 23.01-31.12 Augsburg 2.5km 22 from Hauptbahnhof 300m ap Karlstraße (from May 2006: Pilgerhausstraße) 2 (from May 2006: 1) from Hauptbahnhof 200m ap Stadtwerke (from May 2006: Barfüsserbrücke) 0.4SW x 144 R 1 x

▲ Augustusburg – 22075
"Schloss Augustusburg", 09573 Augustusburg.
(37291) 20256 (37291) 6341
jhaugustusburg@djh.de
www.djh-sachsen.de
Open Dates: 01.01-22.12; 27-31.12
Chemnitz 15km 705, 707 300m ap Schlossberg 0.3E x 130 R 1 x 5.5km

▲ Aurich – 22076
Am Ellernfeld, 26603 Aurich.
(4941) 2827 (4941) 67482
jh-aurich@djh-unterweser-ems.de
www.jugendherberge.de/jh/aurich
Open Dates: 1SW x 111 CC

▲ Bacharach – Jugendherberge Burg Stahleck, Jugendgästehaus – 22077
55422 Bacharach.
(6743) 1266 (6743) 2684
bacharach@diejugendherbergen.de
www.DieJugendherbergen.de
Open Dates: 01.01-23.12; 27-31.12
Bacharach 1.5km x 166 R CC 5 x 13km

▲ Bad Bentheim – 22079
Am Wasserturm 34, 48455 Bad Bentheim.
(5922) 2480 (5922) 6043
jh-badbentheim@djh-unterweser-ems.de
www.jugendherberge.de/jh/badbentheim
Open Dates: 1E x 121 CC

▲ Bad Bergzabern – 22080
Altenbergweg, 76887 Bad Bergzabern.
(6343) 8383 (6343) 5184
bad-bergzabern@diejugendherbergen.de
www.DieJugendherbergen.de
Open Dates: 01.01-23.12; 27-31.12 Bad Bergzabern 1.5km x 141 R CC 4 x 1.3km

▲ **Bad Blankenburg** – 22082
Jugendherberge 1, 07422 Bad Blankenburg.
(36741) 2528 (36741) 47625
jh-bad.blankenburg@djh-thueringen.de
www.djh-thueringen.de
Open Dates: 01.01-23.12; 27-31.12 Erfurt 50km Bad Blankenburg 1km 1km x 141 R CC TV P

▲ **Bad Brambach** – 22083
Röthenbach 4, 08648 Bad Brambach.
(37438) 20541 (37438) 21517
jhbadbrambach@aol.com
www.djh-sachsen.de
Open Dates: 01.01-20.12; 29-31.12. 2km Plauen-Schönberg 2km x 38 R TV 1 x i P 1km

▲ **Bad Doberan** – Tempelberg – 22084
Tempelberg 1a, 18209 Bad Doberan.
(38203) 62439 (38203) 62228
jh-bad-doberan@djh-mv.de
www.djh-mv.de
Open Dates: 01.03-30.11 Bad Doberan, 200m in Richtung Stadt, Überquerung der B105, ca. 10min Fußweg x 116 R TV 5km

▲ **Bad Driburg** – Kulturjugendherberge – 22085
Schirrmannweg 1, 33014 Bad Driburg.
(5253) 2570 (5253) 3882
jh-bad.driburg@djh-wl.de
www.djh.de/westfalen
Open Dates: 01.01-23.12; 27-31.12 Hannover 130km Bad Driburg 2km 438 1km x 124 R TV 6 x i P

▲ **Bad Ems** – Lahntal-Jugendherberge, Jugendgästehaus – 22086
Alte Kemmenauer Str. 41, 56130 Bad Ems.
(2603) 2680 (2603) 50384
bad-ems@diejugendherbergen.de
www.DieJugendherbergen.de
Open Dates: 01.01-23.12; 27-31.12 Bad Ems 2.9km x 117 R CC TV 3 x i P

▲ **Bad Fallingbostel** – 22088
Liethweg 1, 29683 Bad Fallingbostel.
(5162) 2274 (5162) 5704
jh-fallingbostel@djh-hannover.de
www.jugendherberge.de/jh/fallingbostel
Open Dates: 01.01-23.12; 27-31.12 Hannover 70km Bad Fallingbostel 2km x 92 TV i P 1.5km

▲ **Bad Freienwalde** – 22089
Hammerthal 3, 16259 Bad Freienwalde.
(3344) 3875 (3344) 31598
jh-bad-freienwalde@t-online.de
www.hostel.de
Open Dates: 12 2.5km 2W x 48 R 1 x i P

▲ **Bad Herrenalb** – Ev. Ferienheim – 22090
Aschenhüttenweg 44, 76332 Bad Herrenalb.
(7083) 2430 (7083) 51031
info@jugendherberge-bad-herrenalb.de
jugendherberge-bad-herrenalb.de
Open Dates: 12 113 ap Gasthaus Linde (20min walk to YH) ap S1 from NHF Karlsruhe x 108 TV 6 x P

Bad Homburg ☛ **Frankfurt - Bad Homburg**

▲ **Bad Honnef** – 22092
Selhofer Str. 106, 53604 Bad Honnef
(2224) 71300 (2224) 79226
bad-honnef@jugendherberge.de
www.bad-honnef.jugendherberge.de
Open Dates: 01.01-23.12; 27-31.12 Köln/Bonn 35km Bad Honnef 1km 566 to Bad Honnef 1km ap St. Martinskapelle 66, Bonn 1km ap Bad Honnef x 193 R CC TV 7 x P 1km

▲ **Bad Iburg** – 22093
Offenes Holz, 49186 Bad Iburg.
(5403) 74220 (5403) 9770
jh-badiburg@djh-unterweser-ems.de
www.jugendherberge.de/jh/badiburg
Open Dates: 12 15N x 142 CC TV P

Bad Karlshafen – 22094
Winnefelder Str 7, 34385 Bad Karlshafen.
(5672) 338 (5672) 8361
bad-karlshafen@djh-hessen.de
www.djh-hessen.de/jh/bad-karlshafen
Open Dates: 01.01-29.12; 27-31.12 0.5N
x 86

Bad Karlshafen – Helmarshausen – 22095
Gottsbürener Straße. 15,
34385 Bad Karlshafen-Helmarshausen.
(5672) 1027 (5672) 2976
helmarshausen@djh-hessen.de
www.djh-hessen.de/jh/helmarshausen
Open Dates: 01.01-19.12; 27-31.12 1SE
x 173

Bad Kissingen – JH "Der Heiligenhof" – 22096
Alte Euerdorfer Str. 1,
97688 Bad Kissingen (Bavaria).
(971) 71470 (971) 714747
info@heiligenhof.de
www.bad-kissingen.jugendherberge.de
Open Dates: 01.01-23.12; 27-31.12
Frankfurt am Main 130km Bad Kissingen 2.5km Bad Kissingen 2.5km
3S x 123 1 x 3km

Bad Kreuznach –
Nahetal-Jugendherberge, Jugendgästehaus – 22097
Auf dem Kuhberg, Rheingrafenstr. 53,
55543 Bad Kreuznach.
(671) 62855 (671) 75351
bad-kreuznach@diejugendherbergen.de
www.DieJugendherbergen.de
Open Dates: 01.01-23.12; 27-31.12 Bad Kreuznach 3km x 136 4 x 2.5km

Bad Lausick – "Natur- und Musikhaus" – 22098
Herbergsweg 2,
04651 Bad Lausick/OT Buchheim.
(34345) 7270 (34345) 72723
jhbadlausick@djh.de
www.djh-sachsen.de
Open Dates: 01.01-22.12; 27-31.12 (23-26.12) Leipzig 35km Bad Lausick 2.5km 3E x 146 3 x 2.5km

Bad Lauterberg – 22099
Flösswehrtal 25, 37431 Bad Lauterberg.
(5524) 3738 (5524) 5708
jh-lauterberg@djh-hannover.de
www.jugendherberge.de/jh/lauterberg
Open Dates: 01.01-23.12; 27-31.12
Scharzfeld/Bad Lauterberg 8km
Meilerplatz 450m x 131 1km

Bad Marienberg – Westerwald Jugendherberge, Jugendgästehaus Bad Marienberg – 22100
Erlenweg 4, 56470 Bad Marienberg.
(2661) 5008 (2661) 61898
bad-marienberg@diejugendherbergen.de
www.DieJugendherbergen.de
Open Dates: 01.01-23.12; 27-31.12
Nistertal/Bad Marienberg 6km
Nistertal/Bad Marienberg 1km
x 125 6 x 2km

Bad Mergentheim-Igersheim – 22300
Erlenbachtalstr 44, 97999 Igersheim.
(7931) 6373 (7931) 52795
info@jugendherberge-igersheim.de
www.jugendherberge-igersheim.de
Open Dates: 12 Bad Mergentheim
x 162 4 x 1km

Bad Münstereifel – 22101
Herbergsweg 1-5, 53902 Bad Münstereifel
(2253) 7438 (2253) 7483
bad-muenstereifel@jugendherberge.de
www.bad-muenstereifel.jugendherberge.de
Open Dates: 01.01-23.12; 27-31.12 Bad Münstereifel x 164 9 x 2km

Bad Neuenahr-Ahrweiler – Jugendgästehaus – 22102
St. Piusstr. 7, 53474 Bad Neuenahr-Ahrweiler.
(2641) 34924 (2641) 31574
bad-neuenahr-ahrweiler@diejugendherbergen.de
www.DieJugendherbergen.de
Open Dates: 01.01-23.12; 27-31.12 Bad Neuenahr-Ahrweiler 1.5km x 140 10 x 500m

▲ Bad Oldesloe – 22103
Konrad-Adenauer-Ring 2, 23843 Bad Oldesloe.
(4531) 5945 (4531) 67574
jholdesloe@djh-nordmark.de
www.jugendherberge.de/jh/oldesloe
Open Dates: 06.01-30.11 Hamburg 30km Bad Oldesloe 1km 200m x 106 100m

▲ Bad Saarow-Pieskow – 22104
Dorfstr. 20, 15526 Bad Saarow
(33631) 2664 (33631) 59023
jh-bad-saarow@jugendherberge.de
www.hostel.de
Open Dates: (01.11-28.02) A 300m 3km Bad Saarow - Bahnhofstraße 500m x 92 2 x 200m 200m

▲ Bad Sachsa – 22105
Jugendherbergsstr 9-11, 37441 Bad Sachsa.
(5523) 8800 (5523) 7163
jh-sachsa@djh-hannover.de
www.jugendherberge.de/jh/sachsa
Open Dates: 01.01-23.12; 27-31.12 x 121

▲ Bad Salzungen – 22106
Kaltenborner Str. 70, 36433 Bad Salzungen.
(3695) 622208 (3695) 628833
jh-bad-salzungen@djh-thueringen.de
www.djh-thueringen.de
Open Dates: 01.01-23.12; 27-31.12 Erfurt 60km Bad Salzungen 3km x 63 1 x 10m

▲ Bad Schandau-Ostrau – 22107
Dorfstr 14, 01814 Bad Schandau-Ostrau.
(35022) 42408 (35022) 42409
jhbadschandau@djh.de
www.djh-sachsen.de
Open Dates: 01.03.-31.12 (01.01-28.02) 50km 2km 3km L 255 200m ap Ostrauer Scheibe x 101 2 x 3km

▲ Bad Segeberg – 22108
Kastanienweg 1, 23795 Bad Segeberg.
(4551) 2531 (4551) 4518
jhsegeberg@djh-nordmark.de
www.jugendherberge.de/jh/segeberg
Open Dates: 06.01-04.12 Bad Segeberg 1km x 152 1km

▲ Bad Sulza – "August Bebel" – 22109
August Bebel Str. 27, 99518 Bad Sulza.
(36461) 20567 (36461) 20963
jh-badsulza@djh-thueringen.de
www.djh-thueringen.de
Open Dates: 01.01-23.12; 27-31.12 Erfurt 65km Bad Sulza 1km x 94 4 x 2km

▲ Bad Urach – 22110
Burgstr 45, 72574 Bad Urach.
(7125) 8025 (7125) 40358
info@jugendherberge-bad-urach.de
www.jugendherberge-bad-urach.de
Open Dates: Bad Urach 500m ap Krankenhaus 300m x 123 2 x 1.5km

▲ Bad Zwischenahn – 22111
Schirrmannweg 14, 26160 Bad Zwischenahn.
(4403) 2393 (4403) 64588
jh-badzwischenahn@djh-unterweser-ems.de
www.jugendherberge.de/jh/badzwischenahn
Open Dates: x 90 100m 100m

▲ Baden-Baden – Werner-Dietz JH – 22112
Hardbergstr 34, 76532 Baden-Baden.
(7221) 52223 (7221) 60012
info@jugendherberge-baden-baden.de
www.jugendherberge-baden-baden.de
Open Dates: Baden-Baden 201 ap Große Dollenstraße 2NW x 151 2 x 3km

▲ Balingen – 22113
Schlossstr 5, 72336 Balingen.
(7433) 20805 (7433) 5911
info@jugendherberge-balingen.de
www.jugendherberge-balingen.de
Open Dates: 01.03-30.11 Balingen 1km ap Volksbank x 46 1 x 1km

▲ **Balingen-Lochen** – 22114
Auf der Lochen 1, 72336 Balingen-Lochen.
(7433) 37383 (7433) 382296
info@jugendherberge-lochen.de
www. jugendherberge-lochen.de
Open Dates: Balingen x 104
3 x
1km

▲ **Bamberg** – JH "Wolfsschlucht" – 22115
Oberer Leinritt 70, 96049 Bamberg (Bavaria).
(951) 56002 (951) 55211
jh-bamberg@stadt.bamberg.de
www.bamberg.jugendherberge.de
Open Dates: 01.02-19.12 Nürnberg 60km
Bamberg 6km 18 Rodelbahn - YH
2N x 92
4 x 4km

▲ **Barth** – Donnerberg – 22116
Donnerberg, 18356 Barth.
(38231) 2843 (38231) 2090
jh-barth@djh-mv.de www.djh-mv.de
Open Dates: 01.01-23.12; 27-31.12
Barth (30min journey) x 175
1 x

▲ **Bautzen** – 22117
Am Zwinger 1, 02625 Bautzen.
(3591) 40347 (3591) 40348
jhbautzen@djh.de
www.djh-sachsen.de
Open Dates: 1.5km 1km 1.5SE
x 112
3 x
1.5km

▲ **Bayerisch-Eisenstein** – 22118
Brennesstr 23,
94252 Bayerisch-Eisenstein (Bavaria).
(9925) 337 (9925) 730
jhbayerisch-eisenstein@djh-bayern.de
www.bayerisch-eisenstein.jugendherberge.de
Open Dates: 01.01-30.10
Bayerisch-Eisenstein 2.5km
ap YH 2.5N x 142
4 x
2km

▲ **Bayreuth** – 22119
Universitätsstr 28, 95447 Bayreuth (Bavaria).
(921) 764380 (921) 512805
jhbayreuth@djh-bayern.de
www.bayreuth.jugendherberge.de
Open Dates: 01.02-17.12 6km 6,
10 5min 3S x 138
3 x
100m

▲ **Bayrischzell** – JH Sudelfeld – 22120
Unteres Sudelfeld 9,
83735 Bayrischzell (Bavaria).
(8023) 675 (8023) 274
jhsudelfeld@djh-bayern.de
www.sudelfeld.jugendherberge.de
Open Dates: 01.01-31.10; 27-31.12
Munich 90km Bayrischzell 7km
500m 13SE x 92

▲ **Beckerwitz** – 22121
Haus Nr. 21, 23968 Gramkow OT. Beckerwitz.
(38428) 60362 (38428) 61986
jh-beckerwitz@djh-mv.de
www.djh-mv.de
Open Dates: 01.03-31.10 241
Wismar-Hohen Wieschendorf ap Beckerwitz
Dorf x 100 2 x
800m

▲ **Benediktbeuern** – "Don-Bosco-JH" – 22122
Don-Bosco-Str 3,
83671 Benediktbeuern (Bavaria).
(8857) 88350
www.benediktbeuern-don-bosco.jugendherberge.de
Open Dates: 11.01-14.12 x 177

▲ **Benediktbeuern** – "JH Miriam" – 22123
Bahnhofstr 58,
83671 Benediktbeuern (Bavaria).
(8857) 9050 (8857) 694680
djh-miriam.bb@t-online.de
www.benediktbeuern-miriam.jugendherberge.de
Open Dates: 16.01-14.12 x 130
4 x

▲ **Berchtesgaden** – JH Berchtesgaden – 22527
Struberberg 6,
83483 Bischofswiesen (Bavaria).
(8652) 94370 (8652) 943737
jhberchtesgaden@djh-bayern.de
www.berchtesgaden.jugendherberge.de
Open Dates: 01.01-31.10; 27-31.12
Salzburg 30km Berchtesgaden 2km
39 2km ap Strub Kaserne 2E x 307

Berlin – JH Berlin - Am Wannsee 22124
Badeweg 1 (Ecke Kronprinzessinnenweg) 14129 Berlin.
(30) 8032034; R (30) 2649520
(30) 8035908; R (30) 264 952 10
jh-wannsee@jugendherberge.de
www.hostel.de
Open Dates: 01.01-18.12; 27-31.12
Open Times:
Beds: 288 - 72x4
Price Range: € 21 BBinc
Directions: 20SW from city centre
Tegel 25km Berlin-Wannsee 1.5km
118 Badeweg 30m (S-Bahn) S1, S7 - Nikolassee 500m R
1km 2km

Berlin – JH Berlin - Am Wannsee

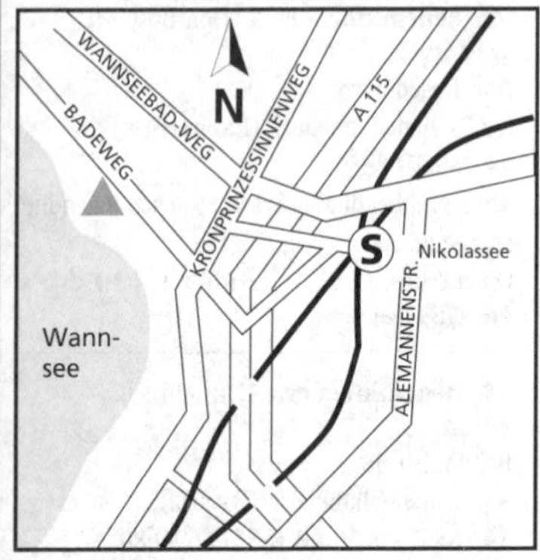

▲ **Berlin** – JH Berlin - Ernst Reuter 22037
Hermsdorfer Damm 48-50, 13467 Berlin.
(30) 2649520; R (30) 2649520
(30) 26495210; R (30) 26495210
jh-ernst-reuter@jugendherberge.de
www.hostel.de
Open Dates: 01.01-04.12; 27-31.12 Tegel 5km Berlin-Zoo 15km 125 10m ap YH (S-Bahn) S 25 Tegel 2km U U 6 ALT-Tegel 2km 15N x 111 R

Berlin – JH Berlin - International 22022 FNM
Kluckstr. 3, 10785 Berlin.
(30) 2649520; R (30) 2649520
(30) 26495210; R (30) 26495210
jh-berlin@jugendherberge.de
www.hostel.de
Open Dates: 12 Open Times:
Beds: 350
Price Range: € 21 BBinc
Directions: 3W from city centre
Berlin-Tegel 10km A 109, X 9 (to Zoologischer Garden) 2km
Zoologischer Garden 2km 129 ap Gedenkstätte U U 1 Kurfürstenstrasse 800m R
3 x 5km

Berlin – JH Berlin - International

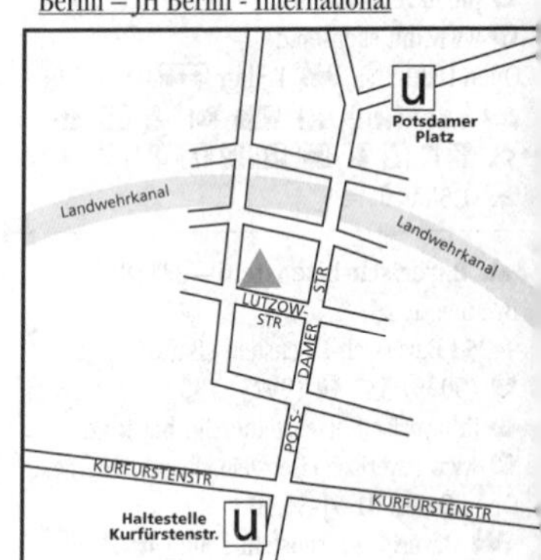

Berlin ... Travel Tips

- **For budget eats check out...** Goltzstrasse, Winterfeldplatz, Youth Hostel, Potsdamer Strasse, Potsdamer Platz
- **For great nightlife try...** Hakische Höfe, Kurfürstendamm, Potsdamer Platz, Prenzlauer Berg, Kreuzberg
- **Don't miss...** Brandenburger Tor, Reichstag (Parliament Building), Potsdamer Platz, Sony Centre, Kulturforum, Gendarmenmarkt, Charlottenburg Castle, Kurfürstendamm, Zoo, Potsdam

▲ **Bernburg** – 22125
Krumbholzallee 2, 06406 Bernburg.
(3471) 352027 (3471) 352027
jh_bbg@t-online.de
www.jugendherberge.de/jh/bernburg
Open Dates: 01.02-30.11 Halle-Leipzig 60km Aschersleben-Dessau 2.5km Cityline ap YH x 65 1 x 2.5km

▲ **Bernkastel-Kues** – 22126
Jugendherbergsstr. 1, 54470 Bernkastel-Kues.
(6531) 2395 (6531) 1529
bernkastel-kues@diejugendherbergen.de
www.DieJugendherbergen.de
Open Dates: 01.01-23.12; 27-31.12
Wittlich 25km x 96 3 x 3km

▲ **Biberach** – 22127
Heusteige 40, 88400 Biberach.
(7351) 21885 (7351) 21315
info@jugendherberge-biberach.de
www.jugendherberge-biberach.de
Open Dates: Biberach - 20 min. x 120 4 x 3km

▲ **Biedenkopf** – 22128
Am Freibad 15, 35216 Biedenkopf.
(6461) 5100 (6461) 2425
biedenkopf@djh-hessen.de
www.djh-hessen.de/jh/biedenkopf
Open Dates: 01.01-23.12; 27-31.12 0.5W x 194 10m

▲ **Bielefeld** –
Jugendgästehaus/Bildungszentrum – 22040
Dürkopp Tor 6 Hermann-Kleinewächter-Str.1, 33602 Bielefeld.
(521) 522050 (521) 52205110
jgh-bielefeld@djh-wl.de
www.djh.de/westfalen
Open Dates: 01.01-23.12; 27-31.12
Paderborn 50km Bielefeld 3km 21, 26 2km ap Jahnplatz 3 300m ap August-Schröder-Str. 1W x 160 5 x 8 2km

▲ **Biggesee** – 22129
Auf dem Mühlenberg, 57462 Olpe-Stade.
(2761) 6775 (2761) 64714
jh-biggesee@djh-wl.de
www.djh.de/westfalen
Open Dates: 01.01-23.12; 27-31.12 Olpe 80 ap Rhode x 240 6 x 1km

▲ **Bilstein** – 22130
"Burg Bilstein", Von-Gevore-Weg 10, 57368 Lennestadt-Bilstein
(2721) 81217 (2721) 83016
jh-burg.bilstein@djh-wl.de
www.burg-bilstein.de
Open Dates: 01.01-23.12; 27-31.12
Grevenbrück 6km 500m ap Lennestadt-Bilstein x 220 10 x

▲ **Bingen** – Rhein-Nahe-Jugendherberge, Jugendgästeshaus Bingen – 22131
Herterstr. 51, 55411 Bingen.
(6721) 32163 (6721) 34012
bingen@diejugendherbergen.de
www.diejugendherbergen.de
Open Dates: 01.04-23.12; 27-31.12
Bingen/Rhein (Bingerbrück) 1km x 116 5 x 1.5km

▲ **Binz** – 22132
Strandpromenade 35,
18609 Ostseebad Binz/Rügen.
(38393) 32597 (38393) 32596
jh-binz@djh-mv.de www.djh-mv.de
Open Dates: 01.01-23.12; 27-31.12
IC-Verbindung über Stralsund ap Binz 0.1N x 143 3 x

▲ Bispingen – 22133
Töpinger Str 42, 29646 Bispingen.
(5194) 2375 (5194) 7743
jh-bispingen@djh-hannover.de
www.jugendherberge.de/jh/bispingen
Open Dates: 01.01-23.12; 27-31.12
Hamburg 70km Hamburg 65km
Soltau 20km Haltestelle 800m
x 121 1.5km

▲ Blankenheim – "Blankenheim Castle" – 22134
Burg 1, 53945 Blankenheim
(2449) 95090 (2449) 950910
burg-blankenheim@jugendherberge.de
www.burg-blankenheim.jugendherberge.de
Open Dates: 01.01-23.12; 27-31.12 x 164
5 x 3km

▲ Blaubeuren – 22135
Auf dem Rucken 69, 89143 Blaubeuren.
(7344) 6444 (7344) 21416
info@jugendherberge-blaubeuren.de
www.jugendherberge-blaubeuren.de
Open Dates: Blaubeuren 700m
400m x 110
5 x 500m

▲ Blomberg – Sport-Jugendherberge – 22136
Ulmenallee 15, 32825 Blomberg.
(5235) 7255 (5235) 2130
jh-blomberg@djh-wl.de
www.djh.de/westfalen
Open Dates: 01.01-23.12; 27-31.12
Schieder-Stausee 8km 760 1km
ap Altenheim x 163
5 x 500m

Bockswiese ☛ Hahnenklee

▲ Bodenwerder – 22138
Richard-Schirrmann-Weg,
37619 Bodenwerder.
(5533) 2685 (5533) 6203
jh-bodenwerder@djh-hannover.de
www.jugendherberge.de/jh/bodenwerder
Open Dates: 01.01-23.12; 27-31.12
Hannover 70km Hameln 26km
x 124
300m

▲ Bollendorf – Südeifel-Jugendherberge, Jugendgästehaus – 22139
Auf der Ritschlay 1, 54669 Bollendorf.
(6526) 200 (6526) 1204
bollendorf@diejugendherbergen.de
www.DieJugendherbergen.de
Open Dates: 01.01-23.12; 27-31.12
x 156
6 x 2km

▲ Bonn – The Cultural Experience 22026
Haager Weg 42, 53127 Bonn.
(228) 289970 (228) 2899714
bonn@jugendherberge.de
www.bonn.jugendherberge.de
Open Dates: 01.01-23.12; 27-31.12
Köln/Bonn 35km A 670 4km
Bonn Central 4km 621 Central Bus Station ap YH x 249
9 x

▲ Bonndorf/Black Forest – 22140
Waldallee 27, 79848 Bonndorf.
(7703) 359 (7703) 1686
info@jugendherberge-bonndorf.de
www.jugendherberge-bonndorf.de
Open Dates: Neustadt
ap Bonndorf x 218
11 x

▲ Borgwedel – 22142
Kreisstr 17, 24857 Borgwedel.
(4354) 219 (4354) 1305
jhborgwedel@djh-nordmark.de
www.jugendherberge.de/jh/borgwedel
Open Dates: 06.01-22.12 Schleswig 10km 500m x 298

▲ Borkum – 22143
Reedestr.231, 26757 Borkum, (North Sea).
(4922) 579 (4922) 7124
jh-borkum@djh-unterweser-ems.de
www.jugendherberge.de/jh/borkum
Open Dates: x 582
5km
5km

▲ **Born-Ibenhorst** – 22144
Im Darßer Wald, 18375 Born-Ibenhorst.
(38234) 229 (38234) 231
jh-born@djh-mv.de www.djh-mv.de
Open Dates: 01.01-23.12; 27-31.12
Ribnitz-Damgarten 25km
Born-Ibenhorst 600m ap YH x 192
3 x
2.5km

▲ **Braunlage** – 22145
Von-Langen-Str 28, 38700 Braunlage.
(5520) 2238 (5520) 1569
jh-braunlage@djh-hannover.de
www.jugendherberge.de/jh/braunlage
Open Dates: 01.01-23.12; 27-31.12 x 130

▲ **Braunsdorf** – 22147
Dorfstr. 17, 15518 Braunsdorf.
(33633) 635 (33633) 635
jh-braunsdorf@jugendherberge.de
www.hostel.de
Open Dates: (01.11-28.02) x 54

▲ **Breisach** – Deutsch-Französische Jugendbegegnungsstätte – 22148
Rheinuferstr 12, 79206 Breisach.
(7667) 7665 (7667) 1847
info@jugendherberge-breisach.de
www.jugendherberge-breisach.de
Open Dates: Breisach x 164
6 x
1km

Bremen – 22006
Kalkstr 6, 28195 Bremen.
(421) 163820 (421) 1638255
jh-bremen@djh-unterweser-ems.de
www.jugendherberge.de/jh/bremen
Open Dates: Open Times:
Beds: 237 - 17x2 20x4 16x6
Price Range: € 20.90-23.90 BBinc
Directions: 1NW from city centre
Bremen 5km Bremen Central 3km
26 200m ap Brill 1, 8 200m
ap Brill x 6
7 x 1km

Bremen

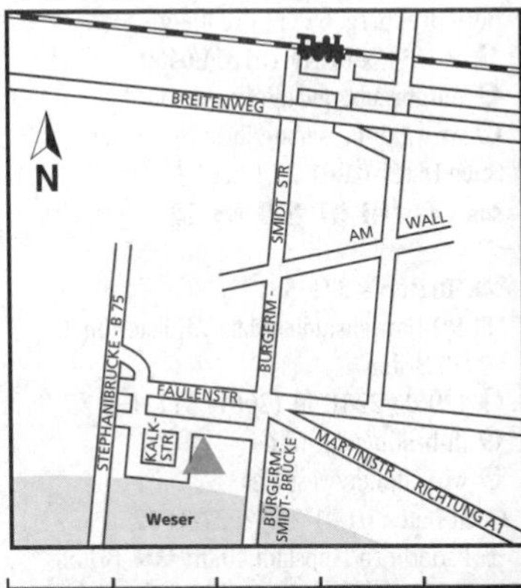

Bremen... Travel Tips

- **For budget eats check out...** JMBISS (snack bar), Fast food outlets, Pizzeria (near hostel), Speciality restaurants (Madame Ho)
- **For great nightlife try...** Weser River promenade & embankment, Schnoor Quarter & Böttcherstr., Universum Science Centre and Botanika, Cinema (Station), Theatres
- **Don't miss...** Old Town & Schnoor Quarter, Universum Science Centre & Botanika, Becks Brewery tour, Harbour tour & river trip, Town tour (bus from Zob), Overseas & Boat Museum, Art Gallery & New Weserburg Museum, Wagenfeldhaus, Bremerhaven & Helgoland, Parks

▲ **Bremerhaven** – 22149
YH + YGH Gaußstr 54-56, 27580 Bremerhaven.
(471) 982080 (471) 87426
info@jgh-bremerhaven.de
www.jgh-bremerhaven.de
Open Dates: x 174

▲ **Bremsdorfer Mühle** – 22151
Bremsdorf 1, 15890 Schlaubetal.
(33654) 272 (33654) 49044
jh-bremsdorfer-muehle@jugendherberge.de www.hostel.de
Open Dates: 01.01-01.12 x 30

▲ **Breuberg** – Burg Breuberg – 22152
Burg Breuberg, 64747 Breuberg.
(6165) 3403 (6165) 6469
burgbreuberg@djh-hessen.de
www.djh-hessen.de/jh/burgbreuberg
Open Dates: 01.01-23.12; 27-31.12 3E
x 139 R P

▲ **Brilon** – 22153
"EURO-Umweltstudienplatz", Hölsterloh 3, 59929 Brilon.
(2961) 2281 (2961) 51731
jh-brilon@djh-wl.de
www.djh.de/westfalen
Open Dates: 01.01-23.12; 27-31.12
Paderborn/Lippstadt 40km Brilon Wald 6km 482 200m ap YH x 165 R 5 x i P 1km

▲ **Brotterode** – 22154
Am Zainhammer 4, 98599 Brotterode.
(36840) 32125 (36840) 32125
jh-brotterode@djh-thueringen.de
www.djh-thueringen.de
Open Dates: 01.01-23.12; 27-31.12 Erfurt 70km 100m ap YH x 65 R CC TV P 2km

▲ **Brüggen** – 22155
Auf dem Eggenberg 1, 41379 Brüggen
(2163) 5161 (2163) 59967
brueggen@jugendherberge.de
www.brueggen.jugendherberge.de
Open Dates: 01.01-23.12
Mönchengladbach Central 5 x 132 R TV 5 x P 1.5km

Buchheim ☛ **Bad Lausick**

▲ **Buckow** – 22156
Berliner Str 36, 15377 Buckow.
(33433) 286 (33433) 56274
jh-buckow@jugendherberge.de
www.hostel.de
Open Dates: 12 (R 01.11-28.02) 1.5S
x 106 R i P

▲ **Büdingen** – 22157
Richard-Schirrmann-Weg 1, 63654 Büdingen
(6042) 3697 (6042) 68178
buedingen@djh-hessen.de
www.djh-hessen.de/jh/buedingen
Open Dates: 01.01-23.12; 27-31.12 2NE
x 130 TV P

▲ **Burg auf Fehmarn** – 22159
Mathildenstr 34, 23769 Fehmarn.
(4371) 2150 (4371) 6680
jhburg@djh-nordmark.de
www.jugendherberge.de/jh/burg
Open Dates: 06.01-22.12 Puttgarden 9km 300m x 182 TV P 1.5km 1.5km

▲ **Burg Stargard** – 22160
Dewitzer Chausse 07, 17094 Burg Stargard.
(39603) 20207 (39603) 20255
jh-burg-stargard@djh-mv.de
www.djh-mv.de
Open Dates: 01.01-23.12; 27-31.12
Burg Stargard x 105 R 5 x P

Burg Wildenstein ☛ **Wildenstein**

▲ **Burg/Spreewald** – 22161
Jugendherbergsweg 8, 03096 Burg/Spreewald
(35603) 225 (35603) 13248
jh-burg@jugendherberge.de
www.hostel.de
Open Dates: 12 (R 01.11-28.02)
x 203 R TV i P

▲ **Burghausen** – 22162
Kapuzinergasse 235, 84489 Burghausen (Bavaria).
(8677) 4187 (8677) 911318
jhburghausen@djh-bayern.de
www.burghausen.jugendherberge.de
Open Dates: 01.01-30.11 Munich 90km 2.5km 0.5S x 111 R CC TV 2 x 8 P 800m

▲ **Büsum** – 22163
Dr Martin-Bahr-Str 1, 25761 Büsum.
(4834) 93371 (4834) 93376
jhbuesum@djh-nordmark.de
www.jugendherberge.de/jh/buesum
Open Dates: 06.01-30.11 Büsum 1km x 206 R CC TV P 1km 1km

▲ Cappenberger See – 22164
Richard-Schirrmann-Weg 7, 44534 Lünen.
(2306) 53546 (2306) 73000
jh-cappenberger.see@djh-wl.de
www.djh.de/westfalen
Open Dates: 01.01-23.12; 27-31.12
Dortmund 22km Lünen Central 3.5km R 19 8km ap Waldfriedhof x 122 4 x

▲ Carolinensiel – 22165
Herbergsmense 13, 26409 Wittmund.
(4464) 252 (4464) 655
jh-carolinensiel@djh-unterweser-ems.de
www.jugendherberge.de/jh/carolinensiel
Open Dates: 01.03-30.09 x 95

▲ Celle – 22166
Weghausstr 2, 29223 Celle.
(5141) 53208 (5141) 53005
jh-celle@djh-hannover.de
www.jugendherberge.de/jh/celle
Open Dates: 01.01-23.12; 27-31.12 2km 100m x 122

▲ Chemnitz – 22167
Augustusburger Str 369, 09127 Chemnitz.
(371) 71331 (371) 73331
jhchemnitz@djh.de
www.djh-sachsen.de
Open Dates: 01.01-22.12; 28-31.12
Hauptbahnhof 6km L 704, Chemnitz-Augustusburg 150m ap Walter-Klippel-Str. L 5 Gablenz 1.5km ap Pappelhain x 58 2 x 1km

▲ Clausthal-Zellerfeld – 22169
Altenauer Str 55, 38678 Clausthal-Zellerfeld.
(5323) 84293 (5323) 83827
jh-clausthal@djh-hannover.de
www.jugendherberge.de/jh/clausthal
Open Dates: 01.01-23.12; 27-31.12
Hannover 100km Goslar 30km Tannenhöhe 100m x 122

▲ Coburg – 22170
Parkstr 2, 96450 Coburg (Bavaria).
(9561) 15330 (9561) 28653
jhcoburg@djh-bayern.de
www.coburg.jugendherberge.de
Open Dates: 01.02-30.11 Nürnberg 100km Coburg, Lossaustraße 2.5km 1, 1a to railway station and city 100m ap YH x 128 3 x 4km

▲ Cochem – Moseltal-Jugendherberge, Jugendgästehaus – 22171
Klottener Str. 9, 56812 Cochem.
(2671) 8633 (2671) 8568
cochem@diejugendherbergen.de
www.DieJugendherbergen.de
Open Dates: 01.01-23.12; 27-31.12
Cochem 700m x 146 7 x 500m

▲ Colditz – 22172
Haingasse 42, 04680 Colditz.
(34381) 43335/mobile 0173-7167252
(34381) 43335
servicecenter-sachsen@djh.de
www.djh-sachsen.de
Open Dates: 01.01-22.12; 28-31.12
Großbothen 8km Leipzig - Colditz 45km ap Sportplatz x 35 1.5km

Cologne ☛ **Köln**

▲ Cottbus – 22173
Klosterplatz 2/3, 03046 Cottbus.
(355) 22558 (355) 23798
service@jugendherberge.de
www.hostel.de
Open Dates: (01.11-28.02) x 64

▲ Creglingen – 22174
Erdbacher Str 30, 97993 Creglingen.
(7933) 336 (7933) 1326
info@jugendherberge-creglingen.de
www.jugendherberge-creglingen.de
Open Dates: Weikersheim 12km ap Schulzentrum x 153 6 x 4km

Cuxhaven-Duhnen – 22175
Schlensenweg 2, 27476 Cuxhaven.
(4721) 48552 (4721) 45794
jhcuxhaven@djh-nordmark.de
www.jugendherberge.de/jh/cuxhaven
Open Dates: 16.01-14.12 Cuxhaven 4km 300m x 277 500m 300m

Dachau – JGH 22025
Rosswachtstrasse 15,
85221 Dachau (Bavaria).
(8131) 322950 (8131) 3229550
jghdachau@djh-bayern.de
www.dachau.jugendherberge.de
Open Dates: Munich 60km Dachau 5km 722 5km x 116 6 x

Dahlen – Kreativjugendherberge – 22176
Belgernsche Str 25, 04774 Dahlen.
(34361) 55002 (34361) 55003
jhdahlen@djh.de www.djh-sachsen.de
Open Dates: 3km Oschatz-Dahlen 1km ap Dahlen 1NE x 125 2 x 3km

Dahme – 22629
Leuchtturmstr. 1, 23747 Dahme
(40) 6559950 (40) 65599544
service@djh-nordmark.de
www.jugendherberge.de/nordmark
Open Dates: Opening Summer 2006 15km 2km x 102 100m 100m

Dahmen – 22177
Dorfstr 14, 17166 Dahmen.
(39933) 70552 (39933) 70650
jh-dahmen@djh-mv.de www.djh-mv.de
Open Dates: 01.03-31.10 Teterow, Malchin ap Dahmen Teterow, Malchin ap Dahmen x 150 6 x

Dahn – 22178
Am Wachtfelsen 1, 66994 Dahn.
(6391) 1769 (6391) 5122
dahn@diejugendherbergen.de
www.DieJugendherbergen.de
Open Dates: 01.01-23.12; 27-31.12 x 108 4 x 300m

Damme – 22179
Neuer Jugendherbergsweg 2, 49401 Damme.
(5491) 96720 (5491) 967229
jh-damme@djh-unterweser-ems.de
www.jugendherberge.de/jh/damme
Open Dates: 1.5NW x 171

Darmstadt ☛ **Frankfurt - Darmstadt**

Daun – Eifelmaar-Jugendherberge, Jugendgästehaus – 22181
Maria-Hilf-Str. 21, 54550 Daun.
(6592) 2884 (6592) 1506
daun@diejugendherbergen.de
www.DieJugendherbergen.de
Open Dates: 01.01-23.12; 27-31.12 x 147 3 x 500m

Dessau – 22182
Waldkaterweg 11, 06846 Dessau.
(340) 619452 (340) 619452
jh-dessau@djh-sachsen-anhalt.de
www.jugendherberge.de/jh/dessau
Open Dates: 01.01-23.12; 27-31.12 Magdeburg-Leipzig, Berlin-Halle, 2km x 63 1 x 4km 4km

Detmold – 22183
Schirrmannstr 49, 32756 Detmold.
(5231) 24739 (5231) 28927
jh-detmold@djh-wl.de
www.jh-detmold.de
Open Dates: 01.01-23.12; 27-31.12 Paderborn 40km Detmold 2km x 126 2 x 1km

Diez – Schloss-Jugendherberge, Jugendgästehaus Diez – 22184
65582 Diez.
(6432) 2481 (6432) 4504
diez@diejugendherbergen.de
www.diejugendherbergen.de
Open Dates: 01.04-23.12; 27-31.12 Diez 1km x 128 5 x 1.5km

Dilsberg ☛ **Neckargemünd**

Dinkelsbühl – 22185
Koppengasse 10,
91550 Dinkelsbühl (Bavaria).
(9851) 9509 (9851) 4874
CBallheimer@t-online.de
www.dinkelsbuehl.jugendherberge.de
Open Dates: 01.03-30.09 Nürnberg 100km Ansbach 45km ap 20mins walk from YH x 148 2 x

Donauwörth – 22186
Goethestr 10, 86609 Donauwörth (Bavaria).
(906) 5158 (906) 243817
jhdonauwoerth@djh-bayern.de
www.donauwoerth.jugendherberge.de
Open Dates: 15.02-15.11 Donauwörth 3km 1 (9107) 400m ap Sallingerstraße x 108 2 x 1.5km

Dornstetten-Hallwangen – Pfahlberg – 22187
Auf dem Pfahlberg 39,
72280 Dornstetten-Hallwangen.
(7443) 6469 (7443) 20212
info@jugendherberge-hallwangen.de
www.jugendherberge-hallwangen.de
Open Dates: Freudenstadt 8km ap Grüner Baum x 126 3 x

Dorsten-Wulfen – Jugendherberge Herrlichkeit-Lembeck – 22188
Im Schöning 83, 46286 Dorsten-Wulfen.
(2369) 8722 (2369) 23867
jh-dorsten@djh-wl.de
www.djh.de/westfalen
Open Dates: 01.01-23.12; 27-31.12
Deuten 3km x 102 4 x 10km

Dortmund – "JGH Adolph Kolping" – 22042
Silberstr. 24-26, 44137 Dortmund.
(231) 140074 (231) 142654
jgh-dortmund@djh-wl.de
www.djh.de/westfalen
Open Dates: 01.01-23.12; 27-31.12
Open Times:
Beds: 319 - 6x1 94x2 5x3 20x4 5x6
Price Range: € 20.40 BB inc
Directions: Dortmund 14.4km
Dortmund Central 500m 2 x
1km

Dortmund – "JGH Adolph Kolping"

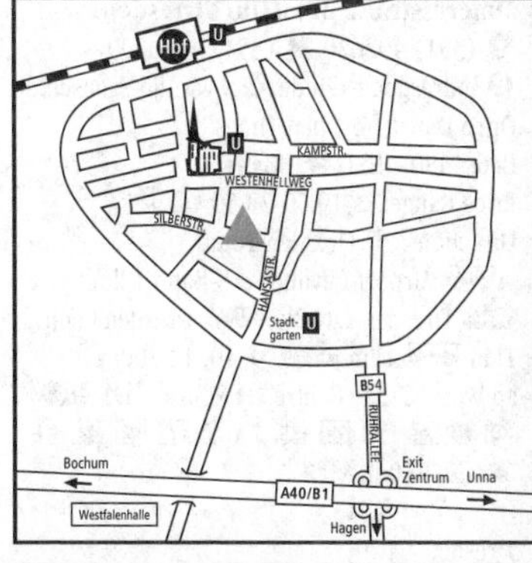

Dortmund... Travel Tips

- **For budget eats check out...** Neue Mühle, Café Extrablatt, Steakhaus Maredo, Brückstraße (a lot of restaurants), Mama Mia
- **For great nightlife try...** Konzerthaus Dortmund, Theater in Depot, Prisma Groß - Disco, Chart Noir, Soundgarten (Disco)
- **Don't miss...** Zoo Dortmund, Cycling tours, Kletter Max, Canoeing on the river Ruhr, DASA, Revierpark Wischlingen, Fredenbaumpark, Kokerei Hansa (Industrial monument), Zeche Zollern, Westfalenpark

Dreisbach – Jugendherberge an der Saarschleife, Jugendgästehaus – 22189
Herbergstr. 1, 66693 Dreisbach-Mettlach.
(6868) 270 (6868) 556
dreisbach@diejugendherbergen.de
www.DieJugendherbergen.de
Open Dates: 01.01-23.12; 27-31.12 x 122
5 x 10km

Dresden – "Rudi Arndt" – 22190
Hübnerstr 11, 01069 Dresden.
(351) 4710667 (351) 4728959
jhdresden.rudiarndt@djh.de
www.djh-sachsen.de
Open Dates: 01.01-21.12; 28-31.12 12km 1km 400m ap Nürnberger Platz 8,3 ap Nürnberger Platz x 77 2 x 3km

Dresden – JGH 22028
Maternistraße 22, 01067 Dresden.
(351) 492620 (351) 4926299
jhdresden@djh.de www.djh-sachsen.de
Open Dates: Open Times:
Beds: 480 - 162x2 38x4
Price Range: € 19.50-23.50 BBinc
Directions: Dresden 10km
A Airport-Cityliner & S-Bahn 12km
Dresden-City 2km Dresden Central 1km 1km 7, 9, 10, 12 200m ap World Trade Centre x 38 R
7 x
250m

Dresden – JGH

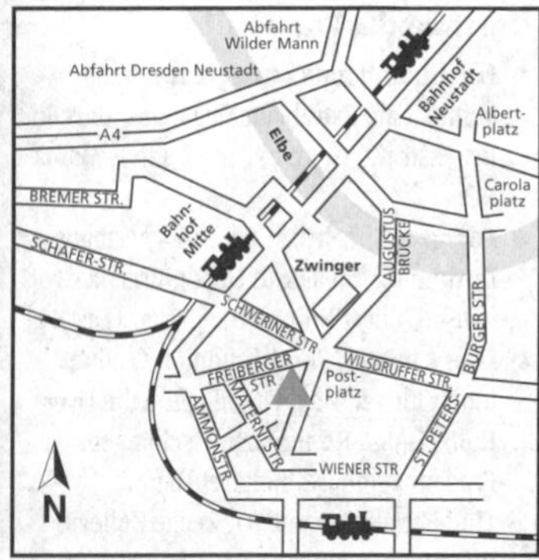

Dresden... Travel Tips

- **For budget eats check out...** Arnis Rennstall, New town with a lot of trendy bars and restaurants, Seafood
- **For great nightlife try...** Herkuleskeule (cabaret), Theatre (town centre), Operetta, New Town, Summer open air events in parks etc
- **Don't miss...** Collections and Exhibitions, Pfunds Dairy & Kunsthof passage, Old Town & new town centre, Frauenkirche (church), Pillnitz Castle grounds, Steam boat trip on the river Elbe, Meißen (porcelain factory), Sächsische Schweiz (mountains & scenery), Music Festivals, Striezel market (December)

▲ **Dresden - Radebeul** – 22191
Weintraubenstr 12, 01445 Radebeul.
(351) 8382880 (351) 8382881
jhradebeul@djh.de
www.djh-sachsen.de
Open Dates: 01.03.-31.10 (01.11-31.12)
Dresden 8km Dresden-Radebeul 300m ap Weintraube 10W x 79
1 x

▲ **Duisburg** – Duisburg-Meiderich – 22192
Lösorter Str. 133, 47137 Duisburg
(203) 417900 (203) 4179010
duisburg-meiderich@jugendherberge.de
www.duisburg-meiderich.jugendherberge.de
Open Dates: 01.01-23.12; 27-31.12
Düsseldorf 35km 903, Duisburg Main Station ap Landschaftspark 8S x 142
R 4 x

▲ **Duisburg** – Duisburg-Wedau – 22193
Kalkweg 148 E, 47279 Duisburg
(203) 724164 (203) 720834
duisburg-wedau@jugendherberge.de
www.duisburg-wedau.jugendherberge.de
Open Dates: 03.01-23.12 Düsseldorf 35km Duisburg 934, 944 Central Station 10m ap YH 45W x 126
R 4 x 1km

Düsseldorf – City-Hostel 22001
Düsseldorfer Str. 1, 40545 Düsseldorf
(211) 557310 (211) 572513
duesseldorf@jugendherberge.de
www.duesseldorf.jugendherberge.de
Open Dates: 01.01-23.12; 27-31.12
Open Times: 06.00-01.00hrs
Beds: 368 - 20x2 61x4 14x6
Price Range: from €20.90-22.00 BBinc
Directions: 3W from city centre
Düsseldorf 12km Düsseldorf Central 6km 835, 836 Kirchplatz 100m ap YH
U 74, 75, 76, 77, Luegplatz 1km x 61
R 8 x
3km

Düsseldorf – City-Hostel

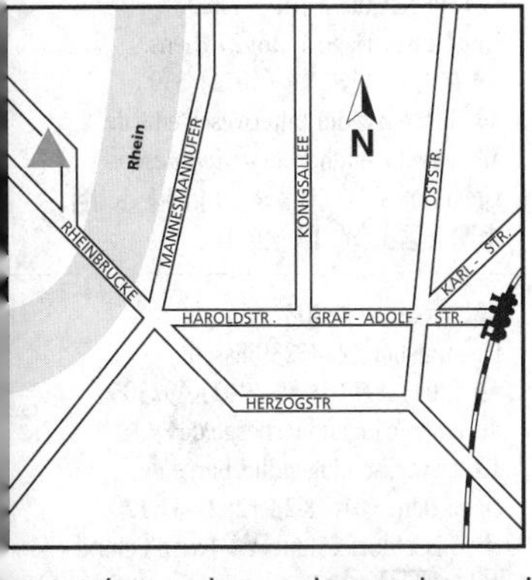

Düsseldorf... Travel Tips

- **For budget eats check out...** The old quarter of the city: more than 260 pubs, restaurants and home-brew taverns
- **For great nightlife try...** The old quarter of the city, Media Harbour, The Rhine Promenade
- **Don't miss...** Rhine Tower, Kaiserswerth Castle, Königsallee, Aqua Zoo, Museum Kunstpalast, Nord Park & Japanese Gardens, Media Harbour with Gehry Buildings, Benrath Castle

▲ Eckernförde – 22194

Sehestedter Str 27, 24340 Eckernförde.
(4351) 2154 (4351) 3604
jheckernfoerde@djh-nordmark.de
www.jugendherberge.de/jh/eckernfoerde
Open Dates: 06.01-22.12 Eckernförde 1km x 164 1km 500m

▲ Ehrenfriedersdorf – 22195

Greifensteinstr. 46, 09427 Ehrenfriedersdorf
(37346) 1253 (37346) 69727
servicecenter-sachsen@djh.de
www.djh-sachsen.de
Open Dates: 01.01-22.12; 27-31.12 (23-26.12) Schönfeld-Wiesa 8km Ehrenfriedersdorf 2km ap Markt 4SW x 43 2.5km

▲ Eichstätt – 22196

Reichenaustr 15, 85072 Eichstätt (Bavaria).
(8421) 980410 (8421) 980415
jheichstaett@djh-bayern.de
www.eichstaett.jugendherberge.de
Open Dates: 01.02-30.11 Munich 90km Eichstätt-Stadt 1km Burgberg 500m ap Elias-Holl-Straße 100m 1NW x 122 4 x 1km

▲ Eisenach – "Artur Becker" – 22197

Mariental 24, 99817 Eisenach.
(3691) 743259 (3691) 743260
jh-eisenach@djh-thueringen.de
www.djh-thueringen.de
Open Dates: 01.01-23.12; 27-31.12 Erfurt 55km Eisenach Central 2.5km 3, 10 100m ap Liliengrund x 102 3 x 2km

▲ Eisenberg – "Froschmühle" – 22198

Mühltal 5, 07607 Eisenberg.
(36691) 43462 (36691) 60034
jh-eisenberg@djh-thueringen.de
www.djh-thueringen.de
Open Dates: 01.01-22.12; 27-31.12 x 123

▲ Ellwangen – 22199

Schloß ob Ellwangen, 73479 Ellwangen.
(7961)53880 (7961) 563442
Open Dates: 12 Ellwangen x 70 2 x

▲ Emden – 22200

An der Kesselschleuse 5, 26725 Emden.
(4921) 23797 (4921) 32161
jh-emden@t-online.de
www.jugendherberge.de/jh/emden
Open Dates: 01.03-30.10 x 102

▲ Erbach – 22201

Eulbacher Str 33, 64711 Erbach.
(6062) 3515 (6062) 62848
erbach@djh-hessen.de
www.djh-hessen.de/jh/erbach
Open Dates: 01.01-23.12; 27-31.12 1.5NE x 162 1km

Erfurt – "Jugendherberge Hochheimerstraße" – 22043
Hochheimerstr 12, 99094 Erfurt.
(361) 5626705 (361) 5626706
jh-erfurt@djh-thueringen.de
www.djh-thueringen.de
Open Dates: 01.01-23.12; 27-31.12 Erfurt 2.5km Erfurt Central 1.8km Linie 5 300m ap Steigerstraße x 201 R CC TV 3 x 200m

Erfurt – "Jugendherberge Klingenstraße" – 22202
Klingenstraße 4, 99094 Erfurt.
(361) 5626705 (361) 5626706
jh-erfurt@djh-thueringen.de
www.djh-thueringen.de
Open Dates: 01.01-23.12; 27-31.12 Erfurt 3km Erfurt 3km 5 200m ap Steigerstraße x 40 R CC TV 2km

Erlangen – JH Frankenhof – 22203
Südliche Stadtmauerstr 35, 91054 Erlangen (Bavaria).
(9131) 862555 (9131) 862119
jugendherberge@stadt.erlangen.de
www.erlangen.jugendherberge.de
Open Dates: 10.01-23.12 Nürnberg 20km 600m ap Langemarckplatz x 66 R TV 3 x

Erpfingen – 22204
Auf der Reute 1, 72820 Sonnenbühl.
(7128) 1652 (7128) 3370
info@jugendherberge-erpfingen.de
www.jugendherberge-erpfingen.de
Open Dates: 12 Reutlingen 24km Sonnenbühl-Erpfingen ap Marktplatz (2.5 km to YH) 2W x 150 R CC TV 5 x

Eschwege – 22206
Fritz-Neuenroth-Weg 1, 37269 Eschwege.
(5651) 60099 (5651) 70916
eschwege@djh-hessen.de
www.djh-hessen.de/jh/eschwege
Open Dates: 01.01-23.12; 27-31.12 0.3NE x 175 1km

Esens-Bensersiel – "Ewald-Neemann-JH" – 22207
Grashauser Flage 2, 26427 Esens.
(4971) 3717 (4971) 659
jh-esens@djh-unterweser-ems.de
www.jugendherberge.de/jh/esens
Open Dates: 12 1N x 146 R CC

Essen – 22208
Pastoratsberg 2, 45239 Essen
(201) 491163 (201) 492505
essen@jugendherberge.de
www.essen.jugendherberge.de
Open Dates: 01.01-23.12; 27-31.12 Düsseldorf 25km Essen Central 10km 190 Central Station 300m ap YH S6 2km ap Essen-Werden 10N x 174 R 5 x

Eutin – 22210
Jahnhöhe 6, 23701 Eutin.
(4521) 2109 (4521) 74602
jheutin@djh-nordmark.de
www.jugendherberge.de/jh/eutin
Open Dates: 06.01-22.12 Eutin 1km x 163 TV 1km

Falkenberg – JH Tannenlohe – 22594
Tannenlohe 1, 95685 Falkenberg (Bavaria).
(9637) 267 (9637) 276
jhfalkenberg@djh-bayern.de
www.falkenberg.jugendherberge.de
Open Dates: 01.02-14.12 Reuth 6km x 162 R CC TV 6 x 10km

Falkenhain – "Talsperre Kriebstein" – 22211
Talsperrenstr. 16, 09648 Mittweida.
(3727) 2952 (3727) 600050
jhfalkenhain@djh.de
www.djh-sachsen.de
Open Dates: 01.05-30.09
Lauenhain/Mittweida-Kriebstein to YH 7km Mittweida-Waldheim S 919 1km 6NE x 220 TV 2 x

▲ **Feldberg** – 22212
Robert-Kahn-Weg 1, 17258 Feldberg.
(39831) 20520 (39831) 22178
jh.feldberg@t-online.de
www.djh-mv.de
Open Dates: 01.01-23.12; 27-31.12
Neustrelitz 30km 619 ap Strelitzer Straße x 87 R 2 x

▲ **Feldberg/Schwarzwald** – Hebelhof – 22213
Passhöhe 14, 79868 Feldberg.
(7676) 221 (7676) 1232
info@jugendherberge-feldberg.de
www.jugendherberge-feldberg.de
Open Dates: 12 Bärental ap Hebelhof 10min x 268 R CC 9 x

▲ **Feuchtwangen** – 22214
Dr.-Hans-Güthlein-Weg 1,
91555 Feuchtwangen (Bavaria).
(9852) 670990 (9852) 6709920
jhfeuchtwangen@djh-bayern.de
www.feuchtwangen.jugendherberge.de
Open Dates: 15.02-30.11 Nürnberg 80km Ansbach 25km 805 ap YH 1SE x 77 R CC 3 x 500m

▲ **Finnentrop-Heggen** – Gesundheitsjugendherberge – 22216
Ahauser Str 22-24, 57405 Finnentrop-Heggen.
(2721) 50345 (2721) 79460
jh-finnentrop.heggen@djh-wl.de
www.djh.de/westfalen
Open Dates: 01.01-23.12; 27-31.12
Köln-Bonn 100km
Finnentrop-Heggen 5km 298 1km ap Ahauser Str. x 208 R 4 x 7km

▲ **Flensburg** – 22217
Fichtestr 16, 24943 Flensburg.
(461) 37742 (461) 312952
jhflensburg@djh-nordmark.de
www.jugendherberge.de/jh/flensburg
Open Dates: 24.01-18.12 Flensburg 3.5km 300m 4NE x 198 CC

▲ **Flessenow** – 22218
Am Schweriner See 1B, 19067 Flessenow.
(3866) 82400 (3866) 82401
jh-flessenow@t-online.de
www.djh-mv.de
Open Dates: 01.04-30.09 (other dates on request) Schweriner 102 to Flessenow x 123 R 100m 100m

▲ **Forbach** – "Heinrich-Kastner-JH" – 22219
Birket 1, Postfach 1175, 76594 Forbach.
(7228) 2427 (7228) 1551
info@jugendherberge-forbach.de
www.jugendherberge-forbach.de
Open Dates: 12 Forbach (30min) 2E x 74 R 2 x

▲ **Forbach** – Environmental Study Centre, Franz-Köbele-JH – 22220
OT Herrenwies, Haus Nr 33, 76596 Forbach.
(7226) 257 (7226) 1318
info@jugendherberge-herrenwies.de
www.jugendherberge-herrenwies.de
Open Dates: 12 Bühl/Baden BusLine ap Herrenwies - YH x 145 R CC 4 x

▲ **Forchheim** – "Don-Bosco-JH" – 22221
Don-Bosco-Str. 4,
91301 Forchheim (Bavaria).
(9191) 70710 (9191) 707111
info@donbosco-forchheim.de
www.forchheim.jugendherberge.de
Open Dates: 08.01-21.12 Nürnberg 40km Forchheim/Oberfranken 500m 1.5E x 83 R 3 x 1km

Frankfurt 22017
"Haus der Jugend" Deutschherrnufer 12, 60594 Frankfurt.
(69) 6100150 (69) 61001599
jugendherberge-frankfurt@t-online.de
www.jugendherberge-frankfurt.de
Open Dates: 01.01-21.12; 28-31.12
Open Times: 06.30-02.00hrs
Beds: 441 - 7x1 50x2 4x3 59x4 11x6+
Price Range: € 16-34 BB inc
Directions: 1SE from city centre
Frankfurt am Main 12km A S1, S9 to Central Station, 46 ap Frankensteiner Platz
Frankfurt Central 3km Bus 46, 30 m 30m ap Frankensteiner Platz 16, S-Bahn 3-6 500m ap Lokalbahnhof R
1 x 8 800m

Frankfurt

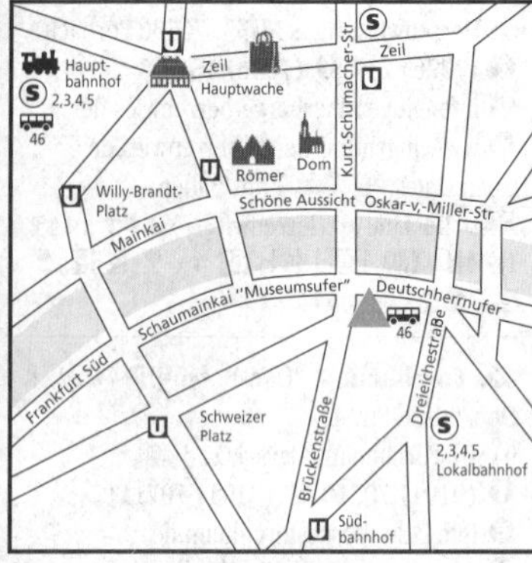

Frankfurt... Travel Tips

- **For budget eats check out...** Imbiss Soya (Chinese), Borsalino, Old Sachsenhausen, Champions Bar (Marriot Hotel), Zum Klaa Sachsenhäuser
- **For great nightlife try...** Alt Sachsenhausen, Schweizer Strasse, Pulse, Hanauer Landstrasse, Main River (summer only)
- **Don't miss...** Exhibition Tower, Hammering Man, Old Opera House, Cathedral, Modern Art Museum, Senckenberg Museum, Goethehaus, Main River Tour, Town hall, Alt Sachsenhausen

▲ **Frankfurt - Bad Homburg** – Bad Homburg – 22091
Mühlweg 17, 61348 Bad Homburg.
(6172) 23950 (6172) 22312
bad-homburg@djh-hessen.de
www.djh-hessen.de/jh/bad-homburg
Open Dates: 01.01-23.12; 27-31.12
Frankfurt am Main 20km Bad Homburg 2km U Bad Homburg-Gonzenheim 2km 0.5SW x 201
R 8 x
2km

▲ **Frankfurt - Darmstadt** – Darmstadt – 22180
Landgraf-Georg-Str 119, 64287 Darmstadt.
(6151) 45293 (6151) 422535
darmstadt@djh-hessen.de
www.djh-hessen.de/jh/darmstadt
Open Dates: 01.01-23.12; 27-31.12 0.8E
x 130 100m

▲ **Frauenau** – 22222
Hauptstr 29a, 94258 Frauenau (Bavaria).
(9926) 735 (9926) 735
www.frauenau.jugendherberge.de
Open Dates: 01.01-30.11 x 24

Frauenberg ☛ Haidmühle

▲ **Frauenstein** – Kulturerlebnistreff – 22223
Walkmühlenstr. 13, 09623 Frauenstein
(37326) 1307 (37326) 84400
jhfrauenstein@djh.de
www.djh-sachsen.de
Open Dates: 01.01-23.12; 27-31.12 (23-26.12) 373
Dresden-Olbernhau-Frauenstein 500m ap Markt 0.5SW x 100 R
2 x P

Freiburg 22224
Kartäuserstr 151, 79104 Freiburg.
(761) 67656 (761) 60367
info@jugendherberge-freiburg.de
www.jugendherberge-freiburg.de
Open Dates: Open Times: 07.00-23.30hrs
Beds: 424 - 13x2 65x4 6x5 18x6
Price Range: 1 night € 20.30; 2 nights or more € 17.10 BBinc
Directions: 6E from city centre
Strasbourg 70km Freiburg No. 1 Littenweiler 500m ap Römerhof x 4 10 x 2km

Freiburg

Freiburg... Travel Tips

- **For budget eats check out...** Feierling-Brauhaus (Augustinerplatz), Laubfrosch (Italian, Schreiberstraße), Lindenmatten (Littenweiler), Zum Schwarzwaldblick (Schwarzwaldstraße), Schlappen (Löwenstraße)
- **For great nightlife try...** Jazzhaus, Municipal Theatre , Alemannische Bühne (theatre), Irish Pub (Augustinerplatz), Agar (disco Löwenstr.)
- **Don't miss...** Minster and City Centre, Feldberg and Schauinsland (Mountains), Titisee (Lake), Europa Park (Leisure Park), Strasbourg and Colmar (Alsace), Basel (Switzerland)

▲ **Freudenstadt** – 22225
Eugen-Nägele-Str 69, 72250 Freudenstadt.
(7441) 7720 (7441) 85788
info@jugendherberge-freudenstadt.de
www.jugendherberge-freudenstadt.de
Open Dates: Freudenstadt ap Berufsschule x 132 4 x 500m

▲ **Freusburg** – 22226
Burgstrasse 46, 57548 Kirchen-Freusburg.
(2741) 61094 (2741) 63135
jh-freusburg@djh-wl.de
www.djh.de/westfalen
Open Dates: 03.01-23.12; 27-31.12
Köln/Bonn 100km
Freusburg-Siedlung 2km x 219 7 x 3km

▲ **Friedrichshafen** – Graf-Zeppelin-JH – 22227
Lindauer Str 3, 88046 Friedrichshafen.
(7541) 72404 (7541) 74986
info@jugendherberge-friedrichshafen.de
www.jugendherberge-friedrichshafen.de
Open Dates: Friedrichshafen 3km RAB-Bus Kressbronn, 7 ap YH or Eberhardtstraße 2E x 235 7 x 1km 1km

▲ **Friedrichstadt** – 22228
Ostdeutsche Str 1, 25840 Friedrichstadt.
(40) 6559950 (40) 65599544
service@djh-nordmark.de
www.jugendherberge.de/nordmark
Open Dates: Opening Summer 2006
Friedrichstadt 700m x 84

▲ **Fulda** – 22230
Schirrmannstraße 31, 36041 Fulda.
(661) 73389 (661) 74811
fulda@djh-hessen.de
www.djh-hessen.de/jh/fulda
Open Dates: 01.01-23.12; 27-31.12 2SW
x 122

▲ Furth im Wald – 22231
Daberger Str 50,
93437 Furth im Wald (Bavaria).
(9973) 9254 (9973) 2447
jhfurth@djh-bayern.de
www.furth.jugendherberge.de
Open Dates: 15.02-15.12 Furth im Wald 2km 500m x 128 R CC 3 x 8 200m

▲ Füssen H 22014
Mariahilferstr 5, 87629 Füssen (Bavaria).
(8362) 7754 (8362) 2770
jhfuessen@djh-bayern.de
www.fuessen.jugendherberge.de
Open Dates: 01.01-14.11; 27-31.12
Füssen 1km 1km x 134 2 x 8 1km

▲ Garmisch-Partenkirchen – 22233
Jochstr 10,
82467 Garmisch-Partenkirchen (Bavaria).
(8821) 2980 (8821) 58536
jhgarmisch@djh-bayern.de
www.garmisch.jugendherberge.de
Open Dates: 27.12-14.11
Garmisch-Partenkirchen 4km
Burgrain 200m 4N x 202 6 x 8 2km

▲ Geesthacht – 22234
Berliner Str 117, 21502 Geesthacht.
(4152) 2356 (4152) 77918
jhgeesthacht@djh-nordmark.de
www.jugendherberge.de/jh/geesthacht
Open Dates: 06.01-22.12 Hamburg 30km Hamburg-Bergedorf 10km 300m x 107 (B) 1km

Gehringswalde ☛ **Warmbad**

▲ Gerolstein – 22235
Zur Büschkapelle 1, 54568 Gerolstein.
(6591) 4745 (6591) 7243
gerolstein@diejugendherbergen.de
www.DieJugendherbergen.de
Open Dates: 01.01-23.12; 27-31.12
Gerolstein 2km x 172 R CC 5 x 500m

▲ Gersfeld – 22236
Jahnstraße 6, 36129 Gersfeld.
(6654) 340 (6654) 7788
Gersfeld@djh-hessen.de
www.djh-hessen.de/jh/gersfeld
Open Dates: 01.01-23.12; 27-31.12 0.5SE
x 107

▲ Geyer – Gut Drauf-JH – 22237
Anton-Günther-Weg 3, 09468 Geyer.
(37346) 1364 (37346) 1770
jhgeyer@djh.de www.djh-sachsen.de
Open Dates: 01.01-22.12; 27-31.12 (23-26.12) Annaberg 12km
Annaberg 1km ap Markt 2W x 91 R 1 x 2km

▲ Gießen – 22238
Richard-Schirrmann-Weg 53, 35398 Gießen.
(641) 65879 (641) 9605502
Giessen@djh-hessen.de
www.djh-hessen.de/jh/giessen
Open Dates: 01.01-23.12; 27-31.12 3SW
x 78

▲ Glörsee – 22239
Glörtalsperre 1, 58339 Breckerfeld.
(2338) 434 (2338) 3674
jh-gloersee@djh-wl.de
www.djh.de/westfalen
Open Dates: 01.01-23.12; 27-31.12
Dortmund 40km Dahlerbrück 5km
84 2km ap Branten 4 x 124 R 4 x

▲ Gommern – 22240
Manheimerstr 12, 39245 Gommern.
(39200) 40080 (39200) 40082
jh-gommern@djh-sachsen-anhalt.de
www.jugendherberge.de/jh/gommern
Open Dates: 01.01-23.12; 27-31.12
Halle-Leipzig 120km
Magdeburg-Dessau 1.7km x 100 R 3 x 500m 500m

Göppingen – JH Hohenstaufen – 22241
Schottengasse 45, 73037 Göppingen.
(7165) 438 (7165) 1418
info@jugendherberg-hohenstaufen.de
www.jugendherberge-hohenstaufen.de
Open Dates: Göppingen
Hohenstaufen ap YH x 121
R CC TV 1 x 3km

Gorenzen – "Carl Wentzel" – 22242
Hagen 2-4, 06343 Gorenzen.
(34782) 20384; 21356
(34782) 21357
jh-gorenzen@djh-sachsen-anhalt.de
www.jugendherberge.de/jh/gorenzen
Open Dates: 01.01-23.12; 27-31.12
Hettstedt 20km YH 800m
ap Hettstedt x 122 R
TV 3 x 3km

Görlitz – "Friedensgrenze" – 22243
Goethestr 17, 02826 Görlitz.
(3581) 406510 (3581) 661775
jugendherbergegoerlitz@t-online.de
www.djh-sachsen.de
Open Dates: 01.01-22.12; 27-31.12 1km
3 ap Goethestr. 1S x 92 R
TV 2 x
800m

Goslar – 22244
Rammelsberger Str 25, 38644 Goslar.
(5321) 22240 (5321) 41376
jh-goslar@djh-hannover.de
www.jugendherberge.de/jh/goslar
Open Dates: 01.01-23.12; 27-31.12
Goslar 4km 500m x 163
R CC TV 4 x
2.5km

Göttingen – 22245
Habichtsweg 2, 37075 Göttingen.
(551) 57622 (551) 43887
jh-goettingen@djh-hannover.de
www.jugendherberge.de/jh/goettingen
Open Dates: 01.01-23.12; 27-31.12
Hannover 140km 2km 100m
x 161 R CC
TV 4 x 8 3km

Gräfenroda – "Olga Benario" – 22247
Waldstr 134, 99330 Gräfenroda.
(36205) 76290 (36205) 76421
jh-graefenroda@djh-thueringen.de
www.djh-thueringen.de
Open Dates: 01.01-23.12; 26-31.12 Erfurt
40km Haltepunkt Dörrberg 1km
Gräfenroda 1km ap Buswendeplatz
x 60 R CC TV
1km

Grävenwiesbach – 22248
Hasselborner Straße. 20,
61279 Grävenwiesbach.
(6086) 520 (6086) 970352
Graevenwiesbach@djh-hessen.de
www.djh-hessen.de/jh/graevenwiesbach
Open Dates: 01.01-23.12; 27-31.12 2.5NE
x 154

Greifswald – 22249
Pestalozzistr. 11/12, 17489 Greifswald.
(3834) 51690 (3834) 516910
jh-greifswald@djh-mv.de
www.djh-mv.de
Open Dates: 01.01-23.12; 27-31.12
Greifswald 1 ap Feldberg 1SE
x 122 R
6 x

Groß Reken – 22251
Coesfelder Str 18, 48734 Reken.
(2864) 1023 (2864) 2044
jh-gross.reken@djh-wl.de
www.djh.de/westfalen
Open Dates: 01.01-23.12; 27-31.12
Münster/Osnabrück 70km Maria
Veen 4km x 126 R
TV 3 x 1km

Grumbach – "Raummühle"-
Umweltstudienplatz – 22252
Jöhstädter Str. 19,
09477 Jöhstadt/OT Grumbach.
(37343) 2288 (37343) 88003
jhgrumbach@djh.de
www.djh-sachsen.de
Open Dates: 01.01-23.12; 27-31.12 (
23-26.12) Annaberg 16km
Annaberg-Jöhstadt 100m ap YH 2E
x 62 R TV
4km

▲ **Günzburg** – 22253
Schillerstr 12, 89312 Günzburg (Bavaria).
(8221) 34487 (8221) 31390
jhguenzburg@djh-bayern.de
www.guenzburg.jugendherberge.de
Open Dates: 16.01-14.11 1km x 34 2km

▲ **Gunzenhausen** – 22254
Spitalstr. 3, 91710 Gunzenhausen (Bavaria).
(9831) 67020 (9831) 670211
jhgunzenhausen@djh-bayern.de
www.gunzenhausen.jugendherberge.de
Open Dates: 12 Gunzenhausen 1km 1km 0.5N x 132 R CC 3 x i P 1km 1km

▲ **Güstrow** – 22255
Schabernack 70, 18273 Güstrow.
(3843) 840044 (3843) 840045
jh-guestrow@djh-mv.de
www.djh-mv.de
Open Dates: 01.01-23.12; 27-31.12
Güstrow 252
ap Güstrow-Schabernack 6SE x 110 R TV 1 x i P 1km 1.5km

▲ **Hagen** – 22257
Eppenhauser Str 65a, 58093 Hagen.
(2331) 50254 (2331) 588576
jh-hagen@djh-wl.de
www.djh.de/westfalen
Open Dates: 01.01-23.12; 27-31.12
Dortmund 40km Hagen Central 5km 520, 527, 541 100m ap Emsterstr. x 133 R TV 6 x i P 5km

▲ **Hahnenklee** – 22258
Hahnenkleer Str 11,
38644 Goslar - OT Hahnenklee- Bockswiese.
(5325) 2256 (5325) 3524
jh-hahnenklee@djh-hannover.de
www.jugendherberge.de/jh/hahnenklee
Open Dates: 01.01-23.12; 27-31.12
Goslar 15km 200m x 122 CC TV P

▲ **Haidmühle** – JH Frauenberg – 22259
Frauenberg 45, 94145 Haidmühle (Bavaria).
(8556) 467 (8556) 1021
jhhaidmuehle@djh-bayern.de
www.haidmuehle.jugendherberge.de
Open Dates: 01.01-31.10; 16-31.12; (only 01.11-15.12) Passau 55km 250m ap Frauenberg x 157 R CC TV 2 x P 3.9km

▲ **Haldensleben** – 22260
Bornsche Str 94, 39340 Haldensleben.
(3904) 40386 (3904) 499023
JH-Haldensleben@djh-sachsen-anhalt.de
www.jugendherberge.de/jh/haldensleben
Open Dates: 02.01-23.12 line Magdeburg-Oebisfelde 3km 2 from ap YH 2N x 40 R TV P

▲ **Halle** – 22261
August-Bebel-Str 48a, 06108 Halle.
(345) 2024716 (345) 2025172
jh-halle@djh-sachsen-anhalt.de
www.jugendherberge.de/jh/halle
Open Dates: 01.01-23.12; 27-31.12
Halle-Leipzig 25km A 300 3km Central 3km 5, 2 500m ap J.-Curie-Platz 0.5N x 72 R TV 2 x P 1.5km

Hallwangen ☛ **Dornstetten**

▲ **Haltern am See** – 22262
Stockwieser Damm 255,
45721 Haltern am See.
(2364) 2258 (2364) 169604
jh-haltern@djh-wl.de
www.djh.de/westfalen
Open Dates: 01.01-23.12; 27-31.12
Münster 60km Haltern am See 6km 272, Haltern 1km ap Haus Niemen x 138 R TV 5 x i P 300m

Hamburg – Auf dem Stintfang 22008
Alfred-Wegener-Weg 5, 20459 Hamburg.
(40) 313488; 3191037 (40) 315407
jh-stintfang@djh.de
Open Dates: 01.01-29.01; 27.02-22.12; 27-31.12 Open Times: 06.30-10.00hrs; 12.30-02.00hrs
Beds: 359 - 26x2 7x3 23x4 6x5 23x6 3x6+
Price Range: € 18.80-23.30 BBinc
Directions: 2SW from city centre
Hamburg 10km Hamburg 200m
Hamburg Central 2km 112 200m
U S1, S3, U3 Landungsbrücken 200m
x 33 1km

Hamburg – Auf dem Stintfang

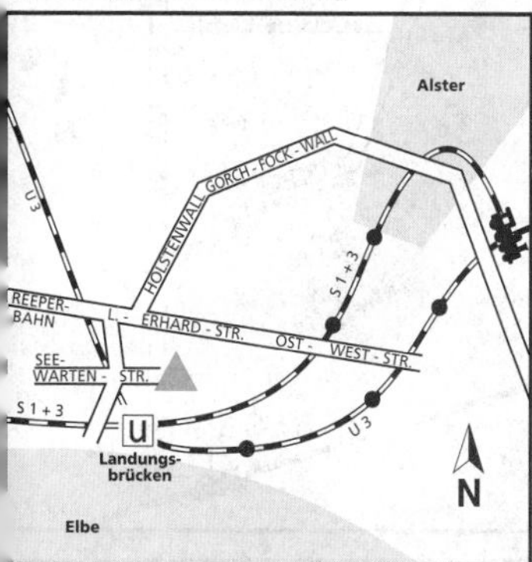

Hamburg – Horner Rennbahn
22007
Rennbahnstr 100, 22111 Hamburg.
(40) 6511671 (40) 6556516
jgh-hamburg@t-online.de
www.jugendherberge.de/jh/hamburg-horn
Open Dates: 01.02-22.12 Hamburg 10km
Hamburg Central 5km
Tribünenweg 300m U Horner Rennbahn 700m 5E x 247
1.5km

Hamburg... Travel Tips

- **For budget eats check out...** Harbour district, St Pauli, Karolinen district, Schanzen district
- **For great nightlife try...** St Pauli
- **Don't miss...** Harbour Cruise, Alster Lake Cruise, St Michaelis Church, Musicals, St Pauli, Fish Market (Sundays), Hagenbecks Zoo, Museums, Theatres, Speicherstadt

Hameln – 22263
Fischbecker Str 33, 31785 Hameln.
(5151) 3425 (5151) 42316
jh-hameln@djh-hannover.de
www.jugendherberge.de/jh/hameln
Open Dates: 01.01-23.12; 27-31.12 3km
200m x 106
1 x

Hankensbüttel – 22265
Helmrichsweg 24, 29386 Hankensbüttel.
(5832) 2500 (5832) 6596
jh-hankensbuettel@djh-hannover.de
www.jugendherberge.de/jh/hankensbuettel
Open Dates: 01.01-23.12; 27-31.12
Hannover 100km Wittingen 10km
120 120m ap Einkaufszentrum
x 142 2 x

Hann. Münden – 22266
Prof-Oelkers-Str 10, 34346 Hann. Münden.
(5541) 8853 (5541) 73439
jh-hann-muenden@djh-hannover.de
www.jugendherberge.de/jh/hannmuenden
Open Dates: 01.01-23.12; 27-31.12
Hannover 150km 2km 50m
x 129
2km

Hannover – 22267
Ferdinand-Wilhelm-Fricke-Weg 1, 30169 Hannover.
(511) 1317674 (511) 18555
jh-hannover@djh-hannover.de
www.jugendherberge.de/jh/hannover
Open Dates: 17.60-25.50 Open Times:
Beds: 270 - 1x1 45x2 46x4
Price Range: € 17.60-25.50 BBinc
Directions: 2S from city centre
Hannover-Langenhagen 20km
Hannover 5km 3, 7 1km
ap Fischerhof x 26
6 x
500m

Hannover

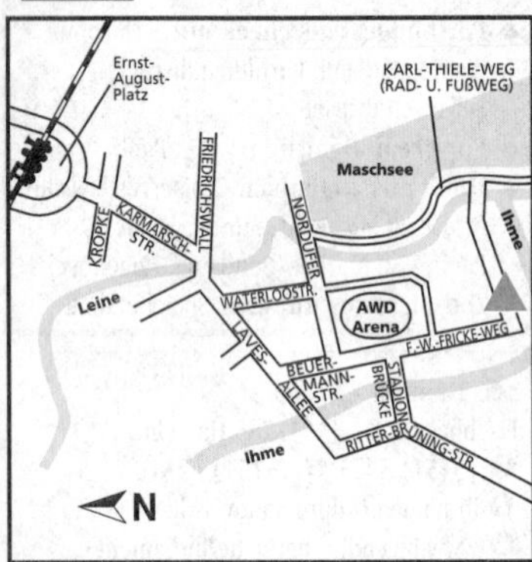

Hannover... Travel Tips

- **For budget eats check out...** Youth Hostel, Old Town, Artemis (Greek), Shogun (Chinese)
- **For great nightlife try...** Old Town, GOP Varieté (theatre), Opera House, Theatre, Play House
- **Don't miss...** Maschsee (lake), Zoo, Herrenhäuser (gardens), Museums, Regenwaldhaus, Historical Old Town, Exhibition Centre

Hardter Wald ☛ Mönchengladbach

Harsberg ☛ Lauterberg

▲ **Hartenstein** – 22269
Salzlecke 10, 91235 Hartenstein (Bavaria).
t (9152) 1296 f (9152) 1328
e jhhartenstein@djh-bayern.de
w www.hartenstein.jugendherberge.de
Open Dates: 01.02-14.12 x 66

▲ **Heide** – 22271
Poststr 4, 25746 Heide.
t (481) 71575 f (481) 72901
e jhheide@djh-nordmark.de
w www.jugendherberge.de/jh/heide
Open Dates: 02.02-22.12 Heide 1km
x 82 TV P
2km

Heidelberg HI 22272
Tiergartenstr 5, 69120 Heidelberg.
t (6221) 65119-0/-13
f (6221) 65119-28
e info@jugendherberge-heidelberg.de
w www.jugendherberge-heidelberg.de
Open Dates: 12 Open Times:
Beds: 485
Price Range: 1 night € 20.30; 2 nights or more € 17.10 BBinc
Directions: 4NW from city centre
Heidelberg 33 - 10 min ap YH
R CC TV
12 x i 8 P 500m

Heidelberg

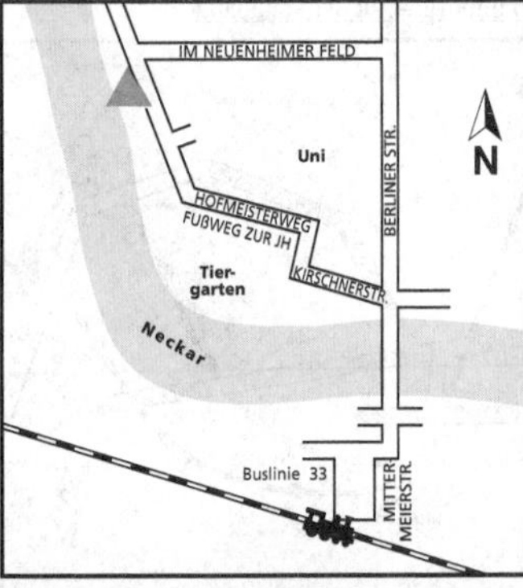

Heidelberg... Travel Tips

- **For budget eats check out...** O'Reilly's Pub, Mandy's Diner, Wok 2, Palmbräugasse, Merlin
- **For great nightlife try...** Schwimmbad (music club), Nachtschicht (disco), Hauptstraße (Palmbräugasse restaurant), Untere Straße (restaurants & pubs), Karlstorbahnhof (station)
- **Don't miss...** Heidelberg Castle, Königstuhl, Old Bridge, Main Street, Neckarwiese, Tiergartenbath, Heiliggeistkirchen (church), Museums, Philosophenweg, Thingstätte

▲ **Heidenheim** – 22273
Liststr 15, 89518 Heidenheim.
t (7321) 42045 f (7321) 949045
e info@jugendherberge-heidenheim.de
w www.jugendherberge-heidenheim.de
Open Dates: 12 Heidenheim 15 ap Liststraße x 128 R CC
TV 5 x P 1km

Heilbronn – JH Rheinhardt – 22274
Schirrmannstr 9, 74074 Heilbronn.
(7131) 172961 (7131) 164345
info@jugendherberge-heilbronn.de
www.jugendherberge-heilbronn.de
Open Dates: Heilbronn 1, (15min) x 110 2 x 4km

Heldrungen – "Wasserburg" – 22275
Schloßstr. 13, 06577 Heldrungen.
(34673) 91224 (34673) 98136
jh-heldrungen@djh-thueringen.de
www.djh-thueringen.de
Open Dates: 01.01-23.12; 27-31.12 Erfurt 60km Heldrungen 3km 501, 509, 520 1km ap Heldrungen Stadt x 52 2 x

Helgoland – 22276
"Haus der Jugend", Postfach 580,
27487 Helgoland.
(4725) 341 (4725) 7467
Haus-der-Jugend-Helgoland@t-online.de
www.jugendherberge.de/jh/helgoland
Open Dates: 01.03-31.10; 28.12-03.01
500m x 136 300m 1km

Hellenthal – Experimential learning with an outdoor center – 22277
Platiß 3, 53940 Hellenthal
(2482) 2238 (2482) 2557
hellenthal@jugendherberge.de
www.hellenthal.jugendherberge.de
Open Dates: 01.01-23.12; 27-31.12 Kall 808, Kall ap Hellenthal x 170 5 x

Heppenheim – Starkenburg – 22278
Starkenburgweg 53, 64646 Heppenheim.
(6252) 77323 (6252) 78185
starkenburg@djh-hessen.de
www.djh-hessen.de/jh/starkenburg
Open Dates: 01.01-23.12; 27-31.12 1.5N
x 121

Heringsdorf – 22279
Puschkinstr 7-9, 17424 Seebad Heringsdorf.
(38378) 22325 (38378) 32301
jh-heringsdorf@djh-mv.de
www.djh-mv.de
Open Dates: 01.01-23.12; 27-31.12
Heringsdorf ap Richtung Promenade (10min) x 167 6 x 100m

Hermeskeil – Hunsrück-Jugendherberge, Jugendgästehaus – 22280
Adolf-Kolping-Str. 4, 54411 Hermeskeil.
(6503) 3097 (6503) 6146
hermeskeil@diejugendherbergen.de
www.DieJugendherbergen.de
Open Dates: 01.01-23.12; 27-31.12 x 111 3 x 500m

Herrenwies ☛ **Forbach**

Hilchenbach – 22281
Wilhelm-Münker-Str 9, 57271 Hilchenbach.
(2733) 4396 (2733) 8085
jh-hilchenbach@djh-wl.de
www.djh.de/westfalen
Open Dates: 01.01-23.12; 27-31.12 x 86 3 x

Hilders – 22282
An der Jugendherberge 1,
36115 Hilders/Rhön.
(6681) 365 (6681) 8429
hilders@djh-hessen.de
www.djh-hessen.de/jh/hilders
Open Dates: 01.01-23.12; 27-31.12 1.5E
x 144

Hilders – Oberbernhards – 22283
Hauptstraße 5,
36115. Oberbernhards-Hilders.
(6657) 240 (6657) 8896
oberbernhards@djh-hessen.de
www.jugendherberge-oberbernhards.de
Open Dates: 01.01-23.12; 27-31.12 8NW
x 257

Hildesheim – 22284
Schirrmannweg 4, 31139 Hildesheim.
(5121) 42717 (5121) 47847
jh-hildesheim@djh-hannover.de
www.jugendherberge.de/jh/hildesheim
Open Dates: 01.01-23.12; 27-31.12 6km 1km x 104 5km

▲ Hitzacker – 22285
Wolfsschlucht 2 (An der Elbuferstrasse), 29456 Hitzacker.
(5862) 244 (5862) 7767
jh-hitzacker@djh-hannover.de
www.jugendherberge.de/jh/hitzacker
Open Dates: 01.01-23.12; 27-31.12
Hannover-Langenhagen 120km
Hitzacker 2km
Hitzacker/Lüneburger Landstraße 1km
x 165 R CC 4 x 1km

▲ Hochspeyer – Naturpark- und Wald-Jugendherberge – 22286
Trippstadter Straße 150, 67691 Hochspeyer.
(6305) 336 (6305) 5152
hochspeyer@diejugendherbergen.de
www.DieJugendherbergen.de
Open Dates: 01.01-23.12; 27-31.12
Hochspeyer 1.8km x 147 R CC 4 x 1.5km

▲ Hof – 22287
Beethovenstr 44, 95032 Hof (Bavaria).
(9281) 93277 (9281) 92016
jhhof@djh-bayern.de
www.hof.jugendherberge.de
Open Dates: 15.02-15.11 8km
A 2.5km Hof 1.5km 500m
4SW x 89 R CC 2 x 1km 1.5km

▲ Hohenberg – 22288
Auf der Burg, 95691 Hohenberg (Bavaria).
(9233) 77260 (9233) 772611
sswhohenberg@t-online.de
www.hohenberg.jugendherberge.de
Open Dates: 01.01-20.12; 27-31.12 x 130 1 x

Hohenstaufen ☛ **Göppingen**

▲ Holzminden – 22289
Am Steinhof, 37603 Holzminden.
(5531) 4411 (5531) 120630
jh-holzminden@djh-hannover.de
www.jugendherberge.de/jh/holzminden
Open Dates: 01.01-23.12; 27-31.12
Holzminden 3km x 123 R CC 500m

▲ Homburg –
Hohenburg-Jugendherberge, Jugendgästehaus Homburg – 22290
Am Mühlgraben 30, 66424 Homburg.
(6841) 3679 (6841) 120220
homburg@diejugendherbergen.de
www.DieJugendherbergen.de
Open Dates: 01.01-23.12; 27-31.12
Homburg 8.1km x 126 R CC 9 x 1.5km

▲ Hormersdorf – Sportjugendherberge – 22291
Am Greifenbachstauweiher, 09468 JH Hormersdorf
(37346) 1396 (37346) 1645
jhhormersdorf@djh.de
www.djh-sachsen.de
Open Dates: 01.01.-31.10 (01.11-31.12)
4SW x 205 R 3 x 300m

▲ Horn-Bad Meinberg – 22292
Jahnstr 36, 32805 Horn-Bad Meinberg.
(5234) 2534 (5234) 69199
jh-horn.bad.meinberg@djh-wl.de
www.djh.de/westfalen
Open Dates: 01.01-23.12; 27-31.12
Paderborn 30km Horn 2km
x 122 R 5 x 400m

▲ Hörnum – 22293
Friesenplatz 2, 25997 Hörnum/Sylt.
(4651) 880294 (4651) 881392
jhhoernum@djh-nordmark.de
www.jugendherberge.de/jh/hoernum
Open Dates: 08.03-22.12 Westerland 18km 300m x 170 CC 800m 1km

▲ Höxter – 22294
"Umweltstudienplatz",
An der Wilhelmshöhe 59, 37671 Höxter.
(5271) 2233 (5271) 1237
jh-hoexter@djh-wl.de
www.djh.de/westfalen
Open Dates: 01.01-23.12; 27-31.12
Höxter-Rathaus 591 ap Fachhochschule x 131 R 6 x

▲ **Hude** – 22295
Linteler Str 3, 27798 Hude.
(4408) 414 (4408) 970322
jh-hude@djh-unterweser-ems.de
www.jugendherberge.de/jh/hude
Open Dates: x 94

▲ **Hümpfershausen/Rhön** – "Schloss Sinnershausen" – 22296
98634 Hümpfershausen.
(36940) 5810 (36940) 58112
jabzschloss@aol.com
www.djh-thueringen.de
Open Dates: 04.01-23.12 Erfurt 75km Wasungen 13km 412 200m ap Hümpfershausen x 70 2 x

▲ **Hürth** – "Villehaus" – 22297
Adolf-Dasbach-Weg 5, 50354 Hürth.
(2233) 42463 (2233) 16351
info@villehaus.de www.villehaus.de
Open Dates: 01.01-23.12; 27-31.12
Köln/Bonn 15km Köln Central 11km Hürth-Hermülheim 979 2km ap Alte Luxemburger Str./Kendenich Köln HBF 18 9km ap Hürth-Hermülheim x 68 2 x 2.5km 2.8km

▲ **Husum** – 22298
Schobüller Str 34, 25813 Husum.
(4841) 2714 (4841) 81568
jhhusum@djh-nordmark.de
www.jugendherberge.de/jh/husum
Open Dates: 06.01-22.12 Husum 2.5km 500m x 181 1km

▲ **Idar-Oberstein** – Nahe-Hunsrück-Jugendherberge, Jugendgästehaus – 22299
Alte Treibe 23, 55743 Idar-Oberstein.
(6781) 24366 (6781) 26712
idar-oberstein@diejugendherbergen.de
www.DieJugendherbergen.de
Open Dates: 01.01-23.12; 27-31.12
Idar-Oberstein 2km x 128 5 x 4km

Igesheim ☛ **Bad Mergentheim**

▲ **Ihrlerstein** – JH Kelheim – 22301
Kornblumenweg 1,
93346 Ihrlerstein (Bavaria).
(9441) 3309 (9441) 21792
jhkelheim@djh-bayern.de
www.kelheim.jugendherberge.de
Open Dates: 01.02-30.11 Saal/Donau 8km 2, Schlesierstraße 500m 1.5N x 112

▲ **Ilmenau** – 22302
Am Stollen 49, 98693 Ilmenau
(3677) 884681 (3677) 884682
jh-ilmenau@djh-thueringen.de
www.djh-thueringen.de
Open Dates: 01.01-23.12; 28-31.12 Erfurt 30km Ilmenau 2km A, B, C 100m ap YH x 130 1 x

▲ **Ingolstadt** – 22303
Friedhofstr 4 1/2, 85049 Ingolstadt (Bavaria).
(841) 3051280 (841) 3051289
jugendherberge@ingolstadt.de
www.ingolstadt.jugendherberge.de
Open Dates: 01.02-14.12 Munich 60km Ingolstadt 3km 500m 0.5W x 84

▲ **Inselsberg** – "Großer Inselsberg" – 22304
Inselsbergstraße 126, 99891 Tabarz
(36259) 62329 (36259) 30821
jh-inselsberg@djh-thueringen.de
www.djh-thueringen.de
Open Dates: 01.01-23.12; 27-31.12 Erfurt 50km Friedrichroda 9km 857 1.5km ap Kleiner Inselsberg x 60 6km

▲ **Inzmühlen** – 22305
Wehlener Weg 10, 21256 Handeloh.
(4188) 342 (4188) 7858
jhinzmuehlen@djh-nordmark.de
www.jugendherberge.de/jh/inzmuehlen
Open Dates: 01.01-22.12 Handeloh 2km x 161

▲ **Itzehoe** – 22307
Juliengardeweg 13, 25524 Itzehoe.
(4821) 62270 (4821) 5710
Jugendherberge@itzehoe.de
www.jugendherberge.de/jh/itzehoe
Open Dates: 16.01-14.12 Itzehoe 1km
x 75 1km

▲ **Jena** – "Internationales Jugendgästehaus" – 22308
Am Herrenberge 3, 07745 Jena.
(3641) 687230 (3641) 687202
jugendgaestehaus.jena@internationaler-bund.de www.internationaler-bund.de
Open Dates: 05.01-19.12 Erfurt 50km
Westbahnhof 3km 10, 13, 40 1km
1, 31 2km 3.5SW x 140 R
3km

▲ **Jever** – 22309
Jahnstraße 12, 26441 Jever.
(4461) 909202 (4461) 909209
jh-jever@djh-unterweser-ems.de
www.jugendherberge.de/jh/jever
Open Dates: 12 x 138 CC
5 x 100m

▲ **Johanngeorgenstadt** – 22310
Hospitalstr. 5, 08349 Johanngeorgenstadt
(3773) 882194 (3773) 889150
jhjohanngeorgenstadt@djh.de
www.djh-sachsen.de
Open Dates: 01.01-23.12; 27-31.12 (
23-26.12) 2km 800m
ap Marktplatz 1S x 60 R
1 x i
2km

▲ **Jonsdorf** – "Dreiländereck" – 22311
Hainstr 14, 02796 Kurort Jonsdorf
(35844) 72130 (35844) 72131
jhjonsdorf@djh.de
www.djh-sachsen.de
Open Dates: 01.02-31.10 (01.11.-31.01)
200m 200m x 71 R
3 x
50m

▲ **Juist** – 22312
Loogster Pad 20, 26571 Juist, (North Sea).
(4935) 92910 (4935) 8294
jh-juist@djh-unterweser-ems.de
www.jugendherberge.de/jh/juist
Open Dates: 03.01-01.12 1.5W x 300
R CC 7 x
300m 300m

▲ **Kandern** – Platzhof – 22313
Platzhof 1, 79400 Kandern.
(7626) 484 (7626) 6809
info@jugendherberge-kandern.de
www.jugendherberge-kandern.de
Open Dates: 12 Steinen
ap Platzhof x 53 R
2 x

▲ **Kappeln** – 22314
Eckernförder Str 2, 24376 Kappeln.
(4642) 8550 (4642) 81086
jhkappeln@djh-nordmark.de
www.jugendherberge.de/jh/kappeln
Open Dates: 06.01-22.12 Süderbrarup
12km 500m x 166
CC

▲ **Karlsruhe** – 22315
Moltkestr 24, 76133 Karlsruhe.
(721) 28248 (721) 27647
info@jugendherberge-karlsruhe.de
www.jugendherberge-karlsruhe.de
Open Dates: 12 Karlsruhe 2, 4
ap Europaplatz 4NW x 167 R
CC 3 x

▲ **Kassel** – 22047
Schenkendorfstraße 18, 34119 Kassel.
(561) 776455 (561) 776832
kassel@djh-hessen.de
www.djh-hessen.de/jh/kassel
Open Dates: 01.01-23.12; 27-31.12 1.5NW
x 209 R

▲ **Katzhütte** – 22316
Bahnhofstr 82, 98746 Katzhütte
(36781) 37785 (36781) 33806
jh-katzhuette@djh-thueringen.de
www.djh-thueringen.de
Open Dates: 01.01-23.12; 27-31.12 Erfurt
70km Katzhütte 300m L 502
300m ap Katzhütte x 70 R
CC

▲ **Kehl** – 22317
Altrheinweg 11, 77694 Kehl.
(7851) 2330 (7851) 76608
info@jugendherberge-kehl.de
www.jugendherberge-kehl.de
Open Dates: 12 Kehl 1SW x 122
R CC 4 x
1km

▲ **Kelbra** – 22318
Forsthaus, 06537 Kelbra/OT Sittendorf.
(34651) 55890 (34651) 55891
JH-Kelbra@djh-sachsen-anhalt.de
www.jugendherberge.de/jh/kelbra
Open Dates: 01.01-23.12; 27-31.12
Halle-Leipzig 50km
Halle-Sangerhausen-Kassel ap Berga
5km 2.5S x 136 R
3 x 5km
5km

Kelheim ☛ Ihrlerstein

▲ **Kevelaer** – 22320
Am Michelsweg 11, 47626 Kevelaer
(2832) 8267 (2832) 899432
kevelaer@jugendherberge.de
www.kevelaer.jugendherberge.de
Open Dates: 01.01-23.12; 27-31.12
Kevelaer 2km 53 800m
ap Schravelener Heide x 130 R
5 x 1km

▲ **Kiel** 22016
Johannesstr 1, 24143 Kiel.
(431) 731488 (431) 735723
jhkiel@djh-nordmark.de
www.jugendherberge.de/jh/kiel
Open Dates: 27.12-19.12 Kiel 7km
Norwegenkai 500m Kiel 1km
500m 2SE x 270 R
CC 100m
4km

▲ **Kirchberg** – 22321
Gaggstatter Str 35, 74592 Kirchberg.
(7954) 230 (7954) 1319
info@jugendherberge-kirchberg.de
www.jugendherberge-kirchberg.de
Open Dates: 12 Schwäbisch Hall,
Crailsheim ap Frankenplatz 800m
x 85 R 3 x

▲ **Kleve** – Family Youth Hostel – 22322
St. Annaberg 2, 47533 Kleve
(2821) 23671 (2821) 24778
kleve@jugendherberge.de
www.kleve.jugendherberge.de
Open Dates: 01.01-23.12 Kleve 4km
57 300m ap YH x 118 R
4 x
4km

▲ **Klingenthal am Aschberg** –
Tschechisch-Deutsche
Musik-Begegnungsstätte – 22323
Grenzweg 22, 08248 Klingenthal
(37467) 22094 (37467) 22099
jhklingenthal@djh.de
www.djh-sachsen.de
Open Dates: 01.01-22.12 (23-31.12)
6km T-48 1.5km ap Sporthotel 6N
x 131 R
2 x

Koblenz – Jugendherberge Festung Ehrenbreitstein, Jugendgästehaus – 22324
56077 Koblenz.
(261) 972870 (261) 9728730
koblenz@diejugendherbergen.de
www.DieJugendherbergen.de
Open Dates: 01.01-23.12; 27-31.12
Open Times:
Beds: 183
Directions: 6NE from city centre
Koblenz 6.6km R CC
5 x
3km

Koblenz – Jugendherberge Festung Ehrenbreitstein

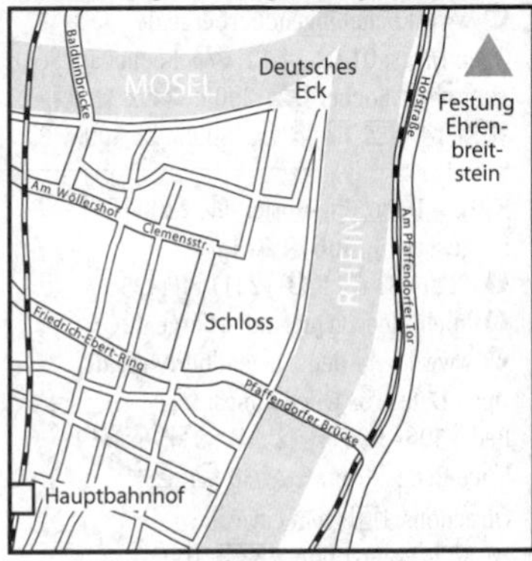

Koblenz... Travel Tips

- **For budget eats check out...** La Guarida (Spanish Restaurant), Weihwasser Kessel (German Restaurant), McDonalds, Hotel zum Sessellift (Indian Restaurant), Gretchens Garten (German Restaurant)
- **For great nightlife try...** Diskothek CB 9 (Discotheque), Kino Apollo/Odeon (Cinema), Bowling Centre, Havanna Bar, Enshilda (Bar and Restaurant)
- **Don't miss...** Sightseeing tour, Marksburg Braubach (Castle), Schmetterlingspark Bendorf (Park known for butterflies), Nürburgring (Formula One race area), Rhine Valley with Loreley and castles, Tauris Freizeit - and Erlebnisbad Mühlheim-Kerlich (Leisure Park), Greifvogelvorführung in Bendorf (performance with birds of prey), Schloss Stolzenfels (Castle), Weingut Göhlen (Winery), Vulkanpark Eifel (Geological Park)

▲ **Kochel** – 22325
Badstr 2, 82431 Kochel (Bavaria).
(8851) 5296 (8851) 7019
jhkochel@djh-bayern.de
www.kochel.jugendherberge.de
Open Dates: 01.02-14.12 Kochel am See 1km Kochel 200m x 31
800m 300m

Köln – Deutz City-Hostel 22004
Siegesstr. 5, 50679 Köln
(221) 814711 (221) 884425
koeln-deutz@jugendherberge.de
www.koeln-deutz.jugendherberge.de
Open Dates: Open Times:
Beds: 506 - 69x² 72x⁴ 8x⁵ 6x⁶
Price Range: from €23.30 BB inc
Directions: 0.6E from city centre
Köln/Bonn 12km A 100m
Köln-Deutz 200m x 72
7 x
5km

Köln – Deutz City-Hostel

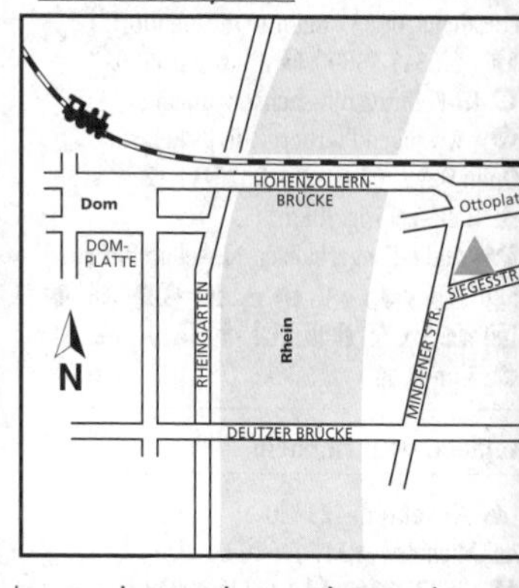

Köln – Riehl City-Hostel – 22041
An der Schanz 14, 50735 Köln
(221) 767081 (221) 761555
koeln-riehl@jugendherberge.de
www.koeln-riehl.jugendherberge.de
Open Dates: 01.01-23.12; 27-31.12
Open Times:
Beds: 369 - 18x¹ 30x² 6x³ 54x⁴ 9x⁶
Price Range: from €22.50 BB inc
Directions: 6NE from city centre
Köln/Bonn 14km A 170 to Köln Central Köln Central 3km U 17,19,18 Boltensternstraße 300m x 52
11 x

Köln – Riehl City-Hostel

Köln... Travel Tips

- **For budget eats check out...** Old Town, Southern part of town, Monheimer Hof, Sion-Brauhaus, Frühkölsch
- **For great nightlife try...** Old Town, Southern part of town, Nippes, Kölner Ringe (ring road), Love Boat
- **Don't miss...** Cologne Cathedral, Old Town, Chocolate Museum, Phantasialand theme park, Roman-Germanic Museum, Ludwig-Richard Museum, Köln Arena, Rhein Park, Roman Churches

▲ **Königsberg** – 22326
Schlossberg 10, 97486 Königsberg (Bavaria).
(9525) 237 (9525) 8114
jhkoenigsberg@djh-bayern.de
www.koenigsberg.jugendherberge.de
Open Dates: 30.01-30.11 Hassfurt 8km Königsberg 400m x 80 2 x

▲ **Konstanz** – Otto-Möricke-Turm – 22328
Zur Allmannshöhe 16, 78464 Konstanz.
(7531) 32260 (7531) 31163
info@jugendherberge-konstanz.de
www.jugendherberge-konstanz.de
Open Dates: Konstanz 5km 4, 1 5km ap YH or Allmannsdorf-Post 5NE x 178 6 x 1km 1km

▲ **Korbach** – 22329
Enser Straße 9, 34497 Korbach.
(5631) 8360 (5631) 4835
korbach@djh-hessen.de
www.djh-hessen.de/jh/korbach
Open Dates: 01.01-23.12; 27-31.12 0.5W x 98

▲ **Köriser See** – 22330
Am See 5, 15746 Groß Köris, OT Klein Köris.
(33766) 62730 (33766) 62734
jh-koeriser-see@jugendherberge.de
www.hostel.de
Open Dates: 12 (R 01.11-28.02) 300m x 84 R 2 x

▲ **Köthener See** – 22331
Dorfstr 20, 15748 Märkisch-Bucholz.
(33765) 80555 (33765) 84870
jh-koethener-see@jugendherberge.de
www.hostel.de
Open Dates: 12 (R 01.11-28.02) x 110 R 2 x 100m

▲ **Kretzschau** – 22332
06712 Kretzschau.
(3441) 210173 (3441) 210174
jh-kretzschau@djh-sachsen-anhalt.de
www.jugendherberge.de/jh/kretzschau
Open Dates: 01.03.-31.10 (Nov-Feb on inquiry) Halle-Leipzig 60km Weißenfels to Naumburg-Zeitz 6km Zeitz ap Kretzschau 2 km 2N x 204 R 4 x 100m 100m

▲ **Kreuth** – JH Kreuth am Tegernsee – 22333
Nördliche Hauptstr 91,
83708 Kreuth (Bavaria).
(8029) 99560 (8029) 995629
jhkreuth@djh-bayern.de
www.kreuth.jugendherberge.de
Open Dates: 01.01-13.11; 27-31.12 Tegernsee 8km Kreuth-Scharling 500m 2.5N x 101 R CC 3 x 3.5km

▲ **Kronach** – 22334
Festung 1, 96317 Kronach (Bavaria).
(9261) 94412 (9261) 629109
www.kronach.jugendherberge.de
Open Dates: 16.01-14.12 Nürnberg 150km 500m x 106 500m

▲ **Lam** – 22336
Jugendherbergsweg 1, 93462 Lam (Bavaria).
(9943) 1068 (9943) 2936
jhlam@djh-bayern.de
www.lam.jugendherberge.de
Open Dates: 01.01-31.10; 28-31.12 Munich 200km Lam 1.5km RBO 590 500m ap Marktplatz 0.5N x 127 R CC 1km

▲ **Landshut** – 22337
Richard-Schirrmann-Weg 6,
84028 Landshut (Bavaria).
(871) 23449 (871) 274947
jugendherberge@landshut.de
www.landshut.jugendherberge.de
Open Dates: 08.01-22.12 Munich 40km Landshut 500m Landshut 2km Obere Altstadt 150m x 100 4 x 1km

▲ **Langeoog** – 22339
Domäne Melkhörn, 26465 Langeoog, (North Sea).
(4972) 276 (4972) 6694
jh-langeoog@djh-unterweser-ems.de
www.jugendherberge.de/jh/langeoog
Open Dates: 01.04-31.10 5E x 126

▲ **Lauenburg** – 22340
Am Sportplatz 7, 21481 Lauenburg.
(4153) 2598 (4153) 2310
jhlauenburg@djh-nordmark.de
www.jugendherberge.de/jh/lauenburg
Open Dates: 06.01-22.12 Lauenburg 2.5km 300m x 134 500m

▲ **Lauterbach** – 22341
Fritz-Ebel-Allee 50, 36341 Lauterbach.
(6641) 2181 (6641) 61200
lauterbach@djh-hessen.de
www.djh-hessen.de/jh//lauterbach
Open Dates: 01.01-23.12; 27-31.12 4NE x 172

▲ **Lauterbach** – "Urwald-Life-Camp" Harsberg – 22633
Harsbergstraße 4, 99826 Lauterbach.
(3643) 850000 (3643) 850002
jh-harsberg@djh-thueringen.de
www.djh-thueringen.de
Open Dates: 01.01-22.12; 27-31.12 Erfurt 70km Lauterbach 2.5km ap Lauterbach x 60 2 x 2.5km

▲ **Leer** – 22342
Süderkreuzstr 7, 26789 Leer.
(491) 2126 (491) 61576
jh-leer@djh-unterweser-ems.de
www.jugendherberge.de/jh/leer
Open Dates: 12 x 125

▲ **Leipzig** – Leipzig-Schönefeld – 22344
Volksgartenstr. 24, 04347 Leipzig
(341) 24570-0 (341) 2457012
jhleipzig@djh.de www.djh-sachsen.de
Open Dates: 01.01-22.12 (23-31.12)
12km 4.2km 1, Richtung Schönefeld 300m ap Haltestelle Löbauerstraße 3NE x 170 5 x 2km

▲ **Lenggries** – 22345
Jugendherbergsstr 10,
83661 Lenggries (Bavaria).
(8042) 2424 (8042) 4532
jhlenggries@djh-bayern.de
www.lenggries.jugendherberge.de
Open Dates: 01.01-30.10; 27-31.12
Munich 80km Lenggries 2km 300m 1.3NW x 91

▲ **Lichtenstein** – 22347
An der Jugendherberge 3, 09350 Lichtenstein.
(37204) 2718 (37204) 87387
jhlichtenstein@djh.de
www.djh-sachsen.de
Open Dates: 01.03.-31.10 (01.11-28.02)
4km Zwickau-Lichtenstein 1km ap Stadtrand 1SE x 60 1 x

▲ **Liepnitzsee** – 22348
Wandlitzer Str. 6, 16359 Lanke/Ützdorf.
(33397) 21659 (33397) 62750
jh-liepnitzsee@jugendherberge.de
www.hostel.de
Open Dates: 12 (01.11-28.02)
x 39 200m

▲ **Limburg** – 22349
Auf dem Guckucksberg,
65549 Limburg/Lahn.
(6431) 41493 (6431) 43873
limburg@djh-hessen.de
www.djh-hessen.de/jh/limburg
Open Dates: 01.01-23.12; 27-31.12 1.5S x 162

▲ **Lindau** – 22018
Herbergsweg 11, 88131 Lindau (Bavaria).
(8382) 96710 (8382) 967150
jhlindau@djh-bayern.de
www.lindau.jugendherberge.de
Open Dates: 09.02-10.12; 25.12-07.01
Friedrichshafen (FDH) 20km Lindau 1.5km Lindau 1.5km to 200m ap YH 1N x 240 R CC 6 x 8 P 100m 1km

▲ **Lindlar** – Center for Environmental Studies – 22350
Jugendherberge 30, 51789 Lindlar
(2266) 5264 (2266) 45517
lindlar@jugendherberge.de
www.lindlar.jugendherberge.de
Open Dates: 01.01-23.12; 27-31.12
Gummersbach 38, 332 500m ap Engelskirchen, Voßbrucher Straße 2N x 160 R 7 x P 2km

▲ **Lingen** – 22351
Umweltstudienplatz, Lengericher Str 62, 49811 Lingen.
(591) 973060 (591) 76954
jh-lingen@djh-unterweser-ems.de
www.jugendherberge.de/jh/lingen
Open Dates: 12 x 152 CC 6 x P 300m

▲ **Linsengericht** – 22352
Jugendherberge, 63589 Linsengericht-Geislitz.
(6051) 72029 (6051) 75694
linsengericht@djh-hessen.de
www.djh-hessen.de/jh/linsengericht
Open Dates: 01.01-23.12; 27-31.12 6S
x 130 P

▲ **List** – 22353
JH Mövenberg, 25992 List/Sylt.
(4651) 870397 (4651) 871039
jhlist@djh-nordmark.de
www.jugendherberge.de/jh/list
Open Dates: 07.01-31.10 List 3km Westerland 18km 100m x 336 CC P 2km 1km

▲ **Lohr** – 22355
Brunnenwiesenweg 13, 97816 Lohr (Bavaria).
(9352) 2444 (9352) 70873
jhlohr@djh-bayern.de
www.lohr.jugendherberge.de
Open Dates: 15.02-15.11 Frankfurt am Main 90km Lohr 2km 1NW x 94 R CC 1km

▲ **Lörrach** – 22356
Steinenweg 40, 79540 Lörrach.
(7621) 47040 (7621) 18156
info@jugendherberge-loerrach.de
www.jugendherberge-loerrach.de
Open Dates: 12 Lörrach-Stetten 7 ap YH 3SE x 168 R CC 5 x P 3km

▲ **Lübben** – 22357
Zum Wendenfürsten 8, 15907 Lübben.
(3546) 3046 (3546) 182597
jh-luebben@jugendherberge.de
www.hostel.de
Open Dates: 12 (R 01.11-28.02) 2.5SE x 127 R 2 x P

▲ **Lübeck** – "Altstadt" – 22358
Mengstr 33, 23552 Lübeck.
(451) 7020399 (451) 77012
jghluebeck@djh-nordmark.de
www.jugendherberge.de/jh/luebeck-jgh
Open Dates: 06.01-23.12 Hamburg 60km A Hl Nr. 6 Travemünde 12km Lübeck Central 1.5km 3, 12, 30B 100m ap Beckergrube 1W x 83 R CC (B) 12km

Lübeck – "Vor dem Burgtor" HI 22034
Am Gertrudenkirchhof 4, 23568 Lübeck.
(451) 33433 (451) 34540
jhluebeck@djh-nordmark.de
www.jugendherberge.de/jh/luebeck-jh
Open Dates: 01.01-23.12; 27-31.12
Open Times: 07.00-24.00hrs
Beds: 211 - 1x^{1} 16x^{2} 8x^{4} 4x^{5} 21x^{6}
Price Range: € 16.50 BB inc
Directions: 2NE from city centre
Hamburg 60km Travemünde 10km 2km 1,3,11,12 200m ap Gustav-Radbruch-Platz x 12 CC 1 x P

Lübeck – "Vor dem Burgtor"

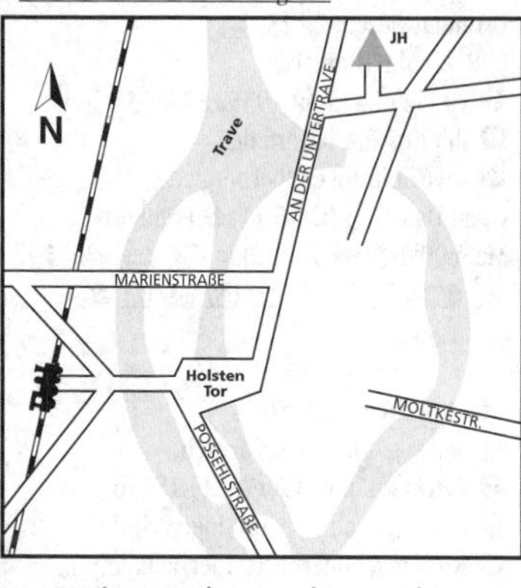

Lübeck... Travel Tips

- **For budget eats check out...** Youth Hostel, Kartoffelkeller (German), La Villetta (Italian), Schiffergesellschaft (traditional), Bolero (Mexican)
- **For great nightlife try...** Body & Soul (disco), Hux (disco), Queens Club (disco), Eishaus (disco), Bolero (pub)
- **Don't miss...** Holstentor, Buddenbrookhaus, Heiligen-Geist-Hospital, St Annen Museum, Salt Reservoir, St Marien Church, Monastery, St Aegidien Church, Town Hall, Travemünde (beach)

▲ **Ludwigsburg** – 22359
Gemsenbergstr 21, 71640 Ludwigsburg.
(7141) 51564 (7141) 59440
info@jugendherberge-ludwigsburg.de
www.jugendherberge-ludwigsburg.de
Open Dates: Ludwigsburg 422 ap Schlösslesfeld x 121 5 x 4km

▲ **Ludwigstein** – 22360
"Jugendburg", 37214 Witzenhausen.
(5542) 501710 (5542) 501712
Open Dates: x 170

▲ **Lüneburg** – 22361
Soltauer Str 133, 21335 Lüneburg.
(4131) 41864 (4131) 45747
jh-lueneburg@djh-hannover.de
www.jugendherberge.de/jh/lueneburg
Open Dates: 01.01-23.12; 27-31.12
Hamburg 58km Lüneburg 3km
11, 12 ap Scharnhorststr ap YH 200m
x 148 2 x 500m

▲ **Maasholm** – 22362
24404 Maasholm.
(4642) 8550 (4642) 81086
jhkappeln@djh-nordmark.de
www.jugendherberge.de/jh/maasholm
Open Dates: 01.04-31.10 Süderbrarup 22km x 33

Magdeburg – Magdeburger Hof – 22363
Leiterstrasse 10, 39104 Magdeburg.
(391) 5321010 (391) 5321020
jh-magdeburg@djh-sachsen-anhalt.de
www.jugendherberge.de/jh/magdeburg
Open Dates: 01.01-23.12; 27-31.12
Open Times:
Beds: 250 - 26x2 2x3 17x4 16x6
Price Range: € 18.00-20.70 BBinc
Directions: Hannover 150km  Weisse Flotte 1km Central 300m 400m 200m 6 x

Magdeburg – Magdeburger Hof

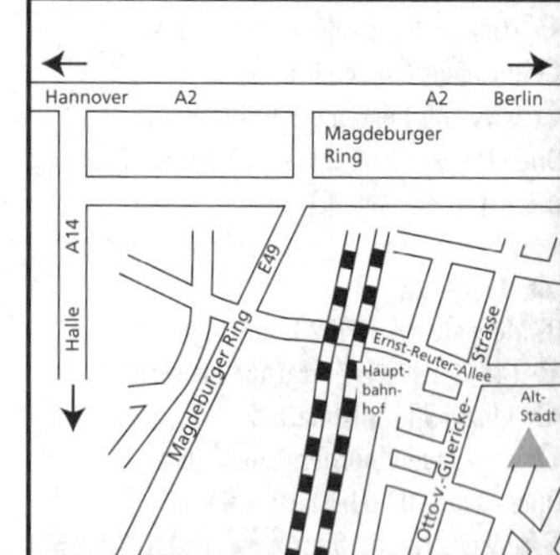

Magdeburg... Travel Tips

- **For budget eats check out...** Asteria (Leiterstrasse), La Piazza, Amadeus (Leiterstrasse), Alex Bistro (Ulrichsplatz), The Fan (O-V- Guericke-Strasse)
- **For great nightlife try...** Cabaret "Die Zwickmühle", "Die Kugelblitze", Theatre (Freie Kammerspiele), Disco "Nautic", Bowling - US Play, Cinemaxx
- **Don't miss...** Magdeburger Cathedral, Monastery "Unser Lieben Frauen", Elbauenparc with Thousand Years Tower, Gruson Greenhaus, Water Way Crossing - Ship Lift, Culture History Museum, Culture Park "Rote Horn", Johannischurch, Lucasklause, Zoo

Maibrunn ☛ **St Englmar**

▲ **Mainz** – Rhein-Main-Jugendherberge, Jugendgästehaus Mainz – 22048
Otto-Brunfels-Schneise 4, 55130 Mainz.
(6131) 85332 (6131) 82422
mainz@diejugendherbergen.de
www.DieJugendherbergen.de
Open Dates: 01.01-23.12; 27-31.12
Mainz Central 3.5km 62, 63 400m ap YH Mainz 5SE x 166 5 x 3km

▲ **Malchow** – 22364
Platz der Freiheit 3, 17213 Malchow.
(39932) 14590 (39932) 14579
jh-malchow@t-online.de
www.djh-mv.de
Open Dates: 01.01-23.12; 27-31.12
Malchow 2km 500m ap Biesdorfer Weg x 141

▲ **Malente** – 22365
Kellerseestr 48,
23714 Bad Malente-Gremsmühlen.
(4523) 1723 (4523) 2539
jhmalente@djh-nordmark.de
www.jugendherberge.de/jh/malente
Open Dates: 06.01-04.12 Malente 2km x 206

▲ **Manderscheid** – Vulkaneifel-Jugendherberge, Jugendgästehaus – 22366
Mosenbergstr. 17, 54531 Manderscheid.
(6572) 557 (6572) 4759
manderscheid@diejugendherbergen.de
www.DieJugendherbergen.de
Open Dates: 01.01-23.12; 27-31.12 x 105 4 x 500m

▲ **Mannheim** – 22367
Rheinpromenade 21, 68163 Mannheim.
(621) 822718 (621) 824073
info@jugendherberge-mannheim.de
www.jugendherberge-mannheim.de
Open Dates: 12 Mannheim 7 ap Lindenhofplatz 2W x 109 2 x 3km

▲ **Marburg** – 22368
Jahnstr 1, 35037 Marburg.
(6421) 23461 (6421) 12191
marburg@djh-hessen.de
www.djh-hessen.de/jh/marburg
Open Dates: 01.01-23.12; 27-31.12 0.5E x 163

▲ **Mardorf** – 22369
Warteweg 2, 31535 Neustadt-Mardorf.
(5036) 457 (5036) 1554
jh-mardorf@djh-hannover.de
www.jugendherberge.de/jh/mardorf
Open Dates: 01.01-23.12; 27-31.12
Hannover 45km Neustadt a. Rbge. 12km 830 200m x 164 3 x 2.5km

▲ **Marktredwitz** – 22370
Wunsiedlerstr 29,
95615 Marktredwitz (Bavaria).
(9231) 81082 (9231) 87346
jhmarktredwitz@djh-bayern.de
www.marktredwitz.jugendherberge.de
Open Dates: 12 Marktredwitz 2.5km 3, 4, 7, 10 ap YH, Wunsiedlerstraße x 40

▲ **Martinfeld** – 22371
Bernteröderstr. 10, 37308 Martinfeld
(36082) 89339 (36082) 90296
jh-martinfeld@djh-thueringen.de
www.djh-thueringen.de
Open Dates: 01.01-23.12; 27-31.12
Heiligenstadt 20km 8 100m ap Martinfeld x 47 3km

▲ **Mauth** – 22372
Jugendherbergsstr 11, 94151 Mauth (Bavaria).
(8557) 289 (8557) 1581
jhmauth@djh-bayern.de
www.mauth.jugendherberge.de
Open Dates: 01.01-31.10; 27-31.12
Munich 190km Passau 51km Mauth 100m ap Mauth x 106 1 x 11km

▲ **Mayen** – 22373
Am Knüppchen 5, 56727 Mayen.
(2651) 2355 (2651) 78378
mayen@diejugendherbergen.de
www.DieJugendherbergen.de
Open Dates: 01.01-23.12; 27-31.12
Mayen 2.6km x 131 4 x 1km

▲ **Meinerzhagen** – 22374
Bergstr. 1, 58540 Meinerzhagen.
(2354) 2280 (2354) 14341
jh-meinerzhagen@djh-wl.de
www.djh.de/westfalen
Open Dates: 01.01-18.12; 27-31.12
Brügge 20km 58 1km ap Meinerzhagen-Stadion x 150 5 x 1km

▲ **Meisdorf** – 22375
Falkensteiner Weg 2B, 06463 Meisdorf.
(34743) 8257 (34743) 92540
jh-meisdorf@djh-sachsen-anhalt.de
www.jugendherberge.de/jh/meisdorf
Open Dates: 01.01-23.12; 27-31.12
Halle-Aschersleben-Halberstadt 6km 3W x 101 1 x 25km

▲ **Melle** – 22376
Fr.-Ludwig-Jahn-Str 1, 49324 Melle.
(5422) 2434 (5422) 3988
jh-melle@djh-unterweser-ems.de
www.jugendherberge.de/jh/melle
Open Dates: 12 x 80

▲ **Melsungen** – 22377
Lindenbergstraße 23, 34212 Melsungen.
(5661) 2650 (5661) 51928
melsungen@djh-hessen.de
www.djh-hessen.de/jh/melsungen
Open Dates: 01.01-23.12; 27-31.12 1W x 128

▲ **Menzenschwand** – St. Blasien – 22379
Vorderdorfstr 10,
79837 St Blasien-Menzenschwand
(7675) 326 (7675) 1435
info@jugendherberge-menzenschwand.de
www.jugendherberge-menzenschwand.de
Open Dates: 12 Schluchsee-Seebrugg 20km x 104 3 x

▲ **Meppen** – Jugend-und Kulturgästehaus "Koppelschleuse Meppen" – 22380
Helter Damm 1, 49716 Meppen.
(5931) 4099770 (5931) 4099773
koppelschleuse-meppen@djh-unterweser-ems.de
www.jugendherberge.de/jh/meppen
Open Dates: 12 x 140

▲ **Meschede** – 22382
Zur Jugendherberge 1, 59872 Meschede.
(291) 6666 (291) 1589
jh-meschede@djh-wl.de
www.djh.de/westfalen
Open Dates: 01.01-23.12; 27-31.12
Paderborn 65km Meschede 4.7km Meschede 4.7km x 100

▲ **Milow** – JH Milow - Carl Bolle – 22383
Friedensstr 21, 14715 Milower Land,
OT Milow
(3386) 280361 (3386) 280369
jh-milow@jugendherberge.de
www.hostel.de
Open Dates: 12 (R 01.11-28.02)
x 96 2 x

▲ **Mirow** – 22384
Retzower Straße, 17252 Mirow
(39833) 26100 (39833) 261030
jh-mirow@djh-mv.de www.djh-mv.de
Open Dates: 01.01-23.12; 27-31.12
Mirow (45min journey) x 138
4 x

▲ **Mittenwald** – 22385
Buckelwiesen 7, 82481 Mittenwald (Bavaria).
(8823) 1701 (8823) 2907
jhmittenwald@djh-bayern.de
www.mittenwald.jugendherberge.de
Open Dates: 01.01-14.11; 28-31.12
Innsbruck 40km Mittenwald 5km
Schmalensee 2km 5N x 110
4 x
5km 5km

▲ **Möhnesee** – 22386
Südufer 20, 59519 Möhnesee-Körbecke.
(2924) 305 (2924) 2788
jh-moehnesee@djh-wl.de
www.djh.de/westfalen
Open Dates: 01.01-23.12; 23-31.12
Dortmund 50km Soest 10km
549, 550 2km ap Körbecke Post
x 203
6 x 100m

▲ **Mölln** – 22387
Am Ziegelsee 2, 23879 Mölln.
(4542) 2601 (4542) 86718
jhmoelln@djh-nordmark.de
www.jugendherberge.de/jh/moelln
Open Dates: 28.01-14.12 Mölln 1.5km
x 149
2km

▲ **Mönchengladbach** – Center for Environmental Studies – 22388
Brahmsstr. 156, 41169 Mönchengladbach
(2161) 560900 (2161) 556464
moenchengladbach@jugendherberge.de
www.moenchengladbach.jugendherberge.de
Open Dates: 01.01-23.12
Mönchengladbach Station 13, 23
1.2km ap Hardt Markt x 131
5 x 6km

▲ **Monschau** – Hargard – 22390
Hargardsgasse 5, 52156 Monschau
(2472) 2180 (2472) 4527
monschau-hargard@jugendherberge.de
www.monschau-hargard.jugendherberge.de
Open Dates: 01.01-23.12 166
Central-Station Aachen ap Hargard x 148
7 x

▲ **Monschau** – Monschau Castle – 22389
Auf dem Schloss 4, 52156 Monschau
(2472) 2314 (2472) 4391
burg-monschau@jugendherberge.de
www.burg-monschau.jugendherberge.de
Open Dates: 31.01-23.12; 27-31.12 x 96
4 x 700m

▲ **Montabaur** – 22391
Richard-Schirrmann-Straße,
56410 Montabaur.
(2602) 5121 (2602) 180176
montabaur@diejugendherbergen.de
www.DieJugendherbergen.de
Open Dates: 01.01-23.12; 27-31.12
Montabaur 2.3km x 136
2 x
2km

▲ **Morsbach** – Family Youth Hostel – 22393
Obere Kirchstr. 21, 51597 Morsbach
(2294) 8662 (2294) 7807
morsbach@jugendherberge.de
www.morsbach.jugendherberge.de
Open Dates: 01.01-23.12; 27-31.12
Wissen (Sieg) 12km 1.5W x 161
6 x

▲ **Mosbach** – Mutschlers Mühle – 22394
Beim Elzstadion (OT Neckarelz),
74821 Mosbach.
(6261) 7191 (6261) 61812
info@jugendherberge-mosbach.de
www. jugendherberge-mosbach.de
Open Dates: 12 Neckarelz 600m 3SW
x 140
5 x 3km

▲ **Müden** – 22395
Wiesenweg 32, 29328 Müden.
(5053) 225 (5053) 1021
jh-mueden@djh-hannover.de
www.jugendherberge.de/jh/mueden
Open Dates: 01.01-23.12; 27-31.12 x 164
3 x
2km

GERMANY - ALLEMAGNE - DEUTSCHLAND - ALEMANIA

▲ Mühldorf a. Inn – 22396
Friedr.-Ludwig-Jahn-Str 19,
84453 Mühldorf a. Inn (Bavaria).
(8631) 7370 (8631) 7437
jugendherberge@muehldorf.de
www.muehldorf.jugendherberge.de
Open Dates: Munich 65km
Mühldorf 2km 3, 10 400m 0.5E
x 66 R
1.5km

▲ Mühlhausen – 22397
Auf dem Tonberg 1, 99974 Mühlhausen
(3601) 813318 (3601) 813320
jh-muehlhausen@djh-thueringen.de
www.djh-thueringen.de
Open Dates: 01.01-23.12; 27-31.12 Erfurt 50km Mühlhausen 3.5km 5, 6 1km ap Blobach x 78 R CC
2 x

▲ Mülheim – "JH Kahlenberg" – 22398
Mendener Str 3, 45470 Mülheim
(208) 382191 (208) 382196
jugendherberge@stadt-mh.de
Open Dates: 01.01-23.12 Düsseldorf 30km
Mülheim 2km 151 500m
ap Kahlenberg 110 500m ap Spielplätze
x 70 R 3 x
2km

▲ Münchehofe – 22399
Strasse der Jugend 2,
15374 Stadt Müncheberg, OT Münchehofe.
(33432) 8734 / -44 (33432) 73154
post@jh-muenchehofe.de
www.jh-muenchehofe.de
Open Dates: 12 (R 01.11-28.02) x 96
R 1 x

München – JH München-Neuhausen
22002
Wendl-Dietrich Str 20,
80634 München (Bavaria).
(89) 131156 (89) 1678745
jhmuenchen-neuhausen@djh-bayern.de
www.muenchen-neuhausen.jugendherberge.de
Open Dates: 01.01-30.11 Open Times:
Beds: 351 - 4x1 17x2 32x4 28x6
1x6+
Price Range: from € 19.50 upwards
BB inc

Directions: 4NW from city centre
Munich 30km A Central Station - Airport 30km 3km 12, 16, 17 (5mins) ap Rotkreuzplatz/Burghausener Strasse U 1 Rotkreuzplatz 200m R
CC 1 x 8
5km

München – JH München-Neuhausen

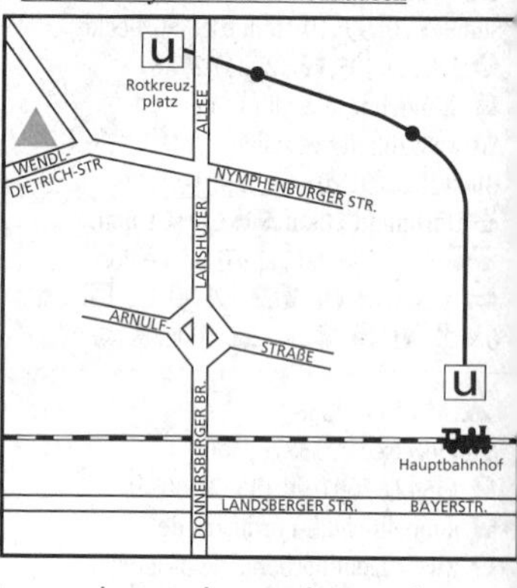

München – JH München-Thalkirchen
22011
Miesingstr 4, 81379 München (Bavaria).
(89) 7236550; 7236560
(89) 7242567
jhmuenchen-thalkirchen@djh-bayern.de
www.muenchen-thalkirchen.jugendherberge.de
Open Dates: 31.01-31.12 Open Times:
Beds: 365 - 58x2 11x3 42x4 6x6+
Price Range: from € 19.50 upwards
BB inc

Directions: Munich (40min by public transport) 10km U 3 Thalkirchen 350m R CC
3 x 8

München – JH München-Thalkirchen

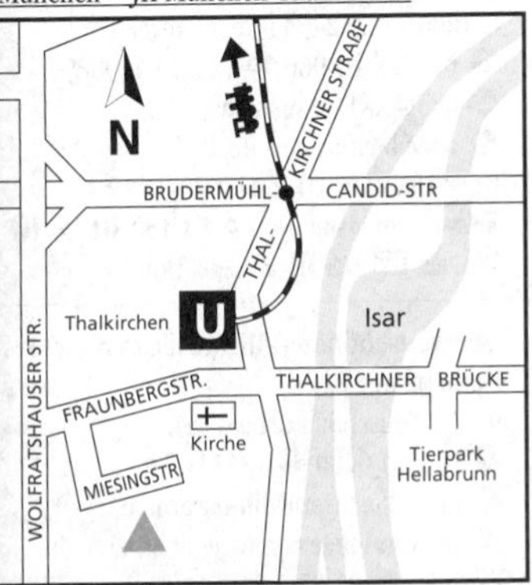

München... Travel Tips

- **For great nightlife try...** Kultfabrik, Schwabing, Haidhausen
- **Don't miss...** Marienplatz & Town Hall, Olympic Centre, Nymphenburg Castle, Frauenkirche (church), Bavaria (film theme park), Englischer Garten (park), Picture Gallery, German Museum of Science, Schleißheim Castle, Botanic Garden

▲ **Münster** – Aasee HI 22024
"JGH", Bismarckallee 31, 48151 Münster.
(251) 5302810; 5302812
(251) 5302850
jgh-muenster@djh-wl.de
www.djh.de/westfalen
Open Dates: 01.01-23.12; 27-31.12
Münster/Osnabrück 25km Münster 2km 10, 34 500m ap Hoppendamm 2W x 208 8 x 3km

▲ **Murchin** – 22400
Jugendherberge Nr. 1, 17390 Murchin.
(3971) 210732 (3971) 259411
samuel-murchin@t-online.de
www.djh-mv.de
Open Dates: 01.01-23.12; 27-31.12
Anklam Usedom ap YH x 48 (B)

▲ **Murrhardt** – Eugen-Nägele-JH – 22401
Karnsberger Str 1, 71540 Murrhardt.
(7192) 7501 (7192) 29058
info@jugendherberge-murrhardt.de
www. jugendherberge-murrhardt.de
Open Dates: 12 Murrhardt 3N x 134 6 x 4km

▲ **Naumburg** – 22403
Am Tennisplatz 9, 06618 Naumburg.
(3445) 703422 (3445) 779560
JH-Naumburg@djh-sachsen-anhalt.de
www.jugendherberge.de/jh/naumburg
Open Dates: 01.01-23.12; 27-31.12
Halle-Leipzig 62km Berlin, Erfurt 3.5km 2.5km ap YH 1.5S x 204 4 x 3.8km

▲ **Nebra** – 22404
Altenburgstrasse 29, 06642 Nebra.
(34461) 25454 (34461) 25456
JH-Nebra@djh-sachsen-anhalt.de
www.jugendherberge.de/jh/nebra
Open Dates: 01.01-23.12; 27-31.12
Naumburg-Artern 1.1km
Naumburg 610, Querfurt 700, Eckartsberga 633 500m 0.5N x 140 3 x 200m

▲ **Neckargemünd-Dilsberg** – JH Dilsberg – 22405
OT Dilsberg, Untere Str 1,
69151 Neckargemünd.
(6223) 2133 (6223) 74871
info@jugendherberge-dilsberg.de
www.jugendherberge-dilsberg.de
Open Dates: 12 Neckargemünd, Heidelberg x 78 3 x

▲ **Neidenberga** – "Niedenburg" – 22406
Ortsstr 1, 07338 Neidenberga
(36737) 22262 (36737) 32503
jh-neidenberga@djh-thueringen.de
www.djh-thueringen.de
Open Dates: 28.02-31.10 Erfurt 100km Saalfeld 22km 46 100m ap Neidenberga x 80 CC 1 x 2km

▲ **Neschwitz** – 22407
Kastanienallee 1, 02699 Neschwitz.
t (35933) 30040 f (35933) 30070
e info@jugendherberge-neschwitz.de
w www.djh-sachsen.de
Open Dates: 01.01-22.12; 27-31.12
Dorfmitte 300m x 64 1 x 3km

▲ **Nettetal-Hinsbeck** – Circus Youth Hostel – 22408
Heide 1, 41334 Nettetal-Hinsbeck
t (2153) 6492 f (2153) 89598
e hinsbeck@jugendherberge.de
w www.hinsbeck.jugendherberge.de
Open Dates: 01.01-23.12 Kempen, Kaldenkirchen 7km 93 1.5km ap Hinsbeck x 183 5 x

▲ **Neudorf** – "Am Fichtelberg" – 22409
Vierenstr 26, 09465 Sehmatal/OT Neudorf
t (37342) 8282 f (37342) 8220
e jhneudorf@djh.de w www.djh-sachsen.de
Open Dates: 01.01-22.12; 27-31.12 (23-26.12) Cranzahl, Oberwiesenthal, Vierenstr. 300m 1km ap Neudorf-Vierenstr. x 132 3 x

▲ **Neuhaus am Rennweg** – "Am Rennweg" – 22410
Apelsbergstr 61, 98724 Neuhaus a. R.
t (3679) 722862 f (3679) 700384
e jh-neuhaus@djh-thueringen.de
w www.djh-thueringen.de
Open Dates: 01.01-23.12; 27-31.12 Erfurt 60km Neuhaus a.R. 1km 505 1km x 70

▲ **Neuhausen** – Jugendbaude – 22411
Bergstr. 12, 09544 Neuhausen
t (37361) 45634; 45633
f (37361) 45626
e jugendbaude@tiscali.de
w www.djh-sachsen.de
Open Dates: Seiffen 2km Gasthoff Dittersbach 500m x 60 1 x 1.5km

▲ **Neumünster** – 22412
Gartenstr. 32, 24534 Neumünster.
t (4321) 419960 f (4321) 4199699
e info@kiek-in-nms.de
w www.kiek-in-nms.de
Open Dates: 01.01-23.12; 29-31.12
Neumünster 1km x 180 1km

▲ **Neuschönau** – JH Waldhäuser – 22414
Herbergsweg 2,
94556 Neuschönau (Bavaria).
t (8553) 6000 f (8553) 829
e jhwaldhaeuser@djh-bayern.de
w www.waldhaeuser.jugendherberge.de
Open Dates: 01.01-31.10; 30-31.12
Spiegelau 10km Spiegelau 10km x 117 1 x 18km

▲ **Neuss** – Family Youth Hostel – 22415
Macherscheiderstr 109, 41468 Neuss
t (2131) 718750 f (2131) 7187510
e neuss@jugendherberge.de
w www.neuss.jugendherberge.de
Open Dates: 01.01-23.12 Düsseldorf 30km Neuss Station 8km 851 300m ap Macherscheider Straße x 142 4 x

Neustadt/Schw ☛ Titisee-Neustadt

▲ **Neustadt/Weinstr.** – Pfalz-Jugendherberge, Jugendgästehaus – 22416
Hans-Geiger-Str. 27, 67434 Neustadt/Weinstr.
t (6321) 2289 f (6321) 82947
e neustadt@diejugendherbergen.de
w www.DieJugendherbergen.de
Open Dates: 01.01-23.12; 27-31.12
Neustadt/Weinstraße 1.5km x 122 5 x 500m

▲ **Nideggen** – 22417
Rather Str. 27, 52385 Nideggen
t (2427) 1226 f (2427) 8453
e nideggen@jugendherberge.de
w www.nideggen.jugendherberge.de
Open Dates: 01.01-23.12. Köln/Bonn 20km Düren 221 100m ap Jungholz x 165 6 x 8km

▲ **Niebüll** – "Deezbüll-Deich" – 22418
Deezbüll-Deich 2, 25899 Niebüll
(4661) 937890 (4661) 9348744
jhniebuell@djh-nordmark.de
www.jugendherberge.de/jh/niebuell-deezbuelldeich
Open Dates: 01.04-31.10 Niebüll 2km
x 36

▲ **Niebüll** – "Mühlenstrasse" – 22419
Mühlenstr. 65, 25899 Niebüll.
(4661) 937890 (4461) 9348744
jhniebuell@djh-nordmark.de
www.jugendherberge.de/jh/niebuell-muehlenstrasse
Open Dates: 16.02-22.12 Niebüll 2km
0.7W x 84
100m

▲ **Norddeich** – 22420
Strandstr 1, 26506 Norden.
(4931) 8064 (4931) 81828
jh-norddeich@djh-unterweser-ems.de
www.jugendherberge.de/jh/norddeich
Open Dates: 12 x 142
200m 200m

▲ **Nordenham** – 22421
Strandallee 12, 26954 Nordenham.
(4731) 88262 (4731) 88034
jh-nordenham@djh-unterweser-ems.de
www.jugendherberge.de/jh/nordenham
Open Dates: 12 x 158
300m

▲ **Norderney** – Dünensender – 22422
Am Dünensender 3, 26548 Norderney, (North Sea).
(4932) 2574 (4921) 83266
jh-norderney-duenensender@djh-unterweser-ems.de
www.jugendherberge.de/jh/norderneyduene
Open Dates: 01.03-31.10 4E x 142
400m 400m

▲ **Norderney** – Südstrasse – 22423
Südstr 1, 26535 Norderney, (North Sea).
(4932) 2451 (4921) 83600
jh-norderney-sued@djh-unterweser-ems.de
www.jugendherberge.de/jh/norderneysued
Open Dates: 01.03.-31.10 1E x 121
300m 300m

▲ **Nordhausen** – Jugendgästehaus Rothleimmühle – 22424
Parkallee 2, 99734 Nordhausen
(3631) 902391 (3631) 902393
rothleimmuehle@t-online.de
www.djh-thueringen.de
Open Dates: 09.01-20.12; 27.12-03.01
Erfurt 80km Nordhausen 3km
Linie 2 200m ap Am Alten Tor x 90
2 x

▲ **Northeim** – 22425
"Adolf-Galland-Jugendheim", Brauereistr 1, 37154 Northeim.
(5551) 8672 (5551) 911108
Open Dates: 01.01-23.12; 27-31.12 x 103

▲ **Nottuln** – Annette-von-Droste-Hülshoff-Jugendherberge – 22426
St.-Amand-Montrond-Str 6, 48301 Nottuln.
(2502) 7878 (2502) 9619
jh-nottuln@djh-wl.de
www.djh.de/westfalen
Open Dates: 01.01-23.12; 27-31.12
Münster-Osnabrück 50km Münster Central 25km S 60, R 63 1km ap Steinstr. x 133
4 x 300m

Nürnberg 22020
Burg 2, 90403 Nürnberg (Bavaria).
(911) 2309360 (911) 23093611
jhnuernberg@djh-bayern.de
www.nuernberg.jugendherberge.de
Open Dates: 01.01-24.12; 27-31.12
Open Times: 07.00-01.00hrs
Beds: 312 - 10x2 2x3 33x4 13x5 15x6
Price Range: 1 night: from € 20.05; 2-3 nights: from € 19.45; 4 nights or more: from € 18.90 BBinc
Directions: Nürnberg 6km Nürnberg Central 1.5km 9 to Krelingstraße 500m U 1 Lorenzkirche 700m
4 x
3km

Nürnberg

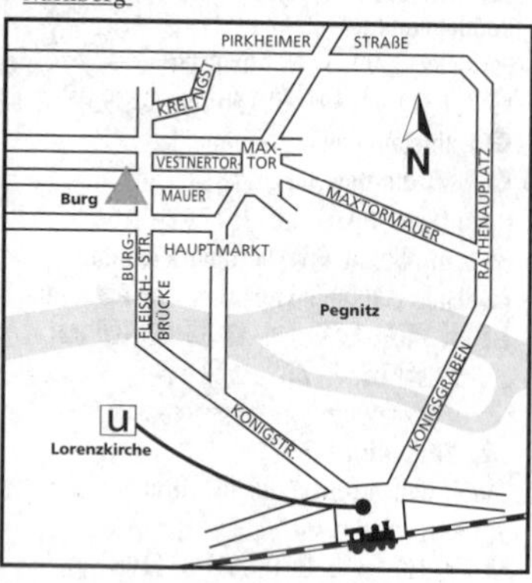

Nürnberg... Travel Tips

- **For budget eats check out...** Old town
- **For great nightlife try...** Cine-Città & IMAX cinemas, Old Town restaurants, Lederer Kulturbrauerei, WON - World of Nightlife (Disco), Rockfabrik (disco)
- **Don't miss...** Old Town & churches, Imperial Castle, German National Museum, Reichsparteitag exhibition centre, Zoo, Fränkische Schweiz (scenery), Toy Museum, Traffic Museum

▲ **Oberammergau** – 22427
Malensteinweg 10,
82487 Oberammergau (Bavaria).
(8822) 4114 (8822) 1695
jhoberammergau@djh-bayern.de
www.oberammergau.jugendherberge.de
Open Dates: 01.01-01.11; 27-31.12
Munich 140km Oberammergau 2km
500m x 132 R CC
2 x
2km

▲ **Oberhundem** – 22428
Wilhelm-Münker-Weg 1, 57399 Kirchhundem.
(2723) 72640 (2723) 73597
jh-oberhundem@djh-wl.de
www.djh.de/westfalen
Open Dates: 01.01-23.12; 27-31.12 Köln 100km Lennestadt-Althundem 7km 2
x 106 R 4 x

▲ **Oberstdorf-Kornau** – 22430
Kornau 8,
87561 Oberstdorf-Kornau (Bavaria).
(8322) 2225 (8322) 80446
jhoberstdorf@djh-bayern.de
www.oberstdorf.jugendherberge.de
Open Dates: 01.01-06.11; 26-31.12
Munich 177km Oberstdorf 4km
1 300m ap Reute/YH 4W x 204
R CC 2 x
4km 4km

▲ **Oberwesel** – Jugendgästehaus – 22431
Auf dem Schönberg, 55430 Oberwesel.
(6744) 93330 (6744) 7446
oberwesel@diejugendherbergen.de
www.DieJugendherbergen.de
Open Dates: 01.01-23.12; 27-31.12
Oberwesel 1km x 179
R CC 15 x
8km

▲ **Ochsenfurt** – 22432
Hauptstr 1, 97199 Ochsenfurt (Bavaria).
(9331) 2666 (9331) 2696
sieber_kj@web.de
www.ochsenfurt.jugendherberge.de
Open Dates: 15.04-15.10 900m
50m x 30 2km

▲ **Oderwitz** – 22429
Zur Lindenallee 5, 02791 Oderwitz
(35842) 26544 (35842) 27726
jhoderwitz@djh.de
www.djh-sachsen.de
Open Dates: 01.03.-22.12 (27.12-28.02)
Dresden-Zittau/Oberoderwitz 1km
L 51, Oberoderwitz 1km
ap Landmannsheim 1E x 138
R 2 x
3km

Oelsnitz ☛ **Taltitz**

▲ **Oerlinghausen** – 22433
Auf dem Berge 11, 33813 Oerlinghausen.
(5202) 2053 (5202) 15456
jh-oerlinghausen@djh-wl.de
www.djh.de/westfalen
Open Dates: 01.01-23.12; 27-31.12
Paderborn 50km
Oerlinghausen/Asemissen 2km
783 ap Brachtshof x 127
4 x 1km

▲ **Oldenburg/Holstein** – 22435
Göhler Strasse 58a,
23758 Oldenburg/Holstein.
(4361) 7670 (4361) 60731
jholdenburg@djh-nordmark.de
www.jugendherberge.de/jh/oldenburg
Open Dates: 27.12-21.12
Oldenburg/Holstein 1.5km x 80 500m

▲ **Oldenburg/Oldenburg** – 22436
Alexanderstr 65, 26121 Oldenburg/Oldb.
(441) 87135 (441) 8852493
jh-oldenburg@djh-unterweser-ems.de
www.jugendherberge.de/jh/oldenburgOldb
Open Dates: 1NE x 104

▲ **Ortenberg** – Schloss Ortenberg – 22437
Burgweg 21/Schloss, 77799 Ortenberg.
(781) 31749 (781) 9481031
info@jugendherberge-schloss-ortenberg.de
www.jugendherberge-schloss-ortenberg.de
Open Dates: Offenburg or Gengenbach 7134 x 146 4 x

▲ **Osnabrück** – 22438
Iburger Str 183A, 49082 Osnabrück.
(541) 54284 (541) 54294
jh-osnabrueck@djh-unterweser-ems.de
www.jugendherberge.de/jh/osnabrueck
Open Dates: 01.03-31.12 2S x 152

▲ **Ossa** – 22439
Ossa 69, 04657 Narsdorf
(34346) 60587 (34346) 60587
servicecenter-sachsen@djh.de
www.djh-sachsen.de
Open Dates: 01.01-22.12; 27-31.12
Geithain 5km x 52 1 x 5km

▲ **Otterndorf** – 22440
Schleusenstr 147, 21762 Otterndorf.
(4751) 3165 (4751) 4577
jhotterndorf@djh-nordmark.de
www.jugendherberge.de/jh/otterndorf
Open Dates: 06.01-22.12 Otterndorf 2km x 212 500m 500m

▲ **Ottobeuren** – 22441
Kaltenbrunnweg 11,
87724 Ottobeuren (Bavaria).
(8332) 368 (8332) 7219
jhottobeuren@djh-bayern.de
www.ottobeuren.jugendherberge.de
Open Dates: 01.02-14.12 Munich 100km
Memmingen 12km to Memmingen 1.5km ap YH x 98 3 x 1.5km

▲ **Paderborn** – 22442
Meinwerkstr 16, 33098 Paderborn.
(5251) 22055 (5251) 280017
jh-paderborn@djh-wl.de
www.djh.de/westfalen
Open Dates: 01.01-23.12; 27-31.12
Paderborn Central 3km 2, 5 3km ap Detmolder Tor o. Maspernplatz x 118 3 x

▲ **Pahlen** – 22443
Mühlenberg 45, 25794 Pahlen.
(4835) 642 (4835) 8462
jhalbersdorf@djh-nordmark.de
www.jugendherberge.de/jh/pahlen
Open Dates: Heide 15km 100m x 41 100m

▲ **Papenburg** – 22444
Kirchstr 38-40, 26871 Papenburg.
(4961) 2793 (4961) 916554
jh-papenburg@djh-unterweser-ems.de
www.jugendherberge.de/jh/papenburg
Open Dates: x 72

▲ **Passau** – 22445
Veste Oberhaus 125, 94034 Passau (Bavaria).
(851) 493780 (851) 4937820
jhpassau@djh-bayern.de
www.passau.jugendherberge.de
Open Dates: 27.12-30.11 Munich 180km
A Bahnhof 2km
Donau-Schiff-Fahrt 1km Passau 2km 1, 2, 3, 4 500m ap Pendelbus 1NE x 131 2 x 4km

▲ **Pforzheim** – Burg Rabeneck – 22446
OT Dillweissenstein, Kräheneckstr 4, 75180 Pforzheim.
(7231) 972660 (7231) 972661
info@jugendherberge-pforzheim.de
www.jugendherberge-pforzheim.de
Open Dates: Pforzheim 3 to Dillweissenstein ap Papierfabrik 3SW x 96 3 x 1km

▲ **Pirna-Copitz** – "Tor zur Sächsischen Schweiz" – 22447
Zum Wesenitzbogen 9, 01796 Pirna-Copitz
(3501) 445601 (3501) 445602
jhpirna@djh.de www.djh-sachsen.de
Open Dates: 01.03.-31.10 (01.11-28.02) 25km Pirna 2km Liebetal, Graupa 50m ap Sportplatz 2km ap Pirna 2.5NE x 166 5 x 150m

▲ **Plön** – 22450
Ascheberger Str 67, 24306 Plön.
(4522) 2576 (4522) 2166
jhploen@djh-nordmark.de
www.jugendherberge.de/jh/ploen
Open Dates: 06.01-22.12 Plön 2km 200m x 207 1.5km

▲ **Plothen** – "Am Hausteich" – 22451
07907 Plothen
(36648) 22329 (36648) 26013
jh-plothen@djh-thueringen.de
www.djh-thueringen.de
Open Dates: 01.01-22.12; 28-31.12 Erfurt 100km Schleiz 12km 102, 147 Schleiz 1.5km ap Plothen x 167 2 x

▲ **Pöcking** – JH Possenhofen – 22452
Kurt-Stieler-Str. 18, 82343 Pöcking (Bavaria).
(8157)996611 (8157)996612
jhpossenhofen@djh-bayern.de
www.possenhofen.jugendherberge.de
Open Dates: 01.01-30.11 Munich 80km Pöcking 800m 0.8NE x 142 3 x 8 200m

▲ **Porta Westfalica** – 22453
Kirchsiek 30, 32457 Porta Westfalica.
(571) 70250 (571) 7100047
jh-porta.westfalica@djh-wl.de
www.djh.de/westfalen
Open Dates: 01.01-23.12; 27-31.12 Porta Westfalica 2km 408 2km ap Schalksburg Passage x 99 2.5km

▲ **Potsdam** – JH Potsdam - Haus der Jugend HI 22622
Schulstrasse 9, 14482 Potsdam.
(331) 5813100 R (30) 2649520
(331) 5813111 R (30) 26495210
jh-potsdam@jugendherberge.de
www.hostel.de
Open Dates: Berlin-Tegel 30km Potsdam Central 3km S7 Potsdam Babelsberg 300m 3E x 152 3 x 3km 3km

▲ **Pottenstein** – 22454
Jugendherbergsstr 20, 91278 Pottenstein (Bavaria).
(9243) 92910 (9243) 929111
jhpottenstein@djh-bayern.de
www.pottenstein.jugendherberge.de
Open Dates: 16.01-14.12 Pegnitz 17km 3km 3W x 163 5 x 6km

▲ **Prebelow** – 22455
Prebelow 2, 16831 Rheinsberg, OT Prebelow.
(33921) 70222 (33921) 70362
jh-prebelow@jugendherberge.de
www.hostel.de
Open Dates: (R 01.11-28.02) x 98 2 x 500m 200m

▲ **Prien** – 22456
Carl-Braun-Str. 66, 83209 Prien (Bavaria).
(8051) 68770 (8051) 687715
jhprien@djh-bayern.de
www.prien.jugendherberge.de
Open Dates: 01.02-30.11 Prien 2km 2E x 109 8 300m

▲ Prüm – Veranstaltungs- und Kongresszentrum, Jugendgästehaus Prüm – 22457
Kalvarienbergstr. 5, 54595 Prüm.
t (6551) 2500 f (6551) 70030
e pruem@diejugendherbergen.de
w www.DieJugendherbergen.de
Open Dates: 01.01-23.12; 27-31.12 x 150
9 x

▲ Pullach – JH "Burg Schwaneck" – 22458
Burgweg 4-6, 82049 Pullach (Bavaria).
t (89) 74486670 f (89) 74486680
e info@jugendherberge-burgschwaneck.de
w www.pullach.jugendherberge.de
Open Dates: 16.01-20.12 Munich 40km
U S-Bahn 7 1km x 138 5 x
500m

▲ Quedlinburg – 22459
Neuendorf 28, 06484 Quedlinburg.
t (3946) 811703 f (3946) 811705
e JH-Quedlinburg@djh-sachsen-anhalt.de
w www.jugendherberge.de/jh/quedlinburg
Open Dates: 01.01-23.12; 27-31.12
Magdeburg-Halberstadt-Thale 2km
Berlin-Thale 500m 0.3N x 58
3 x

Radebeul ☛ **Dresden**

▲ Radevormwald – 22460
Telegrafenstr 50, 42477 Radevormwald
t (2195) 6888-11 f (2195) 6888-10
e radevormwald@jugendherberge.de
w www.radevormwald.jugendherberge.de
Open Dates: 01.01-23.12; 27-31.12
Düsseldorf 50km 626
Wuppertal-Oberbarmen 200m
ap Lindenbaumschule 1.5W x 126
6 x 200m

▲ Radis – 22461
Bahnhofstr. 18, 06773 Radis.
t (34953) 39288 f (34953) 21429
e JH-Radis@djh-sachsen-anhalt.de
w www.jugendherberge.de/jh/radis
Open Dates: 01.01-23.12; 27-31.12
route Berlin-Halle-Leipzig 1km
200m x 114
1 x 5km 5km

▲ Ratingen – 22462
Götschenbeck 8, 40882 Ratingen
t (2102) 20400 f (2102) 204010
e ratingen@jugendherberge.de
w www.ratingen.jugendherberge.de
Open Dates: 01.01-23.12 Düsseldorf
15km Main Station Düsseldorf
016 Ratingen-Ost 1.1km
ap Götschenbeck U S6 Ratingen Ost
x 167
5 x 8 1.5km

▲ Ratzeburg – 22463
Fischerstr 20, 23909 Ratzeburg.
t (4541) 3707 f (4541) 84780
e jhratzeburg@djh-nordmark.de
w www.jugendherberge.de/jh/ratzeburg
Open Dates: 01.02-30.11 Ratzeburg
2.5km 300m x 133
100m
100m

▲ Ravensbrück – JH Ravensbrück - Internationale Jugendbegegnungsstätte – 22056
Strasse der Nationen 16798 Fürstenberg/Havel
t (33093) 605 90 f (33093) 605 85
e jh-ravensbrueck@jugendherberge.de
w www.hostel.de
Open Dates: 12 (R 01.11-28.02) 4NE
x 96
6 x 200m

▲ Ravensburg – Veitsburg – 22464
Veitsburgstr 1, 88212 Ravensburg.
t (751) 25363 f (751) 13769
e info@jugendherberge-ravensburg.de
w www.jugendherberge-ravensburg.de
Open Dates: 12 Ravensburg x 104
4 x

▲ Rechenberg – Schloss – 22465
Zum Schloß 7, 74597 Stimpfach.
t (7967) 372 f (7967) 8985
e info@jugendherberge-schloss-rechenberg.de
w www.jugendherberge-schloss-rechenberg.de
Open Dates: 12 Jagstzell 4km x 100
2 x
4km

▲ Regensburg – 22019
Wöhrdstr 60, 93059 Regensburg (Bavaria).
(941) 57402 (941) 52411
jhregensburg@djh-bayern.de
www.regensburg.jugendherberge.de
Open Dates: 30.01-22.12 Regensburg HBF 1.5km 3, 8, 9 Wöhrdstraße ap YH 1W x 166 4 x 3km

▲ Rheine – 22467
Kupernikusstr. 82, 48429 Rheine.
(5971) 2407 (5971) 13526
jh-rheine@djh-wl.de
www.djh.de/westfalen
Open Dates: 01.01-23.12; 27-31.12 x 60 2 x

▲ Ribnitz-Damgarten – 22468
Am Wasserwerk, 18311 Ribnitz-Damgarten.
(3821) 812311 (3821) 812311
mecklenburger_folkloreensemble@t-online.de www.djh-mv.de
Open Dates: 01.01-23.12; 27-31.12
Ribnitz-Damgarten(West) (5min)
x 50 6km

▲ Rinteln – 22469
Am Bären 1, 31737 Rinteln.
(5751) 2405 (5751) 44630
jh-rinteln@djh-hannover.de
www.jugendherberge.de/jh/rinteln
Open Dates: 01.01-23.12; 27-31.12 3km x 96 3km

▲ Rittersgrün – 22470
Zur Jugendherberge 2, 08355 Rittersgrün
(37757) 7260 (37757) 18636
jugendherberge@rittersgruen.de
www.djh-sachsen.de
Open Dates: 01.01-22.12; 27-31.12
Antonsthal 3km Rittersgrün 1.5km ap Arnoldshammer x 48 5km

▲ Rochlitz – "Schweizerhaus" – 22471
Zaßnitzer Str 1, 09306 Rochlitz.
(3737) 42131 (3737) 149053
servicecenter-sachsen@djh.de
www.djh-sachsen.de
Open Dates: 01.02-31.10 (01.11.-31.01) 1km ap Markt 3E x 49 1 x 1km

▲ Rostock – Jugendgästeschiff – 22051
MS "Georg Büchner", Am Stadthafen 71/72, 18057 Rostock.
(381) 6700320 (381) 6700321
jugendgaesteschiffrostock@t-online.de
www.djh-mv.de
Open Dates: 12 x 50

▲ Rotenburg (Wümme) – 22473
Verdener Str 104,
27356 Rotenburg (Wümme).
(4261) 83041 (4261) 84233
jh-rotenburg@djh-unterweser-ems.de
www.jugendherberge.de/jh/rotenburg
Open Dates: 12 1SW x 224 12 x

▲ Rotenburg/Fulda – 22474
Obertor 17, 36199 Rotenburg/Fulda.
(6623) 2792 (6623) 43177
rotenburg@djh-hessen.de
www.djh-hessen.de/jh/rotenburg
Open Dates: 01.01-23.12; 27-31.12 0.5N x 125

▲ Rothenburg-Tauber HI 22013
Mühlacker 1, 91541 Rothenburg (Bavaria).
(9861) 94160 (9861) 941620
jhrothenburg@djh-bayern.de
www.rothenburg.jugendherberge.de
Open Dates: 30.01-31.12 Nürnberg 78km Rothenburg 2km Citybus 100m 0.5S x 184 2 x 1km

▲ **Rothenfels am Main** – JH Burg Rothenfels – 22475
97851 Rothenfels am Main (Bavaria).
(9393) 99999 (9393) 99997
verwaltung@burg-rothenfels.de
www.rothenfels.jugendherberge.de
Open Dates: 05.01-20.12 Frankfurt am Main 100km Lohr 8km Lohr 12km 8050 (17.05hrs and 18.15hrs) 500m ap Bergrothenfels x 168 5km 500m

Rudenberg ☛ Titisee-Neustadt

▲ **Rüdesheim** – 22476
Jugendherberge 1, 65385 Rüdesheim.
(6722) 2711 (6722) 48284
ruedesheim@djh-hessen.de
www.djh-hessen.de/jh/ruedesheim
Open Dates: 01.01-23.12; 27-31.12 1SE x 155

▲ **Rudolstadt** – "Fröbelhaus" – 22477
Schillerstr. 50, 07407 Rudolstadt
(3672) 313610 (3672) 313611
jugendgaestehaus@froebelhaus.org
www.djh-thueringen.de
Open Dates: 01.01-17.12; 25.12-31.12
Erfurt 54km Rudolstadt 1km 11 - 27, 502 1km ap YH x 60 6 x

▲ **Rüthen** – 22479
Am Rabenknapp 4, 59602 Rüthen.
(2952) 483 (2952) 2717
jh-ruethen@djh-wl.de
www.djh.de/westfalen
Open Dates: 01.01-23.12; 27-31.12
Lippstadt 562 x 132 5 x 100m

▲ **Saarbrücken** – Europa-Jugendherberge, Jugendgästehaus – 22052
Meerwiesertalweg 31, 66123 Saarbrücken.
(681) 33040 (681) 374911
saarbruecken@diejugendherbergen.de
www.DieJugendherbergen.de
Open Dates: 01.01-23.12; 27-31.12
Saarbrücken 2km x 192 5 x 2km

▲ **Saarburg** – 22481
Bottelter Str. 8, 54439 Saarburg.
(6581) 2555 (6581) 1082
saarburg@diejugendherbergen.de
www.DieJugendherbergen.de
Open Dates: 01.01-23.12; 27-31.12 x 102 3 x 1km

▲ **Saldenburg** – 22482
Ritter-Tuschl-Str 20,
94163 Saldenburg (Bavaria).
(8504) 1655 (8504) 4449
jhsaldenburg@djh-bayern.de
www.saldenburg.jugendherberge.de
Open Dates: 24.01-30.11 Munich 170km Passau 35km x 130 3 x

▲ **Sandhatten** – 22483
Wöschenweg 28, 26209 Hatten.
(4482) 330 (4482) 8498
service-san@djh-unterweser-ems.de
www.jugendherberge.de/jh/sandhatten
Open Dates: 12 1.5NW x 122

▲ **Sargenroth** – Wald-Jugendherberge – 22484
Kirchweg 1, 55471 Sargenroth.
(6761) 2500 (6761) 6378
sargenroth@diejugendherbergen.de
www.DieJugendherbergen.de
Open Dates: 01.01-23.12; 27-31.12 x 134 4 x 7km

▲ **Sayda** – "Begegnungs- und Tagungsstätte" – 22485
Mortelgrund 8, 09619 Sayda
(37365) 1277 (37365) 1337
jhsayda@djh.de www.djh-sachsen.de
Open Dates: 01.01-23.12; 27-31.12 (23-26.12) Freiberg, Olbernhau 28km Freiberg-YH 28km ap YH Mortelgrund 3SW x 130 5 x 8 3.5km

▲ **Scharbeutz** – Scharbeutz-Strandallee – 22631
Strandallee 98, 23693 Scharbeutz
(4503) 72090 (4503) 75375
jhscharbeutz-strandallee@djh-nordmark.de
www.jugendherberge.de/jh/scharbeutz-strandallee
Open Dates: Scharbeutz 2km
300m x 142
100m

▲ **Scharbeutz-Uhlenflucht** – 22486
Uhlenflucht 30, 23684 Scharbeutz.
(4524) 428 (4524) 1637
jhscharbeutz-uhlenflucht@djh-nordmark.de
www.jugendherberge.de/jh/scharbeutz-uhlenflucht
Open Dates: 21.01-14.12 Pönitz 3km
300m x 260
4km 4km

▲ **Schierke** – JH – 22488
Brockenstrasse 48, 38879 Schierke.
(39455) 51066 (39455) 51067
JH-Schierke@djh-sachsen-anhalt.de
www.jugendherberge.de/jh/schierke
Open Dates: 01.01-23.12; 27-31.12
Brockenbahn 2km 265
Wernigerode-Schierke-Braunlage 200m 1.5W
x 272
4 x 7km

▲ **Schillighörn** – 22489
Inselstr 6, 26434 Wangerland.
(4426) 371 (4426) 506
jh-schillighoern@djh-unterweser-ems.de
www.jugendherberge.de/jh/schillighoern
Open Dates: 0.5N x 124
100m

▲ **Schleiden-Gemünd** – Nationalpark Eifel Youth Hostel – 22490
Im Wingertchen 9, 53937 Schleiden-Gemünd
(2444) 2241 (2444) 3386
gemuend@jugendherberge.de
www.gemuend.jugendherberge.de
Open Dates: 01.01-23.12; 27-31.12 Kall 6km 829 Kall 2km
ap Schleiden-Gemuend x 162
6 x

▲ **Schleswig** – 22491
Spielkoppel 1, 24837 Schleswig.
(4621) 23893 (4621) 20796
jhschleswig@djh-nordmark.de
www.jugendherberge.de/jh/schleswig
Open Dates: 16.01-14.12 Schleswig 2km
150m x 120
300m

▲ **Schliersee** – 22492
Josefsthaler Str. 19,
83727 Schliersee (Bavaria).
(8026) 97380 (8026) 71610
jhschliersee@djh-bayern.de
www.schliersee.jugendherberge.de
Open Dates: 01.01-31.10; 27-31.12
Munich 70km Fischhausen-Neuhaus 2km Josefsthaler Straße 30m x 105
2 x 2km 2km

▲ **Schluchsee** – Seebrugg – 22493
Haus 9, 79859 Schluchsee, (OT Seebrugg).
(7656) 494 (7656) 1889
info@jugendherberge-schluchsee-seebrugg.de
www.jugendherberge-schluchsee-seebrugg.de
Open Dates: Seebrugg 500m 3SW
x 134
3 x 500m

▲ **Schluchsee** – Wolfsgrund – 22494
Im Wolfsgrund 28, 79859 Schluchsee.
(7656) 329 (7656) 9237
info@jugendherberge-schluchsee-wolfsgrund.de
www.jugendherberge-schluchsee-wolfsgrund.de
Open Dates: Schluchsee 1NE
x 117 3 x
500m 500m

▲ **Schmallenberg** – Erlebnis-Jugendherberge am Rothaarsteig – 22495
Im Lenninghof 20, 57392 Schmallenberg.
(2972) 6098 (2972) 4918
jh-schmallenberg@djh-wl.de
www.djh.de/westfalen
Open Dates: 01.01-23.12; 27-31.12
Altenhundem x 134
5 x

▲ **Schmitten** – Oberreifenberg – 22496
Limesstraße 14,
61389 Schmitten-Oberreifenberg
(6082) 2440 (6082) 3305
oberreifenberg@djh-hessen.de
www.djh-hessen.de/jh/oberreifenberg
Open Dates: 01.01-23.12; 27-31.12 3SW
x 222

▲ **Schnett** – "Auf dem Simmersberg" – 22497
Kirchberg 25, 98666 Schnett
(36874) 39532 (36874) 39532
jh-schnett@djh-thueringen.de
www.djh-thueringen.de
Open Dates: 01.01-22.12; 28-31.12 Erfurt 75km Suhl 30km 1km ap Schnett
1.2N x 61
1 x

▲ **Schönberg** – 22498
Stakendorfer Weg 1, 24217 Schönberg.
(4344) 2974 (4344) 4484
jhschoenberg@djh-nordmark.de
www.jugendherberge.de/jh/schoenberg
Open Dates: 06.01-22.12 Kiel 20km 500m x 214 3.5km

▲ **Schöneck** – 22499
Am Stadtpark 52, 08261 Schöneck
(37464) 8106 (37464) 8107
jhschoeneck@djh.de
www.djh-sachsen.de
Open Dates: 01.01-22.12; 27-31.12 (23-26.12) 500m 500m 1E
x 60
1 x 300m

▲ **Schöningen am Elm** – 22500
Richard-Schirrmann-Str 6a,
38364 Schöningen am Elm.
(5352) 3898 (5352) 3752
jh-schoeningen@djh-hannover.de
www.jugendherberge.de/jh/schoeningen
Open Dates: 01.01-23.12; 27-31.12 x 92
3km

▲ **Schotten** – Hoherodskopf – 22502
Ausserhalb 25,
63679 Schotten-Hoherodskopf.
(6044) 2760 (6044) 784
hoherodskopf@djh-hessen.de
www.djh-hessen.de/jh/hoherodskopf
Open Dates: 01.01-23.12; 27-31.12 8NE
x 130

▲ **Schwäbisch Hall** – 22503
Langenfelderweg 5, 74523 Schwäbisch Hall.
(791) 41050 (791) 47998
info@jugendherberge-schwaebisch-hall.de
www.jugendherberge-schwaebisch-hall.de
Open Dates: Schwäbisch Hall, Hessental 1 ap Bausparkasse x 143
3 x 2km

▲ **Schwarzburg** – "Hans Breuer" – 22504
Am Buschbach 2, 07427 Schwarzburg
(36730) 22223 (36730) 33555
jh-schwarzburg@djh-thueringen.de
www.djh-thueringen.de
Open Dates: 01.01-23.12; 27-31.12 Erfurt 58km 16, 502 500m ap Schwarzburg
x 163
2 x 1km

▲ **Schweinfurt** – 22505
Niederwerrnerstr 17 1/2,
97421 Schweinfurt (Bavaria).
(9721) 21404 (9721) 23581
jugendherberge@afz-sw.de
www.schweinfurt.jugendherberge.de
Open Dates: 09.01-21.12 Nürnberg 100km Schweinfurt 1.5km
Mozartstraße 50m
ap Nikolaus-Hofmann-Straße 0.5NE x 110
2 x

▲ **Schwerin** – 22506
Waldschulweg 3, 19061 Schwerin.
(385) 3260006 (385) 3260303
jh-schwerin@djh-mv.de
www.djh-mv.de
Open Dates: 01.01-23.12; 27-31.12
Schwerin Central 14 Marienplatz
ap YH 1 ap Marienplatz x 91

Seebrugg ☛ **Schluchsee**

▲ **Sellin** – 22628
Kiefernweg 4, 18586 Sellin (Rügen)
(38303) 95099 (38303) 95098
jh-sellin@djh-mv.de www.djh-mv.de
Open Dates: 01.01-23.12; 27-31.12
Bergen/Rügen and Binz 414a, 414 b Sellin Ost ap YH x 156 500m 500m

▲ **Sigmaringen** – Hohenzollern-JH – 22507
Hohenzollernstr 31, 72488 Sigmaringen.
(7571) 13277 (7571) 61159
info@jugendherberge-sigmaringen.de
www.jugendherberge-sigmaringen.de
Open Dates: Sigmaringen 2 x 90 2 x 500m

▲ **Silberborn** – 22508
Schießhäuser Str 4, 37603 Silberborn.
(5536) 568 (5536) 1533
jh-silberborn@djh-hannover.de
www.jugendherberge.de/jh/silberborn
Open Dates: 01.01-23.12; 27-31.12
Holzminden 12km YH 200m x 161 3 x

▲ **Simmerath** – Rurberg For nature and adventure sports – 22478
52152 Simmerath-Rurberg
(2473) 2200 (2473) 4911
rurberg@jugendherberge.de
www.rurberg.jugendherberge.de
Open Dates: 01.01-23.12; 27-31.12
Aachen 68 ap Rurberg x 188 6 x

▲ **Singen** – 22509
Friedingerstr 28, 78224 Singen.
(7731) 42590 (7731) 48842
info@jugendherberge-singen.de
www.jugendherberge-singen.de
Open Dates: Singen 1, 7364 ap Hallenbad-Waldeckstraße 1NE x 100 500m

▲ **Soest** – 22510
Kaiser-Friedrich-Platz 2, 59494 Soest.
(2921) 16283 (2921) 14623
jh-soest@djh-wl.de
www.djh.de/westfalen
Open Dates: 01.01-23.12; 27-31.12
Paderborn 25km Soest 3km 642 ap Stadthalle x 105 5km

▲ **Solingen-Burg** – Multicultural Youth Hostel – 22158
An der Jugendherberge 11, 42659 Solingen
(212) 41025 (212) 49449
solingen-burg@jugendherberge.de
www.solingen-burg.jugendherberge.de
Open Dates: 01.01-23.12; 27-31.12
Köln/Bonn 43.7km A 266, then 260, then 170 300m Bremerhaven 360km Köln Central 38.4km 266 300m ap YH 8SE x 118 5.5km

▲ **Solingen-Gräfrath** – 22511
Flockertsholzerweg 10, 42653 Solingen
(212) 591198 (212) 594179
solingen-graefrath@jugendherberge.de
www.solingen-graefrath.jugendherberge.de
Open Dates: 01.01-23.12
Wuppertal-Vohwinkel 621 Station Vohwinkel ap Roßkamper Höhe x 146 5 x 2km

▲ **Sondershausen** – "Juventas" – 22512
Güntherstr 26/27, 99706 Sondershausen.
(3632) 601193 (3632) 782259
info@juventas.de
www.djh-thueringen.de
Open Dates: Erfurt 50km Sondershausen 1km 10km ap Bergstraße x 50 3 x 500m 2km

Sonnenbühl ☛ **Erpfingen**

▲ **Sorpesee** – 22513
Am Sorpesee 7, 59846 Sundern-Langscheid.
(2935) 1776 (2935) 7254
jh-sorpesee@djh-wl.de
www.djh.de/westfalen
Open Dates: 01.01-23.12; 27-31.12
Dortmund 80km Arnsberg 16km
332 500m ap Langscheid Turmcafe
x 166
1 x 500m

▲ **Sosa** – "Skihütte" – 22514
Am Frölichwald 9, 08326 Sosa
(37752) 8268; mobil 0174-7817163
(37752) 8268
servicecenter-sachsen@djh.de
www.djh-sachsen.de
Open Dates: 01.01-22.12; 27-31.12
Aue-Sosa 200m ap Buswendeschleife
1W x 28
3.5km

▲ **Spalt** – JH Wernfels – 22515
Burgweg 7-9, 91174 Spalt (Bavaria).
(9873) 976120 (9873) 244
burg@cvjm-bayern.de
www.wernfels.jugendherberge.de
Open Dates: 01.01-19.12; 28-31.12
Nürnberg 35km Schwabach 16km
602 to Schwabach ap Wernfels Mitte
6SE x 167
9 x

▲ **Speyer** – Kurpfalz-Jugendherberge, Jugendgästehaus – 22516
Geibstr. 5, 67346 Speyer.
(6232) 61597 (6232) 61596
speyer@diejugendherbergen.de
www.DieJugendherbergen.de
Open Dates: 01.01-23.12; 27-31.12
Speyer 3km x 160
CC 5 x
300m

▲ **Springe** – 22517
In der Worth 25, 31832 Springe.
(5041) 1455 (5041) 2963
jh-springe@djh-hannover.de
www.jugendherberge.de/jh/springe
Open Dates: 01.01-23.12; 27-31.12 3km
500m x 92
500m

St Blasien ☛ **Menzenschwand**

▲ **St Englmar** – JH Maibrunn – 22518
Haus Nr 5, 94379 St Englmar (Bavaria).
(9965) 271 (9965) 1342
jhsankt-englmar@djh-bayern.de
www.sankt-englmar.jugendherberge.de
Open Dates: 01.01-31.10; 16-31.12
Bogen 23km 13 100m
ap Maibrunn 4E x 59 CC

▲ **St Goar** – Loreley-Jugendherberge – 22519
Bismarckweg 17, 56329 St. Goar.
(6741) 388 (6741) 2869
st-goar@diejugendherbergen.de
www.DieJugendherbergen.de
Open Dates: 01.01-23.12; 27-31.12 St Goar 900m x 126 CC
4 x 2km

▲ **St Michaelisdonn** – 22520
Am Sportplatz 1, 25693 St. Michaelisdonn.
(4853) 923 (4853) 8576
haus-am-klev@dithmarschen.de
www.jugendherberge.de/jh/stmichaelisdonn
Open Dates: 16.01-09.12 St. Michaelisdonn 1km x 70

▲ **Stade** – 22521
Kehdinger Mühren 11, 21682 Stade.
(4141) 46368 (4141) 2817
jhstade@djh-nordmark.de
www.jugendherberge.de/jh/stade
Open Dates: 06.01-22.12 Stade 1.5km
x 139 CC
8 500m

▲ **Steinbach/Donnersberg** – 22522
Brühlstraße 41, 67808 Steinbach.
(6357) 360 (6357) 1583
steinbach@diejugendherbergen.de
www.DieJugendherbergen.de
Open Dates: 01.01-23.12; 27-31.12 x 104
CC
4 x 15km

▲ **Stralsund** – 22524
Strandstraße 21, 18439 Stralsund OT. Devin.
(3831) 490289 (3831) 490291
jh-stralsund@djh-mv.de
www.djh-mv.de
Open Dates: 01.03-31.10 Stralsund Central 3 ap Ortsteil Devin x 130

▲ **Straubing** – 22525
Friedhofstr 12, 94315 Straubing (Bavaria).
(9421) 80436 (9421) 12094
juhe-sr@web.de
www.straubing.jugendherberge.de
Open Dates: 01.04-31.10 Munich 120km 8km Straubing 1km 300m ap Aeußere Passauerstraße 1N x 53 R 1km

▲ **Strehla** – 22526
Torgauer Str. 33, 01616 Strehla
(35264) 92030 (35264) 92031
jhstrehla@djh.de www.djh-sachsen.de
Open Dates: 01.03-31.10 (01.11-28.02) Riesa 8km Riesa-Strehla 1km ap Markt 1W x 72 R 200m

Streitberg ☛ Wiesenttal

Stuttgart 22528
Haußmannstr 27, 70188 Stuttgart
(711) 241583 (711) 2361041
info@jugendherberge-stuttgart.de
www.jugendherberge-stuttgart.de
Open Dates: Open Times:
Beds: 307
Price Range: 1 night €20.10; 2 nights or more €17.10 BBinc
Directions: 1SE from city centre
Stuttgart 500m 42 200m ap Eugensplatz 15 200m ap Eugensplatz x 41 R CC 9 x 3km

Stuttgart

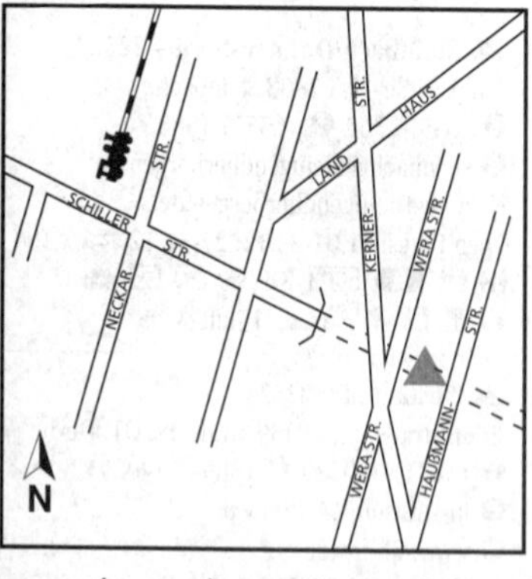

Stuttgart... Travel Tips

- **For budget eats check out...** Spaghettissimo (pizzeria, Tübinger Str. 8), Hacienda (Mexican, Tübinger Str. 8), s'Mäxle (traditional German, Tübinger Str. 8), California Sidewalk Café (Schellingstr. 7), Subway (Sandwiches, Königstr. 31)
- **For great nightlife try...** Bosch-Areal (M1, Paris, Mash, Seidenstr. 20), Stereo (Fritz-Elsas Str. 60), Barcode (Theodor-Heuss Str. 30), Altes Schützenhaus (Burgstallstr. 99), Perkins Park (Stresemannstr. 39)
- **Don't miss...** State Gallery and New Art Museum, 1. TV Tower of the World, Musicals, Royal Court Theatre, Wilhelma Botanical Gardens & Zoo, Mercedes and Porsche Museum, Old & New Castle, Market Hall, Planetarium and Observatory, Solitude & Ludwigsburg Castles & Gardens

Sudelfeld ☛ Bayrischzell

▲ **Taltitz** – "Talsperre Pirk" - Wassersport-JH – 22530
Dobenecker Weg 27, 08606 Oelsnitz, OT Taltitz
(37421) 23019 (37421) 20202
jhtaltitz@djh.de www.djh-sachsen.de
Open Dates: 01.01-22.12; 27-31.12 (23.-26.12.) Oelsnitz, Pirk 5km Oelsnitz 500m ap Neue Welt 5W x 82 R 2 x 1km

▲ **Tambach-Dietharz** – 22531
Oberhoferstr 3, 99897 Tambach-Dietharz
(36252) 36149 (36252) 36564
jh-tambach@djh-thueringen.de
www.djh-thueringen.de
Open Dates: 01.01-23.12; 27-31.12 Erfurt 25km Georgenthal 6km 851 500m ap Bahnhofstraße x 120 R CC 3 x

Tannenlohe ☛ Falkenberg

▲ **Tauberbischofsheim** – 22532
Schirrmannweg 2,
97941 Tauberbischofsheim.
(9341) 3152 (9341) 95052
info@jugendherberge-tauberbischofsheim.de
www.jugendherberge-tauberbischofsheim.de
Open Dates: Tauberbischofsheim 2NW x 108 R 3 x

▲ **Tecklenburg** – Kulturjugendherberge – 22533
Am Herrengarten 5, 49545 Tecklenburg.
(5482) 360 (5482) 7937
jh-tecklenburg@djh-wl.de
www.djh.de/westfalen
Open Dates: 01.01-23.12; 27-31.12
Münster Osnabrück 20km Lengerich 8km R 45 1km ap Kreisverwaltung Tecklenburg x 130 R 5 x 1km

---

▲ **Teterow** – 22534
Am Seebahnhof 7, 17166 Teterow.
(3996) 172668 (3996) 158812
info@jugendherberge-teterow.de
www.djh-mv.de
Open Dates: 01.01-23.12; 27-31.12
Teterow (20min) x 80 R

▲ **Thale** – 22535
Waldkater-Bodetal 1, 06502 Thale.
(3947) 2881 (3947) 91653
JH-Thale@djh-sachsen-anhalt.de
www.jugendherberge.de/jh/thale
Open Dates: 01.01-23.12; 27-31.12
Halle-Halberstadt, Magdeburg-Halberstadt 500m x 204 R 3 x

▲ **Thallichtenberg** – Musikantenland-Jugendherberge, Jugendgästehaus Burg Lichtenberg – 22536
66871 Thallichtenberg.
(6381) 2632 (6381) 80933
thallichtenberg@diejugendherbergen.de
www.DieJugendherbergen.de
Open Dates: 01.01-23.12; 27-31.12 x 106 R CC 4 x 4km

▲ **Tholey** – Schaumberg-Jugendherberge, Jugendgästehaus – 22537
Am Schaumberg, 66636 Tholey.
(6853) 2271 (6853) 5534
tholey@diejugendherbergen.de
www.DieJugendherbergen.de
Open Dates: 01.01-23.12; 27-31.12 x 164 R CC 5 x 500m

▲ **Thülsfelder Talsperre** – 22538
Am Campingplatz 7, 49681 Garrel-Petersfeld.
(4495) 475 (4495) 365
jh-thuelsfelde@djh-unterwesser-ems.de
www.jugendherberge.de/jh/thuelsfelde
Open Dates: x 160 CC 300m 300m

▲ **Titisee-Neustadt** – JH Rudenberg – 22539
Ortsteil Neustadt, Rudenberg 6,
79822 Titisee-Neustadt.
(7651) 7360 (7651) 4299
info@jugendherberge-titisee-rudenberg.de
www.jugendherberge-titisee-rudenberg.de
Open Dates: Titisee-Neustadt 2NE x 146 R 5 x 100m

▲ **Titisee-Neustadt** – JH Veltishof – 22540
Ortsteil Titisee, Bruderhalde 27,
79822 Titisee-Neustadt.
(7652) 238 (7652) 756
info@jugendherberge-titisee-veltishof.de
www.jugendherberge-titisee-veltishof.de
Open Dates: Titisee 7300 Titisee-Todtnau 2km ap Feuerwehrsheim/YH 2NW x 128 R CC 4 x 3km

---

▲ **Todtnauberg** – Fleinerhaus – 22541
OT Todtnauberg, Radschertstr 12,
79674 Todtnau.
(7671) 275 (7671) 721
info@jugendherberge-todtnauberg.de
www.jugendherberge-todtnauberg.de
Open Dates: Freiburg 7215 ap Todtnauberg 1N x 146 R CC 6 x 5km

GERMANY – ALLEMAGNE – DEUTSCHLAND – ALEMANIA

▲ **Tönning** – 22542
Badallee 28, 25832 Tönning.
(4861) 1280 (4861) 5956
jhtoenning@djh-nordmark.de
www.jugendherberge.de/jh/toenning
Open Dates: 23.01-14.12 Tönning 1km
x 208 500m 10km

▲ **Torfhaus** – 22543
Nr 3, 38667 Torfhaus.
(5320) 242 (5320) 254
jh-torfhaus@djh-hannover.de
www.jugendherberge.de/jh/torfhaus
Open Dates: 01.01-23.12; 27-31.12 x 174
2 x

▲ **Traben-Trarbach** –
Mittelmosel-Jugendherberge, Jugendgästehaus – 22544
Hirtenpfad 6, 56841 Traben-Trarbach.
(6541) 9278 (6541) 3759
traben-trarbach@diejugendherbergen.de
www.DieJugendherbergen.de
Open Dates: 01.01-23.12; 27-31.12
Traben-Trarbach 1.5km x 172
8 x
3km

▲ **Traunstein** – 22545
Traunerstr 22, 83278 Traunstein (Bavaria).
(861) 4742 (861) 12382
jhtraunstein@djh-bayern.de
www.traunstein.jugendherberge.de
Open Dates: 01.03-31.10 Traunstein
1.5km Traunstein 1.5km 1.2SE x 57
1km

▲ **Trausnitz** – 22546
Burggasse 2, 92555 Trausnitz (Bavaria).
(9655) 92150 (9655) 921531
jhtrausnitz@djh-bayern.de
www.trausnitz.jugendherberge.de
Open Dates: 01.02-05.12 Nürnberg 90km
Pfreimd 9km Trausnitz x 137
5 x

▲ **Travemünde** – 22547
"Jugendfreizeitstätte Priwall",
Mecklenburger Landstr 69,
23570 Travemünde.
(4502) 2576 (4502) 4620
info@jfs-priwall.de www.jfs-priwall.de
Open Dates: 02.04-29.09
Lübeck-Travemünde 1.5km x 77
1km 300m

▲ **Triberg/Schwarzwald** – 22548
Rohrbacher Str 35, 78098 Triberg.
(7722) 4110 (7722) 6662
info@jugendherberge-triberg.de
www.jugendherberge-triberg.de
Open Dates: Triberg 2SE x 125
3 x
8km

▲ **Trier** – Jugendgästehaus – 22053
An der Jugendherberge 4, 54292 Trier.
(651) 146620 (651) 1466230
trier@diejugendherbergen.de
www.DieJugendherbergen.de
Open Dates: 01.01-23.12; 27-31.12
Trier 2.2km 3SW x 242
5 x
800m

▲ **Tübingen** HI 22549
Gartenstr 22/2, 72074 Tübingen.
(7071) 23002 (7071) 25061
info@jugendherberge-tuebingen.de
www.jugendherberge-tuebingen.de
Open Dates: 01.01-23.12; 27-31.12
Tübingen x 159
5 x
1km

▲ **Überlingen** – Martin-Buber-JH and Jugendbegegnungsstätte – 22550
Alte Nussdorfer Str 26, 88662 Überlingen.
(7551) 4204 (7551) 1277
info@jugendherberge-ueberlingen.de
www.jugendherberge-ueberlingen.de
Open Dates: Überlingen-West,
Nussdorf 7395 ap Kramer/YH 2SE
x 259
9 x 1km 1km

▲ **Ueckermünde** – 22551
Dorfstraße, 17373 Ueckermünde, OT Bellin.
(39771) 22411 (39771) 22554
jh-ueckermuende@djh-mv.de
www.djh-mv.de
Open Dates: 01.03-14.11 Ueckermünde Altwarp-Luckow ap Dorfmitte 7W x 93 3 x

▲ **Uelsen/Grafschaft Bentheim** – 22552
Linnenbachweg 12, 49843 Uelsen.
(5942) 718 (5942) 922935
jugendherberge@uelsen.de
www.jugendherberge.de
Open Dates: 01.03-31.10 2S x 104

▲ **Uelzen** – 22553
Fischerhof 1, 29525 Uelzen.
(581) 5312 (581) 14210
jh-uelzen@djh-hannover.de
www.jugendherberge.de/jh/uelzen
Open Dates: 01.01-23.12; 27-31.12
Hannover 95km Uelzen 4km 7, 8 Fischerhof 1km x 166 CC 3 x 4km

▲ **Ulm** – Geschwister-Scholl-JH – 22554
Grimmelfinger Weg 45, 89077 Ulm.
(731) 384455 (731) 384511
info@jugendherberge-ulm.de
www.jugendherberge-ulm.de
Open Dates: 12 Ulm 4, 8 Kuhberg ap Schulzentrum 1 ap Ehinger Tor x 126 R CC 2 x 5km

Urach ☛ **Bad Urach**

Urfeld ☛ **Walchensee**

▲ **Uslar** – 22555
Kupferhammer 13, 37170 Uslar.
(5571) 2298 (5571) 1288
jh-uslar@djh-hannover.de
www.jugendherberge.de/jh/uslar
Open Dates: 01.01-23.12; 27-31.12 x 104 R CC 2 x 500m

▲ **Velbert** – 22556
Am Buschberg 17, 42549 Velbert
(2051) 84316 (2051) 81202
niermannrolf@compuserve.de
www.djh-velbert.de
Open Dates: 29.01-30.11 Düsseldorf 20km Wuppertal 12km 649, 169 100m ap Velbert Schloßstraße, Am Buschberg 2N x 120 R 4 x 500m

▲ **Verden / Aller** – 22557
Saumurplatz 2, 27283 Verden/Aller.
(4231) 61163 (4231) 68121
jh-verden@djh-unterweser-ems.de
www.jugendherberge.de/jh/verden
Open Dates: 12 x 124 CC 100m

▲ **Villingen** – 22558
OT Villingen, St-Georgener-Str 36,
78048 Villingen-Schwenningen.
(7721) 54149 (7721) 52616
info@jugendherberge-villingen.de
www.jugendherberge-villingen.de
Open Dates: 12 Villingen 5, 6 ap Triberger Straße 2NW x 133 R 4 x 4km

▲ **Vöhl** – Hohe Fahrt am Edersee – 22561
Hohe Fahrt 1, 34516 Vöhl-Asel.
(5635) 251 (5635) 8142
hohefahrt@djh-hessen.de
www.djh-hessen.de/jh/hohefahrt
Open Dates: 01.01-23.12; 27-31.12 4SW x 231 R

▲ **Vöhl-Ederbringhausen** – Burg Hessenstein – 22560
34516 Vöhl-Ederbringhausen.
(6455) 300 (6455) 8771
burghessenstein@djh-hessen.de
www.djh-hessen.de/jh/burghessenstein
Open Dates: 01.01-23.12; 27-31.12 12S x 136

▲ **Walchensee** – JH Urfeld – 22563
Mittenwalder Str 17,
82432 Walchensee (Bavaria).
(8851) 230 (8851) 1022
jhwalchensee@djh-bayern.de
www.walchensee.jugendherberge.de
Open Dates: 01.01-14.11; 27-31.12
Kochel 9km x 97 2 x

▲ **Waldeck** – Waldeck/Edersee – 22564
Klippenberg 3, 34513 Waldeck.
(5623) 5313 (5623) 6254
waldeck@djh-hessen.de
www.djh-hessen.de/jh/waldeck
Open Dates: 01.01-23.12; 27-31.12 2.5NW
x 161

Waldhäuser ☛ **Neuschönau**

▲ **Waldmünchen** – 22565
Schlosshof 1, 93449 Waldmünchen (Bavaria).
(9972) 94140 (9972) 941433
office@jugendbildungsstaette.org
www.waldmuenchen.jugendherberge.de
Open Dates: Nürnberg 130km
Waldmünchen 500m 500m
x 120 R
13 x 500m

▲ **Walldürn** – 22566
Auf der Heide 37, 74731 Walldürn.
(6282) 283 (6282) 40194
info@jugendherberge-wallduern.de
www.jugendherberge-wallduern.de
Open Dates: Walldürn 3N x 102
R 4 x
2km

▲ **Waltersdorf** – "Gut Drauf-JH" – 22567
Jägerwäldchen 2, 02763 Bertsdorf-Hörnitz.
(35841) 35099 (35841) 37773
jhwaltersdorf@djh.de
www.djh-sachsen.de
Open Dates: 01.01-23.12; 27-31.12 (
23-26.12) Großschönau, Jonsdorf 3km
Großschönau ap YH x 166
R 6 x
1.5km

▲ **Wandlitz** 22050
Prenzlauer Chaussee 146, 16348 Wandlitz.
(33397) 22109 (33397) 62735
jh-wandlitz@jugendherberge.de
www.hostel.de
Open Dates: (R 01.11-28.02)
x 148 R
4 x 200m

▲ **Wangerooge** – 22568
"Westturm", 26486 Wangerooge,
(North Sea).
(4469) 439 (4469) 8578
jh-wangerooge@djh-unterweser-ems.de
www.jugendherberge.de/jh/wangerooge
Open Dates: 4W x 168
R CC 4 x
300m

▲ **Waren (Müritz)** – 22569
An der Feisneck 1a, 17192 Waren (Müritz).
(3991) 186900 (3991) 186904
jh-waren@djh-mv.de www.djh-mv.de
Open Dates: 01.01-23.12; 27-31.12
Waren Stadtbus ap Altes
Wasserwerk 1S x 102 R

▲ **Warmbad** – 22570
An der Jugendherberge 68,
09429 Wolkenstein, OT Warmbad
(37369) 9437 (37369) 5665
info@jugendherberge-warmbad.de
www.djh-sachsen.de
Open Dates: 01.02-31.10 (01.11.-13.01)
Warmbad 3km Dresden-Annaberg
1km ap Silbertherme 3NW x 62
R 2 x
7km

Warnemünde – 22571
Parkstraße 47,
18119 Rostock OT. Warnemünde.
(381) 548170 (381) 5481723
jh-warnemuende@djh-mv.de
www.djh-mv.de
Open Dates: 01.01-23.12; 27-31.12
Open Times:
Beds: 191
Price Range: € 21.15 BBinc
Directions: 1W from city centre
Rostock-Laage 40km A 604 15km
Rostock 10km Warnemünde
1.5km 36 ap Am Strand x 10
R 1 x
1.5km 100m

Warnemünde

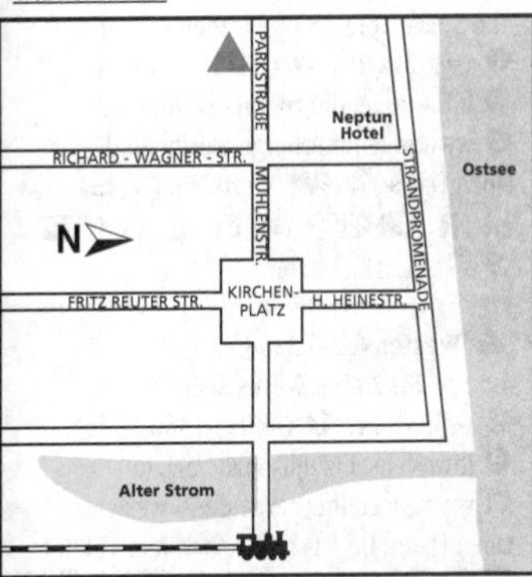

Warnemünde... Travel Tips

- **For budget eats check out...** Casablanca, Speciality restaurants (sea food) in Rostock City & Warnemünde, Salsarico, Alabama
- **For great nightlife try...** Cine Star, Escape (Warnemünde), Space and Mambo (Rostock-Lütten Klein), HCC (Rostock-Schmarl), Hotel Neptun (disco)
- **Don't miss...** Hanse Sail, Museums, Rostock Zoo, Cruise boats, Yachting harbour, Lighthouse, Historical City Centre

---

▲ **Weilburg** – 22573
Am Steinbühl, 35781 Weilburg-Odersbach.
(6471) 7116 (6471) 1542
weilburg@djh-hessen.de
www.djh-hessen.de/jh/weilburg
Open Dates: 01.01-23.12; 27-31.12 2E
x 135

▲ **Weimar** – "Am Poseckschen Garten" – 22574
Humboldtstr 17, 99423 Weimar
(3643) 850792 (3643) 850793
jh-posgarten@djh-thueringen.de
www.djh-thueringen.de
Open Dates: 01.01-21.12; 27-31.12 Erfurt 20km Weimar 3km 6 200m ap Cranachstraße 0.5S x 104 R CC 1 x 1km

---

▲ **Weimar** – "Germania" – 22575
Carl-August Allee 13, 99423 Weimar
(3643) 850490 (3643) 850491
jh-germania@djh-thueringen.de
www.djh-thueringen.de
Open Dates: 01.01-21.12; 28-31.12 Erfurt 20km Weimar Central 120m 1, 7, 6, 5, 8 120m 0.5N x 120 R CC 1 x 1km

---

▲ **Weimar** – "Jugendgästehaus am Ettersberg" – 22576
Ettersberg-Siedlung, 99427 Weimar.
(3643) 421111 (3643) 421112
jgh-weimar@djh-thueringen.de
www.djh-thueringen.de
Open Dates: 12 Erfurt 22km Weimar 5km 6 500m ap Obelisk 5N x 66 R CC 2 x P 1km

---

Weimar – "Jugendgästehaus Maxim Gorki" – 22577
Zum Wilden Graben 12, 99425 Weimar
(3643) 850750 (3643) 850749
jgh-weimar@djh-thueringen.de
www.djh-thueringen.de
Open Dates: 01.01-21.12; 28-31.12
Open Times:
Beds: 60 - 2x1 3x2 1x3 4x4 4x5 3x6
Price Range: € 18-21 BBinc
Directions: 4S from city centre
Erfurt 20km Weimar 4km 8, 5 200m ap Friedhof x 10 R CC 2 x i P 2km

---

Weimar – "Jugendgästehaus Maxim Gorki"

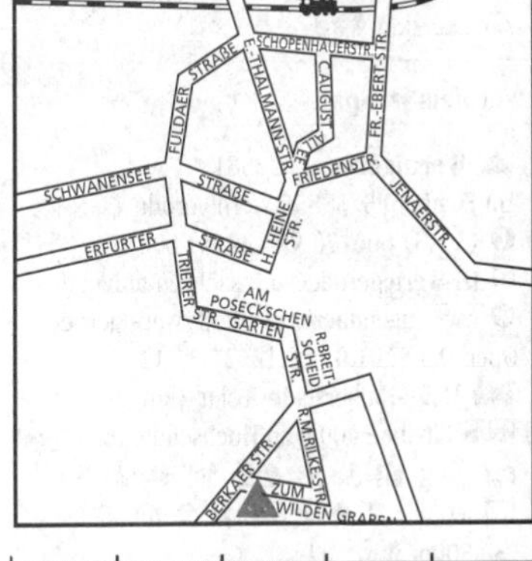

Weimar... Travel Tips

- **For budget eats check out...** Weisser Schwan, Jacobs Klause, Apollon (Greek restaurant), Scharfe Ecke, Ratskeller
- **For great nightlife try...** Student Club Kasseturm, Mon Ami Youth Club, Stellwerk, Bowling Centre, ACC
- **Don't miss...** National Theatre, Weimarhaus, Goethe's residence & garden house, Schillerhouse, Art Collection, Belvedere & Tiefurt Castles, Buchenwald

▲ **Weinheim/Bergstraße** – 22578
Breslauer Str 46, 69469 Weinheim.
(6201) 68484 (6201) 182730
info@jugendherberge-weinheim.de
www.jugendherberge-weinheim.de
Open Dates: 12 Weinheim
Mannheim, Weinheim ap Stahlbad 2W
x 129 R CC
6 x 1km

▲ **Weiskirchen** – 22579
Jugendherbergsstr 12, 66709 Weiskirchen.
(6876) 231 (6876) 1444
weiskirchen@diejugendherbergen.de
www.DieJugendherbergen.de
Open Dates: 01.01-23.12; 27-31.12 x 126
R CC
6 x 700m

▲ **Werdau** – 22580
Jugendheimweg 1, 08412 Werdau
(3761) 3514 (3761) 3514
kosaksjuhe@web.de
www.djh-sachsen.de
Open Dates: 01.01-22.12; 27-31.12
Werdau 1.5km Werdau 300m
ap Kaufhalle-West 1.5W x 44 R
2 x
2km

Wernfels ☛ **Spalt**

▲ **Wernigerode** – 22581
Am Eichberg 5, 38855 Wernigerode.
(3943) 606176 (3943) 606177
JH-Wernigerode@djh-sachsen-anhalt.de
www.jugendherberge.de/jh/wernigerode
Open Dates: 01.01-23.12; 27-31.12
Halle-Halberstadt-Goslar 3km
City-line 400m ap Hochschule Harz 1.5NW
x 242 R
4 x
500m

▲ **Wertheim** – Frankenland – 22582
Alte-Steige 16, 97877 Wertheim.
(9342) 6451 (9342) 7354
info@jugendherberge-wertheim.de
www.jugendherberge-wertheim.de
Open Dates: 12 Wertheim 2W x 99
R CC 3 x
1km

▲ **Westensee** – 22583
Am See 24, 24259 Westensee.
(4305) 542 (4305) 1360
jhwestensee@djh-nordmark.de
www.jugendherberge.de/jh/westensee
Open Dates: 06.01-22.12 Kiel 15km
500m x 145

▲ **Westerland** – Dikjen-Deel – 22623
Fischerweg 36-40, 25980 Westerland/Sylt
(4651) 8357825 (4651) 8357826
jhwesterland@djh-nordmark.de
www.jugendherberge.de/jh/westerland
Open Dates: 06.01-22.12 Westerland
4km 500m x 50 R
6km 200m

▲ **Westerstede** – 22584
"Hössensportzentrum", Jahnallee 1,
26655 Westerstede, Postfach 1129,
26641 Westerstede.
(4488) 84690 (4488) 78317
hoessen-sportzentrum@westerstede.de
www.jugendherberge.de
Open Dates: 03.01-21.12 2SW x 68
200m

▲ **Wetzlar** – 22585
Richard-Schirrmann-Straße 3, 35578 Wetzlar.
(6441) 71068 (6441) 75826
wetzlar@djh-hessen.de
www.djh-hessen.de/jh/wetzlar
Open Dates: 01.01-23.12; 27-31.12 2SW
x 186

▲ **Wewelsburg** – 22586
Burgwall 17, 33142 Büren-Wewelsburg.
(2955) 6155 (2955) 6946
jh-wewelsburg@djh-wl.de
www.djh.de/westfalen
Open Dates: 01.01-23.12; 27-31.12
Paderborn 7km Paderborn 20km
400, 460 20km ap Wewelsburg-Schule
x 204 R
5 x 9km

▲ **Wiehl** – 22588
An der Krähenhardt 6, 51674 Wiehl
(2262) 93410 (2262) 91598
wiehl@jugendherberge.de
www.wiehl.jugendherberge.de
Open Dates: 01.01-23.12; 27-31.12
Dieringhausen 302 Dieringhausen ap Zirrerstraße x 176 R
5 x

Wiesbaden – 22589
Blücherstr 66-68, 65195 Wiesbaden.
(611) 48657 (611) 441119
wiesbaden@djh-hessen.de
www.djh-hessen.de/jh/wiesbaden
Open Dates: 01.01-23.12; 27-31.12
Open Times:
Beds: 220
Price Range: € 19-25 BBinc
Directions: 2W from city centre
Wiesbaden 3km 14 300m ap Gneisenaustraße R TV
1km

Wiesbaden

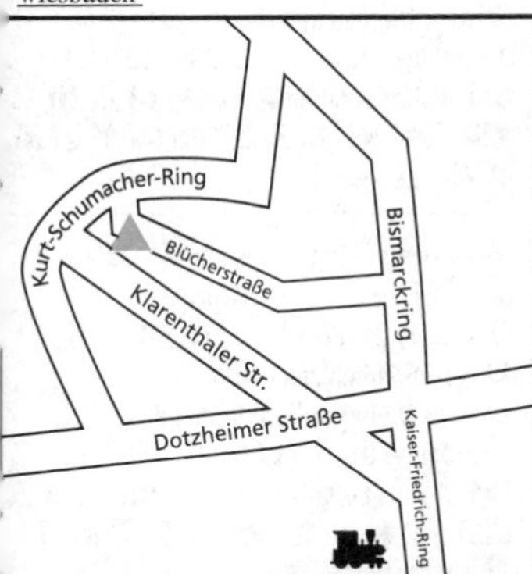

Wiesbaden... Travel Tips

- **For budget eats check out...** Alt-Wiesbaden (Italian), Zum Dortmunder, Paulaner, Becks am Bäckerbrunnen, Maredo Steakhouse
- **For great nightlife try...** Europa Palace (disco), Casino, Theatre, Schlachthof (live music), Bowling Centre
- **Don't miss...** Boating on the Rhine, Kaiser-Friedrich-Thermals, Cable Railway, Pheasant House, Freudenberg Castle, Harlekinäum, Museum, Greek Chapel

▲ **Wiesenttal-Streitberg** – JH Streitberg – 22590
Am Gailing 6,
91346 Wiesenttal-Streitberg (Bavaria).
(9196) 288 (9196) 1543
jhstreitberg@djh-bayern.de
www.streitberg.jugendherberge.de
Open Dates: 15.02-14.11 Nürnberg 60km
Ebermannstadt 5km Streitberg 400m 0.3SW x 122 CC
8 1km

▲ **Wildenstein - Burg** – 22591
88637 Leibertingen
(7466) 411 (7466) 417
info@jugendherberge-burg-wildenstein.de
www.jugendherberge-burg-wildenstein.de
Open Dates: 12 Beuron 5km x 156
R CC TV 6 x

▲ **Willingen** – 22592
Am Lukasheim 9-12,
34508 Willingen-Schwalefeld.
(5632) 6347 (5632) 4343
willingen@djh-hessen.de
www.djh-hessen.de/jh/willingen
Open Dates: 01.01-23.12; 27-31.12 4NE
x 132

▲ **Windeck-Rosbach** – Forest Youth Hostel – 22593
Herbergsstr. 19, 51570 Windeck-Rosbach
(2292) 5042 (2292) 6569
windeck@jugendherberge.de
www.windeck.jugendherberge.de
Open Dates: 01.01-23.12; 27-31.12
Rosbach 3km Rosbach 3km
x 142 R
7 x 3km

▲ **Windischleuba** – "Schloß Windischleuba" – 22595
Pestalozziplatz 1, 04603 Windischleuba
(3447) 834471 (3447) 832702
jh-windischleuba@djh-thueringen.de
www.djh-thueringen.de
Open Dates: 01.01-23.12; 27-31.12
Altenburg 5km Altenburg 5km
264 ap Alte Schmiede x 140
R CC TV 5 x

▲ Wingst – 22596
Molkereistr 11, 21789 Wingst.
(4778) 262 (4778) 7594
jhwingst@djh-nordmark.de
www.jugendherberge.de/jh/wingst
Open Dates: 31.01-14.12 Wingst 1km
x 205 1km

▲ Winterberg – 22597
Astenberg 1, 59955 Winterberg-Neuastenberg.
(2981) 2289 (2981) 569
jh-winterberg@djh-wl.de
www.djh.de/westfalen
Open Dates: 01.01-23.12; 27-31.12
Winterberg R 28 ap YH x 170
6 x

▲ Wipperfürth – Sport Youth Hostel – 22598
Ostlandstr 34, 51688 Wipperfürth
(2267) 1228 (2267) 80977
wipperfuerth@jugendherberge.de
www.wipperfuerth.jugendherberge.de
Open Dates: 01.01-23.12 427, 429
Bergisch Gladbach 1.5km ap Wipperfürth
Central Bus Station x 144
5 x 200m

▲ Wirsberg – 22624
Sessenreuther Str. 31, 95339 Wirsberg.
(9227) 6432 (9227) 902767
www.wirsberg.jugendherberge.de
Open Dates: Neuenmarkt/Wirsberg
2.5km KBS 8358 x 68
3 x 8
900m

▲ Wismar – 22599
Juri-Gagarin-Ring 30a, 23966 Wismar.
(3841) 32680 (3841) 326868
jh-wismar@djh-mv.de www.djh-mv.de
Open Dates: 01.01-23.12; 27-31.12
Wismar C, D
ap Phillip-Müller-Straße/Krankenhaus
x 134 1 x

▲ Wittdün – 22600
Mittelstr 1, 25946 Wittdün/Amrum.
(4682) 2010 (4682) 1747
jhwittduen@djh-nordmark.de
www.jugendherberge.de/jh/wittduen
Open Dates: 02.02-30.11 Wittdün 300m
x 216
100m

▲ Wittenberg-Lutherstadt – 22601
Schloss, 06886 Lutherstadt-Wittenberg.
(3491) 403255 (3491) 409422
jugendherberge@wittenberg.de
www.jugendherberge.de/jh/wittenberg
Open Dates: 01.01-22.12; 28-31.12
Berlin-München, ap Altstadt 300m
2km x 104

▲ Wolfsburg – 22602
Lessingstr 60, 38440 Wolfsburg.
(5361) 13337 (5361) 16630
jh-wolfsburg@djh-hannover.de
www.jugendherberge.de/jh/wolfsburg
Open Dates: 01.01-23.12; 27-31.12
Wolfsburg 1.5km 201 500m
x 68
2 x 2km

▲ Wolfstein – Königsland-Jugendherberge
Wolfstein/Pfalz – 22603
Rötherweg 24, 67752 Wolfstein.
(6304) 1408 (6304) 683
wolfstein@diejugendherbergen.de
www.DieJugendherbergen.de
Open Dates: 01.01-23.12; 27-31.12
Wolfstein 600m x 139
6 x
1km

▲ Worms – Jugendgästehaus – 22604
Dechaneigasse 1, 67547 Worms.
(6241) 25780 (6241) 27394
worms@diejugendherbergen.de
www.DieJugendherbergen.de
Open Dates: 01.01-23.12; 27-31.12
Worms 800m x 114
5 x
1.2km

▲ Worpswede – 22605
Hammeweg 2, 27726 Worpswede.
(4792) 1360 (4792) 4381
jh-worpswede@djh-unterweser-ems.de
www.jugendherberge.de/jh/worpswede
Open Dates: x 164
4 x

▲ **Wunsiedel** – 22607
Am Katharinenberg 4,
95632 Wunsiedel (Bavaria).
(9232) 1851 (9232) 70629
jhwunsiedel@djh-bayern.de
www.wunsiedel.jugendherberge.de
Open Dates: 11.01-30.11 Nürnberg 150km Marktredwitz 8km 3, 5, 9 500m ap YH x 112 R CC 6 x 1km

▲ **Wuppertal** – 22608
Obere Lichtenplatzerstr 70, 42287 Wuppertal
(202) 552372 (202) 557354
wuppertal@djh-rheinland.de
www.wuppertal.jugendherberge.de
Open Dates: 01.01-23.12; 27-31.12
Düsseldorf, Köln 40km A S-Bahn 7 40km Barmen 300m 640 Barmen 100m ap YH 1N x 126 R CC 4 x 1.5km

▲ **Würzburg** 22012
Burkarderstr 44, 97082 Würzburg (Bavaria).
(931) 42590 (931) 416862
jhwuerzburg@djh-bayern.de
www.wuerzburg.jugendherberge.de
Open Dates: Frankfurt am Main 110km Würzburg HBF 2km Sanderring 1km Löwenbrücke 500m 0.5NE x 254 R CC 5 x 500m

▲ **Wüstewohlde** – 22609
Wüstewohlde Nr 20,
27624 Wüstewohlde-Ringstedt.
(4708) 234 (4708) 152492
www.jugendherberge.de
Open Dates: 01.04-31.10 x 74

▲ **Wyk auf Föhr** – 22610
Fehrstieg 41, 25938 Wyk auf Föhr.
(4681) 2355 (4681) 5527
jhwyk@djh-nordmark.de
www.jugendherberge.de/jh/wyk
Open Dates: 15.02-22.12 Wyk auf Föhr 3.5km x 162 R 1km 300m

▲ **Xanten** – South See – 22626
Bankscher Weg 4, 46509 Xanten.
(2801) 98500 (2801) 985010
xanten@jugendherberge.de
www.xanten.jugendherberge.de
Open Dates: 01.01-23.12; 27-31.12
Xanten 3km SL 42 Xanten ap YH 2N x 190 R 7 x 500m

▲ **Zeven-Bademühlen** – 22611
Haus Nr 1, 27404 Zeven.
(4281) 2550 (4281) 80293
jh-zeven@djh-unterweser-ems.de
www.jugendherberge.de/jh/zeven
Open Dates: 01.01-31.11 4W x 133 CC

▲ **Zielow** – 22612
Seeufer 10, 17207 Ludorf, OT. Zielow.
(39923) 2547 (39923) 28096
jh-zielow@djh-mv.de www.djh-mv.de
Open Dates: 01.03-31.10 Waren Waren-Röbel, Richtung Neustrelitz ap Viperow (3km journey) x 98 R 2 x 100m 100m

▲ **Zingst** – 22613
Glebbe 14, 18374 Ostseebad Zingst.
(38232) 15465 (38232) 12285
jh-zingst@djh-mv.de www.djh-mv.de
Open Dates: 01.01-23.12; 27-31.12
Ribnitz-Damgarten(West), Barth Jeweils 210 ap Zingst 0.8W x 162 R 4 x 1km 1km

▲ **Zinnwald** – "Jägerhütte" – 22614
Bergmannsweg 8, 01773 Altenberg,
OT Zinnwald
(35056) 32361 (35056) 32317
jhzinnwald@djh.de
www.djh-sachsen.de
Open Dates: 01.01-22.12; 27-31.12 (23-26.12) Altenberg 5km Altenberg-Zinnwald 1km ap Wendeplatz 1SE x 70 R 2 x 6km

▲ **Zinnwald** – "Klügelhütte" – 22615
Hochmoorweg 12, 01773 Altenberg, OT Zinnwald.
t (35056) 35882 f (35056) 32458
e heuer.ralf@gmx.de
w www.djh-sachsen.de
Open Dates: 01.01-22.12; 27-31.12
Altenberg 4km Zinnwald 300m ap Grenzsteinhof 3S x 35 R 1 x 300m

▲ **Zuflucht** – 22617
Zuflucht 1, 72250 Zuflucht.
t (7804) 611 f (7804) 1323
e info@jugendherberge-zuflucht.de
w www.jugendherberge-zuflucht.de
Open Dates: 12 Freudenstadt 16km x 192 R 8 x

▲ **Zwingenberg** – 22619
Die Lange Schneise 11, 64673 Zwingenberg.
t (6251) 75938 f (6251) 788113
e zwingenberg@djh-hessen.de
w www.djh-hessen.de/jh/zwingenberg
Open Dates: 01.01-23.12; 27-31.12 1NE
x 125

Hungary

Magyarországi Ifjúságí Szállások Szövetsége
(Almássy Leisure Time and Cultural Centre)
H-1077 Budapest VII., Almássy tér IV/404, Hungary.
Postal Address: PO Box 116, 1410 Budapest, Hugary.

t (36) (1) 3435167
f (36) (1) 3435167
e miszsz@axelero.hu
w www.miszsz.hu

Office Hours: Monday-Thursday 08.00-16.00hrs;
Friday 08.00-14.00hrs

Mellow Mood Ltd.
1056 Budapest
Molnàr u. 3. Hungary

t (36) (1) 4112390
f (36) (1) 2663725
e info@youthhostel.hu
w www.mellowmood.hu

Office Hours: Monday-Friday 08.00-17.00hrs

A copy of the Hostel Directory for this Country can be obtained from:
Tourinform Offices eg Keleti Rail Station, Budapest,
All Hostels
The National Office

National Tourist Authority/Board:	www.malev.hu; www.mav.hu www.volan.hu www.budapestinfo.hu www.tourinform.hu
Capital:	Budapest
Language:	Hungarian
Currency:	Ft (forints)
Population:	10,750,000
Size:	93,030 sq km
Telephone Country Code:	36
eKit Access Number:	06800-17053

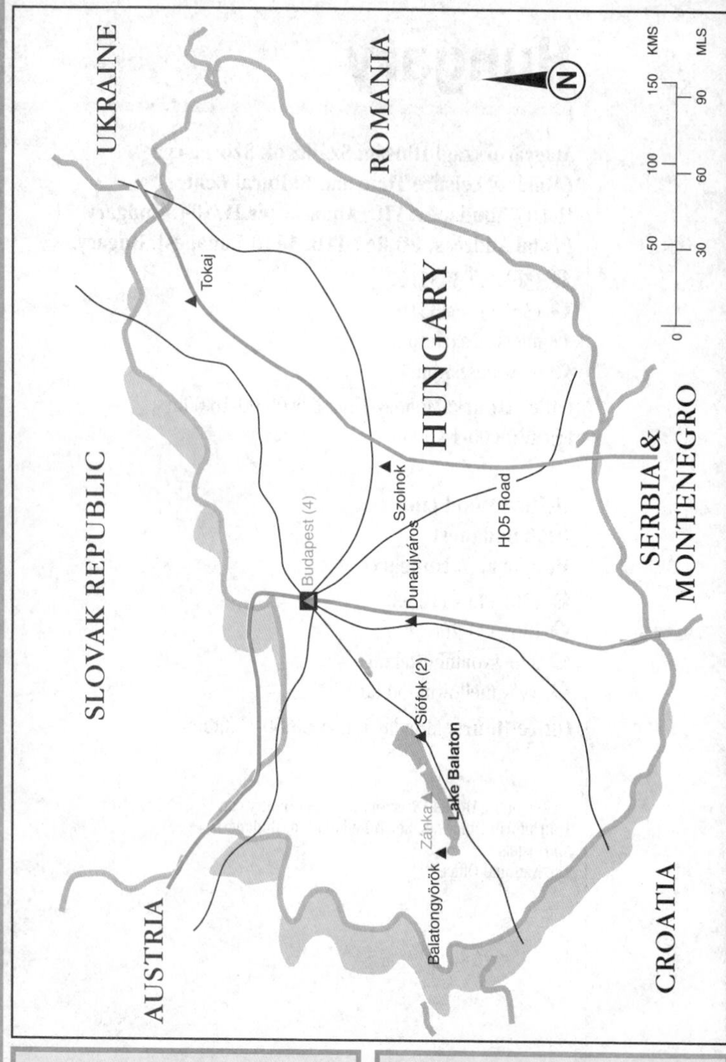

Hungary, the country of Bartok and Liszt, has a significant and distinguished history going back a thousand years, most recently to the Austro-Hungarian Empire that came into being in 1848 but ended badly after WWI at the Treaty of Versailles, when it lost a third of its original land to neighbouring countries.

Hungary is also Europe's odd man out insofar as it has a unique culture and language, which are totally unrelated to its Germanic and Slavic neighbours.

It is the only member of the Eastern bloc in the Communist era to have proclaimed its independence (1956), which was brutally repressed twelve days later by Soviet tanks ordered by the then Soviet leader Nikita Khrushchev. Today, as a recently joined member of the European Union, Hungary is liberated from its historic sense of isolation, and is coming to terms with the difficult challenges of moving to a free-enterprise market economy.

Its fine baroque capital, Budapest, straddles the River Danube – the two halves of the city being Buda and Pest – and is home to about two million of the country's ten million population. Amazingly, there are about the same number of Hungarians living outside the country, and from this relatively small Hungarian 'tribe' have come a whole array of other great names, including a considerable number of Nobel Prize-winners (most recently Imre Kertesz for Literature in 2002), along with a great many international names, from Sir George Solti, the acclaimed conductor, to the tennis superstar Monica Seles.

A few other Top Tips from **CULTURE SMART!**:

- Hungarians are generally people of style and elegance, like their architecture and music, which translates into the way they dress – formal when it has to be but invariably smart and tasteful.
- On meeting, the Continental habit of shaking hands on every occasion prevails. This is customary, not just on meeting for the first time. Hungarians believe in a hearty, sincere handshake, which includes women: so be prepared for a 'bone-cruncher' even from the most reserved!
- Like the Germans, Hungarians honour the status of the people they meet, as in 'Mr President', 'Mr Teacher', 'Mr Minister'; but always Doctor for scholars, medical doctors and surgeons. On the other hand, Hungarians have a much more highly developed sense of humour, not least bawdy jokes!
- Hungarian's love their food, including their world-renowned sausages, salami and the cherry-paprika that puts the 'bite' in many of their dishes, including *gulyás* (goulash), which is in fact a rich, meaty soup in Hungary. Paprika veal and paprika chicken are also hot favourites! But beware of all the rich cream that goes into much of the cooking.

You can find out a lot more on our website - a visit to www.HIhostels.com is essential for planning your trip!

Pour en savoir plus, rendez-vous sur notre site Internet, www.HIhostels.com une visite incontournable pour préparer votre voyage!

Viele weitere Informationen auf unserer Website: www.HIhostels.com - unverzichtbar für die Reiseplanung!

Puedes averiguar mucho más en nuestro sitio web. Es imprescindible que visites la página www.HIhostels.com para planear tu viaje.

△ ***Balaton*** *– Zánka* Ⓗ *25008*
Zánkai Gyermek és Ifjúsági Centrum, 8250 Zánka/Balaton Nord.
Ⓣ *(87) 568500* Ⓕ *(87) 568578*
Ⓔ *marketing@zanka.hu*
Ⓦ *www.zanka.hu*
Open Dates: 12 *Zánka*
Zánkafürdő *Zánka* x 3000
R
5 x P

△ ***Balaton Siófok*** *– Villa Benjamin – 25010*
H-8600 Siófok-Ezüstpart/Balatonszéplakfelső, Siófoki ut 9.
(84) 350704 (84) 350704
ssaaa@freeweb.hu
http://ssssq.freeweb.hu
Open Dates: Siófoki 1.5km
Ezüstpart 150m x 38 R
(B)
250m 150m

△ ***Balatongyörök*** *– Györöki Ifitàbor – 25012*
H-8313 Balatongyörök-Szépkilàtó.
(83) 346018; (92) 312770; (92) 312771
(92) 312770 info@ifitabor.hu
www.ifitabor.hu
Open Dates: 15.05-15.09
Balatongyörök 1km 1km
500m x 218 R
5 x
50m 50m

▲ **Budapest** – Boatel Fortuna Budapest – 25017
1137 Bp., Szt. István park, alsó rakpart.
(12) 888100 (12) 700351
fortunahajo@chello.hu
www.fortunahajo.hu
Open Dates: Szent István; Rakpart on Danube West 1km; East 5km; South 6km 76 Trolley 200m; 79 Trolley ap St. István Park 150m; 2, 4, 6 at Jászai Mari Square 300m x 29 R CC
3 x 500m
300m

△ ***Budapest*** *– Csillebérci Szabadidö és Ifjúsági Központ – 25049*
H-1121 Budapest, Konkoly-Thege M. utca 21.
(1) 3956537 (1) 3957327
csill@mail.datanet.hu
www.csilleberciszabadido.hu
Open Dates: 90 from Moszkvatér ap Csillebèrc x 284 R CC
9 x

Budapest – Hostel Fortuna Mellow Mood Kft
HI 25004 FNM
H-1097 Budapest, Gyáli Út 3/B.
(1) 2150660 (1) 2170666
info@fortunahotel.hu
www.fortunahostel.hu
Open Dates: Open Times:
Beds: 81 - 1x¹ 13x² 6x³ 9x⁴
Price Range: from € 45 BB inc
Directions: 2SW from city centre
Ferihegy 15km A 150m Vigadó Square (International Harbour) 4km
Keleti Pu 3km U Metro No 3 (Blue) ap "Nagyvárad Square" 300m R
CC
2km 2km

Budapest – Hostel Fortuna Mellow Mood Kft

Budapest – Hostel Marco Polo HI 25005 FNM
H-1072 Budapest, Nyár utca 6.
(1) 4132555 (1) 4136058
gazd@marcopolohostel.com
www.marcopolohostel.com
Open Dates: Open Times:
Beds: 156 - 36x² 6x⁴ 5x⁶⁺
Price Range: € 18-68 BB inc
Directions: Ferihegy 15km Keleti 1km 7A, 7 300m 74 Trolley 300m; 4, 6 500m U Blue Metro 3, Red Metro 2 - Stations Blaha Lujza 500m; Astoria 800m
R
5km 5km

Budapest – Hostel Marco Polo

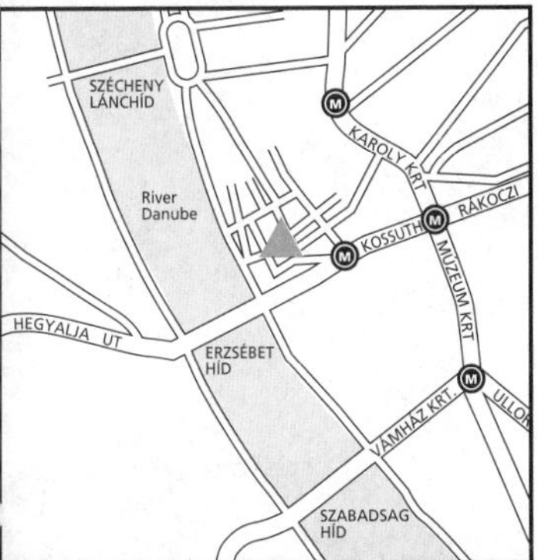

Dunaújváros Föiskola Kerpely Antal Kollégium

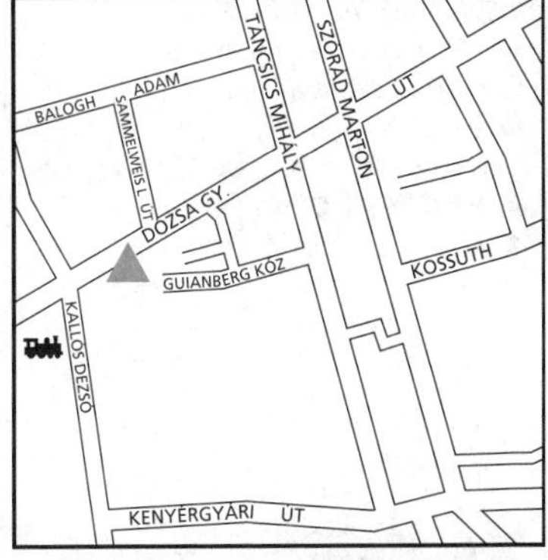

Budapest... Travel Tips

- **For budget eats check out...** Liszt Ferenc Square, Dohá'ny Street , Kodály Köröndi Square, Rákoczy Square, Andrássy Road
- **For great nightlife try...** Old Man's, Café del Rio (open air), Club Seven, Bahnhof, Fat Mo's
- **Don't miss...** Citadella of Buda, Zoo, Amusement Park, Szemlö-Hegy Cave, Castle Cavern, Palace of Miracles, St. Stephen's Circular Look-out, Opera, Cathedral, St. László Basilica

Dunaújváros – Dunaújváros Föiskola Kerpely Antal Kollégium – 25034 (FNM)
H-2400 Dunaújváros,
Dózsa György út 33.
(25) 551155 (25) 410434
kerpely@makacs.poliod.hu; tit-koll@mail.poliod.hu www.kac.poliod.hu/kollegium
Open Dates: (10.07-20.08 high season)
Open Times:
Beds: 121
Price Range: € 15 BBinc
Directions: Kisapostag 7km A 200m 3km 1.5km Budapest West Railway Station to Dunaújváros every 20 mins Nos 16, 19, 20, 24 from Vasútállomás; Bus station 200m from Kollégium in Dunaújváros ap "Dózsa Mozi" Bus Station 500m; "Béke Tér" Bus Station 300m R 1 x 200m 200m

Dunaújváros... Travel Tips

- **For budget eats check out...** Arauyhordo Restaurant, Halászcsárda, Kiskoharz Restaurant, Geronimo Pub, Topo Pizzeria & Salad Bar
- **For great nightlife try...** Haugulat Disco, Kontiki Club, Dome Disco, Bowling Center, Kiscsillag Pub
- **Don't miss...** Sutercisa Museum, Danubian Steel-Statue Park, Smith Museum, Roman Catholic Church, Evangelic Church, Rost Pal Photo Art Exhibition, Pentelei Moluar János Painter's House, Socialist Statues and Houses, Roman Stone Garden, Reformed Church

△ ***Siófok*** *– Hotel Ezüstpart – 25038*
Liszt Ferenc sétány 2-4, 8609 Siófok, Balatonszéplak Felsö.
(84) 350793 (84) 351095 (84) 350622 www.hunguesthotels.hu
Open Dates: 01.04-31.10 600m
1 3.5km x 400 R CC 4 x 8

△ ***Szolnok*** *– Turisztikai Ès Szabadidöközpont – 25043*
5000 Szolnok, Tiszaliget PF.: 178.
(56) 424705 (56) 424335
turisztikaikozpont@axelero.hu
www.turistztikaikozpont.hu
Open Dates: Szolnoki 3km
15 10m ap Tiszaligeti 1.5E x 320 R 1 x 1km 1km

△ ***Tokaj*** – *Vizisport Turistaház – 25052*
H-3910 Tokaj, Horgasz u. 3.
(47) 352645 *(47) 352640*
turistahaz@tokaj-hostel.hu
www.tokaj-hostel.hu
Open Dates: *1.5km* 0.6E x 100
1 x
100m 100m

Iceland

Bandalag Íslenskra Farfugla,
(Hostelling International Iceland)
Sundlaugavegur 34,
105 Reykjavík, Iceland.

t (354) 553 8110
f (354) 588 9201
e info@hostel.is
w www.hostel.is

Office Hours: Monday-Friday 09.00-17.00hrs

A copy of the Hostel Directory for this Country can be obtained from:
The National Office

Capital:	Reykjavík
Language:	Icelandic
Currency:	Kr (kronúr)
Population:	290,000
Size:	103,000 sq km
Telephone Country Code:	354
eKit Access Number:	800-8326

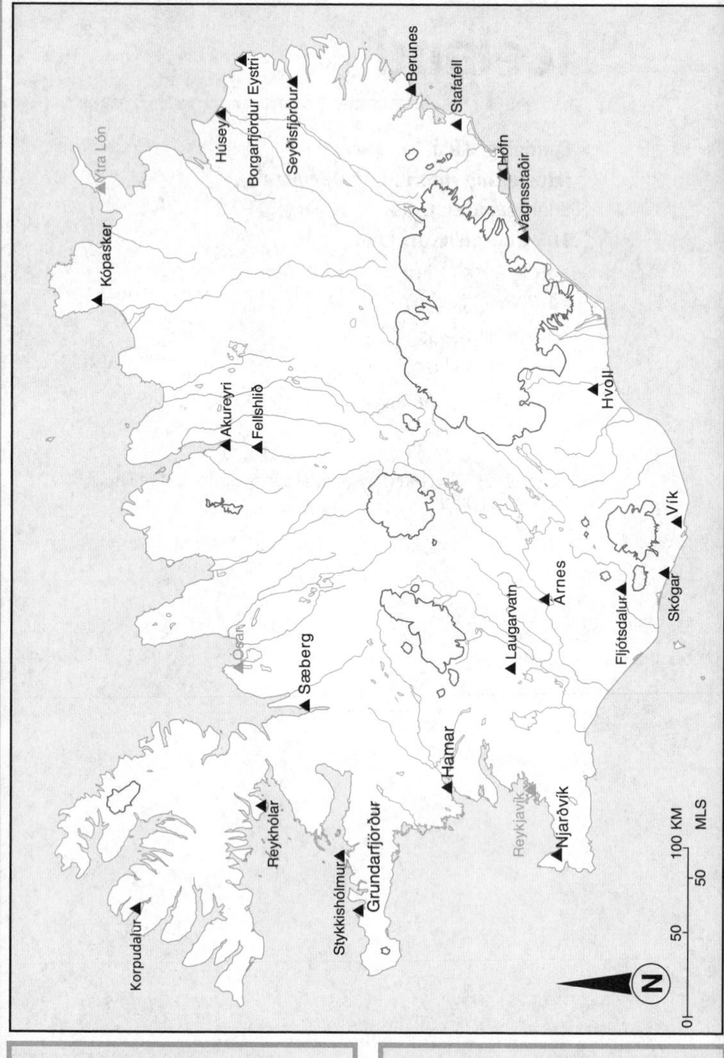

HI Suggests...

Iceland is an island of 103,000 sq km situated on the Mid-Atlantic Ridge. Glaciers, including the largest in Vatnajökull, which is the largest glacier in Europe, measuring 8,000 sq m, cover over 11% of the country. Iceland is a hot spot of volcanic and geothermal activity; 30 post-glacial volcanoes have erupted in the past two centuries. Natural hot water supplies much of the population with cheap, pollution-free heating. Rivers are also harnessed to provide inexpensive hydroelectric power.

In 930 the Icelandic settlers founded one of the world's first republic governments; the Old Commonwealth Age, which lasted until 1262, when Iceland lost its independence. In 1944 the present republic was founded. The country is governed by Althing (parliament), whose 63 members are elected every 4 years.

Out of a population of, approximately, 280,000 inhabitants, half live in the capital, Reykjavík, and in neighbouring towns in the southwest. The highland interior is uninhabited (and uninhabitable). Most centres of population are situated along the coast.

Iceland means new and different things for you to see and do whatever the season. Every part of the year has its special attractions, character and charm, and offers you different experiences. Don't let the name deceive you – Iceland can be surprisingly warm in the summer, when the sun shines virtually around the clock, while January temperatures drop to around 0°C.

Between north, south, west and east Iceland lies the "fifth dimension" the great interior of the Central Highlands where man can never make his home and is still a rare visitor. Here the nature is still at the rawest and most archetypal; glaciers, deserts of black sand, barren glacial moraine, steaming hot springs, active and extinct volcanoes and strange oases of vegetation, thriving against all the sub-artic odds.

Visiting Iceland is an experience of a lifetime and the opportunities for activities are endless. Hiking in the highlands, whale watching, riding tours, bird watching, river rafting, seeing the northern lights and swimming in outdoor geothermal pools are among the popular activities in Iceland.

There are 26 HI Hostels over the entire country, which welcome you. Over the last few years Hostelling International Iceland has worked to implement its environmental policy into the Hostels daily work. This has been well received and successful. The Hostels that already fulfil certain criteria in environmental work have received permission to be called Green Hostels and to use an environmental logo. Those Hostels are specially marked on our website and in our brochures. In June 2004, Reykjavík City Hostel received the Nordic Ecolabel, *The Swan*, for its environmental work.

The easiest way to travel around Iceland is by bus or car, as there are no trains in the country. The Travel section of Hostelling International Iceland offers packages consisting of rental cars or bus passes and overnight vouchers at hostels. Check our prices for those packages when planning your trip to Iceland. The Travel section also provides ideas relating to different tours and activities.

You can find out a lot more on our website - a visit to www.HIhostels.com is essential for planning your trip!

Pour en savoir plus, rendez-vous sur notre site Internet, www.HIhostels.com une visite incontournable pour préparer votre voyage!

Viele weitere Informationen auf unserer Website: www.HIhostels.com - unverzichtbar für die Reiseplanung!

Puedes averiguar mucho más en nuestro sitio web. Es imprescindible que visites la página www.HIhostels.com para planear tu viaje.

Akureyri – 26004
Stórholt 1, 600 Akureyri.
T 4623657; 8944299 F 4612549
e akureyri@hostel.is W www.hostel.is
Open Dates: 10.01-15.12 Open Times:
Beds: 62 - 3x1 6x2 6x3 2x4 1x5 2x6+

Akureyri

Akureyri... Travel Tips

- **For budget eats check out...** Greifinn, Bautinn, Litla Kaffistofan, Dominoz Pizza, Crown Chicen (all near Hostel)
- **For great nightlife try...** Græni Hatturinn, Kaffi Amor, Kaffi Akureyri, Pollurinn, Kaffi Carolina (all near Hostel)
- **Don't miss...** Botanic Garden, Akureyri Swimming Pool, Listagilið - Gallery Art Street, Mývatn, The waterfalls Godafoss & Aldeyjarfoss, National Park of Ásbyrgi, Grímsey/Hrísey, Ólafsfjördur & Siglufjördur, Laufás, Davidsshus

▲ Árnes – 26005
Gnúpverjahreppur, 801 Selfoss.
4866048; 8612645 4866044
arnes@hostel.is www.hostel.is
Open Dates: x 26 R CC

▲ Berunes – 26006
Berufjörd, 765 Djúpivogur.
4788988; 8697227 4788902
berunes@hostel.is www.hostel.is
Open Dates: 01.05-01.10 x 34 R CC

▲ Borgarfjördur Eystri – 26027
Ásbyrgi, 720 Borgarfjördur Eystri.
4729962; 8663913; 4729920 4729961
borgarfjordur@hostel.is www.hostel.is
Open Dates: 01.05-17.09 x 17 R TV

▲ Fellshlíð – 26028
Fellshlíð, 601 Akureyri.
4612491; 8498857 fellshlid@hostel.is
www.hostel.is
Open Dates: x 10 R TV 12km

*△ **Fljótsdalur** – 26007*
Fljótshlið, 861 Hvolsvollur.
4878498; 4878497 www.hostel.is
Open Dates: 15.04-15.10 x 15 R

▲ Grundarfjordur – 26008
Hlíðarvegur 15, 350 Grundarfjordur.
5626533; 6911769; 8956533 438643
grundarfjordur@hostel.is
www.hostel.is
Open Dates: 15.01-15.12 x 23 R CC (B)

▲ Hamar – 26009
Golfskálinn Hamri, 310 Borgarnes.
4371663 4372063
hamar@hostel.is www.hostel.is
Open Dates: x 18 R CC (B) 4km

▲ Höfn – Nýibær – 26010
Hafnarbraut 8, 780 Höfn.
4781736; 8642159 4781965
hofn@hostel.is www.hostel.is
Open Dates: 01.03-31.12 x 33 R CC

▲ Húsey – 26011
Tungnahreppur, 701 Egilsstadir.
4713010; 8548554 4713009
husey@simnet.is www.hostel.is
Open Dates: x 16 R CC

▲ Hvoll – 26013
Skaftárhreppur, 880 Klaustur.
4874785; 4874784 4874890
hvoll@hostel.is www.hostel.is
Open Dates: 01.03-01.11 x 70 R CC (B)

▲ Kópasker – 26014
Akurgerði 7, 670 Kópasker.
4652314; 8612314 8722105
hostel@kopasker.is www.hostel.is
Open Dates: 01.05-31.10 x 14 R

▲ **Korpudalur** – 26017
Korpudalur Kirkjubol, 425 Flateyri.
4567808; 8922030 4567808; (Winter) 5573620 korpudalur@hostel.is
www.hostel.is
Open Dates: 01.06-01.09 x 24
(B)
12km

▲ **Laugarvatn** – Dalsel – 26015
840 Laugarvatn.
4861215; 8995409 4861215
laugarvatn@hostel.is www.hostel.is
Open Dates: x 51
(B)

▲ **Njarðvík** – 26016
Fitjabraut 6a, 260 Njarðvík.
4218889 4218887
airport@hostel.is www.hostel.is
Open Dates: 01.05-01.10 Keflavík International 4km x 80
(B)

▲ **Ósar** 26018
Þverárhreppi, V-Hún, 531 Hvammstangi.
8622778; 4512678 4512978
osar@hostel.is www.hostel.is
Open Dates: 01.03-01.11 x 57

▲ **Reykhólar** – 26029
Álftaland, 380 Reykhólar, A-Barðarstrandasýslu.
4347878; 8659968 4347941
reykholar@hostel.is www.hostel.is
Open Dates: x 28
(B)

Reykjavík 26001
Sundlaugavegur 34, 105 Reykjavík.
5538110 5889201
reykjavik@hostel.is www.hostel.is
Open Dates: Open Times:
Beds: 164 - 10x2 18x4 12x6
Price Range: 1700-3500 IKR
Directions: 3W from city centre
Keflavík International 50km A The flybus drives passengers to the hostel on request. There is also a pick up service from the hostel for most international flights.
14 (10 mins to City Centre & Central Bus Station) 100m ap 1 x 30
(B) 1 x
200m

Reykjavík

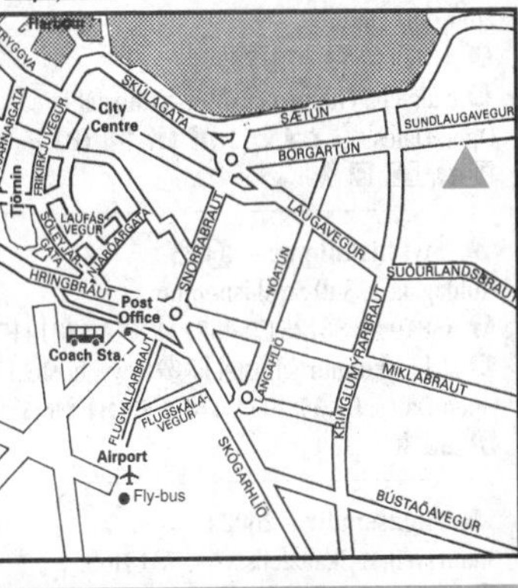

Reykjavík... Travel Tips

- **For budget eats check out...** The Culture House, Vegamót, One Woman Restaurant, Litli Ljóti Andarunginn (all in City Centre)
- **For great nightlife try...** Kaffibarinn, Kaffibrennslan, Ölstofan, Kaffi List, Vegamót (all in City Centre)
- **Don't miss...** the Spounting Geysers, to splash about in Blue Lagoon, local concerts, elves, relaxing in a hot tub, glacier hiking, the northern lights (winter), husky dog racing (winter), New Years Eve in Reykjavík, Tickets for sightseeing tours available from the hostel

▲ **Sæberg** – 26019
Reykir, Hrútafjörður, 500 Brú.
4510015; 8945504 4510034
saeberg@hostel.is www.hostel.is
Open Dates: 01.01-30.11 x 42
(B)

▲ **Seyðisfjörður** – Hafaldan – 26020
Ránargata 9, 710 Seyðisfjörður.
4721410; 8917010 4721610
seydisfjordur@hostel.is www.hostel.is
Open Dates: 15.04-15.10 x 28

▲ **Skógar** – 26030
Skógar, 861 Hvolsvöllur.
4878801; 8995955 4878955
skogar@hostel.is www.hostel.is
Open Dates: 15.05-15.09 x 30

▲ **Stafafell** – 26022
Lóni, 781 Höfn.
t 4781717 f 4781785
e stafafel@eldhorn.is w www.hostel.is
Open Dates: 12 x 52 (B)

▲ **Stykkishólmur** – 26023
Höfðagata 1, 340 Stykkishólmur.
t 4381095; 8612517; 4381417 f 4381417
e stykkisholmur@hostel.is w www.hostel.is
Open Dates: 01.05-30.09 x 50

▲ **Vagnsstadir** – 26024
Sudursveit, A-Skaftafellssysla, 781 Höfn.
t 4781048; 4781567 f 4782167
e glacierjeeps@simnet.is w www.hostel.is
Open Dates: 10.06-01.09 x 28
R CC (B)

▲ **Vík** – Norður - Vík – 26025
Suðurvíkurvegur 5, 870 Vík.
t 4871106; 8672389 f 4871303
e vik@hostel.is w www.hostel.is
Open Dates: 01.04-01.11 x 36
R CC

▲ **Ytra Lón** HI 26026
Langanes, 681 Þórshöfn.
t 4681242; 8543797 f 4681242
e ytralon@hostel.is w www.hostel.is
Open Dates: 12 x 16 (B)
14km

India

Youth Hostels Association of India,
5 Nyaya Marg, Chanakyapuri,
New Delhi 110 021, India.
t (91) (11) 26871969; 26110250
f (91) (11) 26113469
Telegraphic address: 'Youthostel, New Delhi 110 021'
e yhostel@del2.vsnl.net.in
w www.yhaindia.org

A copy of the Hostel Directory for this Country can be obtained from: The National Office.

National Tourist Authority/Board:	www.Indiaconsulate.org; www.tourisminindia.com/traveltips
Capital:	New Delhi
Language:	Hindi
Currency:	Rs (rupees)
Population:	1,065,898,900
Size:	3,287,590 sq km
Telephone Country Code:	91
eKit Access Number:	000-800-100-3004

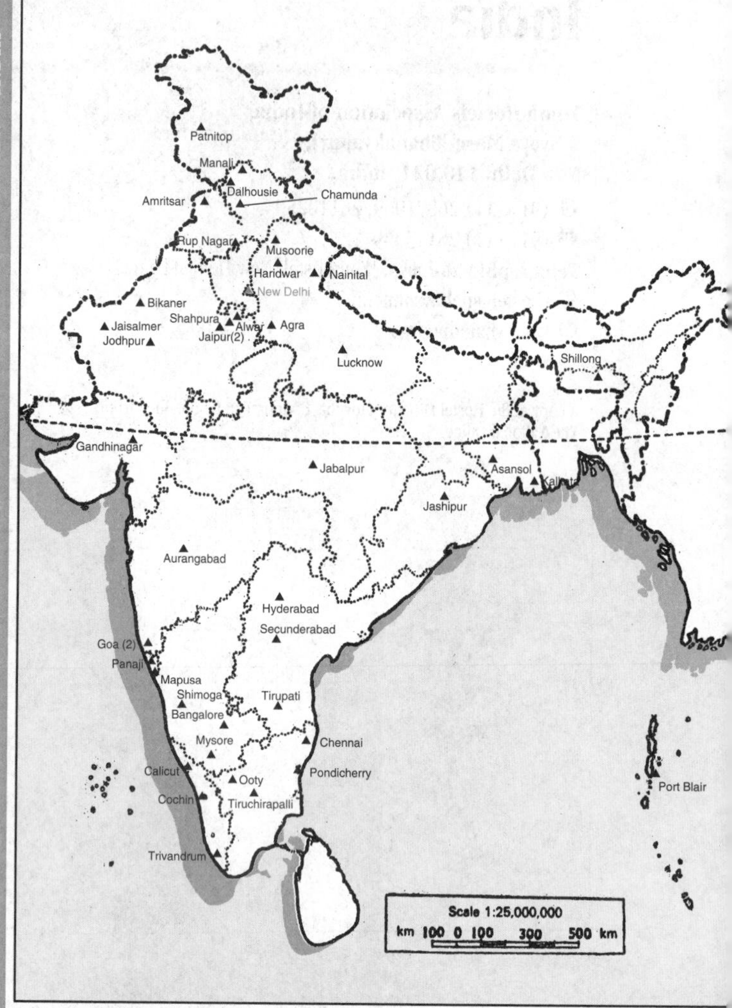

India has a rich and distinct identity that has arisen from the surges of migrating people who have entered the country over the last several thousand years. It is impossible to speak of any one Indian culture, although there are deep cultural continuities that unite its people. English is the major language of trade and politics, Hindi is the most spoken language, and there are fourteen other official languages. There are twenty-four languages that are spoken by a million people or more, and numerous other dialects.

New Delhi, the capital city, is located in the northern part of the country, in the Indo-Gangetic plain. This is southwest of the great Himalayan range, which includes some of the world's highest mountains. India is the second most populous nation in the world, with nearly a billion citizens, so it's hardly surprising that the city streets are crowded, bustling and full of noise and colour.

Religion is primary to Indian culture,

and religious customs can be seen in practically every aspect of life. The dominant faith of India is Hinduism, practised by approximately 80 percent of the population; 10 percent follow Islam; 5 percent are Sikhs and Christians; the rest (excluding a few smaller religious groups) are Buddhists, Jains and Bahai.

The Indian people are quite particular about whom they associate with outside their society, and can consequently appear to be somewhat "closed," or insulated. However, outwardly they are friendly, warm and hospitable to visitors.

A few other Top Tips from **CULTURE SMART!**:

- Indians believe in *karma*, which is based on the idea that "what goes around will come around again;" consequently they tend to worry less than Westerners about such matters as missed opportunities; and believe that your behaviour in this life will affect you in your next life. If, for example, you did something wicked in a past life, you will, according to the rules of *karma*, be suffering now.
- Try to ensure that the food you eat has been thoroughly cooked and is served hot. It is also essential to drink water that has been boiled or otherwise sterilized, to avoid the dreaded "Delhi belly."
- The standard greeting in India is a Hindu gesture known as the *namaste*. You make a slight bow, with the palms of your hands together and the fingertips at about chin level.
- Visitors should be aware that traditional Indian clothes should be worn in the correct way. For example the *salwar* and the *kameez* should always be worn together.

Cultural Top Tips supplied by Culture Smart! guides. These essential guides to customs and etiquette will help you steer clear of embarrassing gaffes and sensitive issues, enabling you to discover new cultures whilst developing new friendships. Order online at www.culturesmartguides.co.uk

You can find out a lot more on our website - a visit to www.HIhostels.com is essential for planning your trip!

Pour en savoir plus, rendez-vous sur notre site Internet, www.HIhostels.com une visite incontournable pour préparer votre voyage!

Viele weitere Informationen auf unserer Website: www.HIhostels.com - unverzichtbar für die Reiseplanung!

Puedes averiguar mucho más en nuestro sitio web. Es imprescindible que visites la página www.HIhostels.com para planear tu viaje.

△ ***Agra*** *– Youth Hostel Agra – 27003*
Sanjay Place, M G Rd, Hari Parwat Crossing, Agra 282002, Uttar Pradesh.
(0562) 2854462
Open Dates: x 86

▲ **Alwar** – Youth Hostel Alwar – 27005
1 C.E.B, Near P.W.D. Rest House, Near Railway Station, Alwar - 301001, Rajasthan.
(144) 2339354; 2332883; 2332011; Mob: 9828112101 (144) 2332011
hotelaravali@rediffmail.com; achal_kakkar@hotmail.com
Open Dates: 100m x 44

△ ***Amritsar** – Youth Hostel Amritsar – 27053*
G.T. Road, Nr. Panch Peer, Amritsar - 143 001 (Punjab).
(0183) 5534993
Open Dates: x 59

▲ **Asansol** – Youth Hostel Asansol – 27059
c/o Jubilee Resorts JRO Complex Kanyapur Asansol Bypass, NH-2, Dist. Burdwan West Bengal.
(0341) 2254842; 2254845
jubileeresortsasansollyh@yahoo.com
Open Dates: 6km 2km x 32

△ ***Aurangabad** – Youth Hostel Aurangabad – 27006*
Padampura Corner, Station Rd, Aurangabad 431005, Maharashtra.
(240) 2334892
Open Dates: x 60

▲ **Bangalore** – Youth Hostel Bangalore – 27048
65/2 Milers Road, Benson Town Cantt., Bangalore - 560 046 Karnataka.
(080) 23540849; 25924040; 25924343
bangalore_youthhostel@yahoo.co.in
Open Dates: 10km Bangalore Cantt (5mins walk); Bangalore 14km 1.5km x 64

▲ **Bikaner** – Youth Hostel Bikaner – 27054
c/o Shri Ram Hotel, A-228 Sadul Ganj, Bikaner - 334 003 Rajasthan.
(0151) 2522651; 2521320; Mob: 09351201102 (0151) 2209181
shriramhotel@yahoo.com
Open Dates: Jodhpur 250km 3km 3.5km x 26

△ ***Calicut (Kozhikode)** – Youth Hostel Calicut (Kozhikode) – 27009*
East Hill, PO West Hill, Calicut - 673005, Kerala.
(495) 2381354
Open Dates: 30km 14km 7km 7NE x 50

▲ **Chamunda** – Youth Hostel Chamunda – 27050
Mata Shri Chamunda Devi, Chamunda (Dharamshala) Kangra Valley, Himachal Pradesh.
(01892) 252207; 201411; 236538; Mob: 09418105034 atithi@sancharnet.in
Open Dates: 8km 1km x 26

▲ **Chennai** – Youth Hostel Chennai – 27010
2nd Avenue, Indira Nagar, Chennai - 600 020, Tamil Nadu.
(44) 24420233
Open Dates: 15km 15km 14km 15NE x 44

△ ***Cochin** – Youth Hostel Kochi – 27011*
NGO Qtrs Junction Thrikkakara, Kakanadu Route Distt Ernakulam, Cochin, 682021 Kerala.
(484) 2422808; 2424399
Open Dates: A *25km 23km 8km* 10NE x 51

▲ **Dalhousie** – Youth Hostel Dalhousie – 27012
Near bus-stand, Dalhousie 176304, Himachal Pradesh.
(1899) 242189 (1899) 240929
yh_dalhousie@rediffmail.com
Open Dates: A 500m x 66

△ ***Gandhinagar** – Youth Hostel Gandhinagar – 27014*
Opposite Government Arts & Science College, Sector -16, Gandhinagar 382016, Gujarat.
(79) 23222364 (79) 23242057
Open Dates: 1km 2NE x 56 (BD)

▲ **Goa** – Youth Hostel Calangute – 27052
c/o Anup Guest House, Calangute Beach, Goa.
(0832) 2281095; 2281249; Mob: 09326100119
anuphome@yahoo.co.in
Open Dates: 45km Margaon 20km Panjim 20km x 40

▲ **Goa** – Youth Hostel Dona Paula – 27058
c/o M/s Sea View Hotel,
Next to Dona Paula Police Station,
P.O. N.I.O. Dona Paula, Tiswadi Goa 403 004.
(0832) 2453427
hotelsea_view@yahoo.com
Open Dates: 23km 8km
x 56

▲ **Haridwar** – Youth Hostel Haridwar – 27061
c/o Hotel Sant, Sant Kabir Marg,
Nr. UCO Bank, Sharvan Nath Nagar, Haridwar, Uttaranchal.
(01334) 227534; Mob: 09412025255
santhotel@rediffmail.com
Open Dates: JollyGrant, Dehradoon 35km 500m 500m x 18

▲ **Hyderabad** – Youth Hostel Hyderabad – 27049
c/o Sri Sai Guardian, The Main/ 1-8-702/26,
Padma Colony, Beh. Shenkermutt, Nallakunta, Hyderabad.
(040) 27620960; 55508393;
Mob: 09396539854; 09246539854
sai_theguardian@yahoo.co.in;
youthhostel_hyderabad@yahoo.co.in
Open Dates: x 90

△ ***Jabalpur*** *– Youth Hostel Jabalpur – 27018*
Sports Complex, Patrakar Colony, Ranital,
Jabalpur 482 002 (Madhya Pradesh).
(761) 22415256; 25016734
Open Dates: 250m 35km
x 35

▲ **Jaipur** – Licensee Youth Hostel Jaipur – 27060
c/o. Hotel Residency Inn,
D-81 Shiva Hira Path, Chomu House,
Jaipur-302001 Rajasthan.
(0141) 2369966; 2361971;
Mob: 09829222230 (0141) 5125354
residencyinnjaipur@hotmail.com
Open Dates: Jaipur 15km 1km
1km x 28
1 x

▲ **Jaipur** – Youth Hostel Jaipur – 27019
Janpath, Near S.M.S Stadium, Jaipur 302004, Rajasthan.
(141) 2740515; 2741130
Open Dates: 13km 4NE x 75

▲ **Jaisalmer** – Youth Hostel Jaisalmer – 27062
c/o Hotel Payal, Nr. Gadisar Gate, Jaisalmer, Rajasthan.
(2992) 251230; 251231;
Mob: 09414149237 (2992) 251228
hotelpayal@yahoo.co.in
Open Dates: x 18

▲ **Jodhpur** – Youth Hostel Jodhpur – 27020
Circuit House Rd, Ratanada, Jodhpur 342011, Rajasthan.
(291) 2517160; 2629902
(291) 2510160
youthhosteljodhpur@indiatimes.com;
youthhosteljodhpur@yahoo.com.in
Open Dates: 3km 2NE x 60

▲ **Kolkata** – Youth Hostel Kolkata – 27063
c/o. Vulcan House, 1D, Hem Dey Lane,
Kolkata - 700 050 West Bengal.
(33) 25569394
vulcantrading@vsnl.net
Open Dates: 9km 9km
100m x 18

▲ **Lucknow** – Youth Hostel Lucknow – 27046
Jawahar Lal Nehru Youth Centre,
Niket Rumi Gate Chowk,
Lucknow Uttar Pradesh.
(522) 2253340
youthhostellko@yahoo.com
Open Dates: 20km 9km
3km x 82

▲ **Manali** – Youth Hostel Manali – 27022
c/o Sarthak Resorts, Vill. & PO Khakhnal, Naggar Road,
Teh. Manali Distt. Kullu - 175143, Himachal Pradesh.
(0192) 259623; Mob: 09816002323
(0192) 259623
manaliyouthhostel@yahoo.com
www.sarthak.resorts.com
Open Dates: Bhuntar 49km x 50

▲ **Mapusa** – Youth Hostel Mapusa – 27024
Paddam Sports Complex, Peddam,
Goa Mumbai Road, Mapusa 403 507,
Goa (North).
(832) 2257534; 2257741
Open Dates: 45km 45km
5km 2NE x 80

▲ **Mussoorie** – Youth Hostel Mussoorie – 27025
Bhatta Village, Nr Mussoorie Lake,
Dist. Dehradun, Mussoorie, Uttaranchal.
(135) 2630504; 2635190; 2633190
Mob: 09358125768 (135) 2630504
yh_musoorie@sancharnet.in
Open Dates: x 72

▲ **Mysore** – Youth Hostel Mysore – 27026
Opp. Maruthi Temple, HUDCO 2nd Stage,
Gangotri Layout, Saraswatipuram,
Mysore 570009, Karnataka.
(821) 2544704 (821) 2542012
yhmysore@sancharnet.in;
warden@inablers.com
www.yhmysore.com
Open Dates: 5.5km x 112
(BD)

△ ***Nainital** – Youth Hostel Nainital – 27028*
Ardwell, Mallital, Nainital 263001, Uttaranchal.
(5942) 236353; 236168
Open Dates: 60km 35km 1NE
x 48 (LD)

New Delhi – International YH 27001
5 Nyaya Marg, Chanakyapuri,
New Delhi 110021.
(11) 26116285; 24101246
(11) 26113469
yhostel@del2.vsnl.net.in
www.yhaindia.org
Open Dates: Open Times:
Beds: 166
Price Range: Rs 70-250 (Dormitory); Rs 300-700 (Rooms)
Directions: Indira Gandhi International 16km A White Line Bus 16km New Delhi 8km, Delhi Main 16km, Nizamuddin 8km 604, 620, 640, 680, 720 ap Chanakyapuri Police Station, New Delhi 350m x 4
3km

New Delhi – International YH

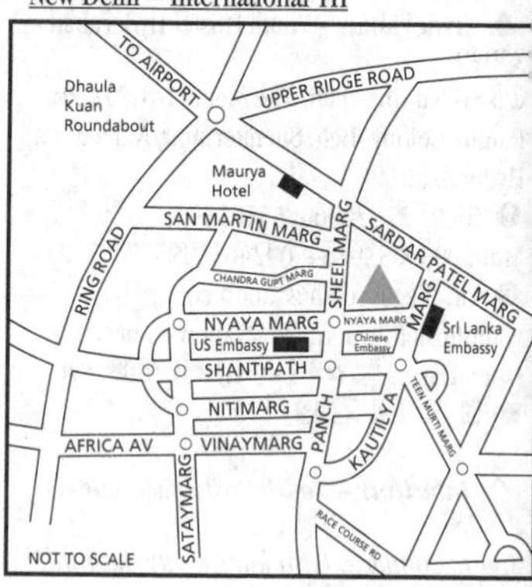

New Delhi... Travel Tips

- **For budget eats check out...** International Youth Hostel, Nirulas Chain of Hotels, Shah-en-Shah, Talkatora Stadium, Moti Mahal (Malcha Marg), Lazeaz Affair (Malcha Marg)
- **For great nightlife try...** Floats Hotel Park Royal (Nehru Place), Ghunghroo Bar & Pub - Maurya Sheratan Hotel, Rodeo Inner Circle (Connaught Place)
- **Don't miss...** Qutab Minar, Red Fort, Lotus Temple, India Gate, Birla Temple, Lodhi Tomb, Gurudwara Bangla Sahib, Jama Masjid, National Museum, Raj Ghat

▲ **Ooty** – Youth Hostel Ooty – 27030
42, South Lake Road, Fern Hills,
Ooty - 643004, Tamil Nadu.
(423) 2447506
ootyyouthhostel@hotmail.com
Open Dates: 12 A 2km 2km
x 54 R P

▲ **Panaji** – Youth Hostel Panaji – 27031
Miramar, Panaji 403001, Goa.
(832) 2225433 (832) 2420735
yhpanaji@rediffmail.com
Open Dates: 12 x 60 R
P

△ ***Patnitop*** – *Youth Hostel Patnitop – 27034*
PO Kud 182142, Dist Udhampur, J&K.
(1992) 287524
Open Dates: 12 1NE x 44 R
P

△ ***Pondicherry*** – *Youth Hostel Pondicherry – 27035*
Neithal St, Solai Nagar, Muthialpet, 605003, Pondicherry.
(413) 2237495
Open Dates: 12 x 36 R
P

△ ***Port Blair*** – *Youth Hostel Port Blair – 27036*
Aberdeen Bazar, PO 744104, Port Blair, Andaman and Nicobar Islands.
(3792) 232459; 232438
Open Dates: 12 x 38 P

△ ***Rup Nagar (Ropar)*** – *Youth Hostel Rupnagar – 27038*
Near New Bus Stand,
Opposite Nehru Stadium,
Rup Nagar (Ropar), 141001 Punjab.
(1881) 220350
Open Dates: 12 *50km* *1km* 1NE
x 48 R TV
8 P

△ ***Secunderabad*** – *Youth Hostel Secunderabad – 27039*
5-4-203 Near Sailing Club, Secunderabad, Andhra Pradesh.
(40) 27540763; 27543004
ramamturaga@yahoo.com;
secunderabadyouthhostel@yahoo.com
Open Dates: 12 3NE x 100 R
P

▲ **Shahpura** – Youth Hostel Shahpura – 27040
H.P.I., Shahpura Industrial Area, NH-8,
Shahpura, Jaipur (Rural) - 303103,
Rajasthan.
(1422) 222322 (1422) 223023
sinhankur@rediffmail.com
Open Dates: 12 1km 2NE x 34
P

▲ **Shillong** – Youth Hostel Shillong – 27041
Opposite Central Telegraph Office,
Vivekananda Marg, Shillong 793001,
Meghalaya.
(364) 2224382; 2222246
(364) 2222246
Open Dates: 12 35km 0.25NE x 49
R 8 P

▲ **Shimoga** – Youth Hostel Shimoga – 27064
c/o. Hotel Mathura Regency, Balraj Urs Road,
Shimoga 577 021 Karnataka.
(8182) 260255; 260244
(8182) 260255
mathurashimoga@indiatimes.com
Open Dates: 12 R

△ ***Tiruchirapalli*** – *Youth Hostel Tiruchirapalli – 27042*
Near Anna Stadium, Khaja Malai,
Tiruchirapalli 620 023, Tamil Nadu.
(431) 2421508
yhtrichy@rediffmail.com
Open Dates: 12 *4km* *3km* 3E
x 46 R P

△ ***Tirupati*** – *Youth Hostel Tirupati – 27043*
Near Reserve Police Quarters, M R Palli,
Tirupati - 517 502, Andhra Pradesh.
(877) 2240300
yhtirupati@hotmail.com;
yhtirupati@yahoo.co.in
Open Dates: 12 *15km* *1.5km* 1.5S
x 46 R 8 P

△ ***Trivandrum (Thiruvananthapuram)*** – *Youth Hostel Veli – 27044*
Near Boat Club, Veli, Trivandrum 695021, Kerala.
(471) 2501230
yh.veli@123india.com
Open Dates: 12 *4km* *15km* *6km*
x 44 P

Ireland (Northern)

Hostelling International - Northern Ireland,
22 Donegall Road, Belfast,
BT12 5JN, Northern Ireland.
t (44) (28) 9032 4733
f (44) (28) 9043 9699
e info@hini.org.uk
w www.hini.org.uk

Office Hours: Monday-Friday 09.00-17.00hrs

A copy of the Hostel Directory for this Country can be obtained from:
The National Office

National Tourist Authority/Board:	www.discovernorthernireland.com
Capital:	Belfast
Language:	English
Currency:	£ (Sterling)
Population:	1,578,100
Size:	14,120 sq km
Telephone Country Code:	44
eKit Access Number:	0800-032-6297

HI Suggests...

Northern Ireland is fast emerging as a new land to be discovered. A land of immense history and culture, Northern Ireland is now embracing the future and turning its attention to welcoming visitors to their undiscovered world.

Although small in size, Northern Ireland offers a wealth of experiences for any discerning traveller. It is home to some of the most spectacular scenery, the friendliest locals and a new and exciting vibe in its cities. Beneath all this lies the heart of Northern Ireland, the history and culture, which tell the story of thousands of years and makes this land the unique and passionate place that it is today.

As a country that is taking its first major steps in tourism, Northern Ireland is hugely supportive and welcoming to its guests. The people are laid back, friendly and more than willing to provide advice or help to make your stay more enjoyable.

Tradition and customs in Northern Ireland are strong and it is well worth experiencing these in order to appreciate the true nature of this land. Pipe bands, Irish dancing, native Gaelic sports and the many murals illustrate the passion of the people in Northern Ireland and the history and tradition, which underpins the two main communities.

Time out in Northern Ireland can take a variety of forms. Mainly rural in landscape there are many areas of great natural beauty and activities include hiking in the Mourne Mountains, taking in the breathtaking North coast, exploring the beautiful forest parks or relaxing on the Fermanagh Lakelands. Activity sports, on land or water, are also widely available. Time can also be spent delving into the history of Northern Ireland by taking a tour of the murals in Belfast, visiting the many museums and exploring heritage sites such as the burial ground of St. Patrick, the patron saint of Ireland. Attractions to visit include the World heritage Site, the Giants Causeway; the Carrick-A-Rede Ropebridge; the Marble Arch Caves; the Aquarium in Portaferry and the historic walls of Derry City.

As the sun sets in Northern Ireland the action does not stop and pubs can be found in even the smallest village where the locals will finish the day with a pint and enjoy some traditional music.

Belfast is a new and vibrant city which plays host to the many bars, clubs and award winning restaurants that make this city come alive. The Odyssey in Belfast is a new entertainment complex with clubs, bars and the arena, which is home to the Belfast Giants ice hockey team and a multitude of international stars stop to perform there.

Getting around Northern Ireland is relatively easy by train and bus, which service even the most rural communities. Dublin is only two hours away by train and low cost flights now link with most main cities in Europe and the UK.

You can find out a lot more on our website - a visit to www.HIhostels.com is essential for planning your trip!

Pour en savoir plus, rendez-vous sur notre site Internet, www.HIhostels.com une visite incontournable pour préparer votre voyage!

Viele weitere Informationen auf unserer Website: www.HIhostels.com - unverzichtbar für die Reiseplanung!

Puedes averiguar mucho más en nuestro sitio web. Es imprescindible que visites la página www.HIhostels.com para planear tu viaje.

▲ **Armagh City** (H) 29011
39 Abbey St, Armagh BT61 7EB.
(t) (28) 3751 1800 (f) (28) 3751 1801
(e) info@hini.org.uk (w) www.hini.org.uk
Open Dates: 02.01-23.12 ✈ Belfast International 64km [ferry] Belfast 64km [train] Poradown 20km [bus] 1km [0.2SW]
[beds] x 62

Belfast – International YH (H) 29002
22 Donegall Rd, Belfast BT12 5JN.
(t) (28) 9031 5435 (f) (28) 9043 9699
(e) info@hini.org.uk (w) www.hini.org.uk
Open Dates: [12] Open Times: [clock]
Beds: 202 - 25x2 22x4 5x6 2x6+
Price Range: £12.50-£13.50 € 20.00-21.60
Directions: [1SW] from city centre
✈ Belfast International 30.6km [ferry] Larne 35.7km, Donegall Quay 3.2km [train] Central 5km [bus] 89, 90 from City centre ap YH

Belfast – International YH

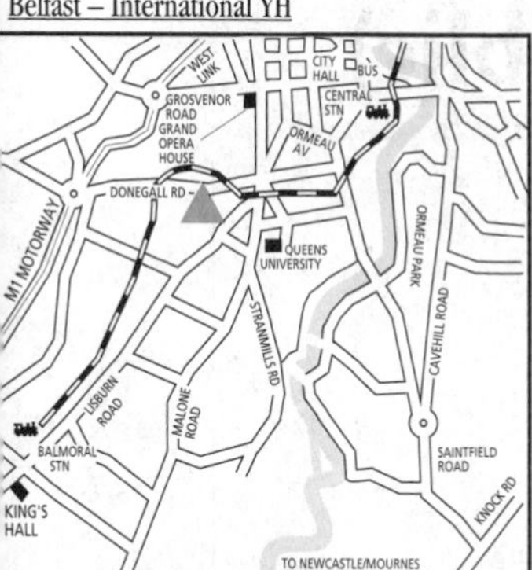

Belfast... Travel Tips

- **For budget eats check out...** Bishops - Fish and Chips, Maggie May's Belfast Café, The Other Place, Wok Express, Flannigans
- **For great nightlife try...** Grand Opera House, U.G.C. Cinema, The Crown, The Fly, Belfast Superbowl
- **Don't miss...** Botanic Gardens, Ulster Museum, W5 (Odyssey), St. Anne's Cathedral, Wall Mural Tour, Joyce Boat Trip, City Hall Tour, Ulster Folk & Transport Museum, Lagan Lookout, St. George's Market

▲ **Bushmills** – Hostelling International Bushmills HI 29013
49 Main Street, Bushmills,
County Antrim BT57 8QA.
t (28) 2073 1222 f (28) 2073 0493
e info@hini.org.uk w www.hini.org.uk
Open Dates: 02.01-23.12 ✈ Belfast International 80km ⛴ Belfast 104km 🚂 Portrush 8km 🚌 Portrush 50m
x 74 1 x

▲ **Enniskillen** – Hostelling International Enniskillen HI 29012
Belmore Street, Enniskillen,
Co. Fermanagh BT74 6AA.
t (28) 6634 0110 f (28) 6634 6873
e info@hini.org.uk w www.hini.org.uk
Open Dates: 02.01-23.12 ✈ Belfast 130km ⛴ Belfast 130km 🚂 Sligo 72km 🚌 500m x 70 2 x

▲ **Gortin** – Gortin Youth Hostel – 29015
62 Main Street, Gortin, Omagh,
Co. Tyrone BT79 8NH.
t (28) 8164 8346 f (28) 8164 8346
e visit.gortin@virgin.net w www.gortin.net
Open Dates: 12 ✈ Belfast International 130km ⛴ Belfast 130km 🚌 200m
x 40 1 x

▲ **Newcastle** HI 29005
30 Downs Rd, Newcastle, Co Down BT33 0AG.
t (28) 4372 2133 f (28) 4372 2133
e info@hini.org.uk
Open Dates: 01.03-23.12 ✈ Belfast International 70km ⛴ Belfast 50km 🚌 200m x 40

▲ **Whitepark Bay** HI 29006
157 Whitepark Bay Rd, Ballintoy,
Co Antrim BT54 6NH.
t (28) 2073 1745 f (28) 2073 2034
e info@hini.org.uk w www.hini.org.uk
Open Dates: 01.03-31.10 ✈ Belfast International 80km 🚂 Portrush 19km 🚌 200m 9W x 54

Ireland (Republic)

An Óige, Irish Youth Hostel Association,
61 Mountjoy Street,
Dublin 7, Republic of Ireland
t (353) (1) 8304555
f (353) (1) 8305808
e mailbox@anoige.ie; groups@anoige.ie
w www.irelandyha.org

Office Hours: Monday-Friday 09.00-17.30hrs

A copy of the Hostel Directory for this Country can be obtained from:
The National Office or the Irish Tourist Board (office in most countries).

National Tourist Authority/Board:	www.ireland.travel.ie; www.tourismireland.com
Capital:	Dublin
Language:	English/Irish
Currency:	€ Euro
Population:	4,000,000
Size:	70,283 sq km
Telephone Country Code:	353
eKit Access Number:	1800-992-363

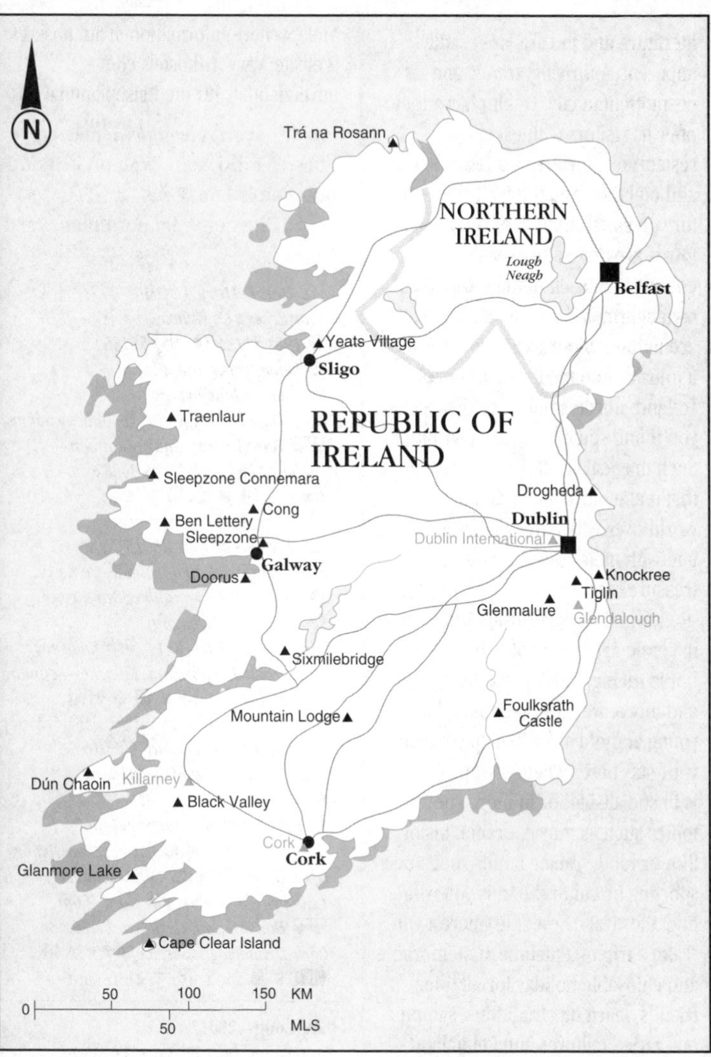

HI Suggests...

Cead Mille Fáilte – A Thousand welcomes to the Emerald Isle where enchanting people, landscape and spectacular scenery await you. The warm and friendly Irish people are the very heartbeat of Ireland where visitors are greeted in an old-age tradition of hospitality. It has been said that once you visit Ireland you will not forget it and this will be evident by the fond memories of our people and land you take with you and cherish.

Vast amounts of historical castles, quaint Irish cottages and emerald rolling hills all add to the truly magical scenery throughout the island. Fifty shades of green describes the colors of Ireland – just one of the reasons why we call it the Emerald Isle.

Visit our capital and world famous city of Dublin, which has always had a reputation, as a great historical city, and its strong links with world literature and the arts are readily apparent. A thriving, trendy and cosmopolitan city, Dublin has a lot to offer its visitors with excellent restaurants, theatres, galleries, bars and nightlife. And if the city life is not for you small traditional villages and towns are dotted all over the countryside, each of them with their own charm and characteristics that are unique to our native country. Take a journey into the four corners of Ireland, north, south, east or west and you'll find something for everyone. Such magical scenery and greenery that make our country famous the world over will leave you breathless and with memories that you will treasure forever.

Renowned for its festivals and events, its 'craic agus ceol', St Patrick's Day, horse racing, hurling, Gaelic football and more, we have something for the young and old alike to help you enjoy your stay here. Whether your interest is in socialising, or in more specific topics such as music, drama, history, film or food, tracing family roots, or in sporting or cultural events you will find a festival or event to interest you.

Take a trip of a lifetime, a memorable and enjoyable holiday for all. Meet friends, learn our traditions, sample our varied cultures and Celtic land – simply come to Ireland and just have fun!

You can find out a lot more on our website - a visit to www.HIhostels.com is essential for planning your trip!

Pour en savoir plus, rendez-vous sur notre site Internet, www.HIhostels.com une visite incontournable pour préparer votre voyage!

Viele weitere Informationen auf unserer Website: www.HIhostels.com - unverzichtbar für die Reiseplanung!

Puedes averiguar mucho más en nuestro sitio web. Es imprescindible que visites la página www.HIhostels.com para planear tu viaje.

△ ***Ben Lettery*** *– 28014*
Near Recess, Co Galway.
(95) 51136 (95) 51136
benlettery@hotmail.com
www.irelandyha.org
Open Dates: 01.03-30.11 Galway 64km Bus Eireann: Galway-Clifden - Michael Nee Coaches 095 34682 ap YH x 50

△ ***Black Valley*** *– 28015*
Near Beaufort, Gap of Dunloe, Co Kerry.
(64) 34712 mailbox@anoige.ie
www.irelandyha.org
Open Dates: 01.03-30.11 Killarney 30km Bus Eireann: Killarney-Kenmare Service x 46

△ ***Cape Clear Island*** *– 28016*
South Harbour, Cape Clear Island, Skibbereen, Co Cork.
(28) 41968 mailbox@anoige.ie; anoige@fenlon.net www.irelandyha.org
Open Dates: Cape Clear Ferry 11.00hrs & 14.00hrs Cork 100m Bus Eireann: Cork-Skibbereen or Cork-Drimoleague service x 36 R 1 x 8 13km

▲ **Cong** – 28017
Lisloughrey, Quay Rd, Cong, Co Mayo.
(94) 9546089 (94) 9546448
mailbox@anoige.ie
www.irelandyha.org
Open Dates: Galway 39km; Westport 42km x 80 CC 1 x

▲ **Connemara** – Sleepzone Connemara – 28038
Leenane, Connemara, Co. Galway.
(1) 8304555 (1) 8305808
mailbox@anoige.ie
www.irelandyha.org
Open Dates: x 91 R TV

Cork – International Youth Hostel 28004
1-2 Redclyffe, Western Rd, Cork.
(21) 4543289 (21) 4343715
corkyh@gofree.indigo.ie
www.irelandyha.org
Open Dates: Open Times:
Beds: 98 - 2x 7x 8x 2x
Price Range: € 14-25
Directions: 2W from city centre
Cork 5km A to Central Bus Station 1km Cork (Seasonal) 16km Cork 2km No 8 from City 1km ap YH x 18

Cork – International Youth Hostel

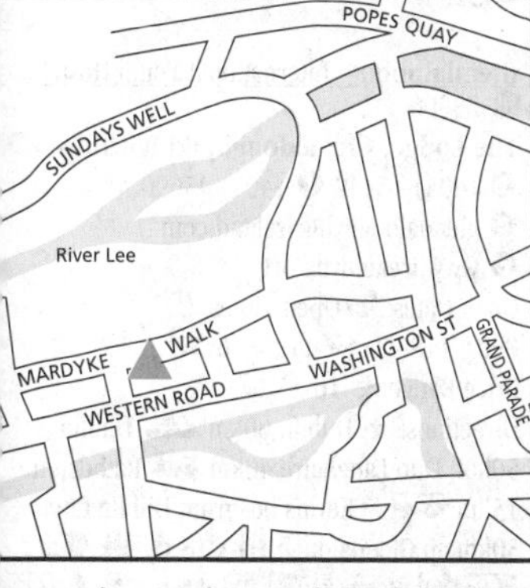

Cork... Travel Tips

- **For budget eats check out...** Supermac's (City Centre Locations), Castelli - Italian Bar & Restaurant, (29 Prince's St.), Kafkas (7 Maylor St.), Nash 19 (19 Prince's St.), Yumi Yuki Club - Triskel Arts Centre
- **For great nightlife try...** O'Riordans (Washington St.), The Washington (Washington St.), Everyman Palace Theatre (MacCurtain St.)
- **Don't miss...** Cork City Gaol, Blarney Castle Estate, Riverstown House, Ballincollig Gun Powder Mills, Old Middleton Distillery, West Cork Model Railway Village, Cobh Heritage Trust, Barryscourt Castle, Millstreet Country Park, Lisselan Estate Gardens

△ ***Doorus House*** *– 28019*
Near Kinvara, Co Galway.
(91) 637512 (91) 637512
doorushouse@kinvara.com
www.irelandyha.org
Open Dates: Galway 29km Galway 29km Galway-Dublin service via Ballyvaughan x 56 1km

△ ***Downings*** *– Trá na Rosann – 28020*
Downings, Co. Donegal.
(74) 9155374 mailbox@anoige.ie
www.irelandyha.org
Open Dates: 27.05-30.09 Derry 71km Gallaghers Bus from Letterkenny x 24

▲ **Drogheda** – Green Door Hostel – 28021
47 John Street, Drogheda, Co. Louth.
(41) 9834422 (41) 9800854
mailbox@anoige.ie
www.irelandyha.org
Open Dates: Dublin 25km A Bus Eireann: Dublin-Drogheda Bus Eireann: Dublin-Drogheda x 50 1 x

Dublin – International Youth Hostel
28001
61 Mountjoy St., Dublin 7.
(1) 8301766 (1) 8301600
dublininternational@anoige.ie
www.irelandyha.org
Open Dates: Open Times:
Beds: 289 - 2x 3x 7x 9x 22x
Price Range: € 18-26 (discounts for HI members) BB inc
Directions: 1NW from city centre
Dublin 6km A 41/41a/41b/41c 500m Dublin 4km; Dun Laoghaire 10km Connolly 2km; Heuston 3km 10, 16A, 19, 120 ap 747 Airlink to Bus Áras U Connolly 2km x 14 R CC 1 x 1.5km

Dublin – International Youth Hostel

Dublin... Travel Tips

- **For budget eats check out...** McGowans, Thunder Road Café, Judge Roy Beans, Flanagans, The Berkley
- **For great nightlife try...** Temple Bar, Oliver St. Gogarty's, The Pod, The Kitchen, The Auld Dubliner
- **Don't miss...** Guinness Storehouse, Trinity College, Old Jameson Distillery, Dublin Castle, Irish Music Hall of Fame, Dublin Zoo, GAA Museum, Dublin Writers Museum, Viking Splash Tours, Wax Museum

▲ **Dún Chaoin** – 28022
Near Ballyferriter, Co Kerry.
(66) 9156121 (66) 9156355
mailbox@anoige.ie
www.irelandyha.org
Open Dates: 01.02-30.11 Shannon 192km; Cork 195km Tralee 64km; Killarney 97km Killarney-Dún Chaoin (summer only) x 52

△ ***Foulksrath Castle** – 28024*
Near Jenkinstown, Co Kilkenny.
(56) 7767674 (56) 7767144
mailbox@anoige.ie
www.irelandyha.org
Open Dates: Kilkenny 15km Countrywide services to Kilkenny x 52

▲ **Galway** – Sleepzone – 28036
Bóthar na mBan, Woodquay, Galway City.
(91) 566999 (91) 566996
mailbox@anoige.ie
www.irelandyha.org
Open Dates: Galway 8km 100m 100m x 190

△ ***Glanmore Lake** – 28026*
Near Lauragh, Killarney, Co Kerry.
(64) 83181 mailbox@anoige.ie
www.irelandyha.org
Open Dates: 27.05-30.09 Killarney 56km Killarney to Castletownbere ap Lauragh - 6km to hostel x 36

Glendalough – International Youth Hostel
28006
The Lodge, Glendalough, Co Wicklow.
(404) 45342 (404) 45690
glendaloughyh@ireland.com
www.irelandyha.org
Open Dates: Open Times:
Beds: 118 - 1x2 11x4 6x6 2x6+
Price Range: € 16-25
Directions: Dublin 60km Dublin 50km; Dun Laoghaire 40km Rathdrum 13km St Kevins bus from Dublin City 50km ap Glendalough x 18 2 x

Glendalough – International Youth Hostel

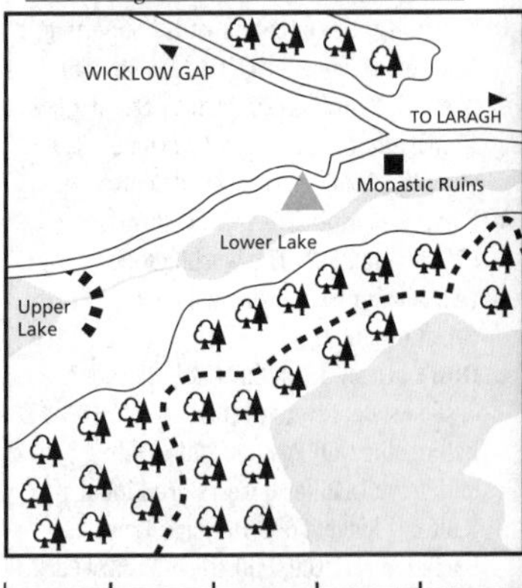

Glendalough... Travel Tips

- **For budget eats check out...** Glendalough Hotel, Glendalough Hostel
- **Don't miss...** Powerscourt Estate, Avondale House, Wicklow Gaol, Glendalough Round Tower, Mount Usher Gardens, Irish National Stud & Japanese Gardens, Larchill Arcadia Gardens, Greenan Farm Museum & Maze

△ ***Glenmalure** – 28027*
Near Greenane, Co Wicklow.
(01) 8304555 (01) 8305808
mailbox@anoige.ie
www.irelandyha.org
Open Dates: 01.07-31.08 (+ Sat evenings 12) Rathdrum 16km St. Kevins Bus: Dublin-Laragh x 16

Killarney – International Youth Hostel
28002
Ring of Kerry Rd, Aghadoe House, Killarney, Co. Kerry.
(64) 31240 (64) 34300
anoige@killarney.iol.ie
www.irelandyha.org
Open Dates: 12 Open Times:
Beds: 184 - 5x2 20x4 5x6 6x6+
Price Range: € 13.00-22.50
Directions: 4W from city centre
Kerry International 10km; Cork 92km; Shannon 120km Cork (Seasonal) 92km
Killarney 5km Free transfer from station (summer only) ap YH x 26
1 x

Killarney – International Youth Hostel

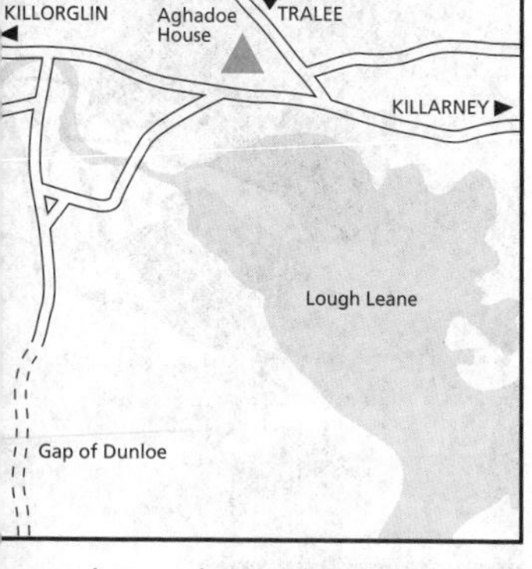

Killarney... Travel Tips

- **For budget eats check out...** Allegro's Pizza (Plunkett St.), Continental Café (Innisfallen Mall), Country Kitchen (New St.), Cronin's Restaurant (College St.)
- **For great nightlife try...** The Golden Nugget, O'Connor's Pub, Scotts Gardens, O'Mearas (High St.), Mustang Sallys
- **Don't miss...** Killarney National Park, Kate Kearneys Cottage, Ring of Kerry, Vintage Car Museum, Dingle, Gap of Dungloe, Lakes of Killarney, Kerry Woollen Mills

△ ***Knockree** – 28029*
Lacken House, Knockree, Near Enniskerry, Co Wicklow.
(1) 2864036 (1) 2767892
knockree@eircom.net
www.irelandyha.org
Open Dates: 12 Bray 10km
Alpine Coaches to Bray/Knockree
x 56

△ ***Mountain Lodge** – 28030*
Near Burncourt, Cabir, Co Tipperary.
(52) 67277 mailbox@anoige.ie
www.irelandyha.org
Open Dates: 26.03-25.09 Cabir 16km
Cork-Athlone or Cork-Dublin service ap YH x 24

▲ **Sixmilebridge** – Jamaica Inn – 28031
Sixmilebridge, Co. Clare.
(61) 369220 (61) 369377
mailbox@anoige.ie
www.irelandyha.org
Open Dates: 12 Shannon 12km
Limerick or Ennis 14km
Limerick-Sixmilebridge ap Shannon Airport, Sixmilebridge x 60
1 x

△ ***Sligo** – Yeats Village – 28037*
Ballinode, Sligo.
(71) 9138945 (71) 9138945
mailbox@anoige.ie
www.irelandyha.org
Open Dates: 12 Sligo 8km Sligo 2.5km Sligo 2.5km x 60
1 x

△ ***Tiglin*** *– 28032*
Near Ashford, Co Wicklow.
(404) 49049 *(404) 49049*
mailbox@anoige.ie
www.irelandyha.org
Open Dates: 01.02-30.11 *Wickow Town 11km* *Bus Eireann: Dublin-Rosslare service ap Ashford (6km to hostel)* x 50

△ ***Traenlaur Lodge*** *– 28033*
Lough Feeagh, Near Newport, Co Mayo.
(98) 41358 *mailbox@anoige.ie*
www.irelandyha.org
Open Dates: 27.05-30.09 *Westport 19km* *Bus Eireann: Westport-Achill service ap Newport (8km to hostel)*
x 32

Israel

Israel Youth Hostels Association (IYHA),
1 Shazar Street, P.O. Box 6001
Jerusalem 91060, Israel.
t (972) (2) 6558400; (972) (1) 599510511 (Reservation Centre)
f (972) (2) 6558430; 6558432 (Travel)
e iyha@iyha.org.il
w www.iyha.org.il (Online reservations)

Office Hours: Sunday-Thursday 08.00-16.00hrs

A copy of the Hostel Directory for this Country can be obtained from:
All I.Y.H.A. Hostels

National Tourist Authority/Board:	www.tourism.org.il
Capital:	Jerusalem
Language:	Hebrew/Arabic
Currency:	NIS
Population:	6,500,000
Size:	20,770 sq km
Telephone Country Code:	972
eKit Access Number:	180-920-3300

This is the country of the Patriarchs Abraham, Isaac and Jacob, the Bible, the Holy City of Jerusalem and the birthplace of Christianity; but for many in the new state of Israel, which is barely sixty years old, it is also the 'Promised Land', home to a myriad different nationalities for whom culture and customs mean many different things. Since the Declaration of Independence in 1948, the historic Jewish Diaspora has been working in reverse, with Jews 'returning home' from all over the world, whether from persecution or otherwise, most recently the many thousands from the former Soviet Union, bringing the current population to some 6.8 million.

Whilst there are many different 'tongues' spoken, Hebrew is the so-called language of integration, and service in the Israeli Defence Forces—compulsory for all, both men and women – has played an essential part in the processes of social exchange and harmony, as have the Kibbutz communities, though these are far less prominent today.

Modern Israel, despite the ongoing challenges of making peace with its Palestinian neighbours, is a vibrant, progressive and outward-looking country – no longer the 'prickly pear' it once was, now a big player in the hi-tech industries as well as a major exporter of fruit, vegetables and juices. Tourism is also a vital ingredient of the economy, although now dependent on the Road Map to peace being agreed by all sides.

A few other Top Tips from **CULTURE SMART!:**

- For security reasons, it is mandatory to carry identity cards in Israel at all times; so visitors are advised to keep their passports with them whenever they go out. All countries provide guidance about visiting Israel and the Occupied Territories. Of course, everybody, both Arab and Jew, goes about their daily business in the usual way. But it is best to be circumspect at all times.
- Informality in dress and behaviour is very much a keyword in Israel – from the Knesset (parliament) to the classroom. First-name usage is common as is the handshake, though be aware that Orthodox Jew's men will not shake hands with a woman.
- It is important to remember that the Sabbath (Shabbat) in Israel begins at dusk on a Friday and lasts through to nightfall on Saturday. Public transport ceases, as do all other public services. Consequently, Israel's 'Monday' (first day of the working week) is Sunday!
- As you would expect, Israeli restaurant food choices reflect the cuisine from many parts of the world. On the other hand, snacking is very common, including *falafel* (fried chickpea batter served with salad in pita bread) and *shwarma* – slices of roast lamb served in a large pita roll).

Cultural Top Tips supplied by Culture Smart! guides. These essential guides to customs and etiquette will help you steer clear of embarrassing gaffes and sensitive issues, enabling you to discover new cultures whilst developing new friendships. Order online at www.culturesmartguides.co.uk

You can find out a lot more on our website - a visit to www.HIhostels.com is essential for planning your trip!

Pour en savoir plus, rendez-vous sur notre site Internet, www.HIhostels.com une visite incontournable pour préparer votre voyage!

Viele weitere Informationen auf unserer Website: www.HIhostels.com - unverzichtbar für die Reiseplanung!

Puedes averiguar mucho más en nuestro sitio web. Es imprescindible que visites la página www.HIhostels.com para planear tu viaje.

▲ **Arad** 30015
4 Ha'atad St, POB 34, Arad 81900.
(08) 9957150 (08) 9955078
arad@iyha.org.il www.iyha.org.il
Open Dates: 12 Ben Gurion 130km
386 & 388 from Beer Sheva; 389 from Tel Aviv 15 x 203 R CC
TV 2 x P 2km

▲ **Be'er Sheva** – 30046
79 Ha' Atzmaut St, PO Box 7,
Be'er Sheva 84221.
(08) 6277444 (08) 6275735
beit_yatziv@silverbyte.com
www.iyha.org.il
Open Dates: Ben Gurion 113km
13 from Be'er Sheva Central Station 1W
x 212 33 x

▲ **Beit Shean** 30048
129 Menachem Begin Rd, POB 863,
Beit Shean.
(04) 6060760 (04) 6060766
beitshean@iyha.org.il www.iyha.org.il
Open Dates: Ben Gurion 150km
412 from Afula, 829 direct from Tel Aviv, 961 from Tiberias and Jerusalem 1.5NW
x 243 7 x

Eilat 30006
Arava Rd, POB 152, Eilat.
(08) 6370088 (08) 6375835
eilat@iyha.org.il www.iyha.org.il
Open Dates: Open Times:
Beds: 462 - 13x2 28x4 17x5 19x6+
Price Range: $15-25 € 12-20 BBinc
Directions: 2S from city centre
Ben Gurion 354km Eilat 1km
394 from Tel Aviv Central Bus Station to Eilat, 444 from Jerusalem Central Bus Station to Eilat x 102 2 x

Eilat

Eilat... Travel Tips

- **For budget eats check out...** Batzal Yarok, Halleluia, Colombus, Pizzicato, Boston Fish & Grill
- **For great nightlife try...** The 3 Monkeys, Club Hotel, Hilton Queen of Sheba, Wow - Royal Garden Hotel, Yacht Pub - King Solomon Hotel
- **Don't miss...** Dolphin Reef, Kings City, Coral Beach, Underwater Observatory & Marine Park, Camel Tours (Khan Shaharut), Cruise Red Sea, Jeep Sea, WOW Isrotel Theater, Imax - 3 dimensions cinema, Timna Park

▲ **Ein Gedi** – Beit Sarah 30003
Ein Gedi, Mobile Post, Dead Sea 86980.
(08) 6584165 (08) 6584445
eingedy@iyha.org.il www.iyha.org.il
Open Dates: Ben Gurion 175km
421 from Tel Aviv Bus Station, 486/487 from Jerusalem x 252 3 x 100m

▲ **Haifa** 30018
18 Tzvia Velzhak St. Kfar Zamir, Haifa.
(04) 8531944 (04) 8532516
haifa@iyha.org.il www.iyha.org.il
Open Dates: Ben Gurion 100km
43 from Haifa Central Station 8S
x 80 3km

▲ **Jerusalem** – Bayit Vegan – 30055
8 Hapisga St, PO Box 16350, Bayit Vegan, Jerusalem.
(02) 6420990 (02) 6423362
rachely@baitvegan-gh.co.il
www.iyha.org.il
Open Dates: Ben Gurion 55km
18, 20, 39, 40 from Jerusalem Central Station 3SW x 460 30 x

▲ **Jerusalem** – Beit Shmuel – 30051
6 Shama St, Jerusalem.
(02) 6203456 (02) 6203467
btshmuel@netvision.net.il
www.iyha.org.il
Open Dates: Ben Gurion 55km
13, 18 from Jerusalem Central Station 1E x 170 7 x

▲ **Jerusalem** – City Center Agron
Ⓗ 30050
6 Agron St, Jerusalem.
(02) 6217555 (02) 6221124
agron@iyha.org.il www.iyha.org.il
Open Dates: ✈ Ben Gurion 55km 7, 8, 14, 31, 32 from Jerusalem Central Station
1E x 200 R CC 5 x

△ ***Jerusalem** – Ein Kerem – 30052*
PO Box 16091, Jerusalem.
(02) 6416282 www.iyha.org.il
Open Dates: ✈ Ben Gurion 55km
17 from Jerusalem Central Station
6SW x 40 R CC

▲ **Jerusalem** – Jerusalem Forest – 30053
PO Box 3353, Jerusalem 91032.
(02) 6752911 (02) 6413522
zippori@zippori.org.il www.iyha.org.il
Open Dates: ✈ Ben Gurion 55km 6SW
x 120 R CC P

Jerusalem – Yitzhak Rabin Ⓗ 30010
1 Nahman Avigad St, PO Box 39100, Jerusalem 91390.
(02) 6780101 (02) 6796566
rabin@iyha.org.il www.iyha.org.il
Open Dates: Open Times:
Beds: 308 - 10x² 72x⁴
Price Range: $15-25 € 12-20 BBinc
Directions: 4SE from city centre
✈ Ben Gurion 55km 9, 17, 24 from Central Bus Station x 77 R
CC TV 11 x i P

Jerusalem – Yitzhak Rabin

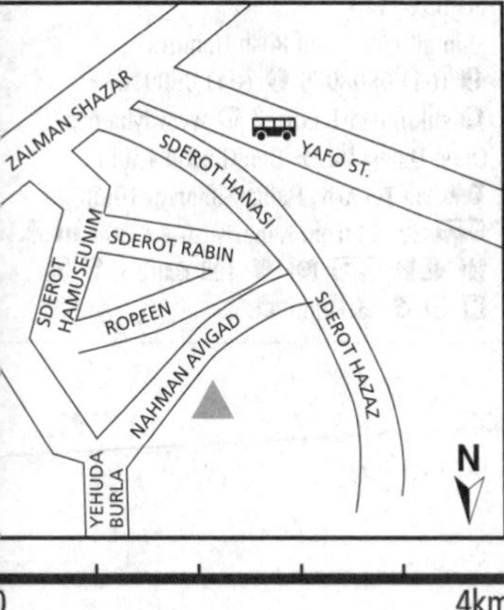

Jerusalem... Travel Tips

- **For budget eats check out...** Fink's Bar and Restaurant, Ima (Restaurant), Ben Yehuda Pedestrian Area, Malcha Mall, Falafel
- **For great nightlife try...** Nahalat Shiva, Russian Compound, Ian (pub near the theatre), Talpiot Ha Uman 17, The Underground
- **Don't miss...** Jerusalem Biblical Zoo, Soreq Stalactite Caves, Second Temple Model, Time Elevator, Old City, Israel Museum, Bible Lands Museum, Knesset, Armon Hanatziv Promenade, Mount Herzel & Yad Va Shem

---

Karei Deshe Ⓗ 30057
Mobile Post, Korazim 12365.
(04) 6720601 (04) 6724818
kdeshe@iyha.org.il www.iyha.org.il
Open Dates: Open Times:
Beds: 296 - 10x² 24x⁴ 30x⁶
Price Range: $15-25 € 12-20 BBinc
Directions: ✈ Ben Gurion 150km 459, 841 from Tiberias Central Bus Station - Tiberias 10km from Youth Hostel x 64
R CC TV 3 x P
100m

Karei Deshe

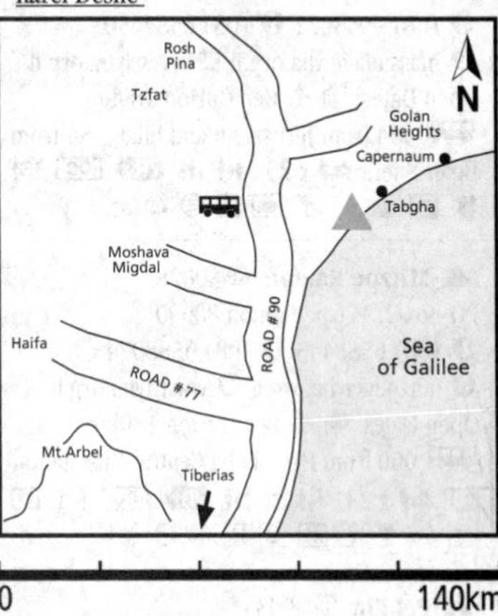

ISRAEL – ISRAEL – ISRAEL – ISRAEL

Karei Deshe... Travel Tips

- **For budget eats check out...** Beit Gabriel, Hapagoda, Cherry, Tanurin, Tveria Haktana
- **For great nightlife try...** Papaya Pub, Al-Hanahar (Kinneret), Tzel-Tamar
- **Don't miss...** Orcha Bagalil, Hamat Gader Park, Tiberias Hot Springs Spa, Holy Land Sailing, Baptism Site, Luna Gal (water park), Abu Kayak, Jeep Trip, Rob Roy (Canoe), Horse Ranch (Holiday Inn Hotel)

▲ **Kfar Etzion** – 30058
Gush Etzion 90912.
(02) 9935162 (02) 9938152
www.iyha.org.il
Open Dates: Ben Gurion 80km
x 180 R CC

▲ **Ma'ayan Harod** HI 30021
PO Box 863 Beit Shean.
(04) 6531669 (04) 6531660
mayanh@iyha.org.il www.iyha.org.il
Open Dates: Ben Gurion 120km
412 from Afula to Beit Shean x 144
R CC 8 x P 50m

▲ **Massada** HI 30025
Mobile Post, Dead Sea 86935.
(08) 9953222 (08) 6584650
massada@iyha.org.il www.iyha.org.il
Open Dates: Ben Gurion 189km
444 from Jerusalem and Eilat, 384 from Be'er Sheva x 294 R CC
TV 5 x P

▲ **Mitzpe Ramon** HI 30028
PO Box 2, Mitzpe Ramon 80600.
(08) 6588443 (08) 6588074
mitzpe@iyha.org.il www.iyha.org.il
Open Dates: Ben Gurion 180km
060 from Beersheba Central Bus Station
0.1E x 237 R CC TV
4 x i P

▲ **Peki'in** HI 30034
PO Box 910, Peki'in 24914.
(04) 9574111 (04) 9574116
pkiin@iyha.org.il www.iyha.org.il
Open Dates: Ben Gurion 172km
271 from Haifa to Nahariya; 44 from Nahariya to Peki'in x 244
R CC TV 10 x P

▲ **Petah Tikva** – 30061
Yalahom St 34, Petah Tikva 49404.
(03) 9226666 (03) 9217222
petachtikva@iyha.org.il
www.iyha.org.il
Open Dates: Ben Gurion 15km
50, 51 from Tel Aviv - Dan Line
x 214 R CC TV 1 x P

▲ **Poriya** HI 30037
Poria, PO Box 232, Tiberias 14101.
(04) 6750050 (04) 6751628
poria@iyha.org.il www.iyha.org.il
Open Dates: Ben Gurion 128km
Taxi from Tiberias x 200
R CC TV 4 x P 4km
4km

▲ **Ramot Shapira** – 30047
D.N. Harey Yehuda,
Beit Meir 90865 (20km W Jerusalem).
(02) 5331666 (02) 5331662
www.iyha.org.il
Open Dates: Ben Gurion 40km
x 426 R CC P

▲ **Safed** – 30040
1 Lohamei Ha Getaot St., PO Box 1139,
Safed 13401.
(04) 6921086 (04) 6973514
tzfat@iyha.org.il www.iyha.org.il
Open Dates: Ben Gurion 168km
6, 7 from Safed Central Station 2SW
x 96 R CC TV
3 x P

▲ **Shlomi** HI 30043
PO Box 2120,
Shlomi. (5km E of Rosh Haniqra).
(04) 9808975 (04) 9809163
shlomi@iyha.org.il www.iyha.org.il
Open Dates: Ben Gurion 130km
via Tel Aviv, Haifa, Nahariya 10km
22, 23 from Nahariya x 400
R CC TV 2 x
P 4km

Tel Aviv 30004
36 Bnei Dan St, Tel Aviv 62260.
(03) 5441748 (03) 5441030
telaviv@iyha.org.il www.iyha.org.il
Open Dates: Open Times:
Beds: 182 - 2x 2x 37x 4x
Price Range: $15-25 € 12-20 BBinc
Directions: 3N from city centre
Ben Gurion 20km Arlozorov 3km
5 from Tel Aviv Central Bus Station 3km
7 x 2km

Tel Aviv

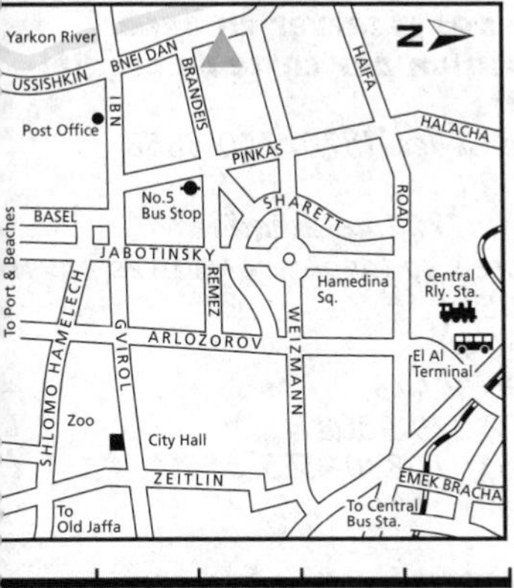

Tel Aviv... Travel Tips

- **For budget eats check out...** Kerem HaTeimanim, Hatikvah, Promenade along the beach, Old Jaffa
- **For great nightlife try...** Shenkin, Beach Promenade, Cinemateque, Old Jaffa, Dizengoff St.
- **Don't miss...** Luna Park, Beach, Yarkon River Boating - Water Skiing, Ha Aretz Museum, Azrieli Tower, Ganei Yehoshua, Ramat Gan Zoo - Safari, Water Park (Meimadion), Diaspora Museum, Old City of Jaffa

▲ Tel Hai 30007
Mobile Post, Upper Galilee 12100.
(04) 6940043 (04) 6941743
tel-hai@iyha.org.il www.iyha.org.il
Open Dates: Ben Gurion 200km
841, 842, 845 from Tel Aviv Central Bus Station 19.4km; 20, 23 Kiriat Shmone to Tel Hai 3km 3N x 240
9 x
10km

▲ Tiberias 30005
2 Jordan St, PO Box 81, Tiberias 14100.
(04) 6721775 (04) 6720372
tiberias@iyha.org.il www.iyha.org.il
Open Dates: Ben Gurion 132km
961 from Jerusalem to Tiberias, 830, 835, 840 from Tel Aviv to Tiberias 0.1NW
x 98
1km

Italy

Associazione Italiana Alberghi per la Gioventù,
Via Cavour 44, 00184 Roma, Italy.

t (39) (06) 4871152
f (39) (06) 4880492
e aig.sedenazionale@ostellionline.org
w www.ostellionline.org

Office Hours: Monday-Thursday 07.30-17.00hrs;
Friday 07-30-15.00hrs

Travel Section:
Via Farini 48/50, 00184 Roma, Italy.

t (39) (06) 48907740
f (39) (06) 48987982

Office Hours: Monday-Friday 08.00-17.30hrs

A copy of the Hostel Directory for this Country can be obtained from:
The National Office

National Tourist Authority/Board:	www.enit.it
Capital:	Roma
Language:	Italian
Currency:	€ Euro
Population:	57,000,000
Size:	301,225 sq km
Telephone Country Code:	39
eKit Access Number:	800-985-675

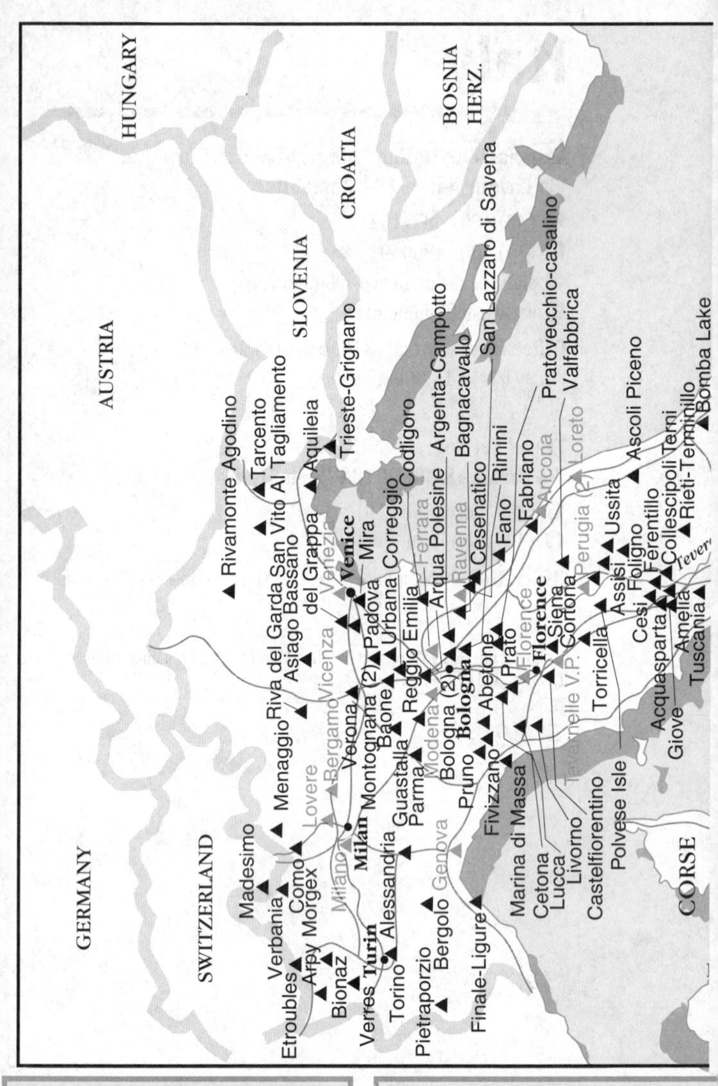

It was only in 1870 that Italy achieved political unity. Until then it was a multitude of quarrelling city-states, kingdoms, dukedoms and Papal States controlled by exterior powers. Although no longer divided politically, Italy still consists of regions that are so different that they are almost like separate countries. Each one has its own cuisine, landscape, history, dialect, architecture and artistic styles, and it is interesting that an Italian will identify himself first and foremost by the region he comes from, rather than describing himself as "Italian."

A few other Top Tips from **CULTURE SMART!**:

- Most Italians consider it a matter of personal pride to turn out beautifully groomed and tailored every day of the week. Italian fashion is, of course, known all over the world. Gucci, Valentino, Ungaro, Versace and Armani are just a few of the

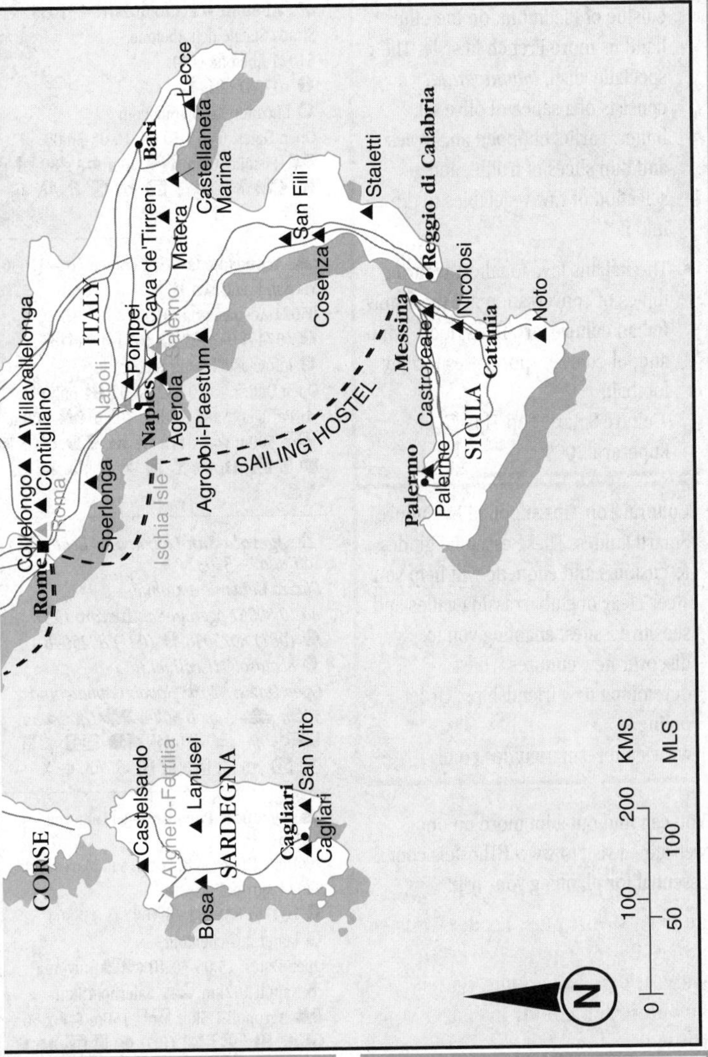

internationally famous names whose creations fill boutiques from Milan to Rome.

- Like the French, the Italians love to spend time over their meals, and to talk about their food while they are eating. Wine is almost always served with the evening meal, and it is reassuring to know that if you knock your glass over, wine spilled on the tablecloth is a sign of good luck!

- Stand up to be introduced if you are a man; but a woman need not stand unless she is being introduced to someone of particular importance.
- Italian cuisine varies from region to region, and can be described as Venetian, Florentine, Milanese, Neapolitan, and so forth. Tuscany is renowned for simple food, and its signature dish is a T-bone steak, lightly seasoned with pepper and oil and grilled on a wood fire. The

cuisine of Piedmont, on the other hand, is more French in style. The speciality dish, *bagnacauda*, consists of a sauce of olive oil, butter, garlic, chopped anchovies and thin slices of truffle, and a selection of raw vegetables to dip into it.

- The Italians love to talk. Favourite topics of conversation are the family, Italian culture, art, films, food, wine and, of course, sports – especially football!

Culture Smart! Top Tips © Kuperard 2005

Cultural Top Tips supplied by Culture Smart! guides. These essential guides to customs and etiquette will help you steer clear of embarrassing gaffes and sensitive issues, enabling you to discover new cultures whilst developing new friendships. Order online at www.culturesmartguides.co.uk

You can find out a lot more on our website - a visit to www.HIhostels.com is essential for planning your trip!

Pour en savoir plus, rendez-vous sur notre site Internet, www.HIhostels.com une visite incontournable pour préparer votre voyage!

Viele weitere Informationen auf unserer Website: www.HIhostels.com - unverzichtbar für die Reiseplanung!

Puedes averiguar mucho más en nuestro sitio web. Es imprescindible que visites la página

▲ **Abetone** – Renzo Bizzarri – 31035
Strada Statale dell'Abetone,
51021 Abetone (PT).
(0573) 60117
bucaneve@abetone.com
Open Dates: 01.12-30.04; 10.06-30.09
Pistoia 50km 50m x 80

▲ **Acquasparta** – San Francesco – 31036
Via San Francesco 1,
05021 Acquasparta (TR).
(0744) 943167 (0744) 944168
info@ostellosanfrancesco.it
Open Dates: (01.02-28.02 only)
Perugia "Sant' Egidio" 70km 500m
500m x 118 1 x

△ ***Agerola-San Lazzaro*** – *"Beata Solitudo" – 31037*
Piazza Generale Avitabile,
no 10 80051 Agerola-San Lazzaro (NA).
(081) 8025048 (081) 8025048
beatasol@tiscalinet.it
Open Dates: Napoli Capodichino 50km Napoli 40km Gragnano
50m x 16

▲ **Agropoli-Paestum** – La Lanterna – 31038
Via Della Lanterna 8, Loc.tà San Marco,
84043 Agropoli (SA).
(0974) 838364 (0974) 838364
lanterna@cilento.it
Open Dates: 15.03-30.10 (July-Aug)
Napoli 102km Salerno 48km
Agropoli 1.5km 150m x 56
(BD)

▲ **Alessandria** – Santa Maria Di Castello – 31039
Piazza Santa Maria Di Castello 14,
15100 Alessandria.
(0131) 288187 (0131) 220280
serenity.2000@libero.it
Open Dates: (Sat and Sun)
Genova 100km; Milano (Malpensa) 150km Genova 80km 2km
Line 2 500m x 70

Alghero-Fertilia – Hostal de l'Alguer
31029
Via Parenzo, 07040 Alghero.
(079) 930478 (079) 932039
alghero@ostellionline.org
Open Dates: Open Times: 07:00-10:00hrs; 15:00-24:00hrs
Beds: 99 - 6x2 4x3 5x4 5x5 5x6
Price Range: € 16 standard room; € 18 (€ 20 01.07-31.08); € 20 (€ 25 01.07-31.08); € 9 L, D BBinc
Directions: 6NW from city centre
Fertilia 6km A 200m Porto Torres 30km Alghero 6km 200m ap Piazza Venezia Giulia R (BD)

Alghero-Fertilia – Hostal de l'Alguer

Alghero-Fertilia... Travel Tips

- **For budget eats check out...** Youth Hostel (€9 for lunch)
- **Don't miss...** Nuraghi, Storic Centre, Stintino Beach

Amelia – Giustiniani – 31040
Piazza Mazzini 9, 05022 Amelia (TR).
(0744) 978673 (0744) 978673
info@ostellogiustiniani.it
Open Dates: 01.03-31.12 Narni 10km; Orte 18km ATC 20m x 56 CC (BD) 1 x

Ancona – Ostello Ancona 31021
Via Lamaticci 7, 60126 Ancona (AN).
(071) 42257 (071) 42257
aigancona@tiscalinet.it
Open Dates: Falconara 15km A 300m 1km Ancona Centrale 200m 200m x 56 CC

Aquileia – Domus Augusta – 31041
Via Roma 25, 33051 Aquileia (UD).
(0431) 91024 (0431) 917105
info@ostelloaquileia.it
Open Dates: Trieste Ronchi dei Legionari 10km A 200m
Cervignano 6km 200m x 50 R CC 1 x

Argenta – Campotto – 31042
Via Cardinala 27,
44010 Campotto di Argenta (FE).
(0532) 808035 (0532) 808035
ostellodicampotto@libero.it
Open Dates: Bologna-Borgo Panigale 50km Argenta 8km Linea Bologna-Argenta 50m x 52 - for only 7km

Arpy Morgex – "Valdigne. M. Blanc" – 31043
Loc.Arpy, 11017 Morgex (AO).
(0165) 841684 (0165) 841684
info@ostellodiarpy.it
Open Dates: 01.12-02.04; 10.06-03.09 (R) Torino Caselle 99km A Private bus on request Morgex 7km x 130 CC 1 x

Arquà Polesine – Ostello Del Canal Bianco – 31044
Loc. Valmolin, 45031 Arquà Polesine (RO).
(0425) 465213 (0425) 465213
ostellocanalbianco@libero.it
Open Dates: Venezia "Marco Polo" 80km Rovigo 9km
Rovigo-Polesella Line 100m ap Bosaro 100m x 102 1 x

Ascoli Piceno – "Ostello de Longobardi" – 31045
Via Soderini 26, Palazzetto Longobardo, 63100 Ascoli Piceno (AP).
(0736) 261862 (0736) 259191
Open Dates: 1km 500m
x 30 1 x

Asiago – Ekar – 31046
Via Ekar 2, 36012 Asiago (VI).
(0424) 455138 (0424) 455138
ostelloechar@libero.it
Open Dates: 01-07.01; 01-30.04; 15.06-30.09; 27-31.12 ( )
Bassano del Grappa 25km 100m
x 120 (BD)
1 x

Assisi – Ostello della Pace – 31047
Via Di Valecchie 177, 06082 Assisi (PG).
(075) 816767 (075) 816767
assisi.hostel@tiscalinet.it
Open Dates: 01.03-02.11 (03.11-06.01 on request) Perugia "Sant' Egidio" 11km
2km 800m 0.8S x 64
2.5km

Bagnacavallo – Antico Convento Di San Francesco – 31048
Via Cadorna 10, 48012 Bagnacavallo (RA).
(0545) 60622 (0545) 937228
info@ostellosanfrancesco.com
Open Dates: 01-07.01; 01.02-31.10; 15-31.12
Bologna 65km Bagnacavallo 800m
x 91 (B)
1 x

Baone Valle San Giorgio – Colli Euganei – 31049
Via Donna Daria, no 2 35030 Baone (PD).
(0429) 604286 (0429) 615567
ideogrammi.ostelli@libero.it
Open Dates: 01.03-31.10 Venezia Marco Polo 65km Venezia 65km
Monselice 8km Padova-Este Line (via Colli) 200m x 54 (B)
1 x

Bassano Del Grappa – Don Cremona – 31124
Via Chini 6, 36061 Bassano del Grappa (VI).
(0424) 219137 (0424) 219137
associazioneoscaronlus@virgilio.it
Open Dates: Venezia 60km; Treviso 45km Bassano Centro 600m x 84
200m

Bergamo – Nuovo Ostello di Bergamo
31014
Via Galileo Ferraris 1,
24123 Bergamo (BG).
(035) 361724 (035) 361724
bergamo@ostellionline.org
Open Dates: Open Times: 07.00-24.00hrs
Beds: 84 - 2x1 6x2 3x3 4x4 5x6 2x6+
Price Range: € 15.50 standard room; € 18; 1 € 23; 2 € 20; € 9 L, D BB inc
Directions: 3NW from city centre
Orio al Serio 7km Bergamo 2km
3 from Città Alta to hostel x 10
(BD)
1 x
4km

Bergamo – Nuovo Ostello di Bergamo

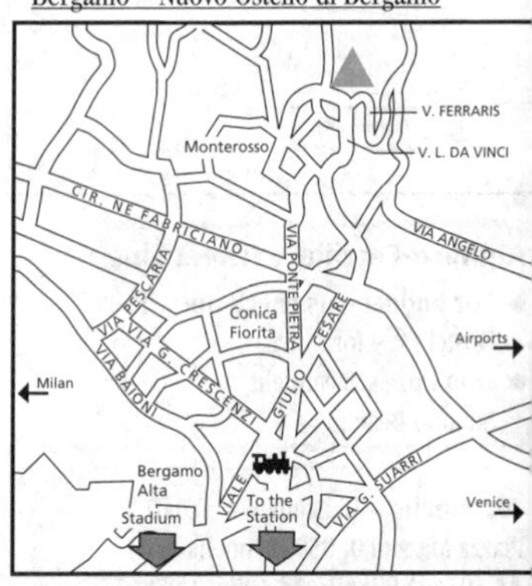

0 300m

Bergamo... Travel Tips

- **Don't miss...** The Upper City, Accademia Carrara (museum), Orto Botanico (botanic garden), Museo Diocesano, Mini Italia (park), Gardaland (park), Caneva, Museo Donizettiano, Castello San Vigilio, Il Mercato Dell' Antiquariato

△ ***Bergolo** – Le Langhe – 31051*
Via Roma 22, 12070 Bergolo (CN).
(0173) 87222 (0173) 87222
bergolo@bergolo.com
Open Dates: 01.05-15.09 ( )
Torino Caselle 120km Acqui Terme 38km; Saliceto 30km; Alba 30km
100m x 34
(B) 1 x
300m

▲ **Bionaz** – La Bâtise – 31052
Plan de Veyne 25, - 11010 Bionaz (AO).
(0165) 730105; Mobile (328) 4879702
(0165) 730214 info@labatise.com
Open Dates: 01.12-31.12; 01.01-04.11
Torino Caselle 110km Aosta 25km
Aosta-Bionaz 50m x 36
(B) 1 x

Bologna – Due Torri-San Sisto – 31030
Via Viadagola 5, 40127 Bologna BO.
(051) 501810 (051) 501810
hostelbologna@hotmail.com
Open Dates: Open Times: 07.00-10.00hrs; 15.30-23.30hrs
Beds: 85 - 7x 4x 12x 1x 1x
Price Range: € 15.50 standard room; € 17; € 18; € 9 for dinner BBinc
Directions: 6NE from city centre
Marconi 10km Centrale 6km
21/B, 93-301 150m ap San Sisto
(BD)

Bologna – Due Torri-San Sisto

▲ **Bologna** – San Sisto – 31053
Via Viadagola 14, 40127 Bologna.
(051) 501810 (051) 501810
hostelbologna@hotmail.com
Open Dates: ( ) Marconi 10km Centrale 6km 21/B, 93-301 150m ap San Sisto x 33
(BD)

Bologna... Travel Tips

- **For budget eats check out...** Youth Hostel (€ 9 for lunch/dinner, please reserve in the morning)
- **Don't miss...** Piazza Maggiore, University Area (via Zamboni, via delle Moline, via delle Bele Arti), Abbazia di San Luca, Piazza del Nettuno, Chiesa di Santa Maria dei Servi (church), Chiesa di San Francesco (church), Underground City, Jewish District, The Two Towers

▲ **Bomba Lake** – Isola Verde – 31054
Via Lago, 66042 Bomba (CH).
(0872) 860475; 860568
(0872) 860450 isolaverde@tin.it
Open Dates: (Closed 24-25.12) lago di Bomba 150m from Pescara 800m
x 28 1 x

△ ***Bosa** – Malaspina – 31055*
Via Sardegna 1-08013, Bosa Marina (NU).
(0785) 375009 (0785) 375009
Open Dates: Alghero-Fertilia 40km
50m 200m x 48

▲ **Cagliari** – Cagliari – 31134
Piazza Del S. Sepolcro, 09100 Cagliari (CA).
(Info) (070) 402033 (070) 402033
Open Dates: during 2006 Cagliari "Elmas" 5km 200m 200m ap Last bus stop x 135
1 x

▲ **Castelfiorentino** – 31057
Viale Roosevelt 26,
50051 Castelfiorentino (FI).
(0571) 64002 (0571) 64002
hostelcast@interfree.it
Open Dates: Pisa 50km Livorno 40km Castelfiorentino 600m x 84

▲ **Castellaneta Marina** – Villini Paradiso – 31058
Via Zond 2, 74010 Castellaneta Marina (TA).
(099) 8431015 (099) 8430892
Open Dates: Bari 80km
Bari-Brindisi (Porto) 30km
Taranto 30km 200m x 100
1 x

▲ **Castelsardo** – Golfo Dell' Asinara – 31059
Via Sardegna 1,
07031 Loc Lu Bagnu Castelsardo (SS).
(079) 474031; 587008
(079) 587008; 474031
ostello.asinara@tiscali.it
Open Dates: 01.06-15.09 & Easter ( ) Alghero-Fertilia 50km; Olbia 120km
Porto Torres 30km Sassari 30km
Line Lu Bagnu-Castelsardo 200m
ap Bore Tabacos x 110
300m

▲ **Castroreale** – "Ostello Delle Aquile" – 31060
Salita Federico II d'Aragona,
98053 Castroreale Centro (ME).
(Info) (091) 6797807 (Info) (091) 6912376 (Info)
aig.sicilia@ostelllionline.org
Open Dates: during 2006 Catania
Barcellona 11km 100m

▲ **Cava De' Tirreni** – Borgo Scacciaventi – 31061
Piazza San Francesco 1,
84013 Cava De' Tirreni (SA).
(089) 466631 (089) 466631
cavatirreni@ostellionline.org
Open Dates: 24.03-31.10 Napoli 50km
800m Lines 4-9 x 140
1 x

▲ **Cesenatico** – Stella Marina – 31128
Via Colombo n.15, 47042 Cesenatico (FO).
(0547) 75581 (0547) 82145
stellamarinafun@libero.it
Open Dates: Forli 30km; Rimini 35km
A A.T.R. 350m Ravenna 30km
Cesenatico 3km A.T.R. 350m
x 97
2 x

▲ **Cesi** – Palazzo Contelori – 31062
Piazza I° Maggio, 05030 Cesi (TR).
(0744) 248410 (0744) 248221
info@palazzocontelori.it
Open Dates: Perugia "S. Egidio" 77km
2km 500m x 18
3 x

▲ **Cetona (SI)** – La Cocciara – 31112
Via San Sebastiano 18, 53040 S1.
(0578) 237931 (0578) 238052
info@ostellocetona.it
Open Dates: Florence 130km
8km 300m x 34
(L) 1 x

▲ **Codigoro** – Pomposa – 31130
Loc. Pomposa sud; 44021 Pomposa di Codigoro (FE).
(Info) (051)224913
(Info) (051) 224913
Open Dates: 01.03-31.10 ( )
Bologna 90km Codigoro 5km
Bus from/for Pomposa x 60
(B)

▲ **Collelongo** – Chiaravalle – 31063
Via Casarine, 67050 Collelongo (AQ).
(0863) 948368 (0863) 948065
info_chiaravalle@libero.it
Open Dates: 01.04-30.09 (Christmas holiday on request) ( ) Avezzano 24km
Arpa 200m x 41
1 x

▲ **Collescipoli-Terni** – Garibaldini YH – 31064
Corso Dei Garibaldini 61,
05033 Collescipoli TR.
(0744) 800467 (0744) 800467
info@ostellogaribaldini.it
Open Dates: (01.01-28.02)
Perugia "Sant' Egidio" 90km Terni 5km Line 9 150m x 37
1 x

▲ **Como** – 'Villa Olmo' – 31065
Via Bellinzona 2, 22100 Como (CO).
(031) 573800 (031) 573800
ostellocomo@tin.it
Open Dates: 01.03-30.11
Milano-Malpensa 43km; Bergamo Orio al Serio 60km A Line C250-C46 1.5km
Como San Giovanni 1.5km 1, 6, 11 20m ap Villa Olmo x 76 R
(BD)

▲ **Contigliano** – Villa Franceschini – 31113
Via Ettore Franceschini no 7, Contigliano (Ri).
(0746) 706123 (0746) 706123
ostello.franceschini@libero.it
Open Dates: Civitavecchia 120km
Contigliano 1km Cotral 250m
x 64

▲ **Correggio** – La Rocchetta – 31066
Corso Cavour 19, 42015 Correggio (RE).
(0522) 632361 (0522) 632361
la.rocchetta@libero.it
Open Dates: Bologna 65km Carpi 6km 600m x 25

▲ **Cortona** – "San Marco" – 31067
Via Maffei 57, 52044 Cortona (AR).
(0575) 601392 (0575) 601392
ostellocortona@libero.it
Open Dates: 15.03-15.10 ( )
Camucia 3km; Terontola 6km
70m x 80
1 x

▲ **Cosenza** – Re Alarico – 31135
Vico 2, G. Marini Serra 10,
87100 Cosenza (CS).
(0984) 25535
Open Dates: Lamezia Terme 80km
Cosenza 2km 50m x 24
(B)

▲ **Etroubles** – Dortoir Echevennoz – 31068
Frazione Echevennoz, 11014 Etroubles (AO).
(0165) 78225 (0165) 78225
ruffierdidier@libero.it
Open Dates: 01.01-14.09; 01.10-31.12
Torino Caselle 90km Aosta 14km
Savda 200m x 15
(B)

▲ **Fabriano** – San Biagio in Caprile – 31114
Loc. Campodonico, 60044 Fabriano (AN).
(0732) 259466 (0732) 259466
hostellosanbiagio@libero.it
Open Dates: Ancona-Falconara 70km
Ancona 70km Fabriano 12km
Line Terni-Ferentillo 100m x 25

▲ **Fano** – Internazionale – 31129
Viale Cappellini n85, 61032 Fano (PU).
(0721) 884585 (0721) 884585
Open Dates: 02.04-30.09 Rimini 70km
Rimini 70km Marotta 3.5km; Fano 12km Line Fano-Marotta 300m
x 92

▲ **Ferentillo** – Il Tiglio – 31069
Via Abruzzo, 05034 Ferentillo (TR).
(0744) 389104 (0744) 388710
atreks2001@yahoo.it
Open Dates: Terni 18km
Terni-Ferentillo Line 100m (on request) x 25

▲ **Ferrara** – Estense 31025
Corso Biagio Rossetti 24, 44100 Ferrara.
(0532) 204227 (0532) 204227
hostelferrara@hotmail.com
Open Dates: Bologna 45km 1km
3C-4C from the Station 0.5N x 70
CC (B)

▲ **Finale-Ligure** – 'Vuillermin Castle' – 31070
Via Generale Caviglia 46,
17024 Finale-Ligure (SV).
(019) 690515 (019) 690515
castellofinaleligure@tiscali.it
Open Dates: 16.03-15.10 Genova "Cristoforo Colombo" 70km
Savona-Vado Ligure 25km 1km
x 70 R CC
1km

△ ***Fivizzano*** – *Ostello Degli Agostiniani – 31121*
Piazza Garibaldi, no 1,
54013 Fivizzano (MS).
(0585) 948282 (0585) 948282
Open Dates: Pisa 120km Soliera Apuana 10km C.A.T 200m x 59
1 x

Florence – Villa Camerata 31004
Viale Augusto Righi 2-4,
50137 Firenze (FI).
(055) 601451 (055) 610300
firenze@ostellionline.org
Open Dates: 12 Open Times: 07.00-24.00hrs
Beds: 322 - 6x3 34x4 9x5 3x6 12x6+
Price Range: € 17.50 standard room; 2 € 30; 3 € 23; 4 € 20; € 18.50 BB inc

Directions: 3NE from city centre
Firenze "Vespucci" 10km Livorno 99km Santa Maria Novella 5km 17 400m ap Salviatino x 7 R (BD) 1 x

Florence – Villa Camerata

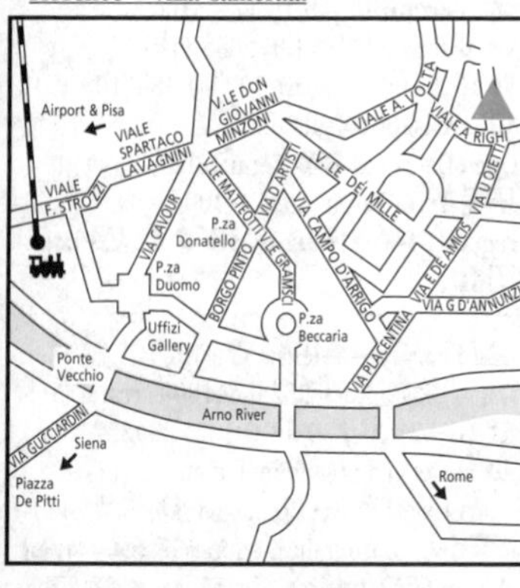

Florence... Travel Tips

- **For budget eats check out...** Youth Hostel (€ 9 for dinner)
- **Don't miss...** Museo degli Uffizi, Fiesole district, Piazza Santa Croce, Ponte Vecchio, Duomo Santa Maria del fiore (church), Palazzo Pitti, Giardino di Boboli (park)

Foligno – Ostello Pierantoni – 31031
Via Pierantoni 23, 06034 Foligno (PG).
(0742) 342566 (0742) 343559
foligno@ostellionline.org
Open Dates: 12 Open Times: 00.00-11.00hrs; 14.00-00.00hrs
Beds: 199 - 8x2 2x3 15x4 12x6 2x6+
Price Range: € 15 standard room; € 17; 1 € 22; € 9 for L, D BB inc
Directions: 0.4E from city centre
Perugia "Sant' Egidio" 26km Ancona 120km Foligno 500m Navetta B 100m 3 x 1km

Foligno – Ostello Pierantoni

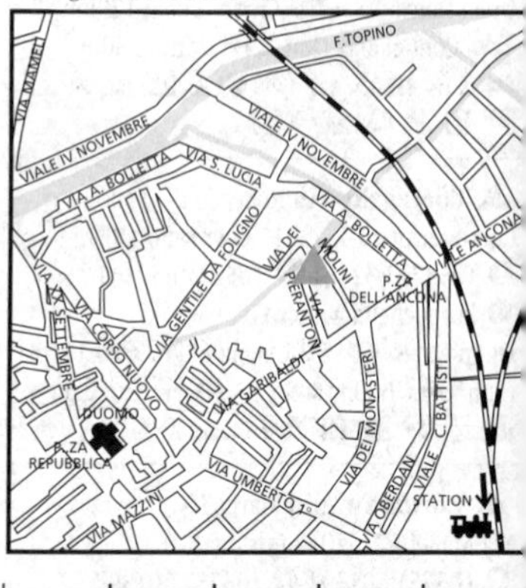

Foligno... Travel Tips

- **For budget eats check out...** Youth Hostel (€ 9 for lunch/dinner)
- **Don't miss...** Duomo (church), Pinacoteca comunale (art gallery), Giostra della Quintana (jousting tournament June-September), Palazzo Trinci museum, Oratorio Nunziatella, Santa Maria Infraportas Church, San Francesco Basilica, Santianna Monastry, Humor Fest, Sassovivo Abbey

Genoa – Genova 31005
Via Costanzi 120N, 16135 Genova (GE).
(010) 2422457 (010) 2422457
hostelge@iol.it
Open Dates: 01.02-19.12
Open Times: 07.00-11.30hrs; 15.30-24.00hrs
Beds: 213 - 13x4 19x6
Price Range: € 15 standard room; 3-4 € 16; 2 € 20; 1 € 22; € 9 for dinner BBinc
Directions: 3N from city centre
Cristoforo Colombo 8km Genova 3km Principe 3km, Brignole 4km
from Principe 35/40; from Brignole 40 50m ap Via Costanzi x 9 R (BD) TV 1 x 8

Genoa – Genova

Genoa... Travel Tips

- **For budget eats check out...** Youth Hostel (Menu: € 9)
- **For great nightlife try...** Walk and have a drink around the old port, Walk and have a drink along the Passegiata Di Nervi, Have a drink in the Old Town near Piazza Delle Erbe
- **Don't miss...** Via Garibaldi and its museums, Palazzo Ducale, Cathedral Di S. Lorenzo, Acquario e Padiglione del Mare, Passeggiata di Nervi, Palazzo Reale, The fishing village of Boccadasse, 1 day trips to Portofino and Cinque Terre

▲ **Giove** – Torre Al Borgo – 31138
Via Piave, 05024 Giove (TR).
(0744) 978673 (0744) 978673
info@ostellogiustiniani.it
Open Dates: 01.03-30.09 (01.10-31.12 R) Roma-Fiumicino 80km
Civitavecchia 100km Attigliano 13km; Orte 13km 10m x 25 (B) TV 1 x

△ ***Guastalla*** – *"Quadrio Michelotti" – 31071*
Via Lido Po 11-13, 42016 Guastalla (RE).
(0522) 839228; Mobile (335) 5230406
lunetia@tin.it
Open Dates: 01.04-15.10 (12 R)
Bologna 95km; Verona 60km
1.5km 1.5km x 50 1 x 1km

Ischia Isle – Il Gabbiano 31019
SS. Forio-Panza N.182,
80075 Forio D'Ischia (NA).
(081) 909422 (081) 909422
ischia@ostellionline.org
Open Dates: 24.03-31.10 Open Times:
Beds: 100 - 3x2 13x4 7x6
Price Range: € 14 (01-20.04; 03-31.05; 01.09-31.10); € 16.50 (13.04-02.05; 01.06-31.08) BBinc
Directions: Napoli-Capodichino (by boat) 38km Forio D'Ischia 1.5km Napoli (by boat) 20m R CC TV

Ischia Isle – Il Gabbiano

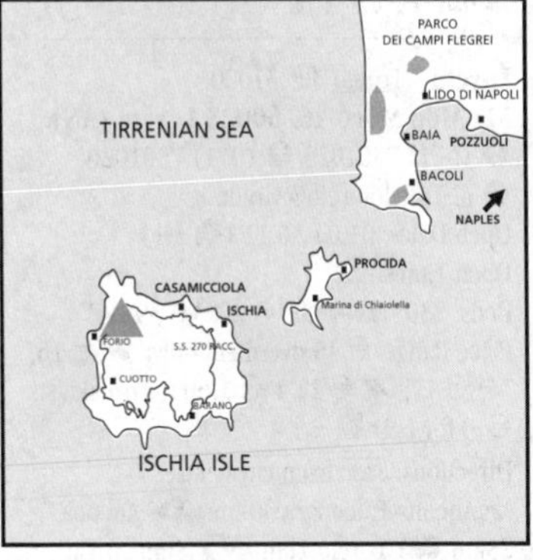

Ischia Isle... Travel Tips

- **For great nightlife try...** Walk and have a drink around the port
- **Don't miss...** Aragonese Castle (via Castello Aragonese 1), The Cathedral (Via L.Mazzella), Royal Palace (Piazza Antica Reggia 1), Guevara Tower (Via Nuoua Cartaromana), Clock Palace (Via Giovanni Da Procida), Thermal Garden

▲ **Lanusei** – La Nuova Luna – 31137
Via Indipendenza 31/35, 08045 (OG).
(0782) 41051 (0782) 480366
ostello@lanuovaluna.it
Open Dates: 01.03-31.10 (R)
Cagliari 160km; Olbia 200km A Arst Line 500m Arbatax 20km Touristic Train 1km FDS/ARST 500m x 24
(BD)
1 x

△ *Lecce – Namaste Camping/Hostel – 31143*
Via Lecce-Novoli, Km 4.5, Lecce.
(0832) 329647 (1782) 738000
info@ostellolecce.it
Open Dates: Brindisi 38km
Lecce 6km; Brindisi 38km 26
x 20

▲ **Livorno** – Villa Morazzana – 31119
Via Curriel 110, 57100 Livorno LI.
(0586) 500076 (0586) 502426
info@villamorazzana.it
Open Dates: Pisa 20km Livorno 3km Livorno Central 3km x 64
1 x

Loreto – Loreto 31020
Via Aldo Moro 46, 60025 Loreto (AN).
(071) 7501026 (071) 7501026
aigostelloloreto@virgilo.it
Open Dates: 01.04-30.11 ()
Open Times:
Beds: 230 - 4x[1] 5x[2] 20x[3] 39x[4]
Price Range: € 15 overnight only; [3] € 16; [2] € 17; [1] € 22 + € 1.60 for breakfast; € 9 for L, D
Directions: 0.5NE from city centre
Ancona-Falconara 30km Ancona 25km Loreto 1km 50m ap Via Marconi x 20 R CC
4 x
400m

Loreto – Loreto

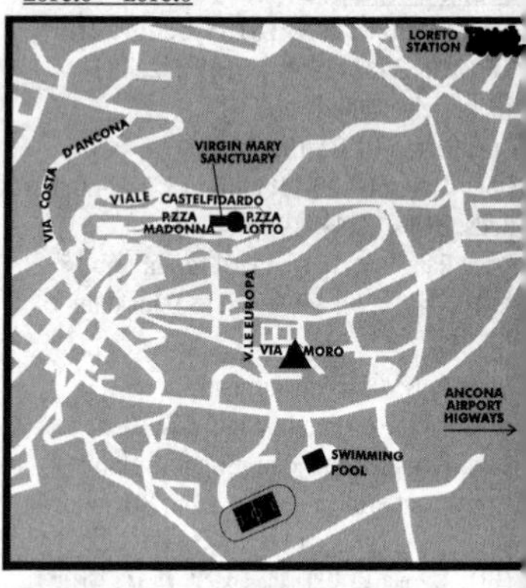

Loreto... Travel Tips

- **Don't miss...** Piazza della Madonna, Santuario della Santa casa, Sala del Pomarancio, Adriatic Coast & Conero, Recanati (town of Giacomo Leopardi)

▲ **Lovere** – Ostello Del Porto 31110
Via G. Paglia 70, Lido Di Cornasola, 24065 Lovere (BG).
(035) 983529 (035) 983529
lovere@ostellionline.org
Open Dates: 01.03-30.09 (R)
Bergamo-Orio Al Serio 40km
Cornasola 20m Bergamo 41km
to and from Bergamo 100m x 56
1 x

Lucca – San Frediano – 31032
Via della Cavallerizza 12, 55100 Lucca (LU).
(0583) 469957 (0583) 461007
info@ostellolucca.it
Open Dates: Open Times: 07.00-13.00hrs; 15.30-24.00hrs
Beds: 148 - 10x[4] 9x[6] 5x[6]
Price Range: € 16.50 standard room; € 18 with bath; /[2] € 45 + € 1.60 for breakfast
Directions: Pisa 20km Livorno 40km Lucca 500m 3 100m ap Piazza San Frediano R CC (BD)
1 x

Lucca – San Frediano

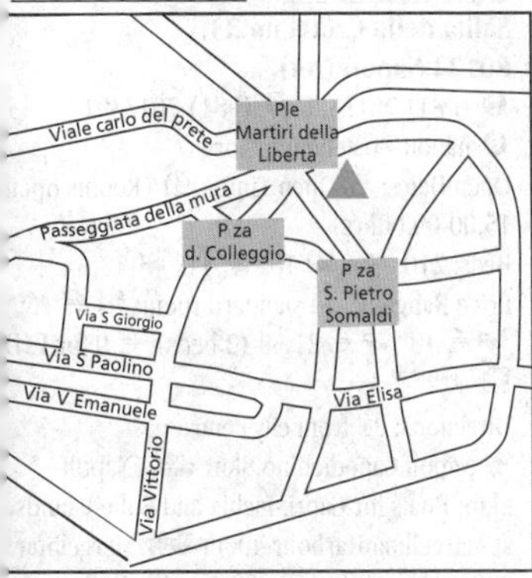

Lucca... Travel Tips

- **Don't miss...** Antiques Market (3rd Weekend of each month), Palazzo Mansi (Art Museum), Botanical Gardens, Palazzo Pfanner, River Park - for a nice bike tour, Guinigi Tower with stunning view to the town, A walk along the Middle-Age walls, Anfiteatro Square (Just 200m from the hostel), Carfagnana Area and wonderful trekking sites, Beaches and discos in the Versilla Area (15 minutes drive)

▲ **Madesimo** – Casa Delle Nevi – 31131
Via Cantonale 5, S.S.36,
23024 Madesimo (SO).
(0343) 53649 info@casadellenevi.it
Open Dates: Chiavenna 14km
Milano-Madesimo Line x 25

▲ **Marina di Massa e Carrara-Partaccia** – Ostello Apuano – 31074
Viale delle Pinete 237, 54037 Marina di Massa e Carrara Partaccia (MS).
(0585) 780034 (0585) 774266; 74858 ostelloapuano@hotmail.com
Open Dates: 16.03-30.09 Pisa 50km
Carrara 4km Line 53 50m ap Via Avenza Mare x 160
10m 10m

▲ **Matera** – Le Monacelle – 31140
Via Riscatto 9/10, 75100 Matera.
(0835) 344097 (0835) 336541
info@lemonacelle.it
Open Dates: Bari Palese 65km
Bari 60km 400m
"Tempesta" on request x 31
(B) 3 x
800m

▲ **Menaggio** – La Primula – 31075
Via Quattro Novembre106,
22017 Menaggio (CO).
(0344) 32356 (0344) 32356
menaggiohostel@mclink.it
Open Dates: 15.03-05.11 Varenna 4km by boat 100m x 35
(BD) 1 x

Milano – "Piero Rotta" 31076
Via Martino Bassi 2 (access from via Salmoiraghi 1) (QT8-San Siro), 20148 Milano (MI).
(02) 39267095 (02) 33000191
milano@ostellionline.org
Open Dates: 13.01-23.12 Open Times:
Beds: 367 - 2x 6x 8x 6x 13x 40x
Price Range: € 19 standard room (€ 19.50 April, Sept, Oct); € 22 BB inc
Directions: 4NW from city centre
Milano-Malpensa 40km; Linate 15km; Bergamo-Orio al Serio 55km Centrale 8km 90, 91, 68 200m U QT8 300m
(B)
1 x

Milano – "Piero Rotta"

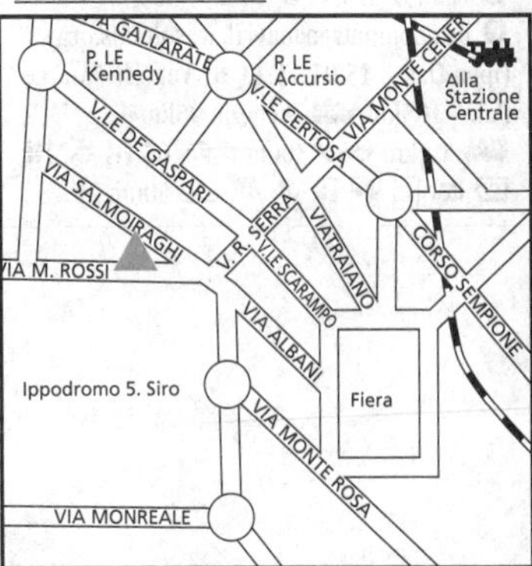

Milano... Travel Tips

- **Don't miss...** Historic Centre, The Dome, Castello Sforzesco, Theatre "La Scala", Vittorio Emanuele II Gallery

▲ **Mira** – Ostello Di Mira Casa Del Sole – 31077
Via Giare 169, 30030 Mira-Giare (VE).
(041) 5679203 (041) 5676457
mira@casasoleluna.it
Open Dates: 01.04-30.09 (R)
Venezia Marco Polo 20km
A Venezia-Sotto Marina no 80 800m
Venezia 18km Venezia-Mestre 10km Venezia-Sotto Marina no 80 800m ap Giare x 56 (B) 1 x

▲ **Modena** – San Filippo Neri 31026
Via Santa Orsola 48/52, 41100 Modena.
(059) 234598 (059) 234598
hostelmodena@hotmail.com
Open Dates: Bologna 40km 300m x 81 CC

▲ **Montagnana** – "Rocca degli Alberi" – 31078
Castello degli Alberi (Porta Legnago), 35044 Montagnana (PD).
(0429) 81076 (0429) 805301
ostellomontagnana@ilgirasole-ms.org
Open Dates: 01.04-30.09 500m 200m x 24 R

▲ **Montagnana 2** – Città Murata – 31141
Via Circonvallazione Nord, 35044 Montagnana.
(0429) 81076 (0429) 805301
ostellomontagnana@ilgirasole-ms.org
Open Dates: 15.03-15.11 Venezia "Marco Polo" 105km Venezia 95km 1.5km 300m x 63 500m

Naples – Mergellina 31007
Salita della Grotta no 23, 80122 Napoli (NA).
(081) 7612346 (081) 7612391
napoli@ostellionline.org
Open Dates: Open Times: (Rooms open 15.00-09.00hrs)
Beds: 210 - 36x2 18x4 11x6
Price Range: € 14 standard room; € 16; 2 € 18; 1 € 21.50 (2 beds); € 9 for L, D BBinc
Directions: 1N from city centre
Napoli Capodichino 8km Napoli 2km; Boats for Capri, Ischia and Eolie Islands at Margellina Harbour 400m Mergellina 200m 150, 152 400m ap Via G. Bruno U Mergellina 200m x 12 R CC

Naples – Mergellina

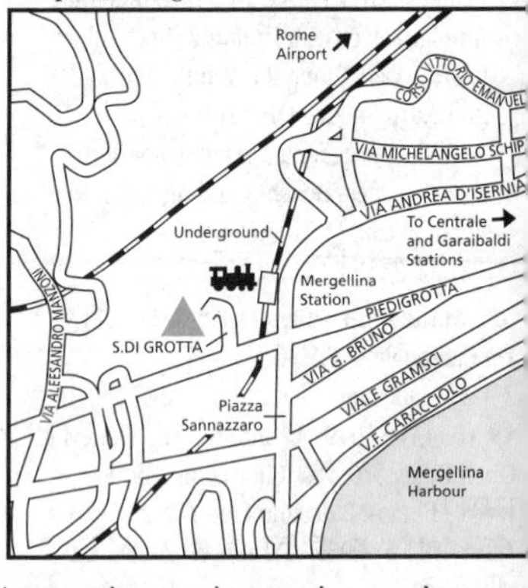

Naples... Travel Tips

- **For budget eats check out...** Youth Hostel (€ 9 for dinner)
- **Don't miss...** Duomo (church), Spaccanapoli street, Castel Sant Elmo, Aquarium, Archaeological Museum, Capodimonte museum and picture gallery, San Carlo Theatre, Museum of the Observatory at Capodimonte, Jolfataro Volcano of Pozzuoli, The Royal Palace Museum and Royal Apartments

▲ **Nicolosi** – Etna Garden Park – 31079
Via della Quercia 7, 95030 Nicolosi (CT).
(095) 7914686 (095) 7914701
ostelloct@tiscalinet.it
Open Dates: Catania Fontanarossa 20km Catania 13km Catania Centrale 13km Line Catani-Nicolosi 300m x 55 1 x

▲ **Noto** – Il Castello – 31080
Via Fratelli Bandiera 1, 96017 Noto (SR).
(0931) 894778 (0931) 894778
ostellodinoto@tin.it
Open Dates: Catania 100km Catania 100km 2km "Sais" ap Giardini Pubblici x 34 (B)

▲ **Padova** – Città Di Padova – 31082
Via A. Aleardi 30, 35122 Padova (PD).
(049) 8752219 (049) 654210
pdyhtl@tin.it
Open Dates: 09.01-21.12 Venezia "Marco Polo" 40km 2km 3, 8, 12, 18, 22 250m x 120 (B) 2 x

Palermo – Baia Del Corallo – 31083
Via Plauto, 27 90148 Palermo (PA).
(091) 6797807 (091) 6912376
palermo@ostellionline.org
Open Dates: 01.03-31.10 (R)
Open Times: 07.00-10.00hrs; 15.30-03.30hrs (closed on Mon from 00.30hrs)
Beds: 70
Price Range: € 17 overnight only; 2 € 18 + € 1.60 for breakfast
Directions: 15NW from city centre
Palermo Falcone e Borsellino 15km
Palermo 12km T.Natale 2km
628 20m U T. Natale R (B) 1 x

Palermo – Baia Del Corallo

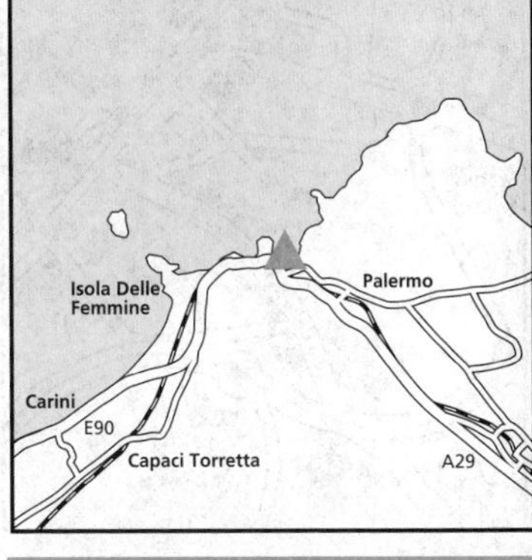

Palermo... Travel Tips

- **Don't miss...** Historic Centre, Palazzo De I Normanni, The Cathedral, I Quatro Canti Place

△ ***Parma*** *– "Cittadella" – 31084*
Parco Cittadella 5, 43100 Parma (PR).
(0521) 961434
ostellocittadella@libero.it
Open Dates: 01.04-31.10 Bologna 95km 1.5km 400m x 25

Perugia – Mario Spagnoli 31085
Via Cortonese 4,
06127 Perugia-Pian Di Massiano.
(075) 5011366 (075) 5026805
perugia1@ostellionline.org
Open Dates: Open Times:
Beds: 172 - 7x2 4x4 18x6 4x6+
Price Range: € 15 standard room; € 17; 1 € 22; € 9 for L, D BBinc
Directions: 3E from city centre
Perugia "Sant' Egidio" 10km
Fontivegge 1km 9, 10, 11 50m ap Via Cortonese 1 x 1km

Perugia – Mario Spagnoli

▲ **Perugia** – Ponte Felcino – 31033
Via Maniconi 97,
06077 Perugia-Ponte Felcino.
(075) 5913991 (075) 5914203
perugia2@ostellionline.org
Open Dates: 05.03-10.11; 26.12-10.01 (12 R) Perugia "Sant' Egidio" 3km
Ponte Felcino 500m 50m x 90

Perugia... Travel Tips

- **For budget eats check out...** Youth Hostel (€ 9 for lunch/dinner, please reserve in the evening and morning)
- **Don't miss...** Umbria Jazz Festival (July), Eurochocolate (October), Sagra musicale dell' Umbria (September), Galleria nazionale dell'Umbria (art gallery), Etruscan archaeological sites, Spagnolia (amusement/zoo park), Rocca Paolina, Parco Naturale Monte Subasio (natural park)

△ ***Pietraporzio*** *– Al Tenibres – 31086*
Via Nazionale 8, 12010 Pietraporzio (CN).
(0171) 96602 riva30@interfree.it
Open Dates: 01.01-30.09; 16.11-31.12
Caselle (Turin) 120km Cuneo 50km Line Cuneo-Bersezio 50m
x 24 (B)

▲ **Polvese Isle - Trasimeno Lake** –
Fattoria Il Poggio YH – 31072
Isola Polvese, 06060 San Feliciano (PG).
(075) 9659550 (075) 9659551
ostelloilpoggio@libero.it
Open Dates: 01.03-31.10 (12) Perugia "Sant' Egidio" 35km 500m
Magione 4km Line Magione-San Feliciano x 76 R 1 x

Pompei – "Casa Del Pellegrino" – 31034
Via Duca D'Aosta no 4,
80045 Pompei (NA).
(081) 8508644 (081) 8508644
pompei@ostellionline.org
Open Dates: 12 Open Times:
(Rooms open from 15.00-09.00hrs)
Beds: 76
Price Range: € 14 standard room;
€ 16.50; € 9 for L, D (only for) BBinc
Directions: Napoli-Capodichino 30km
Napoli 20km; Salerno 30km; Sorrento 15km 200m 50m
U Circumvesuviana 200m x 6 R 1 x

Pompei – "Casa Del Pellegrino"

Pompei... Travel Tips

- **Don't miss...** Archaelogical Area (close to hostel), Virgin Mary Sanctuary, Ercolano Excavations, Castellammare Thermae

▲ **Prato** – Villa Fiorelli – 31087
Parco Di Galceti, Via Di Galceti 64,
59100 Prato (PR).
(0574) 690786 (0574) 691845
cspsrl@interfree.it
Open Dates: 01.02-30.09 Firenze 10km
3km Lam Rossa 13m x 52
R 1 x

▲ **Pratovecchio** – Casalino YH – 31116
Loc. Casalino n. 80/A,
52015 Pratovecchio (AR).
(0575) 558122
info@ostellocasalino.it
Open Dates: 12 Firenze 50km
Pratovecchio 4km Line
"Pratovecchio-Casalino" 50m x 18
TV P

▲ **Pruno** – La Pania – 31088
Via del Teatro 14,
55040 Pruno Di Stazzema (LU).
(0584) 770092 (0584) 790871
ostellolapania@tiscali.it
Open Dates: 12 Pisa 50km A Clap
150m Livorno 50km Pietrasanta
20km Clap 150m ap Pruno x 23
TV 1 x P

Ravenna – Dante HI 31024
Via Aurelio Nicolodi 12
(quartiere Trieste),
48100 Ravenna (RA).
(0544) 421164 (0544) 421164
hostelravenna@hotmail.com
Open Dates: 01.03-15.11 (12)
Open Times: 07.00-10.00hrs; 15.30-23.30hrs
Beds: 110 - 6x1 2x2 15x4 8x5
Price Range: € 14 standard room; € 16
(€ supplement 01.01-15.03; 01.11-31.12)
€ 9 for L, D BBinc
Directions: Bologna "Marconi" 75km;
Forli 26km 1km Ravenna 1km
1, 10, 11, 70 200m R
CC (LD) TV 1 x
8 P 2km

Ravenna – Dante

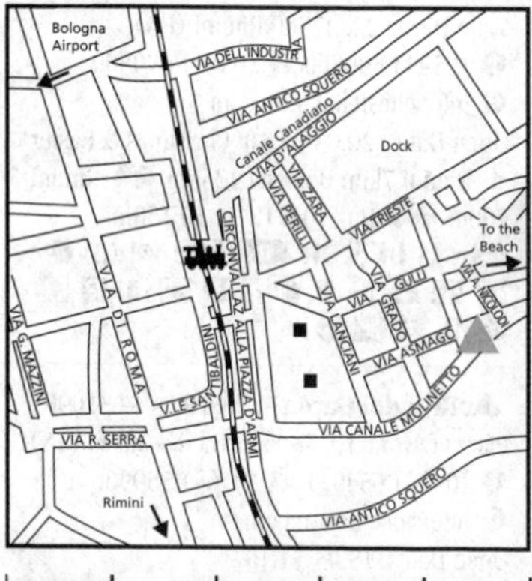

Ravenna... Travel Tips

- **For budget eats check out...** Youth Hostel (€ 9 for lunch/dinner)
- **Don't miss...** Basilica di San Vitale, Museo Nazionale (15th century icons, early byzantine glass), Mausoleo di Galla Placida, Duomo (church), Tomba di Dante, Neonian Baptistery

▲ **Reggio Emilia** – Basilica Della Ghiara – 31089
Via Guasco, 42100 Reggio Emilia.
(0522) 452323 (0522) 454795
Open Dates: 12 Bologna 55km 1km
Mini bus E ap Piazza Gioberti x 100
TV 2 x
P

▲ **Rieti-Terminillo** – "Ostello della Neve" – 31018
Anello Panoramico (Campoforogna),
02017 Rieti-Terminillo (RI).
(0746) 261321 (0746) 261321
Open Dates: 01.12-15.05; 15.06-31.08
Roma-Fiumicino Rieti 25km
250m x 58 R CC
TV 1 x P

Rimini – Hostel Jammin – 31132
Viale Derna 22, 47900 Rimini (RN).
(0541) 390800 (0541) 390800
info@hosteljammin.com
Open Dates: 20.03-31.10; Christmas & Easter
Rimini 7km; Bologna 125km Rimini 700m Bus 10, 11, 18, 19 150m
x 55 (B) 1 x

Riva del Garda – "Benacus" – 31090
Piazza Cavour 10, 38066 Riva del Garda (TN).
(0464) 554911 (0464) 559966
info@ostelloriva.com
Open Dates: 15.03-31.10
Verona-Villafranca 90km 200m
Rovereto 22km 500m x 120

***Rivamonte Agordino** – Imperina – 31091*
Localita le Miniere 3,
32020 Rivamonte Agordino BL.
(0437) 62451 (0437) 62451
ostelloimperina@inwind.it
Open Dates: 01.04-17.10 Venezia "Marco Polo" 150km Belluno 30km Line Belluno-Agordo 1.5km ap Le Campe x 44 (BD) 1 x

Rome – Foro Italico - A F Pessina YH
31003
Viale delle Olimpiadi 61,
00194 Roma (RM).
(06) 3236267 (06) 3242613
roma@ostellionline.org
Open Dates: Open Times: 07.00-24.00hrs
(Rooms open from 14.00hrs)
Beds: 334 - 14x6 35x6+
Price Range: € 18 standard room;
€ 9 for L, D BBinc
Directions: 5NW from city centre
Roma-Leonardo da Vinci 28km
Termini 6km 32, 280, 628 50m
ap Lungotevere Maresciallo Cadorna U Line A Ottaviano 2km 1 x

Rome – Foro Italico - A F Pessina YH

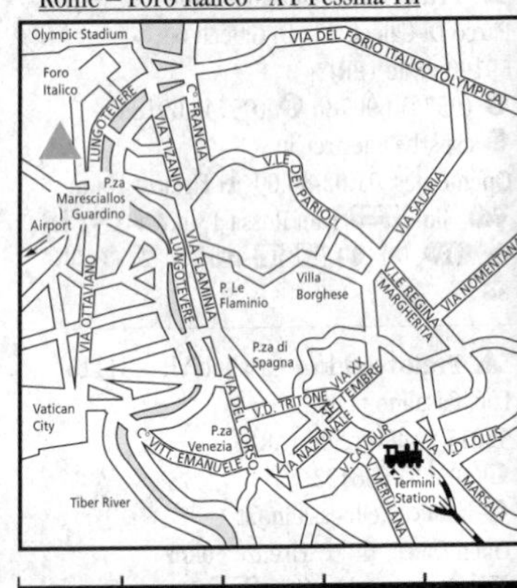

Rome... Travel Tips

- **For budget eats check out...** Youth Hostel (€ 9 for lunch/dinner)
- **For great nightlife try...** Trastevere district, Campo de' fiori square, Via di Monte testaccio street, Ostia district (summer only)
- **Don't miss...** Foro Romano-Palatino-Colosseo (archaeological sites), Piazza Navona, Galleria Borghese (art gallery), Fontana di Trevi, Piazza di Spagna, Campidoglio Hill, Cappella Sistina, San Pietro, Gianicolo Hill, Campo de' Fiori

Salerno – Ave Gratia Plena 31009
Via Dei Canali, 84121 Salerno (SA).
(089) 234776 (089) 2581874
info@ostellodisalerno.it
Open Dates: Open Times:
Beds: 100 - 3x1 13x2 3x3 11x4 3x6
Price Range: € 14 standard room; € 26 1; € 17.50 4; € 20 2; € 9 for dinner BBinc
Directions: Napoli-Capodichino 55km
50m 600m 50m x 9 (BD) 1 x

▲ **Turin** – Torino – 31006
Via Alby 1, 10131 Torino (TO).
(011) 6602939 (011) 6604445
ostello.torino@libero.it
Open Dates: 15.01-21.12 Torino Caselle 16km Porta Nuova 1.8km 52 (64 on Sun) 200m x 76 (BD) 2km

▲ **Tuscania** – Palazzo Ranucci – 31126
Via Della Torretta 8, 01017 Tuscania (VT).
(0761) 445067 (0761) 445067
Open Dates: Roma-Leonardo Da Vinci 100km Civitavecchia 40km Viterbo 40km Acotral 200m x 15 (LD)

▲ **Urbana** – "San Salvaro" – 31106
Via Pozzotto 1, 35044 San Salvaro, Urbana (PD).
(0429) 809216 (0429) 804067
info@ostellosansalvaro.it
Open Dates: 15.03-30.05; 01.07-15.10 ( ) Verona-Catullo 40km A 500m Bevilacqua 3km x 25 (B) 2 x

▲ **Ussita** – Felycita – 31127
Via Frontignano, 62039 Ussita (MC).
(0737) 90121; 90209 (0737) 90121
info@hotelfelycita.com
Open Dates: Perugia 100km; Ancona 120km A Ussita 7km Ancona 110km Camerino 50km Frontignano 10m x 55 1 x

△ ***Valfabbrica*** *– Il Sentiero – 31136*
Via Piave 3, 06029 Valfabbrica (PG).
(075) 901864; Mobile (248) 6000191
Open Dates: Perugia "S.Egidio" 15km A 300m Ancona 85km Bastia Umbra 17km 300m
x 24 (B)

Venice – Venezia 31001
Fondamenta Zitelle 86,
Isola della Giudecca,
30133 Venezia (VE).
(041) 5238211 (041) 5235689
venezia@ostellionline.org
Open Dates: 01.01-11.12; 28-31.12
Open Times: 07.00-24.00hrs (Rooms open from 14.00hrs)
Beds: 260 - 1x² 1x³ 18x⁶⁺
Price Range: € 19.50 standard room; € 24; € 9 for lunch BB inc
Directions: 1S from city centre
Venezia "Marco Polo" 10km Santa Lucia 2km Boat 41, 42, 82 150m ap Zitelle x 2 (BD)

Venice – Venezia

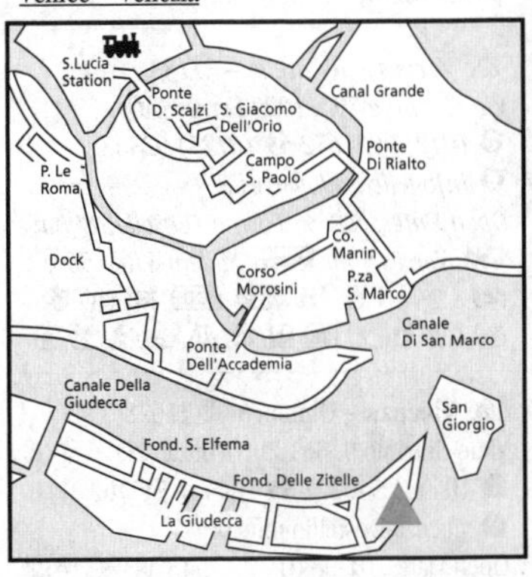

Venice... Travel Tips

- **For budget eats check out...** Youth Hostel (€ 9 for dinner)
- **Don't miss...** Basilica di San Marco (church), Ponte di Rialto, Palazzo Ducale, Galleria dell' Accademia (art gallery), Campo San Moisè, Ca' d'oro Palace, Murano district, Burano district, Correr Museum, Querini Stampalia Museum

▲ **Verbania** – Verbania – 31107
Via Alle Rose 7 - 28922 Verbania (VB).
(0323) 501648 (0323) 507877
ostello_verbania@libero.it
Open Dates: 01.03-31.10 (06-29.02)
Milano-Malpensa 60km Verbania 10km Line Intra-Trobaso 100m ap Piazza Gramsci x 89
1 x

▲ **Verona** – "Villa Francescatti" – 31108
Salita Fontana del Ferro 15,
37129 Verona (VR).
(045) 590360 (045) 8009127
Open Dates: Verona-Catullo 15km
Porto Nuova 3km 73 - 400m (90 - 400m at night) ap Piazza Isolo 3NW x 241
(BD) 1 x

△ ***Verres*** *– Il Casello – 31133*
Via Stazione 79, 11029 Verres (AO).
(0125) 921652 (0125) 923674
info@ilcaselloverres.it
Open Dates: Torino "Caselle" 80km
Verres 50m "Sadem-Vita" 50m
x 25 (B)

▲ **Vicenza** – Olimpico HI 31028
Viale Giuriolo 9, 36100, Vicenza (VI).
(0444) 540222 (0444) 547762
vicenza@ostellionline.org
Open Dates: 01-08.01; 16.03-15.11 ( ) Venezia "Marco Polo" 75km; Verona "Catullo" 65km Venezia 70km
Vicenza 1.5km 1, 2, 4, 5, 7 50m
x 84 1 x
8

▲ **Villavallelonga** – Tre Confini – 31109
Via Aia Canale, 67050 Villavallelonga (AQ).
(0863) 949406 (0863) 949406
ostellotreconfini@virgilio.it
Open Dates: 01.04-30.09; 01.12-29.02
Avezzano 27km 50m x 54
1 x

Japan

Japan Youth Hostels, Inc,
Kanda Amerex Bldg,
3-1-16 Misaki-cho, Chiyoda-ku, Tokyo 101-0061, Japan.

t (81) (3) 32881417
f (81) (3) 32881248
e info@jyh.or.jp
w www.jyh.or.jp

Travel Section: Kanda Amerex Bldg,
3-1-16 Misaki-cho, Chiyoda-ku,
Tokyo 101-0061, Japan.

t (81) (3) 32880260
e travel@jyh.or.jp
w www.jyh.or.jp

A copy of the Hostel Directory for this Country can be obtained from:
The National Office

Capital:	Tokyo
Language:	Japanese
Currency:	¥ (yen)
Population:	125,000,000
Size:	377,780 sq km
Telephone Country Code:	81
eKit Access Number:	0053-112-1399

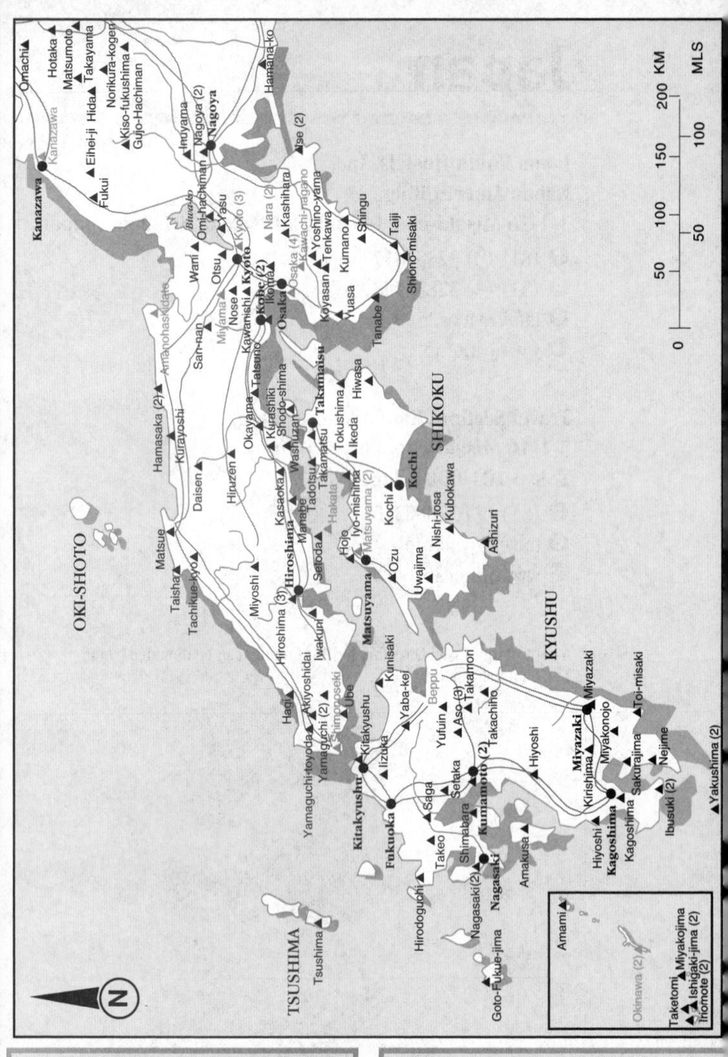

Japan is the world's second largest economy and the industrialized world's most sophisticated and socially-structured society. It is a country of 125 million people where the group, not the individual matters most, where the past continues to echo in the present and where the quality of the packaging of goods and services (both literally and metaphorically) is often deemed to be more important than the contents. Japan is a land of paradoxes and opposites, where 'yes' *(hai)* can often mean 'no' or simply 'I hear you' and where silence is treasured and pauses in conversation are a time for reflection, not a signal to say more. Japan also has an 'inside' and an 'outside' culture. Foreigners, of course, are 'outside' people (as can be other Japanese from outside the circle) but are invariably treated with the respect due to guests.

Be a welcome guest, show deference and good manners at all times and you

will be treated with courtesy wherever you go – from the big department store to the local temple.

A few other Top Tips from **CULTURE SMART!**:

- Most Japanese have not been abroad and therefore have very limited knowledge of other cultures; but they are invariably keen to know what you think of Japan. Your questioners, of course, will expect to hear positive things.

- Gift-giving is an essential lubricant of daily life in Japan. As a visitor you will not be expected to know very much about this; but 'show willing' by bringing little items from your town or region that you can give as souvenirs.

- If you are invited out for a Japanese meal, it is usually best to say that you will enjoy everything, and give your host the pleasure of ordering for you (unless, of course, you have an

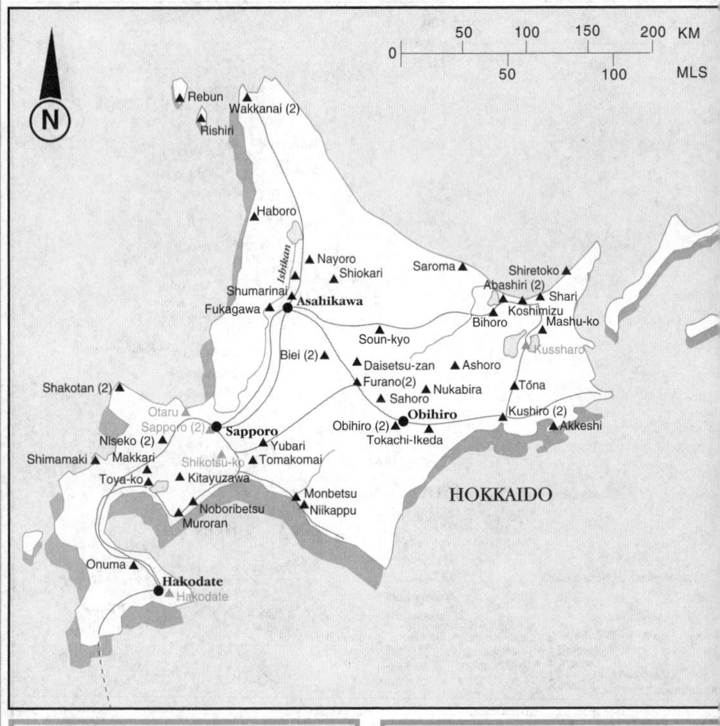

allergy to particular foods). Most first-timers are amazed at how delicious raw fish with rice *(sushi)* and plain raw fish *(sashimi)* are. Eating with Japanese wooden chopsticks is much easier than the Chinese bone or plastic ones you might have tried previously.

- Always remove your shoes on entering a Japanese home or a Japanese room (including a restaurant), which has a *tatami* (straw-mat) floor.
- Like the hot towel *(o-shibori)* you are given before all meals for face and hands, immerse yourself as much as you can in Japanese culture; this includes learning some basic Japanese polite phrases, which will be much appreciated.

Culture Smart! Top Tips © Kuperard 2005

Cultural Top Tips supplied by Culture Smart! guides. These essential guides to customs and etiquette will help you steer clear of embarrassing gaffes and sensitive issues, enabling you to discover new cultures whilst developing new friendships. Order online at www.culturesmartguides.co.uk

You can find out a lot more on our website a visit to www.HIhostels.com is essential for planning your trip!

Pour en savoir plus, rendez-vous sur notre site Internet, www.HIhostels.co[m] une visite incontournable pour préparer votre voyage!

Viele weitere Informationen auf unserer Website: www.HIhostels.com - unverzichtba[r] für die Reiseplanung!

Puedes averiguar mucho más en nuestro sitio web. Es imprescindible que visites la página www.HIhostels.com para planear tu viaje.

▲ **Abashiri** – Genseikaen YH – 32056
208-2 Kita-hama, Abashiri-shi,
Hokkaido 099-3112.
(152) 462630
Open Dates: 26.01-09.04; 26.04-09.11
Kitahama 1km x 24 (BD)

▲ **Abashiri** – Ryuhyo-no-oka YH – 32055
22-6 Meiji, Abashiri-shi, Hokkaido 093-0085.
(152) 438558
Open Dates: Abashiri
Futatsuiwa 700m ap Meij-iriguchi
x 28 (BD)

▲ **Aizu Misato** – Aizuno YH 32047
88 Kakiyashiki, Terazaki, Aizu-Misato-machi,
Onuma-gun, Fukushima-ken 969-6271.
(242) 551020 (242) 551320
aizunoyh@jyh.or.jp
Open Dates: Aizu-Takada 1.4km
x 27 (BD)

▲ **Aizu-shiokawa** – Aizu-no-sato YH – 32057
36 Hatakeda, Kofune, Aizu-shiokawa-cho,
Yama-gun, Fukushima-ken 969-3532.
(241) 272054 (241) 272070
Open Dates: Shoikawa 700m
x 14

▲ **Akita** – Youth-Pal Akita YH – 32058
3-1 Kamiyashiki Terauchi Akita-Shi, Akita-Ken,
011-0905.
(18) 8802303 (18) 8476350
Open Dates: 04.01-27.12 Akita for
Dobashi 400m
ap Akitaken-Seisyonen-Koryu-Center x 52
(BD)

▲ **Akiyoshidai** – Akiyoshidai YH – 32059
4236-1, Akiyoshi, Shuho-cho, Mine-gun,
Yamaguchi-ken, 754-0511.
(837) 620341 (837) 621546
Open Dates: 01.01-16.01; 01.02-31.12
Ogôri Hôfu 1.5km ap Akiyoshidai
x 50 (BD)

▲ **Akkeshi** – Aikappu YH – 32060
2-168-4 Wangetsu-machi, Akkeshi-cho,
Akkeshi-gun, Hokkaido 088-1114.
(153) 522054 (153) 522054
Open Dates: 06.01-29.12 Akkeshi
for Kokutaiji 200m ap Kokutaiji
x 32 (BD)

△ ***Amakusa*** *– Amakusa YH – 32061*
180 Jonan-cho, Hondo-shi,
Kumamoto-ken 863-0034.
(969) 223085 (969) 222257
Open Dates: Misumi for
Hondo 700m ap Hondo x 28 (BD)

▲ **Amami** – Amami YH – 32089
2380 Chinase Naze-shi,
Kagoshima-ken 894-0047.
(997) 548969 (997) 548969
Open Dates: Naze ap Chinase x 9
R

▲ **Amanohashidate** – Amanohashidate
YH 32062
905 Nakano, Miyazu-shi, Kyoto-fu 629-2232.
(772) 270121 (772) 270975
www.5.nkansai.ne.jp/hotel/hasidateyh/
Open Dates: Amanohashidate
for Line 700m ap Jinja-mae x 60
(BD)

▲ **Aomori** – Aomori Moyakogen YH – 32063
9-5 Yamabuki Moya Aomori-Shi Aomori-Ken 0
30-0133.
(17) 7642888 (17) 7642889
Open Dates: 01.01-14.11; 16-31.12
Aomori 9 100m ap Moya-Kogen
x 14 (B)

▲ **Appikogen** – Kamui no Mori YH
32054
661-5 Matsuo, Hachimantai-shi,
Iwate-ken 028-7305.
(195) 735041 (195) 735279
kamuinomori@me.0038.net
Open Dates: Appikogen 2km
x 13 (BD)

▲ **Ashizuri** – Ashizuri YH – 32065
1351-3, Ashizuri-Misaki, Tosa-Shimizu-shi,
Kochi-ken, 787-0315.
(880) 880324 (880) 880327
Open Dates: 04.01-31.12 Nakamura
for Ashizuri-Misaki 300m
ap Ashizuri-Misaki x 13 (BD)

▲ **Ashoro** – Nonaka-onsen YH – 32066
159 Ashoro, Ashoro-cho, Ashoro-gun,
Hokkaido 089-3964
(1562) 97454
Open Dates: 01.01-31.10; 16.11-31.12
Kushiro for Meakan-onsen ap YH
x 24 (BD)

▲ **Aso** – Aso YH – 32067
922-2 Kurokawa, Aso-shi,
Kumamoto-ken 869-2225.
(967) 340804
Open Dates: 03.01-30.12 Aso 1.4km
x 60

△ ***Aso*** *– Senomoto YH – 32068*
6332 Senomoto, Minami-oguni-machi, Aso-shi, Kumamoto-ken 869-2400.
(967) 440157 (967) 440297
senomoto@jyh.gr.jp
www.jyh.gr.jp/aso/next.html
Open Dates: Aso for Beppu 700m ap Senomoto x 56
(BD)

▲ **Aso** – YMCA Aso Camp YH – 32069
358 Kurumakaeri, Asho-shi,
Kumamoto-ken 869-2234.
(967) 350124 (967) 351642
Open Dates: Akamizu 1.7km
x 80 (BD)

▲ **Asuke** – Asuke Satoyama YH – 32070
27-2 Saka, Tsubakidach, Toyota-shi,
Aichi-ken 444-2419.
(565) 622462 (565) 622462
Open Dates: Higashi-Okazaki for Asuke 4km ap Asuke x 24
(BD)

▲ **Bandai** – Ura-Bandai YH – 32071
Goshiki-numa, Ura-bandai,
Kita-shiobara-mura Yama-gun,
Fukushima-ken 969-2701.
(241) 322811
Open Dates: 20.04-30.11 Inawashiro for Bandai-Kogen 500m
ap Goshikinuma-iriguchi x 56
(BD)

▲ **Beppu** – Beppu YH 32035
20-28 Nakashima-Cho, Beppu-shi,
Oita-ken 874-0901.
(977) 234116 (977) 220086
www.4.justnet.ne.jp/~beppuyh/
Open Dates: Beppu 1km x 52

▲ **Biei** – Bibaushi Liberty YH – 32072
Shigaichi, Bibaushi, Biei-cho, Kamikawa-gun,
Hokkaido 071-0472.
(166) 952141
Open Dates: 01.01-31.03; 01.05-10.11; 21-31.12 Bibaushi 100m x 20
(BD)

▲ **Biei** – Potato no Oka YH – 32073
Õmura Murayama, Biei-cho, Kamikawa-gun,
Hokkaido, 071-0218.
(166) 923255
Open Dates: 01.01-10.04; 21.04-30.11; 11-31.12 Biei 3.9km x 26
(BD)

▲ **Bihoro** – Bihoro YH – 32074
31 Moto-machi, Bihoro-cho, Abashiri-gun,
Hokkaido 092-0063.
(1527) 32560 (1527) 32560
Open Dates: 01.04-31.10 Bihoro for Tsubetsu or Ryoyojo 700m
ap Minami-Sanchome x 60 (BD)

▲ **Chiba** – Chiba-shi YH – 32075
955 Yasashido-cho, Midori-ku, Chiba-shi,
Chiba-ken 267-0062.
(43) 2941850 (43) 2265801
Open Dates: 06.01-28.12 Toke for Azumigaoka-minami 700m ap Odori-chuo
x 60 (BD)

△ ***Chita*** *– Chitahanto YH – 32076*
1-6 Onoura, Fukushima, Mihama-cho, Chita-gun, Aichi-ken 470-3236.
(569) 873380
Open Dates: Utsumi 2.4km x 8
(BD)

△ ***Đaisen*** *– Đaisen YH – 32077*
36-32 Đaisen, Đaisen-cho, Saihaku-gun, Tottori-ken 689-3318.
(859) 522501
Open Dates: Yonago for Đaisenji 300m ap Đaisenji x 28
(BD)

▲ **Eihei-ji** – Monzen Yamaguchi-so YH – 32080
22-3 Shihi, Eihei-ji-machi, Yoshida-gun,
Fukui-ken 910-1228.
(776) 633123
Open Dates: Eiheijiguchi 400m Eiheiji 200m ap Eiheiji x 28
(BD)

△ ***Fuji-san*** *– Fuji-yoshida YH – 32081*
339 2-chome, Shimo-yoshida-hon-cho, Fuji-yoshida-shi 403-0004, Yamanashi-ken.
(555) 220533
Open Dates: 04.01-29.12 Fuji-yoshida 1.3km x 30 (BD)

▲ **Fuji-san** – Gotemba YH – 32083
3857 Higashiyama, Gotemba-shi, Shizuoka-ken 412-0024.
(550) 823045
Open Dates: Gotemba for Hakone 1.4km ap Nino-oka x 26 (BD)

▲ **Fuji-san** – Kawaguchi-ko YH – 32084
2128 Funazu, Fujikawaguchiko-machi, Minami-tsuru-gun 401-0301.
(555) 721431 (555) 721431
Open Dates: 20.03-05.11 Shimoyoshida 500m x 50 (BD)

▲ **Fuji-san** – Yamanakakohan-so Seikei YGH – 32085
Asahigaoka, Yamanakako-mura, Minami-Tsuru-gun, Yamanashi-ken, 401-0500.
(555) 620020
Open Dates: Fuji-yoshida for Hirano 200m ap Golf-jomae x 68 CC

△ ***Fuji-san Fujinomiya*** – *Fumoto-no-ie YH – 32082*
251 Sugita, Fujinomiya-shi, Shizuoka-ken 418-0021.
(544) 274314 (544) 274445
www6.shizuokanet.ne.jp/fumoto/
Open Dates: 01.01-31.08; 01.10-31.12
Fuji for Sohina 700m ap Nitta-bashi x 8

▲ **Fukagawa** – Irumu-no-Oka YH – 32086
546-2, Otoe, Otoe-cho, Fukagawa-shi, Hokkaido, 074-1273.
(164) 251000 (164) 251000
Open Dates: 01.01-20.03; 11.04-20.11; 11-31.12 Fukagawa for Takigawa 1km ap Otoe x 14 (BD)

▲ **Fukui** – Fukuiken Seinenkan YH – 32087
3-11-17 Ōte, Fukui-shi, Fukui-ken 910-0005.
(776) 225625 (776) 226009
Open Dates: 04.01-28.12 Fukui 500m x 14 (B)

▲ **Fukushima** – Azuma-Kogen Star Hunt YH – 32018
Takayu-onsen, 1-49 Kami-no-mori, Machiniwasaka, Fukushima-shi, Fukushima-ken 960-2261.
(24) 5911412 (24) 5911417
Open Dates: 01.01-31.05; 21.06-31.12 Fukushima for Takato-onsen 100m ap Kagetsu-highland-mae x 70 CC (BD)

▲ **Fukushima** – YGH Atoma HI 32052 FNM
15-2, Funaishi, Sakuramoto, Fukushima-shi, Fukushima-ken 960-2151.
(24) 5912523 (24) 5912523
yghatoma@ma4.justnet.ne.jp
Open Dates: Fukushima 3 300m ap Kami-ubado x 26 (BD)

▲ **Furano** – Furano YH – 32090
3-20 Oka-cho, Nakafurano-cho, Sorachi-gun, Hokkaido 071-0700.
(167) 444441 (167) 444521
Open Dates: 26.12-31.03; 26.04-30.10 Nakafurano 500m x 15 (BD)

▲ **Furano** – Rokugō Furarin YH – 32091
1 Higashi-Rokugo, Furano-shi, Hokkaido, 076-0162.
(167) 292172
Open Dates: Furano for Rokugo 1.7km ap Rokugo x 25 (BD)

▲ **Goto-Fukue-jima** – Goto-Miiraku Sunset YH – 32093
493 Hamonokuri, Miiraku-cho, Goto-shi, Nagasaki-ken.
(959) 843151
Open Dates: Fukue for Miiraku 1.4km ap Miiraku-Chugakko-mae x 100 CC (BD)

▲ **Gujo-Hachiman** – Gujo-Tosenji YH – 32094
417 Ozaki-machi, Hachiman-cho, Gujo-shi, Gifu-ken, 501-4217.
(575) 670290
Open Dates: 06.01-10.08; 17.08-28.12 Gujo-Hachiman 1.4km x 28 (B)

▲ **Haboro** – Haboro Yuho YH – 32095
260 Sakae-machi, Haboro-cho, Tomamae-gun, Hokkaido 078-4123.
(1646) 22146 (1646) 22146
Open Dates: 01.01-31.10; 01-31.12
Rumoi for Horonobe or Enbetsu 700m ap Sakaemachi-danchi x 23 (BD)

▲ **Hachimantai** – Hachimantai YH – 32096
5-2 Midorigaoka, Hachimantai-shi, Iwate-ken, 028-7304.
/ (195) 782031
Open Dates: Morioka for Hachimantai-chojo 100m ap Hachimantai-Kankohotel-mae x 64 (BD)

▲ **Hagi** – Hagi YH – 32097
109-22 Horinouchi, Hagi-shi, Yamaguchi-ken 758-0057.
(838) 220733
Open Dates: 01-15.01; 10.02-31.12
Tamae 1km x 68 (BD)

▲ **Hakata** – Skycourt Hakata YGH
32049
4-73 Gion-cho Hakata-ku Fukaoka-shi Fukuoka-Ken 812-0038.
(92) 2624400 (92) 2628111
www.skyc.jp/hakata.htm
Open Dates: Hakata 700m
U Kukoline ap Gion 300m x 22

▲ **Hakodate** – Hakodate YGH 32013
17-6 Hourai-cho, Hakodate-shi, Hokkaido 040-0043.
(138) 267892 (138) 260989
Open Dates: 01-09.01; 21.01-09.04; 21.04-19.11; 21-31.12 Hakodate 2 300m ap Horai-cho x 35

▲ **Hakone** – Hakone Lake Villa YH
32098
103-354, Moto-Hakone, Hakone-cho, Ashigara shimo-gun, Kanagawa-ken.
(460) 31610
hakonelakevilla@jyh.or.jp
Open Dates: Hakoneyumoto for Hakone-cho 10m ap Futagochaya x 20 CC (BD)

▲ **Hakone** – Sengokuhara YH – 32099
912 Sengokuhara, Hakone-machi, Ashigara-shimo-gun, Kanagawa-ken, 250-0631.
(460) 48966 (460) 46578
hakone-@pop21.odn.ne.jp
www.theyh.com/
Open Dates: 05.01-27.12
Hakone-yumoto 4 100m ap Senkyoro-mae x 27 CC (B)

▲ **Hakuba** – Hakuba-no-sato Schondorf YH – 32100
Tsugaike-kogen, Otari-mura, Kita Azumi-gun Nagano-ken 399-9422.
(261) 833011
Open Dates: 01.01-09.11; 01-31.12
Hakuba-Oike for Tsugaike-Kogen 1km ap Tsugaike-Kogen x 37 (BD)

▲ **Hamana-ko** – Hamana-ko YH – 32101
223-2 Uchiyama, Arai-machi, Hamana-gun, Shizuoka-ken 431-0304.
(53) 5940670
Open Dates: Arai-machi 1.8km x 108 (BD)

▲ **Hamasaka** – Hamasaka YH – 32026
Shiroyama-enchi, Shin-onsen-cho, Mikata-gun, Hyogo-ken 669-6701.
(796) 821282 (796) 820970
hamasaka@jyh.gr.jp
Open Dates: Moroyose 1km x 80 CC (BD)

▲ **Hamasaka** – Moroyose-so YH – 32102
461 Moroyose, Shin-onsen-cho, Mikata-gun, Hyogo-ken 669-6753.
(796) 821279 (796) 823614
Open Dates: 03.01-30.12 Moroyose 300m x 30 (BD)

▲ **Hanamaki** – Naranosato YH – 32104
10-16-1 Takamatsu, Hanamaki-shi, Iwate-ken 025-0014
(198) 312341 (198) 312341
Open Dates: 06.01-29.12 Hanamaki for Hakeyama 700m ap Fudanadane x 10 (BD)

▲ **Hida Furukawa** – Hida Furukawa YH – 32105
180 Shimpô, Furukawa-machi, Hida-shi, Gifu-ken 509-4272.
(577) 752979 (577) 752979
www.d2.dion.ne.jp/~hidafyh/
Open Dates: 01.01-29.03; 11.04-31.12
Hida-Hosoe 1km x 22
(BD)

▲ **Higashine** – Higashine Barefoot YH – 32106
1-3-39, Minami, Kami-machi, higashine-shi, Yamagata-ken 999-3765.
(237) 471057 (237) 471057
Open Dates: Kami-machi 1km
x 10 (BD)

▲ **Himi** – Karashimaso YH – 32107
8-27 Kita-omachi, Himi-shi, Toyama-ken 935-0004
(766) 720097
Open Dates: 08.01-12.08; 19.08-28.12
Himi 1.4km x 15 (BD)

△ ***Hinohara** – Hinohara YH – 32108*
7779-10 Hinohara-mura, Nishi-Tama-gun, Tokyo
(42) 5981131
Open Dates: 01.04-30.11
Musashi-Itsukaichi for Fujikura 300m ap Hinohara-mura-Kyodo-shiryokan
x 15 (BD)

▲ **Hiradoguchi** – Tabira-Hiradoguchi YH – 32109
1111-3 Okubomen, Tabira-cho, Hirado-shi, Nagasaki-ken 859-4821.
(950) 571443
Open Dates: Tabira-Hiradoguchi 1km
x 38 (BD)

▲ **Hiraizumi** – Motsu-ji YH – 32110
58 Osawa, Hiraizumi-machi, Nishi-iwai-gun, Iwate-ken 029-4102.
(191) 462331
Open Dates: 01.03-30.11 Hiraizumi 600m x 36 (B)

▲ **Hirosaki** – Hirosaki YH – 32111
11 Mori-machi, Hirosaki-shi, Aomori-ken 036-8205.
(172) 337066 (172) 337066
Open Dates: 04.01-29.12 Hirosaki
6 400m ap Daigaku-byoin-mae or Shiyakusho-mae x 24 (B)

▲ **Hiroshima** – Hiroshima Bayside Saka YH – 32112
3-27-5 Ueda, Saka-cho, Aki-gun, Hiroshima-ken 731-4321.
(82) 8840714
Open Dates: Saka 1.8km 13SE
x 16 (B)

Hiroshima – Hiroshima YH – 32113
1-13-6 Ushita-shin-machi, Higashi-ku Hiroshima-shi, Hiroshima-ken 732-0068.
(82) 2215343 (82) 2215377
hyh@mint.ocn.ne.jp
www.ttec.co.jp/~hyh/
Open Dates: Open Times: 07.00-10.00hrs; 15.00-22.00hrs
Beds: 104 - 4x² 1x⁴ 14x⁶⁺
Price Range: ¥2,260-2,440 (Discount for foreigners ¥1,770-1,940)
Directions: 3NW from city centre
Hiroshima 50km A No number 50km
Hiroshima 8km Hiroshima 4km
for Ushita ap Ushita-Shinmachi-Ichome
700m ap Ushita (BD)
60 x

Hiroshima – Hiroshima YH

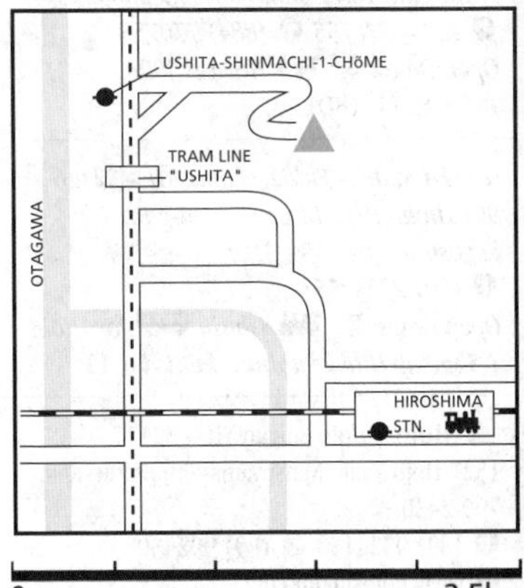

▲ **Hiroshima** – Miyajima-guchi YH – 32114
1-4-14 Miyajima-guchi, Hatsukaichi-shi, Hiroshima-ken 739-0411.
(829) 561444 (829) 561444
Open Dates: Miyajima-guchi 100m
x 30 (BD)

Hiroshima... Travel Tips

- **For budget eats check out...** Okonomimura (Japanese Pizza), Genzo (Hiroshima dishes), Sushitei (Sushi), Andersen (Caféteria)
- **For great nightlife try...** Peace Park, Hiroshima Castle, Nagarekawa, Hiroshima Baseball Stadium
- **Don't miss...** Peace Memorial Ceremony (06 August), Flower Festival (03 to 05 May), Miyajima Firework Festival (14 August), Ota-river Firework Festival (10 August), Miyajima Oyster Festival (11 February), Ebisu Festival (18 to 20 November)

▲ **Hiruzen** – Hiruzenkogen Kawakami YH – 32346
617-1 Yufune Kawakami-mura Maniwa-shi, Okayama-ken 717-0601.
/ (867) 662938
Open Dates: 04.01-29.12 Okayama, Kurayoshi for Hiruzen Haitsu-mae 1.3km x 20 R CC (BD)

△ ***Hiwasa*** *– Hiwasa YH – 32115*
113-1 Teramae, Okukawachi, Hiwasa-cho, Kaifu-gun, Tokushima-ken 779-2305.
(884) 770755 (884) 770755
Open Dates: Hiwasa 300m x 12 (BD)

△ ***Hiyoshi*** *– Fukiagehama YH – 32116*
901 Hioki, Hiyoshi-cho, Hioki-gun, Kagoshima-ken 899-3101
(99) 2923455
Open Dates: Ishuin for Hioki 1.5km ap Hioki-yubinkyoku x 12

▲ **Hojo** – Hojo Suigun YH – 32117
1527 Hojo Tsuji, Matsuyama-Shi, Ehime-Ken, 799-2430.
(89) 9924150 (89) 9924308
www.hojosuigun.com
Open Dates: Iyo-Hojo 400m x 10 CC (BD) P

▲ **Hotaka** – Azumino Pastoral YH – 32118
8508 Ariake, Hotaka-machi, Azumino-shi, Nagano-ken 717-0601.
(263) 836170 (263) 836416
www.user.cnet.ne.jp/p/pastoral
Open Dates: Hotaka 4km x 32 (BD) P

△ ***Ibusuki*** *– Tamaya YH – 32120*
5-27-8 Yuno-hama, Ibusuki-shi, Kagoshima-ken 891-0406.
(993) 223553
Open Dates: Ibusuki for Hotel ap Suzurigahama x 35 (BD) P

▲ **Ibusuki** – Yunosato YH – 32121
2-38-20, Omure, Ibusuki-shi, Kagoshima-ken 891-0401.
(993) 225680
Open Dates: Ibusuki 900m x 15 (BD) P

▲ **Iizuka** – Yakiyama-Kōgen YH – 32122
1270-14 Yakiyama, Iizuka-shi, Fukuoka-ken 820-0047.
(948) 226385 (948) 227234
Open Dates: 03.01-29.12 Hakata for Yakiyama-toge 700m ap Yakiyama-Motomara 20E x 90 (BD) P

▲ **Ikeda** – Awa-Ikeda YH – 32123
3798, Sako, Nishiyama, Ikeda-cho, Miyoshi-gun, Tokushima-ken, 778-0040.
(883) 725277
http://awaikedayh.hp.infoseek.co.jp/
Open Dates: 04.01-01.04; 04.04-29.12 Awa-Ikeda 5.5km x 22 (BD) P

▲ **Ikoma** – Senko-ji YH – 32124
188 Narukawa, Heguri-cho, Ikoma-gun, Nara-ken 636-0945.
(745) 450652 (745) 454408
senkoji@kcn.ne.jp
Open Dates: Motosanjo-guchi Midoriga-oka 1.8km ap Midoriga oka-kita x 30 (BD) P

▲ **Inuyama** – Inuyama International YH – 32125
162-1, Tsugao-Himuro, Inuyama-shi, Aichi-ken, 484-0091.
(568) 611111 (568) 612770
Open Dates: 04.01-28.12 Inuyama-yuen 1.8km x 80 R (BD) P

▲ **Iriomote** – Iriomote-jima Midori-sō YH – 32126
572-5 Uehara, Taketomi-cho, Yaeyama-gun, Okinawa-ken 907-1541.
(9808) 56526
Open Dates: Funaura for Shirahama 100m ap Uehara x 32 (BD)

▲ **Iriomote** – Irumote-sō YH – 32127
870-95 Uehara, Taketomi-cho, Yaeyama-gun, Okinawa-ken 907-1541.
(9808) 56255 (9808) 56076
Open Dates: Funaura 700m x 45 (BD)

▲ **Isawa** – Isawa Onsen YH – 32128
106-2 Yamasaki, Isawa-machi, Fuefuki-shi, Yamanashi-ken 406-0022.
(55) 2622110
Open Dates: Isawa-onsen 500m x 29 (BD)

▲ **Ise** – Ise-shima YH – 32024
1219-82 Anagawa, Isobe-cho, Shima-shi Mie-ken 517-0213.
(599) 550226
Open Dates: 01.01-20.01; 01.02-20.06; 01.07-31.12 Anagawa 900m x 80 CC (BD)

△ ***Ise** – Taikō-ji YH – 32129*
1659 Ei, Futami-cho, Ise-shi, Mie-ken 519-0602.
(596) 432283
Open Dates: Futamino-ura Meotoiwa-higashiguchi 500m ap Meotoiwa-higashiguchi x 28 (BD)

▲ **Ishigaki-jima** – Trek Ishigaki-jima YH – 32130
165-12 Hoshino, Ishigaki-shi, Okinawa-ken 907-0241.
(980) 868257
Open Dates: 04.01-29.12 Ishigaki Hiranoline 200m ap Hoshino x 12 (BD)

△ ***Ishigaki-jima** – Yashimaryokan YH – 32131*
117 Tonoshiro, Ishigaki-shi, Okinawa-ken 907-0004.
(9808) 23157 (9808) 24546
Open Dates: Ishigaki 700m x 20

▲ **Itako** – Itakoso YH – 32132
2031-3 Uwado, Itako-shi, Ibaraki-ken 311-2435.
(299) 624510 (299) 645891
Open Dates: Itako 1.7km x 15 (BD)

▲ **Itō** – Izu-Kogen Aoikaze YH – 32133
1250-34, Yawatano, Ito-shi, Shizuoka-ken, 413-0232.
(557) 513785
Open Dates: Izu-Kogen for Saboten-koen 200m ap Omuro-kogen-nana-chome x 15 (BD)

▲ **Iwaki** – Matsugaoka YH – 32134
127 Furukaji, Taira, Iwaki-shi, Fukushima-ken 970-8026.
(246) 212226
Open Dates: 01.07-30.09 Iwaki 1km x 12 (BD)

▲ **Iwakuni** – Iwakuni YH – 32135
1-10-46 Yokoyama, Iwakuni-shi, Yamaguchi-ken 741-0081.
(827) 431092 (827) 430123
Open Dates: Iwakuni for Kintai-Kyo 700m ap Kintai-Kyo x 50 (BD)

▲ **Iyo-mishima** – Shin-hasedera YH – 32136
3214 Sangawa-cho, Iyo-mishima-shi, Ehime-ken 799-0431.
(896) 250202 (896) 250333
Open Dates: 06.01-09.06; 01.07-12.08; 17.08-29.12 Iyo-Samukawa 1.4km x 20 (BD)

▲ **Joge** – Shizennomori MG – 32357
470-1 Yano, Joge-cho, Fuchu-shi, Hiroshima-ken 729-3423.
/ (847) 623244
Open Dates: Bingo-Yano Yano-Onsen 500m x 24 R (BD)

▲ **Kagoshima** – Shiroyama YH – 32343
2-40-8 Kusamuta, Kagoshima-chi, Kagoshima 890-0014.
(99) 2232648 (99) 2232648
Open Dates: Kagoshima For Road 3 400m ap Nakakusamuta x 12

▲ **Kamakura** – Kamakura Hase YH – 32355
5-11 Sakanoshita Kamakura-shi Kanagawa-ken 248-0021.
(467) 243390
Open Dates: Hase 300m x 12 (BD)

▲ **Kanazawa** – Kanazawa YH 32022
Utatsuyama-koen, 37 Suehiro-cho, Kanazawa-shi, Ishikawa-ken 920-0833.
(76) 2523414 (76) 2528590
kanazawa@jyh.gr.jp
Open Dates: 01-31.01; 15.02-31.12
Kanazawa 90 to Utatsuyama-koen 100m ap YH x 80 (BD)

▲ **Karakuwa** – Riasu Karakuwa YH – 32143
2-8 Nakai, Karakuwa-machi, Motoyoshi-gun, Miyagi-ken 988-0563.
(226) 322490 (226) 323777
Open Dates: Shikaori-Karakuwa for Misaki 100m ap Ezokari x 28 (BD)

▲ **Kasaoka** – Kasaoka-ya YH – 32144
5658 Kasaoka, Kasaoka-shi, Okayama-ken 714-0081.
(865) 634188 (865) 624839
Open Dates: 04.01-30.12 Kasaoka 600m x 21 (BD)

▲ **Kashihara** – Asuka Road YH – 32145
70-8 Kihara-cho, Kashihara-shi, Nara-ken 634-0004.
(744) 210988 (744) 210988
Open Dates: 01-10.01; 01.02-31.12 (except Weds) Yamato-Yagi 500m x 15 (BD)

▲ **Katsunuma** – Katsunuma Budoukyo YH – 32146
861-2 Hishiyama Katsunuma-Cho, Koshu-shi, Yamanashi-ken, 409-1302.
(553) 204733 (553) 204733
www.katsunuma.net/yh
Open Dates: Katsunuma-Budoukyo 1km x 15 (BD)

▲ **Kawachi-Nagano** – Kawachi-Nagano YH 32025
1305-2 Amano-cho, Kawachi-nagano-shi, Osaka-fu 586-0086.
(721) 531010 kawachi@jyh.gr.jp
Open Dates: 01-16.01; 22.01-06.06; 12.06-31.12 Kawachinagano for Cycle Sports Centre 100m ap Oku-Amano x 80 (BD)

△ ***Kawanishi*** *– Inagawa Sansō YH – 32147*
1-21-9 Yato, Kawanishi-shi, Hyogo-ken 666-0131.
(72) 7513565
Open Dates: 06.01-26.12
Tsuzumiga-taki 500m x 15 (BD)

▲ **Kawazu** – Amagi Harris Court YH – 32148
28-1 Nashimoto, Kawazu-machi, Kamo-gun, Shizuoka-ken 413-0501.
(558) 357253 (558) 368931
harris@shizuokanet.ne.jp
Open Dates: Kawazu for Shuzenji 100m ap Gigein x 48 (BD)

▲ **Kijimadaira** – Koshasanroku Miyukinomori YH 32149
3783-12 Kamikijima, Kijimadaira-mura, Shimotakai-gun, Nagano-Ken 389-2303.
(269) 824551 (269) 824551
Open Dates: Iiyama Nukazuka 1km ap Ski-jo-iriguchi x 15 (BD)

△ ***Kirishima*** *– Jingumae YH – 32150*
2459 Taguchi, Kirishima, Kirishima-shi, Kagoshima-ken 889-4201.
(995) 571188 (995) 571187
Open Dates: Kirishima-Jingumae for Hayashida-onsen 100m ap Kirishima-Jingumae x 28 (BD)

▲ **Kiso-Fukushima** – Kiso Ryojoan YH – 32152
634 Shinkai, Kisomachi, Kiso-gun, Nagano-ken 397-0002.
(264) 237716 (264) 237773
Open Dates: Kiso-Fukushima for Ohara 400m ap Ohara x 41 (BD)

▲ Kita Karuizawa – Kita Karuizawa Blue Berry YGH – 32153
1506-12 Kamahara Tsumagoi-muta, Azuma-gun, Gunma-Ken 377-1524.
(279) 843338 (279) 846361
Open Dates: Karuizawa for Kusatsu-onsen 2km ap Kitakaruizawa x 19 (BD)

▲ Kita-kyūshū – Kita-kyūshū YH – 32032
Hobashira-shizenkoen, 7 Hobashira, Yahata-higashi-ku, Kita-kyūshū-shi, Fukuoka-ken 805-0056.
(93) 6818142 kitakyu@jyh.gr.jp
Open Dates: 01-20.01; 01.02-10.06; 21.06-31.12 Yahata 1.8km x 56 (BD)

▲ Kitayuzawa – Kitayuzawa YH – 32154
50 Kitayuzawa-onsen-cho, Otaki-mura, Usu-gun, Hokkaido 052-0316.
(142) 686552 kitayuzawa@jyh.gr.jp
Open Dates: 01.01-20.05; 01.06-20.11; 01-31.12 Datemonbetsu for Kucchan or Otaki 200m ap Kitayuzawa-onsen x 40 CC (BD)

▲ Kiyosato – Kiyosato YH – 32155
3545 Kiyosato, Takane-cho, Kita-koma-gun, Yamanashi-ken 407-0301.
/ (551) 482125
Open Dates: Kiyosato 400m x 50 (BD)

△ ***Kiyotsukyo*** – *Kiyotsukyo-onsen YH – 32156*
168 Nishitajiri, Tokamachi-shi, Niigata-ken 949-8437.
(25) 7632431 (25) 7632431
Open Dates: Echigo-Yuzawa for Mori-miyanohara 300m ap Setoguchi x 30 CC (BD)

▲ Kobe – Kitano YH – 32157
3-12-1 Kitano-cho, Chuo-ku, Kobe-shi, Hyogo-ken 650-0002.
(78) 2214712
Open Dates: Shin-kobe 1km x 12

▲ Kobe – Kobe Tarumi YH – 32158
5-58, Kaigan-dori, Tarumi-ku, Kobe-shi, Hyogo, 655-0036.
(78) 7072133 (78) 7071575
Open Dates: 01-10.01; 01.03-31.12 Tarumi 600m x 24

▲ Kobuchizawa – Yatsugatake Pony YH – 32159
3332-1911, Kamisasao, Kobuchizawa-cho, Kita Koma-gun, Yamanashi-ken 408-0041.
(551) 366401
Open Dates: (except Tues) Kobuchizawa 1.8km x 15 (BD)

▲ Kochi – Kochi YH – 32353
4-5 Fukuihigashi-machi Kochi-shi, Kochi-ken 780-0967.
(88) 8230858 (88) 8230859
www1.quolia.com/sakenokuni
Open Dates: Engyoji 300m x 25 R (BD)

▲ Kōfu – Kōfu Highland YH – 32160
1355 Kamiobina-machi, Kōfu-shi, Yamanashi-ken 400-1101.
(55) 2518020
Open Dates: Kofu for Kami-Obina 300m ap Kami-Obina x 40 (BD)

▲ Komagane – Komagane YH – 32161
25-1 Akaho, Komagane-shi, Nagano-ken, 399-4117.
/ (265) 833856
Open Dates: Komagane for Ropeway 1km ap Komagaike x 46 (B)

▲ Komoro – Komoro YH – 32162
3876-4, Minami-ga-hara, Komoro-shi, Nagano-ken, 384-0063.
(267) 235732
Open Dates: Komoro for Seinen-no-ie 1.8km ap Seinen-no-ie x 40 CC (BD)

▲ Koshimizu – Ohotsuku Koshimizu YH – 32163
137-4 Hama-koshimizu, Koshimizu-machi, Shari-gun, Hokkaido 099-3452.
(152) 642011 (152) 642012
Open Dates: Hama-Koshimizu 1.8km x 75 (BD)

▲ **Koyasan** – Koyasan YH – 32164
628, Koyasan, Koya-cho, Ito-gun, Wakayama-ken, 648-0211.
(736) 563889 (736) 563889
skoyasan@mint.ocn.no.jp
Open Dates: 01-10.01; 20.01-31.12
Koyasan for Rinkan 200m ap Keisatsusho-mae x 13 CC (BD)

▲ **Kubokawa** – Iwamotoji YH – 32165
3-13 Shigekushi-machi, Kubokawa-cho, Takaoka-gun, Kochi-ken 786-0004.
(880) 220376 (880) 224166
Open Dates: Kubokawa 700m x 20 CC (BD)

▲ **Kujukurihama** – Shirako YH – 32166
2722 Sorigane, Shirako-machi, Chosei- gun, Chiba-ken 299-4203.
(475) 332254 (475) 332577
Open Dates: Oami for Shirako-shako 400m ap Asahibashi x 20 (BD)

▲ **Kumamoto** – Suizenji YH – 32168
1-2-20 Hakusan, Kumamoto-shi, Kumamoto-ken 860-0959.
(96) 3719193 (96) 3719218
Open Dates: 03.01-29.12 Suizenji 400m x 20

▲ **Kumamoto** – Youthpia Kumamoto YH – 32167
3-17-15 Suizenji, Kumamoto-shi, Kumamoto-ken, 862-0950.
(96) 3816221
Open Dates: 04.01-28.12 Suizenji 500m x 60 (B) TV

▲ **Kumano** – Kumano-shi Seinen-no-ie YH – 32169
2-13 Arima-cho, Kumano-shi, Mie-ken 519-4325.
(597) 890800 (597) 891115
Open Dates: 04.01-28.12 Kumanoshi 600m x 12 (BD)

▲ **Kunisaki** – Kunisaki-hantō Kunimi YH – 32170
3750 Imi, Kunimi-cho, Higashi-kunisaki-gun, Oita-ken 872-1401.
/ (978) 820104
Open Dates: Usa for Imi 1km ap Imi x 60 CC (BD)

▲ **Kurashiki** – Kurashiki YH – 32028
1537-1 Mukaiyama, Kurashiki-shi, Okayama- ken 710-0044.
(86) 4227355 (86) 4227364
kurashiki@jyh.gr.jp
Open Dates: 01-20.01; 01.02-31.12
Kurashiki 6 for Kojimaeki 1km ap Shiminkaikan-mae x 60 CC (BD)

▲ **Kurayoshi** – Kōhō-ji YH – 32171
195 Shimoasazu, Yurihama-machi, Tottori-ken 682-0711.
(858) 352054
Open Dates: Kurayoshi for Hawai-onsen 700m ap Asozu x 27 (BD)

▲ **Kusatsu** – Kusatsu-kogen YH – 32019
464-1, Kusatsu, Kusatsu-machi, Agatsuma-gun, Gumma-ken 377-1711.
(279) 883895 (279) 886880
kusatsu@jyh.gr.jp
www4.ocn.ne.jp/~kusatsu
Open Dates: 01.01-20.06; 01.07-20.11; 01-31.12 Naganohara-Kusatsuguchi for Kusatsu-onsen 1.8km ap Kusatsu-onsen x 96 CC (BD)

▲ **Kushiro** – Hoshi no Makiba YH – 32172
7-23 Kawakita-cho, Kushiro-shi, Hokkaido 085-0003.
(154) 230852
Open Dates: 01.05-19.10 Kushiro 900m x 44 (BD)

▲ **Kushiro** – Kushiro Shitsugen Toro YH – 32173
7 Toro, Shibecha-cho, Kawakami-gun, Hokkaido 088-2261.
(154) 872510
Open Dates: Toro 200m x 14 (BD)

▲ **Kussharo** – Kussharo-Genya YGH HI 32174
443-1 Kussharo-genya, Teshikaga-cho, Kawakami-gun, Hokkaido 088-3341.
/ (154) 842609
genya@seagreen.ocn.ne.jp
Open Dates: 01.01-31.03; 29.04-31.10; 24-31.12 Mashu 14km x 28 CC (BD)

▲ **Kyoto** – Higashiyama YH Ⓗ 32003
112 Goken-cho, Shirakawa-bashi, San-jō-dōri, Higashiyama-ku, Kyotō-shi, Kyoto-fu 605-0036.
(75) 7618135 (75) 7618138
kyoto-yh@mx.biwa.ne.jp
www.syukuhaku.jp
Open Dates: 01-10.01; 20.01-10.06; 20.06-30.11; 11-31.12 Kyoto 5 300m ap Higashiyama Sanjo 4NE x 150 (BD)

▲ **Kyoto** – Kitayama YH Ⓗ 32004
Koetsuji-han, Takagamine, Kita-ku, Kyoto-shi, Kyoto-fu 603-8478.
(75) 4925345
www.kitayama-net.com
Open Dates: 30.01-29.12 Kitaoji 1 300m ap Takagamine-Genko-an-mae 8N x 28 CC (BD)

▲ **Kyoto** – Utano YH Ⓗ 32001
29 Nakayama-cho Uzumasa, Ukyō-ku, Kyoto-shi, Kyoto-fu 616-8191.
(75) 4622288 (75) 4622289
utano-yh@mbox.kyoto-inet.or.jp
http://.web.kyoto-inet.or.jp/org/utano-yh/
Open Dates: Kansai International 100km JR Hanazono 2km 26 from Kyoto 100m ap YH 8NW x 168 R CC (BD) 1km

△ ***Makabe*** *– Kabasanso YH – 32175*
891 Nagaoka, Sakuragawa-shi, Ibaraki-ken 300-4403.
(296) 553288
Open Dates: Iwase for Tsukuba 4km ap Kabaho-shogakko
x 15 (BD)

▲ **Makkari** – Makkari YH – 32176
94-2 Midorigaoka Makkari-mura, Abuta-gun, Hokkaido 048-1615.
(136) 452432 (136) 452432
Open Dates: Kucchan for Rusutsu-Kogen 1km ap Makkari x 18 (BD)

▲ **Manabe** – Santora YH – 32177
2224 Manabe-jima, Kasaoka-shi, Okayama-ken 714-0037
(865) 683515 (865) 683516
Open Dates: Manabe-jima 1km
x 30 (BD)

▲ **Mashū-ko** – Mashū-ko YH – 32178
883 Genya, Teshikaga-machi, Kawakami-gun, Hokkaido 088-3222.
(15) 4823098 (15) 4824875
Open Dates: 01.01-30.11; 21-31.12
Mashu for Bihoro or Kawayu 200m ap YH x 71 CC (BD)

▲ **Matsue** – Lakeside YH – 32027
1546 Kososhi-machi, Matsue-shi, Shimane-ken 690-0151.
(852) 368620 (852) 368620
Open Dates: Matsue for Asahiga-oka 500m ap Furue x 50 CC (BD)

▲ **Matsumoto** – Asama Onsen YH – 32179
1-7-15 Asama Onsen, Matsumoto-shi, Nagano-ken 390-0303.
(263) 461335
Open Dates: 04.01-27.12 Matsumoto 6 400m ap Shimo-Asama x 70

▲ **Matsushima** – Pila Matsushima YH Ⓗ 32015 FNM
89-48 Minami-akazaki, Nobiru, Higashimatsushima-shi, Miyagi-ken 981-0411.
(225) 882220 matsushima@jyh.gr.jp
Open Dates: Nobiru 1.4km x 100 CC (BD)

▲ **Matsuyama** – Matsuyama Downtown YH – 32180
3-8-3 Đaikaido, Matsuyama-shi, Ehime-ken 790-0004.
(89) 9868880 (89) 9343336
Open Dates: Matsuyama for Đogo-onsen 300m ap Đaikaido x 15 (B)

▲ **Matsuyama** – Matsuyama YH Ⓗ 32031 FNM
22-3 Himezuka Otsu, Dogo, Matsuyama-shi, Ehime-ken 790-2502.
(89) 9336366 (89) 9336378
Open Dates: Matsuyama for Dogo-onsen 600m ap Dogo-onsen x 47 (BD)

▲ **Matsuzaki** – Sanyo-so YH – 32181
73-1 Naka, Matsuzaki-machi, Kamo-gun, Shizuoka-ken 410-3626.
(558) 420408
Open Dates: Izukyushimoda for Matsuzaki or Dogashima ap Youth Hostel-mae
x 45 (BD)

▲ **Minakami** – Tanigawadake Raspberry YH – 32347
75-5 Tanigawa Minakami-machi Tone-gun, Gunma-ken 379-1619.
(278) 724980
Open Dates: Minakami 2km x 20 (BD)

△ ***Minami Zao*** *– Minami Zao YH – 32183*
59-17 Kashiwagi-yama, Shichigashuku-machi, Katta-gun, Miyagi-ken 989-0501.
(224) 372124
Open Dates: Shiroishi for Kan-kaihatsu-center 1.4km ap YH x 46 (BD)

▲ **Misawa** – Kawayo Green YH – 32185
Kawayo-green-farm, 3331 Mukaiyama, Shimoda-machi, Kamikita-gun, Aomori-ken 039-2151.
(178) 562756 (178) 564112
Open Dates: 01.01-07.01; 06.02-31.12 Mukaiyama 700m x 26 CC (BD)

△ ***Mitake*** *– Mitake YH – 32186*
57 Mitake-san, Ōme-shi, Tokyo 198-0175.
(428) 788774
Open Dates: Mitake for Mitake-san 500m ap Mitake-san x 28 (BD)

▲ **Mito** – Kairakuen YH – 32187
1-1-18, Midori-cho, Mito-shi, Ibaraki-ken 310-0034.
(29) 2261388 (29) 2261445
Open Dates: 04.01-28.12 Mito #4 100m ap Kairakuen-iriguchi x 61 (BD)

▲ **Miyako** – Suehirokan YH – 32189
7-27 Suehiro-cho, Miyako-shi, Iwate-ken 027-0084.
(193) 621555 (193) 623052
Open Dates: Miyako 100m x 30 (BD)

▲ **Miyakojima** – Miyakojima YH – 32190
1325-3, Shimozato, Hirara-shi, Okinawa-ken, 906-0013.
(9807) 37700
Open Dates: Miyako 3km Hirara 2km x 28 (BD)

▲ **Miyakonojō** – Miyakonojō YH – 32344
6361-1, Tohoku-cho, Miyakonojō-shi, Miyazaki-ken 885-0004.
(986) 380022
Open Dates: Miyakonojō for Miyazaki 100m ap Matsunomoto x 13 (BD)

▲ **Miyama** – Heimat YH HI 32050
57 Nakasai, Kobuchi, Miyama-cho, Kitakuwata-gun, Kyoto-fu 601-0775.
(771) 750997
Open Dates: Wachi for Sizuhara 100m ap Ikusei-en x 13 R (BD)

▲ **Miyazaki** – Miyazaki-ken Fujin-kaikan YH – 32191
1-3-10 Asahi, Miyazaki-shi, Miyazaki-ken 880-0803.
(985) 245785
Open Dates: 04.01-29.12 Miyazaki 1km x 20 (BD)

▲ **Miyoshi** – Miyoshi YH – 32192
Terato, Miyoshi-machi, Miyoshi-shi, Hiroshima-ken 728-0021.
(824) 631759
Open Dates: 04.01-12.08; 17.08-28.12 Miyoshi 2km x 10 (B)

▲ **Monbetsu** – Toyosato-Muminmura YH – 32193
115 Toyosato, Monbetsu-cho, Saru-gun, Hokkaido, 059-2126.
(1456) 26388
Open Dates: Toyosato 2.7km x 24 (BD)

▲ **Morioka** – Iwate-ken Seisyonen Kaiken YH – 32348
3-38-20 Mitake Morioka-shi Iwate-ken 020-0196.
(19) 6414550 (19) 6419134
isk@isop.ne.jp
Open Dates: 04.01-29.12 Morioka 1.7km 9 for Iwate Bokujyo ap Iwate Seishonen-kaikan-mae 100m x 28 (BD)

▲ **Muika-machi** – Muikamachi onsen International YH – 32021
1920-1 Oguriyama, Minami-uonuma-shi, Niigata-ken 949-6636.
(257) 722842 muikamachi@jyh.gr.jp
Open Dates: 01.01-20.06; 01.07-20.10; 01.11-31.12 Muikamachi 5km
x 180 (BD)

▲ **Muroran** – Muroran YH – 32196
3-12-2 Miyuki-cho, Muroran-shi, Hokkaido 050-0084.
(143) 443357 (143) 455953
Open Dates: 01-15.01; 27.01-31.12
Wanishi 1.7km x 74 (B)

▲ **Myoko** – Ikenoya YH – 32198
Ikentaira-onsen, Myoko-shi, Niigata 949-2100.
(255) 862116 (255) 863871
ikenoyahisao@aol.com
Open Dates: Myoko-kogen for Suginosawa ap Imori-ike x 31 (BD)

▲ **Nagasaki** – Ebisu YH – 32199
6-10 Ebisu-cho, Nagasaki-shi, Nagasaki-ken 850-0056.
(95) 8243823
masamaki-aimeg@mwc.biglobe.ne.jp
Open Dates: Nagasaki 400m x 12
(BD)

▲ **Nagasaki** – YH Nagasaki Catholik Center – 32361
10-34 Uenocho, Nagasaki, Nagasaki 852-8113.
(95) 8464246
Open Dates: Red Bus for Motohara 200m ap Catholic Center Urakami
x 40 (B)

▲ **Nagoya** – Aichi-ken Seinenkaikan YH – 32200
1-18-8 Sakae, Naka-ku, Nagoya-shi, Aichi-ken 460-0008.
(52) 2216001 (52) 2043508
Open Dates: 05.01-27.12 Nagoya
U Higashiyama Line ap Fushimi 600m 1SE
x 50 (D)

▲ **Nakatsugawa** – Kisoji Furusato – 32349
1921 Ochiai Nakatsugawa-shi Gifu-ken 508-0006.
/ (573) 695128
Open Dates: 01-20.01; 01.02-20.06; 01.07-20.09; 01.10-31.12 Nakatsugawa for Magome 1.5km ap Kominkan-mae
x 15 (BD)

▲ **Nara** – Nara YH 32005
1716 Hōren-cho, Nara-shi, Nara-ken 630-8113.
(742) 221334 nara@jyh.gr.jp
Open Dates: 01-10.01; 01.02-10.06; 11.07-31.12 Nara 108, 109, 111, 115, 130 ap Shiei-Kyujo-mae x 200
(BD)

▲ **Nara** – Nara-ken Seishōnen-kaikan YH – 32204
4 Horensahoyama, Nara-shi, Nara-ken 630-8111.
/ (742) 225540
Open Dates: 04.01-28.12 Nara 12, 13, 131, 140 400m ap Ikuei-gakuen x 59
(BD)

▲ **Narita** – Skycourt Narita YGH 32046
161 Shinden, Taiei-machi, Katori-gun, Chiba-ken 287-0224.
(478) 736211 (478) 736212
hsky21@basil.ocn.ne.jp
Open Dates: Narita 10km A 14 (Terminal 1); 26 (Terminal 2) 10km
Kisarazu 70km Narita-Kūkō Terminal 2 5.5km 62E x 20
(B) 1 x

▲ **Nayoro** – Sunpillar YH – 32205
391-2 Nisshin, Nayoro-shi, Hokkaido 096-0066.
(1654) 22921 (1654) 22921
nayoro-yh@gold.ocn.ne.jp
Open Dates: Nisshin 400m x 15
(BD)

▲ **Nejime** – Kinko-wan South Road YH – 32206
718-2, Kawaminami, Nejime, Minamisoumi-cho, Kimotsuki-gun, Kagoshima-ken, 893-2502.
(9942) 45632 (9942) 45632
Open Dates: Kanoya for Nejime 200m ap Neppi-Kan-mae x 14
(BD)

▲ **Niikappu** – Funhorse-Niikappu YH – 32208
489 Takae, Niikappu-cho, Niikappu-gun, Hokkaido, 059-2413.
(1464) 72317 (1464) 74150
Open Dates: 01.03-31.10 Niikappu 1km x 32 (BD)

▲ **Nikko** – Daiyagawa YH – 32209
1075 Naka-hatsuishi-machi, Nikko-shi, Tochigi-ken 321-1402.
(288) 541974 (288) 541974
Open Dates: 01-24.01; 01.02-31.12
Nikko 1.7km x 26 (BD)

▲ **Nikko** – Green Road Nikko Suginamiki YH – 32210
2112-7 Kiwadajima, Imaichi-shi, Tochigi-ken 321-2375.
(288) 260951 (288) 261775
Open Dates: Shimono-Osawa 1.7km x 30 (BD)

▲ **Niseko** – Niseko Annupuri YH – 32212
479-4, Niseko, Niseko-cho, Abuta-gun, Hokkaido, 048-1511.
(136) 582084 (136) 582084
Open Dates: 01.01-31.03; 28.04-10.10; 09-31.12 Niseko for Konbu-onsen 500m ap Annupuri-Kokusai-ski-jo x 18 (BD)

▲ **Niseko** – Niseko Kōgen YH – 32213
336 Niseko, Niseko-cho, Abuta-gun, Hokkaido, 048-1511.
(136) 441171 (136) 441171
kogenyh@rose.ocn.ne.jp
Open Dates: 01.01-08.04; 25.04-31.10; 01-31.12 Niseko for Konbu-onsen or Yumoto-onsen 1km ap Fujiyama x 29 (BD)

▲ **Nishi-Tosa** – Shimanto-gawa YH – 32214
493-2 Hage, Shimanto-shi, Kochi-ken, 787-1323.
/ (880) 541352
Open Dates: 01-20.01; 01.02-10.06; 21.06-03.12; 21-31.12 Ekawasaki for Kuchiyanai 4.5km ap Kuchiyanai x 11 (BD)

△ ***Noboribetsu** – Kanefuku YH – 32215*
132 Noboribetsu Onsen, Noboribetsu-shi, Hokkaido 059-0551.
(143) 842565
Open Dates: 08.01-24.12 Noboribetsu for Noboribetsu-onsen 300m ap Noboribetsu-onsen-Kosenenkin-Byoin-mae x 18

▲ **Nojiriko** – Miyagawaryokan YH – 32216
261-2 Nojiri, Shinano-machi, Kami-Minochi-gun, Nagano-ken 389-1303
(26) 2582501
Open Dates: Kurohime for Nojiriko 100m ap Nojiriko x 51 (BD)

▲ **Norikura** – Norikura-Kogen Onsen YH – 32217
Norikura-kogen, Matsumoto-shi, Nagano-ken 390-1513.
(263) 932748
Open Dates: Shin-Shimashima for Norikura-kogen 700m ap Suzuran-ski-jo-mae x 40 (BD)

△ ***Nose** – Gyokusenji YH – 32218*
1438 Yamabe, Nose-cho, Osaka
(727) 340844 (727) 340214
Open Dates: 06.01-28.12 Yamashita for Nosecho-shukuno 1.4km ap Yamanobe-guchi x 60 (BD)

▲ **Noto Uchiura** – Isaribi YH – 32219
Yo 51-6 Ogi, Noto-cho, Ishikawa-ken 927-0553.
(768) 740150
Open Dates: Kanazawa 1.7km Mawaki tokkyu 400m ap Ogikô x 15 (BD)

△ ***Noto-Monzen** – Minazukiwan YH – 32220*
Minazuki, Monzen-machi, Fugeshi-gun, Ishikawa-ken 927-2271
(768) 462022
Open Dates: 08.01-28.12 Anamizu for Igisu 100m ap Shitsura-nokyo x 15 (B)

▲ **Nukabira** – Higashidaisetsu Nukabira YH – 32221
Nukabira-Onsen, Kamishihoro-cho, Kato-gun, Hokkaido 080-1403
(1564) 42004
Open Dates: Obihiro for Nukabira 300m ap Nukabira-eigyosho-mae x 22 (BD)

▲ **Obihiro** – Obihiro Yachiyo YH – 32222
163-3-7 Kisen, Yachiyo-cho, Obihiro-Shi, Hokkaido 080-2335.
(155) 602373 (155) 602373
Open Dates: 10.01-04.04; 25.04-10.11; 10-31.12 Ohihiro for Yachiyo 1.7km ap Yachiyo x 14 (BD)

▲ **Obihiro** – Toipirka Kitaobihiro YH – 32223
52-8 Kita4senhigashi Shimoshihoro, Otofuke-cho, Kato-gun, Hokkaido 080-0272.
(155) 304165 (155) 304165
Open Dates: 01.01-19.11; 20-31.12 Obihiro for Tokachigawa-onsen 1.7km ap Shimo-Shihoro-Syogakko-mae x 26 (BD)

▲ **Obuse** – Obusenokaze YH – 32224
475-2 Obuse, Obuse-cho, Kamitakai-gun, Nagano-ken 381-0201.
(262) 474489 (262) 474489
Open Dates: Obuse 700m x 15 (BD)

▲ **Ogasawara** – Anna Beach Hahajima YH – 32225
Shizusawa Hahajima, Ogasawara-mura, Tokyo 100-2211
(4998) 32468
Open Dates: Hahajima (approx 1000km from Central Tokyo) 300m x 14 (BD)

▲ **Ogasawara** – Ogasawara YH – 32226
Nishi-machi, Chichi-jima, Ogasawara-mura, Tokyo 100-2101
(4998) 22692
Open Dates: Futami (approx 1000km from Central Tokyo) 700m x 33 (BD)

▲ **Oirase** – Oirase YH – 32228
11-160 Tochikubo Okuse, Towada-shi, Aomori-ken 034-0301.
(176) 742031 (176) 742032
Open Dates: Misawa Yakeyama 400m ap Yakeyama x 40 (BD)

▲ **Ojiya** – Ojiya Furusatono-oka YH – 32229
2063 Oguriyama, Ojiya-shi, Niigata-ken 947-0211.
(258) 592951 (258) 592951
Open Dates: Ojiya for Katsuyatani or Shioya 300m ap Terasawa x 14 (BD)

▲ **Okayama** – Okayama-ken Seinenkaikan YH – 32230
1-7-6 Tsukura-cho, Okayama-shi, Okayama-ken 700-0014.
(86) 2520651 (86) 2527950
LEP02416@nifty.ne.jp
homepage3.nifty.com/okayama-yh
Open Dates: 01-20.01; 01.02-31.12 Okayama 12 Blue line 200m ap Seinenkaikan-mae x 50 (BD)

▲ **Okinawa** – City Front Harumi YH 32037
2-22-10 Tomari, Naha-shi, Okinawa-ken 900-0012.
(98) 8673218 (98) 8625219
Open Dates: Naha 99, 120, 124 300m ap Tomaritakahashi x 38 (BD)

▲ **Okinawa** – Okinawa International YH – 32036
51 Onoyama-cho, Naha-shi, Okinawa-ken 900-0026.
(98) 8570073 (98) 8593567
okinawa@jyh.gr.jp
Open Dates: 05.01-28.12 Naha Tsubokawa 400m x 200 (B)

▲ **Ōmachi** – Hakuba-Sanroku-Onsen YH – 32232
10594 Taira, Ōmachi-shi, Nagano-ken 398-0001.
(261) 221820 (261) 221977
Open Dates: Shinano-Kizaki 1km x 24 (BD)

▲ **Omaezaki** – Omaezaki YH – 32233
43-7 Omaezaki, Omaezaki-shi,
Shizuoka-ken 421-0601.
(548) 634518
Open Dates: Kikugawa
Omaezaki Kaiyo Centre 300m
ap Omaezaki x 35 (BD)

▲ **Omagari** – Omagari YH – 32360
46-1 Komoto Fujiki, Fujiki,
Daisen,Akita 014-1512.
(187) 653451
Open Dates: Meshidume 1km
(BD)

▲ **Õmi-Hachiman** – Õmi Hachiman YH – 32234
610 Maruyama-cho, Õmi-hachiman-shi,
Shiga-ken 523-0805.
(748) 322938
Open Dates: Õmi-Hachiman for Chomeji or Kokuminkyuka-mura 100m ap YH
x 30 (BD)

▲ **Onuma** – Onuma Koen YH – 32236
4-3 Ikusagawa, Nanae-cho kameda-gun,
Hokkaido 041-1352.
(138) 674126
o_koen_yh@hotmail.com
Open Dates: 01-10.11; 01-31.12 Ikedaen 300m x 20 (BD)

▲ **Õsaka** – Hattori Ryokuchi YH – 32237
1-3 Hattori-ryokuchi, Toyonaka-shi,
Õsaka-fu 560-0873.
(6) 68620600
Open Dates: Õsaka for Senri-chuo ap Ryokuchi-Koen 6N x 92
(BD)

Õsaka – Õsaka International YH 32042

Cho Hagoromo-koen, Takaishi-shi, Osaka 592-0002.
(722) 658539 (722) 673682
osakakokusai@jyh.or.jp
www.osaka-yha.com/osakakokusai/
Open Dates: 01.01-08.05; 13.05-13.11; 18.11-31.12 Open Times: 06.00-10.00hrs; 15.00-23.00hrs
Beds: 214 - 4x2 29x6
Price Range: ¥3300
Directions: 16SW from city centre
Kansai International 25km Osaka 20km Hagoromo 1km x 7
CC (BD)
5 x
500m

Õsaka – Õsaka International YH

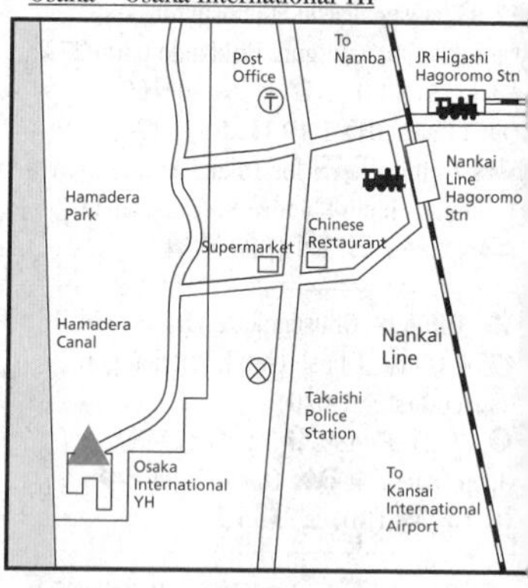

▲ **Õsaka** – Õsaka Municipal Nagai YH – 32238
1-1 Nagai-koen, Higashi-Sumiyoshi-ku,
Osaka-shi, 546-0034.
(6) 66995631 (6) 66995644
www.nagaiyh.com
Open Dates: 05.01-27.12 Osaka U for Nakamozu ap Nagai 700m x 100
(BD)

▲ **Ōsaka** – Shin-Osaka YH 32356
Kokoplaza 10F, 1-13-13 Higashinakajima,
Higashiyodogawa-ku, Osaka-shi,
Osaka 533-0033.
(6) 63705427 (6) 63705428
shin-osaka@jyh.or.jp
www.osaka-yha.com/shin-osaka/
Open Dates: Kansai International 40km Osaka Nanko Port 20km JR Shin-Osaka 400m 30m ap Nakakjima Chuugakko Mae 41 from Osaka Sta U Shin-Osaka 500m x 126 CC (B)

Ōsaka... Travel Tips

- **For budget eats check out...** IMP (Restaurant & Shopping Area), Dotombori, Sennichimae Namba, Osaka Castle OBP, Shingaibashi - Suji
- **For great nightlife try...** Umeda Sky Buildling, BBQs (Kirin Beer Place), Shin Kabukiza Theatre, Wine Bar Namba, National Bungaku Theatre
- **Don't miss...** Osaka Castle, Suntory Museum, Tempozan Marketplace, Universal Studios Japan, Nippon bashi Den Den Town, EXPO '70 Commemoration Park, Tsutenkaku Observation Tower, Kishiwada Danjihi Hall, Rinku Premium Outlets, Aqua Liner

△ ***Ota** – Jofuku-ji YH – 32211*
1114 Nima-machi, Ota-shi,
Shimane-ken 699-2301.
(854) 882233
Open Dates: Nikata 1.7km x 15 (BD)

▲ **Otaru** – Villa Mauntengu YH 32053
2-13-1 Mogami, Otaru-shi,
Hokkaido 047-0023.
(134) 336944 (134) 337081
Open Dates: Otaru 3 ap Tenguyama-Ropeway x 23 CC (BD)

▲ **Ōtsu** – Saikyō-ji YH – 32240
5-13-1 Sakamoto, Ōtsu-shi,
Shiga-ken 520-0113.
(77) 5780013 (77) 5783418
Open Dates: 06.01-09.08; 17.08-24.12 Hieizansakamoto 2km x 15 (BD)

▲ **Ōyu** – Ōyu Onsen Kuromori YH – 32243
63 Kaminoyu, Towada-ōyu, Kazuno-shi,
Akita-ken 018-5421.
(186) 372144 kuromori@ink.or.jp
Open Dates: Towada-minami for Towada-ko or Oyu-onsen 200m ap Oyu-onsen x 26 (BD)

▲ **Ozu** – Ozu-kyodokan YH – 32244
San-no-maru, Ozu-shi, Ehime-ken 795-0012.
/ (893) 242258
fwhy3863@mb.infoweb.ne.jp
Open Dates: Iyo-Ozu 1.7km x 12 (BD)

▲ **Rebun** – Momoiwa-sō YH – 32245
Motochi, Kabuka, Rebun-cho, Rebun-gun,
Hokkaido 097-1201.
(1638) 61421 (1638) 61421
Open Dates: 01.06-30.09 Kafuka for Motoji 500m ap Momoiwa-so-iriguchi x 68 (BD)

▲ **Rikuzen-takata** – Rikuzen-takata YH – 32246
176-6 Takata-Matsubara,
Kesen-cho Sunamori, Rikuzen-takata-shi,
Iwate-ken 029-2204.
(192) 554246 (192) 554260
Open Dates: Rikuzen-takata 1.7km x 68 CC (BD)

▲ **Rishiri** – Green Hill YH – 32247
35-3 Fujino Oshidomari Rishiri-fujicho,
Rishiri-gun, Hokkaido 097-0101.
(1638) 22507
Open Dates: 01.04-30.09 Oshidomari 1.7km x 30 (B)

▲ **Ryozan** – Misato YH – 32248
45-7 Hirohata, Shimo-oguni, Ryozan-machi,
Date-gun, Fukushima-ken 960-0808.
/ (24) 5861828
misatoyh@pop06.odn.ne.jp
Open Dates: Fukushima for Soma 300m ap Tsukitate-iriguchi x 14 (BD)

▲ **Sado-ga-shima** – Sotokaifu YH – 32249
131 Iwayaguchi, Sado-shi,
Niigata-ken 952-2201.
(259) 782911 (259) 782911
Open Dates: Ryotsu for Iwayaguchi 10m ap Iwayaguchi x 24

▲ **Sado-ga-shima** – Green Village YH – 32250
750-4 Niibo Uriuya, Sado-shi,
Niigata-ken 952-0106.
(259) 222719 (259) 222719
greenvyh@cocoa.ocn.ne.jp
Open Dates: 06.01-29.12 Ryotsu for Sawada 200m ap Uriuya x 14 (BD)

△ ***Sado-ga-shima*** *– Kazashimakan YH – 32251*
397 Katanoo, Sado-shi,
Niigata-ken 952-3542.
(259) 292003
Open Dates: 01.03-30.11 Ryotsu for Katanoo 100m ap Kazashima-mae x 14 (BD)

△ ***Sado-ga-shima*** *– Ogi-sakuma-so YH – 32252*
1562 Ogi-machi, Sado-shi,
Niigata-ken 952-0604.
(259) 862565
Open Dates: Ryotsu for Ogi 1.4km ap Ogi x 13 (BD)

▲ **Sado-ga-shima** – Sado Belle Mer YH – 32253
369-4 Himezu, Sado-shi,
Niigata-ken 952-2134.
(259) 752011 (259) 752071
Open Dates: Ryotsu Kaifu Line 400m ap Minami-Himetsu or Himetsu x 26 (BD)

▲ **Sado-ga-shima** – Sado-Hakusan YH – 32254
Yamada, Sado-shi, Niigata-ken 952-1321.
/ (259) 524422
Open Dates: Ryotsu for Aikawa ap Sawada-cho-Kubota x 15 (BD)

▲ **Saga** – Saga-ken Seinen Kaikan YH – 32255
1-21-50 Hinode, Saga-shi,
Saga-ken 849-0923.
(952) 312328 (952) 310608
Open Dates: 04.01-28.12 Saga 1.4km x 20 (BD)

▲ **Sahoro** – Sahoro YH – 32256
26 2-chome, 4-Jō-minami, Shintokuchō,
Kamikawa-gun, Hokkaido 081-0014.
(1566) 46550
Open Dates: 01.01-05.04; 25.04-10.11; 01-31.12 Shintoku 500m x 17 (BD)

▲ **Sakurajima** – Sakurajima YH – 32257
189 Yokoyama-cho, Sakurajima,
Kagoshima-shi, Kagoshima-ken 891-1419.
(99) 2932150
Open Dates: Sakurajima 500m x 100 (BD)

▲ **San-nan** – Tamba no Sato – 32350
447 Tamaki Sannan-cho Tanba-shi Hyogo-ken 669-3122.
(795) 771554
Open Dates: 01-31.01; 01.03-31.10
Tanigawa 1.5km x 15 (BD)

▲ **Sapporo** – Sapporo House YH – 32258
3-1 Nishi 6-chome, Kita 6-jō, Kita-ku,
Sapporo-shi, Hokkaido 060-0806.
(11) 7264235
kokusai@youthhostel.or.jp
Open Dates: 02.01-30.12 Sapporo 500m 0.3W x 100 (BD)

▲ **Sapporo** – Sapporo International YH
HI 32259
5-35 6-Chome 6-jo, Toyohira Toyohira-ku,
Sapporo-shi, Hokkaido 062-0906.
(11) 8253120
Open Dates: Sapporo U Toho Line - Gakuen-mae 100m x 120 R (B) TV

▲ **Saroma** – Saroma-kohan YH – 32260
Saroma-kohan, Hama-Saroma, Saroma-cho,
Tokoro-gun, Hokkaido 093-0423.
/ (1587) 62515
Open Dates: 01.01-04.11; 26-31.12
Abashiri for Nakayubetsu 1.7km ap Hama-Saroma x 60 (BD)

▲ **Sendai** – Dōchūan YH 32017
31 Kitayashiki, Ōnoda, Taihaku-ku, Sendai-shi, Miyagi-ken 982-0014.
(22) 2470511 (22) 2470759
Open Dates: 01.01-04.06; 21.06-04.11; 21.11-31.12 Sendai Nanboku Line - Tomisawa 700m x 30 (BD)

▲ **Sendai** – Esuporu Miyagi YH – 32261
4-5-1 Saiwai-Cho, Miyagino-ku, Sendai-shi, Miyagi-ken 983-0836.
(22) 2934631 (22) 2934634
Open Dates: 04.01-28.12 Higashi-Sendai 1.3km x 24 (BD)

▲ **Sendai** – Maple-Sendai-YH – 32262
1-9-35 Kashiwagi, Aoba-ku, Sendai-shi, Miyagi-ken 981-0933.
(22) 2343922 (22) 2343923
Open Dates: 02.01-30.12 Sendai 25 200m ap Tohokukai-byoin-mae x 23 (B)

▲ **Sendai** – Sendai-Chitose YH – 32263
6-3-8 Odawara, Aoba-ku, Sendai-shi, Miyagi-ken 983-0003.
(22) 2226329 (22) 2657551
Open Dates: 06.01-29.12 Sendai 17 300m ap Miyamachi-Nichome x 23 (BD)

▲ **Setaka** – Runowaru YH – 32264
1380-3 Sakae-cho, Shimonosho, Setaka-machi, Yamato-gun, Fukuoka-ken 835-0024.
/ (944) 622423
Open Dates: 05.01-28.12 Setaka 900m x 15 (BD)

▲ **Setoda** – Setoda Shimanami YH – 32265
58 Tarumi, Setoda-cho, Toyota-gun, Hiroshima-ken 722-2404.
(845) 273137
Open Dates: Setoda 3km Nishimawari 100m ap YH x 28 (BD)

▲ **Shakotan** – Refore Shakotan – 32357
444-7 Fumi-cho, Shakotan-cho, Shakotan-gun, Hokkaido 046-0202.
(135) 443277 (135) 442917
refore@nifty.com
Open Dates: Otaru Yobetsu ap Otaruchaya 300m x 12 R

△ ***Shakotan*** – *Shakotan YH – 32267*
297 Yobetsu-cho, Shakotan-machi, Shakotan-gun, Hokkaido 046-0322.
(135) 465051
Open Dates: Yoichi for Yobetsu ap YH x 48 (BD)

▲ **Shari** – Kiyosato Ihatov YH – 32268
282 Kōyō, Kiyosato-cho, Shari-gun, Hokkaido 099-4403.
(1522) 53995 balloon@vc-net.ne.jp
Open Dates: Kiyosato 1.7km x 24 CC (BD)

▲ **Shibata** – Kadoyonezawaya Ryokan YH – 32269
863 Sugatani, Oaza, Shibata-shi, Niigata-ken 959-2511.
(254) 292008 (254) 292200
k-nikaidou@inet.shibata.or.jp
Open Dates: 11.01-09.08; 21.08-24.12 Shibata for Sugatani 100m ap Sugatani x 15 (BD)

▲ **Shikotsu-ko** – Shikotsu-ko YH 32012
Shikotsuko-onsen, Chitose-shi, Hokkaido 066-0281.
(123) 252311 (123) 252312
Open Dates: Chitose for Shikotsukohan 100m ap Shikotsukohan x 108 CC (BD)

△ ***Shimabara*** – *Shimabara YH – 32270*
7938 Shimo-kawashiri-machi, Shimabara-shi, Nagasaki-ken 855-0861.
(957) 624451
Open Dates: Shimabaragaiko 100m x 38 (BD)

▲ **Shimamaki** – Shimamaki YH – 32271
21 Chihase, Shimamaki-mura, Shimamaki-gun, Hokkaido 048-0631.
/ (136) 745264
Open Dates: 01.03-20.11 Kuromatsunai for Sakaehama or Harauta 400m ap Garodori x 21 (BD)

△ ***Shimojo*** – *Shimojo Land YH – 32273*
7852-98 Mutsuzawa, Shimojo-mura, Shimoina-gun, Nagano-ken 399-2101
(260) 272714
Open Dates: Karakasa 6.7km x 12 CC (BD)

▲ **Shimonoseki** – Hinoyama YH
HI 32043
3-47 Mimosusogawa-machi, Shimonoseki-shi, Yamaguchi-ken 751-0813.
t / f (832) 223753
Open Dates: 01.01-20.06; 01.07-10.11; 21.11-31.12 Shimonoseki for Hinoyama Kokuminsyukusha 200m ap Ropeway-noriba x 52 (BD)

▲ **Shingū** – Hayatama YH – 32274
1-1-9 Kamihon-machi, Shingū-shi, Wakayama-ken 647-0003.
t (735) 222309 f (735) 230721
Open Dates: 02.01-30.12 Shingū 1km x 13 (BD)

▲ **Shingū** – Kajika-sō YH – 32275
1408 Kawayu, Hongu-cho, Tanabe-shi, Wakayama-ken 647-1717.
t (735) 420518 f (735) 420592
Open Dates: Shingū for Kawayu-onsen ap Kawayu-onsen x 30 (BD)

△ ***Shiokari** – Shiokari Onsen YH – 32276*
3 Shiokari, Wassamu-cho, Kamikawa-gun, Hokkaido 098-0125.
t (165) 322168 f (165) 322512
Open Dates: 01.01-20.06; 01.07-20.11
Shiokari 200m x 18 (BD)

▲ **Shiono-misaki** – Misaki Lodge YH – 32277
2864-1 Shiono-misaki, Kushimoto-cho, Nishimuro-gun, Wakayama-ken 649-3502.
t (735) 621474 f (735) 620529
Open Dates: Kushimoto for Shiono-misaki ap Kuroshiomae x 27 (BD)

△ ***Shirahone** – Oishikan YH – 32278*
Shirahone-onsen, Azumi, Matsumoto-shi, Nagano-ken 390-1515.
t (263) 932011 f (263) 932306
Open Dates: Shinshimashima for Shirahone 1km ap Shirahone
x 27 (BD)

▲ **Shirakaba-ko** – Shirakaba-ko YH – 32279
3418 Kitayama, Chino-shi, Nagano-ken 391-0301.
t (266) 682031 f (266) 683378
e hise1103@po.cnet-nc.ne.jp
Open Dates: Chino for Shirakabako 300m ap Nishi-Shirakabako x 50 CC (BD)

▲ **Shirakaba-ko** – Tateshina Kleine YH – 32280
5890 Kitayama, Chino-shi, Nagano-ken 391-0301.
t (266) 772077
Open Dates: Chino for Piratus 2km ap Tateshina-ko-mae x 14 (BD)

▲ **Shirakaba-ko** – Tateshina Shirakaba-kōgen YH – 32281
1020 Megamiko-dori, Tateshina-machi, Kitasaku-gun, Nagano-ken 384-2309.
t (267) 556601 e tateshina@jyh.gr.jp
Open Dates: Sakudaira for Shirakaba-ko 300m ap Tateshina-bokujo x 70 CC (BD)

▲ **Shiretoko** – Iwaobetsu YH – 32282
Iwaobetsu, Shari-machi, Shari-gun, Hokkaido 099-4356.
t (1522) 42311 f (1522) 42312
Open Dates: 01.01-25.03; 29.04-25.11; 24-31.12 Shari for Shiretokogoko or Shiretoko-ohashi 100m ap Iwaobetsu x 49 (BD)

▲ **Shiroishi** – Kimuraya-ryokan YH – 32284
1-51 Kamasaki, Fukuoka-Kuramoto, Shiroishi-shi, Miyagi-ken 989-0231.
t (224) 262161 f (224) 251896
Open Dates: Shiroishi for Kamasaki-onsen 100m ap Kamasaki-onsen x 42 CC (BD)

▲ **Shizukuishi** – Shizukuishi YH – 32285
19-1 Hayasaka, Dai-10-Chiwari, Nagayama, Shizukuishi-cho, Iwate-gun, Iwate-ken 020-0585.
t (19) 6932854
Open Dates: Shizukuishi for Genbu-onsen ap Hayasaka x 14 (BD)

▲ Shōdoshima – Olive YH – 32051
1072 Nishimura, Uchinomi-cho, Shozu-gun, Kagawa-ken 761-4434.
(879) 826161 (879) 826060
Open Dates: 01-20.01; 01.02-20.06; 01.07-31.12 Tonosho for Sakate 100m ap YH x 123 (BD)

▲ Shumarinai – Syumarinaiko Sobano Hana YH – 32351
Shumarinai Horokanai-cho Uryu-gun, Hokkaido 074-0742.
(1653) 64567
Open Dates: Nayoro for Horokanai 100m ap Mimata x 15 (BD)

▲ Shuzenji – Kiya-ryokan YH – 32286
388 Warabo, Izu-shi, Shizuoka-ken 410-2564.
(558) 830146
Open Dates: Shuzenji for Jizo-do 100m ap Waraho x 15 (BD)

▲ Shuzenji – Shuzenji YH 32023
4279-152 Shuzenji, Izu-shi, Shizuoka-ken 410-2416.
(558) 721222 (558) 721771
Open Dates: 01-17.01; 23.01-29.05; 04.06-31.12 Shuzenji for Heta 400m ap Newtown-guchi x 120 (BD)

▲ Sōun-kyō – Sōun-kyō YH – 32287
Sōun-kyō, Kamikawa-machi, Kamikawa-gun, Hokkaido 078-1701.
(1658) 53418
Open Dates: 01.06-31.10 Kamikawa for Soun-kyo 500m ap Soun-kyo buscenter x 75 (BD)

▲ Suwa-ko – Youpen House YH – 32289
8932-2 Takagi, Shimo-suwa-machi, Suwa-gun, Nagano-ken 393-0033.
(266) 277075
Open Dates: Kamisuwa for Okaya 300m ap Higashi-Takagi x 28 (B)

▲ Tachikue-kyō – Tachikue-kyō YH – 32290
Tachikue, Ottachi-machi, Izumo-shi, Shimane-ken 693-0393.
(853) 450102 (853) 450393
Open Dates: 05.01-29.12 Izumo-shi for Susa 400m ap Youth Hostel-iriguchi x 35 (BD)

*△ **Tadotsu** – Kaigan-ji YH – 32291*
997 Nishi-shirakata, Tadotsu-cho, Nakatado-gun, Kagawa-ken 764-0037.
(877) 333333
Open Dates: 04.01-12.08; 16.08-30.12
Kaigan-ji 400m x 34 (BD)

▲ Taiji – Taiji YH – 32292
599-2 Taiji-cho, Higashi-muro-gun, Wakayama-ken 649-5171.
(735) 592636
Open Dates: 21.02-20.05; 21.07-20.11 Taiji for Kajitorisaki 100m ap Hirami-Koen x 14 (BD)

▲ Taira – Taira YH – 32293
26 Kamanodai, Taira Shimokabeya, Iwaki-shi, Fukushima-ken 970-0101.
(246) 347581
Open Dates: 05.01-28.12 Kusano 2.7km x 58 (BD)

▲ Taisetsu-zan – Taisetsu-zan Shirakaba-so YH – 32078
Asahidake-onsen, 1418, Higashikawa-cho, Kamikawa-gun, Hokkaido 071-0372.
(166) 972246
Open Dates: Asahikawa for Asahidake-onsen 100m ap Camp-jomae x 16 (BD)

▲ Taisha – Ebisuya YH – 32294
Shinmon-dori, Taisha-cho, Izumo-shi, Shimane-ken 699-0711.
(853) 532157
Open Dates: 01.01-31.05; 21.06-31.12 Izumoshi for Izumotaisha 100m ap Taisha-mae x 28 (BD)

▲ Takachiho – Takachiho YH – 32295
5899-2 Mitai, Takachiho-cho, Nishi-Usuki-gun, Miyazaki-ken 882-1101.
(982) 723021
Open Dates: Amanoiwato 400m x 25 (BD)

▲ Takamatsu – Takamatsu Sakika YGH – 32297
6-9 Hyakken-cho, Takamatsu-shi,
Kagawa-ken 760-0046.
(87) 8222111
Open Dates: Kotodenchikuko 200m x 43 (BD)

▲ Takamori – Murataya Ryokan YH – 32298
1672 Takamori, Takamori-machi, Aso-gun,
Kumamoto-ken 869-1602.
(9676) 20066
Open Dates: Takamori 600m x 30 (BD)

▲ Takayama – Hida-Takayama-Tensho-ji YH – 32299
83 Tenshoji-cho, Takayama-shi,
Gifu-ken 506-0832.
(577) 326392 (577) 352986
Open Dates: Takayama 1km x 95 (B)

▲ Takeo – Takeo Onsen YH – 32033
16060-1 Nagashima, Takeo-machi, Takeo-shi,
Saga-ken 843-0021.
(954) 222490 (954) 201208
takeo@jyh.gr.jp
Open Dates: Takeo-onsen for Hoyo-center 100m ap YH x 80 (BD)

*△ **Taketomi** – Takanaryokan YH – 32300*
499 Taketomi, Taketomi-cho,
Yaeyama-gun, Okinawa-ken 907-1101
(9808) 52151 (9808) 52129
Open Dates: Taketomi 700m x 15 (BD)

▲ Tanabe – Ohgigahama YH – 32301
35-1 Shinyashiki-cho, Tanabe-shi,
Wakayama-ken 646-0033.
(739) 223433
Open Dates: 01.01-31.05; 01.07-31.12
Kiitanabe 700m x 15

*△ **Tatsuno** – Jounji YH – 32188*
Murotsu, Tatsuno-shi,
Hyogo-ken 671-1332.
(7932) 40030
Open Dates: 06.01-09.08; 18.08-29.12
Sanyo-Aboshi for Murotsu 1km ap Murotsu x 15 (BD)

▲ Tazawa-ko – Tazawa-ko YH – 32302
33-8 Kami-ishikami, Obonai,
Tazawa-ko-machi, Senboku-gun,
Akita-ken 014-1201.
(187) 431281
Open Dates: Tazawako for Tazawako ap Tazawa-ko-koeniriguchi x 24

▲ Tenkawa – Tenkawa YH – 32352
16-1 Kawai Tenkawa-mura Yoshino-gun,
Nara-ken 638-0301.
(747) 630154 (747) 630154
Open Dates: Shimoichi-guchi for Dorokawa or Nakaiozumi 300m ap Tenkawakawai x 10 (BD)

▲ Togakushi-Kogen – Yokokura YH – 32303
3347 Chusha, Togakushi, Nagano-shi,
Nagano-ken 381-4100.
(26) 2542030 (26) 2542540
Open Dates: Nagano for Togakushi 200m ap Togakushi-chushagu-mae x 50

▲ Togari – Kanzanso YH – 32304
6398 Toyota, Iiyama-shi,
Nagano-ken 389-2200.
(269) 652094 (269) 652195
Open Dates: Togari-Nozawa-onsen 1.7km x 30 (BD)

▲ Toi – Takasagoya-ryokan YH – 32305
790-1 Toi, Izu-shi, Shizuoka-ken 410-3302.
(558) 980200
Open Dates: Shuzenji for Toi 300m ap Baba x 21 (BD)

▲ Tokachi-Ikeda – Kitanokotan YH – 32307
99-4 Toshibetsu-nishi-machi, Ikeda-cho,
Nakagawa-gun, Hokkaido 083-0031.
(1557) 23666
Open Dates: 01-08.01; 01.02-19.03; 16.04-10.05; 22.05-19.11; 21-31.12
Toshibetsu 400m x 14 (BD)

▲ **Tokushima** – Tokushima YH – 32029
7-1 Hama, Ohara-machi, Tokushima-shi, Tokushima-ken 770-8012.
(88) 6631505 (88) 6632407
tokushima@jyh.gr.jp
Open Dates: 01-10.01; 01.02-31.12
Tokushima for Omiko 200m ap Omiko x 60 (BD)

▲ **Tokyo** – Skycourt Asakusa YGH 32048
6-35-8 Asakusa, Taito-ku, Tokyo, 111-0032.
(3) 38754411 (3) 38754941
Open Dates: Asakusa 700m x 28

▲ **Tokyo** – Skycourt Koiwa YGH 32044
6-11-4 Kita Koiwa, Edogawa-ku, Tokyo 133-0051.
(3) 36724411 (3) 36724400
koiwa@skyc.jp www.skyc.jp/hotel.htm
Open Dates: Keisei-Koiwa 50m x 37 (B)

▲ **Tokyo** – Sumidagawa YH 32354
2-21-4 Yanagibashi Taito-ku, Tokyo 111-0052.
(3) 38511121 (3) 38511130
Open Dates: Asakusabashi 300m x 40

Tokyo – Yoyogi YH 32002
c/o National Olympics Memorial Youth Center, 3-1 Yoyogi, Kami-zono-cho, Shibuya-ku, Tokyo 151-0052.
(3) 34679163 (3) 34679417
yoyogi@jyh.gr.jp
Open Dates: 05.01-26.12
Open Times: 07.00-09.00hrs (Check-out); 17.00-22.00hrs (Check-in)
Beds: 60 - 60x1
Price Range: ¥3000
Directions: 7W from city centre
Narita 70km A Limousine bus to Shinjyuku 70km Sangubashi Odakyu Line 500m U Yoyogi-Kōen, Chiyoda Line 800m

Tokyo – Yoyogi YH

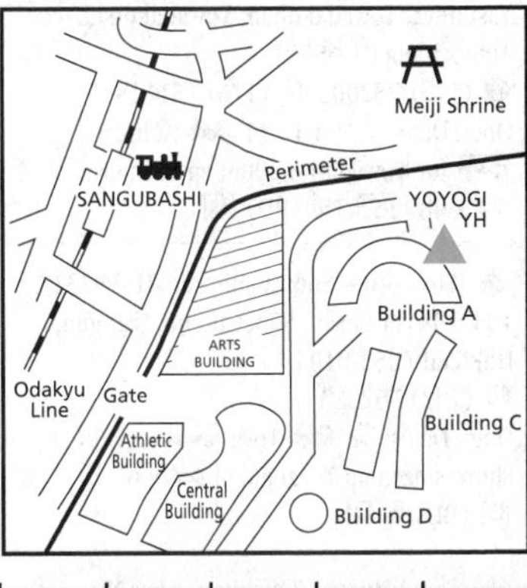

Tokyo... Travel Tips

- **For budget eats check out...** Lots of restaurants (Japanese & Chinese) & fast food outlets, Shops & restaurants in Shinjuku, 3 Caféterias in Youth Centres
- **Don't miss...** Meiji Shrine (adjacent to Youth Centre), Yoyogi Park, New Metropolitan Hall, Opera House, Lots of shops selling cheap consumer electrical goods (Shinjuku)

△ ***Tomakomai*** – *Utonai-ko YH – 32309*
150-3 Uenae, Tomakomai-shi, Hokkaido 059-1365.
(144) 582153
Open Dates: Tomakomai for Chitose 700m ap Utonai-ko YH x 68 (BD)

▲ **Tomari-Toyama** – Tenkyo-ji YH – 32310
913 Ōienoshō, Asahi-machi, Shimo-niikawa-gun, Toyama-ken 939-0722.
(765) 833339
Open Dates: Tomari for Ogawayumoto 400m ap Yanagida x 28

▲ **Tōno** – Tōno YH – 32311
13-39-5, Tsuchibuchi, Tsuchibuchi-cho, Tōno-shi, Iwate-ken 028-0555.
(198) 628736
Open Dates: Tono for Sakonoshita or Oide 700m ap Nitagai x 28 (BD)

▲ **Towada** – Hakubutsukan YH – 32312
Yasumiya, Towadakohan, Towadako-shi,
Aomori-ken 018-5501.
(176) 752002 (176) 751118
Open Dates: 20.04-10.11 Aomori
for Towada-ko 200m ap Yasumiya
x 48 (BD)

▲ **Toya-ko** – Shōwa-shinzan YH – 32313
103 Sōbetsu-onsen, Sōbetsu-chō, Usu-gun,
Hokkaido 052-0103.
(142) 752283
Open Dates: Toya for
Showasinzan ap Tozanguchi x 67
(BD)

▲ **Tsuchitaru** – Tsuchitarusanso YH – 32314
4504-59 Tsuchitaru, Yuzawa-machi,
Minami-Uonuma-gun, Niigata-ken 949-6103.
(257) 873188 (257) 873168
Open Dates: 01.01-11.04; 20.04-10.11;
20.11-31.12 Tsuchitaru 400m x 42
(BD)

▲ **Tsuchiura** – Masuo YH – 32315
1-7-14 Komatsu, Tsuchiura-shi,
Ibaraki-ken 330-0823.
/ (298) 214430
Open Dates: 04.01-28.12 Tsuchiura
for Ami 400m ap Komatsu-sakashita
x 10 (B)

▲ **Tsukuba** – Tsukubasanso YH – 32316
692 Tsukuba, Tsukuba-shi,
Ibaraki-ken 300-4352.
(298) 660022
Open Dates: Tsuchiura for
Tsukuba 400m ap Jingya-mae x 15
(BD)

▲ **Tsuruoka** – Tsuruoka YH – 32317
1-1 Miyanomae, Tsuruoka-Shi, Sanze,
Yamagata-Ken 999-7463.
(235) 733205
kryoma@mail.dewa.or.jp
Open Dates: (except Tues) Sanze
1km x 60 (BD)

▲ **Tsushima** – Seizan-ji YH – 32318
1453 Kokubu, Izuhara-machi, Tsushima-shi,
Nagasaki-ken 817-0022.
(9205) 20444
Open Dates: Izuhara 700m x 16
(B)

△ ***Ube** – Tokiwa-kohan YH – 32320*
3-6-1 Hiraki, Ube-shi,
Yamaguchi-ken 755-0096.
(836) 213613
Open Dates: Ube Shinkawa
for Hirakidai 700m ap Hiraki
x 60

▲ **Ueda** – Fujiya YH – 32321
2689 Tazawa, Aoki-mura, Chiisagata-gun,
Nagano-ken 386-1601.
(268) 493115 (268) 493101
Open Dates: Ueda for
Tazawa-onsen 1.7km ap Aoki x 15
(BD)

▲ **Ueda** – Mahoroba YH – 32322
40-1 Bessho-Onsen, Ueda-shi,
Nagano-ken 386-1431.
(268) 385229
Open Dates: Bessho-onsen 700m
x 15 (BD)

▲ **Uwajima** – Uwajima YH – 32323
Atagokōen, Uwajima-shi,
Ehime-ken 798-0045.
(895) 227177 (895) 227177
Open Dates: (except Thurs) Uwajima
2.7km x 40 (BD)

▲ **Wajima** – Sosogi-kajiyama YH – 32324
4-1 Sosogi-kibe, Machino-machi, Wajima-shi,
Ishikawa-ken 928-0206.
(768) 321145
Open Dates: 04.01-12.08; 19.08-29.12
Wajima for Ushizu 500m
ap Sosogi-guchi x 15 (BD)

▲ **Wakinosawa** – Wakinosawa YH – 32326
41 Senokawame, Wakinosawa, Mutsu-shi,
Aomori-ken 039-5332.
(175) 442341 (175) 442341
t_isoyama@aa.alles.or.jp
Open Dates: 03.01-29.12 Ôminato
for Wakinosawa 700m ap Wakinosawa
x 30 (BD)

▲ **Wakkanai** – Wakkanai Moshiripa YH – 32327
2-9-5 Chuo, Wakkanai-shi,
Hokkaido 097-0022.
(162) 240180
Open Dates: 01.02-10.04; 21.04-31.10;
01-31.12 Wakkanai 400m x 34
(BD)

▲ **Wakkanai** – Wakkanai YH – 32328
3-9-1 Komadori, Wakkanai-shi,
Hokkaido 097-0003.
(162) 237162 (162) 2317179
Open Dates: Minami-Wakkanai 900m
x 48 (B)

△ ***Wani*** *– Wanihama Seinenkaikan YH – 32329*
403 Minami-hama, Shiga-cho, Shiga-gun, Shiga-ken 520-0523.
(77) 5944203 (77) 5943197
Open Dates: Wanihama 1.4km
x 15 (BD)

▲ **Washūzan** – Washūzan YH – 32330
1666-1 Obatake, Kurashiki-shi,
Okayama-ken 711-0924.
(86) 4799280
Open Dates: 04.01-27.12 Kojima
for Tokohai go 25min 300m ap YH
x 60 (BD)

▲ **Yabakei** – Yamaguniya YH – 32331
1933-1 Sogi, Hon-yabakei-machi, Nakatsu-shi,
Oita-ken 871-0202.
/ (979) 522008
Open Dates: 03.01-30.12 Nakatsu
for Kakizaka 200m ap Nakashima
x 15 (BD)

▲ **Yakushima** – Yakushima YH – 32332
258-24 Hirauchi, Yaku-cho, Kumage-gun,
Kagoshima-ken 891-4406.
(997) 473751
Open Dates: 01-10.01; 01.02-10.04;
21.04-31.06; 11.07-30.11; 21-31.12
Anbo for Oko-no-taki 200m
ap Hirauchi-iriguchi x 48 CC
(BD)

▲ **Yakushima-Miyanoura** – Miyanoura Portside YH – 32362
287-2 Miyanoura, Kamiyaku-cho,
Kumage-gun 891-4205.
/ (997) 471316
www.yakushima.info/yh/
Open Dates: Yakushima
Miyanoura 400m for Nagata 200m
ap Miyanourako-iriguchi x 20 CC

▲ **Yamaguchi** – Paltopia Yamaguchi – 32358
1-80 Kanda-cho, Yamaguchi-shi,
Yamaguchi-ken 753-0064.
(83) 9236088 (83) 9230992
http://www.paltopia.com
Open Dates: 04.01-28.12
Shin-Yamaguchi Yuda-Onsen
1.5km ap Yuda-Onsen x 29 R
CC (BD)

▲ **Yamaguchi** – Yamaguchi YH – 32334
801 Miyano-kami, Yamaguchi-shi,
Yamaguchi-ken 753-0001.
(83) 9280057
Open Dates: 01-05.01; 26.01-20.06;
06.07-31.12 Miyano Miyano-onsen
400m ap Miyano-onsen x 16
(BD)

▲ **Yamaguchi-toyoda** – Jinjo-ji YH – 32335
624 Era, Toyota-cho, Toyoura-gun,
Yamaguchi-ken 750-0452.
(837) 660286 (837) 662784
Open Dates: Ozuki Nagato line
ap Ishi-machi x 16 (BD)

▲ **Yasu** – Omikibougaoka YH – 32337
Bunka-koen-mae, 978 Kita-zakura, Yasu-cho,
Yasu-shi, Shiga-ken 520-2321.
(77) 5872201 (77) 5872008
Open Dates: 01-20.01; 01.02-31.12 Yasu
for Kibougaoka-nishi gate
ap Kibougaoka-Bunka-koen-nishi gate
x 122 CC (BD)

▲ **Yokohama** – Kanagawa YH H 32020
1 Momijigaoka, Nishi-ku, Yokohama-shi,
Kanagawa-ken 220-0044.
(45) 2416503
Open Dates: Sakuragi-cho 500m
x 60 (B)

▲ **Yoshino-Yama** – Kizo-in YH – 32338
1254 Yoshino-yama, Yoshino-machi,
Yoshino-gun, Nara-ken 639-3115.
(7463) 20575 (7463) 22519
Open Dates: 01.03-26.12 Yoshinojingu
for Kamisenbon 400m ap Nakasenbon
x 44 (BD)

▲ **Yuasa** – Arida Orange YH – 32339
809 Suhara, Yuasa-machi, Arida-gun,
Wakayama-ken 643-0005.
t (737) 624536 f (737) 641383
Open Dates: 01-20.01; 01.02-31.12
Yuasa 2km x 30 (BD)

▲ **Yubari** – Yubari Forest YH – 32340
554 Numanosawa, Yubari-Shi,
Hokkaido 068-0751.
t /f (1235) 72535
Open Dates: 01.01-31.03; 28.04-24.11;
22-31.12 Numanosawa 1.4km x 15
(BD)

▲ **Yufuin** – Yufuin YH – 32341
441-29 Kawakami, Yufuin-cho, Yufu-shi,
Oita-ken 879-5102.
t (977) 843734
Open Dates: Yufuin for Beppu
200m ap Kuso-no-mori-iriguchi x 21
(BD)

▲ **Zenkoji** – Kyojuin YH – 32342
Zenkoji-nai, 479 Motoyoshi-cho, Nagano-shi,
Nagano-ken 380-0851.
t (26) 2322768
Open Dates: 04.01-19.06; 26.06-19.11;
26.11-29.12 Nagano 1.4km x 15

Kenya

Kenya Youth Hostels Association,
PO Box 48661, Nairobi, Kenya.

Secretariat: Nairobi Youth Hostel,
Ralph Bunche Road, near Nairobi Hospital,
PO Box 48661, Nairobi, Kenya

t (254) (2) 2723012; 2738046
f (254) (2) 2738046; 2656462; 2655321
e kyha@africaonline.co.ke
w www.kyha.or.ke

A copy of the Hostel Directory for this Country can be obtained from:
The National Office

Capital:	Nairobi
Language:	English/Swahili
Currency:	Ksh (shilling)
Population:	30,000,000
Size:	582,646 sq km
Telephone Country Code:	254
eKit Access Number:	Check www.hi.ekit.com for up to date Access Numbers

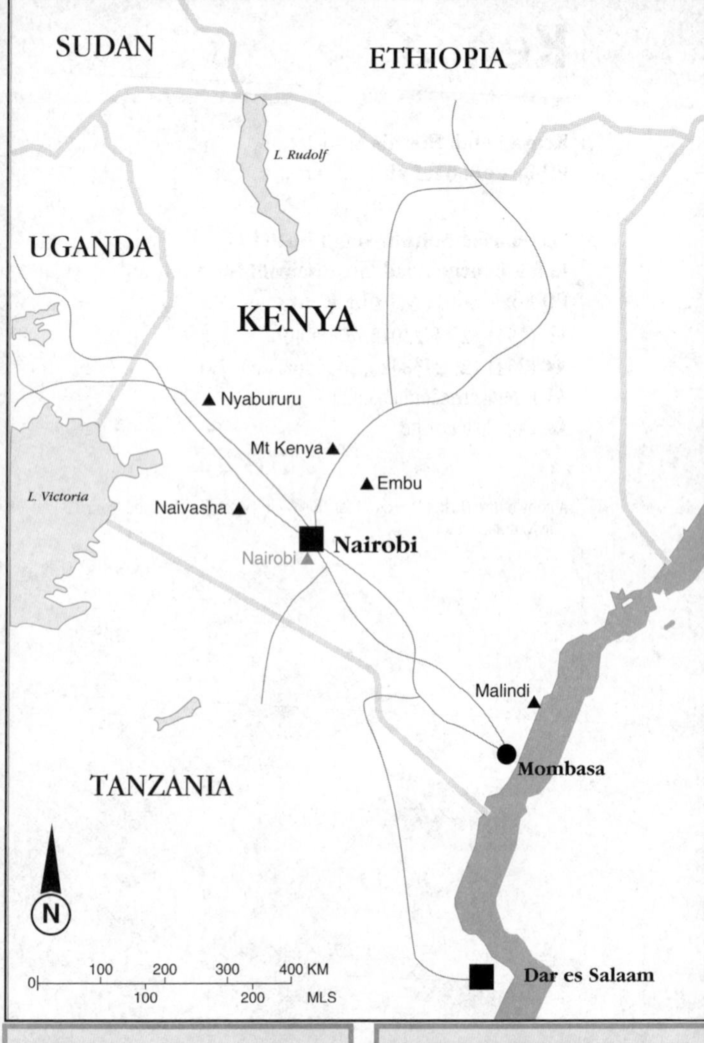

HI Suggests...

Kenya lies to the eastern side of Africa, bordering the Indian Ocean and Somali. Uganda is to the west, Tanzania is to the south, Ethiopia is to the north and Sudan is in the northwest.

There are various places of attraction to visit depending on your interests. For animal lovers check out Masai Mara National Park, which boasts as Africa's finest wildlife area or Amboseli National Park, which is the best place to see elephant herds and views of Kilimanjaro Mountain. Also, visit Lake Nakuru, which is home to flocks of pink flamingos and a beautiful surrounding park. Alternatively, visit Coral Coast with its unspoilt sandy beaches for snorkelling, deep-sea fishing and historic ruins, or Mount Kenya, which is fantastic for climbing, walking, bird watching and plenty of photographic opportunities.

Kenya has several very distinct

geographic regions. Two thirds of it is in the north and east, which is mainly semi arid desert, composed of acacia and commiphora bush. The south and southwest comprise predominantly of tree-dotted savannah at an altitude of between 900 and 1525m (3000 to 5000ft). The east is a narrow fertile strip of land bordered by the Indian Ocean. Cutting through the country in the north and south direction is the Great Rift Valley, containing a string of lakes, most of which are alkaline, and a number of dormant volcanoes. To the centre of Kenya, on the eastern edge of Rift Valley, is an area of high plateau rising above 1829m (6000ft), which is dominated by Mt Kenya, the Aberdare mountain range and Rift Valley. The area is referred to as the highlands, one of the world's richest agricultural areas. West of Rift Valley, in central Kenya, lies the Mau Escarpment, another high lying rich farming area falling low towards Lake Victoria. To the north rift on the border of Kenya and Uganda, is the second highest mountain within the boundary called MT Elgon.

Man's earliest ancestors may well have originated as long as five million years ago in what is now known as northern Kenya. Kenya's indigenous population represents more diversity than any other African country with approximately 30 languages spoken. The most populous ethic group is the Kikuyu, which populates to over 4 million, and then the El-Moro, who live on the shores of Lake Turkana. Other major tribes include Luhya, Luo, Kamba and Kalenjin.

The majority of Kenyans are ambivalent towards their culture; they prefer the world to perceive them as part of a modern and progressive society than as stereotype tribal warriors. 70% of Kenyans are Christians of various denominations, almost every Christian sect is represented and 30% are Islamic. Kenya's official language is English with Kiswahili, the lingua franca, readily understood by the majority of people. In addition, all will speak their tribal language (mother tongue) i.e. Ki-Kikuyu, Ki-Kamba, Ki-Masai, Ki-Jaluo, Ki-Luya etc.

You can find out a lot more on our website - a visit to www.HIhostels.com is essential for planning your trip!

Pour en savoir plus, rendez-vous sur notre site Internet, www.HIhostels.com une visite incontournable pour préparer votre voyage!

Viele weitere Informationen auf unserer Website: www.HIhostels.com - unverzichtbar für die Reiseplanung!

Puedes averiguar mucho más en nuestro sitio web. Es imprescindible que visites la página www.HIhostels.com para planear tu viaje.

▲ **Embu** – Embu Scout - Kenya Scout Association – 33002
PO Box 1859, Embu.
T (161) 20823; 30459 W www.kyha.or.ke
Open Dates: 12 Nairobi 200km 130NE
x 36 R P

△ ***Malindi*** *– Malindi Youth Hostel – 33009*
Lamu Road, P.O. Box 476, Malindi.
T *(42) 30312; 20370* F *(42) 30312*
E *ncts@malindi.com* W *www.kyha.or.ke*
Open Dates: 12 x 28 1 x

△ ***Mt Kenya*** *– 33003*
PO Box 274, Naro Moru, Nyeri.
T *(176) 62412* W *www.kyha.or.ke*
Open Dates: 12 x 38 P

Nairobi – Nairobi Youth Hostel 33001
Ralph Bunche Rd, PO Box 48661, Nairobi (near Nairobi hospital; GPO 2km).
(2) 2723012 (2) 2724862; 2738046
kyha@africaonline.co.ke
www.kyha.or.ke
Open Dates: Open Times: 06.30-23.30hrs
Beds: 96 - 8x² 4x³ 3x⁴ 3x⁶
Price Range: $5.50-25.00
Directions: Jomo Kenyatta International 18km A Stage Coach #34 18km
Central 3km 46 Metro Shuttle - Yay via Lavington, 111, 4, 8, 42, 40, 28 & 135 both Stage Coach & Matatus Mini Coach 3km ap Traffic Police HQ x 2 R
8
500m

Nairobi – Nairobi Youth Hostel

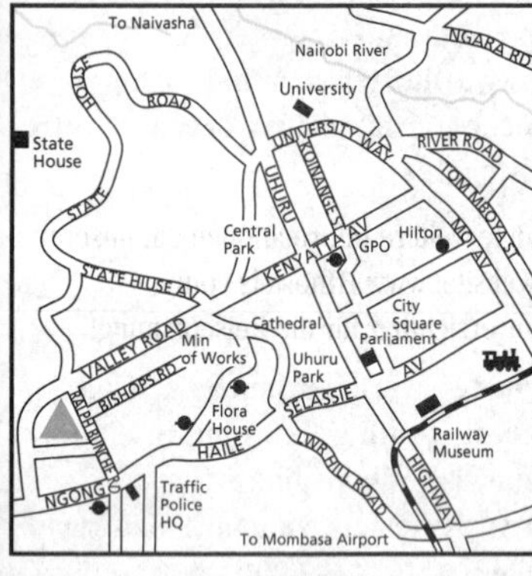

Nairobi... Travel Tips

- **For budget eats check out...** Seasons Restaurant, Visa Place, Lascala, Tratoria, Osewe - next to Nation House down town
- **For great nightlife try...** Dream Village, National Theatre, 20th Century Cinema, Nairobi Cinema, Village Market and Sarit Centre
- **Don't miss...** Swake Park, City Park, Animal Orphanage, Ostrich Farm, Carnivore Restaurant, Karen Blixen, Alboretum, Kenya Archives, Tour to Nairobi City Centre/Slums, Masaai Market (Tues, Sat)

△ ***Naivasha*** – *Naivasha YMCA Hostel – 33005*
PO Box 1006, Naivasha.
(311) 30396 *(311) 30396*
ymcacamp@maj.org *www.kyha.or.ke*
Open Dates: *from Nairobi City 150km* 100NW x 30 R

△ ***Nyahururu*** – *Thompson Falls Hostel & Campsite – 33007*
PO Box 1371,
Nyahururu or PO Box 21553 Nairobi.
(722) 635149
thompsonfalls20@yahoo.co.uk
www.kyha.or.ke
Open Dates:

Korea (South)

Korea Youth Hostels Association,
Rm 408, Jeokseon Hyundai Building,
Jeokseon-dong 80, Jongno-gu,
Seoul 110-756.
South Korea.
t (82) (2) 7253031
f (82) (2) 7253113
e inform@kyha.or.kr
w www.kyha.or.kr

A copy of the Hostel Directory for this Country can be obtained from:
The National Office

National Tourist Authority/Board:	www.knto.or.kr; www.seoul.go.kr; www.visitseoul.net
Capital:	Seoul
Language:	Korean
Currency:	Won
Population:	48,064,878
Size:	99,200 sq km
Telephone Country Code:	82
eKit Access Number:	0030-814-0226

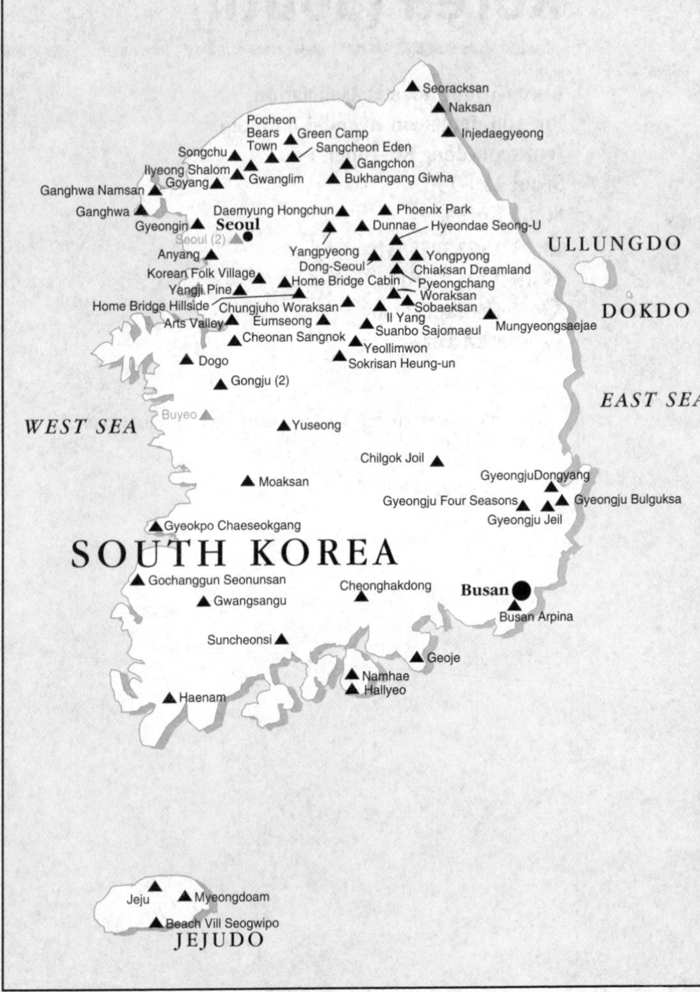

Korea's culture originates as far back as 4000 BC. Its somewhat turbulent history is due to centuries of war games instigated by neighbouring countries. When the Japanese occupied the country from 1910 until the end of the Second World War, the Koreans had to endure the hard times with patience, and this is a characteristic that has stayed with them. They are also known to be extremely hardworking and controlled, and to have a great sense of humour that permeates their traditional art forms.

Korean society is based on the philosophy of Confucianism, a method of ethics developed in China around 500 BC. Confucianism focuses on dedication and respect for parents, family, friends and those in positions of authority, and emphasizes the need for harmony within social relations.

A few other Top Tips from **CULTURE SMART!**:

- Koreans bow when meeting for the first time, and it is customary to say "*Annyong haseyo.*" Otherwise whether to bow will depend on the individuals' relative status: in a greeting between father and son, for example, the father would not bow, but the son would.
- Clothing in Korea is similar to Western clothing, but tends to be more conservative and sophisticated, and less casual. People do not wear shorts, for example, except perhaps in the house, and it is quite usual, when visiting a Korean home, to wait while the host changes into clothing he considers more suitable for receiving guests.
- Koreans smile when they feel happy, as everyone does all over the world, but they and many other Asians smile to cover up feelings of awkwardness or embarrassment. This can be confusing and somewhat difficult for the foreigner to interpret.
- Korean food tends to be very spicy, and is normally served with rice. Every meal includes *Kimchee*, which usually consists of Chinese or *napa* cabbage. Preparation is key to the texture, as the cabbage is washed in salt water and left to ferment overnight, after which spices and herbs are added. Visitors to Korea will find the flavour is unique, and for some it is an acquired taste.

Cultural Top Tips supplied by Culture Smart! guides. These essential guides to customs and etiquette will help you steer clear of embarrassing gaffes and sensitive issues, enabling you to discover new cultures whilst developing new friendships. Order online at www.culturesmartguides.co.uk

You can find out a lot more on our website - a visit to www.HIhostels.com is essential for planning your trip!

Pour en savoir plus, rendez-vous sur notre site Internet, www.HIhostels.com une visite incontournable pour préparer votre voyage!

Viele weitere Informationen auf unserer Website: www.HIhostels.com - unverzichtbar für die Reiseplanung!

Puedes averiguar mucho más en nuestro sitio web. Es imprescindible que visites la página www.HIhostels.com para planear tu viaje.

▲ **Anyang** – Anyang Blu Monte YH – 34005
241-3, Seoksu-dong, Manan-gu, Anyang-si, Gyeonggi-do.
(31) 4728102 (31) 4728106
blumonte@serviceall.co.kr
www.blumonte.com
Open Dates: 12 U Line 1; ap Anyang 4NW
x 292 R CC
1 x P

▲ **Asan** – Dogo YH – 34006
180-1, Sinseong-ri, Seonjang-Myeon, Asan-si, Chungnam-do.
(41) 5448653 (41) 5447656
dopara@paradise.co.kr
www.paradisehoteldogo.co.kr
Open Dates: 12 Dogo 1km; Seonjang 500m Onyang 500m ap St. Seonjang
10S x 858 R CC
2 x P

▲ **Boeun** – Sokrisan Heung-un YH – 34007
238, Sangpan-ri, Naesokri-myeon, Boeun-gun, Chungbuk-do.
(43) 5425799 (43) 5433634
hwyouth@hwyouth.or.kr
www.hwyouth.or.kr
Open Dates: 12 5km ap St. Sangpan-ri
16NE x 710 R CC
TV 1 x P

Boeun – Yeollimwon YH – 34008
285, Galtang-ri, Sanoe-myeon, Boeun-gun, Chungbuk-do.
(43) 5429992 (43) 5429991
master@yollimwon.co.kr
www.yollimwon.co.kr
Open Dates: ap St. Chang-ri 13SE x 570 2 x

Buan – Gyeokpo Chaeseokgang YH – 34066
286 Gyeokpo-ri, Byeonsan-Myeon, Buan-gun, Jeonbuk.
(63) 5831234 (63) 5848098
www.chaesukgang.co.kr
Open Dates: Gimje or Jeongeup ap Gyeokpo Terminal x 206 1 x

Busan – Busan Youth Hostel Arpina – 34071
1417, u-dong, Haeundae-gu, Busan.
(51) 7319800 (51) 7403225
www.arpina.co.kr
Open Dates: Busan International 30km Busan Metro ap Art Museum (Line 2), Exit 3 x 461 1 x

Buyeo – Samjeong Buyeo YH 34002
105-1 Gugyo-ri, Buyeo-eup, Buyeo-gun, Chungnam-do 323-800.
(41) 8353101 (41) 8353791
webmaster@buyeoyh.com
www.buyeoyh.com
Open Dates: 300m ap St. Buyeo 2NE x 582 1 x

Cheonan – Cheonan Sangnok YH – 34009
669-1, Jangsan-ri, Susin-myeon, Cheonan-si, Chungnam-do.
(41) 5609011 (41) 5609019
5401004@naver.com
www.sangnokresort.co.kr
Open Dates: Cheonan Station 12km 500, 50, 42-2, 42-3 from Cheonan-Si ap St. Cheonan Sangnok Resort 30SE x 916 16 x 300m

Cheonghakdong – Cheonghakdong – 34058
1298, Mukgae-ri, Cheongam-myeon, Hadong-gun, Gyeongnam-do.
(55) 8821892 (55) 8826190
Open Dates: Cheonghakdong 50km x 253

Chilgok – Chilgok-Joil YH – 34011
159-4, Yongsu-ri, Gasan-myeon, Chilgok-gun, Gyeongbuk-do.
(54) 9710602 (54) 3536572
Open Dates: ap Gasan Yongsu-dong 40N x 82 1 x

Chugju City – Il Yang YH – 34059
730, Oncheon-ri, Sangmo-myeon, Chungju-si, Chungbuk-do.
(43) 8469200 (43) 8459107
www.ilyangyouth.co.kr
Open Dates: Suanbo Terminal 800m ap St. Suanbo 10SE x 980 3 x

Chuncheon – Bukhangang Gihwa – 34013
365-1, Bangha-ri, Namsan-myeon, Chuncheon-si, Gangwon-do.
(33) 2631151 (33) 2639692
webmaster@kiwayh.com
www.kiwayh.com
Open Dates: Chuncheon 10km ap Gapyeong 25W x 191 4 x 300m

Chuncheon – Gangchon YH – 34014
366, Gangchon-ri, Namsan-myeon, Chuncheon-si, Gangwon-do.
(33) 2621201 (33) 2621204
www.kyh.or.kr
Open Dates: Gangchon 5km St. Gangchon 500m 17W x 254 2 x

Chungju – Suanbo Sajomaeul YH – 34015
641, Oncheon-ri, Sangmo-myeon, Chungju-si, Chungbuk-do.
(43) 8460750 (43) 8461789
sajo@sajoresort.co.kr
www.sajoresort.co.kr
Open Dates: Suanbo Terminal 1km 0.8NE x 796 3 x

▲ **Daejeon** – Yuseong YH – 34016
671-4, Gyesan-dong, Yuseong-gu, Daejeon.
(42) 8229591 (42) 8239965
Open Dates: Seo-Daejeon 10km #103, 110, 115, 133 7E x 360 3 x

▲ **Danyang** – Sobaeksan YH – 34017
23-6, Cheondong-ri, Danyang-eup, Danyang-gun, Chungbuk-do.
(43) 4215555 (43) 4213860
Open Dates: ap Danyang 8E x 1370 2 x

△ ***Eumseong** – Eumseong Surisan YH – 34018*
San 47-1, Chagok-ri, Saenggeuk-myeon, Eumseong-gun, Chungbuk-do.
(43) 8821988 (43) 8777802
www.youthtel.or.kr
Open Dates: ap St. Saenggeuk 3NE x 410 2 x 20m

▲ **Gapyeong** – Green Camp YH – 34064
702 Hwaak-ri, Buk-myeon, Gapyeong-gun, Gyeonggi-do.
(31) 5825304 (31) 5823324
www.greencamp.biz
Open Dates: Gapyeong Hwaakri (from Gapyeong Terminal) ap St. Ansaedangi x 108 1 x

▲ **Gapyeong** – Sangcheon Eden YH – 34019
San 295-4, Sangcheon-ri, Oeseo-myeon, Gapyeong-gun, Gyeonggi-do.
(31) 5812800 (31) 5813900
www.edenyh.co.kr
Open Dates: Cheongpyeong 4.2km 1330 4.2km ap Sangcheon SK gas station 4E x 633 4 x

▲ **Geoje** – Geoje YH – 34020
246-8, Dadae-ri, Nambu-myeon, Geoje-si, Gyeongnam-do.
(55) 6327977; 6329423
(55) 6329423 yes386@geojejoy.com
www.geojejoy.com
Open Dates: Jang Seoung Po Harbour ap Haegumgang 30SE x 120 1 x 7km

▲ **Gimje** – Moaksan YH – 34022
165 Geumsan-ri, Geumsan-myeon, Gimje-si, Jeonbuk-do.
(63) 5484401 (63) 5484403
www.moakyh.co.kr
Open Dates: Jeonju ap St. Gyeokpo 16SE x 669 3 x

▲ **Gochang** – Gochanggun Seonunsan YH – 34023
334, Saman-ri, Asan-myeon, Gochang-gun, Jeonbuk-do.
(63) 5613333 (63) 5613448
Open Dates: Jeongeup 20km ap St. Seonunsan 22NW x 320 2 x

▲ **Gongju** – Gongju YH – 34024
15-8, Samgak-ri, Tancheon-myeon, Gongju-si, Chungnam-do.
(41) 8521212 (41) 8521240
www.gongjuyh.com
Open Dates: 40 from Gongju ap Gongju YH 2NE x 555 1 x

▲ **Gongju** – Gyeryongsan Gapsa YH – 34025
136, Jungjang-ri, Gyeryong-myeon, Gongju-si, Chungnam-do.
(41) 8564666 (41) 8564663
webmaster@kapsayouthhostel.com
www.kapsayouthhostel.com
Open Dates: ap Gapsa 11NE x 530 2 x

▲ **Goyang** – Goyang YH – 34026
278-3 Goyang-dong, Deokyang-gu, Goyang-si, Gyeonggi-do.
(31) 9629049 (31) 9629579
Open Dates: 158-3, 1006 ap Goyang Market 3km 20NW x 220 4 x 10m

▲ **Gwangju** – Gwangsangu YH – 34027
38-3 Songhak-dong, Gwangsan-gu, Gwangju.
(62) 9434378 (62) 9434379
Open Dates: 105, 106, 150 1km ap Gwangsangu YH 22S x 130 2 x

▲ **Gyeongju** – Bulguksa YH – 34028
530-3, Jinhyeon-dong, Gyeongju-si,
Gyeongbuk-do.
(54) 7460826 (54) 7467805
Open Dates: Gyeongju 10, 11
1km ap Bulguksa 11SE x 662 R 1 x

▲ **Gyeongju** – Dongyang – 34068
700-1, Jinhyeon-dong, Gyeongju-si,
Gyeongbuk-do.
(54) 7486577 (54) 7487624
www.hotellife.co.kr
Open Dates: 10, 11 100m
ap Bulguksa x 568 1 x

▲ **Gyeongju** – Gyeongju Fourseason YH – 34065
850-11 Jinhyeon-Dong, Gyeongju-si,
Gyeongbuk-do.
(54) 7432202 (54) 7432206
Open Dates: Gyeongjn 10, 11
1km ap Bulguksa x 500 R CC 1 x

▲ **Gyeongju** – Gyeongju Jeil YH – 34029
63-63, Jinhyeon-dong, Gyeongju-si,
Gyeongbuk-do.
(54) 7460086 (54) 7464215
cheilyh@kornet.net
www.cheil-yh.co.kr
Open Dates: Gyeongju 10, 11
1km ap Bulguksa 13SE x 1068 R CC 1 x

▲ **Haenam** – Haenam YH – 34030
San 7-10, Gurim-ri, Samsan-myeon,
Haenam-gun, Jeonnam-do.
(61) 5330170 (61) 5321730
haenamorg@haenam.or.kr
http://youth.haenam.or.kr
Open Dates: Haenam
ap Daeheungsa 10S x 200 R 2 x

▲ **Hoengseong** – Dunnae YH – 34031
1140, Sapgyo-ri, Dunnae-myeon,
Hoengseong-gun, Gangwon-do.
(33) 3436488 (33) 3436487
www.doonnaeresort.co.kr
Open Dates: Wonju ap Dunnae
4NE x 898 R CC 3 x 800m 65km

▲ **Hoengseong** – Hyeondae Seong-u YH – 34051
476, Duwon-ri, Dunnae-myeon,
Hoengseong-gun, Gangwon-do.
(33) 3403000 (33) 3403173
webmaster@hdsungwoo.co.kr
www.hdsungwoo.co.kr
Open Dates: Shuttle from Wonju
ap Hyeondae Seong-u 40NE x 998 R CC 7 x

▲ **Hongcheon** – Daemyeong Hongcheon YH – 34032
1290-15, Palbong-ri, Seo-myeon,
Hongcheon-gun, Gangwon-do.
(33) 4348311 (33) 4358304
www.daemyungyh.co.kr
Open Dates: ap Daemyeong Hong cheon 32W x 1307 R CC 2 x

▲ **Incheon** – Ganghwa Namsan YH – 34033
439-16, Namsan-ri, Ganghwa-eup,
Ganghwa-gun, Incheon.
(32) 9347777 (32) 9347782
Open Dates: ap Ganghwa 2NE
x 557 R CC
2 x

▲ **Incheon** – Ganghwa YH – 34034
San 177, Oepo-ri, Naega-myeon,
Ganghwa-gun, Incheon.
(32) 9338891/2 (32) 9339335
master@khyh.co.kr www.gh-yh.co.kr
Open Dates: ap Oepo 0.4S x 412
R CC
3 x 2km

▲ **Incheon** – Gyeongin YH – 34035
San 253-1, Gyeongseo-dong, Seo-gu, Incheon.
(32) 5797195 (32) 5797198
Open Dates: ap Cheonglado 28.5S
x 560 R
2 x

▲ **Inje** – Inje Daegyeong YH – 34069
1341-3, Sangnam-ri, Sangnam-myeon,
Inje-gun, Gangwond-do.
(33) 4638853 (33) 4618852
Open Dates: x 565

▲ **Jecheon** – Chungjuho Woraksan YH – 34036
401, Tanji-ri, Hansu-myeon, Jecheon-si, Chungbuk-do.
(43) 6517001 (43) 6517004
woraksan@woraksan.co.kr
www.woraksan.co.kr
Open Dates: ap Naesonggae (from Chungju Terminal) 30SE x 266 R CC 1 x 20m

▲ **Jeju** – Beach Vill Seogwipo YH – 34037
85, Beophwan-dong, Seogwipo-si, Jeju-do.
(64) 7390114 (64) 7397552
master@jejusyh.com www.jejusyh.com
Open Dates: Jeju International 50km A Airport Limousine 20km ap Gyeongnam Hotel 15S x 340 R CC 2 x

▲ **Jeju** – Jeju Fitness Town YH – 34038
483, Nameup-ri, Aewol-eup, Bukjeju-gun, Jeju-do.
(64) 7998811 (64) 7998821
webmaster@chejufitness.co.kr
www.jejufitness.co.kr
Open Dates: Jeju International 30km 15S x 668 R CC 5 x 30m

▲ **Jeju** – Jejusi Myeongdoam YH – 34039
234-66, Bongae-dong, Jeju-si, Jeju-do.
(64) 7218233 (64) 7218235
Open Dates: ap Myeongdoam 15NE x 225 R 2 x

▲ **Mungyeong** – Mungyeong Sae Jae – 34067
355-2, Sangcho-ri, Mungyeong-eup, Mungyeon-si, Gyeongbuk-do.
(54) 5711988 (54) 5711990
www.saejae-yh.co.kr
Open Dates: ap Mungyeongsaejae 1 x

▲ **Namhae** – Namhae YH – 34041
140-1, Geumsong-ri, Samdong-myeon, Namhae-gun, Gyeongnam-do.
(55) 8674848 (55) 8674850
Open Dates: ap Dunchon 30E x 496 R 1 x 500m

▲ **Pocheon** – Bears Town YH – 34042
295, Sohak-ri, Naechon-myeon, Pocheon-gun, Gyeonggi-do.
(31) 5322534 (31) 5338427
bears@bearstown.com
www.bearstown.com
Open Dates: 33 2km ap Naechon 2NE x 600 R CC 3 x

▲ **Pocheon** – Gwanglim YH – 34043
456, Jikdong-ri, Soheul-eup, Pocheon-gun, Gyeonggi-do.
(31) 5440515 (31) 5440519
Open Dates: 21 500m ap Jikdong-ri Seminar House 10S x 454 R 5 x

▲ **Pyeongchang** – Bogwang Phoenix Ville YH – 34061
1095, Myeonon-ri, Bongpyeong-myeon, Pyeongchang-gun, Gangwon-do.
15882828 (33) 3306007
www.phoenixpark.co.kr
Open Dates: ap Phoenix Park 26N x 788 R CC 150m

▲ **Pyeongchang** – Pyeongchang YH – 34044
1477, Ungyo-ri, Bangrim-myeon, Pyeongchang-gun, Gangwon-do.
(33) 3327501 (33) 3328003
www.pcyh.co.kr
Open Dates: 62-3 ap Ungyo-ri 17NW x 742 R CC 4 x

▲ **Pyeongchang** – Yongpyeong YH – 34045
130, Yongsan-ri, Doam-myeon, Pyeongchang-gun, Gangwon-do.
(33) 3355757 (33) 3350160
webmaster@yongpyong.co.kr
www.yongpyong.co.kr
Open Dates: ap Hwenggye 50W x 762 R CC 4 x

▲ **Pyeongtaek** – Arts Valley YH – 34063
462-3 Okgil-ri,
Cheongbuk-Myeon Pyeongtaek-si,
Gyeonggi-do.
(31) 6837677 (31) 6837679
www.artsvalleyyh.com
Open Dates: Osan or Pyeongtaek ap Okgilri (from Osan) x 520 1 x

Seoul – Dreamtel YH 34004
801, Banghwa 3-dong, Gangseo-gu,
Seoul.
(2) 26670535 (2) 22670744
www.idreamtel.co.kr
Open Dates: Open Times:
Beds: 245 - 2x 9x 27x 11x 4x
Price Range: 25,500
Directions: 15W from city centre
22, 41, 68 1km ap Banghwa U Line No 5 Banghwa 1km 4 x

Seoul – Dreamtel YH

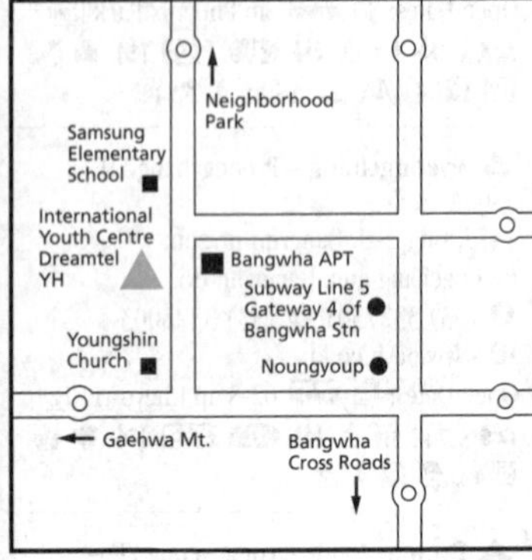

Seoul – Olympic Parktel YH 34003
88, Bang-i-dong, Songpa-gu,
Seoul 138-050.
(2) 4102114 (2) 4102101
parktel@sosfo.or.kr
www.parktel.co.kr
Open Dates: Open Times:
Beds: 967 - 9x[1] 84x[2] 52x[3] 20x[4] 20x[5] 10x[6]
Price Range: 22,000
Directions: 25SE from city centre
Incheon International 40km A 606 or Kal Limousine line 4 40km 569, 568, 212, 21, 813, 16, 70 10m ap Olympic Park U No 8 Line Mongchontoseong Station 200m
x 180 11 x

Seoul – Olympic Parktel YH

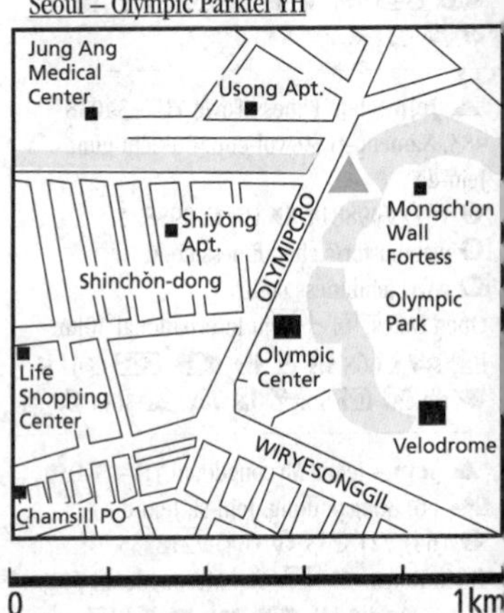

Seoul... Travel Tips

- **For budget eats check out...** Sindang-dong, Daehangno, Insa-dong, Sincheon, Baekjegwan
- **For great nightlife try...** Myeong-dong, Jongno, Dongdaemun Market, Apgujeong-dong, Namdaemun Market
- **Don't miss...** Gyeongbokgung (Palace), Namsan Seoul Tower, Semo Cruise, Namsangol (Traditional Korean Village), Insa-dong, Daehangno, Itaewon, Yeouido & Hangang River, Lotteworld Adventure

▲ **Sokcho** – Seoraksan YH – 34046
246-77, Seorak-dong, Sokcho-si, Gangwon-do.
(33) 6367115 (33) 6367107
www.syh.co.kr
Open Dates: 7 500m ap Seoraksan YH 10N x 844 2 x

▲ **Suncheon** – Suncheonsi YH – 34047
774-1, Unpyeong-ri, Seo-myeon, Suncheon-Si, Jeonnam-do.
(61) 7555522 (61) 7556298
Open Dates: Suncheon 32 3km ap Seo-myeon Jukcheong 12N x 168 2 x

▲ **Suwon** – Korean Folk Village YH – 34048
107, Bora-ri, Giheung-eup, Yongin-si, Gyeonggi-do.
(31) 2856994 (31) 2854374
master@koreanfolk.co.kr
www.koreanfolk.co.kr
Open Dates: Suwon 5500-1 or 1560 (from Seoul) ap Korean Folk Village 10SE x 353 1 x 50m

▲ **Wonju** – Chiaksan Dreamland YH – 34049
223-3, Hakgok-ri, Socho-myeon, Wonju-si, Gangwon-do.
(33) 7321600 (33) 7326888
dream10@dreamland.co.kr
www.dreamland.co.kr
Open Dates: Wonju 41 500m (from Wonju-si) ap Chiaksan Dreamland 30E x 480 3 x 50m

▲ **Wonju** – Dong-Seoul YH – 34050
San 2-4, Wolsong-ri, Jijeong-myeon, Wonju-si, Gangwon-do.
(33) 7323700 (33) 7324282
www.respia.net
Open Dates: Shuttle from Dangye-dong 10S x 741 5 x 35m

▲ **Yangju** – Ilyeong Shalom YH – 34052
San 72, Ilyeong-ri, Jangheung-myeon, Yangju-gun, Gyeonggi-do.
(31) 8558011 (31) 8557085
Open Dates: 35 or 36 3km (from Gupabal Station) ap Jangheun 7SE x 217 4 x

△ ***Yangju*** – *Songchu YH – 34062*
45-1 Kisan-ri, Baeksuk-eop, Yangju-gun, Gyeongi-do.
(31) 8714900 (31) 8764144
Open Dates: ap Changheung 15NW x 384

▲ **Yangpyeong** – Yangpyeong YH – 34053
Seoksan-ri, Danwol-myeon, Yangpyeong-gun, Gyeonggi-do.
(31) 7747800 (31) 7747815
Open Dates: Mogok 4km (Sangbong Terminal) 40W x 1180 4 x

▲ **Yangyang** – Naksan YH – 34054
30-1, Jeonjin-ri, Gangbyeon-Myeon, Yangyang-gun, Gangwon.
(33) 6723416 (33) 6714620
Open Dates: ap Naksan Beach x 400

▲ **Yongin** – Home Bridge Cabin YH – 34055
310, Jeondae-ri, Pogok-myeon, Yongin-si, Gyeonggi-do.
(31) 3208841 (31) 3209747
evermast@everland.com
www.everland.com
Open Dates: Suwon 600, 500-1, 66, 1500, 1500-2, 5002 1km ap Everland 15N x 496 1 x 3km

▲ **Yongin** – Home Bridge Hillside YH – 34056
310, Jeondae-ri, Pogok-myeon, Yongin-si, Gyeonggi-do.
(31) 3208849 (31) 3208843
evermast@everland.com
www.everland.com
Open Dates: Suwon 600, 500-1, 66, 1500, 1500-2, 5002 1km ap Everland 12SE x 458 4 x 3km

▲ **Yongin** – Yangji Pine YH – 34057
34-1, Namgok-ri, Yangji-myeon, Yongin-si, Gyeonggi-do.
(31) 3382001 (31) 3387897
www.pineresort.com
Open Dates: Suwon Shuttle from Yangji Terminal ap Yangji YH 12SE x 643 5 x

Kuwait

Kuwait Youth Hostel Committee,
PO Box 15548, Daiyah 35456, Kuwait.
t (965) 2530463
f (965) 2575922
e info@kyhc.org; kyhc2005@hotmail.com
w www.kyhc.org

Capital:	Kuwait City
Language:	Arabic, English
Currency:	Kuwaiti Dinar
Population:	2,000,000
Size:	17,800 sq km
Telephone Country Code:	965
eKit Access Number:	Check www.hi.ekit.com for up to date Access Numbers

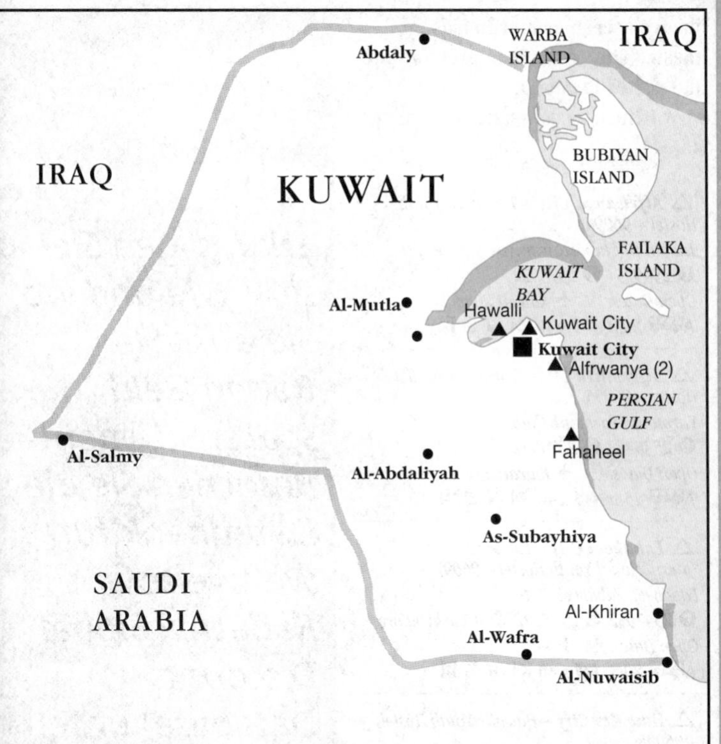

HI Suggests...

After a few troublesome years, Kuwait is once again the prototypical oil state, and travellers looking for a relaxed entry into the Muslim world can look forward to wandering around mosques, souks and other sandy traces of bygone Bedouin days.

The moderate and quite modern Middle Eastern city is today one of the region's most interesting and flourishing cities. Kuwait City has a long history and is home to a friendly population.

Some of the major attractions in Kuwait City are the excellent museums and historical buildings. Including: the Kuwait Towers, which are the city's most famous landmark, and the fantastic Grand Mosque, which can accommodate almost 6000 worshippers at any one time. Other attractions include the National Museum, the Tareq Rajab Museum and the Sadu House.

The selection of restaurants in Kuwait City is not excellent although you will find some good Middle Eastern dining options and several Indian restaurants. Accommodation is plentiful and you will find everything from upscale and luxurious to more reasonably priced accommodation.

You can find out a lot more on our website - a visit to www.HIhostels.com is essential for planning your trip!

Pour en savoir plus, rendez-vous sur notre site Internet, www.HIhostels.com une visite incontournable pour préparer votre voyage!

Viele weitere Informationen auf unserer Website: www.HIhostels.com - unverzichtbar für die Reiseplanung!

Puedes averiguar mucho más en nuestro sitio web. Es imprescindible que visites la página www.HIhostels.com para planear tu viaje.

△ ***Alfrwanya City*** *– Tadamun Youth Hostel – 96094*
Tadamun Club, Farwaniya.
2549751 2575922
Open Dates: Kuwait 20km
A 20m x 40

△ ***Alfrwanya City*** *– Yarmouk Youth Hostel – 96095*
Yarmouk, Yarmouk Club.
2530463 2575922
Open Dates: Kuwait 25km
A 15m x 40

△ ***Fahaheel City*** *– Fahaheel International Youth Hostel – 96097*
Fahaheel, Fahaheel Club.
2547952 2575922 www.kyha.org
Open Dates: Kuwait 15km
A 20m x 30

△ ***Hawally City*** *– Hawally Youth Hostel – 96098*
Beirute Street, Hawally.
2668015 (201) 2575922
Open Dates: Kuwait 15km A 5m
50m x 40

△ ***Kuwait City*** *– Khalidiya Youth Hostel – 96099*
Abdulla Salem Sport Centre, Khalidiya.
2549751 2575922
Open Dates: Kuwait 25km
A 25m x 40

Lebanon

Lebanese Youth Hostels Federation (LYHF),
P.O. Box 116-5073, Beriut, Lebanon.
t (961) 3 313377; (961) 1 752670-1
f (961) 1 1 752670-1
e lyhf@lyhf.org
w www.lyhf.org

Capital:	Beirut
Language:	Arabic, French, English
Currency:	Lebanese Pound
Population:	3,236,000
Size:	10,452 sq km
Telephone Country Code:	961
eKit Access Number:	Check www.hi.ekit.com for up to date Access Numbers

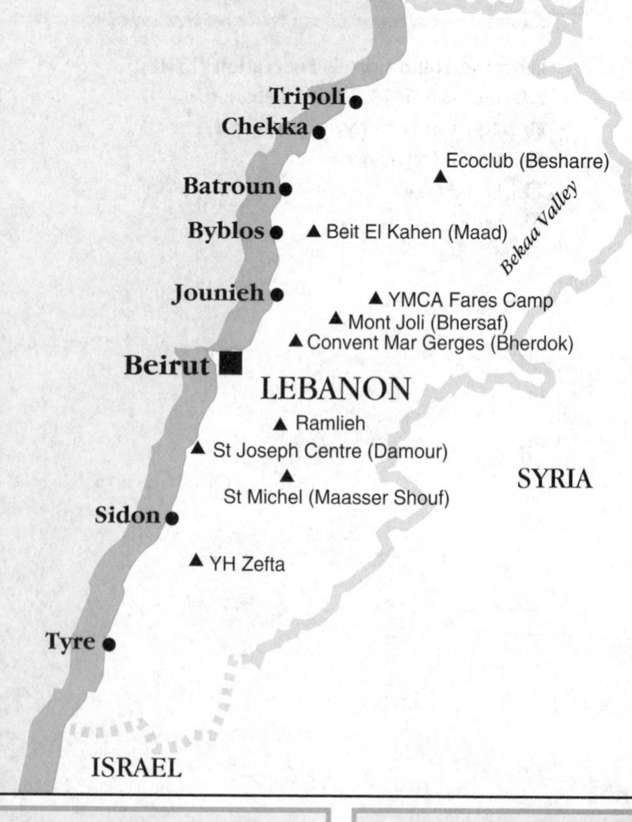

HI Suggests...

Lebanon lies on the eastern side of the Mediterranean Sea, bordered to the North and East by Syria and the South by Israel. It is 55 km at the widest point and 215 km long.

Lebanon is unique in many aspects, unlike any other country in the Middle East. Its rich cultural mix with 6,000 years of history, one of the oldest continuously inhabited countries of the world, influence of various civilizations and religions that passed through its history, makes Lebanon a land of contrast and diversity.

Lebanon has the best ski resorts in the Middle East. With its snow covered mountains in the winter offering skiing facilities, first class hotels and restaurants, and various accommodations make these mountains a favourite destination for locals and tourists all year round.

Alternatively, beach resorts dot the coastline of Lebanon on the Mediterranean Sea, offering a variety of water sports and activities. Sandy beaches, rocky beaches, fresh spring water in the sea, provide a wide choice for beach lovers and sun seekers.

The people of Lebanon are warm, friendly and hospitable, very generous and enjoy living life to the full. Sports activities, partying, nightlife, shopping centres displaying goods from around the world, restaurants and hotels, anything you can think of, you can find in Lebanon.

›u can find out a lot more on our website - visit to www.HIhostels.com is essential for anning your trip!

our en savoir plus, rendez-vous sur otre site Internet, www.HIhostels.com ne visite incontournable pour réparer votre voyage!

ıele weitere Informationen auf unserer /ebsite: www.HIhostels.com - unverzichtbar ïr die Reiseplanung!

'uedes averiguar mucho más en uestro sitio web. Es imprescindible ue visites la página ıww.HIhostels.com para planear tu iaje.

△ ***Becharre** – Ecoclub – 70001*
Becharre North Lebanon
(3) 832060 (6) 678488
info@ecoclub-becharre.org
www.ecoclub-becharre.org
Open Dates: Beirut 120km Beirut 110km ARZ Transport
40N x 25

△ ***Bherdok - Beit Chaber** – Convent Mar Gerges – 70009*
(4) 914002; 3256100 (4) 914002
Open Dates: Beirut 20km 100km x 223 1 x

▲ **Bhershaf** – Mont Joli – 700002
Bhersaf - Mount Lebanon
(4) 982571; 985640 (4) 981923
longuie@cyberin.net.lb
www.longuevie.com
Open Dates: Beirut 30km Beirut 20km x 66 3 x

▲ **Damour** – St Joseph Centre – 70007
Upper part of Damour Village.
(5) 602642; (3) 216270 (5) 602642
jeunesse@arceuciel.org
www.arceuciel.org
Open Dates: 01.06-31.10 Beirut 15km 25km x 35 1 x 5km

▲ **Maad - Casa Jbeil** – Beit el Kahen - Maad – 70006
(9) 750370; (3) 288211 (9) 750370
beitelkahen@yahoo.com
Open Dates: Beirut 55km 45km x 67 2 x 10km

▲ **Maasser El Chouf** – Auberge St Michel-Maasser – 70008
(5) 350452 jeunesse@anceuceil.org
www.anceuceil.org
Open Dates: 01.05-31.10 Beirut 57km 67km x 83 1 x

▲ **Ramlieh - Aley** – MFDCL - AFDC – 70003
Ramlieh Aley - Lebanon
(3) 493281; 848412 (1) 752670-1
afdc@afdc.org.lb www.afdc.org.lb
Open Dates: Beirut 40km Beirut 30km 12 - 15 x 44 2 x

△ ***Ras El Metn** – Ras El Metn - Fares Camp – 70004*
Ras El Metn - Lebanon.
(1) 490740; 490640 (1) 490740
ymca@ymca_leb.org.lb
www.ymca_leb.org.lb
Open Dates: 01.06-30.09 Beirut 1 x

▲ **Zefta (South Lebanon)** – Zefta Nabatiye - Rissala Scout – 70005
Zefta - South Lebanon.
(7) 50 59 50 (7) 50 59 50
Kashaf_risala@hotmail.com
Open Dates: Beirut 65km 55km x 44 1 x

Libya

Libyan Youth Hostel Association,
69 Amr Ben Al-Aas Street, PO Box 10322,
Tripoli, Al-Jamahiriya, Libya.

ⓣ (218) (21) 4445171
ⓕ (218) (21) 3330118
ⓦ www.libyahihostels.com

Office Hours: 08.00-15.00hrs

A copy of the Hostel Directory for this Country can be obtained from:
The National Office

Capital:	Tripoli
Language:	Arabic
Currency:	LD (Libyan Dinar)
Population:	7,495,000
Size:	1,759,540 sq km
Telephone Country Code:	218
eKit Access Number:	Check www.hi.ekit.com for up to date Access Numbers

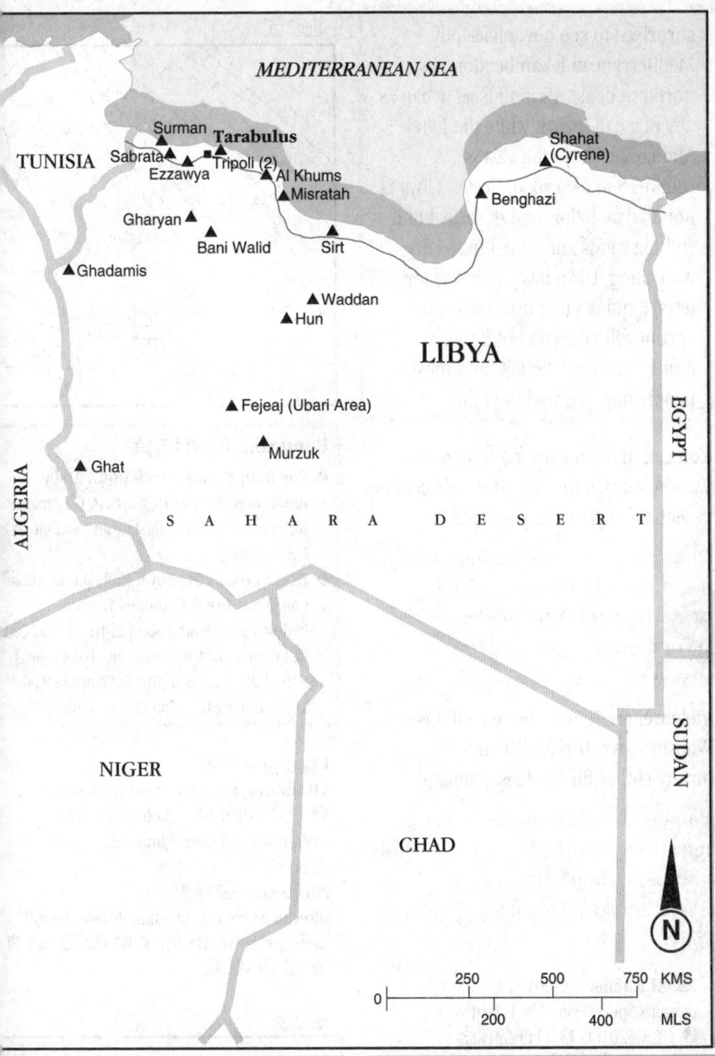

HI Suggests...

Libya is the fourth largest country in Africa with a total area of 1,759,540 square kilometres. It provides a variety of things to see and do, especially for the adventurers. From the World UNESCO heritage sites to the pre-historic ruins, rock painting of Jebel Acacus in the heart of the desert and spectacular landscapes.

Cultural differences between the provinces are important. The population of the west is far more cosmopolitan than that of the east and includes a higher proportion of people with Arab origins. Libyan culture centres on folk art and traditions, which are highly influenced by Islam.

The Libyan people enjoy a well-earned reputation for kindness and hospitality toward visitors, and its streets and souqs are free of the hassles of touts and their hard sell.

For a country that as been all but swallowed by the Sahara, you will be surprised to see how pleasantly Mediterranean it can be along its northern coast. Tripoli is as urban as any place in Africa, while the Jebel Akhdar region to the east is reminiscent of verdant Crete. Libya is not all date palms and deserts, but if shifting sands and camel trains are your thing, Libya has got desert for days, a quick jaunt down into the Fezzan will take you boldly where nomad has gone before, and most people have a grand out time!

You can find out a lot more on our website - a visit to www.HIhostels.com is essential for planning your trip!

Pour en savoir plus, rendez-vous sur notre site Internet, www.HIhostels.com une visite incontournable pour préparer votre voyage!

Viele weitere Informationen auf unserer Website: www.HIhostels.com - unverzichtbar für die Reiseplanung!

Puedes averiguar mucho más en nuestro sitio web. Es imprescindible que visites la página www.HIhostels.com para planear tu viaje.

▲ **Al Khums** – 35001
Alkhums Sport Centre SW 1.2km.
(31) 620180 (31) 621888
Open Dates: City Centre 500m 1.2SW
x 120

Bengazi – 35003
Sport City Bengazi SW 1km.
(61) 2234101
Open Dates: Open Times: 07.00-10.30hrs; 14.00-24.00hrs
Beds: 160
Price Range: 5-7 LYD BBinc
Directions: 1SW from city centre
Benenna 20km A to City Centre
Bengazi 500m 200m ap YH
1 x

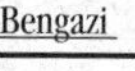
Bengazi

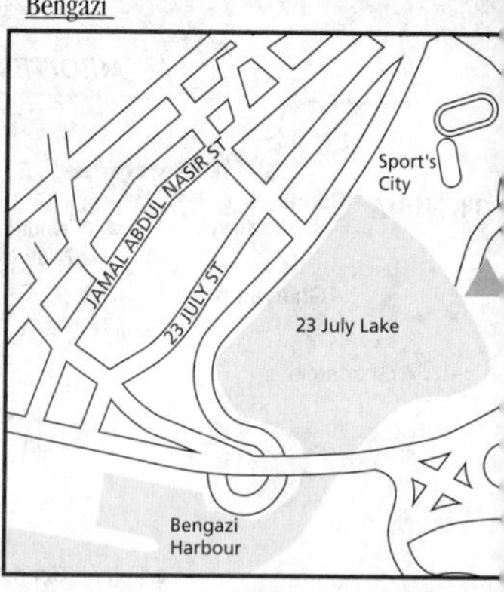

Bengazi... Travel Tips

- **For budget eats check out...** Arabi Restaurant, Alkabir Restaurant, Gharmata Restaurant, Al Sadaf Restaurant, Shahat Restaurant
- **Don't miss...** Old Town Hall, Old Egyptian Consulate, Greek Orthodox Church, Pedestrian Precinct, Souq al-Jreed, The Old Lighthouse, Libyan University, Tokra - was one of the 5 cities of Greek Petapolis (70 km E of Bengazi), The City Museum

Ezzawya – 35007
YH, Ezzawya City: Tripoli NE 0.6km.
(23) 64019 (23) 623119
Open Dates: Open Times:
Beds: 150
Price Range: BBinc
Directions: Tripoli 30km A Tripoli
300m

Ezzawya

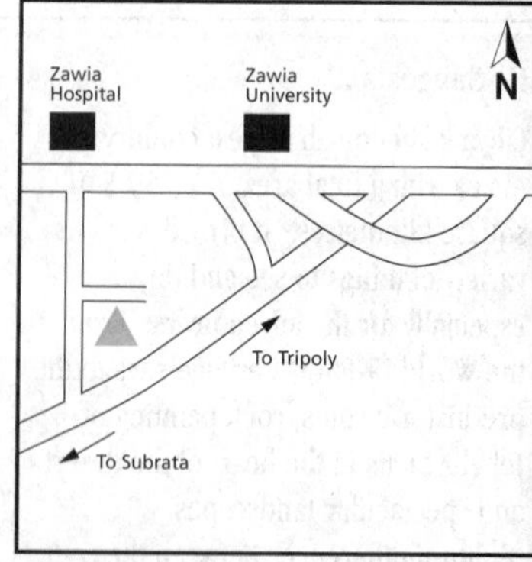

▲ Fejeaj (Ubari Area) – 35008
ejeaj YH, People's Housing Project:
/illage of Fejeaj.
(728) 2902; (71) 28323; (722) 622022
)pen Dates: Sabha 160km x 60

▲ Ghadamis – 35009
YH, Ghadamis.
(484) 63023 (484) 62023
Open Dates: Ghadamis 6km
A City Centre 1km 1SE x 120

△ Ghat – Ghat – 35024
Ghat City Center.
(72) 42991
Open Dates: Ghat International 20km x 30

▲ Gharyan – 35010
YH, Gharyan.
(41) 631491 (41) 634650
Open Dates: A City Centre 2km 2NE
x 120

***△ Hun** – 35011*
Hun YH City Centre.
(57) 602040 (57) 603712
Open Dates: 1SW x 50

▲ Misratah – 35012
YH, Misratah.
(51) 642419 (51) 642435
Open Dates: A City Centre 3km
500m 4W x 160

***△ Murzuk YH** – 35013*
Murzuk City Centre.
(725) 62301
Open Dates: x 50

Sabrata – 35016
Sabrata YH, City Centre,
Sabrata: Tripoli NW 0.5km.
(24) 62821 (24) 621514
Open Dates: Open Times: 07.00-10.30hrs; 14.00-24.00hrs
Beds: 120
Directions: 1NW from city centre
800m

Sabrata

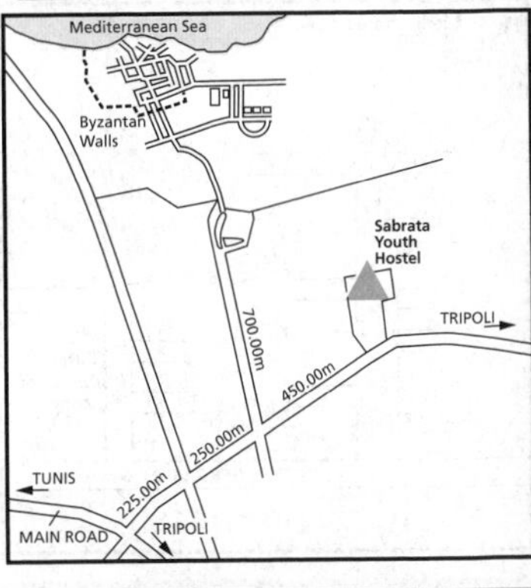

Sabrata... Travel Tips

- **For budget eats check out...** Arous al-Bahar Restaurant, Al-Bawdy Restaurant
- **Don't miss...** The ruins of the ancient city of Sabrata, Roman Museum, Punic Museum

▲ Sirt – 35018
YH, Cost Rd, Sirt N 0.8km.
(54) 61391; 61825
Open Dates: Sirt 15km 2km 0.8N
x 120

***△ Surman** – 35019*
Surman YH, City Centre.
(273) 62581 (73) 620417
Open Dates: 2N x 120
1 x

▲ Tripoli – 35020
69 Amru Ben Al-Aas St, Tripoli.
(21) 4445171; 3333867
(21) 3330118
Open Dates: Tripoli International 20km
200m x 60

Tripoli – Gergarish YH – 35021
Tripoli Gergarish YH, Gergarish Rd, Km 5.
(21) 4776694 (21) 4775187
Open Dates: Open Times: 07.00-10.30hrs; 14.00-24.00hrs
Beds: 160
Directions: 5S from city centre
Tripoli 20km A 200m Tripoli 7km 1km
1 x

Tripoli – Gergarish YH

Tripoli... Travel Tips

- **For budget eats check out...** Eslam Restaurant, El Jadah Restaurant, Al Turkiye Restaurant, Ash-Shark Restaurant, Dahabi Restaurant
- **Don't miss...** Art Galleries, House of Yusuf Karamane, Obman Pashu Mosque, and Madrassa in old city of Tripoli, The Old British & French Consulate, Tripoli Medina (The old city), Souq al Mushir and the Ottman clock tower, Jam Ihiriya Museum, The ruins of Sabratha (60 km W of Tripoli), The ruins of Leptis Magna (100 km E of Tripoli)

▲ **Waddan** – 35022
YH, Waddan W 0.5km.
(581) 632904 (581) 632904
Open Dates: 12 Hun 10km 2SW x 120
R P

YOUTH HOSTEL ACCOMMODATION OUTSIDE THE ASSURED STANDARDS SCHEME

Banī Walid – 35002
Banī Walid YH, El Dahra Road.
(322) 62415
Open Dates: 12 A City Centre 2km
200m 1S x 35 P

El-Marj – 35006
YH, El-Marj Town.
(67) 3669
Open Dates: 12 x 60 P

Shahat (Cyrene) – 35017
The former Cyrene (Shahat) Tourist Hotel.
(851) 62102 (851) 62103
Open Dates: 12 El Bedah 20km 1km
2NW x 160 R P

Luxembourg

Centrale des Auberges de Jeunesse Luxembourgeoises,
2 rue du Fort Olisy, L-2261
Luxembourg.

t (352) 262766-40
f (352) 262766-42
e info@youthhostels.lu
w www.youthhostels.lu

Office Hours: Monday-Friday 08.00-17.00hrs

A copy of the Hostel Directory for this Country can be obtained from:
The National Office

National Tourist Authority/Board:	www.ont.lu
Capital:	Luxembourg
Language:	Lëtzebuergesch
Currency:	€ Euro
Population:	450,000
Size:	2,587 sq km
Telephone Country Code:	352
eKit Access Number:	800-22026

HI Suggests...

The Grand Duchy of Luxembourg is an independent sovereign state, with a constitutional monarchy. A Prime Minister, a cabinet of 12 ministers and the Parliament rule Luxembourg. The eldest son of Grand Duke Henri, Guillaume, officially supports Luxembourg's youth hostels. Steel was a big industry in the past, however, today, the economic structure of the Grand Duchy mainly rests on banking and telecommunication.

There are approximately 450,000 inhabitants. The country has a surface of 2,587 square kilometres. One third- about 1,000 square miles- is covered with forests. Luxembourg is divided into five regions: the Good Land with the capital city, the Ardennes, the Mullerthal or Little Switzerland, the Moselle and the Land of red rocks.

The population is trilingual, speaking Luxembourgish (national language), French and German. Some people also speak English.

As the birthplace of Robert Schuman, father of the European Union, Luxembourg hosts several European institutions.

The Grand Duchy enjoys a temperate climate without extremes. It profits from the moderating influence of the sea. The period from May to mid-October is particularly suitable for vacations. While July and August are the warmest, May and June are the sunniest months. September and October offer an "Indian Summer". The currency used is the Euro.

ou can find out a lot more on our ebsite - a visit to www.HIhostels.com is ssential for planning your trip!

our en savoir plus, rendez-vous ır notre site Internet, ww.HIhostels.com une visite ıcontournable pour préparer votre ɔyage!

ïele weitere Informationen auf unserer 'ebsite: www.HIhostels.com - nverzichtbar für die Reiseplanung!

uedes averiguar mucho más en uestro sitio web. Es imprescindible ue visites la página ww.HIhostels.com para planear tu iaje.

▲ **Beaufort** 36002
6 rue de l'Auberge, L-6315 Beaufort.
(352) 836075 (352) 869467
beaufort@youthhostels.lu
www.youthhostels.lu
Open Dates: 23.01-23.12 Luxembourg 37km Diekirch 21km 107, 414, 500, 848 50m ap "Eglise" 1SW x 80 R CC 1 x

▲ **Bourglinster** 36012
2 rue de Gonderange, L-6161 Bourglinster.
(352) 26780707 (352) 26780717
bourglinster@youthhostels.lu
www.youthhostels.lu
Open Dates: Luxembourg 22km Luxembourg 22km 500m ap "Am Duerf" 0.1E x 51 R CC TV 1 x 22km

▲ **Echternach** 36003
Lac D'Echternach, L-6479 Echternach.
(352) 720158 (352) 728735
echternach@youthhostels.lu
www.youthhostels.lu
Open Dates: Luxembourg 37km Luxembourg 37km 500m ap Centre Secours 0.1W x 118 R CC 4 x

▲ **Hollenfels** 36015
2 rue du Château, L-7435 Hollenfels.
(352) 307037; (352) 621673261
(352) 305783
hollenfels@youthhostels.lu
www.youthhostels.lu
Open Dates: Luxembourg 21km Mersch 7km 0.1W x 103 R CC 1 x 7km

Larochette – Centre Osterbour 36005
45 Osterbour, L-7622 Larochette.
(352) 837081; (352) 661660401
(352) 878326
larochette@youthhostels.lu
www.youthhostels.lu
Open Dates: Open Times: 08.00-10.00hrs; 17.00-23.00hrs
Beds: 77 - 14x2 7x5 1x6+
Price Range: € 16.60-28.60 BBinc
Directions: 1N from city centre
Luxembourg 28km Luxembourg 28km; Mersch 9km no bus on Suns 300m x 7 R CC TV 1 x 2km

Larochette – Centre Osterbour

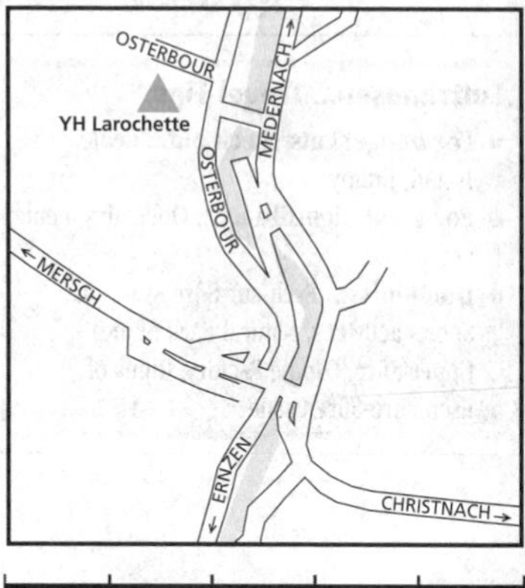

Larochette... Travel Tips

- **Don't miss...** Church, Mini golf, Nommerlayen, Larochette Castle, Meysembourg Castle, Open air swimming pool, Mullerthal waterfall, Diekirch Military Museum, Echternach Basilica, Beaufort Castle

Lultzhausen 36006
rue du Village, L-9666 Lultzhausen.
(352) 26889201 (352) 621531044
lultzhausen@youthhostels.lu
www.youthhostels.lu
Open Dates: 01-15.01; 28.01-03.12; 16-31.12
Open Times: 08.00-10.00hrs; 17.00-23.00hrs
Beds: 112
Price Range: € 16.60-28.60 + tax € 1 per person per night BBinc
Directions: Luxembourg 52km
Mersch 15km 50m ap "An der Driischt"
7 x

Lultzhausen

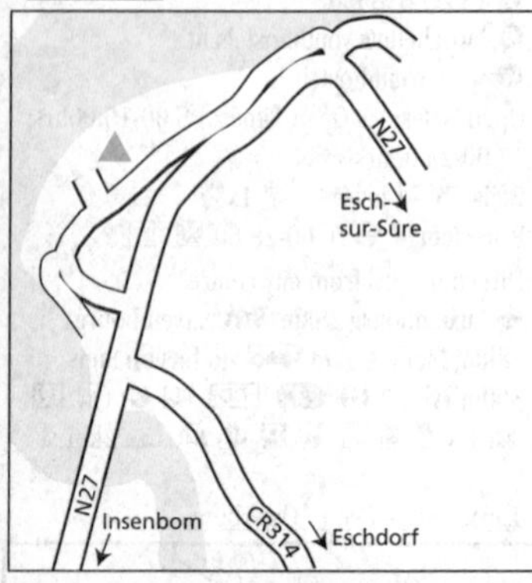

Lultzhausen... Travel Tips

- **For budget eats check out...** Celtic Island, Jimmy
- **For great nightlife try...** Open air cinema at the lake
- **Don't miss...** Esch-sur-Sûre Museums, Sports activities, Natural Park of the Upper-Sûre, Candle Factory, Ruins of Esch-sure-Sûre Castle

Luxembourg City 36001
2 rue du Fort Olisy (Pfaffenthal), L-2261 Luxembourg.
(352) 226889-20 (352) 223360
luxembourg@youthhostels.lu
www.youthhostels.lu
Open Dates: Open Times:
Beds: 240 - 30x[4] 20x[6]
Price Range: € 16.60-28.60 + tax € 1 p.p.p.n. BBinc
Directions: 1NE from city centre
Findel 5km A 9 300m
Luxembourg 2km 9 Plateau Altmünster 300m ap "Montée de Clausen"
x 20
1 x 3km

Luxembourg City

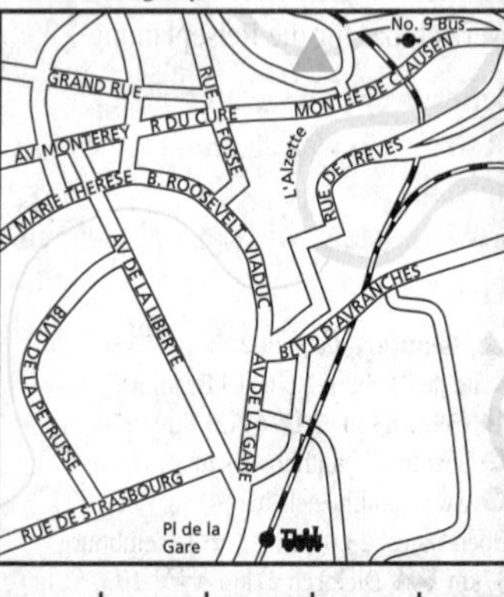

Luxembourg City... Travel Tips

- **For budget eats check out...** Congo (Pitta), Coyote Café (Mexican & American), Jungle Bar (vegetarian), Giorgio's Pizzeria
- **For great nightlife try...** Old Town area, Clausen area, Grund area, Down Town station area, Utopolis
- **Don't miss...** Wenzel Vauban & Goethe trail, Casemates, European quarter, Luxembourg City History Museum, Olympic-size swimming pool, National Art & History Museum, National Natural History Museum, Casino Luxembourg Contemporary Art Forum, Am Tunnel Contemporary Art Gallery

▲ **Remerschen** – 36016
31, Wäistrooss, L-5440 Remerschen.
remerschen@youthhostels.lu
www.youthhostels.lu
Open Dates: 01.07-31.12 Findel 36km
A 10m x 150 R CC
1 x

▲ **Vianden** 36007
3 Montée du Château, L-9408 Vianden.
(352) 834177 (352) 849427
vianden@youthhostels.lu
www.youthhostels.lu
Open Dates: 09.01-23.12 Luxembourg 50km Diekirch 17km 2km
ap "Gare Centrale" 1N x 64 R
CC 3km

▲ **Wiltz** 36008
6 rue de la Montagne, L-9538 Wiltz.
(352) 958039 (352) 959440
wiltz@youthhostels.lu
www.youthhostels.lu
Open Dates: 01-29.01; 11.02-19.11; 02-31.12
Luxembourg 50km 2.5km City Bus 500m 0.5S x 105 R
CC 5 x

HI Member Discounts!
To find out where you can save money on your travels, check out the Global Discounts Database at ***www.HIhostels.com.***

Remises pour les adhérents HI!
Pour savoir où vous pouvez économiser en voyageant, consultez notre base de données des remises sur ***www.HIhostels.com.***

Rabatte für HI-Mitglieder!
Erkundigen Sie sich, wie und wo Sie auf Ihren Reisen Geld sparen können! Besuchen Sie die Datenbank für weltweite Rabatte (Global Discounts Database) unter ***www.HIhostels.com.***

¡Descuentos para los miembros de Hostelling International!
Para saber dónde y en qué puedes ahorrar dinero a lo largo de tu viaje, consulta nuestra base de datos mundial de descuentos en ***www.HIhostels.com.***

Macedonia

Macedonian Youth Hostel Association,
Prolet 25, 1000 Skopje, Macedonia.
t (389) (2) 3216434; 3216433; 3114849
f (389) (3) 165029
e hostelfsm@hotmail.com
w www.myha.org.mk

A copy of the Hostel Directory for this Country can be obtained from:
The National Office

Capital:	Skopje
Language:	Macedonian, Albanian, Turkish, Serbo-Croatian
Currency:	Macedonian denar (MKD)
Population:	2,046,209
Size:	24,856 sq km
Telephone Country Code:	389
eKit Access Number:	Check www.hi.ekit.com for up to date Access Numbers

HI Suggests...

International recognition of The Former Yugoslav Republic of Macedonia's (FYROM) independence from Yugoslavia in 1991 was delayed by Greece's objection to the new state's use of what it considered a Hellenic name and symbols.

Greece finally lifted its trade blockade in 1995, and the two countries agreed to normalize relations, despite continued disagreement over FYROM's use of "Macedonia". FYROM's large Albanian minority and the independence of neighbouring Kosovo continue to be sources of ethnic tension.

Macedonia is medieval monasteries, timeworn Turkish bazaars, Orthodox churches and space-age shopping centres. It is also the drone of the local bagpipes, Turkish-style grilled mincemeat and Balkan cheese pies. The country is unbelievably green; its people are hospitable and welcoming.

There is no bad time to go to Macedonia weather-wise, as the country benefits from its proximity to the Aegean, which keeps it relatively warm in winter and very nice in summer. July and August are the best months to catch festivals: the Balkan Festival of Folk Dances and Songs is held in Ohrid in early July, while the Ohrid Summer Festival takes place later that same month.

You can find out a lot more on our website - a visit to www.HIhostels.com is essential for planning your trip!

Pour en savoir plus, rendez-vous sur notre site Internet, www.HIhostels.com une visite incontournable pour préparer votre voyage!

Viele weitere Informationen auf unserer Website: www.HIhostels.com - unverzichtbar für die Reiseplanung!

Puedes averiguar mucho más en nuestro sitio web. Es imprescindible que visites la página www.HIhostels.com para planear tu viaje.

▲ **Ferijalen Dom-Skopje** – 96272
Prolet 25, 1000 Skopje.
(23) 114849 (23) 165029
hostelfsm@hotmail.com
www.myha.org.mk
Open Dates: Petrovec 17km
A Direction Skopje 500m Skopje 500m 0.5E x 54 1 x
100m

▲ **Kumanovo** – Kopakabana – 96275
Romanovce, Kumanovo.
(31) 465111; 460420 (31) 465555
copacabana@yahoo.com
www.myha.org.mk
Open Dates: Skopje-Petrovec 3km
Miladinovci 2km Romanovce 100m 20S x 90 R

△ ***Mladost Ohrid*** – *YH Letuvaliste Mladost – 96273*
Vasil Stefoski bb, Ohrid.
(23) 114849; (46) 270340
(23) 165029
hostelfsm@hotmail.com
www.myha.org.mk
Open Dates: 01.06-15.09 Ohrid 7km
A Ohri 2km 2W x 350 R
TV

▲ **Negotino** – Hotel Park – 96277
Iko Zarov 14, 1440 Negotino.
(43) 61125 (43) 61605
arsovski@hotelpark.com.mk
www.myha.org.mk
Open Dates: Petrovec 90km
Negotino 1km Negotino 500m 0.5E
x 80 1 x

▲ **Ohrid** – Hotel Ambasador – 96276
Hotel Ambasador, Ohrid.
(46) 282020 autop@mt.net.mk
www.myha.org.mk;
www.hotelambasador.com.mk
Open Dates: Ohrid 1km A Ohrid 500m Ohrid-Struga 500m 6W x 58
TV 3 x
1km 1km

△ ***Ohrid*** – *Mrc Magnus – 96278*
Ohrid.
(23) 216433 (23) 165029
hostelfsm@hotmail.com
www.myha.org.mk
Open Dates: Ohrid 7km A Ohrid 2km Ohrid 2km 2W x 130
1 x

△ ***Prespa Lake*** – *YH Pretor – 96274*
Pretor, Prespa Lake.
(23) 114849; (47) 480218
(23) 165029
hostelfsm@hotmail.com
www.myha.org.mk
Open Dates: 01.06-15.09 Ohrid 50km
Bitola 40km Resen 7km
x 100 R

Malaysia

Malaysian Youth Hostels Association,
KL International Youth Hostel,
21, Jalan Kampung Attap, 50460 Kuala Lumpur,
Malaysia.
t (60) (3) 22736870; 22736871
f (60) (3) 22741115
e myha@pd.jaring.my

A copy of the Hostel Directory for this Country can be obtained from:
The National Office

National Tourist Authority/Board:	www.tourism.gov.my
Capital:	Kuala Lumpur
Language:	Malay, English widely spoken
Currency:	RM (Malaysian Ringgit)
Population:	25,000,000
Size:	330,434 sq km
Telephone Country Code:	60
eKit Access Number:	1800-804-146

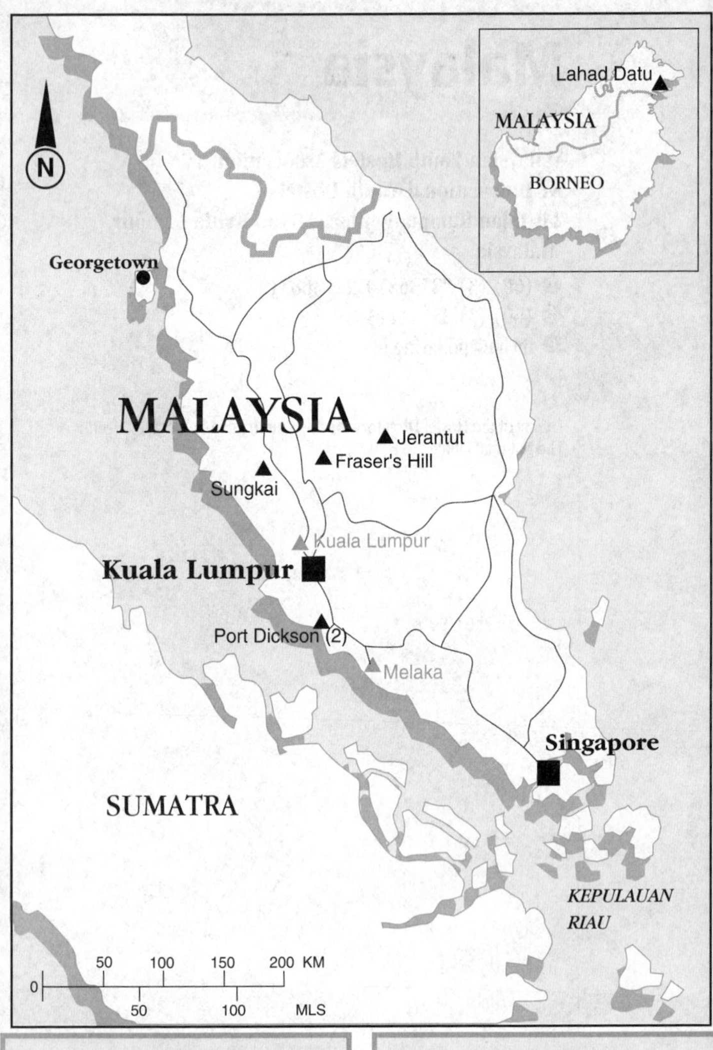

A diversity of cultures has mingled in Malaysia since the very beginning of its history. Situated in the centre of Southeast Asia, at one of the world's primary crossroads, Malaysia has always been pivotal to the trade routes. The Malay Kingdom in Bujang Valley welcomed traders from China and India more than fifteen hundred years ago. When the later Arab traders arrived, they brought with them the beliefs and principles of Islam. Malays, Chinese and Indians make up the majority of the population today.

The people of Malaysia value moderation, harmony and good relations both among family members and within the whole community. Their peaceful, tolerant ways are clearly apparent when you consider the numerous festivals they celebrate throughout the year; among these festivals are Hari Raya, Chinese New Year, Deepavali, Christmas and Gawai Day.

A few other Top Tips from **CULTURE SMART!**:

- The clothing is as varied as the cuisine in Malaysia. The Tamils' attire consists of a white robe similar to that of the *sarong*; male Sikhs wear the turban, and female Sikhs wear the *salwar-khameez* (trouser suit). Indian women of the younger generation tend to follow modern fashion trends.
- The handshake is becoming more common. Foreigners will find the Malaysian handshake is quite soft – it is more of a touch of the hand. In conservative circles, men don't shake hands with women.
- Remember, it is always the *right* hand that is used for eating or for passing dishes. On the subject of eating, the food stalls, which offer an amazing variety, are well worth investigating. Note that pointing with the forefinger is considered rude, so, to order, use your thumb to point out the food you want.
- The Malaysians are not as demonstrative as Westerners, and social kissing is looked down upon. The touching of the head and the hair is also considered to be offensive, as both are considered sacred.

Cultural Top Tips supplied by Culture Smart! guides. These essential guides to customs and etiquette will help you steer clear of embarrassing gaffes and sensitive issues, enabling you to discover new cultures whilst developing new friendships. Order online at www.culturesmartguides.co.uk

You can find out a lot more on our website - a visit to www.HIhostels.com is essential for planning your trip!

Pour en savoir plus, rendez-vous sur notre site Internet, www.HIhostels.com une visite incontournable pour préparer votre voyage!

Viele weitere Informationen auf unserer Website: www.HIhostels.com - unverzichtbar für die Reiseplanung!

Puedes averiguar mucho más en nuestro sitio web. Es imprescindible que visites la página www.HIhostels.com para planear tu viaje.

▲ **Fraser's Hill** – 37010
Lady Guillermard Road, 49000 Fraser's Hill, Pahang.
T (609) 3622263 F (609) 3622263
e fasresorts@felda.net.my
w www.plantationresorts.com.my
Open Dates: 12 x 21 R

▲ **Jerantut** – Tekam Plantation Resort – 37009
Sungai Tekam, 27000 Jerantut, Pahang.
T (609) 4718300 F (609) 4718450
e fasresorts@felda.net.my
w www.plantationresorts.com.my
Open Dates: 12 x 80 R 4 x

▲ **Kuala Lumpur** – Wira Hotel H 37012
123 Jalan Thamboosamy,
50350 Kuala Lumpur.
T (603) 40423333 F (603) 40422833
e whkl@po.jaring.my
w www.wirahotel.com.my
Open Dates: 12 Kuala Lumpur International 65km Putra LRT ap PWTC Station x 80 R 1 x 8 P

▲ **Lahad Datu** – Sahabat Beach Resort – 37011
PO Box 2, Cenderawasih, 91150 Lahad Datu, Sabah.
t (6089) 811300 f (6089) 811302
e fasresorts@felda.net.my
w www.plantationresorts.com.my
Open Dates: 12 x 72 R 2 x P

△ ***Melaka*** *HI 37003*
341A, Jalan Melaka Raya 3,
Taman Melaka Raya,
75000 Melaka. (Next to Malacca Club).
t *(6) 2827915*
Open Dates: 12 x 56 R P

▲ **Port Dickson** – PD Beach Resort – 37001
10 3/4 Mile, Jalan Pantai, 71000 Port Dickson.
t (606) 6626645 f (606) 6627728
e fasresorts@felda.net.my
w www.plantationresorts.com.my
Open Dates: 12 x 40 R 2 x P

▲ **Sungkai** – Trolak Country Resort – 37008
35600 Sungkai, Perak.
t (605) 4388687 f (605) 4388760
e fasresorts@felda.net.my
w www.plantationresorts.com.my
Open Dates: 12 x 108 R 8 x P

YOUTH HOSTEL ACCOMMODATION OUTSIDE THE ASSURED STANDARDS SCHEME

Kuala Lumpur – International YH – 37002
21 Jalan Kampung Attap, 50460 Kuala Lumpur.
t (3) 22736870/71 f (3) 22741115
e myha@pd.jaring.my
Open Dates: 12 65km Kuala Lumpur Central 1km 1km 2SE x 72 R TV 8 P

HI Member Discounts!
To find out where you can save money on your travels, check out the Global Discounts Database at ***www.HIhostels.com.***

Remises pour les adhérents HI!
Pour savoir où vous pouvez économiser en voyageant, consultez notre base de données des remises sur ***www.HIhostels.com.***

Rabatte für HI-Mitglieder!
Erkundigen Sie sich, wie und wo Sie auf Ihren Reisen Geld sparen können! Besuchen Sie die Datenbank für weltweite Rabatte (Global Discounts Database) unter ***www.HIhostels.com.***

¡Descuentos para los miembros de Hostelling International!
Para saber dónde y en qué puedes ahorrar dinero a lo largo de tu viaje, consulta nuestra base de datos mundial de descuentos en ***www.HIhostels.com.***

Malta

NSTS Hostelling International,
220 St. Paul St, Valletta VLT 07, Malta.
t (356) 25 588000
f (356) 25 588200
e nsts@nsts.org
w www.nsts.org

A copy of the Hostel Directory for this Country can be obtained from:
The National Office

National Tourist Authority/Board:	www.visitmalta.com
Capital:	Valletta
Language:	Maltese, English
Currency:	Malta Lira (MLT)
Population:	379,750
Size:	356 sq km
Telephone Country Code:	356
eKit Access Number:	Check www.hi.ekit.com for up to date Access Numbers

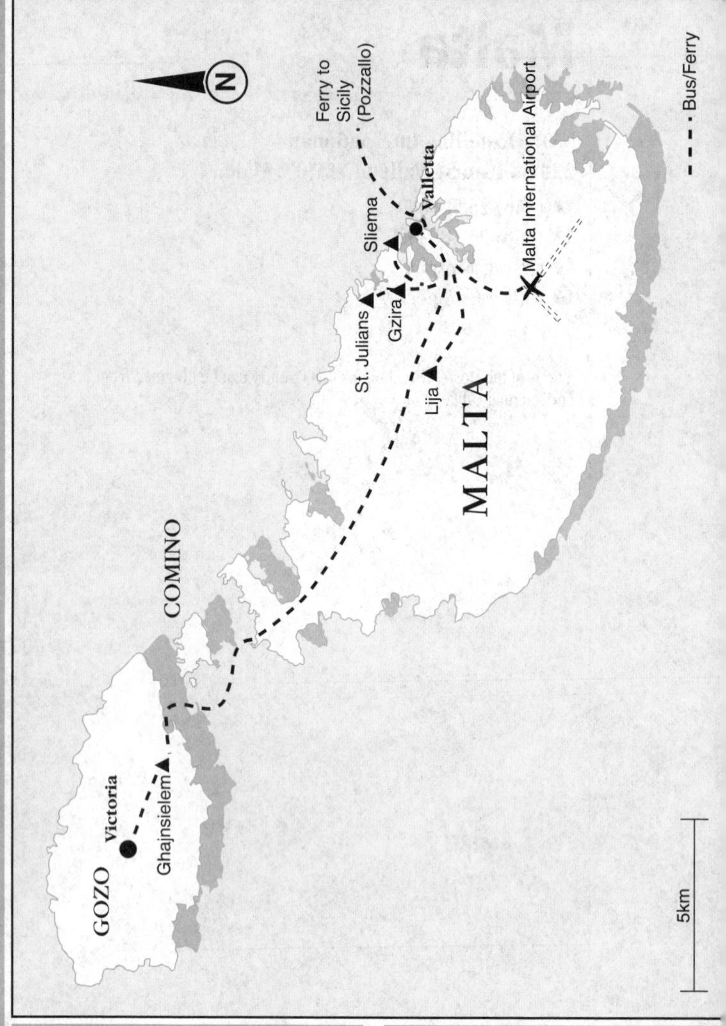

HI Suggests...

In Malta, you will explore 7000 years of history yet live passionately in the present. You will span the millennia with an astonishing array of things to discover and wherever you go, the Islands' scenery and architecture provide a spectacular backdrop. The colours are striking. Honey-coloured stone and sand against the deepest of Mediterranean blues.

The Maltese Islands have been described as one big open-air museum. What makes them unique is that so much of there past is visible today. Delve into the Islands' mysterious prehistory, retrace the footsteps of St Paul, see where the Knights of St John lived and fought or visit the UNESCO monuments.

But Malta is no regular museum. Here life is lived to the full, so make time for some living history and action. Visit locations where Oscar-winning blockbusters were filmed, including Gladiator, or go off the beaten track into ancient villages. Marvel at the fireworks and revelry of the summertime festas and enjoy a packed calendar of events all year round.

Malta is holidaying as the mood takes you. And with near year-round sun, you can indulge in outdoor living at its best.

In just 48 hours and a kilometer or two, you can try a new sport, laze on an island cruise and tour the most important historic sites ... and still have time to join in the nightlife. That's the real advantage of a stay here.

The Islands offer plenty of specialist holidays for those seeking to learn a new skill, discover history or get fit. If you are interested in water sports, NSTS, offer scuba-diving courses for the seasoned enthusiast as well as the first-timer. Sea and land lend themselves to activities from rock-climbing to gentle rambling.

Bilingual (Maltese and English are both official languages) Malta is an enjoyable place to learn or practice English. NSTS offer courses for everyone from youngsters to professionals.

Visit during special times like summer fiesta season, Easter and carnival and you will never be stuck for what to do – simply join the crowd for some fun.

ou can find out a lot more on our vebsite - a visit to www.HIhostels.com is ssential for planning your trip!

'our en savoir plus, rendez-vous ur notre site Internet, vww.HIhostels.com une visite ncontournable pour préparer votre oyage!

'iele weitere Informationen auf unserer Vebsite: www.HIhostels.com - nverzichtbar für die Reiseplanung!

'uedes averiguar mucho más en uestro sitio web. Es imprescindible que visites la página www.HIhostels.com para planear tu viaje.

▲ **Gozo** – St. Joseph Home Hostel – 92063
Mgarr Rd, Ghajnsielem, Gozo.
t 21 556439 f 21 556439
e georgecordina@yahoo.com
w www.stjosephhomstel.com
Open Dates: 08.01-23.12 Malta International A #8 to Valletta From Valletta - 44, 45 ap Gozo Ferry Terminal Hostel 500m up the hill from Gozo Ferry Terminal, walk in the direction of Ghajnsielem 0.2SW x 67 R (B) 1 x P 100m 100m

▲ **Gzira** – Balco Harmony Hostel – 92067
Cuschieri Street.
t 21 676946 e info@balcomalta.com
w www.balcomalta.com
Open Dates: 12 Malta International A #8 to Valetta Bus 60 from Valletta ap Gasan x 22 R 8 1.3km 1.3km

▲ **Lija** – University Residence – 92064
Robert Mifsud Bonnici St, Lija.
t 21 436168 f 21 434963
e info@universityresidence.com
w www.universityresidence.com
Open Dates: 12 Malta International A #8 to Valletta From Valletta - 40 ap Lija Church 0.1E x 250 R 2 x i 8 P

Sliema – Hibernia House Gateway Hostel – 92065
Depiro St, Sliema.
t 21 333859 f 21 230330
e nsts@nsts.org w www.nsts.org
Open Dates: 12 Open Times:
Beds: 130 - 5x1 14x2 5x3 8x4 2x5 4x6 2x6+
Price Range: MLT 5-14 € 12-32 BBinc
Directions: 0.3W from city centre
Malta International - Gudja A #8 to Valletta From Valletta - 62, 64, 66, 68 ap Plaza Hotel R (B) 1 x i 8 P 100m 100m

MALTA - MALTE - MALTA - MALTA - MALTA

Sliema – Hibernia House Gateway Hostel

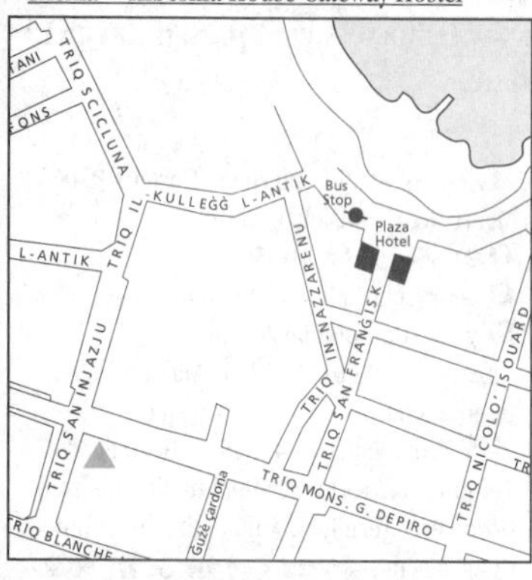

Sliema... Travel Tips

- **For budget eats check out...** Many budget restaurants around
- **For great nightlife try...** Paceville district - Malta's premiere youth entertainment district
- **Don't miss...** Hypogeum underground neolithic temple (Paola), Ggatija oldest building (Temple) in the world (Gozo), Valletta Bastions, Valletta St John's Cathedral, Valletta Museum of Archaeology, Mdina medieval capital, Gozo villages, Beaches to the north of the island, Blue Grotto - Hagar Qim (Zurrieq), Blue Lagoon (Comino)

▲ **St Julian's** – Pinto Guest House – 92066
Sacred Heart Ave, St Julians.
T 21 313897 F 21 319852
E info@pintohotel.com
W www.pintohotel.com
Open Dates: 01.04-31.10 ✈ Malta International A 🚌 #8 to Valletta 🚌 From Valletta - 41, 42 ap Mrabat Street 0.5SW
x 30 R (B) TV P 200m 200m

Mexico

Hostelling International de Mexico AC,
Republica de Guatemala 4,
Colonia Centro, 06020, Mexico DF.

t (52) 55181726
f (52) 55103442
e info@hostellingmexico.com
w www.hostellingmexico.com

A copy of the Hostel Directory for this Country can be obtained from:
The National Office

National Tourist Authority/Board:	www.sectur.gob.mx
Capital:	Mexico City
Language:	Spanish
Currency:	Mexican Peso
Population:	108,000,000
Size:	1,972,000 sq km
Telephone Country Code:	52
eKit Access Number:	01800-088-5000

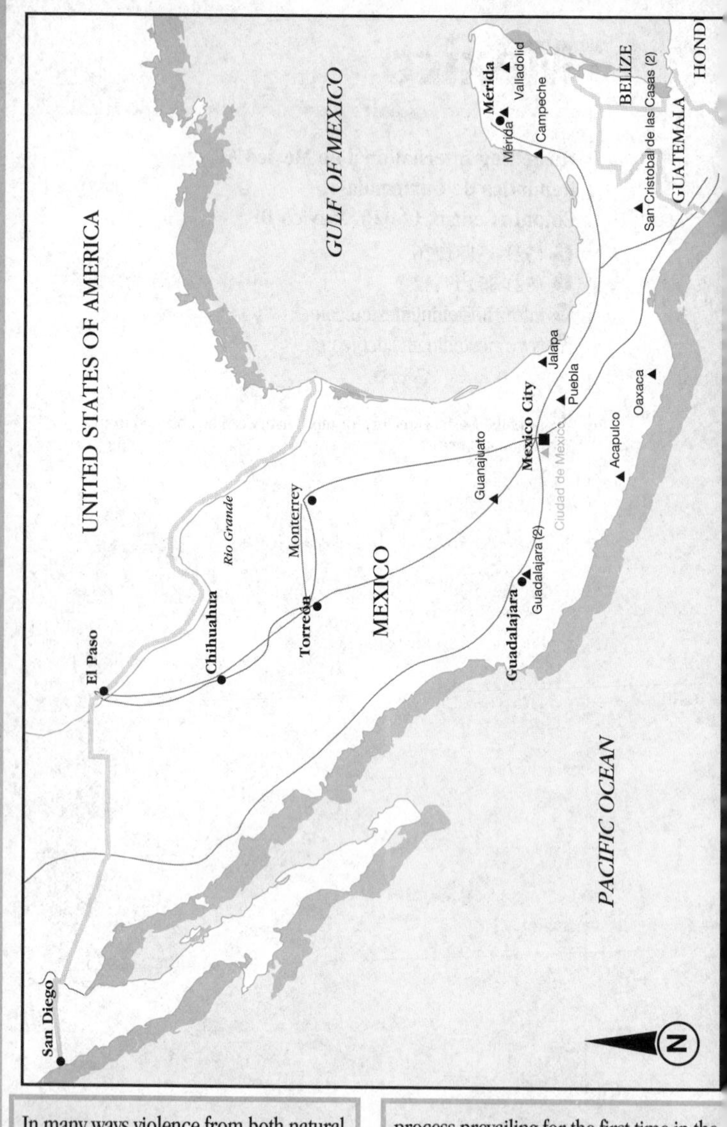

In many ways violence from both natural catastrophes, especially earthquakes, as well as conquest and lawlessness (often featured in Hollywood's 'gringo' films), has driven Mexico's history and culture home, originally to advanced Amerindian civilizations. Yet, from a bizarre and often tragic past, today's country of some 108 million is witnessing a remarkable economic and even political transformation, with the democratic process prevailing for the first time in the 2000 election of the National Action Party, and trade with the US and Canada tripling since the 1994 free trade agreement.

Built on the ruins of the ancient Aztec capital known as Tenochtitlan, Mexico City itself, the fastest growing and most densely populated city in the world, is still expanding and already home to over 20 million people, with the inevitable extremes of wealth and poverty, skyscrapers and shanty suburbs – and serious pollution problems, not least photo-chemical smog.

Mexico is a fantastic and fascinating country to explore geographically and culturally – from the first civilizations of the Olmecs, Mayas and Aztecs to the vibrant café and sports-focused environment of today. Visitors need to be aware that crime is widespread outside the special holiday resort enclaves.

A few other Top Tips from **CULTURE SMART!**:

- Men who are well acquainted greet each other with an embrace and a handshake; otherwise, just a handshake. Similarly, women will greet each other with a kiss on the cheek and a handshake if they know each other well, otherwise just a handshake.
- In addition to so-called 'Western' dress, ethnic dress and regional dress is still widespread in Mexico so when it comes to social occasions it is always best to check what others are doing and follow suit. Rule of thumb is to dress conservatively but informally.
- Status is important, so be sure to respect this when introduced and use the correct terminology, as in *licenciado* (lawyer) and *ingeniero* (engineer). For women, when in doubt use *senorita* (Miss) rather than *senora* (Mrs). Women should also be aware that Mexico is still a 'machismo' culture, although the younger generation is demanding greater respect and equality between the sexes.

You can find out a lot more on our website - a visit to www.HIhostels.com is essential for planning your trip!

Pour en savoir plus, rendez-vous sur notre site Internet, www.HIhostels.com une visite incontournable pour préparer votre voyage!

Viele weitere Informationen auf unserer Website: www.HIhostels.com - unverzichtbar für die Reiseplanung!

Puedes averiguar mucho más en nuestro sitio web. Es imprescindible que visites la página www.HIhostels.com para planear tu viaje.

▲ **Acapulco** – Kingdom – 92624
Carretera Puerto Marquez 104 esq. glorieta Pt o. Marquez.
(744) 4663736
coordinacion@hostellingmexico.com
www.hostellingmexico.com
Open Dates: Acapulco 10km
A 10km 20km 20km
x 72 R CC (B)

▲ **Campeche** – Pirate – 92616
Calle 59 No. 47 Entre 14 y 16 Centro Histórico.
(981) 8111757
coordinacion@hostellingmexico.com
www.hostellingmexico.com
Open Dates: Ciudad Del Carmen 4km
Bus Station 1km x 28 R
CC (B) 8

▲ **Guadalajara** – De María – 92622
Nveva Galicia #924 Centro Histórico.
(33) 36146230
coordinancion@hostellingmexico.com
www.hostellingmexico.com
Open Dates: Miguel Hidalgo 35km
12km 25km x 32 (B)

▲ **Guadalajara** – Guadalajara – 92618
Maestranza 147 Centro Histórico.
(33) 35627520
coordinacion@hostellingmexico.com
www.hostellingmexico.com
Open Dates: Miguel Hidalgo 35km
12km Bus Station 25km 20m
x 35 (B)

▲ **Guanajuato** – Hostelito Guanajuato – 92075
Sangre de Cristo N 9 Centro Histórico.
(473) 7325483
coordinacion@hostellingmexico.com
www.hostellingmexico.com
Open Dates: Leon 40km A 10m
20km x 20 (B)

▲ **Jalapa** – De La Niebla – 92620
Zamora No. 24 Centro.
(228) 8172174 (228) 8182842
coordinacion@hostellingmexico.com
www.hostellingmexico.com
Open Dates: Bus Station 7km
ap 15m x 44 (B)

▲ **Merida** – Nomadas – 92605
Calle 62 No.433x51 Centro.
(999) 9245223
coordinacion@hostellingmexico.com
www.hostellingmexico.com
Open Dates: Mérida 30km Bus
Station 1km x 60 (B)

México DF – Hostel Mundo Joven Catedral
92074
Guatemala #4, Centro, México DF.
(55) 55181726 (55) 55103442
coordinacion@hostellingmexico.com
www.hostellingmexico.com
Open Dates: Open Times:
Beds: 204
Price Range: BB inc
Directions: Benito Juarez 5km
A Zócalo Station 100m Tapo
Terminal 1km; North Terminal 5km ap 10m
500m 200m

México DF – Hostel Mundo Joven Catedral

▲ **Oaxaca** – Paulina – 92613
Trujano 321, Centro Historico.
(951) 5162005 (951) 5011615
coordinacion@hostellingmexico.com
www.hostellingmexico.com
Open Dates: Oaxaca City International
5km Bus Station 1km ap 30m x 95

▲ **Puebla** – Xaman-Ke – 92623
6 norte 1801 entre 18y20 Ote, Centro.
(222) 2425997
coordinacion@hostellingmexico.com
www.hostellingmexico.com
Open Dates: 10km x 23
(B)

▲ **San Cristobal de Las Casas** – Backpackers – 92619
Real de Mexicanos 16, Barrio de Mexicanos.
(967) 6740525
coordinacion@hostellingmexico.com
www.hostellingmexico.com
Open Dates: Bus Station 800m ap 10m x 38 (B)

▲ **San Cristobal de Las Casas** – Posada Mexico – 92621
Dr. Felipe Flores ·16. Col. Centro Histórico.
(967) 6780014
coordinacion@hostellingmexico.com
www.hostellingmexico.com
Open Dates: Bus Station 800m x 49 (B)

▲ **Valladolid** – La Candelaria – 92614
Calle 35 No. 201-F entre 42y44.
(985) 8562267
coordinacion@hostellingmexico.com
www.hostellingmexico.com
Open Dates: Cancun International 160km Bus Station 300m x 44 (B)

HI Member Discounts!
To find out where you can save money on your travels, check out the Global Discounts Database at ***www.HIhostels.com.***

Remises pour les adhérents HI!
Pour savoir où vous pouvez économiser en voyageant, consultez notre base de données des remises sur ***www.HIhostels.com.***

Rabatte für HI-Mitglieder!
Erkundigen Sie sich, wie und wo Sie auf Ihren Reisen Geld sparen können! Besuchen Sie die Datenbank für weltweite Rabatte (Global Discounts Database) unter ***www.HIhostels.com.***

¡Descuentos para los miembros de Hostelling International!
Para saber dónde y en qué puedes ahorrar dinero a lo largo de tu viaje, consulta nuestra base de datos mundial de descuentos en ***www.HIhostels.com.***

Morocco

Fédération Royale Marocaine des Auberges de Jeunes, Parc de la Ligue Arabe, BP No 15998, Casa-Principale, Casablanca 21000, Morocco.

t (212) (22) 470952

f (212) (22) 227677

e frmaj@iam.net.ma

Office Hours: 08.30-12.00hrs & 15.00-18.00hrs (Summer)
08.30-12.00hrs & 14.00-18.00hrs (Winter)

A copy of the Hostel Directory for this Country can be obtained from:
The National Office

National Tourist Authority/Board:	www.morocco.com
Capital:	Rabat
Language:	Arabic
Currency:	Dh (dirham)
Population:	26,073,717
Size:	710,850 sq km
Telephone Country Code:	212
eKit Access Number:	Check www.hi.ekit.com for up to date Access Numbers

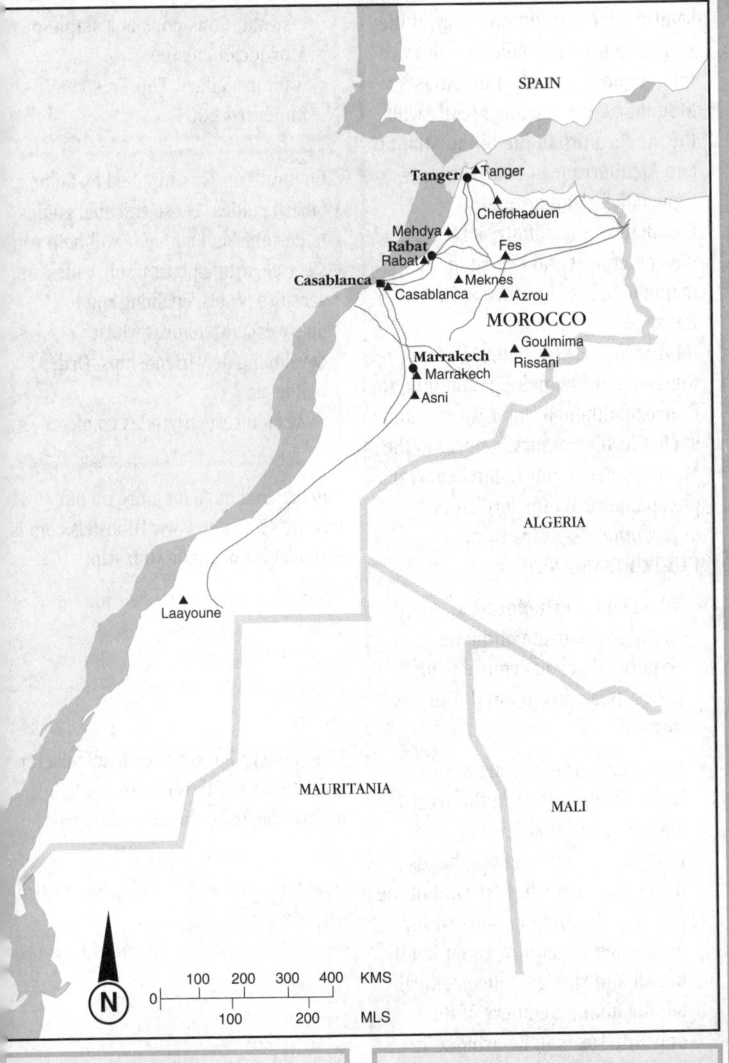

The Kingdom of Morocco – a country of 32 million and Europe's gateway to north Africa – stands as heir to the historic splendour of the Moorish kingdom, which from the eighth century, once populated southern Spain, bringing with them their art, architecture and Muslim faith. (The word Moor comes from the word Mauri, the North African Berber people.) In the late 'empire period' of the early twentieth century Morocco was colonised by the French and Spanish (1912), and gained independence early in 1956 with the return of Tangier, which had been an international autonomous zone, soon after.

So both Arabic and Berber languages are spoken, with French often being used in business and diplomatic contexts. To some extent, the landscape reinforces the historic cultural variations, with a peasant, semi-nomadic traditional way of life still present in the valleys of the vast mountainous region of the Atlas Mountains, contrasting greatly with the modern urban life of the Atlantic and Mediterranean coastal plains, especially in and around Casablanca, the country's largest city, chief port and centre of manufacturing, and the capital Rabat.

Morocco's *souks*, beloved of tourists and filmmakers, continue to flourish, although, interestingly for such a fertile country, central to the Moroccan economy is the export of phosphates used for fertilizers.

A few other Top Tips from **CULTURE SMART!:**

- When entering a Moroccan home traditional Muslim etiquette requires that you remove your shoes. Bear this in mind if you normally wear socks.
- Moroccan greetings are a more leisurely affair than in the West and can last for several minutes, individuals often shaking hands throughout the whole period of the greeting. It would be normal for both sides to enquire about family, health and studies; but specifically talking about members of the opposite sex is to be avoided in case of misunderstandings.
- Moroccans, like the Italians, love to gesticulate, the hands being an integral part of communication. For example, waving the hand over the shoulder indicates that something has already happened, or is in the past.
- The main meal of the day is lunch, which can last for several hours, with office workers taking up to four hours off, in order to include a siesta. Cous cous is a staple of Moroccan cuisine.

Cultural Top Tips supplied by Culture Smart! guides. These essential guides to customs and etiquette will help you steer clear of embarrassing gaffes and sensitive issues, enabling you to discover new cultures whilst developing new friendships. Order online at www.culturesmartguides.co.uk

You can find out a lot more on our website - a visit to www.HIhostels.com is essential for planning your trip!

Pour en savoir plus, rendez-vous su notre site Internet, www.HIhostels.com une visite incontournable pour préparer votre voyage!

Viele weitere Informationen auf unserer Website: www.HIhostels.com - unverzichtbar für die Reiseplanung!

Puedes averiguar mucho más en nuestro sitio web. Es imprescindible que visites la página www.HIhostels.com para planear tu viaje.

△ ***Asni** – Asni Youth Hostel – 96129*
Route d'Amlil par Marrakech,
Asni (Grand Atlas).
(4) 447713 (4) 447713
Open Dates: ✈ Marrakech Menara 55km
x 40

Casablanca – 96131
6 Place Ahmed Al Bidaoui, Ville Ancienne, Casablanca.
(22) 220551 (22) 227677
casa_hostel@caramail.com
Open Dates: Open Times: 08.00-10.00hrs; 12.00-23.00hrs; 12.00-24.00hrs (in summer)
Beds: 76 - 4x2 3x3 6x5 4x6
Price Range: 50-70DH BBinc
Directions: 0.35SW from city centre
✈ Mohamed V International 35km
A CTM (National Bus) 35km
Casablanca 250m Casa Port 350m
11 300m ap Casa Port x 2 R
(B) TV 1 x
8

Casablanca

Casablanca... Travel Tips

- **For budget eats check out...** Rotisserie Marché Central, McDonalds, Restaurant Amine (Derb Ralaf), Pizza Hut, Alfa 55 & Central Market rotisseries
- **For great nightlife try...** La Corniche (coast road - night clubs), Centre 2000, Club 84, Private swimming pools & sports clubs
- **Don't miss...** Hassan II Mosque, Des Habeuss district, La Corniche (coast road), Place des Nations, Commandment Provant, Parc de la ligue Arabe, Mohammadia beach, Prince Moulay Abolellah, Fishing port, Craft centre

△ ***Chefchaouen** – Chaouen Youth Hostel – 96132*
Pres du Camping Municipal, Chefchaouen.
(9) 986031
Open Dates: x 30

▲ **Fes** – 96133
18 Rue Abdeslam Seghrini, Ville Nouvelle, Fes.
(5) 624085
Open Dates: ✈ Fès Saiss 18km Fès Gare 500m x 35

△ ***Goulmima** – Oasis Youth Hostel Palmeraie Goulmima – 96134*
Secteur 3, Hay Ouatman No. 4 Goulmima.
(66) 908442 arjikamal@yahoo.fr
Open Dates: 0.3NE x 50 P

▲ **Laâyoune** – 96135
Laâyoune Complexe Sportif, Laâyoune, Sakiat Alhamra.
(08) 893402
Open Dates: ✈ Laâyoune 15km x 40

△ ***Marrakech** – 96136*
Rue El Jahed,
Quartier Industriel (near camp site),
Marrakech.
(4) 447713 (4) 447713
Open Dates: ✈ Marrakech Menara 25km x 46 R

▲ **Mehdya** – Auberge Internationale Mehdya – 96137
Villa No 6, Lotissement Amria, Mehdya Plage.
(7) 388212
Open Dates: ✈ Rabat-Salé 47km 0.7E
x 35 R P

▲ **Meknès** – 96138
Boulvard Okba Ben Nafii,
Meknès (near Transatlantique Hotel).
(5) 524698
Open Dates: ✈ Saïs 33km 3km
4km x 45

△ ***Rabat** – 96139*
43 Rue Marassa, Bab El Had, Rabat,
BP 488 RP Rabat.
(7) 725769
Open Dates: ✈ Rabat-Salé 20km
Rabat Ville 2km x 38

△ ***Rissani*** *– Rissani Youth Hostel – 96140*
107 Hay Moulay Slimane. Près De Souk Rissani.
(5) 575389
Open Dates: 12 01S x 25

Tanger – 96141
8 rue El Antaki, Av d'Espagne, Tanger.
(9) 946127
Open Dates: 12 Tanger Boukahalef x 3
R

YOUTH HOSTEL ACCOMMODATION OUTSIDE THE ASSURED STANDARDS SCHEME

Azrou – Azrou Youth Hostel – 96130
Route de Midelt, Ifrane, BP 147 (Moyen Atlas).
(5) 563733
Open Dates: 12 x 30

Netherlands

Stayokay,
Postbus 9191, 1006 AD Amsterdam, Netherlands.

t (31) (10) 2646064 (information);
(31) (20) 6392929 (group bookings)

f (31) (10) 2646089

e info@stayokay.com

w www.stayokay.com

Office Hours: Monday-Friday 09.00-17.00hrs

A copy of the Hostel Directory for this Country can be obtained from:
The National Office

National Tourist Authority/Board:	www.holland.com
Capital:	Amsterdam
Language:	Dutch
Currency:	€ Euro
Population:	16,000,000
Size:	40,844 sq km
Telephone Country Code:	31
eKit Access Number:	0800-020-3235

It has sometimes been said that the Netherlands (Holland) exists by the whim of the sea and the will of the people, given the fact that two-fifths of the country is below sea level, including all the main centres of population, and requires the best of human ingenuity to keep if from flooding. Famous for its windmills and waterways, the Netherlands is a wealthy country and its people are adventurous, entrepreneurial, open and progressive – great seafarers of old who continue to be renowned today for their skills in commerce and trade, including their expertise as the world's hub for diamond cutting and polishing.

Here are people who speak Dutch, sometimes still wear clogs and still ride bicycles everywhere. Though it may be another of their stereotypes, they also make excellent cheese and are amongst the world's top horticulturists, including the growing of tulips. Crucially, they are also one of

Europe's top exporters of agricultural products.

A country of 16 million, with a very 'modern monarchy' under Queen Beatrix and one of the founding members of the European Union. The country's 'national colour', orange, derives from the Dutch royal House of Orange that once provided a monarch to the UK (William of Orange).

A few other Top Tips from **CULTURE SMART!**:

- Though very liberal and tolerant, the Dutch are still very conservative in many ways and like to maintain an ordered and orderly society, including their approach to the control of drugs. They do not like 'loudness' either in speech or in their everyday life, including neighbours. There has also been some reaction to the abuse of what they see as their open society.
- It is customary to shake hands in Holland; the Dutch are not so tactile as Europe's Latin races and generally tend to be more demur and much less demonstrative, which applies equally to the way they socialize and their candid, 'down-to-earth ' approach to life.
- The Dutch are great coffee drinkers and produce some of the best blends in the world. Meetings 'over coffee' are commonplace, including home visits, which need to be carefully organized in advance. The Dutch do not like surprises, and that includes people 'dropping in' unannounced!
- Equally, the Dutch sense of family is very strong and the sense of well being that this generates is important to appreciate; it has a significant impact on everyday life and the 'respect' culture that derives from it.

Cultural Top Tips supplied by Culture Smart! guides. These essential guides to customs and etiquette will help you steer clear of embarrassing gaffes and sensitive issues, enabling you to discover new cultures whilst developing new friendships. Order online at www.culturesmartguides.co.uk

You can find out a lot more on our website - a visit to www.HIhostels.com is essential for planning your trip!

Pour en savoir plus, rendez-vous sur notre site Internet, www.HIhostels.com une visite incontournable pour préparer votre voyage!

Viele weitere Informationen auf unserer Website: www.HIhostels.com - unverzichtbar für die Reiseplanung!

Puedes averiguar mucho más en nuestro sitio web. Es imprescindible que visites la página www.HIhostels.com para planear tu viaje.

▲ **Ameland** – Stayokay Ameland Ⓗ 40029 (FNM)
Oranjeweg 59, 9161 CB Hollum Ameland.
Ⓣ (519) 555353 Ⓕ (519) 555355
Ⓦ www.stayokay.com/ameland
Open Dates: 01.04-31.10 & all weekends (12 ⅲ) ✈ Schiphol ⛴ Holwerd - Nes, Ameland 🚂 Leeuwarden 45km 🚌 Bus 6 to Holwerd x 144 ⅲ ♿ ⅲ R CC 10km 500m

Amsterdam – Stayokay Amsterdam Stadsdoelen 40004

Kloveniersburgwal 97, 1011 KB Amsterdam.

(20) 6246832 (20) 6391035

www.stayokay.com/stadsdoelen

Open Dates: (no) Open Times:

Beds: 170 - 13x

Price Range: € 20.00-25.50 (HI-members receive € 2.50 discount p.p.p.n.) inc

Directions: Schiphol 18km A Shuttle Amsterdam Central 1.5km 4, 9, 16, 24 or 25 500m ap Muntplein U Nieuwmarkt 500m R CC 26km

Amsterdam – Stayokay Amsterdam Stadsdoelen

▲ **Amsterdam** – Stayokay Amsterdam Timorplein – 40050

Timorplein 21,1094 CC Amsterdam

(20) 5513155 www.stayokay.com

Open Dates: Expected opening - September 2006 Schiphol 15km Amsterdam central. tram 14 x 464 R CC 28km

Amsterdam – Stayokay Amsterdam Vondelpark 40001

Zandpad 5, 1054 GA Amsterdam.

(20) 5898996 (20) 5898955

www.stayokay.com/vondelpark

Open Dates: Open Times:

Beds: 536 - 19x 35x 38x 21x

Price Range: € 20.00-28.75 (HI-members receive € 2.50 discount p.p.p.n.) (€ 2 supplement p.p.p.n. Fri/Sat) inc

Directions: 0.3N from city centre Schiphol 15km A Interliner 370 every half hour 200m Amsterdam Centra 3km Leidseplein 50m 1, 2, 5 50m ap Leidseplein U Weesperplein 1km x 5 R CC 1 x 300m 28km

Amsterdam – Stayokay Amsterdam Vondelpar

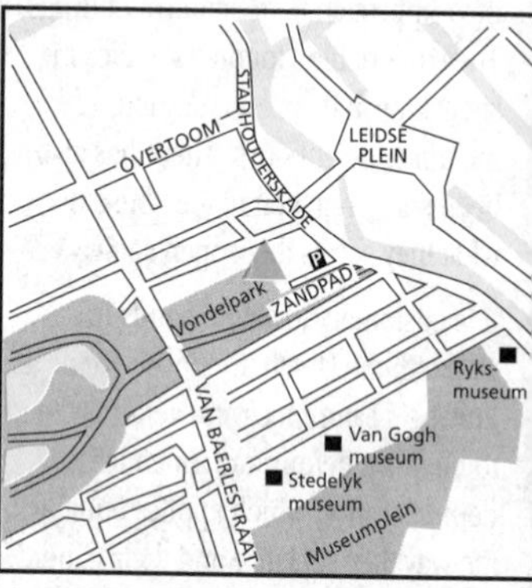

Amsterdam... Travel Tips

- **For budget eats check out...** Brasserie Backpackers, Al Capone Pizza, Café de Jaren, Grand Café l'Opéra, Moko
- **For great nightlife try...** Paradiso (disco), Leidseplein (pubs), Melkweg (disco), Rembrandt plein (pubs)
- **Don't miss...** Van Gogh Museum, Rijksmuseum, City Centre, Canal Tours, Vondelpark, Stedelijk museum, Artis (zoo), Nemo, Anne Frank's House, Rembrandt museum

Apeldoorn – Stayokay Apeldoorn 40036

Asselsestraat 330, 7312 TS Apeldoorn.

(55) 3553118 (55) 3553811

www.stayokay.com/apeldoorn

Open Dates: Open Times:

Beds: 136 - 3x2 17x4 9x6 1x6+

Price Range: € 22.25-28.75 (HI-members receive € 2.50 discount p.p.p.n.) (€ 2 supplement p.p.p.n. Fri/Sat) BBinc

Directions: Schiphol 95km

Apeldoorn 3km 6, stop Driehoek or 7, stop Chamavenlaan 150m x 16

R CC 3 x

2km

Apeldoorn – Stayokay Apeldoorn

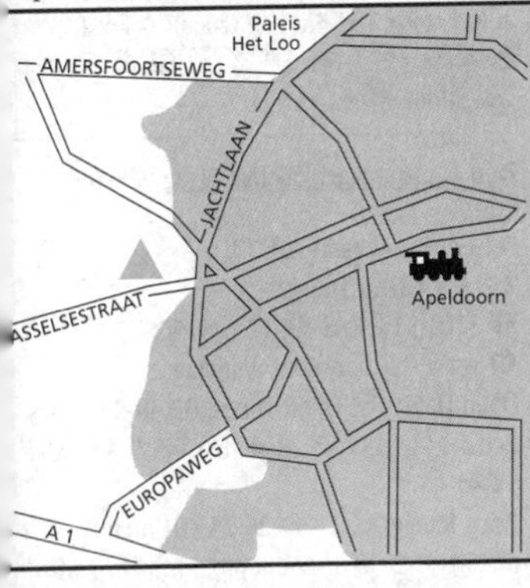

Apeldoorn... Travel Tips

- **For budget eats check out...** Hostel Restaurant, City Centre
- **For great nightlife try...** Caterplein
- **Don't miss...** Apenheul, Paleis 'T Loo (Palace), National Park "De Hoge Veluwe", Kröller Müller museum, Julianatoren (attraction park for kids)

Arnhem – Stayokay Arnhem 40005

Diepenbrocklaan 27, 6815 AH Arnhem.

(26) 4420114 (26) 3514892

www.stayokay.com/arnhem

Open Dates: Open Times: 07.00-24.00hrs

Beds: 181 - 2x2 12x4 4x6 15x6+

Price Range: € 22.25-28.75 (HI-members receive € 2.50 discount p.p.p.n.) (€ 2 supplement p.p.p.n. Fri/Sat) BBinc

Directions: 2NW from city centre

Schiphol 110km Arnhem 2.5km

3 ap Rijnstate Hospital x 14

R CC 5 x

1.5km

Arnhem – Stayokay Arnhem

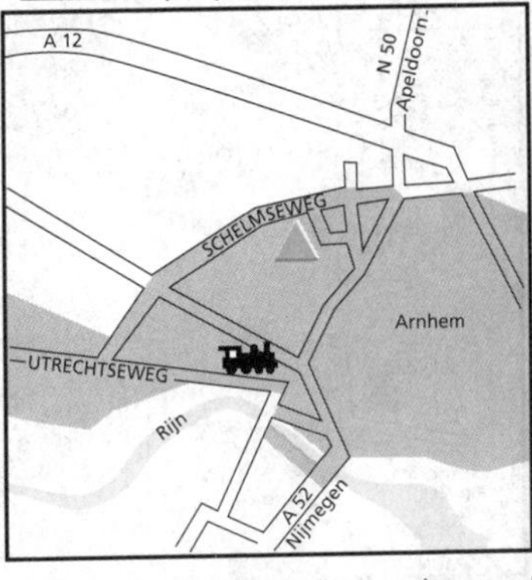

Arnhem... Travel Tips

- **For budget eats check out...** City centre, Hostel restaurant, Korenmarkt
- **For great nightlife try...** City centre, Cinemas, Music performances & theatre, Bars/pubs/discotheques in city centre, Korenmarkt
- **Don't miss...** National Park "de Hoge Veluwe", Kröller Möller museum, Open air museum, Airborne museum Oosterbeek, Museum of Modern Art, Wine museum, Castles, Burgers' Zoo

Bakkum – Stayokay Bakkum 40034
Heereweg 84, 1901 ME Bakkum.
(251) 652226 (251) 670027
www.stayokay.com/bakkum
Open Dates: Open Times: 07.00-01.00hrs
Beds: 178 - 1x2 3x4 2x6 13x6+
Price Range: € 21-26.50 (HI-members receive € 2.50 discount p.p.p.n.) (€ 1.50 supplement p.p.p.n. Fri/Sat) BBinc
Directions: 3S from city centre
Schiphol 40km Castricum 3.5km
NZH 164 ap stop Anthosius
R CC 2 x
2km

Bakkum – Stayokay Bakkum

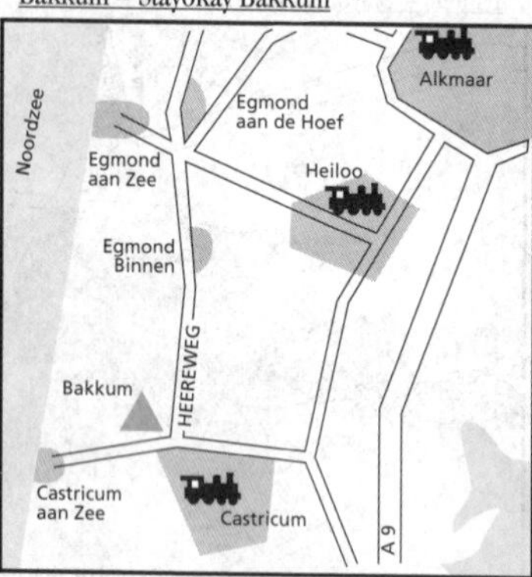

Bakkum... Travel Tips

- **For budget eats check out...** The hostel, Ziltezoen, Gonzales BBQ, Mezza Luna, Pubs on the beach
- **For great nightlife try...** Pubs - Scala, M'dante, Balustrade (Castricum), Bob's (Uitgeest), Waagplein Alkmaar
- **Don't miss...** Cheese Market (10km), Black Market Beverwijk (12km), Beer Museum Alkmaar (10km), Windmill village Zaanse Schans (10km), Nature Museum De Hoep Castricum (1 km), Watersports, Beach

▲ **Bergen op Zoom** – Stayokay Bergen op Zoom 40033
Boslustweg 1, 4624 RB Bergen op Zoom.
(164) 233261 (164) 239133
www.stayokay.com/bergenopzoom
Open Dates: Rotterdam 70km
Intercity - Bergen op Zoom 3km
21, 22 500m ap Lievensberg x 152
R CC
5 x 3km
25km

▲ **Bunnik** – Stayokay Bunnik 40023
Rhijnauwenselaan 14, 3981 HH Bunnik.
(30) 6561277 (30) 6571065
www.stayokay.com/bunnik
Open Dates: 01.03-31.10 & weekends ( ) Schiphol 55km Utrecht CS 5km, Bunnik 3km from Utrecht CS 40, 41 500m ap Rhijnauwen YH x 139
R CC 4 x 8
1km

▲ **Chaam** – Stayokay Chaam 40037
Putvenweg 1, 4861 RB Chaam.
(161) 491323 (161) 491756
www.stayokay.com/chaam
Open Dates: 01.04-31.10 ( )
Schiphol 120km Breda, Tilburg 20km 132 3km ap Chaam x 133
R CC
300m

Den Haag – Stayokay Den Haag 40007
Scheepmakersstraat 27, 2515 VA Den Haag.
(70) 3157888 (70) 3157877
www.stayokay.com/denhaag
Open Dates: Open Times: 07.30-22.30hrs
Beds: 232 - 13x2 2x3 18x4 2x5 7x6 8x6+
Price Range: € 21.50-25.25 (HI-members receive € 2.50 discount p.p.p.n.) (€ 1.50 supplement p.p.p.n. Fri/Sat) BBinc
Directions: Schiphol 46km Hoek van Holland (Ferries to UK) 25km Den Haag Hollands Spoor 400m, Den Haag Centraal 1km ap Holland Spoor 1,9,12,16 ap Rijswijkse Plein x 24 R CC
5 x
8 8km 3km

Den Haag – Stayokay Den Haag

Den Haag... Travel Tips

- **For budget eats check out...** Brasserie Backpackers, Babbelen, Jungle, Naast de Paap, Papocatepet
- **For great nightlife try...** Crazy piano's, Hathor, Get Down, Havana
- **Don't miss...** Madurodam, Sealife Centre, Uithof, Omniversum, Museon, Haags Municipal Museum, Panorama Mesdag, Vitalizee

Domburg – Stayokay Domburg 40030

Duinvlietweg 8, 4356 ND Domburg.

(118) 581254 (118) 583342

www.stayokay.com/domburg

Open Dates: Open Times:

Beds: 116 - 2x 8x 12x 1x

Price Range: € 22.25-28.75 (HI-members receive € 2.50 discount p.p.p.n.) (€ 2 supplement p.p.p.n. Fri/Sat) inc

Directions: Schiphol 170 km, Rotterdam 100km Vlissingen Middelburg 53 ap Westhove

2km

Domburg – Stayokay Domburg

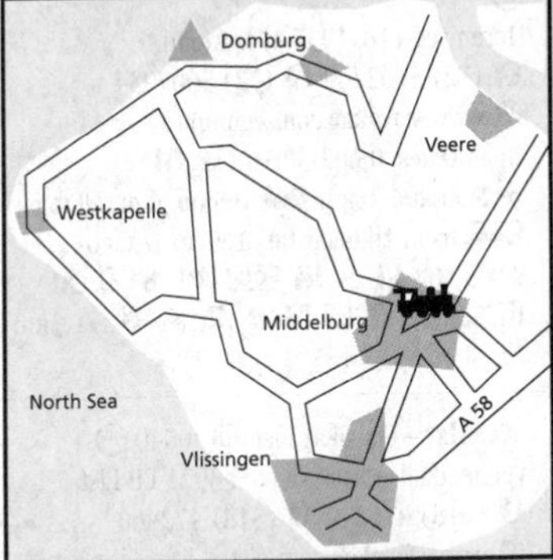

Domburg... Travel Tips

- **For budget eats check out...** The hostel restaurant (3 course dinner €9.75), 't Groentje, Strandpaviljoen, Lage Duintjes en de Piraat
- **For great nightlife try...** Cafe Tramzicht, Discotheque De Hooizolder - Westkapelle, Bars in Middelburg
- **Don't miss...** Waterland Neeltje Jans, Veere historical village, Museum - Vlissingen, Zeeuws Biologisch Museum, Iguana (reptiles) Zoo

▲ **Doorwerth** – Stayokay Doorwerth 40038

Kerklaan 50, 6865 GZ Doorwerth.

(26) 3334300 (26) 3337060

www.stayokay.com/doorwerth

Open Dates: 01.04-30.09

Schiphol 98km Rotterdam, Hoek van Holland 140km Arnhem 7km 86 150m ap Kerklaan x 114

2 x

▲ **Dordrecht** – Stayokay Dordrecht 40039

Baanhoekweg 25, 3313 LA Dordrecht.

(78) 6212167 (78) 6212163

www.stayokay.com/dordrecht

Open Dates: 02.01-30.11

Schiphol 85km Waterbus for hikers & cyclists 1km Dordrecht 5 ap change to Biesbus, stop Moldiepweg x 120

2 x 1km

▲ **Egmond** – Stayokay Egmond 40024
Herenweg 118, 1935 AJ Egmond.
(72) 5062269 (72) 5067034
www.stayokay.com/egmond
Open Dates: 05.02-30.10
Schiphol 25km Heiloo 3km, Alkmaar from Alkmaar bus 165 ap Texaco x 162 1 x 3km 3km

▲ **Elst** – Stayokay Elst 40040
Veenendaalsestraatweg 65, 3921 EB Elst.
(318) 471219 (318) 472460
www.stayokay.com/elst
Open Dates: 15.06-15.08
Schiphol 80km Veenendaal Centrum 51 x 200 6 x 3km

▲ **Gorssel** – Stayokay Gorssel 40016
Dortherweg 34, 7216 PT Gorssel.
(573) 431615 (573) 431832
www.stayokay.com/gorssel
Open Dates: 02.02-30.10
Schiphol 100km Zutphen 10km, Deventer 10km 56 ap De Drie Kieviten x 92 1 x 5km

▲ **Grou** – Stayokay Grou 40020
Raadhuisstraat 18, 9001 AG Grou.
(566) 621528 (566) 621005
www.stayokay.com/grou
Open Dates: 02.01-23.12 Schiphol 140km Grou/Irnsum 13km from Leeuwarden, bus 95 ap Parkstraat x 218 6 x

Haarlem – Stayokay Haarlem 40010
Jan Gijzenpad 3, 2024 CL Haarlem.
(23) 5373793 (23) 5371176
www.stayokay.com/haarlem
Open Dates: Open Times: 07.30-24.00hrs
Beds: 140 - 3x² 19x⁴ 7x⁶ 2x⁶⁺
Price Range: € 22.25-26.50 (HI-members receive € 2.50 discount p.p.p.n.; Weekend surcharge € 1) (€ 2 supplement p.p.p.n. Fri/Sat) BB inc
Directions: Schiphol 15km A Line 236 Train Station Haarlem 15km
Santpoort-Zuid 500m, Haarlem 3km
2 ap Stayokay Haarlem x 29 1 x 500m 7km

Haarlem – Stayokay Haarlem

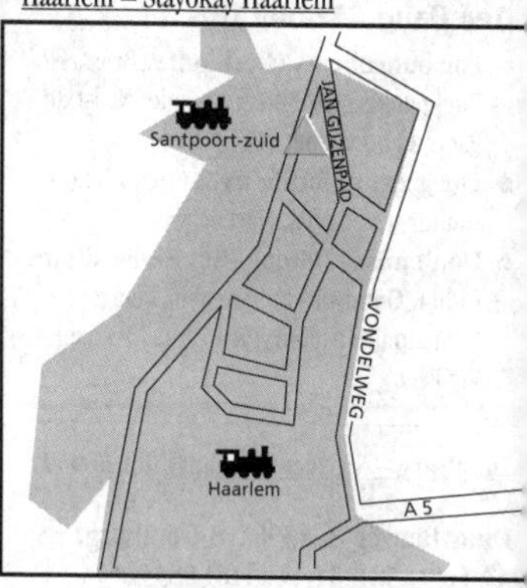

Haarlem... Travel Tips

- **For budget eats check out...** The hostel, the city centre with numerous restaurants and bars
- **For great nightlife try...** Hostel bar "The Shuffle", Claus bowling centre, Bars/discos/cinemas/terraces in city centre, Zandvoort boulevard & casino
- **Don't miss...** Historic city centre, Keukenhof flower garden, Zandvoort beach resort, Zandvoort F1 race circuit, Haarlem Jazz weekend, Haarlem Cartoon weekend, Haarlem try-out weekend, City walks in "hofjes", Dune reserve (cycling, walking - 2km), Frans Hals/Teylers museum

▲ **Heeg** – Stayokay Heeg – 40041
t Eilân 65, 8621 CT Heeg.
(515) 442258 (515) 442550
heeg@stayokay.com
www.stayokay.com/heeg
Open Dates: 25.03-30.10
Schiphol 100km Sneek 10km
500m x 188
4 x 100m

Heemskerk – Stayokay Heemskerk
40027
Tolweg 9, 1967 NG Heemskerk.
(251) 232288 (251) 251024
www.stayokay.com/heemskerk
Open Dates: Closed until 01.05.06 due to renovation Open Times: 07.00-24.00hrs
Beds: 199 - 10x 1x 8x 1x 11x
Price Range: € 21-26.50 (HI-members receive € 2.50 discount p.p.p.n.) (€ 1.50 supplement p.p.p.n. Fri/Sat) BBinc
Directions: 2W from city centre Schiphol 25km
A Train station Beverwijk - Line 74
IJmuiden Beverwijk 2km 74
20m ap Jan van Kuikweg
6 x
1km 4km

Heemskerk – Stayokay Heemskerk

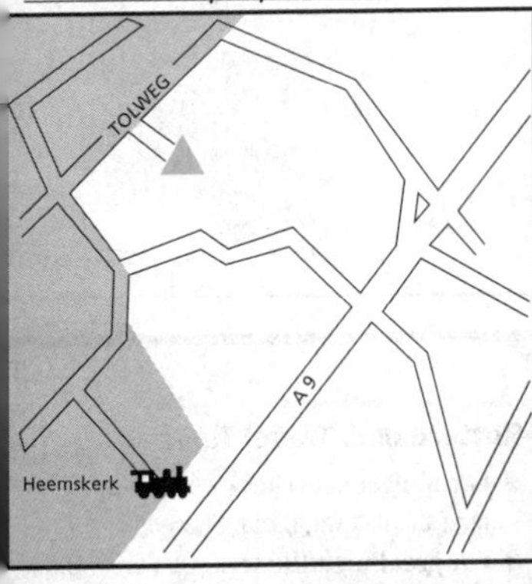

Heemskerk... Travel Tips

- **For budget eats check out...** The hostel
- **For great nightlife try...** The hostel is situated in a medieval castle so check out the castle bar, Waagplein (Alkmaar)
- **Don't miss...** Amsterdam, Haarlem, Alkmaar, Beach, Forest & dunes, Lake, Karting centre/Laser game, Swimming pool, Zaanse Schans

▲ **Maastricht** – Stayokay Maastricht – 40006
Maasboulevard 101,6211 JW Maastricht
(43) 3503270 (43) 3503277
www.stayokay.com/maastricht
Open Dates: Expected opening - August 2006
maastricht 15km x 192

Nijverdal – Stayokay Nijverdal 40042
Duivenbreeweg 43, 7441 EA Nijverdal.
(548) 612252 (548) 615372
www.stayokay.com/nijverdal
Open Dates: 01.03-31.10
Open Times:
Beds: 136 - 1x 22x 1x 5x
Price Range: € 21-26.25 (HI-members receive € 2.50 discount p.p.p.n.) (€ 1.50 supplement p.p.p.n. Fri/Sat) BBinc
Directions: Schiphol 155km
Nijverdal 2km Almelo 71 - 5min, Rijssen 93 - 5min ap Molenweg x 24
3 x

Nijverdal – Stayokay Nijverdal

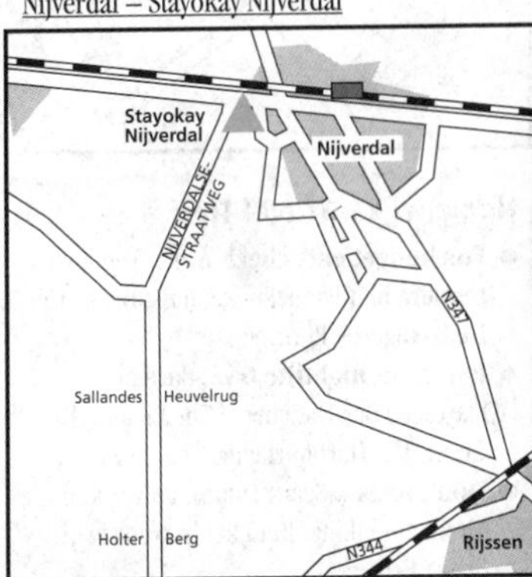

Nijverdal... Travel Tips

- **For budget eats check out...** The hostel restaurant (3 course dinner €9.75), De Strooppot Pancake Restaurant, Sirtaki, Stromboli Pizzeria
- **For great nightlife try...** De Lantaarn (live-music), Discotheek Lucky, Bills Bar
- **Don't miss...** Hellendoorn Adventure Park, Kartplaza Actionworld, Mountainbiking in the Salland rolling hills

Noordwijk – Stayokay Noordwijk 40031

Langevelderlaan 45, 2204 BC Noordwijk.
(252) 372920 (252) 377061
www.stayokay.com/noordwijk
Open Dates: 12 Open Times: 08.00-24.00hrs
Beds: 140 - 3x2 7x4 5x6 9x6+
Price Range: € 21-26.50 (HI-members receive € 2.50 discount p.p.p.n.) BBinc
Directions: Schiphol 35km Leiden 15km 57 ap Brink (30 minutes walk)
R CC 3 x
1.5km

Noordwijk – Stayokay Noordwijk

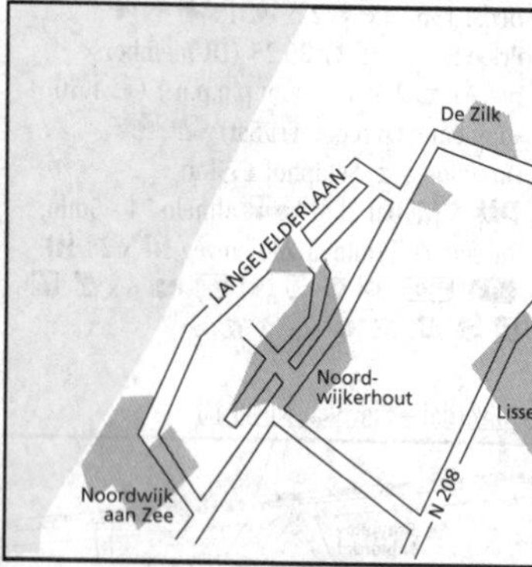

Noordwijk... Travel Tips

- **For budget eats check out...** The hostel restaurant, 't Pannekoekenhuis, Brasserie De Orangerie, El Gringo
- **For great nightlife try...** Surfbar Stayokay, Bar-Dancing at The Champ, De Grent, The Harbourlights, The Coast
- **Don't miss...** Sea & Dunes, Power kiting, Mountain biking, Bulb fields, Noordwijk Space Expo

Rotterdam – Stayokay Rotterdam 40003

Rochussenstraat 107-109, 3015 EH Rotterdam.
(10) 4365763 (10) 4365569
www.stayokay.com/rotterdam
Open Dates: 12 Open Times:
Beds: 138 - 2x2 4x4 5x6 11x6+
Price Range: € 20-25.75 (HI-members receive € 2.50 discount p.p.p.n.) (€ 1 supplement p.p.p.n. Fri/Sat) BBinc
Directions: 2SW from city centre
Schiphol 90km A Line 33 2km
Rotterdam Europoort 20km, Hoek van Holland 30km Rotterdam CS 2km
44 20m ap Dijkzigt/Erasmus MC 4 150m ap Mathenessen Laan U Red Line ap Dijkzigt 10m x 6 R CC
TV 1 x

Rotterdam – Stayokay Rotterdam

Rotterdam... Travel Tips

- **For budget eats check out...** Dizzy Jazzcafé, Ratown, Bazar, Sherry's
- **For great nightlife try...** Off Corso, Old Harbour, Bootleg, Water Front, Baja Beachclub
- **Don't miss...** The Netherlands Architecture Institute (NAI), Kunsthal Rotterdam, Rotterdam Zoo, Boymans Van Beuningen Museum, Euromast and space adventure, Maritime Museum Rotterdam, Het Schielandshuis, Cube Houses, Erasmus Bridge, Kinderdijk Windmills

▲ **Scheemda** – Stayokay Scheemda – 40043 (FNM)
Esbörgstraat 16, 9679 ZG Scheemda.
(597) 591255 (597) 591132
www.stayokay.com/scheemda
Open Dates: 01.04-01.11 (03.01-15.12)
Schiphol 240km Groningen CS - Scheemda 30km 79 - Winschoten 20 min, Groningen 75min ap Esborgstraat
x 78 R CC
2 x

▲ **Sneek** – Stayokay Sneek 40035 (FNM)
Oude Oppenhuizerweg 20, 8606 JC Sneek.
(515) 412132 (515) 412188
www.stayokay.com/sneek
Open Dates: 26.03-31.10 (R)
Schiphol 120km Sneek CS 2km
98 or 99 150m x 112 R
CC
1.5km

Soest – Stayokay Soest 40017 (FNM)
Bosstraat 16, 3766 AG Soest.
(35) 6012296 (35) 6028921
www.stayokay.com/soest
Open Dates: 10.03-01.11 (12)
Open Times: 07.00-00.30hrs
Beds: 142 - 9x2 14x4 6x6 1x6+
Price Range: € 21.00-26.50 (HI-members receive € 2.50 discount p.p.p.n.) (€ 1.50 supplement p.p.p.n. Fri/Sat) BBinc
Directions: Schiphol 50km
Soest-Zuid 500m 70, 72 - Amersfoort-Hilversum x 29 R CC
7 x
1.5km

Soest – Stayokay Soest

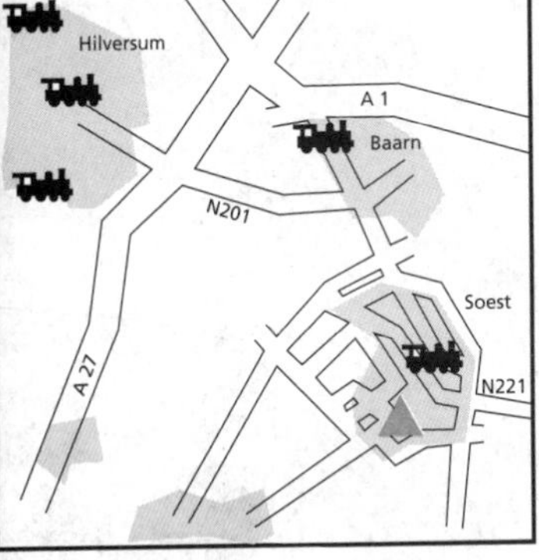

Soest... Travel Tips

- **For budget eats check out...** McDonalds, Pizzeria, Snackbar
- **For great nightlife try...** Amersfoort, Utrecht, Amsterdam
- **Don't miss...** Castles, Fish Village Spakenburg (15km), Amersfoort, Dunes (1km), Flevopolder reclaimed land & Funpark (40km), Six Flags Holland, Amersfoort Zoo, Amersfoort historic city centre & high architecture suburbs, Utrecht architecture & Rietveld

Terschelling – Stayokay Terschelling
40025 (FNM)
Burg Van Heusdenweg 39,
8881 EE West-Terschelling.
(562) 442338 (562) 443312
www.stayokay.com/terschelling
Open Dates: 01.03-31.10 (12)
Open Times:
Beds: 144 - 4x2 23x4 3x6 2x6+
Price Range: € 21-26.50 (HI-members receive € 2.50 discount p.p.p.n.) (€ 1.50 supplement p.p.p.n. Fri/Sat) BBinc
Directions: 0.15W from city centre
Schiphol 130km
Harlingen-Terschelling. Normal ferry 2hrs, Fast ferry 45mins Harlingen-Haven any from ap Dellewal stop
R CC
8 500m

Terschelling – Stayokay Terschelling

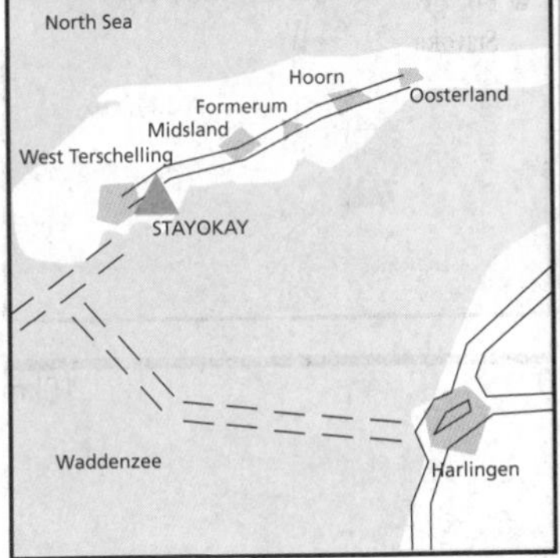

Terschelling... Travel Tips

- **For budget eats check out...** The hostel, de Grië, Restaurant-steakhouse Pickwick, Amsterdamsche Koffijhuis, De Drie Gapen
- **For great nightlife try...** Braskoer, OKA 18, WYB, Café Ké Rijf
- **Don't miss...** the beach, Museum 't Behoudenhuys, Fishing museum Aike van Stien, horseriding or cycling around the island

Texel – Stayokay Texel 40032
Schansweg 7, 1791 LK Den Burg, Texel.
(222) 315441 (222) 313889
www.stayokay.com/texel
Open Dates: Open Times: 07.30-00.30hrs; 00.30-07.30hrs key service
Beds: 139 - 1x3 9x4 1x5 12x6 3x6+
Price Range: € 21-26.50 (HI-members receive € 2.50 discount p.p.p.n.) (€ 1.50 supplement p.p.p.n. Fri/Sat) BBinc
Directions: Schiphol 95km Den Helder to Texel (20 min.) Den Helder 10km 29 ap De Keet x 10 3 x 6km

Texel – Stayokay Texel

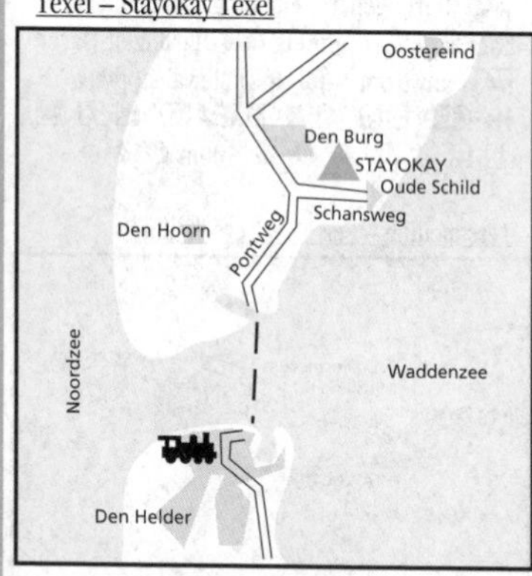

Texel... Travel Tips

- **For budget eats check out...** The hostel, Pizzeria San Remo, Niros the Greek, Café 12 Balcken
- **For great nightlife try...** Question Plaza, Jelleboog, Grooten Slock, Balcker, De Toekomst
- **Don't miss...** Ecomare, Maritiem Jutters Museum, TX 10, Calluna Park

▲ **Valkenswaard** – Stayokay Valkenswaard 40044
Past. Heerkensdreef 20,
5552 BG Valkenswaard.
(40) 2015334 (40) 2047932
www.stayokay.com/valkenswaard
Open Dates: () Schiphol 85km, Eindhoven 10km A 171, 172, 177 from Eindhoven 10km Eindhoven 10km 171, 172, 177 500m x 146 3 x

New Zealand

Youth Hostels Association of New Zealand Inc
PO Box 436,
Christchurch,
New Zealand.

t (64) (3) 3799970
f (64) (3) 3794415
e info@yha.co.nz
w www.yha.co.nz

YHA New Zealand National Reservations Centre
PO Box 436,
Christchurch,
New Zealand.

t (64) (3) 3799808
f (64) (3) 3794415
e book@yha.co.nz

A copy of the Hostel Directory for this Country can be obtained from:
The National Office

National Tourist Authority/Board:	www.purenz.com
Capital:	Wellington
Language:	English
Currency:	NZ$
Population:	4,000,000
Size:	268,676 sq km
Telephone Country Code:	64
eKit Access Number:	0800-445-108

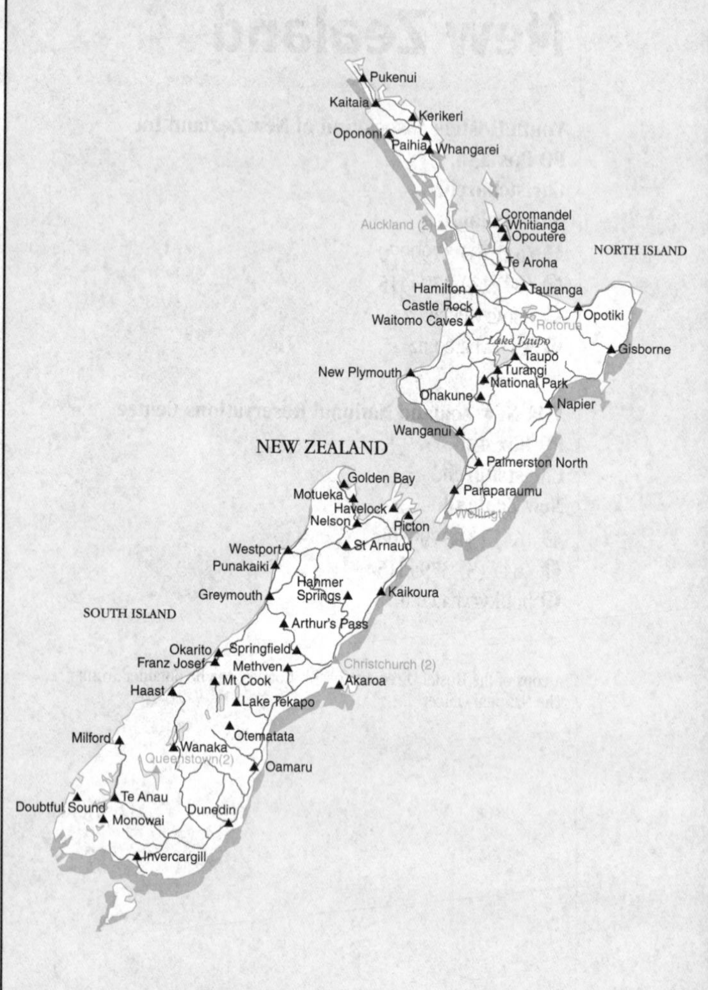

HI Suggests...

Revelling as a movie director's playground, New Zealand's beautiful and diverse landscapes have recently gained worldwide recognition, featuring as the backdrop for the Oscar winning 'Lord of the Rings' film trilogy. The spectacular mountains, breathtaking expanses, forests and startlingly blue lakes, which feature in the film, are all right here for you to experience!

New Zealand lies in the South Pacific Ocean and consists of two major Islands – North Island and South Island, which stretches over 1,600km from top to bottom. There is also the smaller Stewart Island. Because of New Zealand's relatively small size, everything is easily accessible, and with a population of 4 million people (approximately 74% of the population live in the North Island) and 49 million sheep (that's 12.25 sheep per person), New Zealand still remains a rural country.

While New Zealand has a fairly recent history, with the first European settlers arriving in the early 1800's, Polynesian settlers, who were to become the Maori, arrived in New Zealand from the Pacific Islands as early as 800AD. The influence of their culture and language is everywhere. The depth and richness of it is displayed in many ways including traditional Maori arts, such as weaving and moko (tattoo), and in the language as well as in the Maori customs of the Marae.

Visitors to New Zealand can be assured of a very special welcome, New Zealanders are well known for their hospitality, creativity and positive approach to life. This easy-going attitude combines with a sense of adventure to bring the real New Zealand experience to life.

There is plenty to see and do in New Zealand, especially if you're after action and adventure – New Zealand is a Mecca for thrill seekers! Activities include bungy jumping, rafting and jet boating to extreme skiing. Alternatively, for relaxation, explore a beach, sail a yacht or sample New Zealand's cuisine, including fresh seafood and wine tasting at one of the many wineries. New Zealand also offers plenty of art and cultural experiences. To gain an insight into the Maori culture, attend a 'hangi' or visit a Marae to experience their traditions and customs. If you're in the major cities you will find a variety of casinos, cabarets, pubs and live performances to choose from. But, there is no better way of experiencing the real New Zealand than heading outdoors and exploring our coastlines, National Parks, rainforests and alpine areas by hiking or choosing from a variety of walk's available, some of which are said to be the finest in the world.

Because New Zealand is such a compact country, travelling – whether by plane, bus, rail, car or bicycle – is affordable and efficient. It is best to book accommodation and transport in advance, especially, if you're travelling during peak periods (October-March) and visiting Winter Resorts between June and August. As there really is so much to explore and experience in New Zealand, make sure you allow at least six weeks for a comprehensive trip.

You can find out a lot more on our website - a visit to www.HIhostels.com is essential for planning your trip!

Pour en savoir plus, rendez-vous sur notre site Internet, www.HIhostels.com une visite incontournable pour préparer votre voyage!

Viele weitere Informationen auf unserer Website: www.HIhostels.com - unverzichtbar für die Reiseplanung!

Puedes averiguar mucho más en nuestro sitio web. Es imprescindible que visites la página www.HIhostels.com para planear tu viaje.

▲ **Arthur's Pass** – Arthur's Pass Alpine YHA – 41015
Main Rd, Arthur's Pass.
t (3) 3189230 f (3) 3189000
e yha.arthurspass@yha.co.nz
w www.yha.co.nz
Open Dates: 12 Arthur's Pass 500m
Atomic Shuttles, Alpine Coach, Coast to Coast 20m ap Arthur's Pass Store x 17

▲ **Auckland** – City YHA 41001
18 Liverpool St, Corner of City Rd,
PO Box 68-149, Auckland.
(9) 3092802 (9) 3735083
yha.aucklandcity@yha.co.nz
www.yha.co.nz
Open Dates: Auckland International 23km A Super Shuttle Britomart 2km Intercity 500m ap Sky City 0.6N
x 160

Auckland – International YHA 41010
5 Turner St, PO Box 68-149, Auckland.
(9) 3028200 (9) 3028205
yha.aucklandint@yha.co.nz
www.yha.co.nz
Open Dates: Open Times: 07.00-23.00hrs (guest access)
Beds: 170 - 14x2 25x4 4x6
Price Range: $25-44
Directions: 0.5N from city centre
Auckland International 23km
A Super Shuttle Britomart 2km
Intercity 500m ap Sky City x 3

Auckland – International YHA

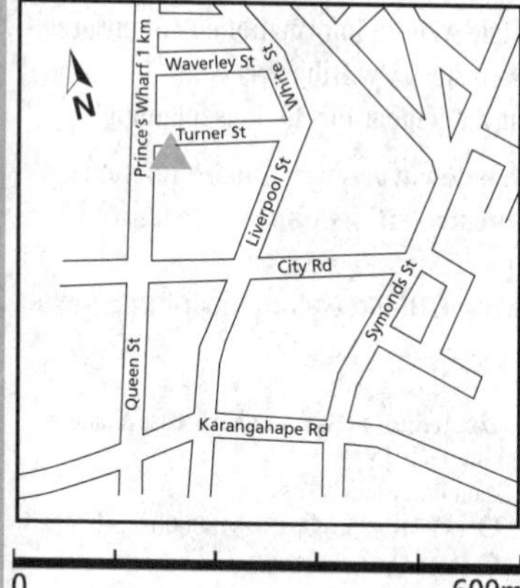

Auckland... Travel Tips

- **For budget eats check out...** Tommy's at Auckland City YHA, Kebabs on Queen, Peter's Pies, Angus Steak House, Shochiko Japanese Restaurant
- **For great nightlife try...** Embargo Bar, Globe Bar, Comedy Club, Dogs Bolix, Sky Tower & Casino
- **Don't miss...** Kelly Tarlton's Antarctic Encounter & Underwater World, Fullers Cruises, Devonport Village, Sky Tower, West Coast Beaches, Viaduct Basin, Auckland Explorer Bus, Stardome Observatory, Auckland Museum & Domain, Auckland Zoo

▲ **CastleRock (Assoc)** – CastleRock Adventure Lodge – 41058
1250 Owairaka Valley Rd, R.D.7, Te Awamutu.
(7) 8722509 (7) 8722507
info@castlerockadventure.co.nz
www.yha.co.nz
Open Dates: Hamilton 40km Te Awamutu 21km Intercity/Newmans, Waitomo Wanderer 21km ap Te Awamutu for Intercity or Front Gate for Waitomo Wanderer
21SE x 38 1 x

Christchurch – City Central YHA 41006
273 Manchester St, Christchurch.
(3) 3799535 (3) 3799537
yha.christchurchcity@yha.co.nz
www.yha.co.nz
Open Dates: Open Times: 07.00-24.00hrs
Beds: 166 - 28x2 4x3 15x4 3x5 2x6
Price Range: $23-37.50
Directions: 0.05NE from city centre
Christchurch International 10km
A City Bus (Airport Bus) or Super Shuttle (to door) 100m Christchurch 4km ap All trams U New Regent Street 20m x 2 20m 10km

Christchurch – City Central YHA

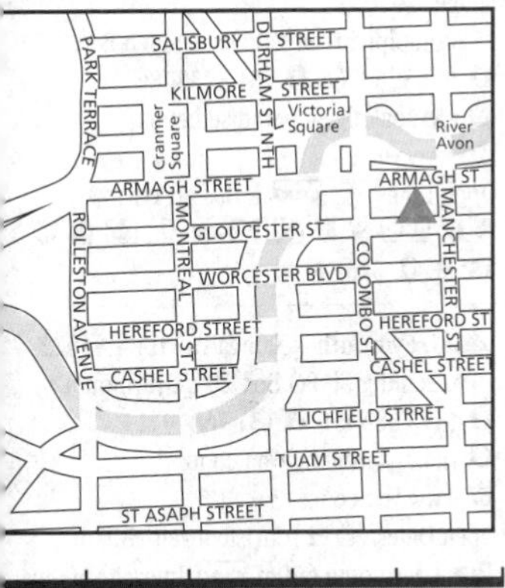

Christchurch – Rolleston House YHA
41004
5 Worcester Blvd (Corner Rolleston Ave), Christchurch.
(3) 3666564 (3) 3655589
yha.rollestonhouse@yha.co.nz
www.yha.co.nz
Open Dates: Open Times: 08.00-10.00hrs; 15.00-22.00hrs (guest access)
Beds: 49 - 2x2 2x3 5x4 2x5 1x6 1x6+
Price Range: $19-35 per person
Directions: 0.5W from city centre
Christchurch International 8km
A Shuttle ap YH Christchurch 2km
x 2 R CC 8 P 1km 10km

Christchurch – Rolleston House YHA

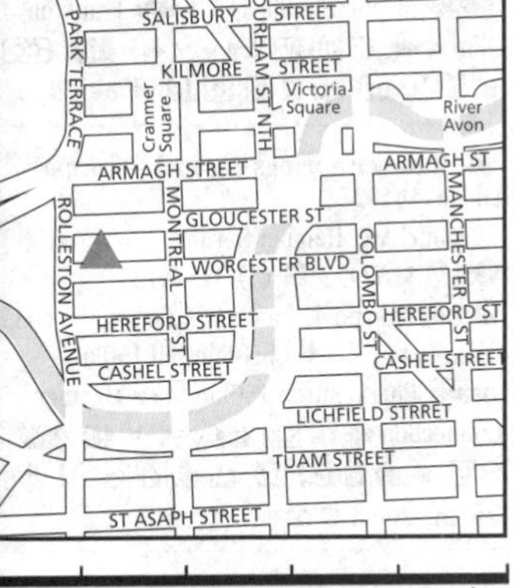

Christchurch... Travel Tips

- **For budget eats check out...** Sampan House, City Seafood Market, Oxford on Avon Restaurant, Osaka Japanese Resaurant, Sophies Café
- **For great nightlife try...** The Strip (Cafés & bars on Oxford Terrace), Christchurch Casino, Theatre Royal, Court Theatre, Manchester Street (restaurants, Cafés & bars)
- **Don't miss...** Christchurch Cathedral, Cathedral Square & the Wizard, Christchurch Arts Centre & Weekend Markets, Antarctic Centre, Christchurch Museum & Botanic Gardens, Christchurch Gondola, Orana Wildlife Park, Nga Hau E Wha National Marae, Willowbank Wildlife Reserve & Kiwis by Night, Banks Peninsula

▲ **Coromandel (Assoc)** – Tidewater Tourist Park – 41016
270 Tiki Rd, Coromandel.
(7) 8668888 (7) 8667231
tidewatr@world-net.co.nz
www.yha.co.nz
Open Dates: Auckland 170km 0.25N
x 28 CC P 250m 3km

▲ **Doubtful Sound (Assoc)** – Fiordland Navigator – 41017
Pearl Harbour, Manapouri.
(800) 656502 (3) 2496603
info@realjourneys.co.nz
www.yha.co.nz
Open Dates: 01.10-30.04 Coach connections available from Queenstown and Te Anau (must be booked at time of reservation) ap Manapouri x 70 R CC (BD) P

▲ **Dunedin** – Stafford Gables YHA – 41018
71 Stafford St, Dunedin.
(3) 4741919 (3) 4741919
yha.dunedin@yha.co.nz
www.yha.co.nz
Open Dates: Dunedin International 25km A Airport Shuttles ap hostel Dunedin 1km St Claire 200m ap Jetty Street 1S x 64 R CC 8 P 1.5km 5km

Franz Josef – Glacier YHA – 41019
2-4 Cron St, Franz Josef Village.
(3) 7520754 (3) 7520080
yha.franzjosef@yha.co.nz
www.yha.co.nz
Open Dates: 12 Open Times: Summer 08.00-21.00hrs; Winter 08.00-20.00hrs (guest access)
Beds: 112 - 1x1 20x2 8x4 3x5 1x6 1x6+
Price Range: $22-45 per person
Directions: 0.5SE from city centre
Christchurch 405km Intercity, Atomic, Kiwi, Magic 50m ap YH x 2

Franz Josef – Glacier YHA

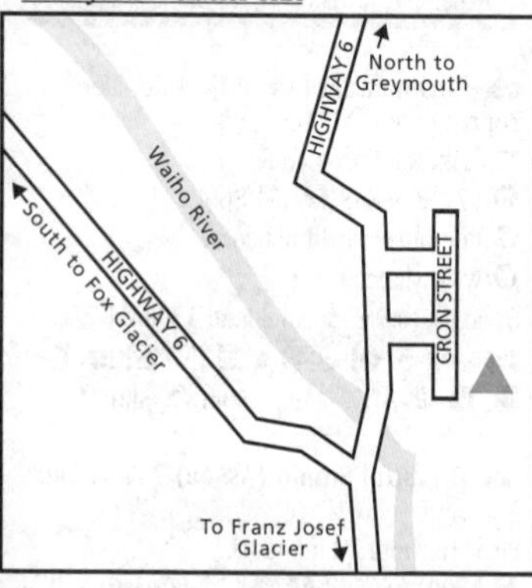

Franz Josef... Travel Tips
- **For budget eats check out...** Cheeky Kea Café, Alice May, Landing, Café Franz
- **For great nightlife try...** Blue Ice Café & Bar, Alice May Café & Bar
- **Don't miss...** Franz Josef Glacier, Kayaking, Bush walks, Guided glacier walks, Wildlife tours, Scenic flights, River rafting, Horseriding, Skydiving, Fishing

▲ **Gisborne (Assoc)** – Gisborne YHA – 41020
32 Harris St, Gisborne.
(6) 8673269 (6) 8673296
yha.gisborne@clear.net.nz
www.yha.co.nz
Open Dates: 12 Gisborne 6km Port Gisborne 100m Gisborne 1.5km City Buses 20m ap YH 0.5N x 34 1.5km 1km

▲ **Golden Bay (Assoc)** – Annies Nirvana Lodge – 41073
25 Motupipi Street, Takaka, Golden Bay.
(3) 5258766 (3) 5258786
nirvanalodge@paradise.net.nz
www.yha.co.nz
Open Dates: 12 K Bus ap YH x 32 5km

▲ **Greymouth** – Kainga-ra YHA – 41022
15 Alexander St, PO Box 299, Greymouth.
(3) 7684951 (3) 7684941
yha.greymouth@yha.co.nz
www.yha.co.nz
Open Dates: 12 Christchurch 280km Greymouth 600m Intercity 600m; All other buses (Atomic, Kiwi Experience, Magic, Coast to Coast, Alpine Coach) ap YH 0.25SE x 42 1km 3km

▲ **Haast (Assoc)** – Haast Lodge – 41023
Marks Rd, Haast.
(3) 7500703 (3) 7500718
haastway@xtra.co.nz www.yha.co.nz
Open Dates: 12 Intercity, Atomic, Magic Bus, Kiwi Experience 150m ap Mid way between Fox Glacier and Wanaka 0.15W x 34 5km

▲ **Hamilton** – Helen Heywood YHA – 41024
1190 Victoria St, Hamilton.
(7) 8380009 (7) 8380837
yha.hamilton@yha.co.nz www.yha.co.nz
Open Dates: 12 Hamilton 12km A Airport Shuttle ap YH Frankton 3km 1.5km 1N x 24

▲ **Hanmer Springs (Assoc)** – Kakapo Lodge – 41025
14 Amuri Ave, Hanmer Springs.
(3) 3157472 (3) 3157472
stay-kakapo@xtra.co.nz www.yha.co.nz
Open Dates: 12 Christchurch 150km A Christchurch 150km Hanmer Connection ap YH 0.2S x 55 200m

Havelock (Assoc) – Rutherford YHA and Travel – 41026
46 Main Rd, Havelock.
(3) 5742104 (3) 5742109
yha@rutherfordtravel.co.nz
www.yha.co.nz
Open Dates: Picton Ferry Terminal 35km Blenheim 42km Intercity 100m, Kiwilink & Knightline ap YH x 30 R CC 10km

---

Invercargill (Assoc) – Tuatara Lodge – 41027
30-32 Dee St, Invercargill.
(3) 2140954 (3) 2140956
tuataralodge@xtra.co.nz
www.yha.co.nz
Open Dates: Invercargill 3km A Spitfire Shuttle picks up/drops off at hostel Stewart Island Ferry at Bluff Harbour 27km Invercargill 100m All City buses pick up/drop off outside front door x 100 R CC 2km 8km

---

Kaikoura – Maui YHA – 41028
270 Esplanade, Kaikoura.
(3) 3195931 (3) 3196921
yha.kaikoura@yha.co.nz
www.yha.co.nz
Open Dates: Kaikoura 2.2km 2N x 39 R CC 800m 100m

Kaitaia (Assoc) – Mainstreet Lodge – 41029
235 Commerce Street, Kaitaia.
(9) 4081275 (9) 4081100
mainstreet@xtra.co.nz www.yha.co.nz
Open Dates: Kaitaia (Domestic) 15km Intercity, Northliner 400m ap Travel Centre 0.5N x 100 R CC 1 x 15km 15km

---

Kerikeri – Kerikeri YHA – 41030
144 Kerikeri Rd, Kerikeri, Bay of Islands.
(9) 4079391 (9) 4079328
yha.kerikeri@yha.co.nz
www.yha.co.nz
Open Dates: KeriKeri (Domestic) 2km A Airport Shuttle (collects from hostel) Intercity, Northliner 500m ap Kerikeri - Cobham Road or YH 0.5NE x 36 R CC 1km 20km

---

Lake Tekapo – Lake Tekapo YHA – 41059
3 Simpson Lane, Lake Tekapo.
(3) 6806857 (3) 6806664
yha.laketekapo@yha.co.nz
www.yha.co.nz
Open Dates: 0.2W x 30 R CC

Methven (Assoc) – Snow Denn Lodge YHA – 41031
Cnr Bank & McMillan Streets, Methven.
(3) 3028999 (3) 3028997
info@methvenaccommodation.co.nz
www.yha.co.nz
Open Dates: Christchurch International 90km A Pick up at YH Intercity 400m ap Methven I-Site 0.05S x 42 R CC (B) 1 x

---

Milford (Assoc) – "Milford Wanderer" Boat – 41032
Milford Harbour, PO Box 12, Milford.
(800) 656501 (3) 2497022
info@realjourneys.co.nz
www.yha.co.nz
Open Dates: 01.10-30.04 A Courtesy Coach 2km Coach connections available from Queenstown and Te Anau (at extra cost, must be booked at time of reservation) x 61 R CC (BD)

NEW ZEALAND – NOUVELLE ZELANDE – NEUSEELAND – NUEVA ZELANDA

▲ **Monowai (Assoc)** – Borland Lodge – 41033
Borland-Monowai Road, Lake Monowai, Blackmount.
(3) 2255464 (3) 2255464
borland@ihug.co.nz www.yha.co.nz
Open Dates: Queenstown, Invercargill Shuttle bus Te Anau to Invercargill 12km ap Borland Lodge turnoff, pick up by arrangement 47N x 35 R CC TV 1 x i P

▲ **Motueka (Assoc)** – Bakers Lodge – 41034
4 Poole St, Motueka.
(3) 5280102 (3) 5280103
bakers@motueka.co.nz www.yha.co.nz
Open Dates: Nelson 45km
A Atomic, K-Bus ap YH Atomic, K-Bus ap YH 0.1N x 71 R CC TV i 8 P 1km 2km

Mount Cook – Mt Cook YHA – 41035
Corner Bowen & Kitchener Drives, Mount Cook.
(3) 4351820 (3) 4351821
yha.mtcook@yha.co.nz www.yha.co.nz
Open Dates: Open Times: Summer 08.00-21.00hrs; Winter 09.00-19.30hrs (guest access)
Beds: 72 - 8x2 2x4 6x6+
Price Range: $24-32
Directions: 1E from city centre
Newmans, Great Sights and Cook Connection all pick-up/drop-off at hostel
x 1 R CC TV i 8 P

Mount Cook – Mt Cook YHA

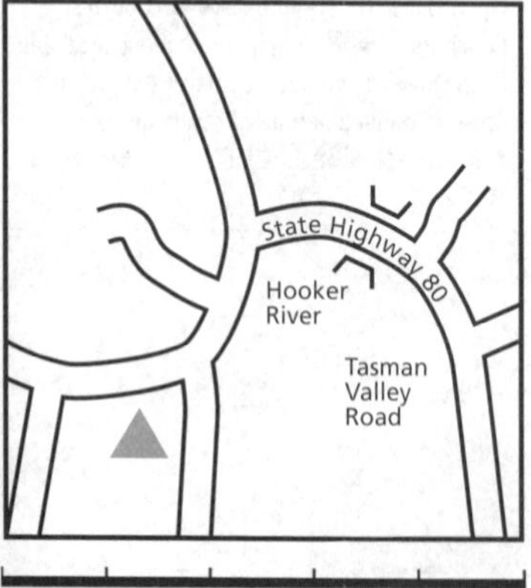

Mount Cook... Travel Tips

- **For budget eats check out...** The Chamois Bar, Mt Cook YHA Hostel Shop
- **For great nightlife try...** The Chamois Bar
- **Don't miss...** Mt Cook - NZ's highest mountain, Scenic flights, A variety of short & long walks, Hooker & Tasman Glaciers, Glacier Lakes, Overnight & extended tramps in the National Park, Advanced & cross-country skiing, Beautiful alpine scenery & wildlife, Horse trekking, Alpine climbing

▲ **Napier** – Napier YHA – 41036
277 Marine Pde, Napier.
(6) 8357039 (6) 8354641
yha.napier@yha.co.nz www.yha.co.nz
Open Dates: Napier/Hastings (Domestic) 6km A Shuttle ap YH 200m 0.2S x 49 R CC TV i 8 P 1km 50m

▲ **National Park (Assoc)** – National Park Backpackers – 41072
Finlay Street, National Park Village.
(7) 8922870 (7) 8922870
nat-park.backpackers@xtra.co.nz
www.yha.co.nz
Open Dates: National Park 800m 0.3S x 96 R CC TV i P

Nelson – Nelson Central YHA – 41037
59 Rutherford St, Nelson.
(3) 5459988 (3) 5459989
yha.nelson@yha.co.nz www.yha.co.nz
Open Dates: Open Times: 08.00-21.30hrs (guest access)
Beds: 92 - 1x1 19x2 3x3 5x4 3x5 1x6
Price Range: $21-40 per person
Directions: Nelson 6km
A Supershuttle ap YH x 5 R CC TV 1 x i 8 2km 5km

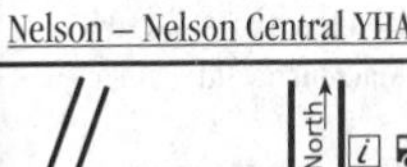

Nelson – Nelson Central YHA

Nelson... Travel Tips

- **For budget eats check out...** Sports Café, Café Affair, Lambrettas, Café Metro, Poppy Thai
- **For great nightlife try...** Victorian Rose Pub (Jazz & Blues nights), Artery (Dance parties), Shark Pool Bar, Movie Theatre, Bridge St. Nightlife Area
- **Don't miss...** World of Wearable Arts, Kayaking & walking in the Abel Tasman National Park, Skydiving, 4WD motor bike excursions, Horse trekking, White water rafting, Local art & craft shops & exhibitions, Wine tours, Orchard & scenic tours, Weekend markets

▲ **New Plymouth (Assoc)** – Egmont Eco Lodge – 41038
12 Clawton St, New Plymouth.
(6) 7535720 (6) 7535782
egmontlodge@taranaki-bakpak.co.nz
www.yha.co.nz
Open Dates: New Plymouth (Domestic) 10km 1.5km 1.5N x 60 R CC 2 x TV 1km 1km

▲ **Oamaru** – Red Kettle YHA – 41039
Corner Reed & Cross Streets, Oamaru.
(3) 4345008 (3) 4345008
yha.oamaru@yha.co.nz www.yha.co.nz
Open Dates: 0.5SW x 19 R CC 300m 1km

▲ **Ohakune (Assoc)** – Matai Lodge YHA – 41040
Corner of Clyde & Rata St, Ohakune.
(6) 3859169 (6) 3859169
matai.lodge@xtra.co.nz
www.yha.co.nz
Open Dates: Palmerston North (Domestic) 200km A Bus drops off 50m Ohakune 2km Intercity 50m 0.3SE x 80 R CC TV P 800m

△ *Okarito (Assoc) – 41041*
Palmerston Street, Okarito.
(3) 7534151
kotukulodge@yahoo.co.nz
www.yha.co.nz
Open Dates: No public transport to Okarito ap 13km from the hostel at "The Forks" then walk or hitch x 12 R

▲ **Opononi (Assoc)** – Okopako "The Wilderness Farm" – 41042
140 Mountain Rd, Opononi, South Hokianga.
(9) 4058815 (9) 4058815
www.yha.co.nz
Open Dates: keriKeri 84km A West Coaster, Northliner, Intercity (Mon, Wed, Fri) Intercity, Magic Bus, Northliner 1.5km ap Mountain Road (Pick up if pre-arranged) 6.5E x 20 R CC (BD) P 6km 6km

▲ **Opotiki (Assoc)** – Opotiki Holiday Park – 41043
Potts Avenue, Opotiki.
(7) 3156050 (7) 3156050
opotiki.holidays@xtra.co.nz
www.yha.co.nz
Open Dates: Intercity 1.5km (free pick up on request) 0.25NW x 19 R CC TV P 2.5km

▲ **Opoutere** – Opoutere YHA – 41044
389 Opoutere Rd, Opoutere. PO Box 36, Whangamata.
(7) 8659072 (7) 8656172
yha.opoutere@yha.co.nz
www.yha.co.nz
Open Dates: 12 Hamilton (Domestic) 140km Auckland/Tauranga
Frankton/Hamilton Intercity, Go Kiwi Shuttle, Whamgamata Taxi ap YH 16km
16N x 40 R CC
P 500m 1km

▲ **Otematata (Assoc)** – Country Inn – 41045
11-12 Rata Drive, Otematata.
(3) 4387797 (3) 4387792
enquiries@otematatacountryinn.co.nz
www.yha.co.nz
Open Dates: 12 Christchurch/Dunedin
Oamaru 100km Mt Cook Connection ap YH 1S x 28 R
CC TV P
500m

▲ **Paihia** – Lodge Eleven YHA – 41046
Cnr Kings Rd and MacMurray Rd, Paihia, Bay of Islands.
(9) 4027487 (9) 4027587
yha.paihia@yha.co.nz www.yha.co.nz
Open Dates: 12 KeriKeri 35km
A Airport Shuttle pick-up/drop-off at hostel Paihia 18km 0.8NE x 55
R CC TV 8
P 400m 400m

▲ **Palmerston North (Assoc)** – Pepper Tree YHA – 41047
121 Grey St, Palmerston North.
(6) 3554054 (6) 3554063
peppertreehostel@clear.net.nz
www.yha.co.nz
Open Dates: 12 Palmerston North 2km
Palmerston North 2km 1km
x 35 R TV
8 P 2km 40km

▲ **Paraparaumu (Assoc)** – Barnacles Seaside Inn – 41048
3 Marine Parade, Paraparaumu Beach.
(4) 9025856; (0800) 555856
(4) 9025856 stay@seasideyha.co.nz
www.yha.co.nz
Open Dates: Wellington International 55km Wellington, Inter-Islander Ferry Terminal 45km Pick up by prior arrangement 3.5km 71, 72 from Train Station 3.5km (Courtesy pick-up if advised at time of booking) 0.3S x 43

▲ **Picton (Assoc)** – Wedgwood House YHA – 41049
10 Dublin St, Picton.
(3) 5737797 (3) 5736426
wedgwoodhouse@xtra.co.nz
www.yha.co.nz
Open Dates: Picton (Koromiko) (Domestic) 5km A Sounds Air drop at hostel Picton 500m Picton 250m 500m 0.03NE x 38
2km 200m

▲ **Pukenui (Assoc)** – Pukenui Lodge – 41050
Cnr State Hwy 1 & Wharf Rd, Pukenui Village, Houhora Harbour.
(9) 4098837 (9) 4098704
pukenui@igrin.co.nz www.yha.co.nz
Open Dates: Northline express or Intercity to Kaitaia 42km; from Kaitaia, take Sand Safaris, Cape Runner Shuttles ap YH (R). 42km 42N x 16

▲ **Punakaiki (Assoc)** – Te Nikau Retreat – 41051
Hartmount Place, Punakaiki.
(3) 7311111 (3) 7311102
www.yha.co.nz
Open Dates: Christchurch 300km Greymouth 50km Intercity, Atomic Shuttles 3km ap Punakaiki 3S x 30 1 x
1km 400m

Queenstown – YHA Queenstown Lakefront
41007
88-90 Lake Esplanade, Queenstown.
(3) 4428413 (3) 4426561
yha.queenstown@yha.co.nz
www.yha.co.nz
Open Dates: Open Times: 06.30-22.00hrs (guest access)
Beds: 147 - 2x[1] 17x[2] 6x[3] 4x[4] 1x[5] 4x[6] 6x[6+]
Price Range: $22-32
Directions: 0.7W from city centre
Queenstown 9km A Airport Shuttle to hostel, drop off by request Intercity ap YH x 4
50m 50m

Queenstown – Queenstown YHA

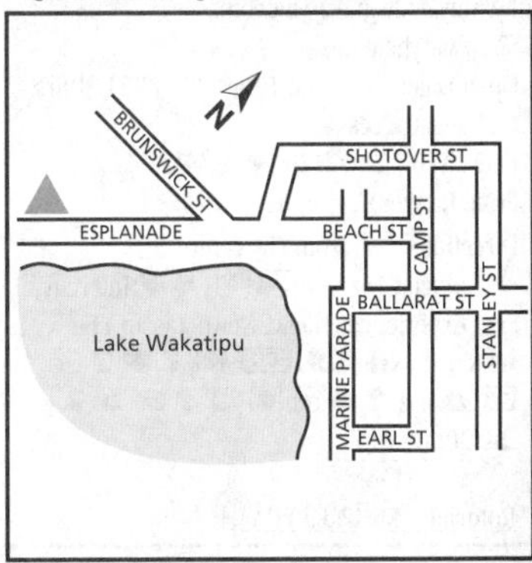

▲ **Queenstown** – YHA Queenstown Central (formerly McFees) – 41075
48A Shotover Street, Queenstown.
(3) 4427400 (3) 4427403
yha.mcfees@yha.co.nz www.yha.co.nz
Open Dates: Queenstown 9km
A Airport Shuttle to hostel, drop off by request Intercity ap YH 0.7W x 110
50m 50m

Queenstown... Travel Tips

- **For budget eats check out...** Pig & Whistle Pub, @ Thai, O'Connells Shopping Precinct (variety of foods available), Lone Star, The World
- **For great nightlife try...** The World, Winnies, Red Rock, Frasers, Chico's
- **Don't miss...** Skyline Gondola & Luge, 3 fantastic ski fields, Skydiving, Hang gliding & parasailing, The home of bungy jumping, Jet boat rides, White water rafting, River surfing & canyoning, Scenic & wine tours, TSS Earnslaw steamship cruise, Access to a multitude of tramping tracks

Rotorua – KiwiPaka YHA 41009
60 Tarewa Rd, Rotorua.
(7) 3470931 (7) 3463167
stay@kiwipaka-yha.co.nz
www.yha.co.nz
Open Dates: Open Times: 07.30-21.30hrs (guest access)
Beds: 116 - 27x 6x 4x
Price Range: $24-35 per person
Directions: 1.5S from city centre
Rotorua 15km A YH Intercity, Kiwi Experience, Magic, Newmans ap YH
x 4 R CC
1 x
20m

Rotorua – KiwiPaka YHA

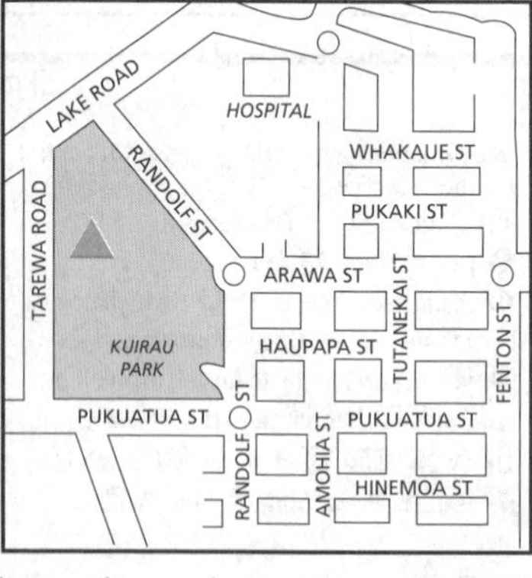

Rotorua... Travel Tips

- **For budget eats check out...** Kiwi Paka YHA Café, Zippie Central, Pig & Whistle, Freos Restaurant, Capers Café
- **For great nightlife try...** Kiwi Paka YHA Bar, Hangi and Concert, Skyline Skyrides Night Luging, Polynesian Spa, Aquatic Centre
- **Don't miss...** Waitapu Thermal Wonderland, New Zealand Maori Arts & Crafts, Waimungu Volcanic Valley, Agrodome Leisure and Adventure Park, Kaitiaki Sledging and River Adventures, Tekiri Trek Day Adventure, Polynesian Spa, Tamaki Tours Hangi & Concert, Kaituna Cascades Rafting, Skyline Luge & Gondola

▲ **Springfield (Assoc)** – Smylie's Accommodation – 41052
Main Rd, Springfield.
(3) 3184740 (3) 3184780
stay@smylies.co.nz www.yha.co.nz
Open Dates: Christchurch International 60km A Arrange with hostel to pick up Springfield 400m Coast to Coast, Atomic, Alpine Shuttles ap YH x 40
R CC
i 8 P

▲ **St Arnaud (Assoc)** – The Yellow House – 41053
Main Rd, St Arnaud,
Nelson Lakes National Park.
(3) 5211887 (3) 5211882
theyellowhouse@xtra.co.nz
www.yha.co.nz
Open Dates: Nelson (Domestic) 90km A YH Picton 130km Atomic Shuttle, Nelson Lakes Shuttle ap YH x 42
R CC (B)
i P

▲ **Taupo** – Action Downunder YHA – 41054
56 Kaimanawa St (Corner Tamamutu St), Taupo.
(7) 3783311 (7) 3789612
yhataupo@xtra.co.nz www.yha.co.nz
Open Dates: Taupo (Domestic) 7km Intercity bus depot (Free pick up by arrangement) 500m x 86
R CC i
8 P 500m

Norway

Norske Vandrerhjem - Hostelling International Norway, Torggata 1, 0181 Oslo, Norway.

t (47) 23139300

f (47) 23139350

e hostel@vandrerhjem.no

w www.vandrerhjem.no

Office Hours: Monday-Friday 08.30-16.00hrs

A copy of the Hostel Directory for this Country can be obtained from: The National Office.

National Tourist Authority/Board:	www.visitnorway.com
Capital:	Oslo
Language:	Norwegian
Currency:	NOK (krone)
Population:	4,513,000
Size:	324,219 sq km
Telephone Country Code:	47
eKit Access Number:	800-11-357

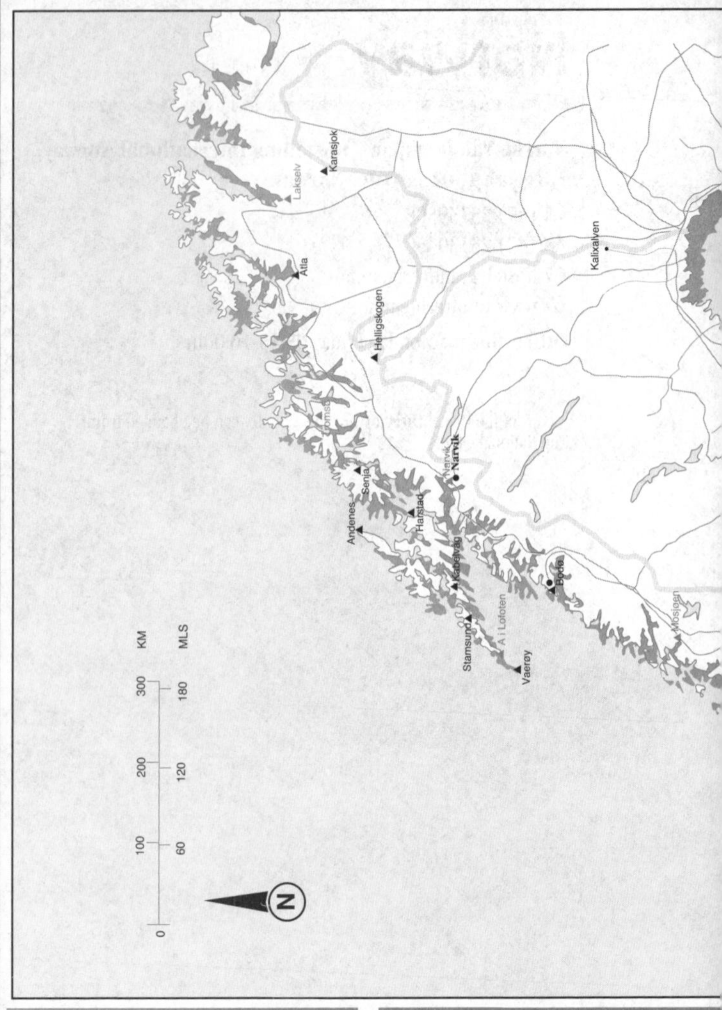

A little like Chile is to South America, Norway is the 'spine' running along the perimeter of northern Europe, hugging the border with Sweden and Finland for over a thousand miles, from Kristiansand in the south to Kirkenes in the north, where it ends in a tail or 'Maelstrom' of islands that have helped generate a rich folklore and cult of the supernatural. Norway today flourishes from its vast oil and gas reserves (its oil capital is Stavanger), and to a lesser extent from its abundant fishing, forestry and mineral resources.

Norway, land of the Midnight Sun, is indeed a very prosperous and picturesque country and has turned itself into a tourist haven, exploiting its colourful villages and spectacular scenery of fjords and monumental cliffs, challenging uplands and forested lowlands. A constitutional monarchy centred on the capital Oslo, Norway has the highest standard of living in Europe but also one of the smallest populations with only 4.5 million people, who take a very egalitarian view of life and so far have chosen not to join the European Union.

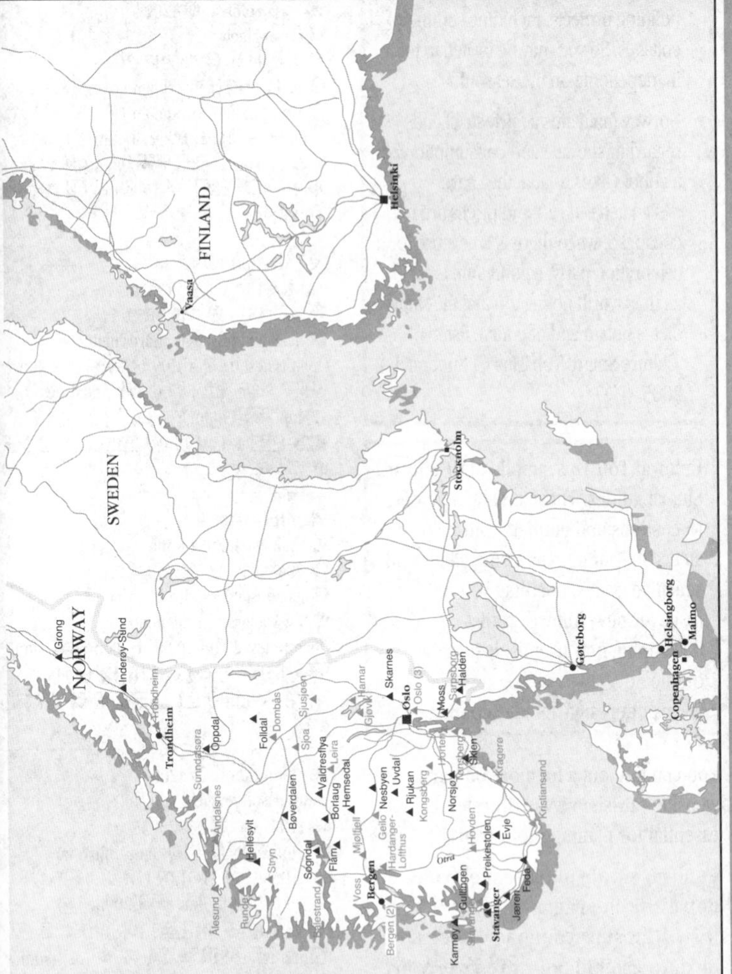

A few other Top Tips from **CULTURE SMART!**:

- There is a simplicity about the Norwegian way of life and its people, which includes food and fashion: they see little need to do anything much for its own sake, choosing rather to live in harmony with nature and the seasons as they have always done. Thus, whether winter or summer, practical but casual dress is the preferred choice.
- Do not equate the simple approach to life with ignorance: Norway has one of the best education and welfare systems in the world and a sense of community, which also helps make it such a welcoming place to visit.
- If invited to a friend's home for dinner, small gifts such as a plant, chocolates or wine would always be welcomed, and be sure to turn up on time. Punctuality is something the Norwegians take very seriously!
- A self-sufficiency heritage has made Norway one of the most active of DIY countries, which extends to significant

building projects, including summer cottages. So you may be invited to join in, depending on the season!

- Norway maintains a fairly strict code regarding the sale and consumption of alcohol (like Canada, they have designated outlets) and prices are not cheap, so, when there is an excuse for a celebration party, a good time is had by all. It is worth noting too that the staple diet is potato and of course fish.

Culture Smart! Top Tips © Kuperard 2005

Cultural Top Tips supplied by Culture Smart! guides. These essential guides to customs and etiquette will help you steer clear of embarrassing gaffes and sensitive issues, enabling you to discover new cultures whilst developing new friendships. Order online at www.culturesmartguides.co.uk

You can find out a lot more on our website - a visit to www.HIhostels.com is essential for planning your trip!

Pour en savoir plus, rendez-vous sur notre site Internet, www.HIhostels.com une visite incontournable pour préparer votre voyage!

Viele weitere Informationen auf unserer Website: www.HIhostels.com - unverzichtbar für die Reiseplanung!

Puedes averiguar mucho más en nuestro sitio web. Es imprescindible que visites la página www.HIhostels.com para planear tu viaje.

▲ **Å – Lofoten** 42063
8392 Sørvågen.
76091121 76091282
aa.hostel@vandrerhjem.no
www.lofoten-rorbu.com
Open Dates: Leknes 64km Moskenes 4km ap Å x 42

▲ **Ålesund** 42028
Parkgaten 14, 6003 Ålesund.
70115830 70115859
aalesund.hostel@vandrerhjem.no
Open Dates: 01.05-01.09 () 22km A 800m 1km Åndalsnes 125km 500m 0.5E x 100 2 x

▲ **Alta** – 42064
Midtbakkvn 52, 9511 Alta.
78434409 78436983
alta.hostel@vandrerhjem.no
www.altavandrerhjem.no
Open Dates: 20.06-20.08 4km 3km 1.5km 1N x 63 (B) 8

▲ **Åndalsnes** 42006
Setnes, 6300 Åndalsnes.
71221382 71226835
aandalsnes.hostel@vandrerhjem.no
Open Dates: 20.05-01.09 (01.04-15.11) 55km 1.5km 200m 1.5W x 84 (BD) 8 400m

△ ***Andenes** – 42065*
Lankanholmen, 8480 Andenes.
76142850; (Off season: 76141222)
76142855; (Off season: 76141933)
Open Dates: 01.06-31.08 Andenes Harbour 200m 200m 0.2N x 18

▲ **Balestrand** 42029
6899 Balestrand.
57691303 57691670
balestrand.hostel@vandrerhjem.no
www.kringsja.no
Open Dates: 26.06-19.08 46km
100m 100m 0.1W x 48
(B)
100m

Bergen – Montana 42003
Johan Blyttsvei 30, 5096 Bergen.
55208070 55208075
bergen.montana.hostel@vandrerhjem.no
www.montana.no
Open Dates: 03.01-22.12 Open Times:
Beds: 262 - 38x2 14x4 26x5
Price Range: NOK 210-440 BBinc
Directions: 4N from city centre
Bergen 20km A 4km
Skoltegrunnskaien 5km 3km
#31 200m R
1 x 8
5km 5km

Bergen – Montana

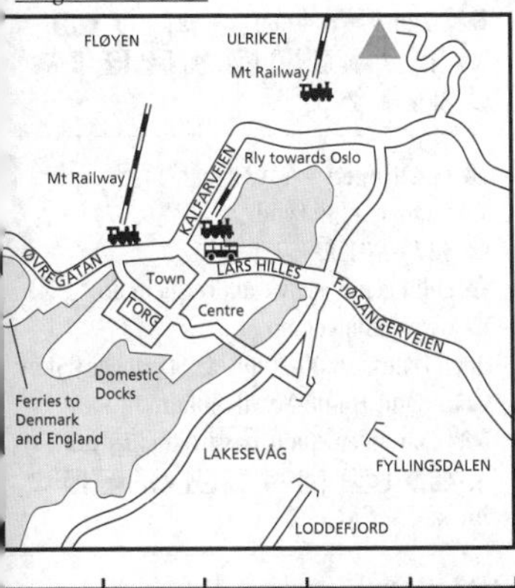

Bergen... Travel Tips

- **For budget eats check out...** Vågens Fetevarer, Café Opera, Holbergstuen (traditional Norwegian food), Zupperiet (soups & salads)
- **For great nightlife try...** Den Stundesløse (concerts), Ricks, Garage, Banco Rotto, Maxim (nightclub)
- **Don't miss...** Hanseatic & Bryggen Museums (Harbour), Håkons Hall, Mariakirken (St. Mary's Church, 12th century), Trollhaugen (composer Edvard Grieg's home), Old Bergen open air museum, Aquarium, Fløyen (funicular), Fish Market, Fantoft Stave Church, Ulriken

▲ **Bergen Vandrerhjem** – YMCA
42030
Nedre Korskirkealm 4, 5017 Bergen.
55606055 55606051
bergen.ymca.hostel@vandrerhjem.no
http://home.broadpark.no/~ymca
Open Dates: 12 (01.10-30.04)
Flesland 18km A Bergen 100m
Skoltegrunnskaien 100m Bergen 1km Bergen x 120
(B) 8

▲ **Bodø** – 42066
Storgata 90, 8006 Bodø.
75520402 75520403
bodo.hostel@vandrerhjem.no
Open Dates: 12 Bodø 10km A 500m
100m 500m x 40
R (B)

▲ **Borlaug** – 42067
6888 Steinklepp.
57668780 57668744
borlaug.hostel@vandrerhjem.no
http://home.online.no/~borvh/eBorlaug.html
Open Dates: 01.02-31.10 Bergen 60km
Lærdal 38km 78km 38E x 53
R (BD)

▲ **Bøverdalen** – 42068
2687 Bøverdalen.
61212064 61212064
boverdalen.hostel@vandrerhjem.no
Open Dates: 02.06-20.10 350km
120km Otta 82km 50m
x 32 R

Dombås 42041
Trolltun, 2660 Dombås.
61240960 61241330
dombaas.hostel@vandrerhjem.no
www.trolltun.no
Open Dates: 02.01-23.12 300km
Dombås 1.5km 1.5km 1.5E
x 78

Evje – 42070
Syrtveit, 4735 Evje
37931177 37931334
evje.hostel@vandrerhjem.no
www.troll-mountain.no
Open Dates: 01.05-01.10 Kristiansand 60km Kristiansand Ferry Terminal 70km Kristiansand 70km 10m 7N
x 35 10m

Feda – 42123
Fosseland Ferie og Aktivitetssenter, 4485 Feda.
38352477 38352515
feda.hostel@vandrerhjem.no
Open Dates: 01.01-20.12 120km
100km 300m x 20
300m

Flåm – 42071
5743 Flåm.
57632121 57632380
flaam.hostel@vandrerhjem.no
Open Dates: 01.05-30.09 250km
Flåm 200m Flåm 200m
200m 0.2W x 31
8km 300m

Folldal – 42072
Sletten Fjellgard, 2584 Dalholen.
62493108 62493108
folldal.hostel@vandrerhjem.no
www.fjellgard.no
Open Dates: 10.06-31.08 ( )
130km Hjerkinn 14km 200m
15W x 63

Geilo 42055
Lienvegen 137, 3580 Geilo.
32087060 32087066
geilo.hostel@vandrerhjem.no
www.oenturist.no
Open Dates: Geilo 2km 200m
2E x 51

Gjøvik 42049
Parkveien 9, 2819 Gjøvik.
61171011 61172602
gjovik.hostel@vandrerhjem.no
www.hovdetun.no
Open Dates: 70km A Gjøvik 900m
130km Gjøvik 800m Gjøvik 100m 0.8NW x 154
100m

Grong – 42118
7870 Grong.
74332000 74331899
grong.hostel@vandrerhjem.no
www.namdals.fhs.no
Open Dates: 01.06-31.07 Namsos 45km
2km 400m 0.4N x 68
(B)
3km

Gullingen – 42121
Mosvannet, 4230 Sand.
52799901 52799937
gullingen.hostel@vandrerhjem.no
www.gullingen.no
Open Dates: 16.06-29.08 Stavanger 95km
Sand 16km; Nesvik 30km
Stavanger 80km 6km 16E x 95

Halden – 42073
Flintveien, Box 604, 1754 Halden.
69216968 69216603
halden.hostel@vandrerhjem.no
Open Dates: 24.06-08.08 Halden 3km
300m 3N x 32
2km

Hamar 42074
Vikingskipet, Åkersvikavn. 24, 2321 Hamar.
62526060 62532460
hamar.hostel@vandrerhjem.no
www.vi-sees.no
Open Dates: 12 Oslo Gardermoen 80km
Hamar 2km 200m 2S x 220
R CC TV
8 P 3km

Hardanger 42075
Lofthus, 5781 Lofthus.
53671400 53671401
lofthus.hostel@vandrerhjem.no
www.hardangervandrerhjem.com
Open Dates: 01.06-10.08 150km
Kinsarvik 10km 70km 50m
1S x 92 CC (B) TV
P 10km

Harstad – 42076
Trondenesvn. 110, 9404 Harstad.
77040077 77040078
harstad.hostel@vandrerhjem.no
www.trondarnes.fhs.no
Open Dates: 01.06-18.08 Harstad/Narvik Evenes 55km A 3km 3km
50m 3NE x 78 CC (B)
TV P 3km

Hellesylt – 42078
6218 Hellesylt.
70265128 70263657
hellesylt.hostel@vandrerhjem.no
Open Dates: 01.06-01.09 100km
Hellesylt 600m 100km
100m 0.8W x 46 (B)
TV P 700m

Helligskogen – 42079
Box 14, 9143 Skibotn.
77715460 77715453
helligskogen.hostel@vandrerhjem.no
Open Dates: 15.06-20.08 & weekends 12
160km 30km x 40 R
CC TV P

Hemsedal – 42080
Fossheim, 3560 Hemsedal.
32060315 32060745
hemsedal.hostel@vandrerhjem.no
www.fossheim.com
Open Dates: 01.06-15-09 270km
90km Gol 26km 100m 4E
x 20 R CC P
4km

Horten 42039
Klokkergården, Sandeveien 5, 3184 Borre.
33031379 33070864
horten.hostel@vandrerhjem.no
www.hortenvh.no
Open Dates: 20.06-15.08 Torp 40km
Horten 2km Horten 4km
100m 2.5S x 114 R CC
TV P 500m
500m

Hovden 42044
Lundane, Box 73, 4755 Hovden.
37939543 37939818
hovden.hostel@vandrerhjem.no
www.hovdenfjellstoge.no
Open Dates: 26.12-30.04; 01.06-30.10 (12) Kristiansand Kjevik 211km
211km 180km 100m 2.9N
x 150 R CC
TV P

Inderøy – 42082
Flagvn. 95, 7670 Inderøy.
74124900 74124910
inderoy.hostel@vandrerhjem.no
www.sund.fhs.no
Open Dates: 01.06-20.08 Trondheim 70km Røra 6km 1km 2NW
x 27 (BD) TV
P 1km

Jæren – 42083
Nordsjøvegen, Hårr, 4362 Vigrestad.
51435755 51437326
jaeren.hostel@vandrerhjem.no
Open Dates: 01.06-31.08 Stavanger 60km
Egersund 33km Vigrestad 2.5km
3km 2.5SW x 28 CC TV
P 5km

▲ **Kabelvåg** – Lofoten – 42084
Finnesveien 24, 8310 Kabelvåg.
t 76069898
e kabelvaag.hostel@vandrerhjem.no
w www.lofotensommerhotell.no
Open Dates: 01.06-13.08 ✈ Svolvær 9km
A 800m Svolvær 5km 200m
1E x 76 R CC (B)
5km

▲ **Karasjok** – 42085
Engholm Husky, 9730 Karasjok.
t 78467166 f 78467176
e karasjok.hostel@vandrerhjem.no
w www.engholm.no
Open Dates: 12 ✈ Lakselv 75km
200km 6km 6E x 20
200m

▲ **Karmøy** – 42124
Austre Karmøyvei 23 - 37, 4250 Kopervik.
t 52846160 f 52846161
e karmoy.hostel@vandrerhjem.no
w www.skolelei.no
Open Dates: 25.05-10.08 ✈ 12km
1.5km 200m 1.5E x 109
8

Kongsberg Vandrerhjem HI 42061
Bergmannen, Vinjesgt 1,
3616 Kongsberg.
t 32732024 f 32720534
e kongsberg.hostel@vandrerhjem.no
w www.kongsberg-vandrerhjem.no
Open Dates: 02.01-22.12
Open Times: 07.00-23.00hrs
Beds: 99 - 2x2 2x3 18x4 4x5
Price Range: NOK 195-445 BBinc
Directions: 0.3SW from city centre
✈ Torp 90km; Gardermoen 120km
A 200m Larvik 80km; Horten 80km; Oslo 100km Kongsberg 600m
200m x 26 R CC
(B) 5 x 8
300m

Kongsberg Vandrerhjem

Kongsberg Vandrerhjem... Travel Tips

- **For budget eats check out...** Peppe's Pizza, Jeppe's Pizza and Meals, Jonas B Gundersen, Kong's (Chinese), Big Horn Steak House/Dolly Dimple Pizza
- **For great nightlife try...** Christians Kjeller (Oppsalgården), Alfa Omega (disco & nightclub), Krag's Møteplass, Velvet, Cirka Bar
- **Don't miss...** Sølvgruvene (silver mines), Norwegian Mining Museum & Silver/Royal Mint/Armory Collections, Lågdal Museum & Labro River Museum, Kongsberg Baroque Church, The Crones at Håvet, Fossesholm Manor, Nestetangen Museum (Hokksund), Kongsberg Skiing Centre (winter)

▲ **Kragerø** HI 42086
Lovisenbergveien 20, 3770 Kragerø.
t 35985700 f 35985701
e kragero.hostel@vandrerhjem.no
w www.kragerosportell.no
Open Dates: 20.06-20.08 ✈ 100km
40km Neslandsvatten 35km
300m 1.5N x 97 CC
(B) 2km

Kristiansand 42052
Skansen 8, 4610 Kristiansand.
38028310 38027505
kristiansand.hostel@vandrerhjem.no
Open Dates: Open Times: 07.00-21.00hrs (15.06-15.08)
Beds: 175 - 15x2 27x4 5x5 1x6
Price Range: NOK 195-395 BBinc
Directions: 0.5SE from city centre
Kristiansand Kjevik 17km A 500m
Kristiansand Ferry Terminal 1.5km
1.5km 500m x 35 R
CC (B)
100m 80m

Kristiansand

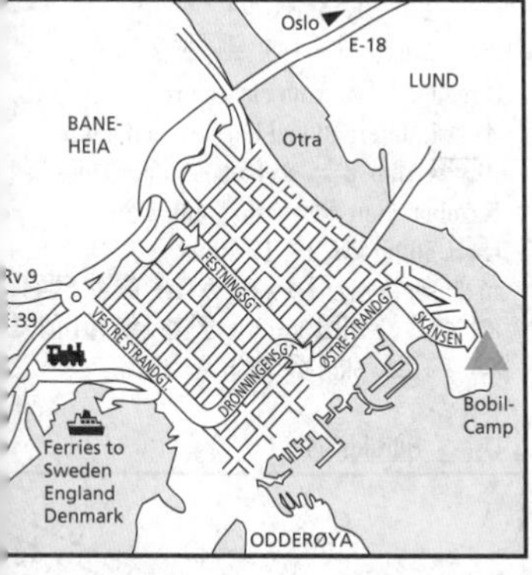

Kristiansand... Travel Tips

- **For budget eats check out...** Frk. Larsen, Glipp, Fish Market (fish restaurants, pizza etc), India (Tandoori), Kjesk
- **For great nightlife try...** Elk Safari at night (10.07-28.08, Weds - contact the Tourist Office), Radisson SAS Hotel (live music & nightclub), Clarion Ernst Hotel (live music & nightclub), Kaptein Sabeltann (family theatre in zoo - 10.07-01.08)
- **Don't miss...** Kristiansand Dyrepark (Zoo), Bronseplassen (reconstruction of Norwegian Bronze Age farm), Agder Nature Museum & Botanical Gardens, Sightseeing boat trips, Posebyen (protected part of town with market), Kristiansand Canon Museum, Søgne Gamle Prestegård (country courtyard - exhibitions, concerts & events), Markens Gate (pedestrian street), Quart Festivalen (annual rock music festival, early July), De Internasjonale Kirkefestspillene (international church music festival)

▲ **Lakselv** 42087
Karalaks, Box 74, 9711 Lakselv.
78461476 78461996
lakselv.hostel@vandrerhjem.no
Open Dates: 01.06-01.09 Lakselv 6km A 2km 2km 5S x 57
R (BD)

▲ **Leira** 42088
Valdres Flokehøyskole, 2920 Leira i Valdres.
61359500 61359501
leira.hostel@vandrerhjem.no
www.valdres.fhs.no/vandrerhjem
Open Dates: 29.05-13.08 Fagernes Leirin 8km Gol 50km 200m 0.2N
x 140 R CC (BD)
1km

▲ **Mjølfjell** 42031
Mjølfjell, 5700 Voss.
56523150 56523151
mjolfjell.hostel@vandrerhjem.no
www.mjolfjell.no
Open Dates: 01.03-20.04; 15.06-30.09 (rest of year R) Bergen Flesland 140km
Ørneberget 300m; Mjølfjell 300m 38W
x 40 R CC

▲ **Mosjøen** 42090
Sandvik Gjestegård, Mjåvatn, 8664 Mosjøen.
75115000 75115001
mosjoen.hostel@vandrerhjem.no
www.sandvik-gjestegard.no
Open Dates: 01.06-15.08 Mosjøen 40km 25km Mosjøen 25km 200m 20N x 40 R CC (BD)

▲ **Moss** – 42091
Nesparken, 1530 Moss.
69255334 69250166
moss.hostel@vandrerhjem.no
Open Dates: 01.06-31.08 (01.09-31.05 R) 70km A 200m Moss 3km Moss 2km 200m 0.3NW x 58 R CC (B) 100m

▲ **Narvik** 42092
Dronningensgate 58, 8514 Narvik.
76962200 76962850
narvik.hostel@vandrerhjem.no
www.narvikvandrerhjem.no
Open Dates: 01.02-25.05; 01.06-20.09 (20.05-30.10) Harstad/Narvik Evenes 70km A 50m Skarberget 80km Narvik 500m 500m x 40 CC 2km

▲ **Nesbyen** – 42093
Sutøya Feriepark, 3540 Nesbyen.
32071397 32070111
nesbyen.hostel@vandrerhjem.no
www.sutoyaferiepark.no
Open Dates: 01.05-15.09 Nesbyen 4km 100m 4W x 40 CC 3.5km

▲ **Norsjø** – 42094
3812 Akkerhaugen.
35958277 35958283
norsjo.hostel@vandrerhjem.no
www.norsjo.no
Open Dates: 01.01-15.12 Bø 7km 1km 7W x 100 R 13km

▲ **Oppdal** – 42095
Sletvold, Gamle Kongevei, 7340 Oppdal.
72404090 72404101
oppdal.hostel@vandrerhjem.no
Open Dates: 01.05-01.12 140km 120km Oppdal 2.5km 2.5km 2.5N x 64 CC (B)

Oslo – Haraldsheim 42001
Haraldsheimvn 4, 0587 Oslo.
Mail: Box 41, Grefsen, 0409 Oslo.
22222965 22221025
oslo.haraldsheim.hostel@vandrerhjem.no
www.haraldsheim.oslo.no
Open Dates: 02.01-23.12 Open Times:
Beds: 270 - 9x2 63x4
Price Range: NOK 185 BBinc
Directions: 4NE from city centre
Oslo International Gardermoen 45km A 1km Stena Line/Color Line Terminal 5km Oslo South 5km 400m 15, 17 400m ap Sinsenkrysset x 62 R CC 5 x 8 3km 8km

Oslo – Haraldsheim

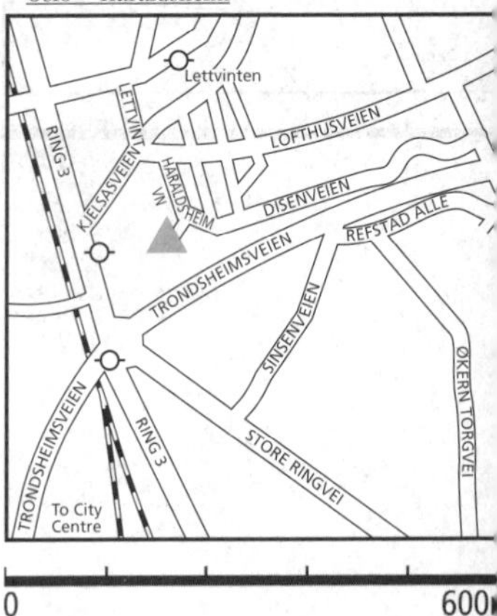

▲ **Oslo** – Holtekilen 42096
Michelets vei 55, 1368 Stabekk.
67518040 67591230
oslo.holtekilen.hostel@vandrerhjem.no
Open Dates: 15.05-20.08 Oslo International Gardermoen 40km Stena Line/Color Line Terminal 6km Stabekk 700m 200m 7W x 179 R CC (B)

▲ Oslo – Rønningen 42120
Myrerskogveien 54, 0495 Olso.
21023600 21023601
oslo.ronningen.hostel@vandrerhjem.no
www.oslohostel.com
Open Dates: 28.05-20.08 Oslo International Gardermoen 48km 6km 5km 200m 700m 40N x 189 R CC (B) 1.5km

Oslo... Travel Tips

- **For budget eats check out...** Central Oslo (Karl Johan Pedestrian Street), Aker Brygge (marina area), Bogstadveien, Majorstuen, Grünerløkka
- **For great nightlife try...** Central Oslo (Karl Johan pedestrian street & Rosenkranzgate Street), Aker Brygge (marina area), Grünerløkka, Bogstadveien Street, Øyafestivalen - (annual rock music festival, 2nd week in August)
- **Don't miss...** Vigeland Park & Vigeland Museum, Holmenkollen Ski Jump & Museum, Norwegian Folk, Viking Ship, Kon-Tiki, & Polar Ship museums (Bygdøy), Akershus Fortress, Norwegian Maritime Museum, Munch Museum, National Gallery, Norwegian Museum of Science & Technology, Tusenfryd Amusement Park, Oslo Cathedral

▲ Preikestolen – 42097
Box 160, 4126 Jørpeland.
97165551 48945551
preikestolen.hostel@vandrerhjem.no
www.preikestolhytta.no
Open Dates: 12.05-17.09 Tau/Oanes 25km 100m 10SE x 62 R CC 100m

▲ Rjukan – Kvitåvatn – 42125
Kvitåvatn, 3660 Rjukan.
35092040 35092095
rjukan.hostel@vandrerhjem.no
www.kvitaavatn.no
Open Dates: 09.06-30.09 Torp 200km; Oslo Gardermoen 250km Oslo/Larvik 200km Kongsberg 110km 12km 17E x 64 CC (B) 16km

▲ Runde 42035
6096 Runde
70085916 70085870
runde.hostel@vandrerhjem.no
www.runde.no
Open Dates: 01.05-31.08 (01.04-30.09) Ålesund 60km 46km 170km 100m x 65 R CC

▲ Sarpsborg 42059
Tuneheimen, Tuneveien 44, 1710 Sarpsborg.
69145001 69142291
sarpsborg.hostel@vandrerhjem.no
www.sarpsborgvandrerhjem.no
Open Dates: 03.01-22.12 Oslo International Gardermoen 140km Moss 34km 1.5km 100m 1N x 96 R CC 3 x 500m 300m

▲ Senja – Skoghus – 42126
9303 Silsand
77844165 77841486
senja.hostel@vandrerhjem.no
Open Dates: 01.06-15.08 (R 16.08-31.05) Bardufoss 50km 7km 200m 7W x 60 R CC 200m

▲ Sjoa 42099
2670 Sjoa.
61236200
sjoa.hostel@vandrerhjem.no
www.heidalrafting.no
Open Dates: 15.05-15.09 (05.01-20.12) 250km Otta 10km 1km 10S x 95 CC 1km

▲ Sjusjøen 42046
Fjellheimen, 2612 Sjusjøen.
62347680 62366591
sjusjoen.hostel@vandrerhjem.no
www.sjusjoen-hotel.no
Open Dates: 12 Oslo International Gardermoen 150km A Lillehammer 20km Lillehammer 20km 50m x 86 R CC 100m

Skarnes – 42100
Solbakken Gård, 2100 Skarnes.
62967080 62967089
skarnes.hostel@vandrerhjem.no
www.revyskolen.no/vandrerhjem
Open Dates: 01.06-15.08; 01.09-15.05 ( ) Oslo International Gardermoen 35km A 200m Skarnes 2km 200m 1E x 92 (BD) 2km 300m

Skien – 42101
Moflatevn. 65, 3733 Skien.
35504870 35546240
skien.hostel@vandrerhjem.no
Open Dates: Sandefjord Torp 50km Skien 4km 200m 3SW x 62 (B) 3km

Sogndal – 42102
Helgheimsvegen 9, Box 174, 6851 Sogndal
57627575 57627570
sogndal.hostel@vandrerhjem.no
Open Dates: 12.06-13.08 (01.06-13.08) Sogndal 20km A 50m 1.5km 1.5km 1E x 63 (B)

Stamsund – 42103
Box 110, 8378 Stamsund, Lofoten.
76089334 76089739
Open Dates: 01.01-15.10; 15.12-31.12
Leknes 15km A 200m x 60

Stavanger 42104
Mosvangen, Henrik Ibsensgt. 19,
4021 Stavanger.
51543636 51543637
stavanger.mosvangen.hostel@vandrerhjem.no
Open Dates: 09.06-18.08 Stavanger Sola 13km A 500m Stavanger 3km Stavanger 3km 300m 3NE x 116 (BL)

Stryn 42036
Geilevegen 14, 6783 Stryn.
57871106 57871106
stryn.hostel@vandrerhjem.no
Open Dates: 01.06-31.08 (01.04-31.10) Sandane 90km Otta 190km 1km 1N x 90 (BD)

Sunndalsøra 42032
Litldalsvegen, 6600 Sunndalsøra.
71698700 71698705
sunndalsora.hostel@vandrerhjem.no
www.tredal-turistsenter.no
Open Dates: Kristiansund 9km 25km Åndalsnes 75km 2km 2S x 50 2km

Tønsberg 42106
Dr. Blancas gt. 22, 3111 Tønsberg.
33312175 33312176
tonsberg.hostel@vandrerhjem.no
www.vandrerhjemmet.no
Open Dates: 05.01-22.12 Sandefjord Torp 29km A 500m 500m 300m 300m 0.3N x 92 1km 600m

Tromsø 42107
Åsgårdveien 9, 9017 Tromsø.
77657628 77657628
tromso.hostel@vandrerhjem.no
Open Dates: 18.06-16.08 Tromsø 4km A 5km No.26 100m ap Åsgård 3SE x 68

Trondheim 42108
Weidemannsvei 41, 7043 Trondheim.
73874450 73874455
trondheim.hostel@vandrerhjem.no
www.trondheim-vandrerhjem.no
Open Dates: Open Times: 06.30-00.00hrs
Beds: 220 - 2x1 6x2 22x4 9x6
Price Range: NOK 235
Directions: 1.5NE from city centre
Trondheim Værnes 35km A 600m 1km 1km Express 100m x 50 2 x 2km

Trondheim

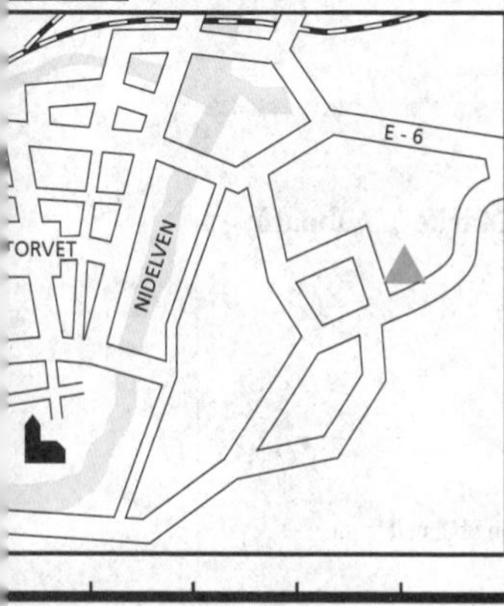

Trondheim... Travel Tips

- **For budget eats check out...** Kings Cross, China House, Ristorantino Italian & Pizzeria, Krambua, Bare Blåber
- **For great nightlife try...** Blæst (live music, theatre), Kings Cross, Den Gode Nabo (Norweigan pub), Mikrobryggeriet, Marina Area
- **Don't miss...** Nidarosdomen Cathedral, Erkebispegården (Archbishop's Palace), Stiftsgården (Royal Residence), Kristiansten Fortress, Gamle Bybro (old city bridge), Munkholmen (Monk Island), Vitensenteret (Scientific Adventure Centre for families), Sverresborg open air folk museum, Tyholt Tower (rotating tower & restaurant)

▲ **Uvdal** – 42110
3632 Uvdal.
T 32743020 F 32743020
E uvdal.hostel@vandrerhjem.no
Open Dates: 12.06-01.09 & Easter (12) Geilo Dagali 35km 105km
30m 10E x 42 R CC
(BD)
100m

△ ***Værøy** – 42111*
8063 Værøy.
T *92618477* F *76095701*
E *vaeroy.hostel@vandrerhjem.no*
Open Dates: 01.05-01.09 *500m*
Værøy 3km 2N x 16 R

▲ **Valdresflya** – 42112
2953 Beitostoelen.
T 95107819 F 22713497
E valdresflya.hostel@vandrerhjem.no
Open Dates: 01.06-15.09 (R Easter & weekends in May) Fagernes Leirin 60km
Express 100m 20NE x 46
R CC

▲ **Voss** HI 42033
Evangerveien 68, 5700 Voss.
T 56512017 F 56510837
E voss.hostel@vandrerhjem.no
W www.vossvandrerhjem.no
Open Dates: 10.01-25.09 (12) Bergen Flesland 120km Voss 700m 700m
1W x 200 R CC
700m

Pakistan

Pakistan Youth Hostels Association,
Shaheed-e-Millat Road, (Near Akhbar Market), Aabparà,
Sector G-6/4, Islamabad, Pakistan.
t (92) (51) 2826899; 2825559; 2825427
f (92) (51) 2824520
e pyha@comsats.net.pk

A copy of the Hostel Directory for this Country can be obtained from:
The National Office.

National Tourist Authority/Board:	www.tourism.govt.pk
Capital:	Islamabad
Language:	Urdu/English
Currency:	Rs (rupee)
Population:	131,600,000
Size:	803,943 sq km
Telephone Country Code:	92
eKit Access Number:	Check www.hi.ekit.com for up to date Access Numbers

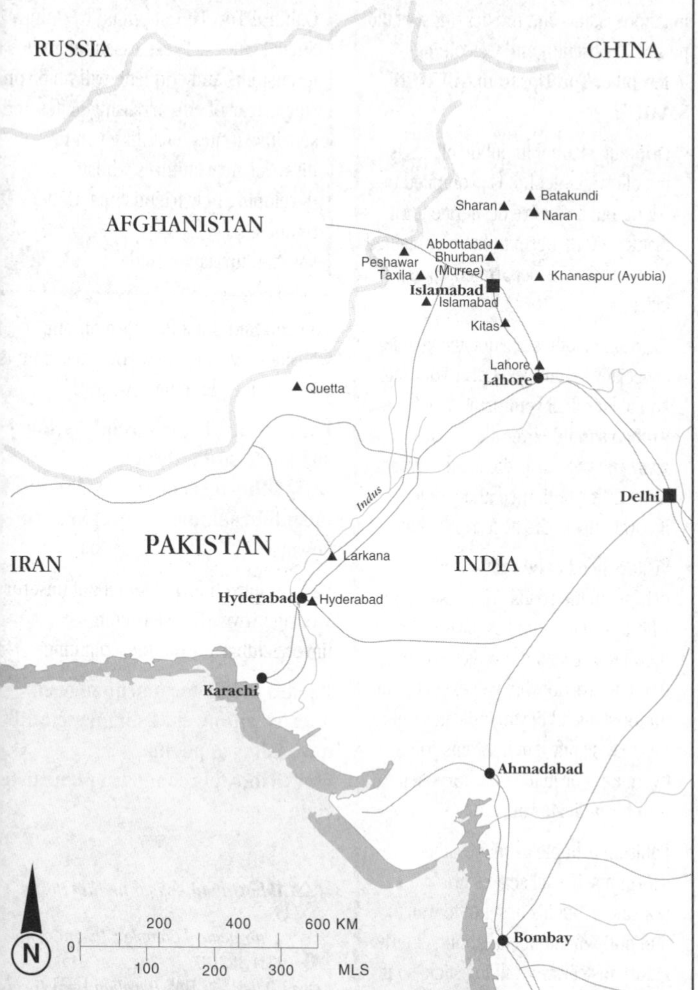

With a cultural ancestry dating back to the third millennium BC, the state of Pakistan was formed in 1947 as a home for the Muslim minority of the population who until that time had been living throughout India.

Geographically, Pakistan has a dramatic landscape, with four main areas. In the mountains of the northwest, pine forests and green valleys contrast with the parched expanse of Baluchistan beside Iran in the west. The southeast is largely wasteland and the Thar Desert. The broad, flat plains around the Indus Valley and the other rivers form much of the remaining area. Architecturally, Pakistan is also diverse; sightseers can visit Hindu temples, Islamic palaces, Anglo-Mogul mansions and Buddhist monuments.

The Punjabis, the Pathans, the Sindhis, the Mohajirs and the Balochis make up the five dominant ethnic groups. Around half of the population is Punjabi, and this group consequently has greater influence over social, political and military matters. There is a strong belief in taboos, saints and mystics. Most of the people are friendly and welcoming.

A few other Top Tips from **CULTURE SMART!:**

- Drinking alcohol in public places is not allowed. Alcohol is prohibited in Islam, but if you are desperate for a drink visitors' permits can be obtained from the Excise Department in the cities.
- Revealing clothes are not acceptable, especially in temples. Cover your legs and at least half your arms, and woman should cover their heads. A *shalwar kameez* is the ideal garment to wear, for both men and women, as it covers up all the necessary areas.
- Visitors need to be cautious when driving on the roads. Motorists, along with rickshaws, donkey carts and bicycles, are very unpredictable, and don't always do what you expect! If the motorist ahead of you indicates right, this may signify that he wants you to overtake – or that he has forgotten to turn his indicator off!
- Pakistan is home to snakes and scorpions. Not all snakes are poisonous but it's best not to wait to find out. When out and about, elderly Pakistanis carry a walking stick, so if need be they can divert the attention of a snake by rapping on the ground or a nearby object.
- A dignified manner is highly respected in Pakistan. Don't rush around the bazaars, as a composed presence and slow body movements and speech make a better impression. The traders are likely to serve impatient customers last, and may even offer them inferior products.

Cultural Top Tips supplied by Culture Smart! guides. These essential guides to customs and etiquette will help you steer clear of embarrassing gaffes and sensitive issues, enabling you to discover new cultures whilst developing new friendships. Order online at www.culturesmartguides.co.uk

You can find out a lot more on our website - a visit to www.HIhostels.com is essential for planning your trip!

Pour en savoir plus, rendez-vous sur notre site Internet, www.HIhostels.com une visite incontournable pour préparer votre voyage!

Viele weitere Informationen auf unserer Website: www.HIhostels.com - unverzichtbar für die Reiseplanung!

Puedes averiguar mucho más en nuestro sitio web. Es imprescindible que visites la página www.HIhostels.com para planear tu viaje.

△ ***Abbottabad*** – *Viqar un Nisa Hostel – 96143*
Near Ayub Medical Complex, Umer Colony.
(992) 382137
Open Dates: 12 *Havalian* *Local Bus ap Mandia* x 80

△ ***Batakundi*** – *96144*
17.6km from Naran.
Open Dates: 01.06-15.10 *Government Bus Service* x 25

△ ***Bhurban (Murree)*** – *96145*
Opposite Pearl Continental Hotel, 12.8km from Murree.
Open Dates: 01.05-30.11 *Local Bus service and Wagon are available ap P.C. More* x 32

△ ***Hyderabad*** *– Jamshoro Youth Hostel – 96280*
University of Sindh, Jamshoro, Hyderabad.
(221) 772310
aslampervez58@hotmail.com
www.pakistanyouthhostel.com
Open Dates: Hyderabad 8km A Public Bus 4km Hyderabad 6km University Bus 2 Furlong
x 50

Islamabad – 96146
Adjoining Akhbar Market, Shaheed-e-Millat Rd, Aabpara, Sector G-6/4, Islamabad.
(51) 2825559; 2826899; 2825427
(51) 2824520 pyha@comsats.net.pk
pakistanyouthhostel.com
Open Dates: Open Times: 09.00-22.00hrs
Beds: 100
Price Range: Rs 65-95 (500-700 for en-suite)
Directions: Islamabad International 20km Rawalpindi 20km Wagon No. 21, 23, 01; Taxi (Yellow Cabs) ap Abbpara ap Abbpara 1 x

Islamabad

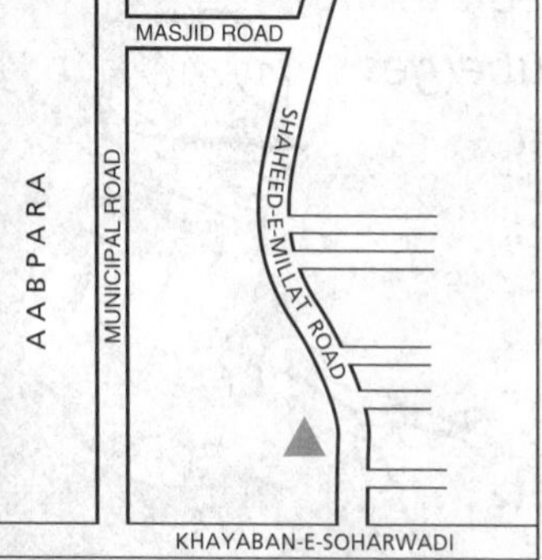

Islamabad... Travel Tips

- **For budget eats check out...** Papa Salis, Food Street, Usmania, Daintyh's, Pizzeria
- **For great nightlife try...** Tennis (Pakistan Sports Board), Squash (Pakistan Sports Board), Theatre and Musical Show, Art Exhibition, Disco Five Star Hotel
- **Don't miss...** Faisal Mosque, Shakir Paryan, Damina Koh, Loke Virsa and Natural History Musuem, Rawal Lake, Murree Hills, Taxila, Terbela Dam, Ayub Park, Trekking

---

△ ***Khanaspur (Ayubia)*** *– 96147*
Bungalow No.33, Ayubia. 27km from Murree on Murree-Abbottabad Rd (rd junction at Kooza Gali, 24km from Murree).
(992) 359012
Open Dates: 01.04-25.12 Local bus service from General Bus Stand Rawalpindi
x 50

△ ***Kitas*** *– 96148*
Cho a Saiden Shah - Katas - Kalax Kahax Road, Chakwal.
(0573) 580156
Open Dates: Local Bus service
x 35

▲ **Lahore** – 96149
110-B-3, Gulberg-III, near Firdaus Market.
(42) 5873612
Open Dates: Lahore International Lahore 10km Wagon No. 43 ap Firdaus Market x 100

△ ***Larkana*** *– Larkana Hostel – 96150*
Satchel Colony, Khorro Stadium, Larkana.
(741) 446893
Open Dates: Mohenjodaro 22km A PIA Bus Local Bus and Taxi service available x 50

△ ***Naran*** *– 96151*
3km before the Naran Village; on the right side of the main rd from Balakot.
Open Dates: 01.06-15.10 Government bus service x 50

△ ***Peshawar*** *– 96152*
Plot No 37, Block B/1, Phase V, Jamrod Rd, Hayatabad.
(91) 824740
Open Dates: International Peshawar Local Bus and Taxi service available
x 50

△ ***Quetta*** *– 96153*
Inside Ayub Stadium, Chaman Phatik, Quetta.
(81) 827498
Open Dates: International Quetta 8km Quetta 3km Local Bus and Taxi available x 50

△ ***Sharan** – 96154*
Post Office, Paras,
Kaghan Valley: 11km from Paras,
YH on left after crossing River Kunhar.
Open Dates: 01.06-15.10 🚌 *Local and Government Transport available* 🛏 x 25

△ ***Taxila** – 96155*
Near Taxila Museum.
☎ *(596) 9314278*
Open Dates: 📅 ✈ *Islamabad International 40km* 🚌 *Local Bus and Wagons available*
🛏 x 35

Peru

Asociación Peruana de Albergues Turísticos Juveniles,
Avda Casimiro Ulloa 328, San Antonio,
Miraflores, Lima 18,
Peru.

t (51) (1) 2423068; 4465488
f (51) (1) 4448187
e hostell@terra.com.pe
w www.hostellingperu.com.pe; www.limahostell.com.pe

A copy of the Hostel Directory for this Country can be obtained from:
The National Office

Capital:	Lima
Language:	Spanish
Currency:	S/. (Sol)
Population:	23,834,000
Size:	1,285,215 sq km
Telephone Country Code:	51
eKit Access Number:	0800-520-08

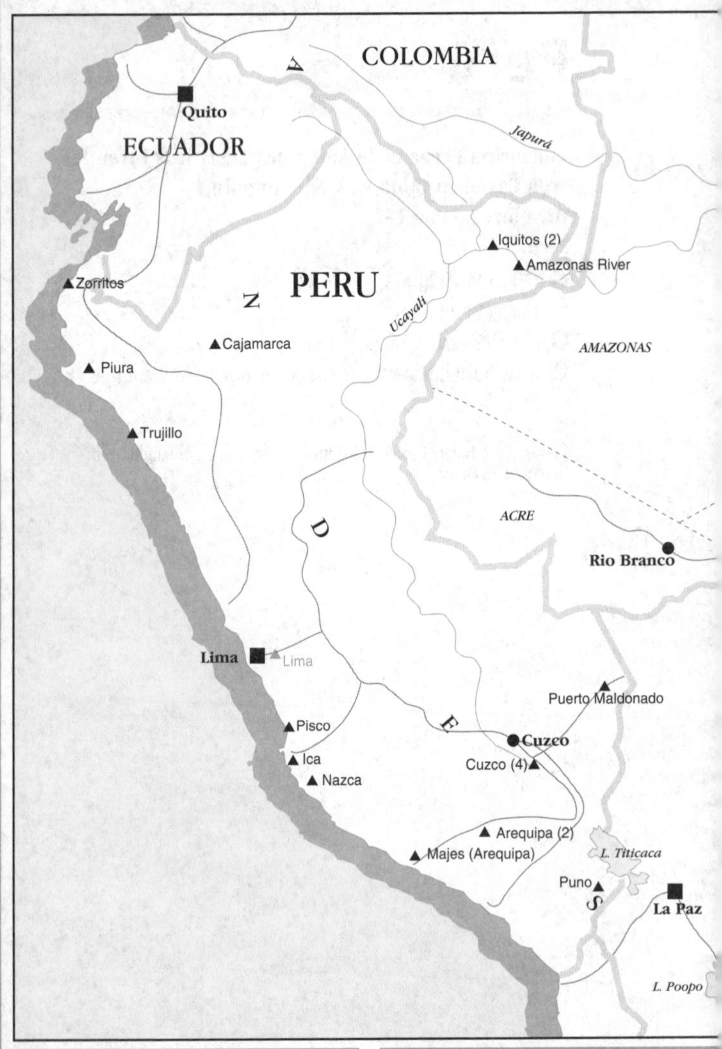

HI Suggests...

Peru is not a common place but is indeed a magical land. The diversity of the ecosystem might account for the magical atmosphere, which attracts travellers from all over the world due to its mountains, rainforests and thrilling deserts.

Visiting Peru is not only to experience its diversity and cultural life, but also to be in touch with the numerous alternatives the country offers - history, culture, nature and unique adventures for all tastes.

If you are interested in the huge Peruvian archaelogical and cultural patrimony, do not miss Cuzco, the capital city of the empire, founded by the Incas and the ruins of Machu Pichu. But remember that the Inca civilization lasted for a short time over the 20 thousand years of the presence of men in the Peruvian territory.

In the Peruvian Andes you can also find various tracks, rivers and mountains, which make a paradise for

those who love adventure sports such as trekking, canoeing and mountain climbing.
Don't miss the Peruvian Amazon rainforest where you can find most national parks and environmental protected areas. The fauna and flora are breath taking, which makes the country a champion of biodiversity.
The Peruvian coastline is a long stretch of desert along the mountains. A region of beautiful beaches and valleys are where the agricultural production is plentiful. A good option would be to start your trip from Lima, the capital city. Rooms are available at the International Tourist Hostel at a super special price and have nice facilities.
Besides that, do not forget that in Peru there are around 3,000 popular festivals a year. Enjoy yourself!

You can find out a lot more on our website - a visit to www.HIhostels.com is essential for planning your trip!

Pour en savoir plus, rendez-vous sur notre site Internet, www.HIhostels.com une visite incontournable pour préparer votre voyage!

Viele weitere Informationen auf unserer Website: www.HIhostels.com - unverzichtbar für die Reiseplanung!

Puedes averiguar mucho más en nuestro sitio web. Es imprescindible que visites la página www.HIhostels.com para planear tu viaje.

▲ **Amazonas River (Iquitos)** – Amazonas Sinchicuy Lodge – 44004
Quebrada Sinchicuysillo 30km de Iquitos.
(65) 231618; (1) 2417576
(1) 4467946
p_amazon@amauta.rcp.net.pe
www.paseosamazonicos.com
Open Dates: 12 Embarcadero 20m 30N
x 80 R CC

▲ **Arequipa** – La Posada Real – 44038
Calle Mollendo 218 Urb. "Municipal" Cercado-Arequipa.
(54) 202222; 284541
posadareal@terra.com.pe
www.posadarealaqp.com
Open Dates: 12 x 40 R CC
TV 1 x i P

▲ **Arequipa** – Majes River Lodge – 44006
Valle del Majes, Central Ongoro.
(54) 280205 (54) 242088
jzuniga79@hotmail.com
www.majesriver.com; www.majesriver.net
Open Dates: 12 x 42 R

▲ **Arequipa** – Premiere – 44008
Av. Quiroz 100
(54) 227821 (54) 227821
hostalpremier@hostalpremier.com
www.hostalpremier.com
Open Dates: 12 x 100 R CC
TV 1 x i P

▲ **Cajamarca** – Complejo Turistico Baños Del Inca – 44010
Plaza de Armas, Calle Atahualpa S/N
(76) 838385; 838563 (76) 838249
ctbinca@terra.com.pe
www.cajamarca.net
Open Dates: 12 x 102 R
TV 1 x P

▲ **Cuzco** – Chaski – 44036
Portal Confiturias 257 Plaza de Armas - Cuzco.
(84) 222691; 632009 (84) 222691
hotelchaski@hotmail.com
Open Dates: 12 x 32 R CC
TV

PERU – PEROU – PERU – PERÚ

▲ **Cuzco** – Maison de la Jeunesse – 44014
Avda. El Sol Cdra, 5 Pasaje Grace (Alt 3000), Edificio San Jorge, Cuzco.
(84) 235617
jeunessecuzco@yahoo.com; pazvent@hotmail.com
Open Dates: x 40

▲ **Cuzco** – Municipal Del Cuzco – 44015
Av. Kiskapata 240 Barrio San Cristóbal, Cuzco
(84) 252506
albergue@municusco.gob.pe
Open Dates: x 64

▲ **Cuzco** – Rupa Wasi Ecolodge – 44035
Calle Huanacaure 180 Macchu Picchu
(84) 211101 (84) 211101
rupawasi@hotmail.com
www.rupawasi.com
Open Dates: x 15
1 x

▲ **Ica** – Belle Sand – 44037
Casuarinas B1-3 Resd. la Angostura - Ica.
(56) 256039; (1) 2410598
(56) 256814
ecotourica@terra.com.pe
www.hotelbellesand.tk
Open Dates: x 40
8

▲ **Iquitos** – Ambassador – 44020
Calle Pevas 260, Iquitos
(65) 233110 (65) 231618
paseosiqt@meganet.com.pe
www.paseosamazonicos.com
Open Dates: x 60

▲ **Iquitos** – Muyuna Amazon Lodge & Expeditions – 44021
140km, Rio Arriba Del Amazonas, Iquitos.
(65) 242858; (1) 4469783
amazonas@muyuna.com
www.muyuna.com
Open Dates: x 48
1 x

Lima – AJ Turístico Internacional 44001
Av Casimiro Ulloa 328, San Antonio, Lima 18
(1) 4465488 (1) 4448187
hostell@terra.com.pe
www.limahostell.com.pe; www.hostellingperu.com.pe
Open Dates: Open Times:
Beds: 100 - 3x 10x 1x 2x
Price Range: US$11.80
Directions: Jorge Chavez 20km A S 100m S, P, 3M, 20, 10 100m ap Puente Benavides 100m
1 x 8
2km 2km

Lima – AJ Turístico Internacional

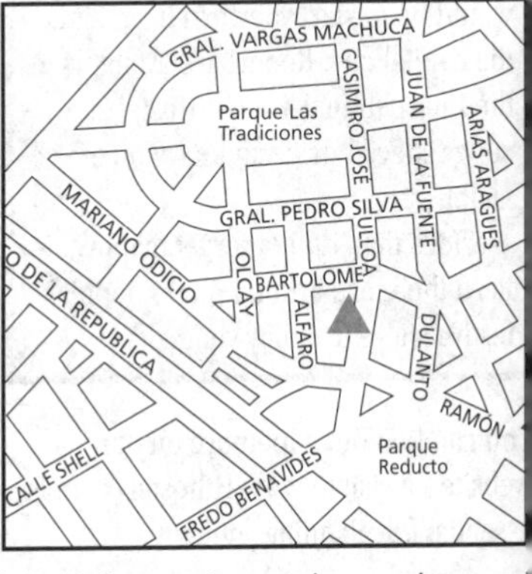

Lima... Travel Tips

- **For budget eats check out...** Pardo's Chicken (Larco Mar), McDonalds (Larco Mar), Pizza Hut (Larco Mar), Kentucky Fried Chicken (Larco Mar), Bembo's (Larco Mar)
- **For great nightlife try...** Barranco District, Larco Mar Shopping Centre
- **Don't miss...** Gold Museum, Lima Town Centre, National Museum, Pachacamac Ruins, Larco Herrera Museum, Huaca Pucllana, Hills of Lachay, St Christopher Hill, Chinese Quarter, Indian Market

▲ **Nazca** – Alegría – 44024
Jr Lima No 168, Nazca
(56) 522444 (56) 523431
alegriatours@hotmail.com; info@alegriatoursperu.com
Open Dates: x 120

Poland

Polskie Towarzystwo Schronisk Mlodziezowych,
ul Chocimska 14, 00-791 Warszawa, Poland.
t (48) (22) 8498128
f (48) (22) 8498354
e hostellingpol.ptsm@pro.onet.pl
w www.ptsm.org.pl; www.hostelling.com.pl

Office Hours: Monday-Friday 08.00-16.00hrs

Travel Section: "Junior" Travel
ul. Chocimska 14, 00-791 Warszawa, Poland
t (48) (22) 8498128; 6428133
f (48) (22) 8498354, 6428305
e hostellingpol.ptsm@pro.onet.pl
w www.ptsm.org.pl; www.hostelling.com.pl

A copy of the Hostel Directory for this Country can be obtained from:
The National Office and Regional Offices

Capital:	Warsaw
Language:	Polish
Currency:	Zl (zloty)
Population:	39,400,000
Size:	312,677 sq km
Telephone Country Code:	48
eKit Access Number:	00800-111-3535

HI Suggests...

Poland is the largest of the East European countries located in the Centre of Europe. It neighbours Germany - to the west, the Czech Republic and Slovakia - to the south, the Ukraine, Belarus, and Lithuania - to the east, and the Russian Federation - to the north. With more than 500 km of coastline the Baltic Sea plays a major part of the northern Polish "border". The capital city is Warsaw, (Warszawa) which has a population of 1.6 million and is located in the central part of the country.

Many Polish tourist sights have already gained a worldwide reputation and are an absolute must. Places to visit include Kraków, Lodz, Wroclaw, Gdansk, Szczecin and Poznan. The tourist season runs from May to September, mainly peaking in July and August. At this time the Baltic beaches are taken over by swarms of people as tourists invade resorts and spas. Masurain lakes become crowded with thousands of sailboats and the range of mountains can hardly been seen for walkers.

The unique nature of various places in Poland is underlined by the fact that some of them have been included in the UNESCO World Cultural and Natural

Heritage List. The lists include places like the historical old Town Halls of Cracow, Torun and Zamosc, the Old Town in Arsaw, the castle of Malbork (the capital of the Teutonic Knights Order), the salt mine of Wieliczka near Cracow (a technology monument). Also included is the State Museum of Oswiecim (the former Nazi concentration camp of Auschwitz).

'ou can find out a lot more on our ,ebsite - a visit to www.HIhostels.com is ssential for planning your trip!

Pour en savoir plus, rendez-vous sur notre site Internet, www.HIhostels.com une visite incontournable pour préparer votre voyage!

Viele weitere Informationen auf unserer Website: www.HIhostels.com - unverzichtbar für die Reiseplanung!

Puedes averiguar mucho más en nuestro sitio web. Es imprescindible que visites la página www.HIhostels.com para planear tu viaje.

△ ***Białowieża*** – *"Paprotka" – 46010*
ul. Gen. Waszkiewicza 6,
17-230 Białowieża.
(85) 6812560 (85) 6812560
sm@paprotka.com.pl
www.paprotka.com.pl
Open Dates: Warszawa 230km
23km 50m x 46 R
TV P

△ ***Białystok*** – *"Podlasie" – 46011*
ul. Piłsudskiego 7b, 15-443 Białystok.
(85) 6524250 (85) 6526069
ssm@ssm.bialystok.ids.pl;
recepcjo@ssm.biolystok.ids.pl
www.ssmbialystok.ids.pl
Open Dates: Warszawa 189km
500m 500m x 52 R
TV P

△ ***Biecz*** – *46012*
ul. Parkowa 1, 38-340 Biecz.
(13) 4471829; 4471014
(13) 4471014
Open Dates: Kraków 300m
300m x 130 R
TV P

△ ***Bielsko-Biała*** – *"Bolka i Lolka" – 46013*
ul. Starobielska 10, 43-300 Bielsko-Biała.
(33) 8167466 (33) 8167466
ssmbielsko@poczta.onet.pl
www.ssmbielsko.republika.pl
Open Dates: 2km x 60
R TV P

△ ***Bóbrkak/Krosna*** – *46014*
38-458 Chorkówka.
(13) 4313097 ptsmbobrkakr@op.pl
Open Dates: 01.05-31.10 Krosno 13km
200m x 30 R

△ ***Bóbrka k/Soliny*** – *46015*
Bóbrka k/Soliny, 38-612 Solina.
(13) 4691861
Open Dates: 01.07-31.08 x 45 TV P

△ ***Buczkowice*** – *46016*
ul. Grunwaldzka 220, 43-374 Buczkowice.
(33) 8177300 (33) 8177300
ssm.buczkowice@wp.pl
www.schronisko.mfirma.net
Open Dates: Bielsko-Biała 12km
300m x 63 R TV
2km

△ ***Bukowiec*** – *"Skalnik" – 46017*
ul. Szkolna 2, 58-533 Mysłakowice.
(75) 7182628 (75) 7182628
Open Dates: 3km x 47
R TV P

▲ **Bydgoszcz** – 46018
ul. Sowińskiego 5, 85-083 Bydgoszcz.
(52) 3227570 (52) 3227570
schronisko@artinfo.com.pl
www.ssm.bydgoszcz.pl
Open Dates: 10km 500m
3km x 100 R P

△ ***Chełm*** – *46019*
ul. Czarnieckiego 8, 22-100 Chełm.
(82) 5640022
Open Dates: 1.5km 800m
x 49 R P

△ ***Chmielno*** – *"Checz Dlo Wanogów" – 46020*
ul. Gryfa Pomorskiego 33,
83-333 Chmielno.
(58) 6842322 (58) 6842216
wanoznik1@wp.pl
www.calekaszuby.prv.pl
Open Dates: 40km 2.5km
30m x 50 R TV P
300m

△ ***Chodzież*** – *"Gontyniec" – 46021*
ul. Kochanowkiego 1, 64-800 Chodzież.
(67) 2812460 (67) 2812460
Open Dates: 1km 1km
x 56 R TV P
1.5km

△ ***Ciechanów*** – *46022*
ul. 17 Stycznia 66, 06-400 Ciechanów.
(23) 6722404; 6724832
(23) 6722404
Open Dates: Warszawa 120km
300m 1.5km x 35 R
P

△ ***Ciężkowice*** – *46024*
ul. Św Andrzeja 6, 33-190 Ciężkowice.
(14) 6510477 schronisko@eranet.pl
www.zsoiz.hopto.pl
Open Dates: 1.7km 250m
x 40 R P

△ ***Cieszyn*** *– 46023*
ul. Błogocka 24, 43-300 Cieszyn.
(33) 8521629 (33) 8521470
ssm@autograf.pl
ssm-cieszyn.republika.pl
Open Dates: 12km 300m
x 65

△ ***Częstochowa*** *– 46025*
ul. Jasnogórska 84/90, 42-200 Częstochowa.
(34) 3243121
Open Dates: 01.07-31.08 1.5km
1.5km x 90

△ ***Ełk*** *– 46028*
ul. Sikorskiego 7a, 19-300 Ełk.
(87) 6102514
Open Dates: 01.07-31.08 x 45

▲ **Gdańsk** – 46032
ul. Wałowa 21, 80-858 Gdańsk.
(58) 3012313 (58) 3012313
biuro@mokf.com.pl
www.mokf.com.pl
Open Dates: 8km 300m
400m x 96
7km

▲ **Gdańsk** – 46030
ul. Grunwaldzka 244,
80-226 Gdańsk-Wrzeszcz.
(58) 3411660 (58) 3411660
biuro@mokf.com.pl
www.mokf.com.pl
Open Dates: 1km 9km
x 196

▲ **Gdańsk** – Hevelius – 46031
ul. Kartuska 245, 80-125 Gdańsk.
(58) 3020581; 3026044
(58) 3020581
hevelius@schronisko-hevelius.com.pl
www.schronisko-hevelius.com.pl
Open Dates: 8km 4km
400m x 62
7km

△ ***Gdynia*** *– 46033*
ul. Energetyków 13a, 81-184 Gdynia.
(58) 6271005 (58) 6271005
ssm-gdynia@wp.pl
Open Dates: Gdańsk 15km 3km
3km x 110

△ ***Gliwice*** *– "Ślązaczek" – 46034*
ul. Krakusa 16, 44-100 Gliwice.
(32) 2302525; 2306831
(32) 2306831 ptsm@zsti.gliwice.pl
www.zsti.gliwice.pl/ptsm
Open Dates: Katowice 47km
3.5km x 50
2km

△ ***Głuchołazy*** *– 46035*
Powstańców Śląskich 33,
48-340 Głuchołazy.
(77) 4391547 (77) 4391547
ssmglucholazy@wp.pl
www.noclegi.glucholazy.pl
Open Dates: 2km 500m
x 150 200m

△ ***Gniezno*** *– 46036*
ul. Pocztowa 11, 62-200 Gniezno.
(61) 4262780 (61) 4262780
www.man.poznan.pl
Open Dates: 300m x 55

△ ***Góra Św. Anny*** *– 46038*
ul. Szkolna 1, 47-154 Góra Św. Anny.
(77) 4615473
www.bip.powiatstrzelecki.pl
Open Dates: 7km 500m
x 50 3km

△ ***Gòrzanka*** *– 46039*
38-613 Wołkowyja.
(13) 4692868
www.bieszczady/gorzanka.pl
Open Dates: 50m x 50

△ ***Gorzòw Wielkopolski*** *– 46040*
ul. St.Wyszyńskiego 8, 66-400 Gorzòw Wlkp.
(95) 7227470 (95) 7227470
Open Dates: 1km 2km
x 86 2km

△ ***Grudziądz*** *– 46041*
ul. Gen. Hallera 37, 86-300 Grudziądz.
(56) 6435540
Open Dates: 2km 2km
x 156

△ ***Iława*** *– 46042*
ul. Mierosławskiego 6, 14-200 Iława.
(89) 6486464 (89) 6486464
oswj@post.pl www.ssm.ilawa.msi.pl
Open Dates: 2km 2km
x 60

△ ***Inowrocław*** *– 46043*
ul. Poznańska 345a, 88-100 Inowrocław.
(52) 3537222
Open Dates: 28.06-28.08 5km
5km x 48

△ ***Istebna Zaolzie*** *– "Zaolzianka" – 46044*
43-470 Istebna 563.
(33) 8556049 (33) 8556049
zaolzianka@op.pl
www.schroniska.wb.pl
Open Dates: 10km x 89
10km

△ ***Jabłonki*** *– "Akademia Bieszczadzka" – 46045*
38-606 Baligród.
(13) 4684026 (13) 4684026
ptsmjablonki@op.pl
www.ptsm.pl/jablonki
Open Dates: 30km 200m
x 80

△ ***Jarosław*** *– 46046*
ul. Reymonta 1, 37-500 Jarosław.
(16) 6233356; 6212563
(16) 6233356
bursajaroslaw@neostrada.pl
www.bursajaroslaw.neostrada.pl
Open Dates: 300m 300m
x 50
150m

△ ***Jelenia Góra*** *– "Bartek" – 46048*
ul. Bartka Zwycięzcy 10,
58-500 Jelenia Góra.
(75) 7525746 (75) 7525746
ssm.bartek@wp.pl
Open Dates: 500m 500m
x 48

△ ***Kamień*** *– "Halny" – 46050*
Kamień k/ Świeradowa, 59-630 Mirsk.
(75) 7834336 (75) 7834336
Open Dates: 8km 300m
x 60

△ ***Karpacz*** *– "Liczyrzepa" – 46051*
ul. Gimnazjalna 9, 58-540 Karpacz.
(75) 7619290 (75) 7619290
www.liczyrzepa.wczasy.net.pl
Open Dates: Wrocław 20km
600m x 50
2km

△ ***Katowice*** *– "Ślązaczek" – 46052*
ul. Sokolska 26, 40-086 Katowice.
(32) 3511956 (32) 3511952
ssm@sltzn.katowice.pl
Open Dates: Katowice 40km
1km 300m x 50
2km

△ ***Kielce*** *– "Wędrownik" – 46053*
ul. Szymanowskiego 5, 25-361 Kielce.
(41) 3423735 (41) 3423735
ssml@poczta.onet.pl
Open Dates: 3km 3km
x 65
100m

Kłębowo – "Świteź" – 46054
11-100 Lidzbark Warmiński,
Kłębowo 50.
(89) 7662382; 7662360
(89) 7662381
smsymsar@poczta.onet.pl
www.ptsm.org.pl
Open Dates: Open Times: 06.00-23.00hrs
Beds: 212 - 1x[1] 3x[2] 8x[3] 12x[4] 7x[5] 16x[6]
Price Range: 20-40 PLN € 6.00-12.00 BB inc
Directions: Olsztyn 8km
ap Lidzbark Warm x 24
1 x
100m

Kłębowo – "Świteź"

△ ***Kletno*** *– MIŚ – 46055*
Kletno 8, 57-550 Stronie Śl.
(74) 8141358
www.kletno.info.pl/noclegi/ptsm.htm
Open Dates: 7km 2km
x 40 R

▲ **Kłodzko** – 46056
ul. Nadrzeczna 5, 57-300 Kłodzko.
(74) 8672524 (74) 8672524
Open Dates: 500m 500m
x 50 R TV P

△ ***Kobylnica*** *– "Sarenka" – 46057*
ul. Poznańska 50, 62-006 Kobylnica.
(61) 8150002 (61) 8150002
Open Dates: 200m 50m
x 45 R P

△ ***Konin-Gosławice*** *– 46058*
ul. Leopolda Staffa 5,
62-505 Konin Gosławice.
(63) 2427235 (63) 2427235
schroniskoptsm@konin.1m.pl
www.man.poznan.pl-ptsm
Open Dates: 8km 500m
x 60 R TV P 1.5km

△ ***Koszalin*** *– "Gościniec" – 46059*
ul. Gnieźnieńska 8, 75-735 Koszalin.
(94) 3426068 (94) 3426068
schroniskomlodziezowe1@neostrada.pl
Open Dates: 2km 2km
x 80 R TV P 2.5km

△ ***Kraków*** *– "Oleandry" – 46060*
ul. Oleandry 4, 30-060 Kraków.
(12) 6338822; 6338920
(12) 6338920
schronisko@smkrakow.pl
www.smkrakow.pl
Open Dates: Kraków 3km
3km x 330 R
P 50m

▲ **Kraków** HI 46002
ul. Grochowa 21, 30-731 Kraków.
(12) 6532432 (12) 6506730
krakov@ssm.com.pl www.ssm.com.pl
Open Dates: Kraków 15km 7km
7km x 250 R TV P
200m

△ ***Kraków*** *– 46061*
ul. Szablowskiego 1C, 30-127 Kraków.
(12) 6371353; 6372441
(12) 6372441
Open Dates: 01.04-30.10 Kraków
x 150 R P

△ ***Kuraszków*** *– "Dworek" – 46062*
ul. Turystyczna 50,
55-120 Oborniki Śląskie.
(71) 3102571 (71) 3102571
Open Dates: 25km 300m
4km x 50 R TV P
3km

△ ***Lądek Zdròj*** *– "Skalniak" – 46063*
Stójków 36, 57-540 Lądek Zdrój.
(74) 8146645 (74) 8146645
sssm_skalniak@wp.pl
www.ssm_skalniak.webpark.pl
Open Dates: 100m 50m
x 45 R TV P 3km

△ ***Łagów/Kielce*** *– 46065*
ul. Zaptotnia 4a, 26-025 Łagów.
(41) 3074104
kierownik.ssm@interia.pl
www.ssm.prv.pl
Open Dates: Kielce 36km Kielce
30km 200m x 48 R
TV P

▲ Lanckorona – 46066
ul. Kazimierza Wielkiego 1,
34-143 Lanckorona.
(33) 8763589 (33) 8763589
ssmlanckorona@interia.pl
Open Dates: 38km 5km 100m x 100

---

*△ **Łańcut** – 46067*
ul. Mickiewicza 3, 37-100 Łańcut.
(17) 2252961 (17) 2252961
Open Dates: 01.07-25.08 x 25

---

*△ **Łazy** – 46068*
Łazy, 32-048 Jerzmanowice.
(12) 3895208 (12) 3895208
ptsm-lazy@ceti.pl www.ptsm.pl/lazy
Open Dates: 20km 25km 2km x 61

---

*△ **Legnica** – 46069*
ul. Jordana 17, 59-220 Legnica.
(76) 8625412 (76) 8628280
Open Dates: 1km 1km x 60

---

*△ **Lesko** – "Bieszczadnik" – 46070*
ul. Jana Pawła II 18B, 36-600 Lesko.
(13) 4696269 (13) 4696269
ptsmlesko@op.pl
www.republika.pl/ptsmlesko
Open Dates: 9km 400m x 200

▲ Łódź – Legionòw 46003
ul. Legionów 27, 91-069 Łódź.
(42) 6306680 (42) 6306683
youthhostellodz@wp.pl
www.youthhostellodz.wp.pl
Open Dates: 2km x 74

---

*△ **Lubsko** – 46073*
ul. Dąbrowskiego 6, 68-300 Lubsko.
(68) 3720398
Open Dates: 1km 1km x 30

---

*△ **Mąchocice** – 46074*
Mąchocice-Scholasteria, 26-001 Masłów.
(41) 3112165
Open Dates: Kielce 18km x 46

---

*△ **Malbork** – 46075*
ul. Żeromskiego 45, 82-200 Malbork.
(55) 2722408 (55) 2722511
gimnazjum@malbork.com
www.malbork.com/gimnazjumm1
Open Dates: 500m 500m x 53

---

*△ **Michałowice** – "Złoty Widok" – 46076*
ul. Kolonijna 14, 58-573 Piechowice.
(75) 7612391 (75) 7612391
Open Dates: 3km 3km x 46
5km

▲ Nagłowice – 46081
ul. Mikołaja, Reja 40, 28-362 Nagłowice.
(41) 3814382 (41) 3814921
dworekreja@wp.pl
www.naglowice.glt.pl
Open Dates: 120km Jedrzejów 15km 500m x 60

---

*△ **Nowa Słupia** – "Pod Pielgrzymem" – 46082*
ul. Świętokrzyska 61, 26-006 Nowa Słupia.
(41) 3177016 (41) 3177016
Open Dates: Kielce 25km Kielce 31km 900m x 53

---

*△ **Nowy Jaromierz** – 46083*
Nowy Jaromierz, 64-220 Kargowa.
(68) 3525545; 3525670
Open Dates: 500m x 25
2km

---

*△ **Nowy Sącz** – 46084*
Rejtana 18, 33-300 Nowy Sącz.
(18) 4423897 (18) 4423897
Open Dates: 100m 200m x 50

---

*△ **Nysa** – "Pod Ziębickim Lwem" – 46085*
ul. Krawiecka 28, 48-300 Nysa.
(77) 4333731 (77) 4333731
ssmnysa@autograf.pl
www.kaolett.ol.pl/nysa
Open Dates: 3km 500m x 48
500m

△ ***Olkusz*** *– "Jura" – 46086*
ul. Legionów Polskich 3, 32-300 Olkusz.
(32) 7546986 *juraol@poczta.fm*
www.schroniska.wb.pl
Open Dates: x 80

△ ***Olsztyn*** *– 46087*
ul. Kosciuszki 72/74 Olsztyn.
(89) 5276650 *(89) 5276770*
ssmolsztyn@ptsm.com.pl
www.ptsm.com.pl/olsztyn/
Open Dates: *700m* *900m*
x 70

△ ***Opole*** *– 46088*
ul. Torowa 7, 45-073 Opole.
(77) 4542855 *(77) 4531178*
ssmopole@02.pl
www.ssm.opole.prv.pl
Open Dates: *Wrocław 100km*
600m *600m* x 48

△ ***Osieczna*** *– "Morena" – 46089*
ul. Kopernika 4, 64-113 Osieczna.
(65) 5350134 *(65) 5350134*
Open Dates: *12km* *400m*
x 60
250m

△ ***Paczków*** *– "Pod Basztą" – 46091*
ul. Kołłątaja 9, 48-370 Paczków.
(77) 4316441 *(77) 4316441*
Open Dates: 01.07-31.08 *2km*
500m x 25

△ ***Pawełki*** *– 46092*
ul. Główna 14, 42-713 Kochanowice.
(34) 3533716
Open Dates: *50km* *4km*
50m x 43

△ ***Piła*** *– "Staszicówka" – 46093*
AL. WP 45, 64-920 Piła.
(67) 2132583 *(67) 2132583*
Open Dates: *1km* *1km*
x 40

▲ **Piotrków Trybunalski** – "Trybunalski" – 46152
97-300, ul. Grota Roweckiego 5.
(44) 6478712 (44) 6478780
schronisko@trybunalskie.pl
www.trybunalskie.pl
Open Dates: Warszawa 147km
50m 50m x 52

▲ **Pobierowo** – "Fala" – 46096
ul. Mickiewicza 19, 72-346 Pobierowo.
(91) 3864243 (91) 3864243
ssm@gryfice.pl
www.republika.pl/fala-pobierowo
Open Dates: 100km 20km
700m x 62
400m

▲ **Poznań** – TPD – 46098
ul. Drzymały 3, 60-613 Poznań.
(61) 8485836 (61) 8490982
www.schronisko.TPD.com.pl
Open Dates: 6km 3km
2.5km x 45

△ ***Poznań*** *– 46097*
ul. Berwińskiego 2/3, 60-765 Poznań.
(61) 8664040 *(61) 8664040*
www.ssm3.prv.pl
Open Dates: *12km* *500m*
1km x 49

▲ **Poznań** – "Hanka" 46004
ul. Biskupińska 27, 60-463 Poznań.
(61) 8407128 (61) 8221063
schroniskohanka@onet.pl
www.schroniskohanka.com
Open Dates: 4km 6km 6km
x 90

▲ **Poznań** – im PE Strzeleckiego – 46099
ul. Głuszyna 127, 61-329 Poznań.
(61) 8788907 (61) 8788461
sp3xph@poczta.onet.pl
www.infhotel.pl
Open Dates: 20km 12km
x 70

△ ***Przemków*** *– 46100*
ul. Głogowska 37, 59-325 Przemków.
(76) 8319465 *(76) 8320613*
Open Dates: *800m* x 53

▲ **Przemyśl** – "Matecznik" – 46101
ul. Lelewela 6, 37-700 Przemyśl.
(16) 6706145 (16) 6706145
www.ptsm-matecznil.pl
Open Dates: 1km 800m
x 54

△ ***Przytok** – 46102*
66-003 Zabór.
(68) 3274410 (68) 3274410
palac@box43.pl
www.osw-przytok.com.pl
Open Dates: 35km 7km
150m x 42

▲ **Puławy** – 46103
ul. Włostowicka 27, 24-100 Puławy.
(81) 8883656; 8863367
(81) 8883656
ssmpulawy@echoson.com.pl
www.ssmpulawy.republika.pl
Open Dates: Warszawa 125km
5km 2.5km x 118
3km

△ ***Radom** – 46150*
ul. Limanowskiego 34/40, 26-600 Radom.
(48) 3602214 (48) 3628701
ssmrandom@neostrada.pl
www.ssmradom.republika.pl
Open Dates: Warszawa 100km
1km x 260
2km

△ ***Radomsko** – 46104*
ul. Piastowska 21, 97-500 Radomsko.
(44) 6834495
Open Dates: 1km 1km
x 30 1km

△ ***Rzeszòw** – "Alko" – 46107*
Rynek 25, 35-064 Rzeszòw.
(17) 8534430
Open Dates: 15km 500m
500m x 90
500m

△ ***Sanok** – 46108*
ul. Konarskiego 10, 38-500 Sanok.
(13) 4630925 (13) 4630925
soswsanok@op.pl
Open Dates: 01.07-31.08 500m
500m x 60

▲ **Sławkòw Niwa** – 46109
ul. Niwa 45, 42-533 Sławkòw.
(32) 2931100; 2619938
(32) 2931100
schronisko_m@turystyczny.pl
www.turystyczny.pl/~schronisko_m
Open Dates: Katowice 20km 4km
x 50

△ ***Śmigiel** – 46111*
ul. M. Konopnickiej 4a, 64-030 Śmigiel.
(65) 5180293
www.man.poznan.pl/~ptsm
Open Dates: 1.5km 500m
x 48 (D)

△ ***Solec n/Wisła** – 46151*
Łoteckiego 24; 27-320 Solec n/Wisła.
(48) 3761202 (48) 3761202
schmomiskosolec@poczta.onet.pl
www.zspsolec.prv.pl
Open Dates: 160km 40km
x 39

△ ***Stalowa Wola** – 46113*
ul. Podleśna 15, 37-450 Stalowa Wola.
(15) 8421772
Open Dates: 01.07-25.08 x 40

△ ***Strużnica** – "Sokolik" – 46114*
58-533 Mysłakowice.
(75) 7137224 (75) 7137224
www.sosm_jeleniagopoczta.onet.pl
Open Dates: 8km x 37
8km

△ ***Sucha Beskidzka** – 46153*
34-200, ul, Kościelna 5B.
(33) 8743189 (33) 8741553
ssmsucha@ssmsuchab.lap.pl
ssmsuchab.lap.pl
Open Dates: 70km 3km
x 60

△ ***Świdnica** – 46115*
ul. Kanonierska 3, 58-100 Świdnica.
(74) 8522645 (74) 8577050
www.zsbt.swidnica.pl
Open Dates: 1km x 90

△ ***Świnoujście*** *– 46117*
ul. Gdyńska 26, 72-6 00 Świnoujście.
(91) 3270613 (91) 3270613
Open Dates: 1.5km 1.5km
x 140

△ ***Szamotuły*** *– 46118*
ul. Obornicka 12, 64-500 Szamotuły.
(61) 2932089 (61) 2932089
Open Dates: 32km 1km
100m x 44
1.5km

▲ **Szczecin** – "Cuma" 46005
ul. Monte Cassino 19a, 70-467 Szczecin.
(91) 4224761 (91) 4235696
ptsm@home.pl www.ptsm.home.pl
Open Dates: 30km 2.5km
2.5km 2NW x 130 CC

△ ***Szczyrk*** *– "Hondrasik" – 46119*
ul. Sportowa 2, 43-370 Szczyrk.
(33) 8178933 (33) 8178933
Open Dates: 100km
Bielsko-Biała 17km 20m
x 50 150m

△ ***Szczytno*** *– "Pod Kasztanem" – 46120*
ul. Pasymska 7, 12-100 Szczytno.
(89) 6243992 aneri@ope.pl
Open Dates: 1.5km 1.5km
x 46

△ ***Szklarska Poręba*** *– "Wojtek" – 46121*
ul. Piastowska 1, 58-585 Szklarska Poręba.
(75) 7172141 (75) 7172141
sssmwojtek@op.pl
www.ptsm.jeleniagóra.prv.pl/wojtek
Open Dates: 1km 2.5km
x 50 1km

△ ***Szydłowiec*** *– "Skałka" – 46122*
ul. Kosciuszki 39a, 26-500 Szydłowiec.
(48) 6174311
schronisko.szydlowiec@wp.pl
Open Dates: 5km 1km
x 45 1km

△ ***Tomaszów Mazowiecki*** *– 46124*
ul. Polskiego Czerwonego Krzyża 10 (MOS), 97-200 Tomaszów Mazowiecki.
(44) 7246334; 7247434
Open Dates: 5km 5km
x 45
500m

△ ***Toruń*** *– 46125*
ul. Św. Józefa 26, 87-100 Toruń.
(56) 6544107; 6544580
(56) 6544791
schronisko@zsmeie.torun.pl
www.zsmeie.torun.pl/glowna/glowna/inter/index.php
Open Dates: 8km x 60
20m

Ustroń-Jaszowiec – "Wiecha" 46006
ul. Stroma 5, 43-450 Ustroń-Jaszowiec.
(33) 8543501; 8542741
(33) 8543501 sm-wiecha@post.pl
www.republika.pl/poniwiec; www.hostelling.com.pl
Open Dates: Open Times: 06.00-23.00hrs
Beds: 170 - 3x1 14x2 10x3 10x4 11x6
Price Range: 20-80 PLN € 6.00-22.00 BB inc
Directions: 3km 3km x 33
3 x
50m

Ustroń-Jaszowiec – "Wiecha"

△ ***Wałcz*** *– 46128*
Al. Zdobywców Wału Pomorskiego 76, 78-600 Wałcz.
(67) 2582749
Open Dates: 01.07-25.08 2km 2km x 25

▲ **Warszawa** – Myśliwiecka – 46131
ul. Myśliwiecka 9 (MOS Agrykola), 00-459 Warszawa.
(22) 6229111 (22) 6229105
recepcja@hotelagrykola.pl
www.hotelagrykola.pl
Open Dates: 15km 5km 1SW x 70

▲ **Warszawa** – "Syrenka" 46008
ul. Karolkowa 53a, 01-197 Warszawa.
(22) 6328829 (22) 6329746
ssmr6@ptsm.com.pl
www.ptsm.com.pl/ssmnr6
Open Dates: 10km 4km x 140

▲ **Warszawa** 46007
ul. Smolna 30, 00-375 Warszawa.
(22) 8278952 (22) 8278952
ssmsmolna@poczta.onet.pl
www.smolna30.pl
Open Dates: 7km 1.5km x 110

△ ***Wetlina*** *– 46133*
38-608 Wetlina 16.
(13) 4684606
www.bieszczady.pl/ssmwetlina
Open Dates: 180km Zagórz 300m x 52 3km

△ ***Włocławek*** *– "Kujawiak" – 46134*
ul. Mechaników 1, 87-800 Włocławek.
(54) 2362410 (54) 2362410
Open Dates: 3km 3km x 48

▲ **Wrocław** – "Tumski" – 46138
ul. Wyspa Słodowa 10, 50-266 Wrocław.
(71) 3226099; 3226088
(71) 3226113
hotel@hotel-tumski.com.pl
www.hotel-tumski.com.pl
Open Dates: 12km 2km 2km 0.2N x 50

△ ***Wrocław*** *– 46136*
ul. Kiełczowska 43, 51-315 Wrocław.
(71) 3457396 (71) 3457396
ssm-lzn@com.pl
www.ssm-lzn.com.pl
Open Dates: 14km 1km 500m x 106 6km

△ ***Wrocław*** *– 46137*
ul. Kołłątaja 20, 50-007 Wrocław.
(71) 3438856 (71) 3438857
mdkkopermik1@wp.pl
Open Dates: 10km 200m 200m x 49 450m

△ ***Zagórze Śląskie*** *– "Gwarek" – 46140*
ul. Główna 17, 58-321 Jugowice.
(74) 8453383
Open Dates: Walbrzych 12km x 52

▲ **Zakopane** – "Szarotka" – 46009
ul. Nowotarska 45G, 34-500 Zakopane.
(18) 2013618; 2066203
(18) 2066203
schroniskoptsm@pro.onet.pl
www.szarotkaptsm.republika.pl
Open Dates: Kraków 100km 500m 500m x 60 19 x

△ ***Zaniemyśl*** *– 46141*
ul. Poznańska 28, 63-020 Zaniemyśl.
(505) 006306 www.zaniemysl.pl
Open Dates: Pozniañ 40km 10km x 45 1km

△ ***Zawoja*** *– 46142*
34-222, Zawoja-Wełcza.
(33) 8775059 (33) 8775059
smzawojawelcza@iap.pl
www.smzawojawelcza@iap.pl
Open Dates: Kraków 90km 20km 800m x 50 3.5km

▲ **Zduńska Wola** – "Czekay" – 46143
ul. Dolna 41, 98-220 Zduńska Wola.
(43) 8232440; 8232374
(43) 8232440
Open Dates: 2km 1.5km x 90

△ ***Zielona Gòra*** *– 46146*
ul. Długa 13, 65-036 Zielona Gòra.
(68) 4530139 (68) 3202571
Open Dates: 45km 1km
x 73
2km

△ ***Złotoryja*** *– Zacisze – 46148*
ul. Kolejowa 2, 59-500 Złotoryja.
(76) 8783674 (76) 8783674
www.sudety.it.pl
Open Dates: x 50
500m

△ ***Żerków*** *– 46144*
ul. Cmentarna 10, 63-210 Żerków.
(62) 7403015 (62) 7403015
www.zerkowszkola.republika.pl
Open Dates: 500m 500m
x 37 1.5km

▲ **Żywiec** – "Pod Grojcem" – 46149
ul. KEN 3, 34-300 Żywiec.
(33) 8612639 (33) 8612939
ssmzywiec@poczta.onet.pl
Open Dates: 50m 10m
x 73

Portugal

MOVIJOVEM - Mobilidade Juvenil
Cooperativa de Interesse Público e Responsabilidade Lda,
Rua Lúcio de Azevedo, 27,
1600-146 Lisboa, Portugal.

t (351) (21) 7232100; Reservations (351) (707) 203030
f (351) (21) 7232101; Reservations (351) (21) 3568129
e movijovem@movijovem.pt (General)
e informacoes@movijovem.pt (Information)
e reservas@movijovem.pt (Reservations)
w www.pousadasjuventude.pt; www.juventude.gov.pt

Office Hours: Monday-Friday 09.00-13.00hrs; 14.00-18.00hrs

A copy of the Hostel Directory for this Country can be obtained from:
The National Office

National Tourist Authority/Board:	www.visitportugal.com
Capital:	Lisboa
Language:	Portuguese
Currency:	€ Euro
Population:	10,500,000
Size:	92,082 sq km
Telephone Country Code:	351
eKit Access Number:	800-812-993

HI Suggests...

Portugal is an easygoing country. There are lots to explore and it's easy to travel around. Although a small country, Portugal is a country full of surprises. For example, the landscape is very rich and diverse. If you have the opportunity to travel through continental Portugal and in the two archipelagos (Açores and Madeira), you will experience different sceneries, ranging from mountainous landscapes, to a green inland and a sweeping coastline, spectacularly located castles, medieval villages and beautiful beaches.

Many different people have inhabited one of the oldest nations in Europe, Portugal, throughout the centuries. D.Afonso Henriques, who was made the first King of Portugal in 1143, gradually gained the land from the Moors, towards the south, and managed to conquer Lisbon. The conquest of the Alentejo and the Algarve took another century, and then the borders of the country were definitively established. A crucial period in Portuguese history was the Maritime Discoveries during the 15th and 16th centuries, when Portugal was one of the richest and most powerful nations in the world.

Apart from history, the Portuguese are generally known for their excellent hospitality and welcoming.

In everyday life, one of the most popular habits is going out for a coffee. Virtually no one goes without an espresso after a meal, not to mention the many 'espressos breaks' throughout the day! It's seen as a good opportunity to go out, even if it's just around the corner, to have a chat with friends or neighbours.

But it isn't just coffee that gets us going, especially from Thursday evening onwards. Restaurants, cinemas, theatres, bars and discos become full of young people looking for leisure and fun. On weekends, whenever the sun is shining people hang out in gardens, parks and outdoor cafés. The Portuguese also love shopping and won't do without the occasional trip to the nearest shopping mall.

Away from the busy city areas, you can find typical villages, where life is lived according to a more tranquil rhythm. Many of these places keep their own traditional way of life – agriculture activities, handicrafts, folk music and dance, or work in small family industries. People are normally very close from their community fellows and like to get together for a chat in the main square of their hometown or outside the church area after mass.

No visit to Portugal is complete without trying one of the country's main attractions, next to its enchanting landscapes and good weather – the traditional Portuguese cuisine! All regions in Portugal have some tempting local delicacies, which can range from fish and meat dishes to cheeses and onto desserts. Dig in!

You can find out a lot more on our website - a visit to www.HIhostels.com is essential for planning your trip!

Pour en savoir plus, rendez-vous sur notre site Internet, www.HIhostels.com une visite incontournable pour préparer votre voyage!

Viele weitere Informationen auf unserer Website: www.HIhostels.com - unverzichtbar für die Reiseplanung!

Puedes averiguar mucho más en nuestro sitio web. Es imprescindible que visites la página www.HIhostels.com para planear tu viaje.

▲ **Abrantes** – 47023
Av. Eng. Adelino Amaro da Costa, 2200-195 Abrantes.
(241) 379210 (241) 379211
abrantes@movijovem.pt
Open Dates: 01.01-23.12; 26-31.12 Lisboa 137km Rossio Abrantes 3km Abrantes 2.5km x 62 1 x 1km 5km

---

▲ **Açores - S.Miguel Island - Ponta Delgada** – 47039
Rua S.Francisco Xavier, 9500-243 Ponta Delgada.
(296) 629431 (296) 629672
pontadelgada@movijovem.pt
Open Dates: 01.01-23.12; 26-31.12 Ponta Delgada 5km x 90 1km 1km

---

▲ Açores - Terceira Island - Angra Do Heroísmo – 47026
Negrito, S.Mateus, 9700 Angra Do Heroísmo.
(295) 642095 (295) 642095
angraheroismo@movijovem.pt
Open Dates: 01.01-23.12; 26-31.12 Lajes 20km Praia Da Vitória 20km
100m ap Negrito 1SW x 71
(B)
24km

▲ Alcoutim – 47024
8970-000 Alcoutim.
(281) 546004 (281) 546332
alcoutim@movijovem.pt
Open Dates: 01.01-23.12; 26-31.12 Faro 114km Vila Real Sto. António 40km
500m ap Alcoutim 0.5N x 70
1 x
500m

Almada 47013
Quinta do Bucelinho-Pragal-Almada, 2805-358 Almada.
(21) 2943491 (21) 2943497
almada@movijovem.pt
Open Dates: 01.01-24.12; 26-31.12
Open Times:
Beds: 126 - 2x 13x 23x 1x
Price Range: € 10-20 (price per person) BB inc
Directions: 2E from city centre
Lisboa 13km Cacilhas 5km
Pragal 2km 400m ap Pragal
2km ap Pragal x 1
2 x
3km 6km

Almada

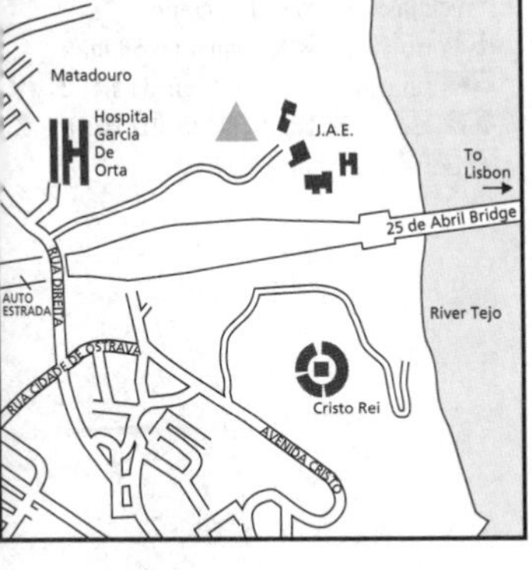

Almada... Travel Tips

- **For budget eats check out...** Atira-Te Ao Rio, A Cabrinha, O Lavrador, A Nau, Europa Mar
- **For great nightlife try...** Hacienda Club, Remédio Santo, Swell Club, Knock Out, Lisbon Night Life (Bairro Alto and Docas)
- **Don't miss...** Cristo Rei Sanctuary/Monument, Almada Museum, Medieval Museum, Botanic Garden, Costa Da Caparica beaches, Panoramic Lift (Boca do Vento), Peace Park, Capuchos Convent, Aroeira Golf

▲ Almograve – 47025
R. do Chafariz, 7630-017 Almograve.
(283) 640000 (283) 647035
almograve@movijovem.pt
Open Dates: 01.01-03.11; 26.11-15.12; 28.12-31.12 Lisboa 157km
Amoreiras - Odemira 50km 200m ap Almograve - Church 0.05E x 92
1 x
8
600m

▲ Areia Branca 47014
Largo João Soldado - Praia da Areia Branca, 2530 - 217 - Lourinhã.
(261) 422127 (261) 419056
areiabranca@movijovem.pt
Open Dates: 01.01-23.12; 26-31.12 Lisboa 71km Torres Vedras 20km 400m ap Praia Areia Branca 0.1SW x 84
1 x
50m

▲ Aveiro – 47027
Rua das Pombas, 3810-150 Aveiro.
(234) 420536 (234) 420536
aveiro@movijovem.pt
Open Dates: 01.01-23.12; 26-31.12 Porto 70km Aveiro 3.5km 5km ap Aveiro 2NW x 36
50m 18km

▲ Beja – 47028
Rua Prof. Janeiro Acabado, 7800-506 Beja.
(284) 325458 (284) 325468
beja@movijovem.pt
Open Dates: 01.01-23.12; 26-31.12 Lisboa 180km Beja 2km 100m ap Beja 1NE x 45
100m

PORTUGAL - PORTUGAL - PORTUGAL - PORTUGAL

▲ **Braga** – 47009
Rua de Santa Margarida 6, 4710-306 Braga.
(253) 616163 (253) 616163
braga@movijovem.pt
Open Dates: 01.01-04.12; 27-31.12 Porto 50km Braga 2km 1.5km ap Braga 2NE x 64 R CC TV 1km 30km

▲ **Bragança** – 47029
Forte de S.João de Deus (near City Hall), 5300-262 Bragança.
(273) 304600 (273) 304601
braganca@movijovem.pt
Open Dates: 01.01-23.12; 26-31.12 Porto 200km Vila Real 120km 400m ap Bragança 1SE x 86 R CC TV 1 x P 50m

▲ **Castelo Branco** – 47030
Rua Dr. Francisco José Palmeiro, 6000-230 Castelo Branco.
(272) 323838 (272) 323838
castelobranco@movijovem.pt
Open Dates: Closed for renovation works during 2006 Lisboa 244km Castelo Branco 2km 1.5km ap Castelo Branco 2E x 64 R CC (B) TV 1km

▲ **Coimbra** 47005
Rua Henriques Seco 14, 3000-145 Coimbra.
(239) 822955 (239) 821730
coimbra@movijovem.pt
Open Dates: 01.01-23.12; 26-31.12 Lisboa 200km Coimbra-A 3km 6, 7, 29 50m ap Coimbra 3NW x 72 R CC TV 3km 50km

▲ **Évora** – 47015
Rua Miguel Bombarda 40, 7000-919 Évora.
(266) 744848 (266) 744843
evora@movijovem.pt
Open Dates: Closed for renovation works during 2006 Lisboa 135km Évora 2km 2km ap Évora 0.1W x 90 R CC (B) TV P 4km

▲ **Faro** 47016
Rua da PSP, 8000-408 Faro.
(289) 826521 (289) 826521
faro@movijovem.pt
Open Dates: 01.01-23.12; 26-31.12 Faro 7km Faro 1.5km 1.5km ap Faro 1.5SW x 52 R CC TV 2km 9km

▲ **Foz do Cávado** 47011
Alameda Bom Jesus, Fão, 4740-322 Fão.
(253) 981790 (253) 981790
fozcavado@movijovem.pt
Open Dates: 01.01-23.12; 26-31.12 Porto 30km Póvoa do Varzim 15km 200m ap Fão 0.1NE x 88 R CC TV 1 x P 1km

▲ **Guarda** – 47031
Av. Alexandre Herculano, Edificio do IPJ 6300-659 Guarda.
(271) 224482 (271) 224482
guarda@movijovem.pt
Open Dates: 01.01-23.12; 26-31.12 Porto 180km Guarda 5km 1km ap Guarda 1N x 52 R CC TV P 3.5km

Guimarães – 47052
Complexo Multifuncional De Couros, Largo do Cidade, 8 - 4800 Guimarães.
(253) 421380 (253) 421381
guimaraes@movijovem.pt
Open Dates: 01.01-23.12; 26-31.12
Open Times:
Beds: 68 - 1x[1] 11x[2] 4x[4] 5x[6]
Price Range: € 8-20 (price per person) BBinc
Directions: 1NE from city centre
Porto 50km Guimarães 500m Guimarães 2km ap Alameda R CC (B) TV 1 x 3km

Guimarães

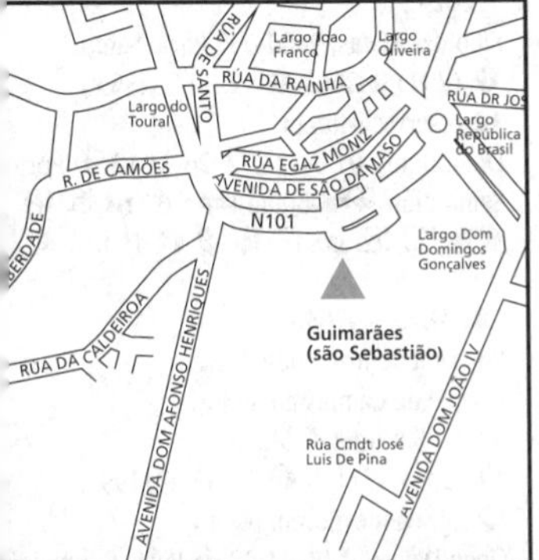

Lagos

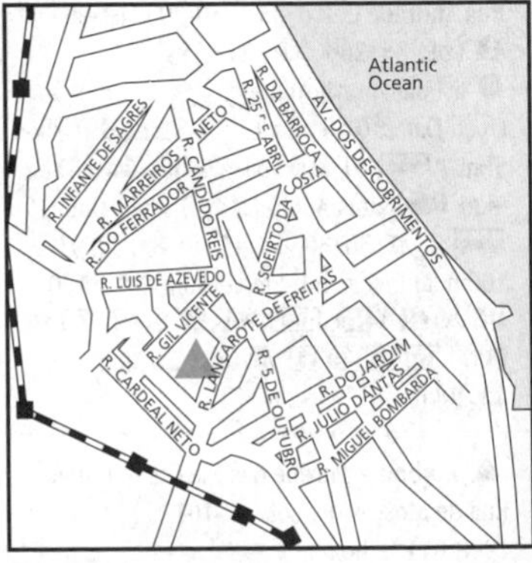

Guimarães... Travel Tips

- **For budget eats check out...** Oriental Etc, Cozinha Regional Santiago, La Presentosa (Italian), Manjares da Horta
- **For great nightlife try...** Século XIX, Ultimatum, Património, Tasquilhado, Secos e Molhados
- **Don't miss...** Guimarães Castle, Ducal Palace, Alberto Sampaio Museum, Martins Sarmento Museum, Mill Museum, Penha Mountain, Guimarães Historic Centre, Santa Marinha da Costa Convent, S. Francisco Church, Misericórdia Church

Lagos... Travel Tips

- **For budget eats check out...** Pátio, Terraço, Piri-Piri, Adega Da Marina, Casinha dos Petiscos
- **For great nightlife try...** Three Monkeys, Whites, Joe's Garage, Zanzibar, RGB
- **Don't miss...** Museum José Formosinho, Senhora Da Luz Castle, Almadena Fortress, Lago's Historic Centre, Slide & Splash Water Park, Lagos Sailing Club, Zoomarine, São Vicente Cape, Santo António Church, Monchique

Lagos Ⓗ 47003
Rua Lançarote de Freitas 50, 8600-605 Lagos.
Ⓣ (282) 761970 Ⓕ (282) 769684
Ⓔ lagos@movijovem.pt
Open Dates: 01.01-23.12; 26-31.12
Open Times: ⌚
Beds: 62 - 5x² 13x⁴
Price Range: € 8.00-22.50 (price per person)
BB inc
Directions: 0.5N from city centre
✈ Faro 88km 🚂 Lagos 1km 🚌 1km ap Lagos
500m 500m

▲ **Leiria** – 47032
Largo Cândido dos Reis 9, 2400-112 Leiria.
Ⓣ (244) 831868 Ⓕ (244) 831868
Ⓔ leiria@movijovem.pt
Open Dates: 01.01-23.12; 26-31.12 ✈ Lisboa 130km 🚂 Leiria 2km 🚌 400m ap Leiria
x 43
600m 21km

Lisboa ☛ Lisbon

▲ **Lisboa** – Catalazete Ⓗ 47006
Estrada Marginal (near Inatel), Catalazete, 2780-267 Oeiras.
Ⓣ (21) 4430638 Ⓕ (21) 4419267
Ⓔ catalazete@movijovem.pt
Open Dates: 01.01-23.12; 26-31.12 ✈ Lisboa 30km 🚂 Oeiras 1km x 86
1 x

▲ **Lisboa** – Central 47001
Rua Andrade Corvo 46, 1050-009 Lisboa.
(21) 3532696 (21) 3537541
lisboa@movijovem.pt
Open Dates: 01.01-24.12; 26-31.12 Lisboa 5km A 91 (Aerobus) 50m Lisboa 4km Santa Apolónia or Oriente 4km 1, 21, 36, 38, 44, 45, 49, 83, 90, 91 100m ap Picoas Picoas 50m x 170 3km 20km

▲ **Lisboa** – Parque das Nações – 47034
Rua de Moscavide, Lote 47-101,
1998-011 Lisboa
(21) 8920890 (21) 8920891
lisboaparque@movijovem.pt
Open Dates: 01.01-24.12; 26-31.12 Lisboa 2km A 44, 5 ap Av. d. João II 500m Oriente 1km 28, 44 500m ap Av. D. João II Oriente 1km 8NE x 92 10km

▲ **Madeira Island - Calheta** – 47060
Sítio dos Serrões Acima, 9370-224 Calheta.
(291) 822500 (291) 822507
reservas@ijm.pt
Open Dates: 01.01-23.12; 26-31.12
Madeira 60km 400m ap Calheta x 32 4km 6km

▲ **Madeira Island - Funchal** – Quinta da Ribeira – 47059
Calçada da Cabouqueira, 5,
9000-171 Funchal.
(291) 741540/381 (291) 742868
reservas@ijm.pt
Open Dates: 01.01-23.12; 26-31.12
Madeira 22km 50m x 125 (B) 1 x 2.5km 6km

▲ **Madeira Island - Porto Moniz** – 47061
Vila do Porto Moniz, 9270-095 Porto Moniz.
(291) 853915 (291) 853915
reservas@ijm.pt
Open Dates: 01.01-23.12; 26-31.12
Madeira 70km 100m x 22 800m

▲ **Madeira - Porto Santo Island** – 47062
Sítio das Matas, 9400-035 Porto Santo.
(291) 982607 (291) 984555
reservas@ijm.pt
Open Dates: 01.01-23.12; 26-31.12 Porto Santo 2km 800m x 67 1km

▲ **Mira** – 47036
Pousada de Juventude de Mira,
Parque de Campismo de Jovens,
3070-752 Praia de Mira.
(231) 471199 (231) 471199
mira@movijovem.pt
Open Dates: 01.06-31.08 Porto 92km Cantanhede 21km 1km ap Mira 7N x 60 1km 1km

▲ **Ovar** – 47037
Av. D. Manuel I (EN 327), 3880-109 Ovar.
(256) 591832 (256) 591832
ovar@movijovem.pt
Open Dates: 01.01-23.12; 26-31.12 Porto 35km Ovar 5km 800m ap Rotunda Carregal 5NW x 88 1 x 3km

▲ **Penhas da Saúde** – 47038
Serra da Estrela - Penhas da Saúde,
6200 Covilhã.
(275) 335375 (275) 335109
penhas@movijovem.pt
Open Dates: 01.01-23.12; 26-31.12 Lisboa 300km Covilhã 12km 12km ap Covilhã x 108 1 x 12km

▲ **Ponte de Lima** – 47053
R. Agostinho José Taveira,
4990-062 Ponte de Lima.
(258) 943797 (258) 943605
pontelima@movijovem.pt
Open Dates: 01.01-23.12; 26-31.12 Porto 86km 1km ap Ponte de Lima 0.5N x 41 (B) 500m 500m

▲ **Portalegre** – 47040
Avenida do Bonfim, Ed. I.P.J. Apartado 205, 7300-901 Portalegre.
(245) 330971 (245) 330971
portalegre@movijovem.pt
Open Dates: 01.01-31.07; 05.09-23.12; 26-31.12 Lisboa 219km Portalegre 4km 1km ap Portalegre 1.5E x 51 R CC TV i P 500m

▲ **Portimão** – 47004
Lugar do Coca Maravilhas, 8500-320 Portimão.
(282) 491804 (282) 491804
portimao@movijovem.pt
Open Dates: Closed for renovation works during 2006 Faro 65km Portimão 500m 4N x 180 R CC TV i P 3km

Porto 47012
Rua Paulo da Gama, 551, 4150-589 Porto.
(22) 6177257 (22) 6177247
porto@movijovem.pt
Open Dates: 01.01-23.12; 26-31.12
Open Times:
Beds: 144 - 34x2 19x4
Price Range: € 12.50-22.50 (price per person) BBinc
Directions: 5NW from city centre
Porto 8km A Airbus (reference to the Youth Hostel needed) 10m
Matosinhos 6km Campanhã e São Bento 4km 1, 35, 78 100m ap Paulo da Gama U Casa da Música, Boavista 3km R CC TV 1 x i 8 P 500m 2km

Porto

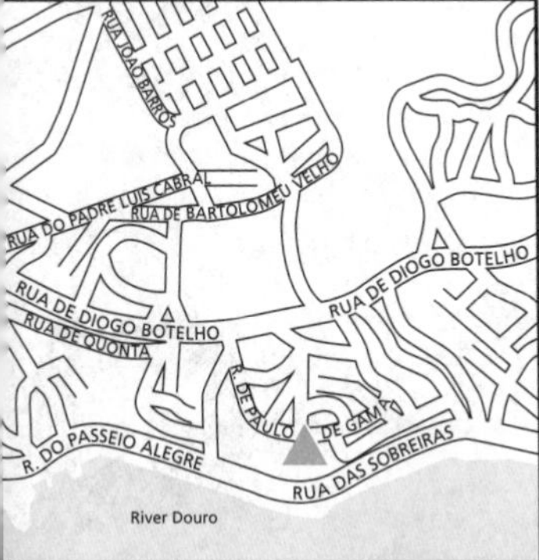

Porto... Travel Tips

- **For budget eats check out...** Casa do Rio, A Marina, Tandoori, Tribunal, Tripeiro (Restaurants)
- **For great nightlife try...** Magestic Café, Ribeira Bars, Indústria Disco, Via Rápida Disco, Alfândega Bar
- **Don't miss...** Serralves Foundation, Guerra Junqueiro Museum, Clérigos Tower, Customers Building, Crystal Palace, Botanical Garden, Fontainhas Pointview, Electric Car Museum, Soares Dos Reis Museum, Port Wine Cellars (Vila Nova De Gaia), Port Wine Museum, Casa Da Música

▲ **S. Pedro do Sul** – 47042
Travessa do Soito, Termas de S.Pedro do Sul, 3660-692 Várzea - S.Pedro do Sul.
(232) 724543 (232) 724541
spedrosul@movijovem.pt
Open Dates: 01.01-23.12; 26-31.12 Porto 120km Nelas 45km 150m ap S. Pedro Sul 0.2W x 136 R CC TV 2 x i P 15km

▲ **Santarém** – 47043
Av. Grupo Forcados Amadores de Santarém, 1, 2000-181 Santarém.
(243) 391914 (243) 391914
santarem@movijovem.pt
Open Dates: Closed for renovation works during 2006 Lisboa 75km Santarém 1N x 36 R CC (B) i P

▲ **São Martinho - Alfeizerão** – 47044
Estrada Nacional 8, 2460-191 Alfeizerão.
(262) 999506 (262) 999506
smartinho@movijovem.pt
Open Dates: Closed for renovation works during 2006 Lisboa 110km São Martinho do Porto 8km 2NE x 60 R CC TV i P 8km

▲ **Setúbal** – 47045
Largo José Afonso, 2900-429 Setúbal.
(265) 534431 (265) 532963
setubal@movijovem.pt
Open Dates: 01.01-23.12; 26-31.12 Lisboa 50km Setúbal 20m 1, 15 400m ap mercado 1E x 48 R CC TV i P 5km 5km

▲ Sintra – 47007
Rua Miguel Torga, Santa Eufémia,
S. Pedro de Sintra, 2710-477 Sintra.
(21) 9241210 (21) 9233176
sintra@movijovem.pt
Open Dates: Closed for renovation works during 2006 Lisboa 26km Sintra 6km 4S x 43 1 x 20km

▲ Viana do Castelo 47018
Rua de Limia, 4900-405 Viana do Castelo.
(258) 800260 (258) 800261
vianacastelo@movijovem.pt
Open Dates: 01.01-23.12; 26-31.12 Porto 73km Viana do Castelo 1km 1km ap Viana Castelo 0.7W x 82 1 x 800m 600m

▲ Viana do Castelo – Navio Gil Eannes – 47054
Doca Comercial, 4900-321 Viana Do Castelo.
(258) 821582 (258) 826251
naviogileannes@movijovem.pt
Open Dates: 01.01-23.12; 26-31.12 Porto 73km Viana do Castelo 1km 1km ap Viana do castelo x 55 (B) 800m 400m

▲ Vila Nova de Cerveira – 47046
Largo 16 de Fevereiro, 21,
4920-249 Vila Nova de Cerveira.
(251) 796113 (251) 796113
cerveira@movijovem.pt
Open Dates: 01.01-23.12; 26-31.12 Porto 95km V.N. Cerveira 300m 300m ap V.N. Cerveira 0.3NE x 50 500m 15km

▲ Vila Nova de Foz Côa – 47047
Caminho Vicinal, Currauteles,
5 5150 Vila Nova de Foz Côa.
(279) 768190 (279) 768191
fozcoa@movijovem.pt
Open Dates: 01.01-11.12; 27-31.12 Porto 195km Pocinho 6km Pocinho 6km 1.5N x 68 1 x

▲ Vila Real – 47048
Rua Dr. Manuel Cardona, 5000-558 Vila Real.
(259) 373193 (259) 373193
vilareal@movijovem.pt
Open Dates: 01.01-23.12; 26-31.12 Porto 85km Vila Real 500m 1km ap Vila Real 1.5W x 53 50m

▲ Vilarinho das Furnas – 47010
Parque Nacional do Gerês, Rua da Pousada,
4840-030 Campo do Gerês.
(253) 351339 (253) 352864
vilarinho@movijovem.pt
Open Dates: 01.01-23.12; 26-31.12 Porto 100km Braga 45km 500m ap Campo do Gerês 0.8N x 58 5km

▲ Viseu – 47050
Rua Aristides de Sousa Mendes,
Portal do Fontelo, 3500-033 Viseu.
(232) 435445 (232) 435445
viseu@movijovem.pt
Open Dates: 01.01-23.12; 26-31.12 Porto 120km Nelas 22km 1km ap Viseu 0.25NW x 64 1km

of Doha.

Some places of interest include:

- Qatar National Museum is located on the Corniche. The museum comprises of five sections: the old palace, the State's section, the lagoon, the marine section and the botanical garden. There are other regional museums such as Al-Wakrah, Al-Zubarah, Al-Khor and others.
- Palm Tree Island is located near to Doha Corniche; the island is accessible by boat and has restaurants, a beach, a popular coffee house and a playground for children.
- Sealine Beach Resort, which is located on the fine beach of Mesaieed, the resort includes a motel and 40 chalets.
- Al-Bida Park is located on the Corniche. The park has play facilities, lawn areas, a popular market and restaurants.
- Khor al-Udeid, which is located 78 km southeast of Doha. This inland sea is characterised by its fine beach and sand dunes that can reach in some places to a height of 40 meters. Fumairit and Dukhan beaches are also worth visiting.
- In Shahaniva Reserve there are herds of rare Arabian oryx and gazelles that were once endangered.
- Al-Zubarah Fort is situated 105km northwest of Doha; the fort was restored in 1987 and turned into a museum.
- Doha Fort (Al-Kout) is one of the few remaining military forts, built on an elevated ground in 1917 at the time of the late Sheikh Abdullah Bin Jassim Al Thani.
- Murwab Fort lies on the coast 15km north of Dukham, and dates back to the abbasid era in the 3rd century of Al-Hijra. 250 houses and two mosques surround the fort.
- Doha Tower, the ethnographic museum, which was built in 1935, is the only remaining wind tower of its kind remaining in Doha. It has a square wind tower called a badjeer with openings on all four sides.

You can find out a lot more on our website - a visit to www.HIhostels.com is essential for planning your trip!

Pour en savoir plus, rendez-vous sur notre site Internet, www.HIhostels.com une visite incontournable pour préparer votre voyage!

Viele weitere Informationen auf unserer Website: www.HIhostels.com - unverzichtbar für die Reiseplanung!

Puedes averiguar mucho más en nuestro sitio web. Es imprescindible que visites la página www.HIhostels.com para planear tu viaje.

Doha – Al Lakta – 96176

Doha YH, Al-Lakta Makka Street.

T 4867180; 4866402 F 4863968

Open Dates: 12 Open Times:

Beds: 60 - 11x1 22x2 33x3 44x4

Price Range: US$14

Directions: Doha International 12km

Doha 10km R TV

8km

6km

Doha – Al Lakta

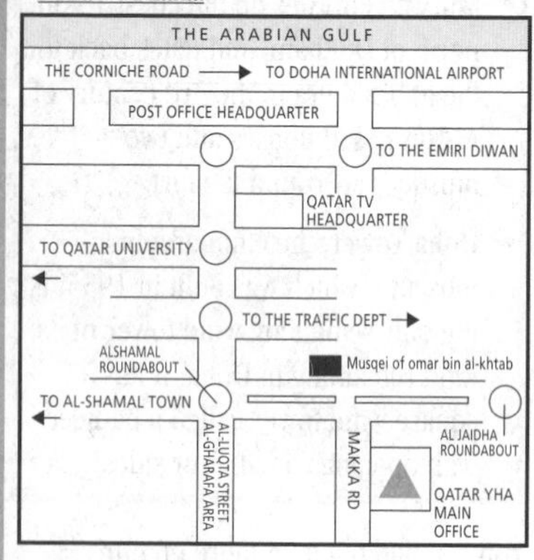

▲ **Doha** – Al Murabaa – 96177
Doha YH, Al-Murabaa
(Behind the Traffic Department Building).
☎ 4863968
Open Dates: 12 ✈ Doha International 20km
⛴ Doha 17km 🛏 x 50 P

Doha... Travel Tips

- **For budget eats check out...** McDonalds, Hardeez, Kentucky Fried Chicken, Dairy Queen, Burger King
- **For great nightlife try...** Sea Sailing, Cinema, Theatre, Old Shopping Places, Sleen Sand Car Race
- **Don't miss...** Aláadeen City, Doha Zoo, Squash Centre, Qatar Museum, City Centre (shopping), Land Mark (shopping), Palm Trees Island, Mall Shopping Centre, Golf Centre, Horse Racing Centre

Romania

Youth Hostel Association Romania
400537 Cluj-Napoca
Clabucet Street Nr 2
Bloc P4, Ap 69 Jud. Cluj, Romania.
t (40) (264) 586616
f (40) (264) 586616
e office@HIhostels-Romania.ro
w www.HIhostels-Romania.ro

Office Hours: 09.00-17.00hrs

National Tourist Authority/Board:	www.romaniatravel.com
Capital:	Bucuresti
Language:	Romanian
Currency:	Lei
Population:	22,545,925
Size:	238,391 sq km
Telephone Country Code:	40
eKit Access Number:	Check www.hi.ekit.com for up to date Access Numbers

HI Suggests...

Romania is a perfect country for all kinds of tourists, with fantastic landscapes like the Black Sea beaches, Danube Delta, the high mountains of Fagaras, Bucegi and Retezat. Alternatively, there are many opportunities to practise a variety of sports and extreme sports such as hiking, mountain biking, fishing, skiing, parapanting, canoeing and caving.

The Carpathian Mountains are a border of cultures. Transylvania's towns are straight out of medieval Hungary or Germany with the imprint of the Austro-Hungarian Empire, while the exotic Orthodox monasteries are apparent and the Turkish influences of Constanta has a totally different background.

Bucharest, "Paris of the East", can show you the face of the 16th-17th century, Franco- Romanian, one which shows the signs of the most ruthless dictators Europe has seen this century. Romania has a calendar of folklore festivals, some of them preserving their authenticity, but making them very difficult for the traveller to attend. Some of the biggest are the "Hora de la Prislop", Whit Sunday Szekely Pilgrimage.

Bram Stoker, an Anglo-Irish writer, presented Dracula, the legend of Romanian history, to the world in the 14th century. Moviemakers have then remade the story countless times. Vlad Tepes (Dracula) was born in Sighisoara. He was ruling Prince of Wallachia (the southern part of Romania) in three turns. Known as one of the most feared enemies of the Ottoman Empire, Vlad Tepes started organising the state, the army, the law and applied the death penalty to those he considered enemies. You can find signs of his time in Sighisoara, near Bucharest.

The public transport is cheap. The railway network is well developed; it covers a large area of country and can be considered the most popular way of transportation. The slowest trains are called "personal" trains and the faster trains, although a little more expensive, are called " Intercity", "Rapid" or "Accelerat" trains.

You can eat out in different types of restaurants in all bigger cities for approximately 5-7 US$, not including alcohol.

When visiting Romania, you must try the Romanian wine; huge variety of regions such as Murfatlar, Vrancea and Odobesti produce this wine. Also, well recognised is the specific cheese, Telemea, which is made from sheep milk.

Local currency is "leu" (lei-plural). Foreign currency may be exchanged to lei upon arrival at airports, banks, hotels or exchange offices. It is advisable to avoid making currency exchanges in the open streets. Traveller's cheques can be cashed in banks; most merchants such as hotels and restaurants do not accept traveller's cheques.

Romania has a temperate climate within the four seasons. The spring can be a changeable season; the warmth of the day can rapidly turn into a cold evening and following morning. In the summer temperatures can easily reach 35-40°C. Autumn is usually rainy and winters are extremely cold with lots of snow from December to March.

You can find out a lot more on our website - a visit to www.HIhostels.com is essential for planning your trip!

Pour en savoir plus, rendez-vous sur notre site Internet, www.HIhostels.com une visite incontournable pour préparer votre voyage!

Viele weitere Informationen auf unserer Website: www.HIhostels.com - unverzichtbar für die Reiseplanung!

Puedes averiguar mucho más en nuestro sitio web. Es imprescindible que visites la página www.HIhostels.com para planear tu viaje.

București-Bucharest – Hostel Helga
HI 69002
Strada Salcâmilor nr.2.
T (21) 6102214 F (21) 6102214
E hostelhelga@yahoo.com
W www.bucharest-hostel.com
Open Dates: 12 Open Times: 24h
Beds: 32 - 1x^{2} 3x^{4} 3x^{6}
Price Range: 40 LEI € 10 BBinc
Directions: 1NE from city centre
✈ Otopeni 18km A 783 1km
Constanta 220km Gara de Nord 3km 79, 86, 133, 226 200m ap Piata Gemeni 5, 14 200m ap Piata Gemeni
U M2 ap Universitate or Piata Romana R

București-Bucharest – Hostel Helga

București-Bucharest... Travel Tips

- **For budget eats check out...** Restaurant Nicoresti - Traditional Romanian dishes (Str. Maria Rosetti 40), Four Seasons Restaurant - Lebanese & Vegetarian dishes (Str. Vasile Lascar), La Mama - Traditional Romanian dishes (Str. Nicolae Golescu), Boema - Traditional Romanian dishes & live music (Str. Maria Rosetti 10), Manuc's Inn
- **For great nightlife try...** La Motor - Bar & open air cinema on the roof of the National Theatre (Bd. Bălcescu 2), Club A - Popular Club (Str. Blanari 14), Twice - 2 different dancefloors & bars (Str. SF. Vineri), Jukebox - band playing everynight, Sardele - live Roma music most nights
- **Don't miss...** The Parliament Palace - world's 2nd largest administrative building, The Village Museum - Open Air Museum, The Triumph Arch - Bucharest as "Little Paris", Revolution Square, Dracula Tomb, University Square, Hanul Lui Manuc (Manuc's Inn), Herestrau Park, Old Court Church, Cotroceni Palace

▲ **București-Otopeni** – Pension Gabriela HI 69009
Margaritarului Vila-A 104.
(21) 2362053 (21) 2362053
pensiuneagabriela@yahoo.com
www.flying.to/Romania
Open Dates: 12 Otopeni 3km Gara de Nord 14km 10N x 12 R (B)

▲ **Cluj-Napoca** – Retro Hostel – 69005
Str. Potaissa nr. 13, Cluj-Napoca.
(264) 450452 (264) 450452
retroinn@rdslink.ro www.retro.ro
Open Dates: 12 Cluj-Napoca 8km
A 300m Cluj-Napoca 2km
29, 30 150m ap Memorandumului
6, 9, 25 150m ap Memorandumului 0.1NW
x 50 R (B)

▲ **Sighișoara** – Burg Hostel – 69007
Str. Bastionului Nr. 4-6.
(265) 778489 (265) 506086
burghostel@ibz.org.ro www.ibz.ro
Open Dates: 12 Targu-Mures 60km
Sighișoara 1km x 70 R
1 x

▲ **Suceava** – Class Youth Hostel – 69011
195, Aurel Vlaicu Street, Itcani, Suceava.
(723) 782328
monika_romania@yahoo.com
www.classhostel.ro
Open Dates: 12 16km Suceava Nord
x 10 R CC

Saudi Arabia

Saudi Arabian Youth Hostels Association
Alshehab Alghassni St. Alnmouzajiyah District
North Almurabb'h, P.O. Box 2359, Riyadh 11451
Kingdom of Saudi Arabia.
t (966) (1) 4055552; 4051478
TX 406560 SAYHAR SJ
f (966) (1) 4021079
e sayha@zajil.net
w www.sayha.org

A copy of the Hostel Directory for this Country can be obtained from:
The National Office

Capital:	Riyadh
Language:	Arabic
Currency:	SR (Saudi riyal)
Population:	21,000,000
Size:	2,240,000 sq km
Telephone Country Code:	966
eKit Access Number:	Check www.hi.ekit.com for up to date Access Numbers

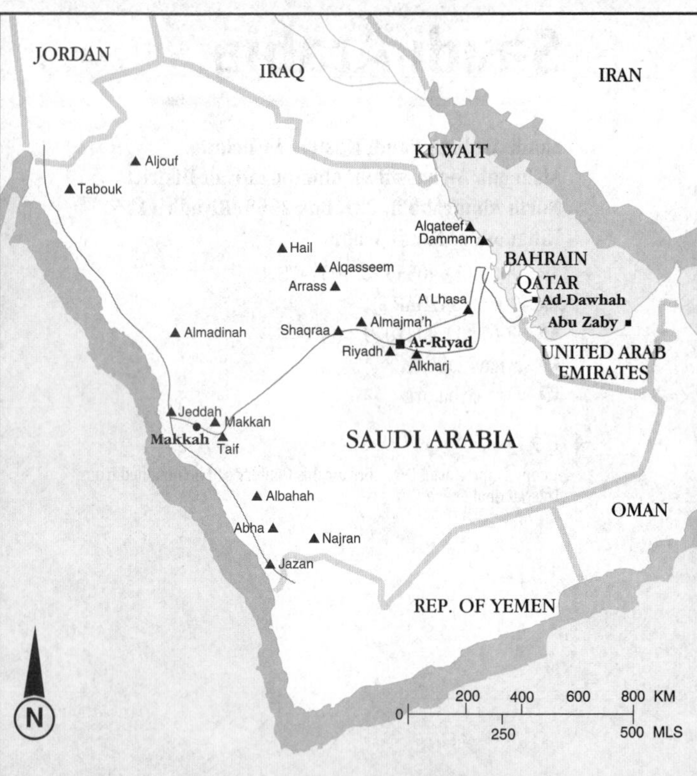

HI Suggests...

The Kingdom of Saudi Arabia is an Islamic State. The capital is called Riyadh. It is a founder member in the Arab League and an efficient member in the United Nations. It is located in the southwestern part of Asia. Its area is about 2,240,000 square kilometers and it has a monarchic regime. It has about 21,000,000 people and its official language is Arabic, which is spoken throughout. The Kingdom of Saudi Arabia has a tropical climate. It is generally hot; mild in mountain areas with rain falls in winter.

The Kingdom is considered the largest producer of oil in the world, which is the main source of income as well as some other modern industries and natural resources.

The Kingdom is the Qiblah of all Muslims from all over the world as it has the Holy Ka'aba in Makkah Al-Mukaramah and the grave of Prophet Muhammad in Al-Madinah Al-Munawarah. Makkah and Al-Madinah are the most famous cities in the world for Muslims worldwide to travel to and perform the rituals of Hajj (Pilgrimage) and Omrah (Lesser Pilgrimage). Saudi Arabia is the world's center of attraction due to its great status in the Islamic world, which plays an active role in spreading love and peace among the countries of the world.

Saudi Arabian Youth Hostels Association (SAYHA) was founded in 1969AD, the Association has been developed greatly, which now includes more than 20 youth hostels that are well equipped with the most modern facilities.

The role of the Association and its youth

hostels is not only of making accommodation available, as is the case known in most youth hostels all over the world, but it exceeds to educational and social purposes due to existing youth hostels set to practicing different sports and cultural activities. Saudi Arabian Youth Hostels Association in participation with all youth hostels in the Kingdom usually carries out its annual accredited plan, which includes cultural, sports, social and art activities. Varied programs are carried out all year inside the youth hostels.

The association has an annual central plan which is carried out centrally with all the Kingdom's youth hostels taking part. The winner youth hostel is awarded with valuable prizes during the Annual Closing Ceremony. HRH General President of Youth Welfare and the President of Saudi Arabian Youth Hostels Association award and honor the winner youth hostel that wins the Yearly Evaluation Competition.

ou can find out a lot more on our ebsite - a visit to www.HIhostels.com is ssential for planning your trip!

our en savoir plus, rendez-vous sur otre site Internet, www.HIhostels.com ne visite incontournable pour réparer votre voyage!

iele weitere Informationen auf unserer /ebsite: www.HIhostels.com - nverzichtbar für die Reiseplanung!

uedes averiguar mucho más en uestro sitio web. Es imprescindible ue visites la página ww.HIhostels.com para planear tu iaje.

▲ **Albahah Area** – 96179
Albahah YH, PO Box 52,
Saud Bin Abdul Aziz Sports City, Albahah,
Alaqeeq Rd, Albahah.
(7) 7250732; 7250385 (7) 7251988
Open Dates: 30km 20km
x 120

▲ **Algateef Governorate** – 96180
Naif Bin Abdul Aziz Sports City, Eastern Area.
(3) 8360897; 8360900 (3) 8360897
Open Dates: 20km 1km x 60

△ ***Al-Jouf Area** – 96178*
Al-Jouf YH, PO Box 211,
Sakaka King Fahd St (Almwasalat), Al-Jouf.
(4) 6241884; 6241883 (4) 6248341
Open Dates: 28km 500m
x 70

△ ***Alkharj Governorate** – 96181*
YH, PO Box 521, Alkharj 11942,
King Fahd Rd,
Next to Sporting Sho'la Club Stadium,
Alkharj.
(1) 5485765 (1) 5485548
Open Dates: 120km 15km
2km x 75

▲ **Almadinah Area** – 96182
YH, Prince Moh Bin Abdelaziz Sporting City,
Alaziziyyah District, Almadinah.
(4) 8303092 (4) 8303244
Open Dates: 13km 50m
x 150

▲ **Almajma'h Governorate** – 96183
YH, PO Box 179,
Prince Salman Bin Abdul Aziz Sports City - the Main Rd, Almajma'h.
(6) 4323028 (6) 4321675
Open Dates: 160km 2km
x 90

▲ **Alqasseem Area** – Buraidah - Alqasseem – 96184
YH, PO Box 949,
Prince Abdallah Bin Abdelaziz Sporting City,
Braidah, Alsafraa, Alqasseem.
(6) 3812361 (6) 3813007
Open Dates: 22km 500m
x 180

△ ***Arrass Governorate** – 96185*
YH, 1986, Northern Alshifa-Riyadh Rd.
(6) 3333315 (6) 3336387
Open Dates: 90km 100m
x 50

▲ **Aseer Area** – Abha – 96186
YH, PO Box 182, Prince Sultan Bin Abdelaziz Sporting City, Almahalah, Abha.
(7) 2277127; 2277237 (7) 2277282
Open Dates: 17km 5km
x 150

▲ **Eastern Area** – Alahsa Governorate – 96187
YH, Prince Abdallah Bin Galawi Sporting City, Alkhalidiyyah District, Hufuf, Alahsa.
(3) 5800028 (3) 5800692
Open Dates: 9km 5km 2km
x 120

Eastern Area – Dammam – 96188
YH, PO Box 2822, Dammam 31461, Dammam - Khobar Rd, adjacent to Gymnasium.
(3) 8575358; 8575384 (3) 8579524
Open Dates: Open Times:
Beds: 200
Price Range: 6-10SR
Directions: 11km 20km 3km
200m

Eastern Area – Dammam

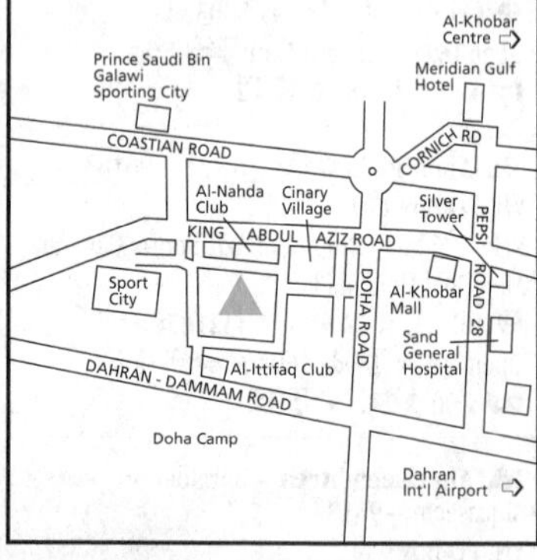

Eastern Area... Travel Tips

- **Don't miss...** Corniche, Half Moon Beach, Kind Fahd Coastal City, King Fahd Bridge, King Abdul Aziz Seaport, King Fahd University of Petroleum and Minerals, Public Gardens

---

▲ **Hail Area** – 96189
YH, Prince Abdelaziz Bin Musaed Bin Galawi Sporting City, Hail: airport district.
(6) 5325734 (6) 5331485
Open Dates: 30km 100m
x 120

▲ **Jazan Area** – Jazan – 96190
YH, 1981, PO Box 319, Jazan King Faisal Bin Abdul Aziz Sports City, Prince Abdullah Rd, Jizan.
(7) 3217529; 3217524 (7) 3217527
Open Dates: 16km 5km
1km x 65

▲ **Jeddah Governorate** – 96191
YH, PO Box 8486, Jeddah 21482, Makkah Rd, K7 West Stadium, Jeddah.
(2) 6886632; 6886692 (2) 6887112
Open Dates: 14km A 10km
50m x 200 R
4 x

▲ **Makkah Area** – Makkah – 96192
YH, 1979, PO Box 5403 King Abdelaziz Sporting City-Al-Sharai, Old Taif Rd, Opposite Jo'ranah Bridge, Makkah.
(2) 5240414 (2) 5240966
Open Dates: 80km 90km
500m x 135

△ ***Najran Area** – Najran – 96193*
King Saud Rd (Al-Khamees Rd) Al-Mukhaiam District opposite Mute Hope Institute for boys, PO Box 155, Najran.
(7) 5236040 (7) 5235900
Open Dates: 35km 1km
x 60

▲ **Riyadh Area** – Prince Faisal Fahd's Youth Hostel – 96194
Riyadh YH, PO Box 2359, Riyadh 11451, West King Fahd Rd, Opposite New Passport Building, Alshehab Alghassani-st.
(1) 4055552; 4051478 (1) 4051376
Open Dates: 45km 7km
50m x 270 R

△ ***Shaqraa Governorate** – 96195*
YH, Al Rowdah District, Alarbaeen St, West Alwashm Club, Shaqraa.
(1) 6220200 (1) 6220200
Open Dates: 200km 1km
x 50

▲ **Tabouk Area** – Tabouk – 96196
YH, King Khalid Bin Abdul Aziz Sports City, Amman Rd, Tabouk.
t (4) 4276425 f (4) 4276426
Open Dates: 25km 5km x 50

▲ **Taif Governorate** – 96197
YH, King Fahd Sporting City, Hawiyyah, Taif.
t (2) 7252000; 7253400 f (2) 7253400
Open Dates: 4km 200m x 160

Scotland

Scottish Youth Hostels Association,
7 Glebe Crescent, Stirling,
FK8 2JA, Scotland.

Central Reservation Service
t (44) (8701) 553255
f (44) (1786) 891336
e reservations@syha.org.uk; groups@syha.org.uk
w www.syha.org.uk; www.rentahostel.com; www.carbisdale.org
Office Hours: CRS Hours 09.00-19.00hrs

The National Office
t (44) (1786) 891400
f (44) (1786) 891333
e info@syha.org.uk
w www.syha.org.uk
Office Hours: Monday-Friday 08.45-17.00hrs

Travel Section: c/o Scottish Youth Hostels Association,
7 Glebe Crescent, Stirling,
FK8 2JA, Scotland.
t (44) (1786) 891400

A copy of the Hostel Directory for this Country can be obtained from:
The National Office

National Tourist Authority/Board:	www.visitscotland.com
Capital:	Edinburgh
Language:	English
Currency:	£ (Sterling)
Population:	5,112,100
Size:	78,781 sq km
Telephone Country Code:	44
eKit Access Number:	0800-032-6297

Well, yes, Scotland has been called the 'Land of the Brave' because of famous characters like Bonnie Prince Charlie and the story of William Wallace (famously depicted by Mel Gibson in *Braveheart*), who were connected with the historic fight to keep Scotland independent of the 'Sassenach South' (the English). This aspect of the country's history, however, was essentially brought to a close with the arrival of James VI of Scotland who ascended the English throne as James I in 1603, which was then followed by the English colonization of the country.

Even so, bravery has been and in many ways still is much more broadly based in Scotland, the population providing many of the intrepid pioneers, including engineers, doctors and scientists who helped build the British Empire, to the many who fought to keep the peace in more modern times.

Also, in 1999, you might say that

Scotland entered the brave new world of independent provincial government with the establishment of the first Scottish Parliament. (Scotland accounts for less than one-tenth of Great Britain's population.) In turn, this partial independence has prompted the Scottish Tourist Board to boost the 'Heritage' agenda so that everything 'Scottish', from tartans and bagpipes to malt whisky and 'Nessie', as well as Scotland's pre-history, is given the appropriate fanfare. But this is not really today's reality for most Scots who are far more focused on contemporary issues of good governance and quality of life, with renewed efforts to reawaken the independence issue fading away.

A few other Top Tips from **CULTURE SMART!**:

- Although most of the population is to be found in the regions of Scotland's two principal cities: Glasgow (Strathclyde) and the capital Edinburgh (Lothian), it is worth remembering that it is a huge country (about a third of the whole of Britain) and includes the Western Isles as well as the Orkney and Shetland Islands in the north.
- The variety of Scotland's great natural beauty, not least its mountains, lochs and forest lands is also reflected in the diversity of regional traditions and ways of life, from city-dweller to crofter. Yet remaining constant wherever you go is the strong character, wit and (sometimes very dry) sense of humour. And for the old stereotype of 'dour', perhaps read 'cautious'.
- You might say, too, that Scotland's polite society is very polite indeed: there is a rigour and strong conservatism about the right time and place, including social hierarchy, dress and manners generally. Paradoxically, Scotland's so-called 'Tartan Army' (football supporters for international matches) provides a dramatic alter ego.
- The Scots are great communicators and are accordingly well represented in the broadcasting media in England. Yet loud voices are not welcome in public places, the preference always being for low-key behaviour. By the same token, handshakes are usually light and social kissing is avoided.

Cultural Top Tips supplied by Culture Smart! guides. These essential guides to customs and etiquette will help you steer clear of embarrassing gaffes and sensitive issues, enabling you to discover new cultures whilst developing new friendships. Order online at www.culturesmartguides.co.uk

You can find out a lot more on our website - a visit to www.HIhostels.com is essential for planning your trip!

Pour en savoir plus, rendez-vous sur notre site Internet, www.HIhostels.com une visite incontournable pour préparer votre voyage!

Viele weitere Informationen auf unserer Website: www.HIhostels.com - unverzichtbar für die Reiseplanung!

Puedes averiguar mucho más en nuestro sitio web. Es imprescindible que visites la página www.HIhostels.com para planear tu viaje.

Aberdeen – The King George VI Memorial Hostel 50026

8 Queen's Rd, Aberdeen AB15 4ZT.

(870) 0041100

Open Dates: Open Times: 07.00-02.00hrs

Beds: 114 - 2x2 13x4 1x5 4x6 3x6+

Price Range: £12.00-£15.00

Directions: 2W from city centre

Aberdeen 10km A outside hostel

Aberdeen 2km Aberdeen 2km

14, 15 2km ap outside hostel x 14

R CC 1 x

8 P 1km

Aberdeen – The King George VI Memorial Hostel

Aberdeen... Travel Tips

- **For budget eats check out...** The Ashvale (Great Western Road), LittleJohns (Schoolhill), The Olive Tree (Queens Road), La Lombarda (King's Street), Estaminet (Littlejohn Street)
- **For great nightlife try...** Cinemas (Odeon, Belmont, Lighthouse, UGC), Cordonas Amusement Park & Beach Leisure Centre, His Majesty's Theatre & the Music Hall, The Lemon Tree, Amadeus - Scotland's largest dance club
- **Don't miss...** The Maritime Museum, St Machar's Cathedral & St Andrew's Cathedral, Footdee - an old sea faring village, Brig O'Balgowrie - one of the oldest bridges in Scotland, Old Aberdeen & Kings College, Marischall College, Duthie Park, Rose Mount & the Winter Gardens, The beach & the Beach Leisure Complex, Hazelhead Park - riding, golf, gardens, maze, The Art Museum & Gordon Highlander's Museum

△ ***Achininver*** *50044*

Achiltibuie, Ross-shire IV26 2YL.

(870) 0041101

Open Dates: 28.04-30.09 Inverness 70km Ullapool 30km Inverness 70km 1km x 20 R CC

P

△ ***Achmelvich Beach*** *50045*

Recharn, nr Lochinver, Sutherland IV27 4JB.

(870) 0041102

Open Dates: 07.04-30.09 Inverness 80km Ullapool 40km Inverness 80km 3km x 36 R CC

P

▲ **Armadale** 50046

Ardvasar, Sleat, Isle of Skye IV45 8RS.

(870) 0041103

Open Dates: 07.04-30.09 Inverness 110km 1km Mallaig 15km by ferry 1km x 42 R CC P

Aviemore 50012

25 Grampian Rd, Aviemore, Inverness-shire PH22 1PR.

(870) 0041104

Open Dates: Open Times: 07.00-02.00hrs

Beds: 106 - 2x2 1x3 12x4 3x5 6x6

Price Range: £12.00-£14.00

Directions: 0.5S from city centre

Inverness 70km Aviemore 400m

Aviemore 400m ap Train Station

x 24 R CC

1 x 8 P 400m

Aviemore

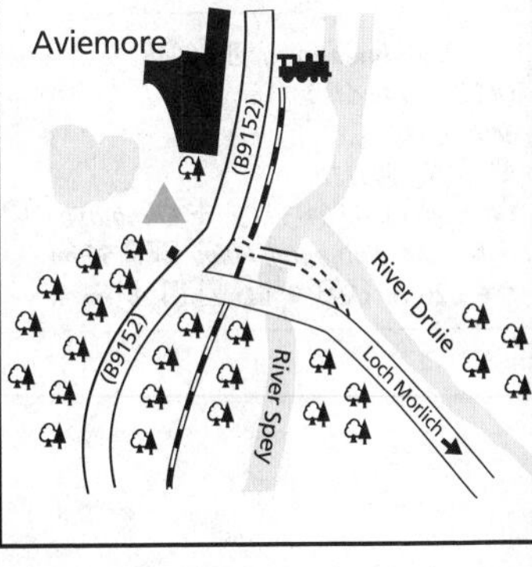

Aviemore... Travel Tips

- **For budget eats check out...** High Range Pizzeria, LittleJohns (burgers etc), Hamblets (pizza & pasta buffet), Mackenzie's Inn, Old Bridge Inn
- **For great nightlife try...** Old Bridge Inn (traditional music), Mamba (nightclub), Crofters AMR (nightclub), The Basement (nightclub), Cairngorn Hotel Bar (pub, sports on TV)
- **Don't miss...** Landmark Forest Heritage Park, Highland Wildlife Centre - see the wolves, Dalwhinnie Distillery - part of the Whisky Trail, Osprey Visitor Centre, Glenmore Forest Park, Aviemore Stables - pony trekking, Rothiemurchus Estate - walking, mountain biking, safari tours, Highland Discovery Day Tours, Aviemore Brewery Tours, Cairngorm Ski Company - skiing in winter

▲ Braemar HI 50023
Corrie Feragie, 21 Glenshee Rd, Braemar, Aberdeenshire AB35 5YQ.
(870) 0041105
Open Dates: 16.12-28.10; 22.12 (only 29.10-21.12) Aberdeen 80km Aberdeen 80km Aberdeen 80km 500m x 49

▲ Broadford HI 50017
Isle of Skye IV49 9AA.
(870) 0041106
Open Dates: 03.03-28.10 (only 29.10-28.02.07) Inverness 90km Kylerhea 10km Kyle of Lochalsh 15km 500m x 63

△ Broadmeadows HI *50048*
Old Broadmeadows, Yarrowford, Selkirk TD7 5LZ.
(870) 0041107
Open Dates: 07.04-30.09 Edinburgh 60km Edinburgh 60km 500m x 26

▲ Cairngorm Lodge (Loch Morlich) HI 50024
Glenmore, Aviemore, Inverness-shire PH22 1QY.
(870) 0041137
Open Dates: 16.12-28.10; 22.12 (only 29.10-21.12) Inverness 80km Aviemore 11km 500m x 82

Carbisdale Castle HI 50008
Carbisdale, Culrain, Ardgay, Ross-shire IV24 3DP.
(870) 0041109 www.carbisdale.org
Open Dates: 03.03-28.10 (only 29.10-28.02.07) Open Times: 07.00-23.45hrs
Beds: 189 - 1x1 2x2 2x3 3x4 2x5 5x6 14x6+
Price Range: £14.50-£15.50
Directions: Inverness 90km Culrain 500m Invershin 1km ap YH x 3 (BD) 1 x 15km

Carbisdale Castle

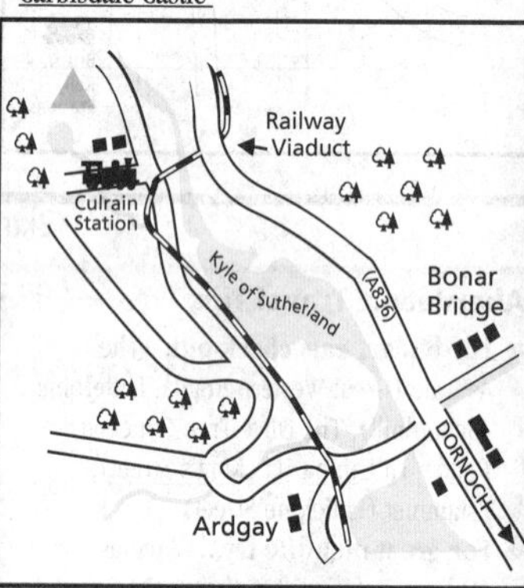

Carbisdale Castle... Travel Tips

- **For budget eats check out...** Invershin Hotel (1 mile), Dunroamin Hotel (4 miles), Falls of Shin Restaurant (4 miles on foot, 12 to drive), Bridge Hotel (5 miles), Lady Ross Hotel (4 miles)
- **For great nightlife try...** Invershin Hotel (occasional live music), Bridge Hotel (occasional live music or disco), Dunroamin Hotel, Lady Ross Hotel (occasional live music or disco), Midnight forest walks to spot foxes & badgers
- **Don't miss...** Clynelish & Glen Morangie Distilleries, Falls of Shin Visitors Centre & Salmon Leap, Dornoch Cathedral & Dornoch Beach, Dunrobin Castle - gardens & falconry display, Croick Church - place of shelter during Highland Clearances, Loch Fleet National Nature Reserve - otters, seals, wildfowl, Boat trips to see dolphins - Dolphin Ecosse, Golf - Bonar Bridge/Ardgay & Royal Dornoch Golf Clubs, Munro bagging & salmon or trout fishing, Ord Hill Archaeological Trail - standing stones, burial cairns

△ ***Carn Dearg*** *50049*
Gairloch, Ross-shire IV21 2DJ.
(870) 0041110
Open Dates: 07.04-30.09 Inverness 90km Ullapool 70km Achnasheen 40km 5km ap Gairloch x 40

▲ **Coldingham Sands** 50029
The Mount, Coldingham, Berwickshire TD14 5PA.
(870) 0041111
Open Dates: 07.04-30.09 (only 01.10-28.02.07) Edinburgh 80km Newcastle 80km Berwick-upon-Tweed 80km 500m x 36

▲ **Crianlarich** 50019
Station Rd, Crianlarich, Perthshire FK20 8QN.
(870) 0041112
Open Dates: Glasgow 80km 500m 500m x 72

▲ **Edinburgh** – Bruntsfield 50003
7 Bruntsfield Crescent, Edinburgh EH10 4EZ.
(870) 0041114
Open Dates: Edinburgh 10km A 3km Rosyth 20km Edinburgh Waverley 3km 11, 15, 16, 17, C1, C11 ap Forbes Rd x 126 2km

Edinburgh – Eglinton 50004
18 Eglinton Crescent, Edinburgh EH12 5DD.
(870) 0041116
Open Dates: Open Times: 07.00-02.00hrs
Beds: 150 - 5x² 9x⁴ 6x⁶ 8x⁶⁺
Price Range: £13.00-£21.00
Directions: 2W from city centre
Edinburgh 10km A to Haymarket 500m Rosyth 20km Haymarket 500m 3, 4, 12, 13, 22, 26, 28, Palmerston 400m ap Haymarket; Palmerston Place x 3 (BD) 1 x

Edinburgh – Eglinton

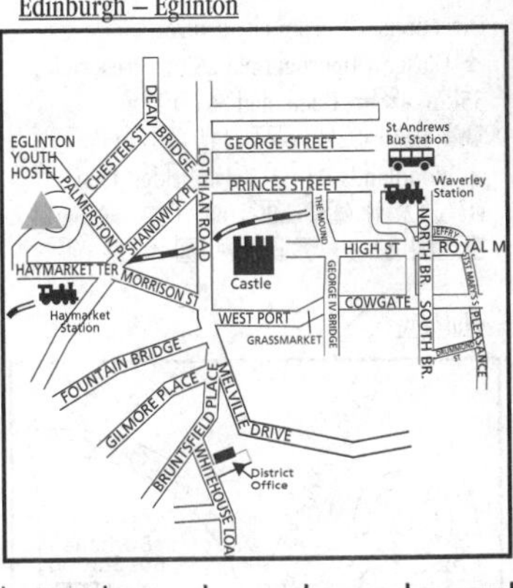

Edinburgh... Travel Tips

- **For budget eats check out...** Italian Connection (Bruntsfield Place), India (Torphin Place), Eastern Cuisine (Dalry Road), Great Wall Chinese Restaurant (Lothian Road), Coconut Grove (Lochrin Terrace)
- **For great nightlife try...** Revolution (Lothian Road), Eros/Elite (Dundas Street), Espionage (Victoria Street), Bongo Club (Calton Road), Three Sisters (Cowgate)
- **Don't miss...** Dynamic Earth, Edinburgh Dungeons, Turbo Venture, Edinburgh Castle & Royal Mile, Royal Yacht Britannia, Witchery/Vaults tours & Mary Kings Close, National & Modern Art Galleries, Museum of Scotland, Edinburgh 200, Gladstone's Land

Glasgow 50001
7/8 Park Terrace, Glasgow G3 6BY.
(870) 0041119
Open Dates: Open Times: 07.00-02.00hrs
Beds: 148 - 1x2 12x4 11x6 4x6+
Price Range: £13.00-£16.00
Directions: 2W from city centre
Glasgow International 25km; Prestwick 55km A Buchanan Street 2km
Central 2km 11, 44 1km ap Woodlands Rd U Kelvinbridge 1km
x 12 R CC (BD)
TV 1 x i 8

Glasgow

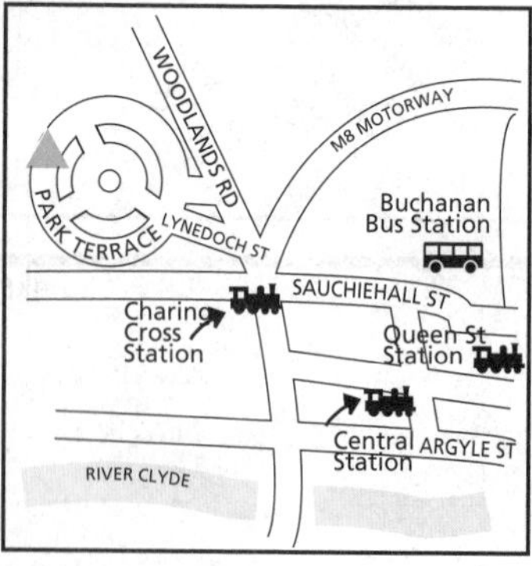

Glasgow... Travel Tips

- **For budget eats check out...** Cul de Sac (Ashton Lane), Big Bites (Woodlands Road), Canton Express (Sauchiehall Street), Grass Roots (St George's Cross), Mother India (North Street)
- **For great nightlife try...** Sub Club (Jamaica Street), Arches (Argyle St), Halt Bar/Uisge Beatha (Woodlands Road), Tron Theatre (Tron Gate), Glasgow Film Theatre (Rose Street)
- **Don't miss...** Art Gallery & Museum (Kelvingrove), Modern Art Museum, House for an Art Lover - built to a design by CR Mackintosh, Glasgow Cathedral & Necropolis, Science Centre (Pacific Quay), The Lighthouse - art & architecture exhibitions, Huntarian Gallery & Mackintosh House (Hillhead Street), People's Palace (Glasgow Green), Burrel Collection (Pollok House & Country Park), Tenement House

△ ***Glen Affric – 50054***
Allt Beithe, Glen Affric, Cannich, by Beauly, Inverness-shire IV47 7ND.
(8701) 553255
Open Dates: 07.04-28.10 Inverness 40km Inverness 40km 10km ap Cannich x 26 R

▲ **Glen Nevis** 50010
Fort William, Inverness-shire PH33 6SY.
(870) 0041120
Open Dates: Inverness 100km
Fort William 5km 5km ap Fort William x 88 R CC
TV i P 5km

▲ **Glenbrittle** 50032
Carbost, Isle of Skye IV47 8TA.
(870) 0041121
Open Dates: 07.04-30.09 (only 01.10-28.02.07) Inverness 120km
Kylerhea 40km Kyle of Lochalsh 45km 500m x 36 CC i
P

▲ **Glencoe** 50020
Ballachulish, Argyll PA49 4HX.
(870) 0041122
Open Dates: Glasgow 100km Fort William 30km 4km x 62 R
CC i P

▲ **Glendevon** 50055
Dollar, Clackmannanshire FK14 7JY.
(870) 0041123
Open Dates: 07.04-30.09 Edinburgh 80km Rosyth 70km Stirling 20km 4km x 32

▲ **Inveraray** 50033
Argyllshire PA32 8XD.
(870) 0041125
Open Dates: 07.04-30.09 (only 01.10-28.02.07) Glasgow 80km Arrochar 25km 500m x 28

△ ***Inverey*** *50059*
By Braemar, Aberdeenshire AB35 5YB.
(870) 0041126
Open Dates: 28.04-30.09 Aberdeen 90km Aberdeen 90km Aberdeen 90km 10km ap Braemar x 14

Inverness 50007
Victoria Dr, Inverness IV2 3QB.
(870) 0041127
Open Dates: Open Times: 07.00-02.00hrs
Beds: 186 - 2x[2] 4x[3] 4x[4] 24x[6]
Price Range: £12.00-£15.00
Directions: 1S from city centre
Inverness 8km Inverness 1km
1km ap Bus Station x 10
(BD)
1 x 3km

Inverness

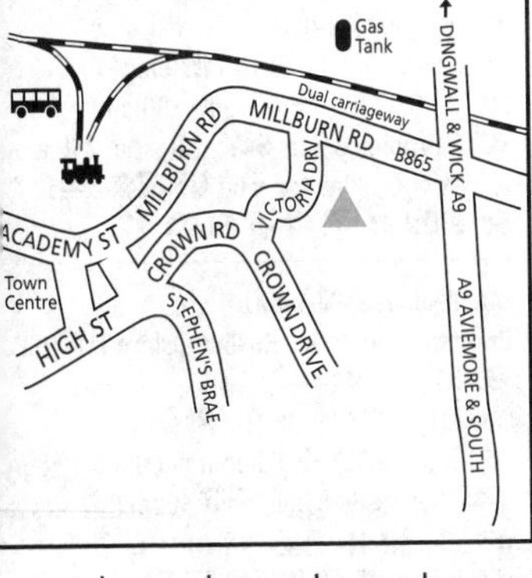

Inverness... Travel Tips

- **For budget eats check out...** LittleJohns (Church Street), Chieftain Hotel (Millburn Road), Castle Restaurant (Castle Street), Il Palio (Queensgate), Quismat (Millburn Road)
- **For great nightlife try...** Warner Village Cinema, Blackfriars Pub (Academy Street), Eden Court Theatre, Blue Nightclub, Johnny Foxes Irish Pub
- **Don't miss...** Culloden Battlefield, Fort George, Cawdor Castle, Highland Wildlife Park & Wolves, Inverness Castle, James Pringle Tartan Weaving Mill, Loch Ness 2000 Exhibition, Black Isle Wildlife Park, Clava Cairns, Dolphin Cruises

▲ **John O' Groats** 50061
Canisbay, Wick, Caithness KW1 4YH.
(870) 0041129
Open Dates: 07.04-30.09 Wick 25km 4km Thurso 30km 500m x 36

△ ***Kendoon*** *50062*
Nr. Dalry, Castle Douglas, Kircudbrightshire DG7 3UD.
(870) 0041130
Open Dates: 07.04-30.09 Prestwick 150km 2km x 36

▲ **Killin** 50034
Killin, Perthshire FK21 8TN.
(870) 0041131
Open Dates: 03.03-28.10 (only 29.10-28.02.07) Glasgow 105km Crainlarich 25km 1km x 40

▲ **Kirk Yetholm** 50064
Kirk Yetholm, Kelso, Roxburghshire TD5 8PG.
(870) 0041132
Open Dates: 07.04-30.09 Edinburgh 100km Newcastle 100km Berwick-upon-Tweed 40km 1km x 20

▲ **Kirkwall** 50035
Old Scapa Rd, Kirkwall, Orkney KW15 1BB.
(870) 0041133
Open Dates: 07.04-30.09 (only 01.10-28.02.07) 3km Stromness 25km 1km x 90

Kyleakin 50013
Kyleakin, Isle of Skye IV41 8PL.
(870) 0041134
Open Dates: Open Times: 07.00-02.00hrs
Beds: 120 - 15x2 2x3 19x4 1x6
Price Range: £11.00-£14.00
Directions: Inverness 80km Kylerhea 15km Kyle of Lochalsh 2km 500m

Kyleakin

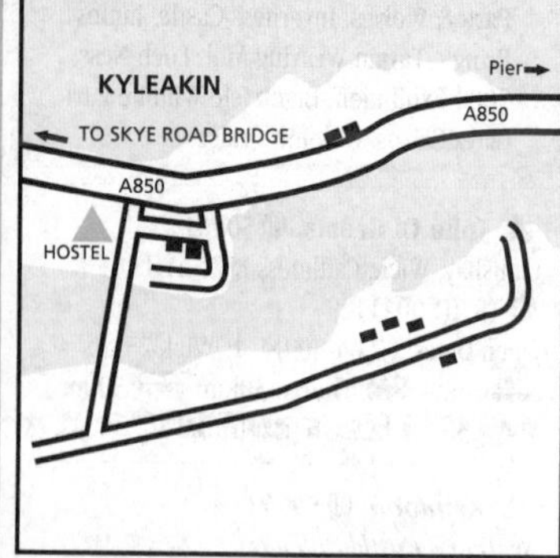

Kyleakin... Travel Tips

- **For budget eats check out...** King Haakon Bar & Restaurant, Saucy Mary's, Harry's Coffee Shop, Creelers Seafood (8 miles), Kyle Hotel (2.5 miles)
- **For great nightlife try...** Haakon Bar (Fri & Sat), Saucy Mary's (Wed & Fri)
- **Don't miss...** Dunvegan Castle, Eilean Donan Castle (on the mainland on approach to Kyle of Lochalsh), Fairy Glen (Uig), Kilmuir Museum of Life, Old Man of the Quiraing, Kilt Rock Waterfall, Boat Trips, Toy Musuem, Serpentarium, Hill Walking & Mountain Climbing in Cuilline Mountains

Lerwick – 50065
Islesburgh House, King Harald St, Lerwick, Shetland ZE1 0EQ.
(1595) 692114
Open Dates: 01.04-30.09 Tingwall 10km 2km 2km x 64

Loch Lochy 50036
South Laggan, Spean Bridge, Inverness-shire PH34 4EA.
(870) 0041135
Open Dates: 07.04-28.10 (only 29.10-28.02.07) Inverness 70km Spean Bridge 20km 500m x 58

Loch Lomond 50009
Arden, Alexandria, Dumbartonshire G83 8RA.
(870) 0041136
Open Dates: 03.03-28.10 (only 29.10-28.02.07) Glasgow 24km Balloch 3.2km ap at driveway x 153 (BD) 2 x 3km

Loch Ness 50037
Glenmoriston, Inverness-shire IV63 7YD.
(870) 0041138
Open Dates: 07.04-28.10 (only 29.10-28.02.07) Inverness 35km Inverness 35km 500m x 50

Loch Ossian *50066*
Corrour, Inverness-shire PH30 4AA.
(870) 0041139
Open Dates: 07.04-28.10 (only 29.10-28.02.07) Glasgow 100km Corrour 2km 15km ap Rannoch x 20

Lochranza 50038
Lochranza, Isle of Arran KA27 8HL.
(870) 0041140
Open Dates: 03.03-28.10 (only 29.10-28.02.07) Glasgow 100km Brodick 25km Ardrossan 25km by ferry 500m x 64

Melrose 50021
Priorwood, Melrose, Roxburghshire TD6 9EF.
(870) 0041141
Open Dates: 03.03-28.10 (only 29.10-28.02.07) Edinburgh 60km Newcastle 65km 500m 0.5E x 83 (BD) 1 x 6km

△ ***Minnigaff*** Ⓗ *50067*
Newton Stewart, Wigtownshire DG8 6PL.
(870) 0041142
Open Dates: 07.04-30.09 Prestwick 50km Stranraer 40km Barrhill 25km 1km x 36

▲ **New Lanark** Ⓗ 50039
Wee Row, Rosedale St, New Lanark ML11 9DJ.
(870) 0041143
Open Dates: 03.03-28.10 (only 29.10-28.02.07) Glasgow 40km Rosyth 55km Lanark 2km 500m 2.5W x 68 (BD) 1 x

Oban Ⓗ 50011
Oban Esplanade & Lodge, Oban, Argyll PA34 5AF.
(870) 0041144
Open Dates: Open Times: 07.00-02.00hrs
Beds: 130 - 2x3 11x4 6x6 4x6+
Price Range: £11.00-£17.00
Directions: 1.5N from city centre
Glasgow 150km Oban 1.5km Oban 1.5km Oban 1.5km
1.5km

Oban

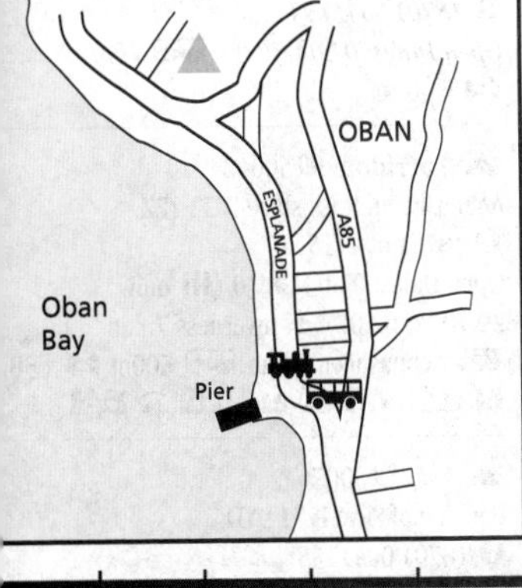

Oban... Travel Tips

- **For budget eats check out...** Oban Inn, Hungry Mac's, Light of India, Chinese Palace, Mondo's
- **For great nightlife try...** Oban Inn, Mondo's, Cooler, Oban Theatre, Oban Cinema
- **Don't miss...** Whale & Dolphin excursions, Sea Life Centre, Oban Rare Breeds Park, Mull/Iona/Staffa Island boat trips & Mull Miniature Railway, Pulpit Hill, Seal Island, Dunollie/Dunstaffanage/Kerrera Castles, Oban Distillery, McCaigs Tower & Oban's new Zoo, Bonawe Iron Foundry

▲ **Pitlochry** Ⓗ 50025
Braeknowe, Knockard Rd, Pitlochry PH16 5HJ.
(870) 0041145
Open Dates: 03.03-28.10 (only 29.10-28.02.07) Edinburgh 110km 1km 1km x 66

▲ **Port Charlotte, Islay** Ⓗ 50060
Port Charlotte, Isle of Islay PA48 7TX.
(870) 0041128
Open Dates: 07.04-30.09 Port Arstaig 20km 500m x 30

△ ***Raasay*** *– 50069*
Creachan Cottage, Raasay, Kyle, Ross-shire IV40 8NT.
(870) 0041146
Open Dates: 28.04-30.09 Inverness 105km 4km Kyle of Lochalsh 30km Sconsar 2km by ferry x 28

▲ **Ratagan** Ⓗ 50040
Glenshiel, Kyle, Ross-shire IV40 8HP.
(870) 0041147
Open Dates: 03.03-28.10 (only 29.10-28.02.07) Inverness 110km Glenelg 15km Kyle of Lochalsh 25km 2km x 38

▲ Rowardennan 50022
Rowardennan by Drymen, Glasgow G63 0AR.
(870) 0041148
Open Dates: 03.03-28.10 (only 29.10-28.02.07) Glasgow 60km
1km Balloch 25km 10km ap Balmaha x 76 R CC

▲ St Andrews – St Andrews Youth Hostel – 50078
David Russell Apartments, Buchanan Gardens, St Andrews KY16 9LY.
(8701) 553255
Open Dates: 01.06-31.08 St Andrews 1km x 60 TV 8

Stirling 50002
St John St, Stirling FK8 1EA.
(870) 0041149
Open Dates: Open Times: 07.00-02.00hrs
Beds: 126 - 4x² 10x⁴ 11x⁵ 3x⁶
Price Range: £12.50-£15.00
Directions: 1W from city centre
Glasgow 50km; Edinburgh 50km
Stirling 1km Stirling 1km x 24 R CC (BD) TV 1 x 8 1km

Stirling

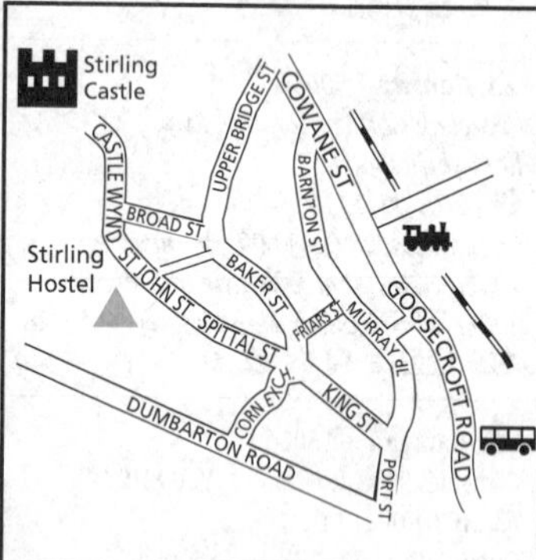

Stirling... Travel Tips

- **For budget eats check out...** Whistlebinkies, Rizzios, Smiling Jacks, The Portcullis, Planet India
- **For great nightlife try...** The Yard Bar, O'Neils Bar, The Fubar Nightclub, Enigma Nightclub, The Sports Bar
- **Don't miss...** Stirling Castle, Stirling Old Bridge, Bannockburn Heritage Centre, Old Town Jail, Argyll's Lodging, Wallace Monument, Smith's Art Gallery, Cambuskenneth Abbey, The Beheading Stone, Arn Prior, Lake of Mentieth

▲ Tobermory 50041
Main St, Tobermory, Isle of Mull, Argyll PA75 6NU.
(870) 0041151
Open Dates: 03.03-28.10 (only 29.10-28.02.07) 1km 500m x 39 R CC

▲ Tomintoul 50074
Main St, Tomintoul, Ballindalloch, Banffshire AB37 9EX.
(870) 0041152
Open Dates: 07.04-30.9 Inverness 100km
Carrbridge 30km 500m x 20 R CC

△ Tongue – 50075
By Lairg, Sutherland, IV27 4XH.
(870) 0041153
Open Dates: 07.04-30.09 1km
x 40

▲ Torridon 50042
Achnasheen, Ross-shire IV22 2EZ.
(870) 0041154
Open Dates: 03.03-28.10 (only 29.10-28.02.07) Inverness 70km
Achnasheen 30km 500m x 58 CC

▲ Uig 50076
Uig, Isle of Skye IV51 9YD.
(870) 0041155
Open Dates: 07.04-30.09 Inverness 130km
4km Kyle of Lochalsh 55km
500m x 62 CC

▲ **Ullapool** 50027
hore St, Ullapool, Ross-shire IV26 2UJ.
(870) 0041156
)pen Dates: 03.03-28.10 (only
29.10-28.02.07) Inverness 70km
500m 500m x 59

YOUTH HOSTEL ACCOMMODATION OUTSIDE THE ASSURED STANDARDS SCHEME

erneray – 50047
sle of Berneray, North Uist, HS6 5BQ.
)pen Dates: Carinish 30km 2km
2km x 20

Durness 50051
moo, Durness, Lairg, Sutherland IV27 4QA.
(870) 0041113
)pen Dates: 07.04-30.09 Inverness 360km
Scrabster 70km Lairg 80km
1km x 40

Eday – 50052
London Bay, Eday, Orkney KW17 2AB.
(1857) 622206
)pen Dates: 01.04-30.09 10km 6km
x 24

Edinburgh – Central 50018
Edinburgh Central YH, 11/2 Robertsons Close,
Cowgate, Edinburgh EH1 1LY.
(870) 0041115
Open Dates: 01.06-31.08 Edinburgh 10km
A 2km Rosyth 20km
Edinburgh Waverley 2km 500m
x 120

Edinburgh – International 50030
Edinburgh International YH, Kincard's Court,
Guthrie St, Edinburgh EH1 1JT.
(870) 0041117
Open Dates: 01.06-31.08 Edinburgh 10km
A 2km Rosyth 20km
Edinburgh Waverley 2km 500m
x 150

Garenin – 50053
Carloway, Isle of Lewis HS2 9AL.
Open Dates: Stornoway 30km
Stornoway 30km 2km x 14

Howmore – 50057
South Uist HS8 5SH.
Open Dates: Carnish 30km
Lochboisdale 20km 1km x 17

Hoy – 50058
Stromness, Orkney KW16 3NJ.
(1856) 873535
Open Dates: Kirkwall 30km by ferry
4km x 26

Kershader – 50063
Ravenspoint, Kershader, South Lochs,
Isle of Lewis HS2 9QA.
(1851) 880236
Open Dates: Melbost 15km
Stornoway 40km 500m x 14

Papa Westray – 50068
Beltane House, Papa Westray,
Orkney KW17 2BU.
(1857) 644267
Open Dates: 4km 4km x 12

Rackwick – 50070
Rackwick Outdoor Centre, Hoy, Stromness,
Orkney KW16 3NJ.
(1856) 873535 Ext 2404
Open Dates: 24.03-03.09 Kirkwall 55km
10km x 8

Rhenigidale – 50071
Isle of Harris HS3 3BD.
Open Dates: Melbost 40km Tarbet
10km 8km ap Maaruig x 11

Serbia & Montenegro

Ferijalni hostelski savez Srbije & Crne Gore,
Youth Hostels Association of Serbia and Montenegro,
11000 Beograd, Makedonska 22/2
Serbia & Montenegro (Fmr. Yugoslavia).
t (381) (11) 322-07-62
f (381) (11) 322-07-62
e info@hostels.org.yu
w www.hostels.org.yu
Office Hours: Monday-Friday 09.00-16.00hrs

Ferijalni savez Srbije,
(Serbian Youth Hostels Association),
11000, Beograd, Obilićev venac 4/3,
Serbia & Montenegro (Fmr. Yugoslavia)
t (381) (11) 2622-956; 2622-584
f (381) (11) 2628-733
Office Hours: Monday-Friday 08.00-15.00hrs

Ferijalni savez Crne Gore,
(Montenegrin Youth Hostels Associations),
8100, Podgorica, Bulevar Lenjina 9, P.fah 209,
Serbia & Montenegro (Fmr. Yugoslavia).
t (381) (81) 225-458
f (381) (81) 241-906
e fscg@cg.yu
Office Hours: Monday-Friday 08.00-15.00hrs

National Tourist Authority/Board:	www.serbia-tourism.org, www.visit-montenegro.com
Capital:	Belgrade
Language:	Serbian
Currency:	Serbia - Din. (Dinar); Montenegro - € Euro
Population:	10,406,742
Size:	107,173 sq km
Telephone Country Code:	381
eKit Access Number:	Check www.hi.ekit.com for up to date Access Numbers

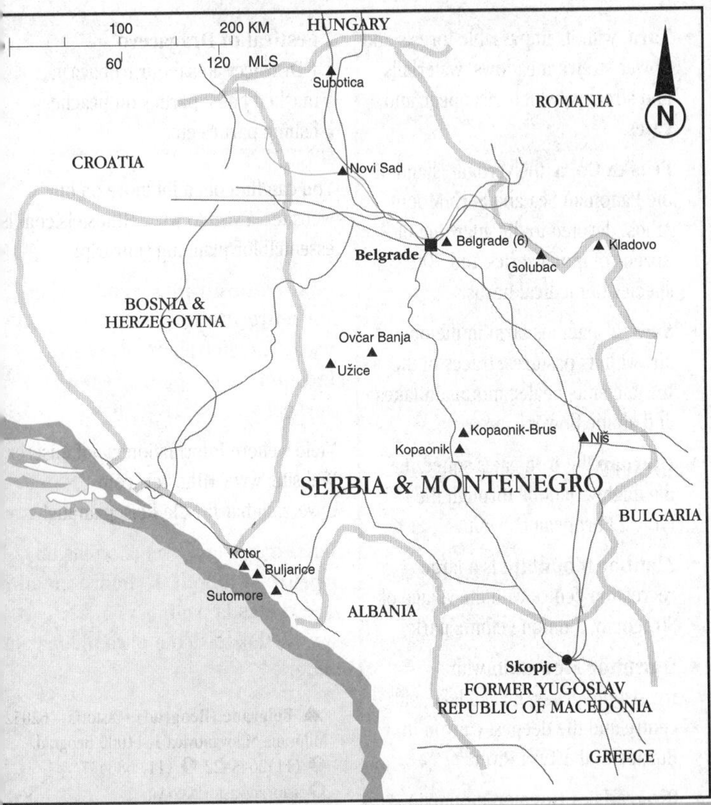

HI Suggests...

The state union of Serbia and Montenegro is made up of two member states, Montenegro and Serbia, which includes the Autonomous Provinces; Vojvodina, Kosovo and Metohija.

It is an unusual unity of contrasts with different civilisation courses present from the earliest times. Bordering between two worlds - The East and the West, which was exactly why these areas resulted in different cultures being present here, in which one can recognise traces from Byzantine, Islam, Venice and Austria- Hungary.

Both the Serbians and the Montenegrins are Orthodox by confession, but there has been a tolerance among all religions for centuries. The official language is Serbian. Two alphabets are used, both Cyrillic and Latin.

It all began six thousand years BC, in **Lepenski Vir** (world famous archaeological site with stone sculptures), on the Danube. Distant ancestors decided to stop and think, and then settle down. Cloaked in silence, hidden among the hills and plum orchards, the world famous monasteries Studenica, Sopocani, Gracanica and Visoki Decani I Ostrog, invaluable heritage of timeless beauty, were created from the 10th to the 17th centuries. Natural attractions include:

- **Kopaonik**, the mountain of contrasts and of all seasons, with monasteries on its slopes, ice-cold water springs at its foot, the sun at its peak and the modern ski centre in the winter.

- **Tara**, with its impassable forests and flower strewn meadows, waterfalls and streams, which disappear into caves.
- **Fruška Gora**, the verdant island of the Panonian Sea and Serb Mount Athos, devoted to the guarding of dozens of monasteries and 700 species of medical herbs.
- **Šara**, a spacious farm in the open air, with its pastures, traces of the Ice Age at its peaks, mountain lakes and alpine flowers.
- **Djerdap** the Iron gates squeezing the mighty Danube through the largest European canyon.
- **Zlatibor Mountain** is a large recreation centre with the village of Sirogojno, a unique ethnic park.
- **Durmitor Mountain** with irresistible peaks, glacial lake, ski centre and the deepest canyon in Europe of the Tara River.
- **Biogradska Gora** on mountain Bjelasica, the last virgin forest in Europe.
- **Kotor Bay**, the southern most fjords in the world.
- **Adriatic Sea**, choose to explore one of the 117 sandy beaches.
- **Belgrade** is the capital city with Kalemegdan fortress, the Cathedral, Princess Ljubica's Home, museums and galleries, stadiums and squares, the Bohemian cafes of Scadarlija and the imposing dome of St. Sava Temple.

Apart from the usual events; music, film, literary, fairs, shows, concerts and exhibitions, some events have been adjusted to the specific offer of every town, events devoted to maintaining traditions, customs, folklore and handicrafts **'Trumpet Festival of Dragacevo'** ('Dragacevski sabour trubaca'), masked balls, parties on beaches, fishing parties etc.

You can find out a lot more on our website - a visit to www.HIhostels.com is essential for planning your trip!

Pour en savoir plus, rendez-vous sur notre site Internet, www.HIhostels.com une visite incontournable pour préparer votre voyage!

Viele weitere Informationen auf unserer Website: www.HIhostels.com - unverzichtbar für die Reiseplanung!

Puedes averiguar mucho más en nuestro sitio web. Es imprescindible que visites la página www.HIhostels.com para planear tu viaje.

▲ **Belgrade (Beograd)** – Astoria – 62052
Milovana Milovanovića 1, 11000 Beograd.
(11)2645422 (11) 686437
astoria@astoria.co.yu
www.astoria.co.yu
Open Dates: 12 Surčin 20km
A 20km Belgrade 2km
Glavna Železnička Stanica 100m
ap Savskitrg ap Savskitrg 0.2S x 120
R 2.5km 3.5km

Belgrade (Beograd) – Jelica – 62004
11000 Beograd, Krunska 8.
(11) 3231268; 3231272; 3304804; 3345519 (11) 3304808 info@hostels.org.yu
www.hostels.org.yu
Open Dates: 22.06-30.08 Open Times:
Beds: 108 - 12x3 18x4
Price Range:
Directions: 0.1SE from city centre
Surčin 20km A Jat Transfer 20km
Belgrade 2km Glavna Železnička Stanica 1.5km 3, 7 100m R
TV 2 x 500m

Belgrade (Beograd) – Jelica

△ ***Belgrade (Beograd)*** *– Lipovička Šuma – 62005*
Lipovica-Barajevo, Beograd.
(11) 8302184 (11) 8302134
info@hostels.org.yu
www.hostels.org.yu
Open Dates: Surčin 40km
Glavna Železnička Stanica 25km
831 Barajevo 50m ap Lipovička Šuma 12, 13 ap Banovo Brdo 20S
x 40 1 x

▲ **Belgrade (Beograd)** – Royal – 62054
Kralja Petra 56 11000 Beograd.
(11) 634222 (11) 626459
toplice@net.yu www.hotelroyal.co.yu
Open Dates: Surčin 22km A Jat Terminal 22km Glavna Luka
Glavna Železnička Stanica 1km 2, 11, 13 300m ap Kalemegdan 0.6NW x 187
2km 4.5km

△ ***Belgrade (Beograd)*** *– "ZMAJ" – 62011*
Tvornička 1, 11080 Zemun.
(11) 3223454 (11) 423248
info@hostels.org.yu
www.hostels.org.yu
Open Dates: 27.06-30.08 Surčin 20km
A Terminal Fontana 2km
Belgrade 6km Glavna Železnička Stanica 5km 83, 18, 17 7W x 80

▲ **Belgrade (Beograd)** – Žoc Hostel – 62049
Zdravka Čelara 14, 11000 Beograd.
(11) 2072600; 2072605 (11) 750868
info@hostels.org.yu
www.hostels.org.yu
Open Dates: 25.06-25.08 x 440
1 x 2km

Belgrade (Beograd)... Travel Tips

- **For budget eats check out...** Tri Kostura (student restaurant), Sunce (vegetable dishes), Stenka (fish), Mornar (national dishes), Klub Kolarac (pizzeria)
- **For great nightlife try...** Skadarlija (food, bars, nightclub & disco), Student Culture Centre, Dom Omladine Beograda (Barutana), BUS (nightclub & disco), Plato (jazz)
- **Don't miss...** Kalemegdan Park & Belgrade Fortress, Knez Mihajlova Street, National Museum, Zemun Gardoš, National Theatre, The Nikola Pašiç Square, St Sava's Church, Košutnjak (sport, recreation & picnic area), Ada Ciganlija, Avala

---

△ ***Buljarice*** *– Toplica – 62014*
"Toplica", 81352 Buljarice.
(86) 461479 (27) 321035
info@hostels.org.yu
www.hostels.org.yu
Open Dates: 01.07-30.08 0.5E x 200

▲ **Golubac** – Golubački Grad – 62019
12223 Golubac, Golubački trg 10.
(12) 78507; 78207 (12) 78207
hotelgograd@ptt.yu
www.hostels.org.yu
Open Dates: 0.2NE x 130
2 x 200m 200m

▲ **Kladovo** – Karataš – 62021
Omladinski Kamp "Djerdap" 19320 Kladovo.
(19) 87577; 87983 (19) 81394
djerdaposk@arkayu.net
www.djerdaposk.co.yu
Open Dates: 01.07-30.08 3km 2W
x 350

▲ **Kopaonik** – Mašinac – 62024
36080 Kopaonik.
t (36) 71065 f (11) 423248
e info@hostels.org.yu
w www.hostels.org.yu
Open Dates: 12 0.1NE x 110 R
200m

▲ **Kopaonik-Brus** – Junior – 62026
Kopaonik, 37220 Brus.
t (37) 823344; (11) 3114556
f (37) 823022; (11) 144828
e junior@tecnicom.net
w www.dpjunior.com
Open Dates: 12 2SW x 150 R
P

▲ **Kotor** – Studentski Hostel "Spasić-Mašera" – 62058
Dobrota BB 85330 Kotor.
t (82) 330258; (69) 041480
f (82) 330258 e sdomkotos@cg.yu
w www.sdomkotor.cg.yu
Open Dates: 01.07-31.08 Tivat 8km
Kotor 1km Bar 65km x 246
R TV 1 x P
100m 100m

△ ***Niš** – Bubanj-Niš – 62057*
18000 Niš Bubanjskih Heroja 3.
t (18) 263801 f (18) 263801
e info@hostels.org.yu
w www.hostels.org.yu
Open Dates: 12 Niš 1km Ledena Stena 100m 2.5W x 50 R
1 x P

▲ **Novi Sad** – "Brankovo kolo" – 62030
Episkopa Visariona 3, 21000 Novi Sad.
t (21) 528263 f (21) 422784
e office@hostelns.com
w www.hostelns.com
Open Dates: 27.06-30.08 Surčin 70km
Ž. Stanica 3.6km 0.2N x 200
R P

△ ***Ovčar Banja** – Dom – 62033*
32240 Ovčar Banja.
t (32) 816763 f (32) 816763
e info@hostels.org.yu
w www.hostels.org.yu
Open Dates: 12 100m Ovčar Banja 600m 0.6NE x 40 R
P

▲ **Subotica** – Studentski Centar – 62037
Subotica 24000, Segedinski Put 11.
t (24) 546637 f (24) 548394
e hostel@scsu.org.yu w www.scsu.org.yu
Open Dates: 01.07-25.08 500m
500m 0.5E x 200 R
TV 63 x P 10km

△ ***Sutomore** – Crveni Krst – 62038*
Odmaralište Crvenog Krsta, 85000 Sutomore.
t (85) 373124; 373608 f (85) 373124
Open Dates: 01.06-31.08 0.3W x 200
R P

△ ***Užice** – Dom PR Užice – 62051*
Nemanjina 52, 31000 Užice.
t (31) 511366; 511336 f (31) 511347
e dompruzice@ptt.yu
w www.hostels.org.yu
Open Dates: 25.06-30.08 x 200 R
TV P

Slovenia

Popotniško združenje Slovenijie - PZS Maribor - Hostelling International Slovenia, Gosposvetska 84, 2000 MARIBOR, Slovenija.

t (386) (2) 2342137
f (386) (2) 2342136
e info@youth-hostel.si
w www.youth-hostel.si

A copy of the Hostel Directory for this Country can be obtained from:
The National Office

National Tourist Authority/Board:	www.slovenia-tourism.si
Capital:	Ljubljana
Language:	Slovene
Currency:	Slovene Tolar (SIT)
Population:	1,965,986
Size:	20,254 sq km
Telephone Country Code:	386
eKit Access Number:	Check www.hi.ekit.com for up to date Access Numbers

HI Suggests...

Slovenia is a relatively small country, tucked into a mountainous corner between Austria, Italy, Hungary, Croatia and the Adriatic Sea.

Everything in Slovenia is in abundance: the majestic Alps with their glacial valleys, rivers and lakes, many forests, mysterious caves and the warm Adriatic Sea. From the steep slopes of the Alps you can reach the world of olives and vineyards in less than three hours. Slovenia's natural features and cultural and historical sites offer plenty of variety for a holiday.

You can explore the underground world of grottoes, walk in the clean mountain air of the Triglav National Park, climb the peaks of the Julian Alps, admire the medieval treasures of old cities and towns and enjoy their museums, concerts, international festivals, fairs and events, or play on spectacular golf courses.

The contrast within the 20,256 square kilometres of Slovenia's landscape will inevitably surprise first time visitors. About fifty kilometres from the capital, Ljubljana, are the Julian Alps, where fairy tale Lake Bled glistens; the Postojna Caves, the largest in Europe, are 35 minutes' drive from the capital on a modern expressway; and Portoroz, a sunny seaside resort, is just over 100 kilometres from Ljubljana.

Peaceful and quiet, Slovenia's population of nearly two million is an integrated society. Nearly 90 percent are Slovene and about 10 percent are Italian, Hungarian, or nationalities from the former Yugoslav republics. Most Slovenes speak English, German, or Italian as their second language.

Ljubljana, Slovenia's attractive medieval capital is very cosmopolitan. The city is dominated by an ancient castle and adorned with baroque churches and classical public buildings. The city has an attractive artistic life, especially in the domain of the performing arts; an international festival is held here every summer.

The Ljubljana Philharmonic Society was founded in 1702 and boasts Beethoven as an honorary member. Performances by Ljubljana's own ballet, symphony and opera companies take place at the National Theatre of Slovenia, the Cankarjev Dom Cultural and Congress Centre, or at the Opera. During the summer months, performances may be seen on the open-air stages of the Ljubljana Festival and elsewhere in the historic old town.

If you are looking for a peaceful, value-laden destination with everything - mountains, lakes, seashore, ski resorts, health spas, historic cities and villages, castles and churches - then discover Slovenia, the beautiful country on the sunny side of the Alps.

ou can find out a lot more on our website - a visit to www.HIhostels.com is ssential for planning your trip!

'our en savoir plus, rendez-vous ur notre site Internet, www.HIhostels.com une visite ncontournable pour préparer votre oyage!

'iele weitere Informationen auf unserer Vebsite: www.HIhostels.com - unverzichtbar für die Reiseplanung!

'uedes averiguar mucho más en uestro sitio web. Es imprescindible que visites la página www.HIhostels.com para planear tu iaje.

▲ **Bilje** – Youth Hostel "Pod Krasom" Kogoj – 92523
Bilje 149/a, 5292 Rence.
(5) 3013097 (5) 3985401
petka.kogoj@siol.net
Open Dates: 12 Trieste 27km; LLjubljana-Brnik 120km Trieste 30km Volcja Draga 3km Bilje-Kogos 20m x 32 R 1 x 8 P 10km

Bled – Bledec - (Advanced Hostel) – 92501
Grajska 17, 4260 Bled.
(4) 5745250 (4) 5745251
bledec@mlino.si www.mlino.si
Open Dates: 12 Open Times:
Beds: 55 - 1x2 3x3 5x4 1x5 2x6 1x6+
Price Range: 3480-4650 SIT € 15-20 BB inc
Directions: 0.5NW from city centre
Ljubljana-Brnik 32km A Taxi
Bled 2km Brnik-Kranj; Kranj-Bled ap Bled Autobusna Postaja R CC 1 x P

Bled – Bledec - (Advanced Hostel)

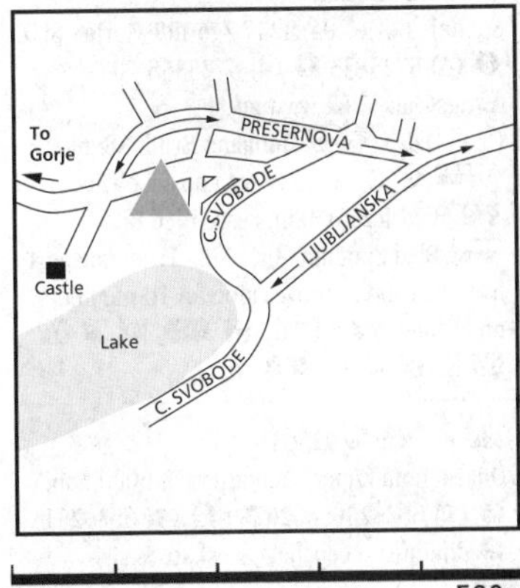

Bled... Travel Tips

- **For budget eats check out...** Restavracija Bledec, Gostilna Pri Planincu, Picerija Matjaž, Gostišce Okarina, Gostišce Mayer
- **For great nightlife try...** Disco Faraon, Bar Dioniz, Rock Bar, Casinó-Black Jack, Casinó-Dancing
- **Don't miss...** Vintgar, Grad Kamen, Pokljuka High Plateu, Lake Bohinj, Bohinj Water Fall, Kropa, Vršic Mountain Pass, Radovljica Bee Musuem, Triglav National Park & The Julian Alps, Radovna Gorge, Babji Zob Cave, Postojna Cave, Oilarina Folk Festival, Violin Festival, Bled & Bohinj have summer festivals with fireworks

▲ **Črnomelj** – Youth Hostel Črnomelj 92529

Ulica Otona Župančica 7, 8340 Črnomelj.
(7) 3062170 (7) 3062175
dd-crnomelj@guest.arnes.si
www.d-crnomelj.nm.edus.si
Open Dates: Zagreb 120 km; Ljubljana-Brnik 140km Crnomelj 800m Crnomelj 800m x 50

▲ **Gorje (near Bled)** – YH Kuralt - (Advanced Hostel) – 92502

Spodnje Gorje 104; 4247 Zgornde Gorje - SLO.
(4) 5725833 (4) 5725358
ats@ats.si www.ats.si
Open Dates: Ljubljana-Brnik 38km A € 35 - arrange with hostel owner Bled-Jezero 3km; Lesce Bled 8km Bled-Spodnje Gorje 5m - Free transport from bus and railway station for HI members on request x 17

▲ **Koper** 92503

Dijaški dom Koper, Cankarjeva 5, 6000 Koper.
(5) 6626250; 6626260 (5) 6626251
ddkoper-recepcija@guest.arnes.si; ddkoper@guest.arnes.si
www.d-dom.kp.edus.si
Open Dates: 10.07-20.08 Trieste 25km Trieste 25km Koper 1.5km Koper 200m ap Vojkovo Nabrežje x 30 1 x 400m 400m

▲ **Koper** – Youth Hostel Port-Koper 92525

Ankaranska Cesta 7.
(5) 6393260; 6393261 (5) 6393259
motel.port@siol.net
www.port-turizem.si
Open Dates: Trieste 20km; Ljubljana-Brnik 150km Trieste 20km Koper 500m Koper 500m 1km

▲ **Kranjska Gora** – Nika 92518

Čičare 2.
(4) 5881000; 5881436; (41) 636266
(4) 5881436 zvone.oreskovic@s5.net
Open Dates: Ljubljana-Brnik 69km; Klagenfurt (Austria) 60km A Transport from airport can be arranged Jesemice; Villach (Austria); Trevissio (Italy) 25km 300m ap Kranjska Gora 0.5S x 55 1 x

▲ **Ljubljana** – Alibi Hostel Ljubljana Center 92531

Cankarjevo Nabrežje 27.
(1) 2511244 (1) 2511567
info@alibi.si www.alibi.si
Open Dates: Ljubljana-Brnik 18km A 750m Koper, Trieste 100km Ljubljana 750m Ljubljana 750m 11, 20 ap Magistrat 200m x 120

▲ **Ljubljana** – Alibi Rooms Hostel 92532

Kolarjeva 30.
(1) 4331331 (1) 5211567
info@alibi.si www.alibi.si
Open Dates: Ljubljana-Brnik 18km A 1km Koper, Trieste 100km 1km 14 ap Podmilščakova 50m 1N x 54 2km

▲ **Ljubljana** – Hostel Park Ljubljana – 92519

Tabor 9, Ljubljana.
(1) 3002500 (1) 4330546
hotel.park@siol.net
Open Dates: Ljubljana-Brnik 25km A Ljubljana 800m Koper 150km Ljubljana 800m ap Ilirska 5 x 22 2 x

▲ **Ljubljana** – Tabor – 92505
Vidovdanska 7, 1000 Ljubljana.
(1) 2348840 (1) 2348855
ssljddta1s@quest.arnes.si
www2.arnes.si/~ssljddta1s/
Open Dates: 25.06-25.08 25km
A 500m 500m 500m ap Line Nr 5. Ilirska x 50 R (B) P

▲ **Ljubljana** – Youth Hostel - Dijaški dom Šiška – 92520
Aljaževa 32.
(1) 5007804; 5007802 (1) 5007820
info@ddsiska.com www.ddsiska.com
Open Dates: 01.06-25.08 Ljubljana-Brnik 25km A Brnik-Ljubljana 30km Trieste 110km; Rijeka 120km Ljubljana 2km 1, 7, 8, 15, 16 800m ap "Stara Cerkev" x 50 R (B) P 100m

▲ **Ljubljana** – Youth Hostel Ljubljana HI 92515
Litijska 57, Ljubljana.
(1) 5480055 (1) 5480056
info@yh-ljubljana.com
www.yh-ljubljana.com
Open Dates: Ljubljana-Brnik 25km A 4km 100km 2km 5, 9, 13 300m ap Emona x 100 R CC (B) TV 8 P

▲ **Maribor** – 92507
Dijaški dom 26 Junij Maribor,
Železnikova UL.12, 2000 Maribor.
/ (2) 4801710; (2) 4801710
vojteh.stefanciosa@guest.arnes.si
www.maribor.uni-mb.si/26junij/html/index.html
Open Dates: A 3km 3km Line 3 300m 6SE x 50 R P 1km

▲ **Maribor** – Group Accommodation Center Gaudeamus – 92509
Gregorčičeva 25, 2000 Maribor.
(2) 2502108 (2) 2502107
info@gaudeamus.si
www.gaudeamus.si
Open Dates: A 100m Maribor 1km Maribor 200m ap Modua Hiša or City x 55 R CC TV i P

▲ **Maribor** – Uni-Hostel Maribor - (Advanced Hostel) HI 92508
Grajski trg 3a, 2000 Maribor.
(2) 2506700 (2) 2518497
uni.hotel@termemb.si
www.termemb.si
Open Dates: A 200m 1km 100m ap Modua Hiša; Vecer x 10 R CC 1 x i 8 P

▲ **Maribor-Ruše** – Youth Hostel Ruše HI 92513
Dijaški dom GSKŠ Ruše, Šolska ulica 16.
(2) 6600800; 6600816 (2) 6300801
info@gimnazija-ruse.org; gsksruse@hotmail.com
www.gimnazija-ruse.org
Open Dates: Ljubljana-Brnik 150km; Graz 80km Ruše Tovarua 300m; Ruše 500m 1km ap Ruše-Vas 11W x 55 R TV 3 x i P

▲ **Murska Sobota** – Dijaški Dom Murska Sobota – 92510
Tomšičeva 15, 9000 Murska Sobota.
(2) 5300310 (2) 5300311
dd.ms-msobota@guest.arnes.si
www.d-dom.ms.edu.si
Open Dates: 1.5km 1km 0.5S x 60 R TV 1 x i P

Piran ☛ **Portorož, Koper**

▲ **Podčetrtek** – Podčetrtek HI 92522
Zdraviliška 10.
(3) 5829109 (3) 5829109
yhostel@podcetrtek.si
www.podcetrtek.si
Open Dates: Zagreb (Croatia) 80km; Ljubljana-Brnik (Slovenia) 110km; Graz (Austria) 110km Podcetrtek-Toplile 100m Podcetrtek-Ciril 10m x 56 TV 1 x i 8 P 100m 100m

▲ **Portorož** – YH Portorož 92530
Šentjane 25.
(5) 6747289 (5) 6747332
residence.panorama@gmail.com
Open Dates: Ljubljana-Brnik 100km; Ronki (Trieste) 80km Trieste 40km (Shuttle on request) Koper 20km (Shuttle on request) Piran 1.6km ap Portorož-Belikriž 300m x 67 800m

▲ **Ptuj** – 92512
Osojnikova 9, 2250 Ptuj.
(2) 7710814 (2) 7710815
csod.yhptuj@guest.arnes.si
Open Dates: Zagreb (Croatia) 80km; Ljubljana-Brnik 130km Ptuj 300m Ptuj 100m 0.15E x 53 1 x

▲ **Rogaška Slatina** – YH Rogaška Slatina 92526
Steklarska 1.
(3) 8182029 (3) 5814616
ema.djorcev@guest.arnes.si
www2.arnes.si/~sscesteks5/
Open Dates: Zagreb 60km; Ljubljana-Brnik 110km Rogaška 1.5km 300m ap Tržišce-Steklarna x 50

▲ **Šmartno Ob Paki** – Youth Hostel Mc Šmartno Ob Paki – 92514
Šmartno Ob Paki 13, 3327 Šmartno Ob Paki.
(41) 938649
mcsmartnoobpaki@siol.net
Open Dates: Ljubljana-Brnik 85km Šmartno Ob Paki 100m 15m ap Šmartno Ob Paki x 44 1 x

▲ **Vransko** – Youth Hostel 'Golobcek' Vransko – 92528
Vransko 31, 3305 Vransko.
(3) 5725360; (31) 724198
(3) 7055038
pizzerija.golobcek@siol.net
Open Dates: Ljubljana-Brnik 70km Vransko 100m x 22

Spain

Red Española de Albergues Juveniles,
c/ Castello n 24,
Esc. Int-6º Decha,
Madrid 28001, Spain.
t (34) (915) 227007
f (34) (915) 228067
e info@reaj.com
w www.reaj.com

c/ Galera, 16, 1º, 41001 Sevilla, Spain.
t (34) (954) 226803
f (34) (954) 221849
e info@reaj.com

Office Hours: Monday-Friday 09.00-14.00hrs

A copy of the Hostel Directory for this Country can be obtained from:
The National Office

Capital:	Madrid
Language:	Spanish
Currency:	€ Euro
Population:	39,433,942
Size:	504,782 sq km
Telephone Country Code:	34
eKit Access Number:	800-099-665

Thanks to membership of the European Union, Spain has achieved a remarkable economic turnaround, with renewal everywhere to be seen in the infrastructure and architecture of the city skylines of, not least Madrid and Barcelona, as well as in the bars and cafes, shops and stores, monuments and museums across the country. Even more so, the flamboyance and flamenco, the pride and passion of traditional Spain continues to enrich everyday life as much as ever, which the world witnessed at the Barcelona Olympic Games in 1992.

Though Castilian Spanish is the official language, regional identity, including local language and culture is very much part of this equation: in fact, Galicia, Catalonia and Euskadi (the Basque region) have their own

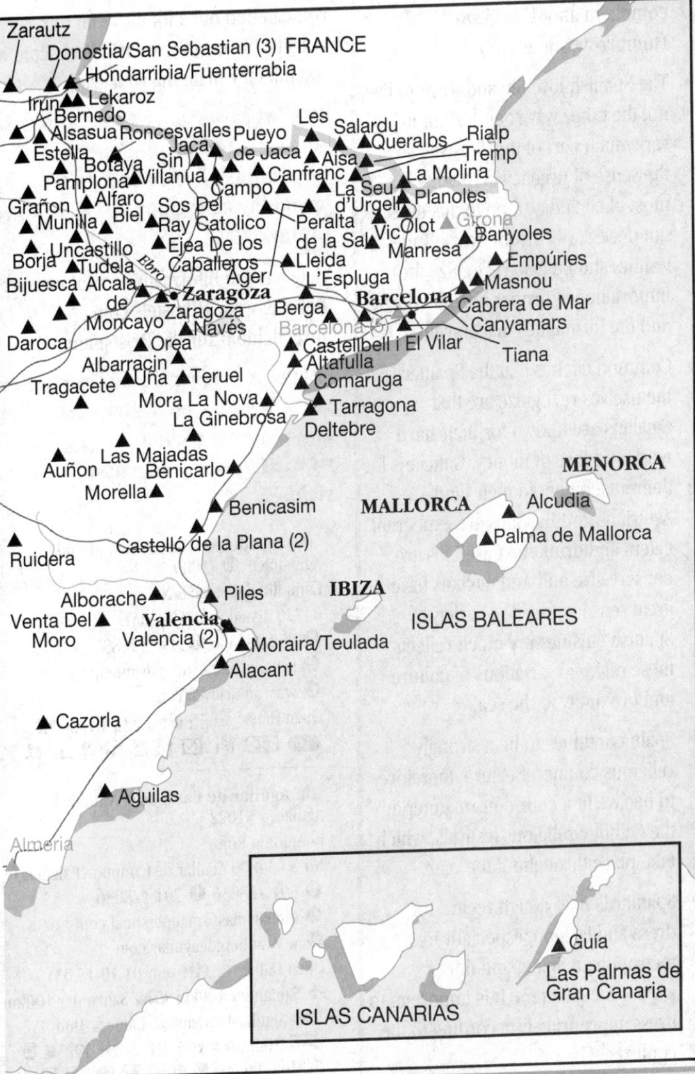

language. The Basques continue to yearn for independence.

Spain is very much a cultural kaleidoscope that over the centuries was home to Greeks, Phoenicians, Carthaginians, Romans, Goths and Arabs (Suni) – the latter staying for 800 years until the end of the fifteenth century, leaving behind a remarkable Moorish Islamic heritage, epitomised in the spectacular design and architecture of the Al-Hambra palace of courts, gardens and water in Granada.

A few other Top Tips from **CULTURE SMART!**:

- The hot climate of Spain undoubtedly impacts on the work ethic the further south you travel, which increasingly gives way to a more relaxed way of life. Hence the common northern European complaint about *'Mañana'* (tomorrow/sometime).

- The Spanish love life and work to live, not the other way round. Humour is very much part of that lifestyle, so is the sense of urgency in making the most of each day, though this does not necessarily involve work! But visitors should also recognize the importance of proper introductions and the formalities that go with it.
- Common clichés that the Spaniards themselves recognize are that Catalans are known for their hard work and love of money, Galicians for their attachment to their land, Asturians and Basques are exuberant eaters and drinkers, Castilians are conservative and Andalucians have a great sense of fun. The variety of Spanish cuisine very much reflects these regional variations of culture and proximity to the sea.
- Spain continues to be a strongly religious country. Be sure, therefore, to behave in a courteous manner at the Catholic religious festivals, which take place throughout the year.
- Spaniards have a high regard for dress and fashion, especially in metropolitan Spain, and thus appearance matters. It is important to dress appropriately according to the context.

Cultural Top Tips supplied by Culture Smart! guides. These essential guides to customs and etiquette will help you steer clear of embarrassing gaffes and sensitive issues, enabling you to discover new cultures whilst developing new friendships. Order online at www.culturesmartguides.co.uk

You can find out a lot more on our website - a visit to www.HIhostels.com is essential for planning your trip!

Pour en savoir plus, rendez-vous sur notre site Internet, www.HIhostels.com une visite incontournable pour préparer votre voyage!

Viele weitere Informationen auf unserer Website: www.HIhostels.com - unverzichtbar für die Reiseplanung!

Puedes averiguar mucho más en nuestro sitio web. Es imprescindible que visites la página www.HIhostels.com para planear tu viaje.

▲ **Aguadulce** – Instalacion Juvenil Aguadulce Ⓗ 51009
Campillo del Moro S/N,
04720 Aguadulce (Almeria).
Ⓣ 950 340346 Ⓕ 950 345855
Ⓔ aguadulce.itj@juntadeandalucia.es
Ⓦ www.inturjoven.com
Open Dates: 12 1S x 222 R CC- TV 1 x

▲ **Aguilar de Campoo** – Nido de las Aguilas – 51022
c/ Antonio Rojo,
No 2 - 34800 Aguilar de Campoo (Palencia).
Ⓣ 791 128036 Ⓕ 791 128036
Ⓔ nidoaguilas@mailpersonal.com
Ⓦ www.albergueaguilas.com
Open Dates: 12 (only 01.10-15.03)
Santander 100km Santander 100km
Aguilar De Campoo-Camesa 3km
100m x 55 TV 2 x 8

▲ **Aguilas** – Calarreona – 51023
Ctra. de Vera Km4, 30880 Aguilas (Murcia).
Ⓣ 968 413029 Ⓕ 968 413029
Ⓔ aj_calarreona@listas.carm.es
Ⓦ www.mundojoven.org
Open Dates: 12 San Javier 100km
A Murcia 105km Aguilas 5km 4SW
x 87 R TV
1 x 50m

Àger – Vall D'Àger – 51216
c/la Font , 9 25691 Àger.
973 455235; 934 838363 (R)
977 650588
albergvalldager@eresmas.com
www.tujuca.com
Open Dates: 12 Balaguer-Àger x 40 R CC

Aisa – Albergue Valle de Aisa – 51211
c/Alta, s/n Aisa 22860.
974 362420 974 364679
Open Dates: 12 x 60 P

Alacant – "La Florida" – 51024
Avda Orihuela 59, 03007 Alicante.
965 113044; R 902 225552 Central Booking 965 282754; R 963 985913
laflorida_ivaj@gva.es; creserves_ivah@gva.es www.ivaj.es
Open Dates: 02.01-23.12; 26-30.12 (please consult) "L'Altet" Alicante 14km
A Alicante 1.5km Alicante 1.5km Alicante 1.5km 3 20m ap Avd. Orihuela 3.5W x 184 R CC TV 1 x 3km

Albarracín – Rosa Bríos – 51025
c/ Santa María, 5, Albarracín 44100 (Teruel).
978 710005; R 976 714797
978 704019
Open Dates: 01-31.01; 01.03-31.10; 01-31.12
x 71 R CC

Alborache – Torre D'Alborache – 51026
Ctra de Macastre, s/n 46369 Alborache (Valencia).
962 508123; R 902 225552 Central Booking 962 508020; R 963 985913
albergalborache_ivaj@gva.es; creserves_ivaj@gva.es www.ivaj.es
Open Dates: 02.01-23.12; 26-30.12
"Manises" Valencia 38km Valencia 48km Buñol 5km Buñol ap at the YH 0.3NW x 116 R CC TV 1 x P 50km

Alburquerque – Castillo de Luna – 51027
c/ Castillo, s/n 06510 Alburquerque (Badajoz).
924 015562 924 015564
Open Dates: 01.03-31.12
Open Times: 08.00-23.00hrs
Beds: 10 - 5x2
Directions: Alburquerque TV 1 x

Alburquerque – Castillo de Luna

0 1.5km

Alburquerque... Travel Tips

- **For budget eats check out...** Machaco, Balanus, Castillo (pub), Castillo de Luna, Tegamar
- **For great nightlife try...** Culture House (films, theatre etc), Medieval Quarter, Way Route 1, Castillo (pub), Balanus Cyber Café
- **Don't miss...** Way Route, Castillo de Luna, Medieval Quarter, Dehesa Zone Route, Pantano del Aguila Route

Alcalá de Moncayo – 51028
c/ Puerta del Lugar s/n, 50591 Alcalá de Moncayo (Zaragoza).
976 646459; 650 396917 976 646459
info@alberguemoncayo.com
alberguemoncayo.com
Open Dates: 12 Vera de Moncayo x 86 R TV P

▲ **Alcúdia** – La Victòria – 51029
Ctra. Cap Pinar Km. 4,
9 07400 Alcúdia (Mallorca).
971 545542; 545395 971 546649
lavictoria@tjove.caib.es
http://turismejove.caib.es
Open Dates: 01.02-30.11 Son Sant Joan 60km Port D'Alcudiac 5km; Palma 60km Sa Pobla 20km
Palma-Alcudia 60km ap Alcudia Church 5km x 203 1 x 50m

▲ **Aldeadávila de la Ribera** – La Noria – 51030
c/ La Noria, s/n - 37250 Aldeadávila de la Ribera (Salamanca).
923 526359 983 140342
aldeadavila@terra.es
Open Dates: x 116

▲ **Alfaro** – 51031
Plaza Azaña, 26540-Alfaro (La Rioja).
941 29100 Ext 6202; 941 291229
Open Dates: x 40

▲ **Algeciras** – Instalacion Juvenil Algeciras
HI 51010
Parque Natural Los Canutos, Ctra. N-340, km 96, 6, 11390 Algeciras (Cádiz).
956 679060 956 679017
algeciras.itj@juntadeandalucia.es
www.inturjoven.com
Open Dates: 8W x 107 1 x

▲ **Almería** – Instalacion Juvenil Almería
HI 51011
c/ Isla de Fuerteventura S/N, 04007 Almería.
950 269788 950 271744
almeria.itj@juntadeandalucia.es
www.inturjoven.com
Open Dates: 1SE x 170 1 x

▲ **Almorox** – "Ecogranja San Pol" – 51032
Camino Cadalso-Pinar,
45900 Almorox (Toledo).
915 419089; 649 473291 915 479946
teatro@teatrosanpol.com
www.teatrosanpol.com
Open Dates: only x 86

▲ **La Almunia de Doña Godina** – Ramón y Cajal" – 51102
Avda Laviaga Castillo, La Almunia de Doña Godina 50100 (Zaragoza).
976 600833; 601088 (Info);
976 714797 976 601080
bgarcias@aragob.es
Open Dates: 01-31.07 6km x 72

▲ **Alsasua** – "Sto Cristo de Otadia" – 51033
Zelai 91, 31800 Alsasua (Navarra).
948 564814; 902 230400 ( )
948 564973 aalsasua@cfnavarra.es
www.cfnavarra.es/indj
Open Dates: 16.01-18.12
Noain-Pamplona/Vitoria Alsasua
Alsasua x 81
1 x

▲ **Altafulla** – "Casa Gran" – 51034
Placeta 12, 43893 Altafulla (Tarragona).
977 650779; 934 838363
977 650588
alberg_altafulla@tujuca.com
www.tujuca.com (online)
Open Dates: 01.01-23.12 Altafulla 500m
x 72

▲ **Aranda de Duero** – Las Francesas – 51035
c/ Antonio Baciero,
s/n - 09400 Aranda de Duero (Burgos).
947 241477; 505030 947 217521; 505030 sprintem@cyl.com
Open Dates: x 70

▲ **Arbejal** – 51036
Carretera Arbejal, 34843 Arbejal (Palencia).
979 870174 albergue@arbejal.com
www.arbejal.com
Open Dates: 2NW x 96

▲ **Arcentales** – La Estacion – 51037
Barrio Laureta s/n,
48879 Arcentales (Bizkaia).
94 6109040 94 4532753
laestacion@agoranet.es
Open Dates: FEVE (Bilbao-Santander) Villaverde
Autobuses ANSA (Bilbao-Lanestosa) 100m ap La Tejera x 34
15km

▲ **Auñon** – "Entrepeñas" – 51039
Poblado de Entrepeñas,
19130 Auñon (Guadalajara).
949 358415; 888869/72 949 888871
alberguesclm@jccm.es
www.rajclm.com
Open Dates: 01.01-30.10; 10-31.12 x 64

▲ **Avila** – "Profesor Arturo Duperier" – 51040
Av de Juventud s/n, 05003 Avila.
920 221716 920 221716
www.jcyl.es/juventud
Open Dates: 01.07-15.09 x 90

▲ **Balmaseda** – "El Peñueco" Aterpetxea – 51041
El Peñueco Auzoa,
s/n 48800 Balmaseda (Bizkaia).
629 535240 gaztezer@balmaseda.net
Open Dates: Loiu 45km
Balmaseda 2km 1.5km x 16

▲ **Banyoles** – "Alberg Banyoles" – 51043
Migdia, 10, 17820 Banyoles (Girona).
972 575454; 934 838363
972 575454
albergbanyoles@teleline.es
www.tujuca.com
Open Dates: 01.01-23.12; 27-31.12
Girona 18km x 100

▲ **Barcelona** – Alberguinn Youth Hostel – 51232
c/Melcior De Palau, 70-74 Entlo.
934 905965; (934 838363)
934 911941
alberguinn@alberguinn.com
www.alberguinn.com; www.tujuca.com
Open Dates: "El Prat" Barcelona 13km
Barcelona 4km Sants 700m Plaça Centre, Sants Estació, Plaça Sants 450m x 50
(B)

▲ **Barcelona** – Inout Alberg – 51231
Major de Rectoret 2, 08017 Barcelona.
932800985; (934 838363)
932801857 reservas@inouthostel.com
www.tujuca.com
Open Dates: "El Prat" Barcelona 17.2km Barcelona 13km
Barcelona South 10.6km
Barcelona North 12.1km x 164

Barcelona – Mare de Déu de Montserrat
51003
Passeig Mare de Déu del Coll 41-51, 08023 Barcelona.
932 105151; 934 838363
932 100798
alberg_barcelona@tujuca.com
www.tujuca.com (online)
Open Dates: 01.01-23.12; 26-31.12
Open Times: 07.00-00.00hrs
Beds: 220 - 25x6 6x6+
Price Range: € 13.59-21.90 BBinc
Directions: "El Prat" Barcelona 20km
A #28 Plaça Catalunya Barcelona 2km Sants (Barcelona 4km) 28, 92 ap next to the hostel Linea 3 - Green "Vallcarca" - exit Republica Argentina 500m
1 x
1km

Barcelona – Mare de Déu de Montserrat

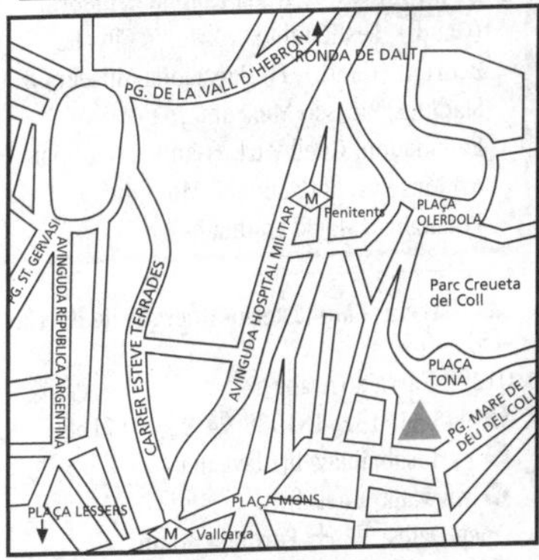

▲ **Barcelona** – Pere Tarrés 51045
Numancia 149-151, 08029 Barcelona.
934 102309 934 196268
alberg@peretarres.org
www.peretarres.org
Open Dates: 01.01-23.12; 27-31.12 "El Prat" Barcelona 12km A 1.5km
Barcelona 3km Sants 1.5km
66 ap Plaçe Catalunya María Cristina L3 x 240
1 x
3km

▲ **Barcelona** – Rambles Center ⓗ 51044
Hospital, 63 08001 Barcelona.
934 124069; ® 934 838363
933 171704
reservas@center-ramblas.com
www.tujuca.com
Open Dates: "El Prat" Barcelona 12km Barcelona 1.5km Plaça Catalunya 1.5km Liceu (Linea 3) x 172 (B)

Barcelona... Travel Tips

- **For budget eats check out...** Gothic Quarter, Les Quinze Nits, Els Quatre Gats, La Fonda
- **For great nightlife try...** Gothic Quarter, Port Olímpic (olympic pool), Maremagnum, El Born, Balmes, Muntaner & Aribau Streets
- **Don't miss...** Sagrada Familia Cathedral (Gaudi), Les Rambles, Olympic City, La Pedrera (Gaudi), FC Barcelona Museum & Stadium, Picasso Museum, Joan Miró Foundation, Guell Park (Gaudi), National Art Museum of Catalonia, Montjuic Fountains (Magic Fountains)

▲ **Barría** – Monasterio-Albergue de Barría – 51046
01208 Narvaja (Araba).
945 317132; 181988 945 317168
carlosabaitua@ifj.alava.net
www.alava.net/ifj
Open Dates: Foronda 30km Salvatierra 10km 100m ap Alegria Hmnos x 200 1 x

▲ **Béjar** – "Llano Alto" – 51047
Ctra. del Castañar, 37715 Béjar (Salamanca).
923 404052; 400702 923 400702
llanoalto@llanoalto.e.telefonica.net
Open Dates: 02.01-30.12 Barajas 240km ap 4km x 150 1 x

▲ **Benicarló** – "Sant Crist del Mar R.J" – 51048
Avda de Yecla 29, 12580 Benicarló (Castelló).
964 470500; 964 470836; ® 902 225552 Central Booking 964 460225; ® 963 985913 benicarlo_ivaj@gva.es; creserves_ivaj@gva.es www.ivaj.es
Open Dates: 02.01-23.12; 26-30.12 (please consult) "Manises" Valencia 175km Valencia 150km Benicarló 2.5km "Benicarló-Peñíscola-Vinaroz" 200m ap Paseo Maritimo 0.5NE x 50 300m

▲ **Benicasim** – Argentina – 51049
Avda Ferrandiz Salvador 40,
12560 Benicàssim (Castelló).
964 300949; 302709; ® 902 225552 Central Booking 964 300473; ® 963 985913 albergbenicassim_ivaj@gva.es; creserves_ivaj@gva.es www.ivaj.es
Open Dates: Closed for repairs "Manises" Valencia 88km Valencia 95km Benicàsim 1.5km from Castellón 100m ap 20 x 70 3 x

▲ **Berga** – Berga – 51050
Vila de Casserres,
5 08600 Berga (Barcelona).
938 214089; ® 934 838363
938 214098
info@alberg.e.telefonica.net
www.tujuca.com (® online)
Open Dates: Berga 1.2km x 190

▲ **Bergondo** – "Albergue Juvenil Gandarío" – 51051
15167 Bergondo (A Coruña).
981 791005 981 794217
albergue.gandario@xanta.es
www.gandario.net
Open Dates: "Alvedro" A Coruña 18km A Coruña 20km "Calpita" A Coruña 20km ap Gandario Beach x 75

SPAIN – ESPAGNE – SPANIEN – ESPAÑA

▲ **Bernedo (Alava)** – Albergue Juvenil de la Montaña Alavesa – 51052
Carretera Santa Cruz, S/n, 01118 Bernedo.
945 378215 945 218045
albergue@konpadeporte.com
Open Dates: only Foronda 40km Vitoria 35km Autobuses Arriaga-Vitoria 40km x 90

▲ **Biel** – 51053
Avda. de la Mina, s/n. Biel, 50619 (Zaragoza).
976 669001 976 669001
biel@dpz.es
Open Dates: Biel x 26 200m

▲ **Bijuesca** – 51055
c/Virgen III, 12, 50316 Bijuesca (Zaragoza).
976 847292
ib310717@public.ibercaja.es
www.alberguedebijuesca.turincon.com
Open Dates: x 50

Bilbao – Bilbao-Aterpetxea – 51056
Carretera Basurto-Kastrexana 70, 48002 Bilbao.
944 270054 944 275479
aterpe@albergue.bilbao.net
http://albergue.bilbao.net
Open Dates: Open Times:
Beds: 142 - 2x[1] 24x[2] 4x[3] 14x[4] 14x[5] 4x[6]
Price Range: € 11.20-17.45 BB inc
Directions: Loiu 12km Bilbao 2km 58, 80

Bilbao – Bilbao-Aterpetxea

Bilbao... Travel Tips

- **For budget eats check out...** La Taberna de los Mundos, Asador Cerveceria Biribilbu, Así Colorano, Txiriboga, Garibulo
- **For great nightlife try...** Casco Viejo (Old Town), Pozas district, Galerias Urkijo, La Granja, Distrito 9
- **Don't miss...** Guggenheim Museum, Fine Art Musem, Ethnological Museum, Historic Oak (Gernika & La Villa), Viejo de Algorta (port), Sopelana beaches, La Arboleda, Theatre Arriaga & Old Town, Iron Transporter Bridge (Portugalete), Durango

▲ **Boñar** – Pardomino – 51057
Avda de Asturias No. 13, 24850 Boñar (León).
987 741581; 735510 987 741581
Open Dates: 1N x 200

▲ **Borja** – "Santuario de la Misericordia" – 51058
Santuario de la Misericordia,
ctra. El Buste s/n 50540 Borja (Zaragoza).
976 867844; 976 714797
976 714049 raaj@aragob.es
Open Dates: 01.01-30.09; 01.11-31.12 (only) Borja 5km x 52

▲ **El Bosque** – Instalacion Juvenil El Bosque – 51083
c/Molino de Enmedio S/N,
11670-El Bosque (Cádiz).
956 716212 956 716258
elbosque.itj@juntadeandalucia.es
www.inturjoven.com
Open Dates: 0.8SW x 131 1 x

▲ **Botaya** – Casa del Herrero – 51059
c/Unica, s/n 22711 Botaya (Huesca).
974 359853; 976 215325
976 215325 acizas@teleline.es
Open Dates: only x 46

▲ **Brañavieja** – "Cantabria" – 51060
39211 Brañavieja (Cantabria).
686 464627; 942 779328;
942 207407 942 779328; 208119
aj_cantabria_branavieja@jovenmania.com
www.jovenmania.com
Open Dates: Parayas 100km Santander 100km Reinosa 25km x 40

▲ **Burgos** – "Gil de Siloe R.J." – 51061
Avda Cantabria s/n, 09006 Burgos.
947 220277 947 220362
gildesiloe@telefonica.net
www.jcyl.es/juventud
Open Dates: 01.07-15.09 Estación de Trenes de Burgos 3.5km Line 3b - 5 - 7 3.2km ap Cantabria 59 x 121

▲ **Bustiello** – 51062
Bustiello, Mieres 33600 (Asturias).
985 421318 985 421318
bustiello@alberguebustiello.com
Open Dates: 01.01-31.10; 01-31.12 Ranon 45km Gijon 60km Bustiello; Renfe Ujo 3km; Sta Cruz: Feve 2km Ujo No 3 7km ap Bustiello x 40

▲ **Cabrera de Mar** – "Torre Ametller" – 51063
Veinat de Sta Elena d'Agell, Cabrera de Mar, 08349 Barcelona.
937 594448; R 934 838363
937 500495
alberg_cabrera@tujuca.com
www.tujuca.com (R online)
Open Dates: 16.02-31.12 Barcelona 35km Vilassar de Mar 4km 1.5km ap Sta Elena D'Agell x 200 4km

▲ **Campo (Huesca)** – 51228
Camino La Paul, s/n 22450 Campo (Huesca).
974 550520 974 550511
campo@sargantana.info
www.sargantana.info
Open Dates: Barcelona 240km Barcelona 240km Monzon 75km Campo 1km x 200 (B)

▲ **Canfranc** – 51065
Plaza del Pilar 2-3,
22880 Canfranc-Estación (Huesca).
974 378016; R 976 714797
974 293040; 976 714049
raaj.iaj@aragob.es
Open Dates: only except Sept Canfranc Jaca 24km x 35

▲ **Canyamars** – Mas Silvestre – 51066
Veinat Rimblas, 14,
08319 Canyamars (Barcelona).
937 955014; R 934 838363
937 955199
alberg_canyamars@tujuca.com
www.tujuca.com (R online)
Open Dates: 01.03-15.11 Mataró 20km x 150

▲ **Caracenilla** – Peñarrubias – 51067
c/ Consuelo, 4, 16540. Caracenilla (Cuenca).
969 272652; 272711 969 272652
Open Dates: x 30

▲ **Carrión de los Condes** – Rio Carrion – 51068
Marcelino Campagnat no.1,
34120 Carrion de los Condes (Palencia).
979 881063 979 881063
cedegesa@jazzfree.com
www.riocarrion.es.vg
Open Dates: 01.07-30.08 ( ) x 230

▲ **Castellbell i El Vilar (Barcelona)** – Viladoms de Baix – 51069
Carretera de la Bauma a Vacarisses, K. 5, 150, 08296 Castellbell I El Vilar (Barcelona).
938 282236; R 934 838363
937 805299
fundacio@torredelpalau.org
www.tujuca.com
Open Dates: 29.02-22.12 Barcelona 50km Barcelona 50km Vacarisses 3km x 90

▲ **Castelló de la Plana** – El Maestrat – 51070
Avd. Hermanos Bou, 26,
12003 Castelló de la Plana.
964 220457; R Central Booking 902 225552 964 237600; R 963 985913
maestrat_ivaj@gva.es;
creserves_ivaj@gva.es www.ivaj.es
Open Dates: 01.07-30.09 "Manises" Valencia 76km A Castellón 2km Valencia 78km Castellón 1km 9 200m ap Borrull x 77 1 x 5km

Castelló de la Plana – Mare de Deu del Lledó – 51212
c/ Orfebres Santalínea 2,
12005 Castelló de la Plana.
964 357979; R 902 225552 Central Booking 964 357970; R 963 985913
lledo_ivaj@gva.es; creserves_ivaj@gva.es
www.ivaj.es
Open Dates: 01.07-30.09 "Manises" Valencia 76km A Castellón 2km Valencia 78km Castellón 1km 1 200m x 100 R CC 1 x 5km

Cazorla – Instalacion Juvenil Cazorla – 51012
Pza Mauricio Martínez 6,
23379 Cazorla (Jaén).
953 720329 953 720203
cazorla.itj@juntadeandalucia.es
www.inturjoven.com
Open Dates: 12 0.05N x 129 R CC 1 x

Cercedilla – Las Dehesas – 51072
Crta de las Dehesas s/n, Cercedilla,
28470 Madrid.
918 520135 918 521836
alb.juv.dehesas@madrid.org
www.madrid.org/inforjoven
Open Dates: 02.01-15.08; 21.09-30.12 Cercedilla 3km Cercedilla 3.3km x 72 R 1 x P

Cercedilla – Villa Castora – 51073
Ctra de las Dehesas s/n, Cercedilla,
28470 Madrid.
918 520334 918 522411
alb.juv.villacastora@madrid.org
www.madrid.org/inforjoven
Open Dates: 02.01-14.08; 22.09-30.12 Cercedilla 3km Cercedilla 3.3km x 80 R 1 x

Chipiona – Instalacion Juvenil Chipiona – 51074
Pinar de la Villa s/n, 11550 Chipiona (Cádiz).
956 371480 956 371480
chipiona.itj@juntadeandalucia.es
www.inturjoven.com
Open Dates: Easter & Summer (12) 4E x 104 R

Cíudad Real – Albergue Juvenil Orea – 51075
Ctra Toledo s/n, 13080 Cíudad Real.
926 690241 926 213005
Open Dates: 12 x 230 P

Comaruga – Sta Maria del Mar – 51076
Av Palfuriana 104,
43880 Coma-Ruga (Tarragona).
977 680008; R 934 838363
977 682959
alberg_comaruga@tujuca.com
www.tujuca.com (R online)
Open Dates: 02.01-18.12 Sant Vicenc de Calders 1.5km Coma-Ruga 1.8km x 150 R CC P 20m

Constantina – Instalacion Juvenil Constantina – 51013
c/ Cuesta Blanca S/N,
41450 Constantina (Sevilla).
955 881589 955 881619
constantina.itj@juntadeandalucia.es
www.inturjoven.com
Open Dates: 12 1SE x 91 R CC 1 x P

Córdoba – Instalacion Juvenil Córdoba
HI 51014
Plaza Judá Leví S/N., 14003 Córdoba.
957 290166 957 290500
cordoba.itj@juntadeandalucia.es
www.inturjoven.com
Open Dates: 12 Open Times:
Beds: 167 - 1x1 29x2 17x3 13x4 1x5
Price Range: € 8.80-17.85 BBinc
Directions: Córdoba 1.5km 3, 12, 50m R CC 1 x

Córdoba – Instalacion Juvenil Córdoba

Córdoba... Travel Tips

- **For budget eats check out...** Sociedad de Plateros Tavern, Juramento Tavern, Salinas Tavern, Rafael Tavern, Juda Levi
- **For great nightlife try...** El Brillante district, El Arenal, Ciudad Jardin, Plaza de la Corredera, Tetería Buen Pastor
- **Don't miss...** Mezquita (Great Mosque), Alcazar Reyes Catolicos (palace-fortress), Synagogue, Calahorra Tower, Medina Al-Zahra ruins, Bullfighting Museum, Julio Romero de Torres Museum, Viana Palace, Archaeology Museum

▲ **Cortes de la Frontera** – Instalacion Juvenil Cortes de la Frontera – 51077
10-Ctra Villamartin - Puerta del Espino, Km 51, 600, 29 380 Cortes de la Frontera (Málaga).
t 952 117162 f 952 117162
e reservas.itj@juntadeandalucia.es
w www.inturjoven.com
Open Dates: 12 4W x 180 R TV P

▲ **Daimiel** – Tablas de Daimiel – 51078
Parque del Carmen s/n Daimiel (Cíudad Real).
t 926 854618; 260639 f 926 854618
e albergue@aytodaimiel.es; reservas@gredosaventura.com
Open Dates: 12 x 68 R P

▲ **Daroca** – Albergue Juvenil Daroca – 51079
c/ Cortes de Aragón, 13, 50360 Daroca (Zaragoza).
t 976 800129; 801268 f 976 800362
e darocaturismo@dpz.es
Open Dates: 12 x 60 R TV P

▲ **Deltebre** – Mn. Antoni Batlle – 51080
Avda de les Goles de L'Ebre, s/n, 43580 Deltebre (Tarragona).
t 977 480136; R 934 838363
f 977 481284
e alberg_deltebre@tujuca.com
w www.tujuca.com (R online)
Open Dates: 01.02-15.12 Amposta 8km x 120 R CC i P 4km

▲ **Derio** – Mañarikua – 51219
Larrauri, 1, 48 Derio.
t 94 4036888 f 94 4036889
e residenciaestudiantes@suspergintza.net
w www.suspergintza.net
Open Dates: 12 Loiu 1km Feve 5mins ap Hostel x 80 R TV i P 500m 20km

▲ **Donostia-San Sebastìan** – Colegio Mayor Olarain – 51225
P-Ondarreta 24.
t (943) 003300 f (943) 003309
e ceservas@olarain.com
w www.olarain.com
Open Dates: 01.01-22.12 Estacion del Norte 2km x 205 TV

▲ **Donostia-San Sebastìan** – Ondarreta La Sirena – 51081
Paseo de Igeldo 25, 20008 Donostia-San Sebastian.
t 943 310268 f 943 214090
e ondarreta@donostia.org
Open Dates: 12 Hondarribia 20km
A from city centre of San Sebastìan
North - San Sebastìan 3km 5, 6, 15, 16, 24, 25, 27 ap "Avda. Zumalakarrepi"
2SW x 96 R CC TV i 8 200m

Layos – El Castillo de Layos – 51106
c/ Conde de Mora 14, Layos (Toledo).
925 376585; 913 572564 913 572564
layoscam@cempresarial.com
Open Dates: only x 192

Lekároz – "Valle de Baztan" – 51107
Bº Huarte/Uharte s/n 31795 Lekároz (Navarra).
948 581804; 902 230400 948 581847
avbaztan@cfnavarra.es
www.cfnavarra.es/indj
Open Dates:
Noain-Pamplona/Fuenterrabia
Pamplona Elizondo x 126
1 x

León – Albergue Municipal de León – 51108
C/ Campos Góticos, s/n 24005 León.
987 081832; 081833 987 261174
alberguedeleon@hotmail.com
Open Dates: x 96

León – Consejo de Europa – 51109
Paseo del Parque 2, 24005 León.
987 200206; 202969 987 251453
www.jcyl.es/juventud
Open Dates: 01.07-15.09 x 79

León – Infanta Doña Sancha – 51110
C/ Corredera 2, 24004 León.
987 203009; 987 203414 987 251525
www.jcyl.es/juventud
Open Dates: 01.07-15.09 x 124

León – Miguel de Unamuno – 51112
San Pelayo 15, 24003 León.
987 233010; 233203 987 233010
migueldeunamuno@terra.es
www.albergueunamuno.com
Open Dates: 01.07-30.09 Barajas 350km
2km x 60

Les – Matacabòs – 51113
Sant Jaume s/n, 25540 Les,
Val D'Aran (Lleida).
973 648048; 934 838363
973 648352 matacabos@aran.org
www.tujuca.com;
aranweb.com/matacabos
Open Dates: 01.01-23.12; 26-31.12
Barcelona 330km Barcelona 330km Barcelona 330km La Pobla de Segur 80km 200m x 56

Llanes – Juventudes – 51114
c/ Celso Amieva 7, 33500 Llanes (Asturias).
98 5400770 98 5400770
Open Dates: Ranon 135km
Santander 100km Llanes 300m
Alsa 600m x 78
1km

Lleida – Sant Anastasi – 51115
Rambla d'Aragó 11, 25003 Lleida.
973 266099; 934 838363
973 261865
alberg_lleida@tujuca.com
www.tujuca.com (online)
Open Dates: 08.01-31.07; 01.09-23.12
Barcelona 190km Lleida 200m
Lleida 1km 200m x 132

Lleida ☛ **La Seu d'Urgell**

Logroño – Residencia Universitaria – 51116
c/ Caballero de la Rosa 38, 26004 Logroño.
941 291145
Open Dates: 01.07-30.09 x 92

Loredo – Playa de Loredo – 51117
Bajada Playa de Loredo s/n,
39140 Loredo (Cantabria).
686 464621; 942 207407
942 208119
aj-playadeloredo_loredo@jovenmania.com
www.jovenmania.com
Open Dates: Parayas 25km
Santander 25km Loredo 500m
x 48 500m

SPAIN - ESPAGNE - SPANIEN - ESPAÑA

▲ **Luarca** – Fernán Coronas – 51118
El Villar S/N, 33700 Luarca (Asturias).
98 5640676 rjuvenil@princast.es
Open Dates: Ranon 65km Luarca 1km Alsa 700m x 110 R
1 x
700m

▲ **Lugo** – Eijo Garay – 51119
c/ Pintor Corredoira 4, 27002 Lugo.
982 220450 982 284748
Open Dates: 01.07-30.09 "Lavacolla", Santiago 100km 800m 1A & 7 400m x 20 R

▲ **Lugo** – Hermanos Pedrosa R.J. – 51120
Pintor Corredoira 2, 27002 Lugo.
982 280432 982 267209
Open Dates: 01.07-30.09 "Lavacolla", Santiago 100km 800m 1A & 7 400m x 20

▲ **Madrid** – Richard Schirrmann – 51121
Casa de Campo, 28011 Madrid.
914 635699 914 644685
alb.juv.richardschirrmann@madrid.org
www.madrid.org/inforjoven
Open Dates: Barajas Atocha
33 300m U 10 El Lago 1km
x 124 R

▲ **Madrid** – "San Fermín" – 51122
Auda. De Los Fueros, 36, 28041 Madrid.
917 920897 915 005134
albergue@san-fermin.org
www.san-fermin.org
Open Dates: Barajas Doce de Octubre 23, 59, 85, 86, 123 ap Iglesia San Fermain U 3 Legazpj x 63
R CC 1 x

Madrid – Sta Cruz de Marcenado – 51007
Calle Sta Cruz de Marcenado No 28, 28015 Madrid.
915 474532 915 481196
alb.juv.marcenado@madrid.org
www.madrid.org/inforjoven
Open Dates: Open Times: 09.00-01.30hrs
Beds: 72 - 2x 6x 2x 4x
Price Range: € 7.80-11.50 BB inc
Directions: Barajas 12km
A Colón-Aeropuerto Chamartin 8km "C" 1, 2, 44, 133, 21 500m
U Linea 4 - Argüelles 500m R
(B)

Madrid – Sta Cruz de Marcenado

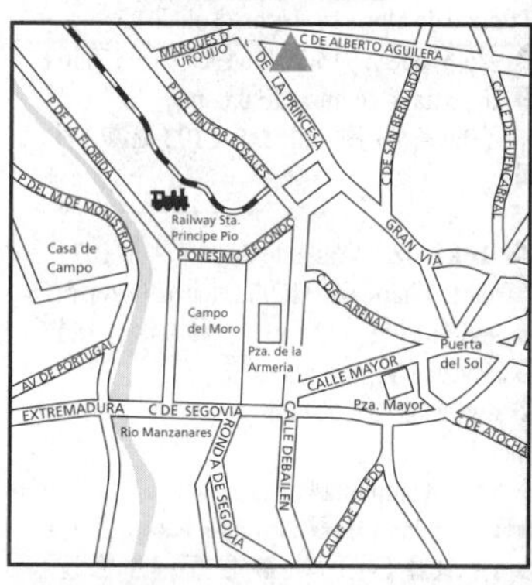

Madrid... Travel Tips

- **For budget eats check out...** El Cinco (C/. Andrés Mellado, 5), Compostela (C/. Serrano Jover, 6), VIPS (restaurant chain), Bocata World (restaurant chain), Sol-Plaza Mayor (bars)
- **For great nightlife try...** Bilbao area (Cardenal Cisneros, Fernando VI, etc), Calle Huertas area (Plaza de Santa Ana), Kapital disco (Atocha), Malasaña district, Flamenco shows (Casa Patas, Cuchilleros, Chinitas etc.)
- **Don't miss...** Museums (El Prado, Thyssen, Reina Sofía etc.), Palacio Real (Royal Palace), El Retiro park, La Casa de Campo park, Paseo de la Castellana (Atocha - Plaza de Castilla), El Escorial, Toledo, Bullfights (Las Ventas bullring), Sol - Plaza Mayor, El Rastro (flea market)

▲ **Las Majadas** – Los Callejones – 51105
Plaza Mayor s/n, 16142 Las Majadas (Cuenca).
964 283052 969 283121
Open Dates: x 45 R CC

▲ **Málaga** – Instalacion Juvenil Málaga HI 51017
Plaza Pio XII 6, 29007 Málaga.
952 308500 952 308504
malaga.itj@juntadeandalucia.es
www.inturjoven.com
Open Dates: 2W x 200 R
CC 1 x

▲ Manresa – Del Carme – 51123
Pl del Milcentenari de Manresa, s/n,
08240 Manresa (Barcelona).
938 750396; (R) 934 838363
938 726838
alberg_manresa@tujuca.com
www.tujuca.com ((R) online)
Open Dates: 08.01-07.08; 01.09-23.12
Manresa Manresa x 89

▲ Marbella – Instalacion Juvenil Marbella
51018
Calle Trapiche 2, 29600 Marbella (Málaga).
952 771491 952 863227
marbella.itj@juntadeandalucia.es
www.inturjoven.com
Open Dates: 0.1N x 158 1 x

▲ El Masnou – Josep Ma Batista i Roca – 51005
Av dels Srs Cusí i Fortunet 52,
08320 El Masnou (Barcelona).
935 555600; (R) 934 838363
935 400552
alberg_elmasnou@tujuca.com
www.tujuca.com ((R) online)
Open Dates: 01.02-08.12 "El Prat" Barcelona 30km Barcelona 20km
Ocata 800m x 100 800m

▲ Mazagón – Instalacion Juvenil Mazagón – 51124
Cuesta de la Barca S/N,
21130 Mazagón (Huelva).
959 536262 959 536201
mazagon.itj@juntadeandalucia.es
www.inturjoven.com
Open Dates: Easter and Summer 1.5E
x 116

▲ Melilla – Albergue Juvenil de Melilla – 51233
c/ Alfonso X, s/n, 52005 Melilla.
952 670008; 952 675180 952 675885
residenciamelilla@hotmail.com
www.residenciamelilla.com
Open Dates: ((R) 952 670008)
Melilla 33 x 40

Miranda de Ebro – Fernán Gonzalez – 51125
c/ Anduva 82,
09200 Miranda de Ebro (Burgos).
947 320932 947 320334
www.jcyl.es/juventud
Open Dates: Open Times:
Beds: 121 - 13x1 12x2 24x3
Price Range: € 7.05-10.50 BBinc
Directions: Miranda de Ebro 1.5km

Miranda de Ebro – Fernán Gonzalez

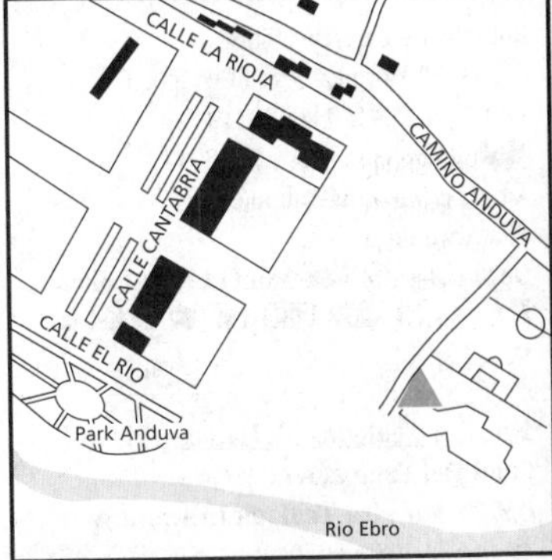

Miranda de Ebro... Travel Tips

- **For budget eats check out...** Cafè Casablanca (C/ Comuneros De Castilla, 6), Cafè Castellano (Avda Comuneros de Castilla, 8), Duque De Frías (C/ Vitoria, 39), La Ferroviaria (Ciudad Jardín, 1), Cervecería Rhin (La Estación, 53)
- **For great nightlife try...** Number One (C/ Juan Ramón Jiménez, 6 - disco-pub), Tras (C/ Juan Ramón Jiménez, 16 - disco-pub), Numer's Pub (C/ Juan Ramón Jiménez, 6), Pub + 3 (C/ La Estación, 68-70), Pub Dos X Dos (C/ Juan Ramón Jiménez, 5)
- **Don't miss...** San Juan del Monte Lagoon, Art & Countryside Route (Shepherd's Monument, Encío, Santa Gadea etc.), Condado de Treviño Route (Albaina, Cucho, Laño, San Vicentejo), Sobrón Reservoir Route, Milagro Route (Valpuesta, Santuario de Angosto), Peñacerrada Route (Ocio, Monte Toloño, Puerto de Herrera), Pancorbo Route (Madrid-Irún main road, area of outstanding natural beauty), Bujedo Convent-College of the La Salle Brothers & Mountains, Villanueva de Teba (archaeology & 12th century necropolis), La Picota (viewpoint)

▲ **La Molina** – Mare de Déu de les Neus – 51126
Ctra de Font Canaleta,
s/n 17537 La Molina (Girona).
972 892012; R 934 838363
972 892050
alberg_lamolina@tujuca.com
www.tujuca.com (R online)
Open Dates: 01.01-31.10; 01-23.12; 27-31.12
La Molina 500m x 170

▲ **Móra La Nova** – Mas De La Coixa – 51127
Rotonda De L'Eix De L'Ebre,
s/n 43770 Móra La Nova (Tarragona).
977 400541; 932 689114
R 934 838363 932 689112
masdelacoixa@yahoo.es
www.tujuca.com
Open Dates: Móra La Nova 1.5km
x 54

Moraira-Teulada – La Marina – 51128
Cami Del Campament, 31,
03724 Moraira-Teulada (Alicante).
966 492030; 492044;
R 902 225552 Central Booking
966 491051; R 963 985913
albergmoraira_ivaj@gva.es;
creserves_ivaj@gva.es www.ivaj.es
Open Dates: 02.01-23.12; 26-30.12
Open Times:
Beds: 130 - 22x2 20x4 1x6
Price Range: € 6.20-10.60
Directions: 0.5S from city centre
"L'Altet" Alicante 90km A Teulada 6km Denia 20km Teulada 6km
Valencia-Teulada/Alicante-Teulada 300m
1 x 150m

Moraira-Teulada – La Marina

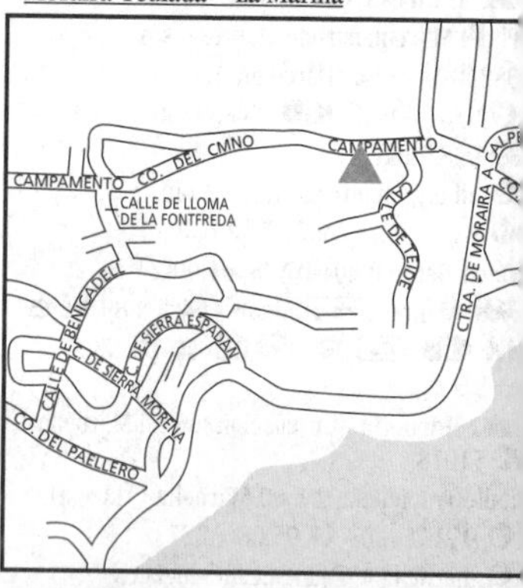

Moraira-Teulada... Travel Tips

- **For budget eats check out...** Restaurante "El Refugio" (Moraira), "Terrasses De LA Torre" (Gata), Bar-Restaurante "Avenidas" (Teulada)
- **For great nightlife try...** Paseo Maritimo (Moraira), Casco Antiguo (Teulada), Paseo Arenal (Xavia)
- **Don't miss...** Fiestas Moros y Cristianos, Fiestas Patronales, Mercado Medieval, Fiestas san Juan, Fiesta Del Moscatel, Terra Mitica, Guadalest, Isla De Tabarca

---

▲ **Morella** – Francesc de Vinatea – 51129
Crta. Morella-Forcall, km. 4, 5,
12300 Morella (Castelló).
964 160100; R 902 225552 Central Booking 964 160977; R 963 985913
albergmorella_ivaj@gva.es;
creserves_ivaj@gva.es www.ivaj.es
Open Dates: ( ) 02.01-23.12; 26-30.12
"Manises" Valencia 195km Valencia 195km Vinaroz 65km
Mediterráneo 4.5km ap Las Cocheras; Altava ap Fábrica Giner 4.5SW x 60
65km

▲ **Munilla** – Hayedo de Santiago – 51130
c/ Cipriano Martinez 29,
26586 Munilla (La Rioja).
941 394213
Open Dates: x 50 R

▲ **Navaluenga** – Sierra de Gredos – 51131
Urb. Fábrica de la Sierra - C/ Los Álamos 12,
05100 Navaluenga (Ávila).
920 286393 920 286393
alberguesierradegredos@yahoo.es
www.infoalbergues.com
Open Dates: 01.03-15.12 (only 01.09-15.12) Barajas Ávila Madrid y Ávila x 55 1 x

▲ **Navamorcuende** – El Chortalillo – 51132
Camino de la Tablada s/n,
45630 Navamorcuende (Toledo.).
925 868256; 811186 925 808008
colclemp@telefonica.net
www.lanzadera.com/chortalillo
Open Dates: only x 150

▲ **Navarredonda de Gredos** – Albergue Juvenil "Navarredonda de Gredos" – 51133
Crta. Comarcal C-500 Km 41.5,
05635 Navarredonda de Gredos (Avila).
920 348005 920 348005
albngredos@jcyl.retecal.es
www.jcyl.es/juventud
Open Dates: x 63

▲ **Navès (Lleida)** – "Rectoria de la Selva" – 51134
La Selva, 25286 Navès (Lleida).
973 299271; 937 899085 ;
934 838363 937 805299
fundacio@torredelpalau.org
www.tujuca.com
Open Dates: 29.02-22.12 Girona 135km; Barcelona 120km Barcelona 120km
x 111

▲ **Olot** – Torre Malagrida – 51135
Passeig de Barcelona 15,
17800 Olot (Girona).
972 264200; 934 838363
972 271896 alberg_olot@tujuca.com
www.tujuca.com (online)
Open Dates: 08.01-24.08; 17.09-22.12
Olot (Teisa Company) x 86

▲ **Orduña** – 51136
Carretera Lendoño, s/n 48460 Orduña.
945 383923 945 383577
Open Dates: Loiu 49km Orduña 1.5km Bizkaibus: Hospital de Galdakao - Orduña; ANSA: Bilbao-Burgos 1.5km
x 104

▲ **Orea** – Albergue el Autillo – 51137
Llano Hoz Seca, 19311 Orea (Guadalajara).
949 836470 949 836435
info@elautillo.com www.elautillo.com
Open Dates: x 60

▲ **Ourense** – Florentino López Cuevillas – 51138
Arturo Perez Serantes 2, 32005 Ourense.
988 252412; 252451 988 242328
Open Dates: 01.07-30.09 "Lavacolla", Santiago 110km 2km 6, 12 250m
x 20

▲ **Oviedo** – Ramon Mendéndez Pidal – 51139
Avda Julian Clavería 14, 33006 Oviedo.
985 966570 985 966571
Open Dates: Ranon 40km Gijon 30km Oviedo 1.5km 2 1.5km ap Julián Clavería x 116

▲ **Palencia** – Palencia – 51213
c/los Chalets, 1 34004 Palencia.
979 712533; 713366 979 712567
www.jcyl.es/juventud
Open Dates: x 36

<u>Palma de Mallorca – "Platja de Palma"</u> – 51142
Costa Brava, 13,
07610 Palma de Mallorca.
971 260892 971 262012
ppalma@tjove.caib.es
http://turismejove.caib.es
Open Dates: 01.02-31.10 Open Times:
Beds: 96
Price Range: BBinc
Directions: Son Sant Joan 4km
Palma 18km 15 30m ap Hotel Acapulco
1 x 150m

Palma de Mallorca – "Platja de Palma"

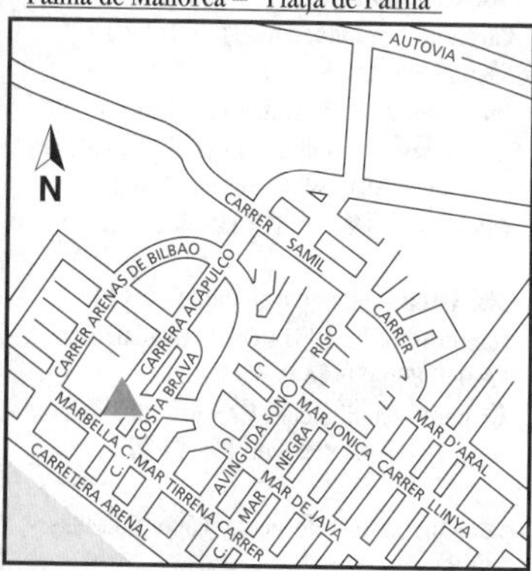

Palma de Mallorca... Travel Tips

- **For budget eats check out...** Cafè Es Pes de sa Palla, Es Mussol Cafè, Es Pinzell, Sa Llimona, Cafè al Vent del Món
- **For great nightlife try...** Cafè al Vent del Món, Sa Font, Sa Llonja, Es Molinar, Promenade
- **Don't miss...** Gran Hotel, Mallorca Museum, Sa Dragonera Island (natural park), L'Almudaina Palace, La Seu Cathedral, Modernism Route, Bellver Castle, Courtyards in Palma, Modern Art Museum, St Francis Basilica

Las Palmas ☛ Guía

▲ **Pamplona** – Fuerte del Principe – 51143
Goroabe 36; 31005 Pamplona-Iruña (Navarra).
948 291206; 902 230400 948 290540
residencia.fuerte.principe@cfnavarra.es
www.cfnavarra.es/indj
Open Dates: 15.07-15.09 Noain-Pamplona Pamplona Pamplona 0.5SE
x 96 R 1 x

▲ **Peñaranda de Bracamonte** – Resid. "Diego de Torres y Villarroel" – 51144
c/ Severo Ochoa 4, 37300 Peñaranda de Bracamonte (Salamanca).
923 540988; 296010 923 540988
alberguepenaranda@eurowind.net
www.jcyl.es/juventud
Open Dates: 12 x 60 R
1 x

▲ **Peralta de la Sal** – Escuelas Pias – 51145
Plaza Escuelas Pias No 1. 22513 Peralta de la Sal (Huesca).
974 411031 974 411203
ep.perl@escolapios.es
Open Dates: 12 x 80 R

▲ **Piles** – Mar i Vent – 51147
Doctor Fleming s/n,
46712 Platja De Piles (Valencia).
962 831748; R 902 225552 Central Booking 962 831121; R 963 985913
albergpiles_ivaj@gva.es;
creserves_ivaj@gva.es www.ivaj.es
Open Dates: 02.01-23.13; 26-30.12
"Manises" Valencia 80km A Gandiá 8km Valencia 80km; Denia 30km
Gandiá 8km "La Amistad" 500m ap Playa de Piles 3E x 90 R
CC 1 x 8
10m 10m

▲ **Planoles** – Pere Figuera – 51006
Ctra de Nevá Prat Cap Riu,
S/N 17535 Planoles, Girona.
972 736177; R 934 838363
972 736431
alberg_planoles@tujuca.com
www.tujuca.com (R online)
Open Dates: 01.01-23.12 Planoles 100m
x 198 R CC

▲ **Plentzia** – A.J. Plentzia – 51148
Ibitoki, 1, 48620 Plentzia (Bizkaia).
946 771866 (R only)
946 773037 R gazteria@bikaia.net
Open Dates: 12 Loiu 20km Plentzia 500m Plentzia 500m x 57 R

▲ **Poble Nou Delta** – L'Encanyissada – 51149
Plaça del Jardí, sn/n Poble Nou Delta, 43549 (Tarragona).
977 742203; R 934 838363
977 742709
alberg_poblenou@tujuca.com
www.tujuca.com (R online)
Open Dates: 18.02-20.12 Amposta 26km
x 65 R CC
1km

▲ **Poo de Llanes** – Fonte del Cai – 51209
arretera General,
3500 Poo de Llanes (Asturias).
658 585865
pen Dates: Ranon 134km Poo
Poo 1km ap Llanes; Alsa x 60
R 300m

▲ **Pradoluengo** – Adolfo Espinosa –
1150
vda. Dionisio Román Zaldo,
5-09260 Pradoluengo (Burgos).
947 586074 690 775688
albergue depradoluengo@
lberguedepradoluengo.org
www.alberguerdepradoluengo.org
Open Dates: 01.07-30.09 only x 100

▲ **Pueyo De Jaca** – "A.J. Quinta Vista
Alegre" – 51151
c/ Afueras, 1,
22662 El Pueyo de Jaca (Huesca).
974 487045 974 487045
alberguedelpueyo@tiscali.es
Open Dates: Sabiñanigo 34km
2 850m ap 1km x 94 R
1 x 600m

▲ **Punta Umbría** – Instalacion Juvenil
Punta Umbría – 51019
Avenida Océano 13,
21100 Punta Umbría (Huelva).
959 311650 959 314229
puntaumbria.itj@juntadeandalucia.es
www.inturjoven.com
Open Dates: x 100 R
CC 1 x

▲ **Queralbs** – Pic de Áliga – 51152
c/ Núria, s/n 17534 - Queralbs-Núria.
972 732048; R 934 838363
972 732043
alberg_nuria@tujuca.com
www.tujuca.com (R online)
Open Dates: 01.01-14.10; 01-21.12
Ríbes de Freser x 174 R
CC

▲ **Rascafria** – Los Batanes – 51153
Finca "Los Batanes" (frente Monasterio
"El Paular") 28740 Rascafria, Madrid.
918 691511 918 690125
alb.juv.batanes@madrid.org
www.madrid.org/inforjoven
Open Dates: 02.01-15.08; 18.09-30.12
Rascafria 2km x 120
R 1 x P

▲ **El Rasillo (La Rioja)** – El Rasillo –
51084
c/ Somera s/n.
941 462027; R 941 291100
941 256120
Open Dates: Haro Grañon
x 35

▲ **Rialp** – Les Estades – 51224
Ctra. De Sort a Rialp, Port-Aine,
Sport Center 25594 Rialp.
973 621216 973 621053
lesestades@port-aine.com
www.tujuca.com
Open Dates: Sport Center Port-Aine
x 172 R CC P

▲ **Ribadesella** – "Roberto Frassinelli" –
51154
c/ Ricardo Cangas,
s/n 33560-Ribadesella (Asturias).
985 861105; 653 787108 985 861105
Open Dates: 01.01-31.10; 01-31.12 Ranon
100km Ribadesella 800m
Ribadesella 300m ap Alsa x 44
R 100m

▲ **Roncesvalles** – Albergue Juvenil
Orreaga/Roncesvalles – 51155
31650 Orreaga/Roncesvalles (Navarra).
948 760302; 760364; 902 230400
948 760362 aroncesv@cfnavarra.es
www.cfnavarra.es/indj
Open Dates: 16.01-18.12 Noain-Pamplona
Pamplona Roncesvalles x 76
R P

▲ **Rucandio** – Modesto Tapia – 51156
39720 Rucandio (Cantabria).
650 413953; 942 207407
942 208119
aj_modestotapia_rucandio@jovenmania.com www.jovenmania.com
Open Dates: Parayas 25km
Santander 25km La Cavada 2km
La Cavada 2km x 28
15km

▲ **Ruidera** – Alonso Quijano – 51157
CRTA. de las Lagunas,
s/n. 13249 Ossa de Montiel (Albacete).
926 528053; 967 596372 967 243575
alberguesclm@jccm.es
www.rajclm.com
Open Dates: x 80

▲ **Ruiloba** – "Gargantia" – 51158
B-° La Iglesia, s/n 39527 Ruiloba (Cantabria).
686 464620; 942 207407
942 208119
aj_gargantia_ruiloba@jovenmania.com
www.informajovencantabria.com
Open Dates: Parayas 45km
Santander 45km Ruiloba 200m
x 40
5km

▲ **Salamanca** – Albergue Juvenil "Salamanca" – 51159
C/ Escoto 13-15, 37008 Salamanca.
923 269141 923 269141; 214227
info@alberguesalamanca.com
Open Dates: x 65
2 x

▲ **Salamanca** – Lazarillo de Tormes – 51221
C/ Lagar s/n 37008 Salamanca.
923 194249 923 194250
info@alberguemunicipalsalamanca.com
Open Dates: Barajas 200km
Salamanca 5km 1, 1B, 5, 8 x 150
1 x

▲ **Salardú** – Era Garona – 51160
CTRA. de Vielha a Baqueira,
s/n 25598 Salardú, Lleida.
973 645271; 934 838363
973 644136 reserves.tojuva@aran.org
www.tujuca.com; aranweb.com/garona
Open Dates: 01.01-23.12; 26-31.12
Barcelona 320km A Barcelona 320km Barcelona 320km La Pobla de Segur 70km Salardú (Alsina Graells Company) 100m x 180

▲ **San Lorenzo del Escorial** – El Escorial – 51161
c/ Residencia 14, San Lorenzo del Escorial, 28200 Madrid.
918 905924 918 900620
alb.juv.res.escorial@madrid.org
www.madrid.org/inforjoven
Open Dates: El Escorial 3km
San Lorenzo del Escorial 500m x 76
1 x

▲ **San Lorenzo del Escorial** – Sta Maria Buen Aire – 51162
Finca de la Herreria s/n,
San Lorenzo del Escorial, 28200 Madrid.
918 903640 918 903792
alb.juv.santamaria@madrid.org
www.madrid.org/inforjoven
Open Dates: x 66

▲ **San Martin de Castañeda** – San Martin de Castañeda – 51163
Ctra. Lago Sanabria, San Martin de Castañeda, 49361 Zamora.
980 622053; 521700 980 622053
www.jcyl.es/juventud
Open Dates: 01.01-30.12 Puebla de Sanabria 18km Parada 6km x 70
1 x

▲ **San Rafael** – El Recreo – 51165
c/ Pinar No. 1, 40410 San Rafael (Segovia).
921 171900 921 171900
albergueelrecreo@yahoo.es
Open Dates: x 76

▲ **San Rafael** – San Rafael – 51164
Paseo de San Juan,
s/n 40410 San Rafael (Segovia).
921 171457; 171258
Open Dates: x 50 1 x

▲ **San Vicente del Monte** – 51166
39592 San Vicente del Monte (Cantabria).
686 464623; R 942 207407
942 208119
aj_sanvicentedelmonte-svmonte
@jovenmania.com www.jovenmania.com
Open Dates: Parayas 53km
Santander 53km Treceño 6km
Treceño 6km x 42 R TV
15km

Santiago de Compostela – Monte do Gozo
– 51210
Carretera de Santiago-Aeropuerto KM 3,
15820 Santiago de Compostela (A Coruña).
981 558942 981 562892
comercial@evacaeionef-montedegozo.com
www.montedegozo.com
Open Dates: Open Times:
Beds: 300 - 38x6
Price Range: € 6.50-9.50
Directions: "Lavacolla", Santiago 8km
Santiago 3.5km 2km ap Santiago
1 x
8 P

Santiago de Compostela – Monte do Gozo

Santiago de Compostela... Travel Tips

- **For budget eats check out...** Casa Manolo, Monte da Condesa (university residence), Auditorio de Galicia, Rey David, San Clodio
- **For great nightlife try...** Rúa do Franco, Rúa da Raiña, Sala Nasa, Modus Vivendi, El Paraíso Perdido
- **Don't miss...** Cathedral, Galicia Modern Art Centre, Auditorio de Galicia, St Domingo de Bonaval Park, Campus Sur, Old Town, Paseo de la Herradura, Carballeira de Santa Susana, Sar Collegiate Church, Museum of the Galician People

---

▲ **Segovia** – Emperador Teodosio – 51167
Paseo Conde Sepúlveda, s/n 40002 Segovia.
921 441111; 441047 921 461027
www.jcyl.es/juventud
Open Dates: 01.07-15.09 x 120
R TV 1 x

▲ **Seseña** – Sta Maria del Sagrario – 51168
Ctra de Andalucía Km 36, 200,
45224 Seseña Nuevo (Toledo).
918 936152; 925 267729 918 936152;
925 267760 alberguesclm@jccm.es
www.rajclm.com
Open Dates: x 56 P

▲ **La Seu d'Urgell** – La Valira – 51103
Joaquim Viola 57,
25700 La Seu d'Urgell (Lleida).
973 353897; R 934 838363
973 353874 alberg_laseu@tujuca.com
www.tujuca.com (R online)
Open Dates: 01.01-03.11; 04-22.12; 26-31.12
Puigcerdá 35km La Seu d'Urgell
x 96 R CC TV
P

Sevilla – Instalacion Juvenil Sevilla 51020
Isaac Peral 2, 41012 Sevilla.
955 056500 955 056508
sevilla.itj@juntadeandalucia.es
www.inturjoven.com
Open Dates: Open Times:
Beds: 289 - 61x2 45x3 8x4
Price Range: € 8.80-17.85
Directions: 4S from city centre
San Pablo 10km A from city centre
"Sta Justa" 2km 6, 34 R
CC TV 1 x

Sevilla – Instalacion Juvenil Sevilla

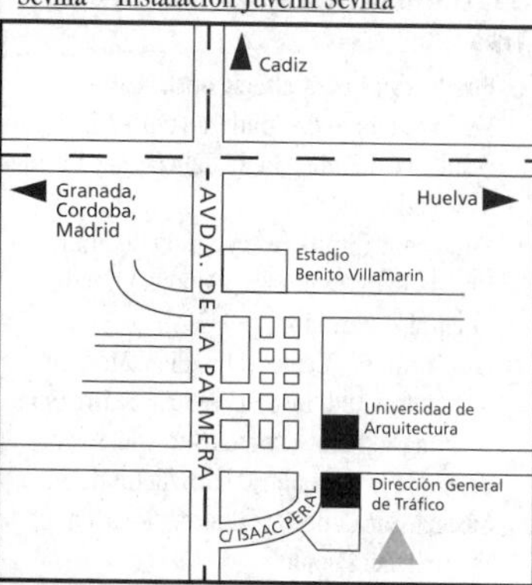

Sevilla... Travel Tips

- **For budget eats check out...** Bar Giralda, Bodega Gongora, Plaza Alfalfa, Santa Cruz district, Casa Modesto
- **For great nightlife try...** Santa Cruz district, El Arenal district, Betis Street, Plaza Alfalfa
- **Don't miss...** Royal Palaces, Cathedral, Maestranza Bullring & Museum, Isla Mágica Theme Park, Guadalquivir River Cruise, Ruins a Itálicas, Plaza España & Maria Luisa Park, Art & Folk Customs Museum, Archaeology Museum, Fine Art Musem

▲ **Sierra Nevada** – Instalacion Juvenil Sierra Nevada – 51169
C/ Peñones, 22,
18196 Sierra Nevada (Granada).
958 480305 958 481377
reservas.itj@juntadeandalucia.es
www.inturjoven.com
Open Dates: x 341

▲ **Sin** – Tella Sin – 51170
Calle Unica, s/n 22366 SIN (Huesca).
974 506212 974 500953
albergue-sin@teleline.es
www.alberguespirineos.com
Open Dates: Aisa 42km x 54

▲ **Siresa** – Albergue Juvenil Siresa – 51171
c/Reclusa, s/n, Siresa-22790 (Huesca).
974 375385; 619 561004 974 375385
albsiresa@arrakis.es
www.alberguesiresa.com
Open Dates: x 51

▲ **Solorzano** – Albergue Juvenil Gerardo Diego – 51172
B-° Quintana, s/n 39739 Solorzano (Cantabria
942 676342; 686 464605;
942 207407 942 676342; 208119
aj_gerardodiego_solorzano@jovenmania.com www.jovenmania.com
Open Dates: Parayas 35km
Santander 35km Beranga 5km
5km ap Beranga x 72
15km

▲ **Soncillo** – 51173
Avda Alejandro Rodriguez Valcarcel, s/n 09572 Soncillo (Burgos).
947 153024 www.jcyl.es/juventud
Open Dates: only Soncillo 1km
x 61

▲ **Soria** – Antonio Machado R.J. – 51174
Plaza José Antonio 1, 42003 Soria.
975 239460 975 239462
www.jcyl.es/juventud
Open Dates: 01.07-15.09 El Cañuelo 1.5km x 97
1 x

▲ **Soria** – Juan A. Gaya Nuño – 51175
Paseo de San Francisco 1, 42003 Soria.
975 221466 975 225621
r.j.gayanuno@telefonica.net
www.jcyl.es/juventud
Open Dates: 01.07-15.09 "El Cañuelo" 1.5km x 105
1 x

▲ **Sos Del Rey Catolico (Zaragoza)** – Albergue De Juventud Sos Del Rey Catolico – 51229
c/ Meca s/n 50680 So Del Rey Cat.
649 055142; 948 888480 948 888480
reservas@alberguedesos.com
www.alberguedesos.com
Open Dates: Pamplona 50km
Pamplona 50km Zaragoza-Sos; Sos-Zaragoza (Lunes Aviernes) x 32

▲ **Soto de Cameros** – Hospital San Jose – 51176
c/ San Jose s/n,
26132 Soto de Cameros (La Rioja).
941 291100 941 256120
Open Dates: x 46

▲ **Talavera de la Reina** – Albergue Juv. Talavera – 51177
Carretera de Cervera km 3, 5, 45600 Talavera de la Reina (Toledo).
925 709482; 709588 925 709588
isbe@alberguetalavera.com
www.alberguetalavera.com
Open Dates: 12 only 35S x 180
P

▲ **Tama** – "Picos De Europa" – 51178
39584 Tama (Cantabria).
649 487571; R 942 207407
942 208119
aj_picosdeeuropa_tama@jovenmania.com
www.jovenmania.com
Open Dates: 12 Parayas 100km
Santander 100km Tama 500m
x 40 R P

▲ **Tarragona** – Sant Jordi – 51179
Lluis Companys 5, 43005 Tarragona.
977 240195; R 934 838363
977 243134 stjordi@resa.es
www.tujuca.com
Open Dates: 12 Reus 15km
Tarragona 2km 0.5SW x 176
R

▲ **Teruel** – Luis Buñuel – 51181
Ciudad Escolar s/n, 44003 Teruel.
978 601712; 602223; R 976 714797
978 605351; 976 714049
rjbunnel_teruel@aragob.es
www.aragob.es/edycul/juve/residen
Open Dates: only 01-31.07; 01-15.09
Teruel 2km 7 50m ap Las Viñas 10m x 160 R TV 1 x
P

▲ **Tiana** – La Conreria – 51182
Crta Badalona-Mollet, Km 6, 08391 Tiana.
933 951011; R 934 838363
933 954850 conreria@peretarres.org
www.peretarres.org/conreria
Open Dates: 12 Barcelona 30km
A Barcelona 30km Barcelona 17km Montgat 5km x 260
R CC TV P
5km

▲ **El Toboso** – El Quijote – 51085
Avda. Castilla-La Mancha, 12, 45820. El Toboso (Toledo).
925 197398
Open Dates: 12 x 50 CC

Toledo – 51183
Castillo de San Servando, 45006 Toledo.
925 224554 925 213954
Open Dates: 12 (Closed 24-25.12; 31.12-01.01) Open Times:
Beds: 96
Directions: 0.8N from city centre
500m 7 10m CC

Toledo

Toledo... Travel Tips

- **For budget eats check out...** Abadia (San Nicolas Square, no 3), La Tabernita (Santa Fé Street, no. 2), Pastucci (Sinagoga Street), La Escalera (La Merced Street), Casa de Damasco (La Síerne Street)
- **For great nightlife try...** Varadero, Catanga, Dublin, Picasso, El Divino, Publico, La Vaca del Cielo, Otto Max (Santa Teresa area around Cuba Square), Picaro, Cason de los Lopez, Dodici, O'Briens (Old Town), Venta de Aires, Venta del Alma (Roman Circus area and around), Playa Safon (by the river)
- **Don't miss...** Alcazar, Primada Cathedral, Greco's House, Santo Tomé Church, Santa Cruz Musuem, Old Town, San Juan de los Reyes Monastery, Santa Maria la Blanca Sinagogue

▲ **Torrejon El Rubio** – Centro De Education Ambiental "La Dehesa" – 51184
c/ Gabriel Y Galán, 17, 10694-Torrejon El Rubio (Cáceres).
927 455178 927 455096
ladehesa@fundacionglobalnature.org
Open Dates: 12 Plasencia 30km
Torrejon El Rubio 13S x 41
R

▲ **Tragacete** – San Blas – 51185
16150 Tragacete (Cuenca).
969 178859 969 178866
alberguesclm@jccm.es
www.rajclm.com
Open Dates: (Only) x 60

▲ **Tremp** – Del Pallars – 51223
Sant Jaume, 28 25620 Tremp.
973 652563 973 652518
alberg_tremp@tujuca.com
www.tujuca.com (online)
Open Dates: Tremp Tremp
x 98

▲ **Tresviso** – Tresviso – 51186
39580 Tresviso.
646 842186; 942 207407
942 208119
aj_tresviso_tresviso@jovenmania.com
www.jovenmania.com
Open Dates: Parayas 140km
Santander 140km x 31

▲ **Tudela** – Albergue Juvenil Municipal de Tudela – 51187
Camino Caritat, 17, 31500 Tudela.
948 402779; 902 230400 948 826367
lestonac@terra.es
www.cfnavarra.es/indj
Open Dates: Zaragoza/Pamplona
Tudela Tudela x 24

▲ **Ugena** – La Chopera – 51188
Camino de Yuncos S/N. 45217 Ugena (Toledo).
608 718721; 916 414422
Open Dates: (only) x 200

▲ **Uña** – La Cañadilla – 51189
16152 Uña (Cuenca).
969 282852 969 281332
Open Dates: x 30

▲ **Uncastillo** – Ayllon – 51190
c/ Mediavilla 30,
50678 Uncastillo (Zaragoza).
976 679400 976 679497
Open Dates: x 50

▲ **Undués de Lerda** – 51191
c/ Herrería, 50689 Undués de Lerda (Zaragoza).
948 888105 948 888105
unduesino@hotmail.com
Open Dates: 01-30.01; 01.03-31.12
Pamplona 50km San Sebastian 120km Pamplona 50km Sangüesa 10km x 56

▲ **Valdeavacas** – La Palaina – 51217
C/ Poyo 1-40185 Valdeavacas (Segovia).
921 500098; 431005 921 440764
segovia@espavila.es
Open Dates: Barajas 125km
Segovia 35km x 24

▲ **Valdeavellano de Tera** – Valdeavellano de Tera – 51192
C/Soledad S/N 42165 Valdeavellano de Tera (Soria).
975 273042; 659 855555 975 273042
albergue-tera@wanadoo.es
www.jcyl.es/juventud
Open Dates: x 60
1 x

▲ **Valdepeñas** – El Cañaveral – 51193
Crta Comarcal de Valdepeñas/San Carlos del V alle, s/n 13300 Valdepeñas (Cíudad Real).
926 338255; 616 982090 915 360254
albergue.canaveral@7estrellas.org
www.7estrellas.org
Open Dates: (only) x 48

▲ **Valencia** – Albergue "C.M. La Paz" – 51194
Avo Del Puerto, 69 46021 Valencia.
963 617459 963 607002
info@alberguelapaz.org
www.alberguelapaz.org
Open Dates: 12.01-18.10; 03-22.12 ( )
"Manises" Valencia 8km A Valencia Bus 3km Valencia 2km Valencia 2km 1, 2, 3, 4 20m ap Abea Al Abbar - Avd. Del Puerto Linea 5 ap Amistad 500m
x 120 1 x
3km

Valencia – Ciutat de Valencia – 51195
almes, 17 - 46001 Valencia.
963 925100 963 153242
albergue@alberguedevalencia.com
www.alberguedevalencia.com
pen Dates: "Manises" Valencia 7km
Valencia Bus 1.5km Valencia
km Valencia 600m 5-B 30m
5-B U Linea 1 - Ángel Guimera 400m
x 50
1 x 8 5km

Valencia de Alcántara – Sta Mª de
uadalupe – 51196
uerto Roque,
0500 Valencia de Alcántara (Cáceres).
927 028516 927 028518
pen Dates: 01.03-31.12 Valencia de
lcántara Valencia de Alcántara
x 10

Valle de Trápaga – Albergue de La
rboleda – 51198
abriel Aresti 2 48 510 Valle de Trápaga.
946 364327 946 604245
albergue@ortzadar.es
pen Dates: Funicular Reineta 2km
Trapagaran 4km x 56

La Vecilla – "Sta. Catalina" – 51104
inca Santa Catalina, 24840 La Vecilla (León).
987 741212 987 741212
granjasantacatalina@hotmail.com
pen Dates: x 80

Venta Del Moro – "Hoces del Cabriel"
- 51199
San Juan, 4 - 46310 - Venta del Moro.
606 362772; 961 235076; 962 178072
961 221184
avensport@avensport.com
www.hocescabriel.com
Open Dates: "Manises" Valencia
100km Valencia 115km Utiel
20km "Utiel - Venta del Moro" 100m
0.1NE x 64
1 x

Vic – Canonge Collell – 51200
Avd. D'Olimpia S/N, 08500 Vic (Barcelona).
938 894938; R 934 838363
938 833062 alberg_vic@tujuca.com
www.tujuca.com (R online)
Open Dates: 07.01-12.04; 23.04-03.08;
23.08-20.12 Vic 1km L-3 ap Bus
stop No7 x 168

Vigo – Altamar – 51201
c/ Cesáreo González 4,
36210 Vigo (Pontevedra).
986 290808 986 211595
Open Dates: 01.07-30.09 "Peinador" Vigo
5km 3km x 20

Villamanín – Villamanín – 51202
Plaza del Ayuntamiento S/N 24680 Villamanín
(León).
987 598243; 985 464361 985 464361
asociacionlaquintana@yahoo.es
www.jcyl.es/juventud
Open Dates: x 54

Villanúa – "Sta. M' del Pilar" – 51203
Camino de la Selva n.18,
22870 Villanúa (Huesca).
974 378016 974 378016; 976 714049
albergue.villanua@aragob.es
Open Dates: 01.01-31.08; 01.10-31.12
Jaca 15km Jaca 15km x 100

Villanueva de la Fuente – Centro De
Vacaciones "Sol Verde" – 51204
Carretera De Albadalejo, s/n,
13330 Villanveva De La Fuente (Cíudad Real).
630 013420; 609 235161 967 396292
sol-verde@sol-verde.com
www.sol-verde.com
Open Dates: only x 96

Vitoria-Gasteiz – Carlos Abaitua –
51205
Escultor Isaac Diez, s/n,
01007 Vitoria-Gasteiz (Araba).
945 148100; 181988 945 148100
carlosabaitua@ifj.alava.net
http://alava.net.ifj
Open Dates: 01.01-14.08; 10.09-31.12
"Foronda" 10km
"Renfe-Vitoria-Gasteiz" 1km x 94

▲ **Vitoria-Gasteiz** – Isla de Zuhatza – 51214
Embalse de Ullibarri-Gamboa,
Aptdo 2030 Vitoria-Gasteiz, Alava.
945 181988 R zuhatza@terra.es
http://alava.net/ifj
Open Dates: Arroyabe - 3km to Zuhatza x 400

▲ **Viznar** – Instalacion Juvenil Viznar – 51021
Camino de Fuente Grande S/N,
18179 Viznar (Granada).
958 543307 958 543448
viznar.itj@juntadeandalucia.es
www.inturjoven.com
Open Dates: x 111 R CC
TV 1 x

▲ **Zamora** – Doña Urraca – 51206
c/ Villalpando No. 7, 49005 Zamora.
980 512671; 512759 980 512759
Open Dates: 01.07-15.09 Line 1 and 4 100m 0.4NW x 115 R
TV i P

Zaragoza – Baltasar Gracián – 51207
c/ Franco y López 4, 50005 Zaragoza.
976 306692; R 976 714797
976 306693 balta@aragob.es
www.aragob.es/edycul/juve/residen/index.html
Open Dates: Open Times: 08.00-23.00hrs (Check in 10.00-20.00hrs)
Beds: 46 - 4x2 8x4 1x6
Price Range: € 9.40-21.80 BBinc
Directions: 15km Zaragoza-Delicias 2km 24, 38, 22 - Zaragoza 200m
R CC TV 50m

Zaragoza – Baltasar Gracián

Zaragoza... Travel Tips

- **For budget eats check out...** Roquelin, Los Baturros, Latre, Itziar, El Fuelle
- **For great nightlife try...** Casco Viejo, Teatro Prinicipal, Auditorio, Tierra Café, Casa del Loco
- **Don't miss...** Plaza del Pilar, Aljafería Palace, Plaza de España, Roman Theatre, Museo Provincial, Museo Pablo Serrano, La Seo, Iglesia San Gil, Iglesia San Pablo, Parque Primo Rivera

▲ **Zarautz** – Igerain – 51208
San Inazio 25, 20800 Zarautz, Gipuzkoa.
943 132910 943 130006
erreserbagunea@gipuzkoa.net
www.gipuzkoa.net/albergues
Open Dates: San Sebastìan 35km
Euskotren Zarautz 600m x 165
TV P 300m

*HI Members save money with Global Discounts! See **www.HIhostels.com.***

*Des économies aux quatre coins du monde pour les adhérents HI! Voir **www.HIhostels.com.***

*HI-Mitglieder erhalten weltweit Rabatte und sparen so Geld! Siehe **www.HIhostels.com.***

*¡Más dinero en la hucha para los miembros de Hostelling International gracias a nuestros descuentos mundiales! Ver **www.HIhostels.com.***

Sudan

Sudanese Youth Hostels Association,
House No 66, Street No 47,
Khartoum East, PO Box 1705,
Khartoum, Sudan
t (249) (183) 480385
f (249) (183) 479318
e info@sudaneseyha.net
w www.sudaneseyha.net

A copy of the Hostel Directory for this Country can be obtained from:
The National Office

Capital:	Khartoum
Language:	Arabic
Currency:	Sudanese dinar (SDD)
Population:	38,114,160
Size:	38,114,160 sq km
Telephone Country Code:	249
eKit Access Number:	Check www.hi.ekit.com for up to date Access Numbers

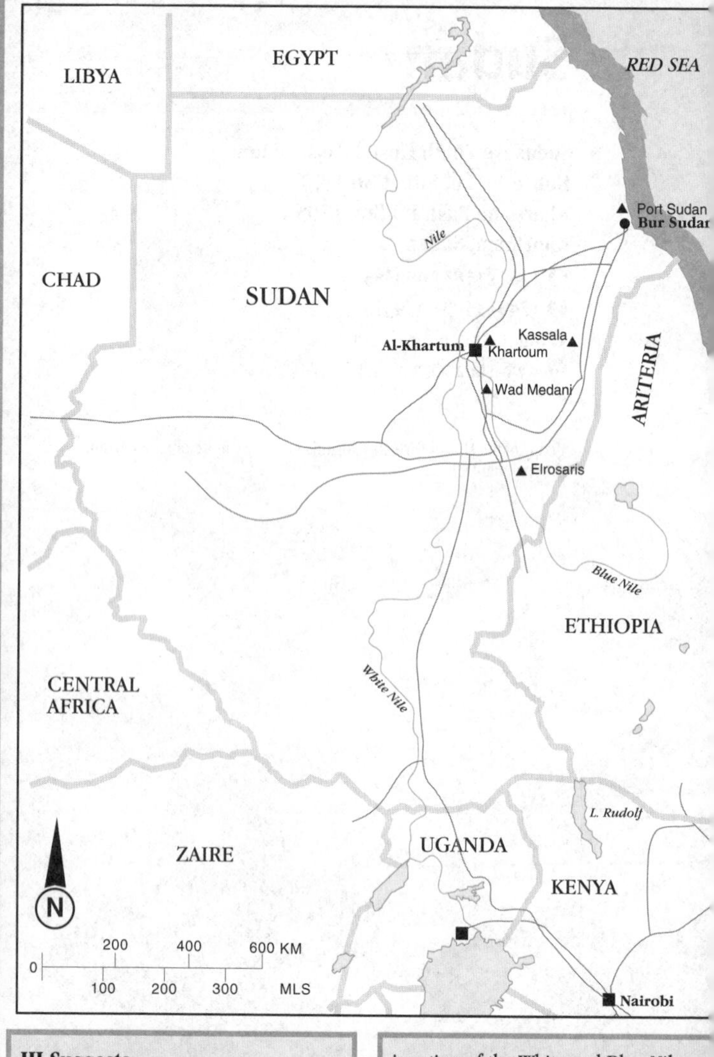

HI Suggests...

As Africa's largest country, Sudan covers 2,505,800 sq km and is divided on ethnic, religious and ideological grounds. Sudan is located in Northern Africa, bordering the Red Sea, between Egypt and Eritre.

Khartoum is Sudan's capital city, which is a quiet city. It has peaceful, tree-lined streets, and in some ways still bears the unmistakable mark of an settlement of the British Empire. The most fascinating sight is the junction of the White and Blue Niles. Al Mogran Family Park, an amusement park, is located at the point where the rivers flow together. After spending time at the joining, take a ferry to Tuti Island for a look at a typical rural village. Consider excursions to Jebel Aulia Dam, which is a great spot for bird watching, fishing and picnics.

Before travelling to or around Sudan, check for the most current information from your embassy.

You can find out a lot more on our website - a visit to www.HIhostels.com is essential for planning your trip!

Pour en savoir plus, rendez-vous sur notre site Internet, www.HIhostels.com une visite incontournable pour préparer votre voyage!

Viele weitere Informationen auf unserer Website: www.HIhostels.com - unverzichtbar für die Reiseplanung!

Puedes averiguar mucho más en nuestro sitio web. Es imprescindible que visites la página www.HIhostels.com para planear tu viaje.

△ ***Kassala** – 96200*
c/o Ministry of Youth & Sports Kassala, Kassala State: near centre of town.
t *(0411) 22949*
e *info@sudaneseyha.net*
w *www.sudaneseyha.net*
Open Dates: x 60 R P

△ ***Khartoum** – 96201*
House No 66, St 47, Khartoum East (Souk Two), PO Box No 1705 Khartoum.
t *(183) 480385* f *(183) 479318*
e *info@sudaneseyha.net*
w *www.sudaneseyha.net*
Open Dates: x 80 R P

▲ **Port Sudan** – 96202
Salabona, Port Sudan YH, Red Sea State, PO Box No 829, Port Sudan.
t (23) 762262 f (23) 762275
e info@sudaneseyha.net
w www.sudaneseyha.net
Open Dates: x 80 R P

YOUTH HOSTEL ACCOMMODATION OUTSIDE THE ASSURED STANDARDS SCHEME

Elrosaris – 96199
Elnile St, Blue Nile Province: c/o Ministry of Youth & Sports, Youth Office.
t (091) 8025610 e info@sudaneseyha.net
w www.sudaneseyha.net
Open Dates: x 60 R P

Wad Medani – 96203
c/o Ministry of Youth & Sports, Wad Medani, Gazeira State: town centre 3km.
t (051) 1826451 e info@sudaneseyha.net
w www.sudaneseyha.net
Open Dates: x 60 R P

Sweden

**Svenska Turistföreningen (STF),
Amiralitetshuset, Skeppsholmen,
PO Box 25,
101 20 Stockholm, Sweden.**
t (46) (8) 4632100
f (46) (8) 6781958
e info@stfturist.se
w www.stfturist.se

Office Hours: Monday-Friday 09.00-17.00hrs

A copy of the Hostel Directory for this Country can be obtained from:
The National Office

National Tourist Authority/Board:	www.visit-sweden.com
Capital:	Stockholm
Language:	Swedish
Currency:	SEK (1Krona/crown = 100 öre)
Population:	9,000,000
Size:	449,964 sq km
Telephone Country Code:	46
eKit Access Number:	0200-888-074

Sweden is about two and a half times the size of the U.K., but its population is little above 9 million. With its sparse population, Sweden appears to be more untouched and unspoiled than almost any other European country. Divided into three regions, the country has developed into a primary producing and exporting nation by exploitation of its natural resources - great forests, rich iron ore deposits and water, used for hydroelectric power. Unemployment is minimal, and the growth of the economy is favourable compared to other parts of Western Europe. Sweden has not been involved in any wartime conflict for almost two hundred years, and neutrality was maintained in both World Wars. The overwhelming majority of Swedes are middle-class, and are proud of their largely egalitarian society. Many people speak good English, but if you make the effort to learn a few phrases of Swedish, along with the local customs,

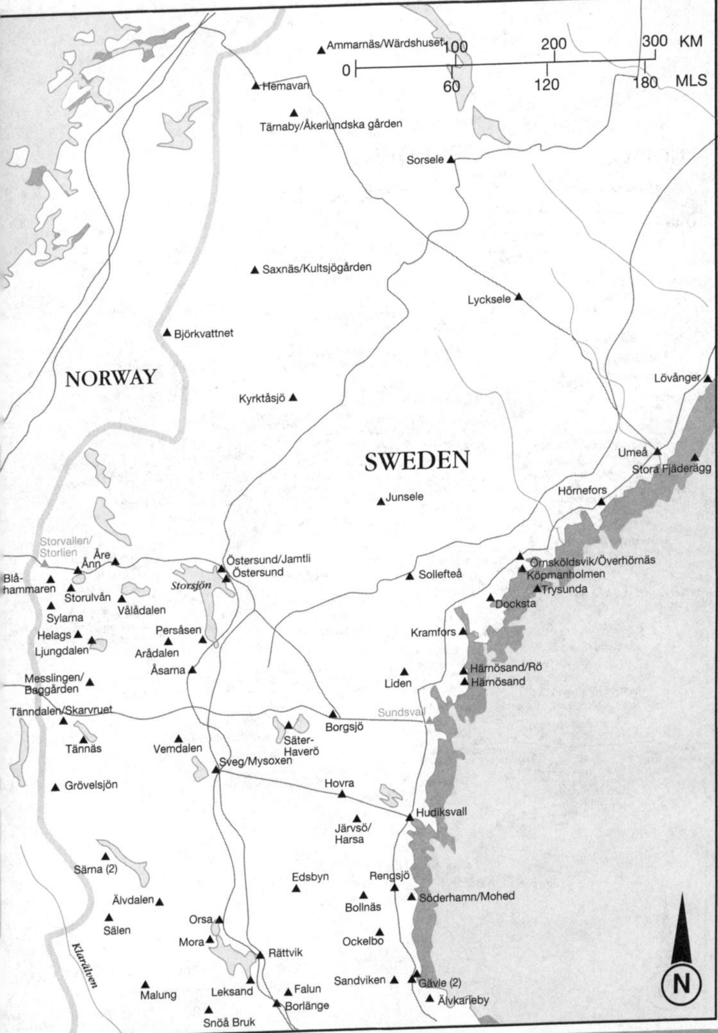

your visit will be greatly enhanced.

A few other Top Tips from **CULTURE SMART!**:

- Swedes place particular importance on punctuality, and would be surprised to be kept waiting for a meeting.
- When visiting a Swedish home, remember to remove your shoes before going indoors – the country's weather conditions have made this a custom for everyone. Do bring flowers, wine, or chocolates as a gift for your hostess.
- When meeting people for the first time, be sure to shake hands and maintain eye contact. Unlike in many other parts of Western Europe, a kiss or hug is uncommon in Sweden – Swedes appreciate their personal space.
- Swedes generally dress casually and comfortably, chiefly because of the practical needs of living in a cold

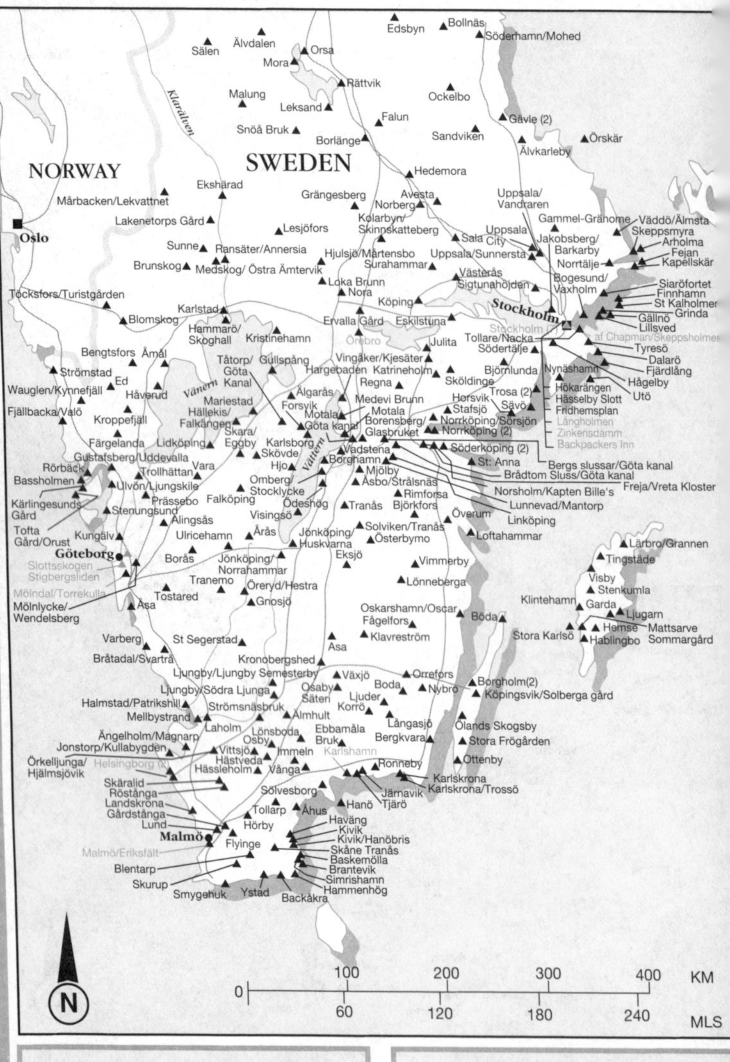

climate. Colours are usually dark or neutral. A good jacket and boots are essential.

- Watch out for queuing systems! When in a post office, chemist or various other shops, remember to take a number from the ticket-dispensing machine, or you will not be served.
- Drivers should note that you need to keep your headlights on at all times while driving in Sweden, and also that the use of seatbelts by drivers and passengers is compulsory. Also, the drink-drive laws are very strict.

'ou can find out a lot more on our ,ebsite - a visit to www.HIhostels.com is ssential for planning your trip!

'our en savoir plus, rendez-vous ur notre site Internet, ,ww.HIhostels.com une visite ncontournable pour préparer votre oyage!

'iele weitere Informationen auf unserer Vebsite: www.HIhostels.com - nverzichtbar für die Reiseplanung!

'uedes averiguar mucho más en uestro sitio web. Es imprescindible ue visites la página ,ww.HIhostels.com para planear tu iaje.

▲ Åhus – 54033
STF Vandrarhem Åhus,""Cigarkingshouse"",
Stavgatan 3, 29631 Åhus.
(44) 248535 (44) 247718
info@cigarrkungenshus.se
www.stfturist.se
Open Dates: Kristianstad 18km
Trelleborg; Ystad 100km
Kristianstad 18km Bus 551 100m
x 32
1km 1km

▲ Älgarås – 54034
STF Vandrarhem Älgarås, Undenäsvägen,
Box 102, 54502 Älgarås.
(506) 40450; 40605 (506) 40237
www.stfturist.se
Open Dates: 01.02-31.10 Töreboda 19km x 26
5km

▲ Alingsås – 54035
STF Vandrarhem Alingsås, Villa Plantaget,
Nyebrogatan 1, 44134 Alingsås.
(322) 636987 (322) 633229
www.stfturist.se
Open Dates: x 39

▲ Älmhult – 54036
STF Vandrarhem Älmhult,
Sjöstugans Camping, Bökhult, 34394 Älmhult.
(476) 71600 (476) 15750
info@sjostugan.com www.stfturist.se
Open Dates: 01.05-01.09 Växjö 70km
Helsingborg 120km Älmhult 2km
Älmhult 2km ap Bökhult 0,2 km 2NE
x 24

▲ Älvdalen – 54037
STF Vandrarhem Älvdalen, Tre Björnar,
Dalgatan 31, 79631 Älvdalen.
(251) 10482 (251) 10482
trebjornar@telia.com www.stfturist.se
Open Dates: Mora 40km Mora 36km 170 50m x 34
(B) 1.5km

▲ Älvkarleby – 54038
STF Vandrarhem Älvkarleby, Laxön 2,
81494 Älvkarleby.
(26) 82122 www.stfturist.se
Open Dates: 15.03-15.10 x 66

▲ Åmål – 54040
STF Vandrarhem Åmål, Gerdinsgatan 7,
66237 Åmål.
(532) 10205 (532) 10205
lokrantz@home.se www.stfturist.se
Open Dates: 04.01-19.12 Landvetter 200km Åmål 1.5km 1.5km
x 48 (B)

▲ Ammarnäs/Wärdshuset – 54471
STF Vandrarhem Ammarnäs/Wärdshuset,
Box 9, 92075 Ammarnäs.
(952) 60024
ammarnas.fiskecentrum@telia.com
www.stfturist.se
Open Dates: Storuman; Arvidsjaure 170km x 52
1 x

▲ Ängelholm/Magnarp – 54042
STF Vandrarhem Ängelholm/Magnarp,
Magnarp, Strandvägen 17, 26263 Ängelholm.
(431) 452364 (431) 452364
www.stfturist.se
Open Dates: 01.04-31.10 6km 40km
10km 300m x 98

Ånn – 54043
STF Vandrarhem Ånn, Ånn 2467, 83015 Duved.
(647) 71070 (647) 71070
www.stfturist.se
Open Dates: 130km A 50m 50m 50m x 33

Arådalen – 54044
STF Vandrarhem Arådalen, Västra Arådalen, 84031 Åsarna.
(687) 14054 www.stfturist.se
Open Dates: 19.06-31.08 Östersund 130km Svenstavik 85km Åsarna 70km x 18

Årås – 54045
STF Vandrarhem Årås, Årås Kvarn, Kölingared, Ulricehamn.
(515) 91151 www.stfturist.se
Open Dates: Jönköping 40km Mullsjö 20km x 28 (B) 1 x 2km

Åre – 54046
STF Vandrarhem Åre, Brattlandsgården 615, 83010 Undersåker.
(647) 30138 (647) 30138
info@brattlandsgarden.se
www.stfturist.se
Open Dates: 01.01-02.05; 06.06-30.09; 20-31.12 Frösö 100km Undersåker 40km; Åre 90 km 157 x 66

Arjeplog – 54048
STF Vandrarhem Arjeplog, Lyktan, Lugnetvägen 4, 93090 Arjeplog.
(961) 61210 (961) 10150
info@hotellyktan-arjeplog.se
www.stfturist.se
Open Dates: 01.05-30.11 90km x 28

Asa – 54011
STF Vandrarhem Asa, 36030 Lammhult.
(472) 263110
vandrarhem@friheten.nu
www.stfturist.se
Open Dates: Växjö 35km Alvesta; Växjö 35km x 60 (B) 1 x 300m

Åsa – 54049
STF Vandrarhem Åsa, Kuggaviksgården, 43031 Åsa.
(340) 651285 (340) 651242
kuggavik@swipnet.se www.stfturist.se
Open Dates: Göteborg 50km Varberg 33km Kungsbacka 18km 732 50m ap Kuggavik x 70 3 x

Åsarna – 54050
STF Vandrarhem Åsarna, Åsarna Skicenter, Olstavägen 45, Box 245, 84031 Åsarna.
(687) 30230 (687) 30360
info@asarnaskicenter.se
www.stfturist.se
Open Dates: 80km 45 100m x 30

Åsbo/Strålsnäs – 54051
STF Vandrarhem Åsbo/Strålsnäs, Åsbogården, 59015 Boxholm.
(142) 57090; 57341 www.stfturist.se
Open Dates: 01.06-31.08 100km 11km 300m x 25

Avesta – 54053
STF Vandrarhem Avesta, Älvbro, Älvbrovägen 33, 77435 Avesta.
(226) 80623 (226) 55871
vandrarhem.avesta@telia.com
www.stfturist.se
Open Dates: Arlanda 160km Avesta-Krylbo 6km x 36

Backåkra – 54054
STF Vandrarhem Backåkra, Östra Kustvägen 1231, 27645 Löderup.
(411) 526080 (411) 526121
backakra.vandrarhem@swipnet.se
www.stfturist.se
Open Dates: 01.06-31.08 (only 15.04-31.10) Sturup 50km Trelleborg 70km Ystad 20km 322 + 392 x 80 (B) 1 x 1km

▲ Baskemölla – 54055
STF Vandrarhem Baskemölla,
Tjörnedalavägen, 27294 Simrishamn.
(414) 26173 (414) 26054
baskevhem@swipnet.se
www.stfturist.se
Open Dates: Sturup 80km
Simrishamn 5km Skåneexpressen
3 500m 5N x 60

5km 500m

▲ Bassholmen – 54056
STF Vandrarhem Bassholmen,
Kärlingesund 60, c/o Uddevalla Kommun,
Kultur/Fritid, 45181 Uddevalla.
(522) 651308 (522) 696425
bassholmen@uddevalla.se
www.stfturist.se
Open Dates: 25.04-04.10 x 38

▲ Bengtsfors – 54057
STF Vandrarhem Bengtsfors, Gammelgården,
66631 Bengtsfors.
(531) 61075
info@gammelgarden.com
www.stfturist.se
Open Dates: x 50 (B)

▲ Bergkvara – 54058
STF Vandrarhem Bergkvara,
Mässen. Storgatan 66, 38542 Bergkvara.
(486) 26040 (486) 26004
ibkarl@spray.se www.stfturist.se
Open Dates: 09.01-30.11 x 51

▲ Bergs Slussar/Göta kanal – 54059
STF Vandrarhem Bergs Slussar/Göta kanal,
Vreta kloster, Hovslagaregatan 8,
S-58246 Linköping.
(13) 60330 (13) 60330
bergsslussar@sverige.nu
www.stfturist.se
Open Dates: 29.04-28.08 Linköping 12km
Linköping 11km 521 400m
x 26 (B)

▲ Björkfors – 54060
STF Vandrarhem Björkfors,
Gamla Landsvägen 13, 59041 Rimforsa.
(494) 60047 (494) 60940
valoborg@telia.com www.stfturist.se
Open Dates: 09.01-20.12 Linköping 60km
Rimforsa 23km Björkfors
x 32 (B)
1 x 1.5km

▲ Björkvattnet – 54061
STF Vandrarhem Björkvattnet,
Björkvattnet 360, 83090 Gäddede.
(672) 23024 (672) 23024
www.stfturist.se
Open Dates: 01.01-20.12 x 28

▲ Björnlunda – 54062
STF Vandrarhem Björnlunda,
Björnlunda Hembygdsgård,
64050 Björnlunda.
(158) 20014 www.stfturist.se
Open Dates: 01.06-20.08
Stockholm-Skavsta 40km Gotland
60km 789-589 1km x 11
(B)

▲ Blentarp – 54063
STF Vandrarhem Blentarp, 27035 Blentarp.
(416) 24377 (416) 24485
bokning@stf-blentarp.com
www.stfturist.se
Open Dates: Sturup 28km Ystad
25 km; Trelleborg 50 km 300m 0.2SE
x 50 (B)

▲ Blomskog – 54065
STF Vandrarhem Blomskog, 67292 Årjäng.
(573) 31035 www.stfturist.se
Open Dates: 07.05-25.09 15S x 34
(B)
3km

▲ Boda – 54066
STF Vandrarhem Boda, Gamla Skolan, Bolet 5,
36065 Boda Glasbruk.
(481) 24230
boda.vandrarhem@telia.com
www.stfturist.se
Open Dates: 01.05-15.09 x 44

Böda – 54067
STF Vandrarhem Böda, Mellböda,
38074 Löttorp.
(485) 22038 (485) 22198
www.stfturist.se
Open Dates: 12.05-27.08 100km
A 100km 100km 100m
x 120 (B)
800m

Bollnäs – 54069
STF Vandrarhem Bollnäs, Lenninge Herrgård,
Lenninge 9365, 82191 Bollnäs.
(278) 23092 (278) 23092
www.stfturist.se
Open Dates: 5km 50m
x 50
1 x 5km 50m

Borås – 54070
STF Vandrarhem Borås, Campinggatan 25,
50313 Borås.
(33) 353280 (33) 140582
info@borascamping.com
www.stfturist.se
Open Dates: 03.01-22.12 Landvetter 50km
A 2.5km Göteborg 70km
2.5km 100m x 44

Borensberg/Glasbruket – 54071
STF Vandrarhem Borensberg/Glasbruket,
Kanalvägen 17, 59033 Borensberg.
(141) 40820 (141) 40820
vandrarhemmet@glasbruket.com
www.stfturist.se
Open Dates: 1.5E x 41

Borghamn – 54072
STF Vandrarhem Borghamn,
Borghamnsvägen 1, 59293 Borghamn.
(143) 20368 (143) 20378
info@borghamnsvandrarhem.nu
www.stfturist.se
Open Dates: 610, 611 600m 15N
x 85
4 x

Borgholm/Ebbas – 54470
STF Vandrarhem Borgholm/Ebbas,
Storgatan 12, 38721 Borgholm.
(485) 10373; Mobile: (70) 9900406
(485) 72602 rum@ebbas.se
www.stfturist.se
Open Dates: 01.05-30.09 40km
300m x 27
1km 1km

Borgholm/Rosenfors – 54073
STF Vandrarhem Borgholm/Rosenfors,
Södra Vägen 7, 38736 Borgholm.
(485) 10756 (485) 77878
rosenfors.vh@telia.com
www.stfturist.se
Open Dates: 15.04-01.10 101, 106
100m ap Rosenfors x 92
(B)
1km 1km

Borgsjö – 54074
STF Vandrarhem Borgsjö, Hembygdsgården,
Borgsjöbyn, 84197 Erikslund.
(690) 20075; 23172 www.stfturist.se
Open Dates: 15.06-15.08 140km
2.5km 10m x 30
(B)

Borlänge – 54075
STF Vandrarhem Borlänge, Tjärna Allé,
Kornstigen 23A, 78452 Borlänge.
(243) 227615 (243) 16411
stf@borlangevandrarhem.se
www.stfturist.se
Open Dates: 02.01-23.12; 27-30.12 Dala
airport 10km A 601 10km
Borlänge 2km 602 2.5km
ap Tjärna centrum x 75
(B) 1 x
500m 3km

Brådtom Sluss/Göta kanal – 54472
STF Vandrarhem Brådtom Sluss/Göta kanal,
Brådtom Sluss, Göta kanal, 61021 Norsholm.
(11) 55055; Mobile (70) 6452949
www.stfturist.se
Open Dates: 01.05-15.09 Norrköping
20km x 15

▲ Brantevik – 54076
STF Vandrarhem Brantevik, Råkullavägen, Råkulle Gård, 27238 Brantevik.
(414) 22020 (414) 22020
www.stfturist.se
Open Dates: 01.04-30.10 Sturup 80km Ystad 45km Simrishamn 6km Bus 577 x 34

▲ Bråtadal/Svartrå – 54077
STF Vandrarhem Bråtadal/Svartrå, Kulturgården Björkekullen Bråtadal, Svartrå, 31060 Ullared.
(346) 23343 (346) 33014
www.stfturist.se
Open Dates: 12.03-10.12 Göteborg 130km Varberg 33km Falkenberg 26km 555, 556 6km ap Köinge x 50 (B)

▲ Brunskog – 54078
STF Vandrarhem Brunskog, Bergamon, 67194 Brunskog.
(570) 52141 (570) 52149
vandrarhem@telia.com
www.stfturist.se
Open Dates: Göteborg 280km; Oslo 150km Oslo 150km Edane 5km 1km ap Vikene x 70 1 x 800m 800m

▲ Docksta – 54085
STF Vandrarhem Docksta, Kustladan, Skoved, 87033 Docksta.
(613) 13064 (613) 13118
kustladan@telia.com www.stfturist.se
Open Dates: 45km 40km 3km x 64

▲ Ebbamåla Bruk – 54454
STF Vandrarhem Ebbamåla Bruk, Hovmansbygdsvägen 610, 29060 Kyrkhult.
(454) 774000 (454) 774001
info@ebbamalabruk.se
www.stfturist.se
Open Dates: 01.03-31.10 x 22

▲ Ed – 54086
STF Vandrarhem Ed, Strömstadsvägen 18, 66831 Ed.
(534) 10191 (534) 10550
www.stfturist.se
Open Dates: 01.06-31.08 Göteborg 180km Ed 700m Bus station 700m x 50 700m

▲ Edsbyn – 54087
STF Vandrarhem Edsbyn, Hogatan 15, 82894 Edsbyn.
(271) 34462 (271) 34176
svante.torngren@telia.com
www.stfturist.se
Open Dates: Arlanda 260km Bollnäs 100 600m ap Hogatan x 37 (B) 1 x 5km

▲ Ekshärad – 54088
STF Vandrarhem Ekshärad, Pilgrimen, Klarälvsvägen 35, 68050 Ekshärad.
(563) 40590 (563) 40590
info@wardshusetpilgrimen.com
www.stfturist.se
Open Dates: x 38

▲ Eksjö – 54089
STF Vandrarhem Eksjö, Norra Storgatan 29, 57580 Eksjö.
(381) 36170 (381) 36179
vandrarhem@eksjo.se www.stfturist.se
Open Dates: Jönköping 70km Oskarshamn 110km Eksjö 500m Eksjö Railway station, several buses 500m x 57 800m 800m

▲ Ervalla Gård – 54091
STF Vandrarhem Ervalla Gård, 71895 Ervalla.
(19) 281199 (19) 222800
info@ervallagard.com www.stfturist.se
Open Dates: 01.02-19.12 ( )
Örebro-Bofors 35km Frövi 8km 314 200m ap Ervalla Gård x 38 (B) 1 x 25km 5km

SWEDEN – SUEDE – SCHWEDEN – SUECIA

Eskilstuna – 54092
STF Vandrarhem Eskilstuna,
Vilsta Sporthotell & Camping,
63229 Eskilstuna.
(16) 513080 (16) 513086
vilsta.sporthotell@telia.com
www.stfturist.se
Open Dates: x 40 R CC

Fågelfors – 54093
STF Vandrarhem Fågelfors, Bruksgården,
Bruksgatan 65, 57075 Fågelfors.
(491) 51250 (491) 51255
info@bruksgarden.se www.stfturist.se
Open Dates: 09.01-22.12 Kalmar 82km
A 300m Oskarshamn 46km
Högsby 12km 153 200m x 35
R CC (B) 2 x
1km 1km

Falköping – 54094
STF Vandrarhem Falköping, Lidgatan 4,
Box 226, 52102 Falköping.
(515) 85020 (515) 10043
www.stfturist.se
Open Dates: x 43 R

Falun – 54005
STF Vandrarhem Falun, Vandrarvägen 3,
79143 Falun.
(23) 10560 (23) 14102
stf.vandrarhem.falun@telia.com
www.stfturist.se
Open Dates: Arlanda 200km
Falun 3km 701/712 Hosjö/Korsnäs
400m ap Koppartorget x 126
R CC (B) 3 x
1km 1km

Färgelanda – 54095
STF Vandrarhem Färgelanda, Dagsholm,
45892 Färgelanda.
(528) 19990 (528) 19999
www.stfturist.se
Open Dates: 01.06-31.08 x 54 R
CC

Fjällbacka/Valö – 54099
STF Vandrarhem Fjällbacka/Valö,
45071 Fjällbacka.
(525) 31234 (525) 31234
info@ostronhummercharter.se
www.stfturist.se
Open Dates: 28.04-27.08 x 12 R

Flyinge – 54465
STF Vandrarhem Flyinge,
Flyinge Kungsgårds elevhem, 24032 Flyinge.
(46) 52087 stfflyinge@telia.com
www.stfturist.se
Open Dates: 23.06-18.08 x 60

Forsvik – 54102
STF Vandrarhem Forsvik, Bruksvägen 11,
54673 Forsvik.
(505) 18840 (505) 41440
info.forsvik@vgregion.se
www.stfturist.se
Open Dates: 01.06-31.08 x 45 R

Freja/Vreta Kloster – 54440
STF Vandrarhem Freja/Vreta Kloster,
59076 Vreta Kloster.
(13) 395020 bokning@villafreja.se
www.stfturist.se
Open Dates: x 30

Gällivare – 54104
STF Vandrarhem Gällivare, Barnhemsvägen 2,
Andra sidan, 98239 Gällivare.
(970) 14380 (970) 16586
info@explorelapland.com
www.stfturist.se
Open Dates: Lapland 6km
Gällivare 300m 0.3S x 89
R CC 1 x
2km 3km

Gammel-Gränome – 54106
STF Vandrarhem Gammel-Gränome, Stavby,
74794 Alunda.
(174) 13108 (174) 13108
www.stfturist.se
Open Dates: 01.01-23.12; 27-30.12
A Uppsala 23km Uppsala 23km
x 27 (B) 1 x

Garda – 54107
STF Vandrarhem Garda, Kommunhuset,
62016 Ljugarn.
(498) 491391 (498) 491181
garda.ik@idrott.nu www.stfturist.se
Open Dates: 01.02-21.12 x 30 R

▲ **Gårdstånga** – 54108
STF Vandrarhem Gårdstånga, Flyingevägen, 24032 Flyinge.
(46) 52087
gorel.stfgardstanga@telia.com
www.stfturist.se
Open Dates: 01.02-31.12 x 34
(B)

▲ **Gävle/Engeltofta** – 54110
STF Vandrarhem Gävle/Engeltofta, Engeltofta, 80595 Gävle.
(26) 96160; 96063 (26) 96055
info@engeltofta.nu www.stfturist.se
Open Dates: 01.05-31.08 7NE x 92

▲ **Gävle/Gamla Gefle** – 54109
STF Vandrarhem Gävle/Gamla Gefle, Södra Rådmansgatan 1, 80251 Gävle.
(26) 621745 (26) 615990
stf.vandrarhem@telia.com
www.stfturist.se
Open Dates: 12.01-17.12 x 72
CC

▲ **Gnosjö** – 54111
STF Vandrarhem Gnosjö, Fritidsvägen 6, 33580 Gnosjö.
(370) 331115 (370) 331110
vandrarhemmet@gnosjo.se
www.stfturist.se
Open Dates: 12 Gnosjö 1km
Gnosjö 1km x 48
3km 3km

▲ **Göteborg** – Kungälv – 54112
STF Vandrarhem Kungälv, Färjevägen 2, 44231 Kungälv.
(303) 18900 (303) 19295
info@kungalvsvandrarhem.se
www.stfturist.se
Open Dates: 12 15N x 68

▲ **Göteborg** – Mölndal/Torrekulla Turiststation HI 54003
STF Turiststation Mölndal/Torrekulla, 42835 Kållered.
(31) 7951495 (31) 7955140
torrekulla@stfturist.se www.stfturist.se
Open Dates: 10.01-22.12 Göteborg 35km
Stena Line 14km Kållered 2km
Torrekulla stop 300m
Mölndal 8km 12S x 148
CC (B) 3 x 8
800m

▲ **Göteborg** – Mölnlycke/Wendelsberg – 54347
STF Vandrarhem Mölnlycke/Wendelsberg, Wendelsbergs folkhögskola, Wendelsvägen, 435 35 Mölnlycke.
(31) 3380536 (31) 3380559
konferens@wendelsberg.se
www.stfturist.se
Open Dates: 12.06-13.08 x 88
(B)

Göteborg – Slottsskogen HI 54015
STF Vandrarhem Slottsskogen, Vegagatan 21, 41311 Göteborg.
(31) 426520 (31) 142102
mail@sov.nu www.stfturist.se
Open Dates: 12 Open Times: 08.00-12.00hrs; 14.00-06.00hrs
Beds: 165 - 17x2 7x3 13x4 5x5 2x6+
Price Range: SEK 120-165
Directions: Göteborg 25km Stena Line Central 2km 52, 60, 87, 755, 764, 765 20m ap Olivedalsgatan/Linnéplatsen
1, 6 200m ap Olivedalsgatan x 20
CC (B)
1 x 8

Göteborg – Slottsskogen

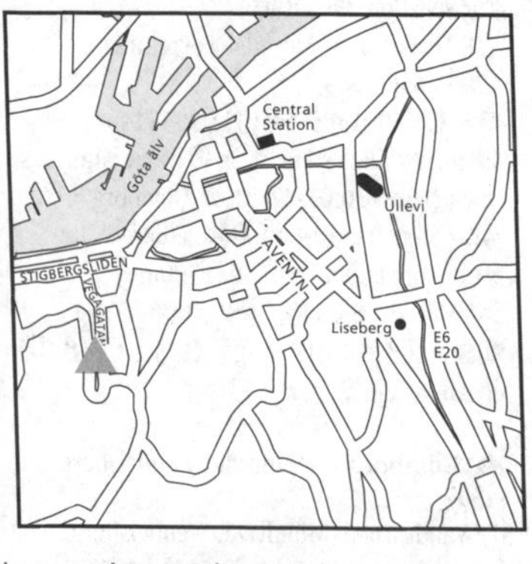

0 8.5km

Göteborg – Stigbergsliden 54006
STF Vandrarhem Stigbergsliden, Stigbergsliden 10, 41463 Göteborg.
(31) 241620 (31) 246520
vandrarhem.stigbergsliden@telia.com
www.stfturist.se
Open Dates: Open Times: 08.00-12.00hrs; 16.00-22.00hrs
Beds: 91 - 1x 10x 1x 7x 7x 1x 1x
Price Range: SEK 135-165
Directions: Göteborg 25km A Central Station 3km Stena Line 300m Central 3km 3, 9, 11 from City Centre (Brunnsparken 10 min) 50m ap Stigbergstorget x 16 (BD) 4km 4km

Göteborg – Stigbergsliden

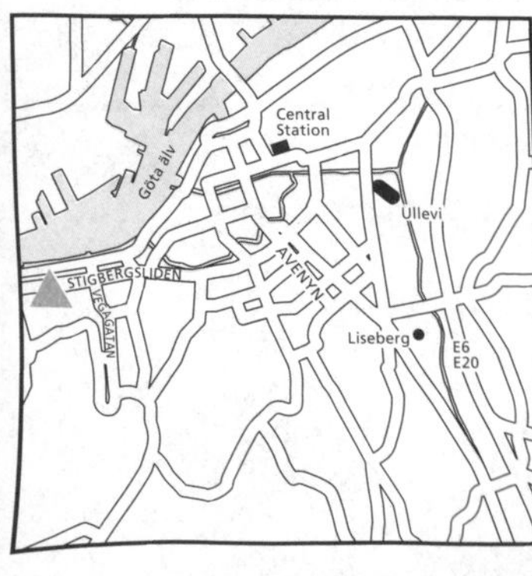

0 8.5km

Göteborg... Travel Tips

- **For budget eats check out...** Cyrano (Prinsgatan 7), Lilla Tavernan (Olivedalsgatan 17), Pasta e Cantorni (Nordenskiöldsgatan 21), Gyllene Prag (Sveagatan 25), Solrosen
- **For great nightlife try...** Nefertiti, Dancing Dingo, Gillestugan, Pusterviksteatern, Avenue Area
- **Don't miss...** Guldhedens Vattentorn (spectacular view), Harbour, Liseberg (amusement park), Haga (old part of the city), Archipelago (boat from Saltholmen), Universeum, Slottsskogen & Botanical Garden, Observatoriet (Slottsskogen), Opera House, Saluhallen (food market)

Gothenburg ☛ Göteborg

▲ **Grängesberg** – 54114
STF Vandrarhem Grängesberg, Bergsmansgården, Hårdtorpsvägen 15, 77240 Grängesberg.
(240) 21830 (240) 21830
jansonskan@hotmail.com
www.stfturist.se
Open Dates: x 45 R

▲ **Gullspång** – 54116
STF Vandrarhem Gullspång, Alhöjden, Järnvägsgatan 4, 54731 Gullspång.
(551) 36140 (551) 20277
vandrarhem@gullspang.se
www.stfturist.se
Open Dates: 15.05-27.08 Göteborg 230km Mariestad 40km 839, 502, 520 300m x 34 R (B)

▲ **Gustafsberg/Uddevalla** – 54117
STF Vandrarhem Gustafsberg/Uddevalla, Gustafsberg 408, 45191 Uddevalla.
(522) 15200 (522) 38658
jan.gustafsberg@telia.com
www.stfturist.se
Open Dates: 15.06-16.08 x 55 R CC

▲ **Hablingbo** – 54118
STF Vandrarhem Hablingbo, 62011 Havdhem.
(498) 487161 (498) 487271
vandrarhem@gutevin.se
www.stfturist.se
Open Dates: 01.05-30.09 x 32 R CC

▲ **Hällekis/Falkängen** – 54120
STF Vandrarhem Hällekis/Falkängen, Falkängsvägen, 53374 Hällekis.
(510) 540653 (510) 540085
info@falkangen.nu www.stfturist.se
Open Dates: 35km 200m Hällekis 200m x 100 2 x

▲ **Halmstad/Patrikshill** – 54462
STF Vandrarhem Halmstad/Patrikshill, Neptunigatan 3, Patrikshill Annex, 30238 Halmstad.
(35) 271200 (35) 271200
reservation@patrikshill-hostel.se
www.stfturist.se
Open Dates: 15.06-15.08 7km
100m 7km 500m
100m ap 100m x 138
(B)
2 x
6km 6km

▲ **Hammarö/Skoghall** – 54121
STF Vandrarhem Hammarö/Skoghall, Djupsundsvägen 1, 66334 Skoghall.
(54) 510440 (54) 518158
www.stfturist.se
Open Dates: 17.06-13.08 x 80
(B)

▲ **Hammenhög** – 54453
STF Vandrarhem Hammenhög, Mariedals Gård, 27655 Hammenhög.
(414) 440074; Mobile: (70) 9963100
(411) 20278 www.stfturist.se
Open Dates: Sturup 65km
Smedstorp 10km 573 500m
ap Hammenhög Mariedalsvägen x 20
(B)
500m 9km

▲ **Hanö** – 54122
STF Vandrarhem Hanö, 29407 Sölvesborg.
(456) 53000
info@boel.tinghog.sbgb.se
www.stfturist.se
Open Dates: (01.10-31.03) x 30

▲ **Hargebaden** – 54124
STF Vandrarhem Hargebaden, Hargebadsvägen 98, 69694 Hammar.
(583) 770556 www.stfturist.se
Open Dates: 27.04-05.09 x 40

▲ **Härnösand** – 54126
STF Vandrarhem Härnösand, Volontärvägen 9-11, 87162 Härnösand.
(611) 10446
vhemmet@harnosandshus.se
www.stfturist.se
Open Dates: 06.06-14.08 40km
A 2km 2km x 67
(B) 1.5km 3km

▲ **Härnösand/Rö** – 54127
STF Vandrarhem Härnösand/Rö, Rö, 87015 Utansjö.
(611) 64011 (611) 64008
soleboab@tiscali.se www.stfturist.se
Open Dates: 15.01-15.12 x 33

▲ **Hässleholm/Hässleholmsgården** – 54128
STF Vandrarhem Hässleholm/Hässleholmsgården, Hovdalavägen 303, 28135 Hässleholm.
(451) 268234 (451) 268232
hassleholmsgarden@hassleholm.se
www.stfturist.se
Open Dates: Hässleholm 1.5km
x 50
3km 3km

▲ **Hästveda** – 54129
STF Vandrarhem Hästveda, Hembygdsparken, Box 97, 28023 Hästveda.
(451) 30273 (451) 30864
info@hastvedavandrarhem.com
www.stfturist.se
Open Dates: 01.04-31.10 x 35

▲ Haväng – 54337
STF Vandrarhem Haväng, Skepparpsgården, 27737 Kivik.
(414) 74071 (414) 74073
www.stfturist.se
Open Dates: 30.04-25.09 Kristianstad 38km Ystad 45km Kristianstad 45km; Simrishamn 25km SkE3 3km ap Ravlunda kyrka x 50 (B) 300m 300m

▲ Håverud – 54130
STF Vandrarhem Håverud, Museivägen 3, 46472 Håverud.
(530) 30275 (530) 30996
www.stfturist.se
Open Dates: Trollhättan 70km Mellerud 15km Håverud 100m x 38 5km

▲ Hedemora – 54131
STF Vandrarhem Hedemora, Hällavägen 1, 77630 Hedemora.
(225) 711350 (225) 596309
hedemoravandrarhem@telia.com
www.stfturist.se
Open Dates: 01.01-22.12; 29.12-31.12 A 2km Hedemora Central 2km Hedemora Central 2km x 40 (B) 500m 10km

▲ Helsingborg/KFUM Nyckelbo – 54132
STF Vandrarhem Helsingborg/KFUM Nyckelbo, Scoutstigen 4, 252 84 Helsingborg.
(42) 92005 (42) 91050
info@nyckelbo.se www.stfturist.se
Open Dates: 09.01-21.12 50km A 7km 7km 7km 300m x 30 500m 500m

▲ Helsingborg/Miatorp 54030
STF Vandrarhem Helsingborg/Miatorp, Planteringsvägen 71, 25230 Helsingborg.
(42) 131130 (42) 132230
boka@miatorp.nu www.stfturist.se
Open Dates: 07.01-21.12 50km A 4km 3km 800m 200m x 140 (B)

▲ Hemavan – 54133
STF Vandrarhem Hemavan, Hemavans Kursgård, Renstigen 1-8, 92066 Hemavan.
(954) 30002 (954) 30510
info@hemavanskursgard.se
www.stfturist.se
Open Dates: 15.06-30.09 Tärnafjällens 10m A Tärnaby Hemavan x 48

▲ Hemse – 54134
STF Vandrarhem Hemse, Tingsåkergatan 4, 62012 Hemse.
(498) 243301 (498) 482424
stf.hemse@sverige.nu www.stfturist.se
Open Dates: Visby 53km Visby 53km Hemse 500m ap Hemse x 24 1 x 500m 10km

▲ Hjo – 54135
STF Vandrarhem Hjo, Stadsparken, 54433 Hjo.
(503) 10085 www.stfturist.se
Open Dates: 01.05-31.08 Skövde 35km Göteborg 200km Skövde Central 32km Hjo bus station 100m x 47 300m

▲ Hjulsjö/Mårtensbo – 54136
STF Vandrarhem Hjulsjö/Mårtensbo, Mårtensbo gård, 71291 Hällefors.
(587) 62102 martensbo@chello.se
www.stfturist.se
Open Dates: Kopparberg 25km 305 500m ap Mårtensbovägen 25SE x 33 (B) 1 x 500m 3km

▲ Hörby – 54138
STF Vandrarhem Hörby, Axona, Kursgården Hotell och Konferens, Råbygatan, 24292 Hörby.
(415) 14830 (415) 14328
info@kursgarden.com www.stfturist.se
Open Dates: Sturup 70km 15km 2km x 36 (B) 3 x 3km

▲ **Hörnefors** – 54139
STF Vandrarhem Hörnefors, Statarlängan, Sundelinsvägen 62, 91020 Hörnefors.
(930) 20480 www.stfturist.se
Open Dates: 01.06-13.08 x 40

▲ **Horsvik** – 54481
STF Vandrarhem Horsvik, Studsvik, 61182 Nyköping.
(155) 263100 (155) 263104
www.stfturist.se
Open Dates: x 40

▲ **Hovra** – 54141
STF Vandrarhem Hovra, Inibyvägen 18, 82042 Korskrogen.
(651) 767093 (651) 767092
www.stfturist.se
Open Dates: Ljusdal 30km 56 100m x 32 R CC

▲ **Hudiksvall** – 54142
STF Vandrarhem Hudiksvall, Malnbaden, 82421 Hudiksvall.
(650) 13260 (650) 13260
information@malnbadenscamping.com
www.stfturist.se
Open Dates: x 36 R CC

▲ **Immeln** – 54144
STF Vandrarhem Immeln, Gamla Byvägen Immeln, 28063 Sibbhult.
(44) 96355
bokning@immelnvikensfritid.se
www.stfturist.se
Open Dates: Kristianstads Airport 40km Åhus 40km Kristianstad 20km 545; 543 200m ap Immeln x 28 R CC (B)

▲ **Järnavik** – 54151
STF Vandrarhem Järnavik, Järnaviksvägen 80, Box 19, 37010 Bräkne-Hoby.
(457) 82200 (457) 82201
gula_huset@swipnet.se
www.stfturist.se
Open Dates: 20km 7km 7km x 33 R (B) 2 x

▲ **Järvsö/Harsa** – 54152
STF Vandrarhem Järvsö/Harsa, Harsagården, 82040 Järvsö.
(651) 49511 (651) 49590
info@harsa.se www.stfturist.se
Open Dates: Stockholm-Arlanda 280km Järvsö 18km Nybo 14km 18NE x 28 R CC 2 x

▲ **Jokkmokk/Åsgård** – 54153
STF Vandrarhem Jokkmokk/Åsgård, 96225 Jokkmokk.
(971) 55977 (971) 58277
info@jokkmokkhostel.com
www.stfturist.se
Open Dates: 08.01-17.12 Luleå 180km Murjek 60km x 47 R CC (B) 4km

▲ **Jönköping/Huskvarna** – 54154
STF Vandrarhem Jönköping/Huskvarna, Odengatan 10, 56132 Huskvarna.
(36) 148870 (36) 148840
148870@telia.com www.stfturist.se
Open Dates: Axamo 20km Jönköping 8km 1 ap Esplanaden x 98 CC (B) 3 x 2km

▲ **Jönköping/Norrahammar** – 54155
STF Vandrarhem Jönköping/Norrahammar, Spånhults herrgård, Spånhultsvägen 19, 56231 Norrahammar.
(36) 61075 (36) 61078
spanhult@swipnet.se www.stfturist.se
Open Dates: Norrahammar 2km Slätten No 25 500m 9S x 45 R CC (B)

▲ **Jonstorp/Kullabygden** – 54156
STF Vandrarhem Jonstorp/Kullabygden, Gamla Södåkravägen 127, 26392 Jonstorp.
(42) 121413 (42) 367898
vandrarhem@jonstorp.com
www.stfturist.se
Open Dates: Ängelholm NE 15km Helsingborg 25km Ängelholm E 10km Jonstorp E 1km ap Jonstorp E (1km) 1W x 48 R (B) 1 x 1km 1km

SWEDEN – SUEDE – SCHWEDEN – SUECIA

▲ Julita – 54157
STF Vandrarhem Julita,
Julita Sveriges lantbruksmuseum,
64025 Julita.
(150) 487555 (150) 487551
julitabokn@nordiskamuseet.se
www.stfturist.se
Open Dates: 10.01-19.12
Stockholm-Skavsta 80km
Katrineholm 25km 405 ap Äs
x 34 (B)
3 x 5km
5km

▲ Junsele – 54158
STF Vandrarhem Junsele, Kullberg 102,
88037 Junsele.
(621) 30000 (621) 30000
kullberg.fritid@home.se
www.stfturist.se
Open Dates: 12N x 55

▲ Kalix – 54159
STF Vandrarhem Kalix, Grytnäs Herrgård,
Herrgårdsvägen 5, Box 148, 95251 Kalix.
(923) 10733 www.stfturist.se
Open Dates: Kallax; Kalix 85km
Kalix - Luleå 75km ap No 3 x 38
25km
25km

▲ Karesuando – 54162
STF Vandrarhem Karesuando, Pajalavägen,
98016 Karesuando.
(981) 20370; 20330 (981) 20305
arctic.tours@telia.com www.stfturist.se
Open Dates: 01.04-15.09 2NW x 36

▲ Kärlingesunds Gård – 54163
STF Vandrarhem Kärlingesunds Gård,
Kärlingesund 316, 45197 Uddevalla.
(522) 651080 stf@kgard.nu
www.stfturist.se
Open Dates: 16.06-06.08 x 28

▲ Karlsborg – 54164
STF Vandrarhem Karlsborg, Ankarvägen 2,
54630 Karlsborg.
(505) 44600 (505) 44600
www.stfturist.se
Open Dates: 01.06-31.08 x 76

▲ Karlshamn 54022
STF Vandrarhem Karlshamn,
Surbrunnsvägen 1C, 37439 Karlshamn.
(454) 14040 (454) 14040
stfturistkhamn@hotmail.com
www.stfturist.se
Open Dates: Kastrup 170km
Karlshamn 5km Karlshamn 300m
300m ap Railway Station 0.3NE x 72
(B)
3km 5km

▲ Karlskrona – 54166
STF Vandrarhem Karlskrona, Bredgatan 16,
Reception at Drottninggatan 39,
37132 Karlskrona.
(455) 10020
trosso.vandrarhem@telia.com
www.stfturist.se
Open Dates: 16.06-13.08 Ronneby 35km
A Karlskrona City 400m
Karlskrona/Verkö 9km Karlskrona
400m Karlskrona 300m
ap Drottninggatan 0,2 km x 50
(B)
500m 300m

▲ Karlskrona/Trossö – 54167
STF Vandrarhem Karlskrona/Trossö,
Drottninggatan 39, 37132 Karlskrona.
(455) 10020
trosso.vandrarhem@telia.com
www.stfturist.se
Open Dates: 09.01-22.12 Ronneby 35km
A Karlskrona City 400m
Karlskrona/Verkö 9km Karlskrona
400m Karlskrona 300m
ap Drottninggatan 0,01 km x 45
(B)
300m 500m

▲ Karlstad – 54168
STF Vandrarhem Karlstad, Ulleberg,
65342 Karlstad.
(54) 566840 (54) 566042
karlstad.vandrarhem@swipnet.se
www.stfturist.se
Open Dates: 07.01-20.12 6km 3km
No 11, 13 600m ap Center- Bellevue
x 102 (B)
1 x 3km
3km

▲ **Katrineholm** – 54169
STF Vandrarhem Katrineholm, Stora Djulö, 64192 Katrineholm.
(150) 10225 www.stfturist.se
Open Dates: 17.05-24.08
Stockholm-Skavsta 50km
Katrineholm Central 3km 2S x 40

▲ **Kiruna** – 54170
STF Vandrarhem Kiruna, Bergmästaregatan 7, Mitt i City, 98133 Kiruna.
(980) 17195 (980) 84142
www.stfturist.se
Open Dates: 12 x 70

▲ **Kivik** – 54171
STF Vandrarhem Kivik, Tittutvägen, 27730 Kivik.
(414) 71195 (414) 71195
www.stfturist.se
Open Dates: 03.03-06.11 Malmö 80km; Kristianstad 40km Bus from Kristianstad No 3 Ystad 50km Simrishamn 20km No 3 Kristianstad, Simrishamn 300m x 30 (B)

▲ **Kivik/Hanöbris** – 54172
STF Vandrarhem Kivik/Hanöbris, Eliselundsvägen 6, 27730 Kivik.
(414) 70050 (414) 70050
www.stfturist.se
Open Dates: 14.04-04.11 Malmö 80km; Kristianstad 40km Bus No 3 from Kristianstad Ystad 50km Simrishamn 20km Simrishamn, Kristianstad No 3 x 33 (B) 1 x

▲ **Klavreström** – 54173
STF Vandrarhem Klavreström, Malmgatan 1, 36072 Klavreström.
(474) 40944 (474) 40944
stfvhem.klavrestroem@swipnet.se
www.stfturist.se
Open Dates: 12 Växjö 42km 200m Karlskrona 120km Växjö 40km Klavreström 200m x 68 2 x 400m 400m

▲ **Klintehamn** – 54174
STF Vandrarhem Klintehamn, Varvsholm, 62020 Klintehamn.
(498) 240010 (498) 241411
warfsholm@telia.com www.stfturist.se
Open Dates: 01.03-30.11 35km 35km 33km x 90 1 x

▲ **Kolarbyn/Skinnskatteberg** – 54456
STF Vandrarhem Kolarbyn/Skinnskatteberg, 3 km East of Skinnskatteberg. Only 2 hours out of Stockholm. See map.
(70) 4007053 info@kolarbyn.se
www.stfturist.se
Open Dates: 01.05-15.10
Stockholm-Västerås 65km
Skinnskatteberg 3km 500; 581; 56 200m ap Skärsjön x 26 (BD) 1 x

▲ **Köping** – 54175
STF Vandrarhem Köping, Ågårdsgatan 2D, 73132 Köping.
(221) 24495 (221) 24495
vandrarhem.koping@swipnet.se
www.stfturist.se
Open Dates: 09.01-09.12 Arlanda 140km Stockholm 140km Central 2km 5 50m 0.5NE x 40 1km 6km

▲ **Köpingsvik/Solberga gård** – 54176
STF Vandrarhem Köpingsvik/Solberga gård, Solberga gård, 38790 Köpingsvik.
(485) 72060 (485) 72060
gk@solbergagard.se www.stfturist.se
Open Dates: 12 Kalmar 45km to Kalmar City Centre, Bus 106 Kalmar 40km 106 2km 2SE x 48 2km 2km

▲ **Köpmanholmen** – 54177
STF Vandrarhem Köpmanholmen, Köpmanholmsvägen 2, 89340 Köpmanholmen.
(660) 223496 www.stfturist.se
Open Dates: 01.02-30.11 Mellansel 30km Local Bus 50m x 36 30km 5km

SWEDEN – SUEDE – SCHWEDEN – SUECIA

Korrö – 54178
STF Vandrarhem Korrö, Korrö Hantverksby, 36024 Linneryd (5km S Linneryd on route 122).
(470) 34249 (470) 34556
korrovandrarhem@home.se
www.stfturist.se
Open Dates: x 87

Kramfors – 54457
STF Vandrarhem Kramfors, Järnvägsgatan 24, 87235 Kramfors.
(612) 13505 www.stfturist.se
Open Dates: Sollefteа; Kramfors 25km Kramfors 200m x 30 (B) 1 x 2km 40km

Kristinehamn – 54179
STF Vandrarhem Kristinehamn, Kvarndammens Camping, Bartilsbrovägen, 68143 Kristinehamn.
(550) 88195 (550) 12393
kvarndammenscamping@kristinehamn.se
www.stfturist.se
Open Dates: 01.05-31.08 x 16 (B)

Kronobergshed – 54180
STF Vandrarhem Kronobergshed, IOGT-NTO Kursgård, Kronobergshed, 34036 Moheda.
(472) 40052 (472) 40135
info@kronobergshed.com
www.stfturist.se
Open Dates: 10.01-18.12 Växjö 15km Alvesta 8km x 43 1 x 8km 400m

Kroppefjäll – 54083
STF Vandrarhem Kroppefjäll, 46450 Dals Rostock.
(530) 18460 (530) 18469
info@kroppefjall.com www.stfturist.se
Open Dates: Trollhättan 60km Mellerud 8km 700 600m, 712 300m ap Dals Rostock x 90 3 x 8km 10km

Kyrktåsjö – 54181
STF Vandrarhem Kyrktåsjö, Kyrktåsjö 190, 83080 Hoting.
(671) 713510 (671) 713511
vandrarhemkyrktasjo@telia.com
www.stfturist.se
Open Dates: x 19

Laholm – 54182
STF Vandrarhem Laholm, Tivolivägen 4, 31230 Laholm.
(430) 13318 (430) 15325
vandrarhem@laholm.se
www.stfturist.se
Open Dates: Halmstad; Ängelholm 30km Laholm 3km Laholm 200m x 70 1 x 800m 7km

Lakenetorps Gård – 54348
STF Vandrarhem Lakenetorps Gård, 683 94 Lakene.
(563) 70097
info@lakenetorpsgard.se
www.stfturist.se
Open Dates: 07.01-20.12 5km 85km 5km x 50 (B) 1 x

Landskrona – 54183
STF Vandrarhem Landskrona, S:t Olovsgatan 15, 26136 Landskrona.
(418) 12063 (418) 13075
www.stfturist.se
Open Dates: 09.01-08.12 Sturup 50km Helsingborg 25km Landskrona 1km 3 200m ap Lasarettet Norra x 45 (B) 1.5km 3km

Långasjö – 54184
STF Vandrarhem Långasjö, Stallgatan, 36195 Långasjö.
(471) 50310 www.stfturist.se
Open Dates: x 43

Lärbro/Grannen – 54190
STF Vandrarhem Lärbro/Grannen, Grannbyn, 62034 Lärbro.
(498) 225033 bokning@grannen.se
www.stfturist.se
Open Dates: 15.05-31.08 Visby 36km Visby 36km 21, 61 700m x 110 3 x 4km 4km

▲ **Leksand** – 54191
STF Vandrarhem Leksand, Parkgården, Källberget, Box 3051, 79335 Leksand.
(247) 15250 (247) 10186
info@vandrarhemleksand.se
www.stfturist.se
Open Dates: Dala Airport 50km Leksand 2.5km 58 100m ap Rutebo x 80 3km 4km

▲ **Lesjöfors** – 54192
STF Vandrarhem Lesjöfors, Esperanto-Gården, Stiftelsevägen 1, 68096 Lesjöfors.
(590) 30909 (590) 30359
egarden@esperanto.se
www.stfturist.se
Open Dates: Karlstad 140km Filipstad 35km 401 50m ap Stiftelsevägen x 88 2 x 4km 4km

▲ **Liden** – 54193
STF Vandrarhem Liden, Larmvägen 2, 86041 Liden.
(692) 10567 (692) 10567
www.stfturist.se
Open Dates: 01.06-31.08 x 34 (B)

▲ **Lidköping** – 54194
STF Vandrarhem Lidköping, Gamla Stadens Torg 4, 53132 Lidköping.
(510) 66430 (510) 23300
info@lidkopingsvandrarhem.com
www.stfturist.se
Open Dates: 09.01-22.12 x 52 R CC (B) 2km

▲ **Linköping** – 54196
STF Vandrarhem Linköping, Klostergatan 52 A, 58223 Linköping.
(13) 359000 (13) 359080
info@lvh.se www.stfturist.se
Open Dates: Linköping 4km Linköping 600m City buses 100m x 74 R CC (B)

▲ **Ljuder** – 54197
STF Vandrarhem Ljuder, Grimsnäs Herrgård, 36053 Skruv.
(478) 20400 (478) 20400
ljudersvandrarhem@bizland.com
www.stfturist.se
Open Dates: Växjö 45km Lessebo 9km 1km x 64 R CC (B) 3km

▲ **Ljugarn** – 54198
STF Vandrarhem Ljugarn, Storgatan 1, Box 36, 62016 Ljugarn.
(498) 493184 (498) 482424
stf.ljugarn@gamma.telenordia.se
www.stfturist.se
Open Dates: 01.05-30.09 x 31 R

▲ **Ljungby/Ljungby Semesterby** – 54349
STF Vandrarhem Ljungby/Ljungby Semesterby, Campingvägen 1, 34140 Ljungby.
(372) 10350 (372) 12235
reservation@ljungby-semesterby.se
www.stfturist.se
Open Dates: x 100

▲ **Ljungby/Södra Ljunga** – 54284
STF Vandrarhem Ljungby/Södra Ljunga, Lingvägen, 34191 Ljungby.
(372) 16011 (372) 16011
reservation@sodraljunga-hostel.se
www.stfturist.se
Open Dates: 6km A 100m 75km 60km 100m x 45 R CC 2 x 5km 5km

▲ **Ljungdalen** – 54199
STF Vandrarhem Ljungdalen, Dunsjögården, LTAB, Box 15, 84035 Ljungdalen.
(687) 20285; 20364 www.stfturist.se
Open Dates: 01.01-30.04; 23.06-24.09; 22-31.12 x 40 R

▲ **Loftahammar** – 54200
STF Vandrarhem Loftahammar, Trillin, Trillinvägen 3, 59095 Loftahammar.
(493) 61110 (493) 61929
trillin@tele2.se www.stfturist.se
Open Dates: Norrköping 100km Gamleby 35km 24 50m x 25 R CC 1km

▲ **Loka Brunn** – 54446
STF Vandrarhem Loka Brunn,
71294 Grythyttan.
(591) 63100 (591) 30000
info@lokabrunn.se www.stfturist.se
Open Dates: 28.04-24.09 Degerfors 40km 342 100m x 33 R CC 22 x 7km

▲ **Lönneberga** – 54202
STF Vandrarhem Lönneberga,
Lönnebergavägen 7, 57794 Lönneberga.
(495) 40036; Mobile: (70) 5745168
(70) 6192851
lonnebergavandrarhem@dof.se
www.stfturist.se
Open Dates: 12km 500m 500m x 55 R CC 1km

▲ **Lönsboda** – 54203
STF Vandrarhem Lönsboda,
Tranebodavägen 12, 28070 Lönsboda.
(479) 20025; 51114 (479) 21520
www.stfturist.se
Open Dates: x 18 R

▲ **Lövånger** – 54204
STF Vandrarhem Lövånger, Kungsvägen 31,
93010 Lövånger.
(913) 10395 (913) 10759
info-kyrkstad@lovangerskyrkstad.se
www.stfturist.se
Open Dates: x 80 R CC 7 x

▲ **Lund** – 54205
STF Vandrarhem Lund, "The Train",
Bjeredsparken, Vävaregatan 22, 22237 Lund.
(46) 142820 (46) 320568
trainhostel@ebrevet.nu
www.stfturist.se
Open Dates: 09.01-15.12 Sturup 30km
A Lund 300m Lund 300m
Central Bus Station Lund 300m 0.1NW
x 108 R (B) 15km 15km

▲ **Lunnevad/Mantorp** – 54206
STF Vandrarhem Lunnevad/Mantorp,
Lunnevads folkhögskola, Sjögestad,
590 48 Vikingstad.
(73) 3403998 (13) 234910
vandrarhem_lunnevad@lio.se
www.stfturist.se
Open Dates: 05.06-20.08 20SW x 90 R

▲ **Lycksele** – 54207
STF Vandrarhem Lycksele, Storgatan 47,
Duvan, 92132 Lycksele.
(950) 14670 (950) 10233
duvan.ab@telia.com www.stfturist.se
Open Dates: 10.06-30.08 x 40 R CC

Malmö/Eriksfält 54025
STF Vandrarhem Malmö/Eriksfält,
Backavägen 18, 21432 Malmö.
(40) 82220 (40) 80759
info@malmohostel.se www.stfturist.se
Open Dates: 09.01-21.12
Open Times: 08.00-10.00hrs; 16.00-20.00hrs
Beds: 177 - 5x1 5x2 5x3 25x4 6x6
Price Range: SEK 130-335 € 15-38
Directions: Sturup 30km
A Södervärn 1km Trelleborg 25km Malmö 3km 2 300m
ap Vandrarhemmet x 25 R CC (B) 2km 3km

Malmö/Eriksfält

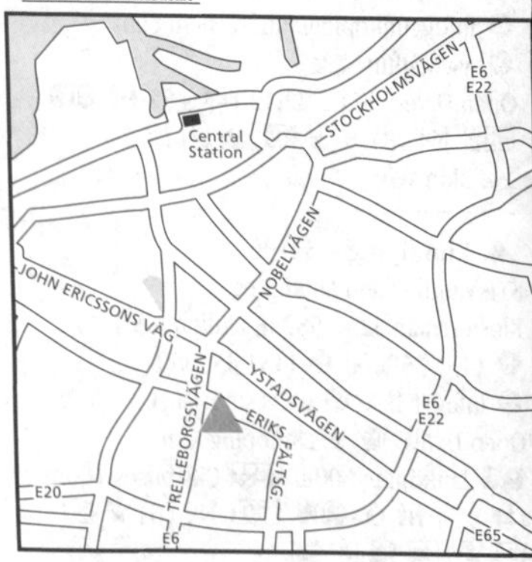

Malmö/Eriksfält... Travel Tips

- **For budget eats check out...** Möllan, Vagabond, Plaka, Lots of Restaurants at Lilla Torg, typical atmosphere of Malmö
- **For great nightlife try...** Kulturbolaget Rock & Nightclub with concerts, Jeriko for Music-lovers, Jazz, Nightclub at the weekends
- **Don't miss...** Malmö Museum of Modern Art, Malmö Art Gallery, Form Design Centre, Spring and Autumn: The Beech Forest & Torup Castle

▲ **Malung** – 54209
STF Vandrarhem Malung, Valleràs Turistgård, Mobyn PL 1448, 78233 Malung.
(280) 14040 (280) 41057
info@vallerasturistgard.se
www.stfturist.se
Open Dates: Malung 4km Valleràs 100m x 46

▲ **Mårbacken/Lekvattnet** – 54210
STF Vandrarhem Mårbacken/Lekvattnet, Skogsgården, Mårbacken, 685 91 Torsby.
(560) 52005 (560) 52005
skogsgarden@spray.se
www.stfturist.se
Open Dates: Oslo 150km Göteborg 320km Torsby 14km 310 300m x 24 (B)

▲ **Mariestad** – 54212
STF Vandrarhem Mariestad, Hamngatan 20, 54230 Mariestad.
(501) 10448 (501) 12345
fredrikssonkerstin@hotmail.com
www.stfturist.se
Open Dates: x 60 (B)

▲ **Mattsarve Sommargård** – 54479
STF Vandrarhem Mattsarve Sommargård, Sproge Mattsarve 251, 62020 Klintehamn.
(498) 241097 (498) 241097
info@mattsarve.com www.stfturist.se
Open Dates: 01.05-30.09 50km 50km 300m x 50 (B) 3km

▲ **Medevi Brunn** – 54213
STF Vandrarhem Medevi Brunn, Medevi Brunn, 59197 Motala.
(141) 91100 (141) 91532
medevibrunn@swipnet.se
www.stfturist.se
Open Dates: 09.06-31.08 Motala 17km 629 100m x 79 3 x 1.5km

▲ **Medskog/Östra Ämtervik** – 54214
STF Vandrarhem Medskog/Östra Ämtervik, 686 96 Östra Ämtervik.
(565) 32123 (565) 32123
medskogaktiv@telia.com
www.stfturist.se
Open Dates: x 38

▲ **Mellbystrand** – 54215
STF Vandrarhem Mellbystrand, Solstickan, Kustvägen 152, 31261 Mellbystrand.
(430) 25220; Mobile: (70) 4148414
(430) 49666 info@solstickan.com
www.stfturist.se
Open Dates: Laholm 2km Next to the hostel x 37 (B) 1 x 200m 200m

▲ **Messlingen/Baggården** – 54350
STF Vandrarhem Messlingen/Baggården, Messlingen 29, 840 95 Funäsdalen.
(684) 26200 (684) 26181
info@fjallvidd.com www.stfturist.se
Open Dates: x 12 1 x

▲ **Mjölby** – 54216
STF Vandrarhem Mjölby, Norrgårdsgatan 14, 59541 Mjölby.
(142) 10016 www.stfturist.se
Open Dates: 10.01-21.12 x 60

Mölndal/Torrekulla ☛ **Göteborg**

▲ **Mora** – 54217
STF Vandrarhem Mora, Målkull Ann's, Fredsgatan 6, 79232 Mora.
(250) 38196 (250) 38195
info@maalkullann.se www.stfturist.se
Open Dates: Mora Siljan 6km A 500m 700m Mora bus station 500m x 62 1 x 700m 2km

▲ Motala – 54218
STF Vandrarhem Motala, Skogsborgsgatan 1, 59152 Motala.
t (141) 57436 f (141) 57435
e skogsborg.vh@telia.com
w www.stfturist.se
Open Dates: 12 x 58 R P

▲ Motala/Göta kanal – 54219
STF Vandrarhem Motala/Göta kanal, Varvsgatan 17, 59146 Motala.
t (141) 210923 f (141) 210923
e motala@ncsab.se w www.stfturist.se
Open Dates: 12 3km 1km 3E x 32 R P

▲ Nora – 54221
STF Vandrarhem Nora, Nora Tåghem, Järnvägsområdet, 71322 Nora.
t (587) 14676 e info@norataghem.se
w www.stfturist.se
Open Dates: 12 x 72 R P

▲ Norberg – 54222
STF Vandrarhem Norberg, Gruvbyn, Klackberg, 73891 Norberg.
t (223) 20247 e info@gruvbyn.com
w www.stfturist.se
Open Dates: 12 150km 70km 15km 1km ap Fagerstavägen Södra 2NW x 50 R TV P 300m 100m

---

▲ Norrköping/Abborreberg – 54223
STF Vandrarhem Norrköping/Abborreberg, Lindö, 60375 Norrköping.
t (11) 319344 e abborreberg@telia.com
w www.stfturist.se
Open Dates: 01.04-15.10 Kungsängen 3km Lindö 2km Norrköping 5km 111, 101 50m ap Abborreberg 5E x 60 CC TV 1 x i P 300m

---

▲ Norrköping/Sörsjön – 54224
STF Vandrarhem Norrköping/Sörsjön, Box 7100, 600 07 Norrköping.
t (11) 61230 f (11) 61130
e info@sorsjon.nu w www.stfturist.se
Open Dates: 12 Kungsängen 30km Norrköping 20km Norrköping 20km 15N x 48 CC TV 1 x i P

▲ Norrköping/Turistgården – 54225
STF Vandrarhem Norrköping/Turistgården, Ingelstagatan 31, 60223 Norrköping.
t (11) 101160 f (11) 186863
e info@turistgarden.se w www.stfturist.se
Open Dates: 10.01-22.12 10km 800m 50m x 102 R CC (B) TV P

▲ Norrtälje – 54226
STF Vandrarhem Norrtälje, Brännäsgården, Bältartorpsgatan 6, Box 803, 76128 Norrtälje.
t (176) 71569 f (176) 71589
e vandrarhemmet@norrtalje.se
w www.stfturist.se
Open Dates: 12.06-13.08
Stockholm-Arlanda 60km Stockholm Central 70km 640 500m x 32 R (B) TV i P 1km

---

▲ Norsholm/Kapten Bille's – 54466
STF Vandrarhem Norsholm/Kapten Bille's, Kapten Bille's Café och Vandrarhem, Slussvägen, 610 21 Norsholm.
t (11) 54550 e kaptenbille@tele2.se
w www.stfturist.se
Open Dates: 18.01-17.12 Norrköping 25km; Linköping 30km, Skavsta 80km Norrköping, Centralstationen 480, 490, 481, 510 50m ap Norsholm Centrum x 44 R CC TV 1 x i P 500m

---

▲ Nybro – 54227
STF Vandrarhem Nybro, Vasagatan 22, 38232 Nybro.
t (481) 10932 f (481) 12117
w www.stfturist.se
Open Dates: 12 Kalmar 30km Kalmar 30km Nybro 1km x 100 R CC TV P

▲ Nynäshamn – 54228
STF Vandrarhem Nynäshamn, Nickstabadsvägen 15-17, 14943 Nynäshamn.
t (8) 52012780 f (8) 52015317
w www.stfturist.se
Open Dates: 16.01-16.12 x 30 (B) 1 x P

▲ **Ockelbo** – 54229
STF Vandrarhem Ockelbo, Södra Åsgatan 28, 81630 Ockelbo.
(297) 42111 www.stfturist.se
Open Dates: x 24
(B)

▲ **Ödeshög** – 54230
STF Vandrarhem Ödeshög, Hembygdsgården, Södra Vägen 63, 59931 Ödeshög.
(144) 10700 (144) 31888
odeshogsvandrarhem@telia.com
www.stfturist.se
Open Dates: 15.05-25.08 x 56

▲ **Ölands Skogsby** – 54231
STF Vandrarhem Ölands Skogsby, 38693 Färjestaden.
(485) 38395 (485) 38324
info@vandrarhskogsby.se
www.stfturist.se
Open Dates: 15.04-30.09 Kalmar 23km Kalmar 17km Kalmar 17km 103 100m x 60
(B) 3km
3km

▲ **Omberg/Stocklycke** – 54232
STF Vandrarhem Omberg/Stocklycke, Stocklycke, Omberg, 59993 Ödeshög.
(144) 33044 (144) 33042
omberg@stocklycke.info
www.stfturist.se
Open Dates: 16.01-08.12 Göteborg 250km Mjölby 40km ap 3 km x 55
2 x 500m

▲ **Örebro** 54233
STF Vandrarhem Örebro, Kaptensgatan 1, 70365 Örebro.
(19) 310240 (19) 310256
vandrarhem@hepa.se www.stfturist.se
Open Dates: 10km Central 2km 16, 31 1km x 110
(B)
1 x 1.1km 3km

▲ **Öreryd/Hestra** – 54234
STF Vandrarhem Öreryd/Hestra, 33027 Hestra.
(370) 337035 (370) 337008
www.stfturist.se
Open Dates: x 27

▲ **Örkelljunga/Hjelmsjövik** – 54352
STF Vandrarhem Örkelljunga/Hjelmsjövik, Östra Spång 540, 28692 Örkelljunga.
(435) 56600 (435) 56619
info@hjelmsjovik.se www.stfturist.se
Open Dates: x 32

▲ **Örnsköldsvik/Överhörnäs** – 54235
STF Vandrarhem Örnsköldsvik/Överhörnäs, Högsnäsgården, Högsnäs 99, 89440 Överhörnäs.
(660) 70244 (660) 70244
stfvandrarhem@sovbra.se
www.stfturist.se
Open Dates: Gideå 20km x 31
(B)

▲ **Orrefors** – 54236
STF Vandrarhem Orrefors, Silversparregatan 14, 38040 Orrefors.
(481) 30020 (481) 30020
www.stfturist.se
Open Dates: 01.05-01.09 x 53
(B)

▲ **Orsa** – 54237
STF Vandrarhem Orsa, Gillevägen 3, 79433 Orsa.
(250) 42170 (250) 42365
stfvandrarhem.orsa@telia.com
www.stfturist.se
Open Dates: Mora 20km Mora 13km No 103 10m x 68
(B)
3km 3km

▲ **Osaby Säteri** – 54452
STF Vandrarhem Osaby Säteri, Osaby Säteri, 35595 Tävelsås.
(470) 776027
maria.drugge@osaby.se
www.stfturist.se
Open Dates: Växjö 20km Växjö 15km x 42 (B)
1 x 2km

▲ **Osby** – 54239
STF Vandrarhem Osby, Stora Hotellet, V Järnvägsgatan 17, 28331 Osby.
(479) 31830 (479) 16222
storahotelletosby@telia.com
www.stfturist.se
Open Dates: 20.06-14.08 x 30

▲ **Oskarshamn/Oscar** – 54240
STF Vandrarhem Oskarshamn/Oscar, Södra Långgatan 15-17, 572 33 Oskarshamn.
(491) 15800 (491) 15801
info@forumoskarshamn.com
www.stfturist.se
Open Dates: 12km 250m 200m 500m x 24 (B) 800m 2km

▲ **Österbymo** – 54241
STF Vandrarhem Österbymo, Ydregården, Box 37, 57060 Österbymo.
(381) 60103 (381) 60937
www.stfturist.se
Open Dates: 01.05-30.09 x 20

▲ **Östersund** – 54242
STF Vandrarhem Östersund, Södra Gröngatan 36, 83135 Östersund.
(63) 139100; 34130
micke2@algonet.se www.stfturist.se
Open Dates: 23.06-09.08 x 112

▲ **Östersund/Jamtli** – 54243
STF Vandrarhem Östersund/Jamtli, Jämtlands Läns Museum, Box 709, 83128 Östersund.
(63) 122060; 150100 (63) 106168
vandrarhemmet@jamtli.com
www.stfturist.se
Open Dates: 09.01-17.12 9km A 1.5km 2km 100m x 30

▲ **Ottenby** – 54244
STF Vandrarhem Ottenby, Ottenby 106, 38065 Degerhamn.
(485) 662062 (485) 662161
info@ottenbyvandrarhem.se
www.stfturist.se
Open Dates: x 146

▲ **Överum** – 54245
STF Vandrarhem Överum, 8 Små Hem, Källarbacken 2, 59096 Överum.
(493) 30302; (70) 6742621
ewo@algonet.se www.stfturist.se
Open Dates: x 30

▲ **Pajala** – 54448
STF Vandrarhem Pajala, Tannaniemi 65, 98431 Pajala.
(978) 74180 (978) 74180
0978.10322@telia.com
www.stfturist.se
Open Dates: Pajala 10km Pajala bus station 1.7km x 24 (B)

▲ **Persåsen** – 54246
STF Vandrarhem Persåsen, Persåsen 3370, 83024 Oviken.
(643) 445550 (643) 445556
stf@persasen.se www.stfturist.se
Open Dates: 25.06-13.08 x 28

▲ **Piteå** – 54247
STF Vandrarhem Piteå, Storgatan 3, 94131 Piteå.
(911) 15880 (911) 15880
www.stfturist.se
Open Dates: x 35

▲ **Prässebo** – 54248
STF Vandrarhem Prässebo, Sommarro, 46012 Prässebo.
(520) 667024
prassebo-hostel@telia.com
www.stfturist.se
Open Dates: 15.05-31.08 Göteborg 80km A 50km Göteborg 50km Älvängen 20km 620 300m ap Prässebo badplats x 33 300m 300m

---

▲ **Ransäter/Annersia** – 54250
STF Vandrarhem Ransäter/Annersia, Geijersvägen 1, 68493 Ransäter.
(552) 30050; 30039 (552) 30039
geijersgarden@telia.com
www.stfturist.se
Open Dates: 01.05-30.09 50km 60km 304 400m x 23 (B)

▲ Rantajärvi – 54251
STF Vandrarhem Rantajärvi, Rantajärvi 110, 95794 Övertorneå.
(927) 23000 (927) 23123
stfvandrarhem@rantajarvi-camp.se
www.stfturist.se
Open Dates: Kallax in Luleå 220km Luleå hamn 220km Haparanda 170km Rantajärvi ap Övertorneå 45km x 28 R CC TV 1 x i 8 P

▲ Rättvik – 54252
STF Vandrarhem Rättvik, Centralgatan, 79530 Rättvik.
(248) 10566 (248) 56113
stfrattvik@rattviksparken.fh.se
www.stfturist.se
Open Dates: Arlanda 300km Stockholm 300km Rättvik 1km 70, 71, 58 1km 1NE x 104 CC (B) TV P 1km 1km

▲ Regna – 54253
STF Vandrarhem Regna, Regnagården, Regna, 64010 Högsjö.
(151) 70127 (151) 70127
www.stfturist.se
Open Dates: x 40 R P

▲ Rengsjö – 54469
STF Vandrarhem Rengsjö, Ohlandersgården, Knyssla 8381, 82198 Rengsjö.
Mobile: (70) 8102966
www.stfturist.se
Open Dates: 01.04-31.10 Bollnäs 15km; Söderhamn 25km 250m ap Knyssla x 22 R (B) TV P

▲ Rimforsa/Kalvudden – 54254
STF Vandrarhem Rimforsa/Kalvudden, 59041 Rimforsa.
(494) 20137; (8) 56032361
info@kalvudden.se www.stfturist.se
Open Dates: 15.05-15.09 Stockholm 280km, Nyköping 150km Rimforsa 3km x 25 R (B) TV 8 P

▲ Ronneby – 54255
STF Vandrarhem Ronneby, Övre Brunnsvägen 54, 37236 Ronneby.
(457) 26300 (457) 26300
www.stfturist.se
Open Dates: 09.01-16.12 Ronneby 5km Ronneby 1km 10m x 104 R (B) TV 1 x i P 300m 2km

▲ Rörbäck – 54256
STF Vandrarhem Rörbäck, Bokenäs, v Rörbäck 29, 45196 Uddevalla.
(522) 650190 rorback@telia.com
www.stfturist.se
Open Dates: 01.06-03.09 x 47 R TV 1 x P

▲ Röstånga – 54257
STF Vandrarhem Röstånga, Röstånga Gästgivaregård, Marieholmsvägen 2, 26024 Röstånga.
(435) 29700 (435) 29799
info@rostangagastgivaregard.se
www.stfturist.se
Open Dates: Ängelholm 45km; Sturup 65km Stehag 25km 200m x 28 CC TV i P

▲ Sala – 54259
STF Vandrarhem Sala, Sofielund, Mellandammen, 73336 Sala.
(224) 12730 www.stfturist.se
Open Dates: 10.02-12.11 ( ) 2.5km x 35 R TV P 900m 1.5km

▲ Sälen – 54260
STF Vandrarhem Sälen, Gräsheden, Box 58, 78067 Sälen.
(280) 82040 (280) 82045
info@salensvandrarhem.se
www.stfturist.se
Open Dates: Mora 120km Oslo 230km Malung 90km Malung 90km, Mora 120km ap Sälen, then take a taxi 25 km x 62 R (B) TV 2 x i 8 P

▲ **Sandviken** – 54262
STF Vandrarhem Sandviken, Svarvargatan 26, 81136 Sandviken.
(26) 251915
svarvaren26@hotmail.com
www.stfturist.se
Open Dates: 02.01-18.12 Arlanda 200km Stockholm 230km Sandviken 2km Odenplan 1.5km ap Valsargatan; 41, 400m x 44 4km 4km

▲ **Sankt Anna** – 54263
STF Vandrarhem Sankt Anna, Gamla Färjeläget, 61498 Sankt Anna.
(121) 51312 (8) 6002352
info@stannagarden.com
www.stfturist.se
Open Dates: 01.06-31.08 55km 55km 300m x 32

▲ **Särna/Björkhagen** – 54264
STF Vandrarhem Särna/Björkhagen, Pl 535, 79090 Särna.
(253) 10308 ltsj@spray.se
www.stfturist.se
Open Dates: 150km A 150km 130km 170 500m ap Särna x 25 (BL) 700m 700m

▲ **Särna/Turistgården** – 54265
STF Vandrarhem Särna/Turistgården, Sjukstugevägen 4, 79090 Särna.
(253) 10437 (253) 10437
turistgarden.stf@tele2.se
www.stfturist.se
Open Dates: Mora 120km Mora 120km 170 to Mora x 32

▲ **Säter-Haverö** – 54266
STF Vandrarhem Säter-Haverö, Haverö Hembygdsgård, Säter, 84193 Östavall.
(690) 30137 www.stfturist.se
Open Dates: 14.06-18.08 x 18

▲ **Saxnäs/Kultsjögården** – 54268
STF Vandrarhem Saxnäs/Kultsjögården, Box 6, 91088 Marsfjäll.
(940) 70044 (940) 70270
info@kultsjogarden.se www.stfturist.se
Open Dates: x 51

▲ **Sigtunahöjden** – 54478
STF Vandrarhem Sigtunahöjden, Hertigvägen 7, Box 502, 19328 Sigtuna.
(8) 59257700 (8) 59257757
kontakt@sigtunahojden.se
www.stfturist.se
Open Dates: 01.01-30.06; 01.08-31.12 x 40

▲ **Simrishamn** – 54270
STF Vandrarhem Simrishamn, Christian Barnekowsgatan 10C, 27232 Simrishamn.
(414) 10540 (414) 71171
www.stfturist.se
Open Dates: 01.03-30.11 Sturup 70km Ystad 40km Simrishamn 400m Simrishamn 500m x 20 (B) 2km 2km

▲ **Skåne Tranås** – 54271
STF Vandrarhem Skåne Tranås, Helgonavägen 7, 27392 Tomelilla.
(417) 20330 (417) 20339
vandrarhem@skanetranas.com
www.stfturist.se
Open Dates: Sturup 50km Trelleborg 90km Malmö 80km Skåne Expressen, 4 200m x 90 3 x 4km 25km

▲ **Skara/Eggby** – 54459
STF Vandrarhem Skara/Eggby, Skärvavägen 3, Eggby, 532 92 Axvall.
(511) 12165 (511) 20206
eggby@home.se www.stfturist.se
Open Dates: 07.01-15.12 Göteborg 130km Göteborg 130km Skövde 20km x 40 (B) 500m

Skäralid – 54273
STF Vandrarhem Skäralid, Pl 750, 26070 Ljungbyhed.
(435) 442025 info@skaralid.com
www.stfturist.se
Open Dates: Kastrup 80km Helsingborg 50km Klippan 15km 518 200m x 40 (B) 2 x

Skellefteå – 54274
STF Vandrarhem Skellefteå, Stiftsgården, Brännavägen 25, 93144 Skellefteå.
(910) 725700 (910) 56863
stiftsgarden.skelleftea@svenskakyrkan.se
www.stfturist.se
Open Dates: 20km A 2km 2km 2E x 22 (B) 4 x 4km 4km

Sköldinge – 54463
STF Vandrarhem Sköldinge, Åsa folkhögskola, 64024 Sköldinge.
(157) 69534 (157) 69528
asa.fhsk@folkbildning.net
www.stfturist.se
Open Dates: Stockholm-Skavsta 60km Stockholm 180km Katrineholm 12km 780 300m ap Asa x 42 5 x 5km 5km

Skövde – 54276
STF Vandrarhem Skövde, Billingens Stugby & Camping, Alphyddevägen, 54133 Skövde.
(500) 471633 (500) 471044
info@billingensstugby.se
www.stfturist.se
Open Dates: 15km Göteborg 150km Skövde 3km 65 300m ap Billingehus x 18 1 x 200m

Skurup – 54277
STF Vandrarhem Skurup, Bruksgatan 3, 27435 Skurup.
(411) 536061 sara.lalle@telia.com
www.stfturist.se
Open Dates: 12.06-13.08 Sturup 24km Trelleborg 44km; Ystad 24km Skurup 600m x 30 400m 20km

Smygehuk – 54278
STF Vandrarhem Smygehuk, Smygehuk fyr, Kustvägen, Pl 314, 23178 Smygehamn.
(410) 24583
info@smygehukhostel.com
www.stfturist.se
Open Dates: 01.02-30.11 30km 15km 45km x 40 (B) 2km 2km

Snöå Bruk – 54279
STF Vandrarhem Snöå Bruk, 78051 Dala-Järna.
(281) 24018 (281) 24045
stf.vandrarhem@snoabruk.se
www.stfturist.se
Open Dates: Arlanda 270km; Borlänge 90km 90km Stockholm 300km Dala-Järn 4km 57 1km ap Snöå Bruk 87W x 91 4 x 10m 10m

Söderhamn/Mohed – 54280
STF Vandrarhem Söderhamn/Mohed, Mohedsvägen 59, 82692 Söderala.
(270) 425233 (270) 425326
minfo@mohedscamping.se
www.stfturist.se
Open Dates: Arlanda 230km Söderhamn 15km 100 500m ap Mohed 15W x 35 100m 100m

Söderköping/Mangelgården – 54281
STF Vandrarhem Söderköping/Mangelgården, Skönbergagatan 48, 61430 Söderköping.
(121) 10213 012110213@telia.com
www.stfturist.se
Open Dates: 01.05-30.09 Norrköping 15km Norrköping 15km 450, 460 500m x 36 1km 20km

▲ **Söderköping/Göta kanal** – 54282
STF Vandrarhem Söderköping/Göta kanal, Skeppsdockan, Box 15, 614 21 Söderköping.
(121) 21630
korskullenscamp@hotmail.com
www.stfturist.se
Open Dates: 12 Norrköping 20km
Klevbrinken/Göta Kanal
Norrköping 20km 450 300m ap Klevbrinken 1NW x 25 R

▲ **Södertälje** – 54283
STF Vandrarhem Södertälje, Tvetagården, 15192 Södertälje.
(8) 55098025 (8) 55098025
tvetagardensvandrarhem@telia.com
www.stfturist.se
Open Dates: 09.01-22.12 Södertälje Central 5km 784 400m ap Tvetaberg 6SW x 45 R CC (B) TV P 100m 1km

---

▲ **Sollefteå** – 54285
STF Vandrarhem Sollefteå, Björklunden, Övergård 7006, 88193 Sollefteå.
(620) 15817 (620) 15917
hotell@hotellbjorklunden.com
www.stfturist.se
Open Dates: 11.01-20.12
Kramfors/Sollefteå 30km
Resecentrum 3km 3E x 32 CC (B) TV P 3km

▲ **Sölvesborg** – 54286
STF Vandrarhem Sölvesborg, Yndegården, Ynde Byväg 22, 294 92 Sölvesborg.
(456) 19811 info@yndegarden.se
www.stfturist.se
Open Dates: 01.03-31.10 Kristianstad 40km A Sölvesborg 3km
Karlshamn 30km Sölvesborg 3km
Sölvesborg 3km 3NW x 26
R (B) TV 1 x P
12km 5km

▲ **Solviken/Tranås** – 54442
STF Vandrarhem Solviken/Tranås, Solviken, 57394 Tranås.
(140) 40100 (140) 40101
solviken@solviken.nu www.stfturist.se
Open Dates: 13.01-17.12 Jönköping 90km
Tranås 15km 2km x 40
R (B) TV P

▲ **Sorsele** – 54287
STF Vandrarhem Sorsele, Torggatan 3, Box 24, 92070 Sorsele.
(952) 10124 (952) 10625
www.stfturist.se
Open Dates: 20.06-31.08 x 80 R P

▲ **Stafsjö** – 54288
STF Vandrarhem Stafsjö, Störnings väg 8, 61895 Stavsjö.
(11) 393384 (11) 393343
www.stfturist.se
Open Dates: 12.01-09.12 Arlanda 180 km; Skafsta 40km Kålmården 8km 563 20m x 28 R CC (B) TV 1 x P 1km 1km

---

▲ **Stenkumla** – 54476
STF Vandrarhem Stenkumla, Gutestugan, 62195 Visby.
(498) 271053; Mobile: (70) 7433883
gutestugan@spray.se www.stfturist.se
Open Dates: 03.01-20.12 17km no 31 from Visby ap Lilla Homa in Stenkumla x 40 R 7km 7km

---

▲ **Stenungsund** – 54289
STF Vandrarhem Stenungsund, Tollenäs, Pl 6109, 44491 Stenungsund.
(303) 82120
tollenas.camping@telia.com
www.stfturist.se
Open Dates: 15.04-15.10 Landvetter Göteborg A 500m 50km 2km x 50 R (B) TV P

Stockholm – af Chapman/Skeppsholmen

Ⓗ 54001

STF Vandrarhem af Chapman/ Skeppsholmen, Flaggmansvägen 8, 11149 Stockholm.

(8) 4632266 (8) 6117155

chapman@stfturist.se www.stfturist.se

Open Dates: 06.01-31.12 - A part of the hostel, the ship "af Chapman", might close due to renovation during 2006. We can as usual offer accomodation on land all year round. For more information see our website.

Open Times:

Beds: 293 - 20x2 8x3 24x4 2x5 8x6 8x6

Price Range: SEK 155-230

Directions: Arlanda 40km A City Terminal 1km Stockholm 2km Central 1km 65 50m ap af Chapman/Östasiatiska museet U Kungsträdgården 300m x 36 R CC (BD) TV 8 P

Stockholm – af Chapman/Skeppsholmen

▲ **Stockholm** – Backpackers Inn

Ⓗ 54339

STF Vandrarhem Backpackers Inn, Banérgatan 56, Box 9116, 10272 Stockholm.

(8) 6607515 (8) 6654039

info@backpackersinn.se

www.stfturist.se

Open Dates: 26.06-13.08 Arlanda 45km A Central Station (T-centralen) 2km Värtahamnen 1.1km Central Station (T-centralen) 2km Karlaplan 200m U Karlaplan 200m x 306 R CC (B) P

▲ **Stockholm** – Bogesund/Vaxholm – 54068

STF Vandrarhem Bogesund/Vaxholm, Per Brahesväg 1, 18593 Vaxholm.

(8) 54132240 (8) 54430011

bogesundsvandrarhem@tele2.se

www.stfturist.se

Open Dates: 08.01-16.12 Arlanda 60km Vaxholm harbour 3.5km Stockholm Central station 35km 670 Tekniska högskolan 35km x 70 R CC TV 2 x P 1km 1km

Stockholm – Fridhemsplan Ⓗ 54458

STF Vandrarhem Fridhemsplan, Sankt Eriksgatan 20, 11239 Stockholm.

(8) 6538800 (8) 6538920

info@fridhemsplan.se www.stfturist.se

Open Dates: 12 Open Times:

Beds: 371 - 8x1 104x2 12x3 28x4

Price Range: SEK 195-495 € 21.05-63.16

Directions: 1NW from city centre Arlanda 40km A Arlanda buses 1km Stadsgården 1.5km Stockholm Central 1km 1, 3, 4, 40, 62, 77 100m U Fridhemsplan 100m R CC (B) TV 8 P 300m 300m

Stockholm – Fridhemsplan

Stockholm – Hässelby Slott – 54468
STF Vandrarhem Hässelby Slott,
Maltesholmsvägen 1, 162 15 Vällingby.
(8) 4455140 (8) 4455141
hasselbyslott@fazer.se www.stfturist.se
Open Dates: 18.06-19.12 Stockholm Arlanda 35km A Stockholm Arlanda 35km Stockholm City 15km Stockholm City 15km U Metrostation "Johannelund" 200m x 24 R CC (B) 1 x 500m 500m

---

Stockholm – Hågelby – 54119
STF Vandrarhem Hågelby, Hågelby gård,
14743 Tumba.
(8) 53062011 (8) 53031153
hagelbyparken@hagelby.se
www.stfturist.se
Open Dates: Arlanda 66km From Alby no 707, 708 400m U Alby 2km
x 28 R CC TV P

Stockholm – Hökarängen – 54464
STF Vandrarhem Hökarängen, Martinskolan,
Munstycksvägen 18, 123 57 Farsta.
(8) 7246504
Open Dates: 24.06-12.08 Arlanda 41km Stockholm Central 8km U line 18 Hökarängen 8km 8S x 50 (B) TV P 1.5km 1.5km

---

Stockholm – Jakobsberg/Barkarby – 54145
STF Vandrarhem Jakobsberg/Barkarby,
Kaptensvägen 7, 17738 Järfälla.
(8) 4457270 (8) 4457273
vandrarhemmet.majorskan@tele2.se
www.stfturist.se
Open Dates: 02.01-21.12 Arlanda 35km Jakobsberg/Barkarby 2km 567 200m ap Stockholm Quality Outlet 1W
x 60 R CC TV 2 x P 4km 6km

Stockholm – Långholmen H 54008
STF Vandrarhem Långholmen,
Kronohäktet, Långholmsmuren 20,
Box 9116, 10272 Stockholm.
(8) 7208500 (8) 7208575
vandrarhem@langholmen.com
www.stfturist.se
Open Dates: Open Times:
Beds: 254 - 71x² 11x³ 13x⁴
Price Range: from SEK 205 € 23
Directions: Arlanda 40km A City Terminal 3km Central 3km 4 700m ap Långholmsgatan U Hornstull 700m
x 30 R CC TV 5 x i 8 P

Stockholm – Långholmen

0 4km

Stockholm – Tollare/Nacka – 54477
STF Vandrarhem Tollare/Nacka, Åhlbergsväg,
Tollare folkhögskola, 13242 Saltsjö-Boo.
(8) 50568600 (8) 50568650
moa.wester.tollare@folkbildning.net
www.stfturist.se
Open Dates: 09.06-20.08 Arlanda 49km Stockholm Central 15km 414 150m ap Tollare x 50 R CC (BL) TV 6 x i P 1.5km 1.5km

---

Stockholm – Tyresö – 54315
STF Vandrarhem Tyresö, Lilla Tyresö,
Kyrkvägen 5, 13560 Tyresö.
(8) 7700304 (8) 7700355
lillatyreso@tyreso.se www.stfturist.se
Open Dates: Arlanda 70km 875 from Gullmarsplan 15km x 44 R CC (B) TV 1 x i 8 P

Stockholm – Zinkensdamm 54007
STF Vandrarhem Zinkensdamm, Zinkens väg 20, 11741 Stockholm.
(8) 6168100 (8) 6168120
mail@zinkensdamm.com
www.stfturist.se
Open Dates: Open Times:
Beds: 490 - 21x2 28x3 91x4 1x6+
Price Range: from SEK 195 € 18.50
Directions: Arlanda 40km A City Terminal 3km Viking Terminal 3km Central 3km U Red line towards Fruängen or Norsborg, Station Zinkensdamm 600m x 91 R CC (BD) 2 x 2km

Stockholm – Zinkensdamm

Stockholm... Travel Tips

- **For budget eats check out...** Systrarna Lundberg (Rörstransgatan), Indira (Bondegatan), Sjöhästen (Långholmsgatan), Ciao Ciao, Chutney Katauna Baugatan
- **For great nightlife try...** Stureplan (many clubs under one square), Berns (music, disco, outdoors with 3 bars and 3 floors), Casino, Hotellet (Linneg 18), Fredsgatan 12 (popular outdoor bar)
- **Don't miss...** Vasa Warship Musuem, Forest Cemetary, Skansen Outdoor Musuem & Gamepark, Sightseeing boat from Grand Hotel, Butterfly - musuem in Hagaparken, Gröna Lund (permanent fairground), Guided walking tour through the Old Town, Beaches (Smedsudden & Rålambshov), Museum of Modern Art, Royal Palace

▲ Hostels in the Archipelago – /AJ dans l'archipel/ JH im Archipel/ Albergues en el Archipiélago

▲ Arholma – 54047
STF Vandrarhem Arholma, Arholma 162, 76041 Arholma.
(176) 56018 www.stfturist.se
Open Dates: x 34

▲ Dalarö – 54082
STF Vandrarhem Dalarö, Lotsen Tullbacken 4, 13054 Dalarö.
(8) 50151636 (8) 50151636
vandrarhem.dalaro@haninge.mail.telia.com
www.stfturist.se
Open Dates: Arlanda A 80km Hotellbryggan in Dalarö Haninge Central 839 ap Hotellbryggan Dalarö 50SE x 8 R 1 x

▲ Fejan – 54097
STF Vandrarhem Fejan, 76015 Gräddö.
(176) 43031 (176) 43205
www.stfturist.se
Open Dates: 01.06-31.08 (01.04-22.12)
x 57 R CC

▲ Finnhamn – 54098
STF Vandrarhem Finnhamn, Finnhamns brygga, Box 84, 13025 Ingmarsö.
(8) 54246212 (8) 54246133
info@finnhamn.se www.stfturist.se
Open Dates: 10.01-18.12 x 80 R CC

▲ Fjärdlång – 54100
STF Vandrarhem Fjärdlång, 13054 Dalarö.
(8) 50156092 (8) 50156634
www.stfturist.se
Open Dates: 02.05-15.10 Dalarö Strömkajen Stockholm x 26 R CC

▲ Gällnö – 54105
STF Vandrarhem Gällnö, 13033 Gällnö by.
(8) 57166117 (8) 57166288
www.stfturist.se
Open Dates: 01.05-30.09 1.2km
x 34 R CC 1.5km
1.5km

SWEDEN - SUEDE - SCHWEDEN - SUECIA

▲ **Grinda** – 54115
STF Vandrarhem Grinda, Grinda,
Södra Bryggan, 18599 Vaxholm, Stockholm.
(8) 54249072 (8) 54249345
grindastugby@telia.com
www.stfturist.se
Open Dates: 28.04-22.10 Södra Grinda 600m x 44

▲ **Kapellskär** – 54161
STF Vandrarhem Kapellskär, Pl 985,
Riddersholm, 76015 Gräddö.
(176) 44169 (176) 239046
www.stfturist.se
Open Dates: Arlanda 80km
Kapellskär 2km Stockholm 100km
631 50m ap Riddersholm x 36
1 x
2km

▲ **Lillsved** – 54195
STF Vandrarhem Lillsved, 13990 Värmdö.
(8) 54138530 (8) 54138316
info@lillsved.gymnastik.se
www.stfturist.se
Open Dates: 01.06-31.08 x 148

▲ **Örskär** – 54238
STF Vandrarhem Örskär, Örskär 141,
74071 Öregrund.
(173) 34021 (173) 34011
orskars.vandrarhem@telia.com
www.stfturist.se
Open Dates: 01.05-30.09 x 18

▲ **Sävö** – 54267
STF Vandrarhem Sävö, Ekviken,
61075 Västerljung.
(156) 40346 (156) 40346
www.stfturist.se
Open Dates: 01.05-31.10 x 35

▲ **Siaröfortet** – 54269
STF Vandrarhem Siaröfortet, Kyrkogårdsön,
Östanå färjeläge, 111 30 Stockholm.
(8) 243090
kontoret@blidosundsbolaget.se
www.stfturist.se
Open Dates: 30.04-15.10 x 40
(B) 1 x

▲ **Skeppsmyra** – 54275
STF Vandrarhem Skeppsmyra,
Lyckhem/Skeppsmyra, 76042 Björkö.
(176) 94027 info@lyckhemhb.se
www.stfturist.se
Open Dates: Arlanda 115km
A Norrtälje 55km Grislehamn 50km Uppsala 110km Skeppsmyra affär 600m x 50
1 x
10km

▲ **Stora Kalholmen** – 54291
STF Vandrarhem Stora Kalholmen,
Stora Kalholmen.
Mailing address: STF Vandrarhem Stora Kalholmen, c/o Skärgårdsstiftelsen, Box 7669, 103 94 Stockholm.
(8) 54246023 www.stfturist.se
Open Dates: 10.06-21.08 x 22

▲ **Utö** – 54321
STF Vandrarhem Utö, Gruvbryggan,
13056 Utö.
(8) 50420315 (8) 50420301
receptionen@uto-vardshus.se
www.stfturist.se
Open Dates: 30.04-30.09 Arlanda 65km
Nynäshamn 15km Stockholm Central 22km Väster Haninge-Årsta Havsbad 10km ap No 846 Årsta Brygga
Stockholm Central-Väster Haninge 30km
x 44
12 x

▲ **Väddö/Älmsta** – 54322
STF Vandrarhem Väddö/Älmsta, Hagavägen,
Älmsta, Box 9, 76040 Väddö.
(176) 50078 (176) 50078
www.stfturist.se
Open Dates: 03.07-09.08 Arlanda 90km
A Norrtälje 30km Grisslehamn 16km Uppsala 80km Elmsta 500m ap Elmsta 0.5 km x 31
2.5km 2.5km

▲ **Stora Fjäderägg** – 54443
STF Vandrarhem Stora Fjäderägg, Lighthouse Station, Holmöskärgården outside Umeå.
(90) 55221 logi@fyrvaktaren.se
www.stfturist.se
Open Dates: 29.05-10.09 Umeå 35km Norrfjärden-Holmön; Holmön-Fjäderägg Umeå 30km Umeå 118, 119 ap Norrfjärden x 16

▲ **Stora Frögården** – 54455
STF Vandrarhem Stora Frögården, Stora Frögården 4, 38062 Mörbylånga.
(485) 36333 post@storafrogarden.se
www.stfturist.se
Open Dates: 20km 20km 1km 10N x 65 (B) 1 x 50m

▲ **Stora Karlsö** – 54292
STF Vandrarhem Stora Karlsö, Stora Karlsö, 62020 Klintehamn.
(498) 240500 (498) 240567
boka@storakarlso.se www.stfturist.se
Open Dates: 01.05-31.08 Visby 36km Visby 33km 31 33km ap Klintehamn Konsum x 33 1 x

---

▲ **Stora Segerstad** – 54293
STF Vandrarhem Stora Segerstad, 33021 Reftele.
(371) 584610 (371) 584619
www.stfturist.se
Open Dates: 16.06-10.08 Reftele 5km Reftele 5km x 56 (B) 1 x

▲ **Storvallen/Storlien** 54014
STF Vandrarhem Storvallen/Storlien, Storvallsvägen 32, 83019 Storlien.
(647) 70050 (647) 70050
info@storvallen.km.scout.se
www.stfturist.se
Open Dates: Vaernes/Trondheim International 65km Storlien 4.5km 571 300m ap Storvallen x 47

▲ **Strömsnäsbruk** – 54294
STF Vandrarhem Strömsnäsbruk, Fågelvägen 2, 28733 Strömsnäsbruk.
(433) 20050; Mobile: (70) 2455929
(433) 20970 hostel.g@swipnet.se
www.stfturist.se
Open Dates: Trelleborg 150km Älmhult 30km Markaryd 11km ap Strömsnäsbruk x 55 2km 70km

---

▲ **Strömstad** – 54295
STF Vandrarhem Strömstad, Crusellska hemmet, Norra Kyrkogatan 12, 45230 Strömstad.
(526) 10193 (526) 66140
info@crusellska.se www.stfturist.se
Open Dates: 10.01-09.12 x 65

▲ **Sundsvall** 54009
STF Vandrarhem Sundsvall, N Stadsberget, Gaffelbyvägen, 85640 Sundsvall.
(60) 612119 (60) 617801
boka@gaffelbyn.se www.stfturist.se
Open Dates: Sundsvall/Härnösand 15km A Navet 1.3km Sundsvall 2.5km Navet 1.3km ap Norra Stadsberget 1.3N x 137 (B) 1km 6km

---

▲ **Sunne** – 54297
STF Vandrarhem Sunne, Hembygdsvägen 7, 68631 Sunne.
(565) 10788 (565) 10788
sunne.vandrarhem@telia.com
www.stfturist.se
Open Dates: x 67

▲ **Surahammar** – 54298
STF Vandrarhem Surahammar, Stationsvägen 2, 73531 Surahammar.
(220) 33008; Mobile: (70) 7361758
(220) 31615
lisbeth.wernerson@suravision.se
www.stfturist.se
Open Dates: Stockholm-Västerås 35km A 30km Surahammar 200m Surahammar 200m x 61 (B) 3km

▲ Sveg/Mysoxen – 54473
STF Vandrarhem Sveg/Mysoxen,
Fjällvägen 12-14, 84232 Sveg.
(680) 17000 (680) 10062
hotell@mysoxen.se www.stfturist.se
Open Dates: 12 300m 300m
x 26 CC (B) TV

▲ Tännäs – 54338
STF Vandrarhem Tännäs, Tännäsgården,
Bygatan 51, 84094 Tännäs.
(684) 24067
kontakt@tannasgarden.nu
www.stfturist.se
Open Dates: 12 Östersund 200km
164 100m ap Tännäs x 30
R CC P

▲ Tänndalen/Skarvruet – 54300
STF Vandrarhem Tänndalen/Skarvruet,
Skarvruets fjällhotell, 84098 Tänndalen.
(684) 22111 (684) 22311
skarvruetfjallhotell@telia.com
www.stfturist.se
Open Dates: 12 Östersund 250km
Östersund 250km Funäsdalen 5km
ap Funäsdalen x 49 R CC
TV 1 x P
3km

▲ Tärnaby/Åkerlundska gården – 54444
STF Vandrarhem Tärnaby/Åkerlundska gården,
Tärnaby, Östra Strandvägen 16, 92064 Tärnaby.
(954) 14595 info@hemavan.nu
www.stfturist.se
Open Dates: 30.06-24.09 Hemavan 20km
Östersund 450km 200m x 31
CC

▲ Tåtorp/Göta kanal – 54301
STF Vandrarhem Tåtorp/Göta kanal,
54993 Moholm.
(506) 53086 (506) 53086
vandrarhemmet@tatorp.se
www.stfturist.se
Open Dates: 15.05-15.10 20SE x 22
R 1 x P

▲ Tingstäde – 54302
STF Vandrarhem Tingstäde, Mistelvägen,
Box 73, 62033 Tingstäde.
(498) 274333
tingstade@hotmail.com
www.stfturist.se
Open Dates: 01.05-31.08 Visby 22km
Visby 22km 21km x 28
R P 1km

▲ Tjärö Turiststation – 54303
STF Turiststation Tjärö, Järnavik,
37010 Bräkne-Hoby.
(454) 60063 (454) 39063
tjaro@stfturist.se www.stfturist.se
Open Dates: 12.05-17.09 (12.05-31.10)
Ronneby/Kallinge 20km Järnavik
2km Bräkne-Hoby 6km x 94
R CC TV 4 x
i P

▲ Töcksfors/Turistgården – 54304
STF Vandrarhem Töcksfors/Turistgården,
E18 väster, Elgerudsvägen, 67010 Töcksfors.
(573) 21040 (573) 21040
www.stfturist.se
Open Dates: 12 Karlstad 120km
Arvika 60km Töcksfors 1km 0.7E
x 48 (B) TV 8 P
500m 500m

▲ Tofta gård/Orust – 54305
STF Vandrarhem Tofta gård/Orust, Tofta gård,
Stockenvägen 6, 47492 Ellös.
(304) 50380 (304) 50298
info@toftagard.se www.stfturist.se
Open Dates: 15.03-15.12 Göteborg 110km
A Göteborg 80km Göteborg 80km
Stenungsund 43km 375 200m
ap Tofta x 80 R CC
TV 4 x P 1km 2km

▲ Tollarp – 54306
STF Vandrarhem Tollarp, Box 74,
Lundgrens Väg 2, 29010 Tollarp.
(44) 310023 (44) 312325
info@axona.se www.stfturist.se
Open Dates: 12 Sturup 80km; Kastrup
90km; Kristianstad 10km 90km Åhus
24km Kristianstad 18km Torget
E22, Skåneexpressen 1 300m, 2 500m, 556
500m ap Tollarp x 104 R
TV 6 x P
500m 20km

▲ Tostared/Lygnern – 54309

STF Vandrarhem Tostared/Lygnern, Stommen, 51995 Tostared.
Mobile: (734) 332205
tostaredsvandrarhem@swipnet.se
www.stfturist.se
Open Dates: 01.05-30.09 Göteborg 40km Kungsbacka 20km 20S x 22 (B) 1km 1km

▲ Tranås – 54310

STF Vandrarhem Tranås, Hembygdsgården, 57339 Tranås.
(140) 15166 www.stfturist.se
Open Dates: x 30 R

▲ Tranemo – 54311

STF Vandrarhem Tranemo, Tranan, Smedsgatan 2, 51432 Tranemo.
(325) 76710 (325) 79278
www.stfturist.se
Open Dates: Göteborg 80km Limmared 6km 301, 350, 900 x 42 R

▲ Trollhättan/Gula Villan – 54312

STF Vandrarhem Trollhättan/Gula Villan, Tingvallavägen 12, 461 32 Trollhättan.
(520) 12960 (520) 38850
trollhattansvandrarhem@telia.com
www.stfturist.se
Open Dates: 09.01-21.12 5km 200m 200m 0.2NE x 40 R CC (B) 400m 5km

▲ Trollhättan/Stenvillan – 54451

STF Vandrarhem Trollhättan/Stenvillan, Reception at Gula Villan Tingvallavägen 12, 461 32 Trollhättan.
(520) 12960 (520) 38850
www.stfturist.se
Open Dates: 09.01-12.12 5km 2km 100m 2NE x 33 R CC 2km 5km

▲ Trosa – 54313

STF Vandrarhem Trosa, Stensunds folkhögskola, 61991 Trosa.
(156) 53200 (156) 53222
stensund@stensund.se www.stfturist.se
Open Dates: 08.06-10.08 Arlanda 200km Vagnhärad 110km Trosa 70km x 15 R

▲ Trosa/Lagnö Studio – 54475

STF Vandrarhem Trosa/Lagnö Studio, Lagnö Gård, 61992 Trosa.
(156) 22470 (156) 22363
per@studiolagno.se www.stfturist.se
Open Dates: Vagnhärad 13km Trosa 6km x 15 CC (B) 700m

▲ Trysunda – 54314

STF Vandrarhem Trysunda, 89301 Bjästa.
(660) 43038 www.stfturist.se
Open Dates: 15.05-15.09 x 24 R CC i

▲ Ulricehamn – 54316

STF Vandrarhem Ulricehamn, Nyboholm, 52337 Ulricehamn.
(321) 10550 (321) 14802
hotell.nyboholm@telia.com
www.stfturist.se
Open Dates: 03.01-16.12 2N x 60 R

▲ Ulvön/Ljungskile – 54317

STF Vandrarhem Ulvön/Ljungskile, Pl. 31482, Ulvösund, 45993 Ljungskile.
(522) 29184 (522) 20171
www.stfturist.se
Open Dates: 14.06-28.08 40km A 2km 5km 5km x 22 R

▲ Umeå – 54318

STF Vandrarhem Umeå, Västra Esplanaden 10, 90326 Umeå.
(90) 771650 (90) 771695
info@umeavandrarhem.com
www.stfturist.se
Open Dates: 09.01-20.12 A 80 200m Holmsund 20km Umeå 500m 1 100m ap Renmarkstorget x 86 R CC (B) 1.5km 3km

SWEDEN – SUEDE – SCHWEDEN – SUECIA

▲ **Uppsala City** – 54460
STF Vandrarhem Uppsala City, Kungsgatan 27, 753 21 Uppsala.
(18)4805055 (18) 4805050
hoteluppsala@profilhotels.se
www.stfturist.se
Open Dates: Arlanda 35km
A 20m Stockholm 70km
Uppsala Central 1km x 100 (B)
4 x 1km

▲ **Uppsala/ Sunnersta Herrgård** – 54319
STF Vandrarhem Uppsala/Sunnersta Herrgård, Sunnerstavägen 24, 75651 Uppsala.
(18) 324220 (18) 324068
info@sunnerstaherrgard.se
www.stfturist.se
Open Dates: 09.01-20.12 Arlanda 35km
A 802 450m Uppsala Central 6km
20, 30 400m ap Herrgårdsvägen 6S
x 50 (B)
3km

▲ **Uppsala/Vandraren** – 54320
STF Vandrarhem Uppsala/Vandraren, Vattholmavägen 16C, 75419 Uppsala
(18) 104300 (18) 241375
info@vandraren.com www.stfturist.se
Open Dates: 16.06-12.08 1.5S x 90

▲ **Vadstena** – 54323
STF Vandrarhem Vadstena, Skänningegatan 20, 59231 Vadstena.
(143) 10302 (143) 76569
vandrarhem@va-bostaelle.se
www.stfturist.se
Open Dates: Arlanda 330km
Mjölby 30km 610, 611, 660 ap Brandstationen x 65
100m
500m

▲ **Vånga** – 54480
STF Vandrarhem Vånga, Furustadsvägen 667, 29038 Villands Vånga.
(44) 94417 (44) 94417
maria_david@telia.com
www.stfturist.se
Open Dates: 45km A 25km
120km 25km 500m
x 50 (B)
1km 1km

▲ **Vara** – 54325
STF Vandrarhem Vara, Torggatan 41, c/o Vara Folkhögskola, Box 163, 53423 Vara.
(512) 57992; 57970 (512) 57999
vandrarhem@vara.fhsk.se
www.stfturist.se
Open Dates: 01.06-15.08 Landvetter, Gothenburg 100km Gothenburg 100km
Vara 500m x 75
(B) 5 x

▲ **Varberg** – 54326
STF Vandrarhem Varberg, Vare 46, 43291 Varberg.
(340) 41173; 41043 (340) 41600
vare.vandrarhem@telia.com
www.stfturist.se
Open Dates: 01.04-30.09 7S x 43

▲ **Västerås** – 54328
STF Vandrarhem Västerås, Svalgången 1, Box 1150, 72129 Västerås.
(21) 303800 (21) 303888
info.vasteras@quality.choicehotels.se
www.stfturist.se
Open Dates: Stockholm airport 10km
A Airport bus Västerås-Arlanda 3km
Västerås Central 3km 12 100m ap 12 100m x 24 5km
7km

▲ **Växjö** – 54329
STF Vandrarhem Växjö, Evedals Brunn, 35263 Växjö.
(470) 63070
vaxjo.vandrarhem@telia.com
www.stfturist.se
Open Dates: 07.01-20.12 Öjaby 10km
Växjö 5km 6NE x 65
1 x
10m 10m

▲ **Vemdalen** – 54330
STF Vandrarhem Vemdalen, Landsvägen 5, 840 92 Vemdalen.
(684) 30640 (684) 30641
info@gestis.com www.stfturist.se
Open Dates: 01.05-30.09 x 50
1 x

▲ **Vimmerby** – 54331
STF Vandrarhem Vimmerby, Hörestadhult, Pl 530, 59895 Vimmerby.
(492) 10275 hhult@nossen.nu
www.stfturist.se
Open Dates: 01.06-31.08 3km 100m x 38 400m

▲ **Vingåker/Kjesäter** – 54450
STF Vandrarhem Vingåker/Kjesäter, Kjesäters folkhögskola, 64392 Vingåker.
(151) 518600 (151) 518610
info@kjesater.fhsk.se www.stfturist.se
Open Dates: Stockholm-Skavsta 60km Vingåker 3km 703 1km ap Kjesäter/Skeppsmyrelund x 130 5 x 4km 5km

▲ **Visby** – 54332
STF Vandrarhem Visby, Alléskolan, Fältgatan 30, 62182 Visby.
(498) 269842 carl.tholin@tjelvar.org
www.stfturist.se
Open Dates: 25.06-13.08 4.5km Visby 2km x 105 (B) 1km 3km

▲ **Visingsö** – 54333
STF Vandrarhem Visingsö, Tunnerstad, Fredängen, 56034 Visingsö.
(390) 40191
STFbokning@visingso-vandrarhem.se
www.stfturist.se
Open Dates: 01.05-01.09 x 30

▲ **Vittsjö** – 54334
STF Vandrarhem Vittsjö, Lehultsvägen 13, 28022 Vittsjö.
(451) 22087 (451) 22488
www.stfturist.se
Open Dates: 01.05-11.11 x 47

▲ **Wauglen/Kynnefjäll** – 54335
STF Vandrarhem Wauglen/Kynnefjäll, Vaglen 12, 45054 Hedekas.
(524) 32015 (524) 32066
kontakta@wauglen.se www.stfturist.se
Open Dates: 19.06-13.08 Göteborg 160km Göteborg 140km Dingle 20km 835 6km x 12 1 x 4km 4km

▲ **Ystad** – 54336
STF Vandrarhem Ystad, Kantarellen, Ystads sandskog, Fritidsvägen, 27160 Ystad.
(411) 66566 (411) 10913
www.stfturist.se
Open Dates: 30km 3km 3km 3km x 104 (B)

▲ **MOUNTAIN LODGES – /Lodges de Montagne/Berggzentren/ Lodges de Montaña**
(For further information, contact STF / Pour de plus amples renseignements, s'adresser à la STF / Nach weiteren Angaben STF fragen / Para más información, diríjase a la STF

▲ **Dalarna** – Grövelsjön Mountain Lodge – 54081
STF Grövelsjöns Fjällstation , 79091 Idre.
(253) 596880 (253) 23225
info@grovelsjon.stfturist.se
www.stfturist.se
Open Dates: 28.12-08.01; 02.02-23.04; 17.06-24.09 Mora 200km Oslo 340km Mora 200km 170 to the entrance x 150 2 x

▲ **Härjedalen** – Helags MC – 54125
STF Fjällstuga Helags, 84035 Ljungdalen.
(687) 20150 (687) 20150
info@helags.stfturist.se
www.stfturist.se
Open Dates: 24.02-01.05; 22.06-24.09 Östersund 200km Östersund 200km 18km ap Ljungdalen x 74 (B)

▲ **Jämtland** – Blåhammaren Mountain Lodge – 54146
STF Blåhammarens Fjällstation , 83015 Duved. (not by the road)
(647) 72200 (647) 70637
info@blahammaren.stfturist.se
www.stfturist.se
Open Dates: 24.02-01.05; 22.06-24.09 Östersund 170km Enafors 18km Storulvåns Fjällstation 12km x 46

▲ **Jämtland** – Storulvån Mountain Lodge – 54147
STF Storulvåns Fjällstation , 83015 Duved.
(647) 72200 (647) 74026
info@storulvan.stfturist.se
www.stfturist.se
Open Dates: 24.02-01.05; 22.06-24.09
Östersund 170km Enafors, pick up is possible 8km x 148 4 x

▲ **Jämtland** – Sylarna Mountain Lodge – 54148
STF Sylarnas Fjällstation,
83015 Duved. (not by the road)
(647) 72200 (647) 75012
info@sylarna.stfturist.se
www.stfturist.se
Open Dates: 24.02-01.05; 22.06-24.09
Östersund, Frösön 170km Enafors 33km Storulvåns Fjäll Station 16km x 92

▲ **Jämtland** – Vålådalen Mountain Lodge – 54149
STF Vålådalens Fjällstation, 83012 Vålådalen.
(647) 35300 (647) 35353
info@valadalen.se www.stfturist.se
Open Dates: 12.12.05-31.12.06 (24.04-05.07 not full service) Östersund 110km Undersåker 27km 562 from Undersåker/Järpen x 200 9 x

▲ **Lappland** – Abisko Mountain Lodge/Hotel – 54185
STF Abisko Turiststation, 98107 Abisko.
(980) 40200 (980) 40140
info@abisko.stfturist.se
www.stfturist.se
Open Dates: 23.12-08.01; 24.02-01.05; 09.06-24.09 Kiruna 120km A Bus 91 120km Abisko Turiststation 300m 91 to Abisko 200m ap Abisko Turiststation x 300 4 x

▲ **Lappland** – Kebnekaise Mountain Lodge – 54186
STF Kebnekaise Fjällstation,
98129 Kiruna. (not by the road)
(980) 55000 (980) 55048
info@kebnekaise.stfturist.se
www.stfturist.se
Open Dates: 24.02-01.05; 19.06-24.09
Kiruna 110km Kiruna 110km
92 Kiruna - Nikkaloukta 110km
ap Nikkaloukta - Kebnekaise walk 19km x 196 1 x

▲ **Lappland** – Kvikkjokk Mountain Lodge – 54187
STF Kvikkjokk Fjällstation, 96202 Kvikkjokk.
(971) 21022 (971) 21039
info@kvikkjokk.stfturist.se
www.stfturist.se
Open Dates: 04.02-23.04; 17.06-17.09
Murjek 180km x 60 (BD)

▲ **Lappland** – Ritsem Mountain Cabin – 54188
STF Fjällstuga Ritsem, Ritsem 4,
98299 Gällivare.
(973) 42030 (973) 42050
info@ritsem.stfturist.se
www.stfturist.se
Open Dates: 13.02-14.05; 19.06-24.09
Gällivare, Lappland 190km Gällivare 183km 93 to Ritsem x 80

▲ **Lappland** – Saltoluokta Mountain Lodge – 54189
STF Saltoluokta Fjällstation, 98299 Gällivare.
(973) 41010 (973) 41013
info@saltoluokta.stfturist.se
www.stfturist.se
Open Dates: 01.02-05.02; 24.02-01.05; 19.06-24.09 Gällivare, Lappland 130km Gällivare 130km 93 to Ritsem 130km ap Kebnatsbryggan x 105 1 x

Mountain Cabins/ *Cabanes de Montagne/ Berghütten/ Cabañas de Montaña*

(For further information, contact STF / Pour de plus amples renseignements, s'adresser à la STF / Nach weiteren Angaben STF fragen / Para más información, diríjase a la STF)

Most of these mountain cabins are far from roads and railways and are situated near rough tracks; these tracks cover more than 4,700km, the best known being Kungsleden, in Lappland. ⊖ 170-320 SEK.

La plupart de ces cabanes de montagne sont loin des routes et des chemins de fer et se trouvent près de sentiers primitifs; ces sentiers couvrent plus de 4700km - le mieux connu est Kungsleden, en Laponie. ⊖ 170-320 SEK.

Die meisten dieser Berghütten sind weit von einer Straße oder Bahnlinie abseits an Wanderwegen gelegen; diese erstrecken sich über mehr als 4700km - der bekannteste ist Kungsleden, in Lappland. ⊖ 170-320 SEK.

La mayoría de las cabañas de montaña están alejados de las carreteras y de los ferrocarriles yse se encuentran cerca de senderos agrestes que cubren más de 4.700km - el más conocido es el Kungsleden, en Laponia. ⊖ 170-320 SEK.

appland

ältsa
årsavagge
biskojaure
nna Allakas
lesjaure
jäktja
istas
allo
älka
arfala
ukejaure
itasjaure
ingi
aitumjaure
eusajaure
akkotavare
Vaisaluokta
Akka
Kutjaure
Sitojaure
Aktse
Pårte
Pieskehaure
Vaimok
Såmmarlappa
Tarrekaise
Njunjes
Aigert
Serve
Tärnasjöstugan
Syterstugan
Viterskalet
Bleriken

Jämtland

Anaris
Lunndörren
Vålåvalen
Stensdalen
Gåsen

Härjedalen

Helags
Fältjägarn
Skedbro
Rogen

Dalarna

Storrödtjärn

Switzerland

Schweizer Jugendherbergen,
Schaffhauserstrasse 14, Postfach,
CH 8042 Zürich, Switzerland.

t (41) (0) 44 3601414
f (41) (0) 44 3601460
e bookingoffice@youthhostel.ch
w www.youthhostel.ch

Office Hours: Monday-Thursday 08.00-12.00hrs and 13.00-18.00hrs; Friday 08.00-12.00hrs and 13.00-17.00hrs

A copy of the Hostel Directory for this Country can be obtained from:
The National Office

National Tourist Authority/Board:	www.myswitzerland.com
Capital:	Bern
Language:	French/German/ Italian/Romansh
Currency:	CHF
Population:	7,367,900
Size:	41,285 sq km
Telephone Country Code:	41
***eKit* Access Number:**	0800-834-578

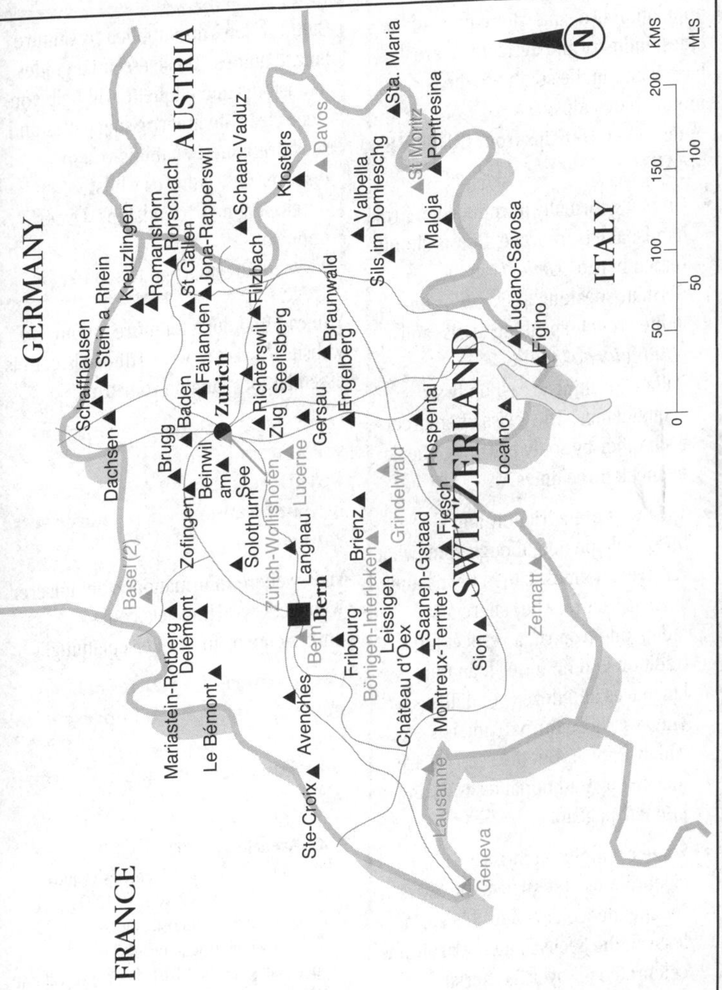

Switzerland is an eclectic mish-mash of world and local history, people, languages and dialects. Despite its size, the country has four official languages – German, French, Italian and Romansh. Many people speak English, however. The Swiss Confederation is divided into twenty-six regions, or cantons, and, despite the fragmentary nature of the government, the Swiss have become one of the world's richest people through a blend of stability, strong work ethic and harmonious relations. France, Germany, Liechtenstein, Austria and Italy surround Switzerland, and these countries have strongly influenced Swiss culture; for instance, Swiss food tends to be based upon traditional French, Italian and German recipes.

Switzerland has three distinct and diverse geographical regions. In the north is the rolling hilly range of the Jura; in the centre is the area known as the Plateau, in which most of the population live, and where most of the cities, industry and agriculture are based; and in the south are the mountainous Alps.

A few other Top Tips from **CULTURE SMART!**:

- On being formally introduced, a firm handshake is in order. Guests should remember to *"Grüezi"* in the German-speaking areas, *"Bonjour"* in the French-speaking areas, and *"Buongiorno"* in the Italian-speaking areas, on first acquaintance. The Swiss often greet each other by softly brushing cheek to cheek three times.
- The Swiss are a friendly and hospitable people, though somewhat reserved at times. Life in towns and cities is secure. They share an independent spirit, a respect for tradition and no fewer than four languages and dozens of dialects. The Swiss love for partying isn't yet widely known. But the seasons are marked by traditional festivals and popular pageants.
- Some examples of Swiss celebrations: 1st August, the Swiss Independence day. Zurich's spring festival, the Sechseläuten. Carnival is celebrated all over Switzerland. Hornussen, a unique sport. Onion market in Berne. Harmless Cow fights in the Valais. Locarno's piazza is a splendid open air cinema during its International Film Festival.
- For a small country, Switzerland has an awful lot of worthwhile attractions. It boasts three World Heritage sites alone: Bern's historic city centre, St. Gallen's cathedral and abbey library, and the convent of St John in Münstair.

Culture Smart! Top Tips © Kuperard 2005

Cultural Top Tips supplied by Culture Smart! guides. These essential guides to customs and etiquette will help you steer clear of embarrassing gaffes and sensitive issues, enabling you to discover new cultures whilst developing new friendships. Order online at www.culturesmartguides.co.uk

You can find out a lot more on our website - a visit to www.HIhostels.com is essential for planning your trip!

Pour en savoir plus, rendez-vous sur notre site Internet, www.HIhostels.com une visite incontournable pour préparer votre voyage!

Viele weitere Informationen auf unserer Website: www.HIhostels.com - unverzichtbar für die Reiseplanung!

Puedes averiguar mucho más en nuestro sitio web. Es imprescindible que visites la página www.HIhostels.com para planear tu viaje.

▲ **Avenches** – 55028
Rue du Lavoir 5, 1580 Avenches (Vaud).
(26) 6752666 (26) 6752717
avenches@youthhostel.ch
www.youthhostel.ch/avenches
Open Dates: 15.04-15.10 Genève 120km
Avenches 800m 200m
ap Restaurant Croix Blanc x 76
1 x

▲ **Baden** – 55034
Kanalstr. 7, 5400 Baden (Aargau).
(56) 2216736 (56) 2217660
baden@youthhostel.ch
www.youthhostel.ch/baden
Open Dates: 13.03-15.12 Zürich 30km
Baden 2km 1, 3, 4 500m
ap Kantonsschule x 83
1 x

Basel – St. Alban Ⓗ 55003
St. Alban-Kirchrain 10,
4052 Basel (Basel).
(61) 2720572 (61) 2720833
basel@youthhostel.ch
www.youthhostel.ch/basel
Open Dates: 02.01-22.12
Open Times: Summer: 07.00-10.00hrs; 14.00-24.00hrs Winter: 07.00-10.00hrs; 14.00-23.00hrs
Beds: 194 - 8x1 10x2 6x4 5x6 14x6+
Price Range: from CHF 31.50 BBinc
Directions: 1SE from city centre
Basel-Mulhouse 7km A Airport Shuttle 1.5km Schifflände 1km Basel SBB 1.5km No 2 500m ap Kunstmuseum x 11 R CC 1 x 1.5km

Basel – St. Alban

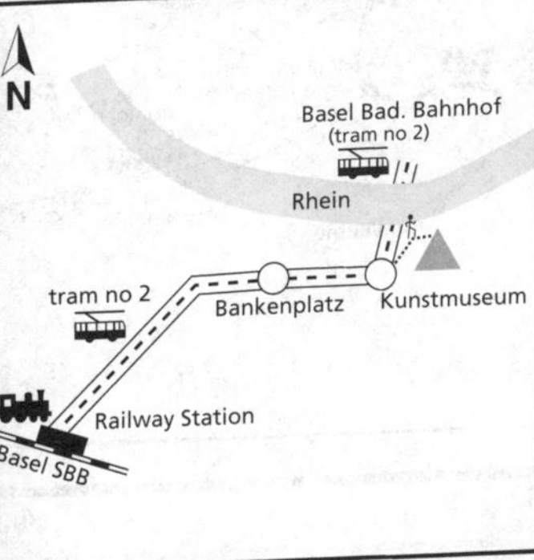

▲ **Basel** – City – 55074
Pfeffingerstr. 8, 4053 Basel (Basel).
(61) 3659960 (61) 3659961
basel.city@youthhostel.ch
www.youthhostel.ch/basel.city
Open Dates: 17.03-26.11 Basel-Mulhouse 7km A Airport Shuttle 1.5km 3min x 128 R CC (B)

Basel... Travel Tips

- **For budget eats check out...** Valentino's Place, Pizzeria Picobello, Château Lapin, Roter Engel, Take aways - Steinenvorstadt
- **For great nightlife try...** Steinenvorstadt, Basel Theatre, NT-Areal, Kaserne (theatre, music, dance, restaurant, bar), Sommercasino (music, events, dance)
- **Don't miss...** Jean Tinguely Museum, Beyeler Foundation Museum, Zoo, Dreiländereck (point where 3 countries meet), Museum Basler Papiermühle (paper mill), Goetheanum (Dornach), Augusta Raurica & Roman museum, The Old Town (cathedral), Waterside of the Rhein, Basel's famous modern architecture

▲ **Beinwil am See** – 55046
Seestrasse 71, 5712 Beinwil am See (Aargau).
(62) 7711883 (62) 7716123
beinwil@youthhostel.ch
www.youthhostel.ch/beinwil
Open Dates: 11.03-26.11 Zürich 56km Beinwil am See Beinwil am See 800m x 98 CC 2 x

▲ **Bellinzona** – 55047
Villa Montebello, Via Nocca 4,
6500 Bellinzona (Ticino).
(91) 8251522 (91) 8354285
bellinzona@youthhostel.ch
www.youthhostel.ch/bellinzona
Open Dates: 01.03-30.11 Lugano Agno 30km Bellinzona 800m 5 100m ap Piazza Indipendenza x 100 R CC 2 x

▲ **Le Bémont** – 55027
2877 Le Bémont (Jura).
(32) 9511707 (32) 9512413
bemont@youthhostel.ch
www.youthhostel.ch/bemont
Open Dates: 14.02-15.10 Genève 170km Le Bémont 20m x 92 CC 2 x

Bern 55037
Weihergasse 4, 3005 Bern (Bern).
(31) 3116316 (31) 3125240
bern@youthhostel.ch
www.youthhostel.ch/bern
Open Dates: 01-01; 16.01-31.12
Open Times: Summer: 07.00-10.00hrs; 15.00-24.00hrs Winter: 07.00-10.00hrs; 17.00-24.00hrs
Beds: 190
Price Range: from CHF 30 BB inc
Directions: Zürich 130km; Bern Belp 15km Bern 800m 1 x

Bern

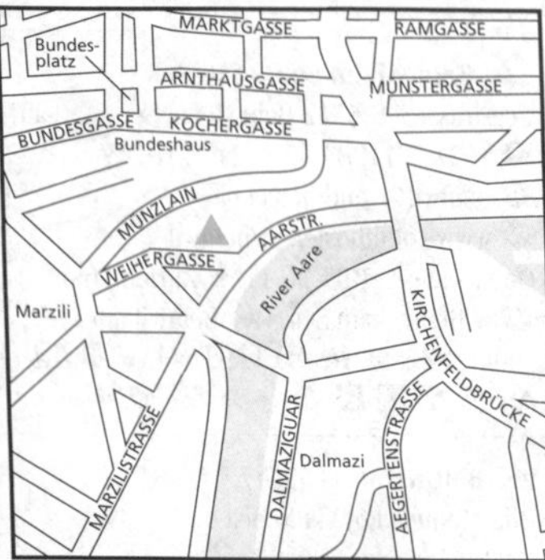

Bern... Travel Tips

- **For budget eats check out...** Fontana (Spitalgasse 24), Hanora (Bubenbergstrasse 5a), Postgasse 48, Anker (Kornhausplatz)
- **For great nightlife try...** Dampfzentrale, Bierhubeli, Silo, Nord-Sud, Artemisia
- **Don't miss...** Tierpark Dählhölzli, Bärengraben, Rosengarten, Münster (Kathedrale), Einstein-Haus, Zytglogge, Altstadt, UNESCO World Heritage

Bönigen-Interlaken 55012
Aareweg 21, Am See, 3806 Bönigen (Bern).
(33) 8224353 (33) 8232058
boenigen@youthhostel.ch
www.youthhostel.ch/boenigen
Open Dates: 01.04-15.10
Open Times: 07.00-10.00hrs; 15.00-23.00hrs
Beds: 150 - 6x4 2x5 8x6 5x6+
Price Range: from CHF 28.20 BB inc
Directions: 2E from city centre
Zürich 130km Interlaken-East 1.8km 3, 4 500m ap Lütschinenbrücke x 6 1 x

Bönigen-Interlaken

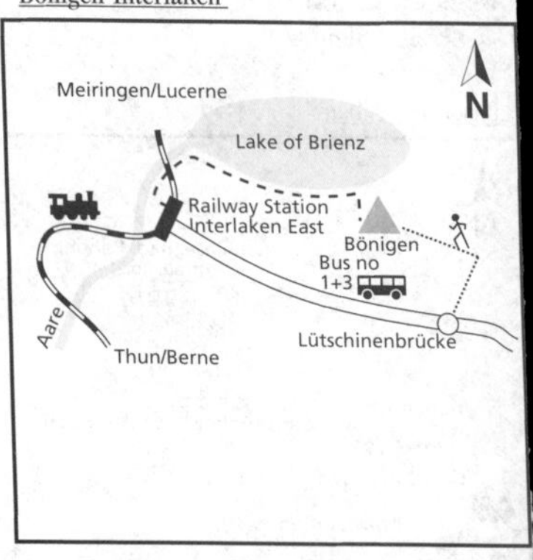

Bönigen-Interlaken... Travel Tips

- **For budget eats check out...** Goldener Anker (Interlaken), Pizzeria Seiler au Lac (Bönigen), Matahari Indonesian Restaurant (Unterseen), Coop Restaurant (Interlaken)
- **For great nightlife try...** Casino, Bars & discos
- **Don't miss...** Jungfraujoch ("Top of Europe", 3545 m), The Schilthorn (featured in James Bond film), Kleine Scheidegg (peak panorama), Schynige Platte (botanic garden), Beatushöhlen (dripstone caves & museum), "Alt Bönigen" with famous wood carvings, Casino Kursaal (park & fountain), Unlimited winter sports, Boat trips (Thuner & Brienz lakes), Giessbachfälle (waterfalls)

▲ **Braunwald** – 55048
"Zwärgehüsli", Im Gyseneggli,
8784 Braunwald (Glarus).
(55) 6431356 (55) 6432435
braunwald@youthhostel.ch
www.youthhostel.ch/braunwald
Open Dates: 01.01-26.03; 30.06-13.08; 22.09-15.10 Zürich 100km Linthal Cablecar 800m x 60 CC

▲ **Brienz** – 55019
Strandweg 10, am See, 3855 Brienz (Bern).
(33) 9511152 (33) 9512260
brienz@youthhostel.ch
www.youthhostel.ch/brienz
Open Dates: 15.04-15.10 Zürich 120km Brienz 500m Brienz 500m x 84 CC

▲ **Brugg** – 55049
"Schlössli Altenburg", im Hof 11,
5200 Brugg (Aargau).
(56) 4411020 (56) 4423820
brugg@youthhostel.ch
www.youthhostel.ch/brugg
Open Dates: 18.03-14.10 Zürich 40km Brugg 800m x 50 CC 2 x

▲ **Château-d'Oex** – 55029
Les Monnaires, 1660 Château-d'Oex (Vaud).
(26) 9246404 (26) 9245843
chateau.d.oex@youthhostel.ch
www.youthhostel.ch/chateau.d.oex
Open Dates: 01.01-12.03, 24.05-15.10, 17-31.12 Genève 150km Château-d'Oex 500m x 50 CC

▲ **Dachsen** – 55050
Schloss Laufen am Rheinfall,
8447 Dachsen (Zürich).
(52) 6596152 (52) 6596039
dachsen@youthhostel.ch
www.youthhostel.ch/dachsen
Open Dates: 17.03-22.10 Zürich 50km Dachsen or Neuhausen 800m, Schloss Laufen (01.04-31.10) 200m x 83 CC 1 x

---

Davos HI 55042
Youthpalace Davos, Horlaubenstr. 27, 7260 Davos Dorf (Graubünden).
(81) 4101920 (81) 4101921
davos@youthhostel.ch
www.youthhostel.ch/davos
Open Dates: 12 Open Times: Summer/Winter: 07.00-10.00hrs; 15.00-23.00hrs May & November: 09.00-11.00hrs; 17.00-20.00hrs
Beds: 250 - 27x2 9x3 25x4 9x6
Price Range: from CHF 45.50 incl halfboard BBinc
Directions: Zürich 160km Davos Dorf 800m 1, 7 200m ap Schiabach R CC TV 3 x

---

Davos

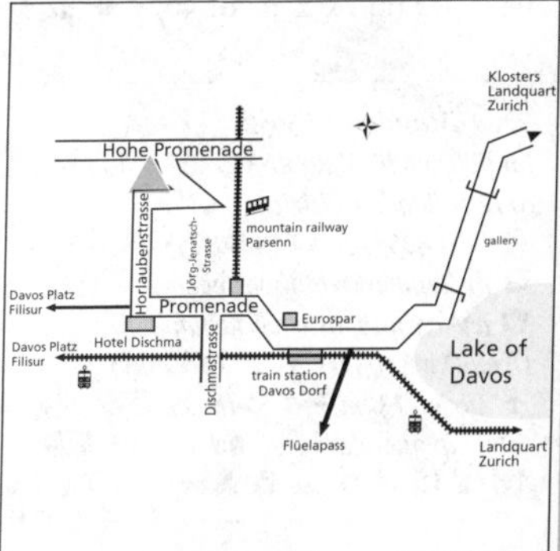

Davos... Travel Tips

- **For budget eats check out...** Scala, Kaffeeklatsch, Café Schneider, Coop Restaurant
- **For great nightlife try...** Chämi Bar, Ex Bar, Bolgenschanze, Rotliechtli, Cabanna Club
- **Don't miss...** 320km of slopes and 75km of cross-coutry tracks in winter, 5 large skiing areas, 450km of hiking trails in summer, Alpinum Schatzalp (botanical gardens), Horsedrawn carriage rides in winter and summer, Kirchner Museum (expressionist artist), Museum of Local History (winter sports), Toy museum, Wellness und Wasserwelten Davos, Sportzentrum

▲ Delémont – 55026
Route de Bâle 185, 2800 Delémont (Jura).
(32) 4222054 (32) 4228830
delemont@youthhostel.ch
www.youthhostel.ch/delemont
Open Dates: 15.04-15.10 Zürich 120km
Delémont 800m Morépont 200m
x 76
1 x

▲ Engelberg – 55051
"Berghaus", Dorfstr 80,
6390 Engelberg (Obwalden).
(41) 6371292 (41) 6374988
engelberg@youthhostel.ch
www.youthhostel.ch/engelberg
Open Dates: 01.01-12.04; 27.04-16.10; 18.11-23.04 Zürich 100km
Engelberg 500m x 106
1 x

*△ **Fällanden** – 55052*
Im Rohrbuck', Maurstr 33,
8117 Fällanden (Zürich).
(44) 8253144 (44) 8255480
faellanden@youthhostel.ch
www.youthhostel.ch/faellanden
Open Dates: 03.03.-29.10 (only)
Zürich 13km Stettbach 743 50m ap outside hostel x 46

▲ Fiesch – 55053
Sport-und Feriencenter, 3984 Fiesch (Wallis).
(27) 9701515 (27) 9701500
fiesch@youthhostel.ch
www.youthhostel.ch/fiesch
Open Dates: Genève 230km
Feriendorf Fiesch 100m x 84
33 x

▲ Figino – 55018
Via Casoro 2, 6918 Figino (Ticino).
(91) 9951151 (91) 9951070
figino@youthhostel.ch
www.youthhostel.ch/figino
Open Dates: 11.03-15.10 Lugano Agno 8km Figino 300m Lugano
Casoro 50m x 160

▲ Filzbach – 55054
"Lihn", Blaukreuz Kurs-und Ferienzentrum,
8757 Filzbach (Glarus).
(55) 6146464 (55) 6146465
filzbach@youthhostel.ch
www.youthhostel.ch/filzbach
Open Dates: 01.01-10.12; 24-31.12 Zürich 85km Näfels-Mollis Postbus Filzbach Post 100m x 50
7 x

▲ Fribourg – 55024
2 rue de l'Hôpital, 1700 Fribourg (Fribourg).
(26) 3231916 (26) 3231940
fribourg@youthhostel.ch
www.youthhostel.ch/fribourg
Open Dates: 01.03-15.10 Genève 140km; Zürich 160km Fribourg 100m x 70
1 x

Genève 55035
30 rue Rothschild,
1202 Genève (Genève).
(22) 7326260 (22) 7383987
geneve@youthhostel.ch
www.youthhostel.ch/geneve
Open Dates: Open Times: 06.30-10.00hrs, 14.00-01.00hrs
Beds: 334 - 13x2 10x4 34x6 3x6+
Price Range: from CHF 25.50 BBinc
Directions: Genève 3km Genève
1 Direction Wilson 50m
1 x

Genève

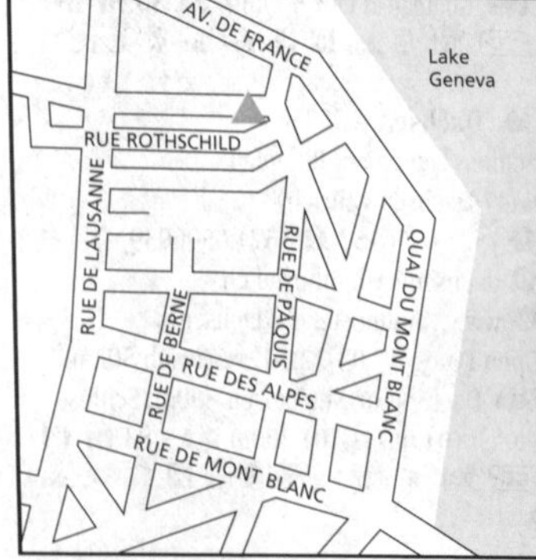

Genève... Travel Tips

- **For budget eats check out...** Manora - self service restaurant, food of all sorts, Mike Womg - Asian food, Chez Ottavio - Italian food, two blocks away from the hostel, Passagio - self service restaurant at the train station, La Vouivre - tea room, great chocolate filled buns
- **For great nightlife try...** Pickwick - Irish pub with live music on Fri nights, L'Usine - multiple events place, Shaker's - old town club, Scandale - contemporary club, Les Cinq Portes - for music and food
- **Don't miss...** CERN - the world's largest particle physics laboratory, CICR - Red Cross museum, Flower clock, Giant water fountain "Jet d'eau" - Geneva's hallmark, Cathedral St. Pierre, overlooking Geneva from the old town, Botanical Gardens, ONU - United Nations building in Europe, Le Salève - for hiking and for a panoramic view of Geneva and the surrounding area, Carouge - artistic quarter

▲ Gersau – 55056
Rotschuo, 6442 Gersau (Schwyz).
(41) 8281277 (41) 8281263
gersau@youthhostel.ch
www.youthhostel.ch/gersau
Open Dates: 01.03-30.11 Zürich 85km
Rotschuo 50m Brunnen/Küssnacht
Rotschuo 50m x 96

Grindelwald 55013
Weid 12, Terrassenweg,
3818 Grindelwald (Bern).
(33) 8531009 (33) 8535029
grindelwald@youthhostel.ch
www.youthhostel.ch/grindelwald
Open Dates: 01.01-09.04; 11.05-21.10; 17-31.12 Open Times: 07.30-09.30hrs; 15.00-23.00hrs
Beds: 125 - 8x2 16x4 6x6 1x6+
Price Range: from CHF 32 BB inc
Directions: 1NW from city centre
Zürich 150km Grindelwald 1km
No. 4 100m ap Terrassenweg-Gaggi Säge x 15
1 x
500m

Grindelwald

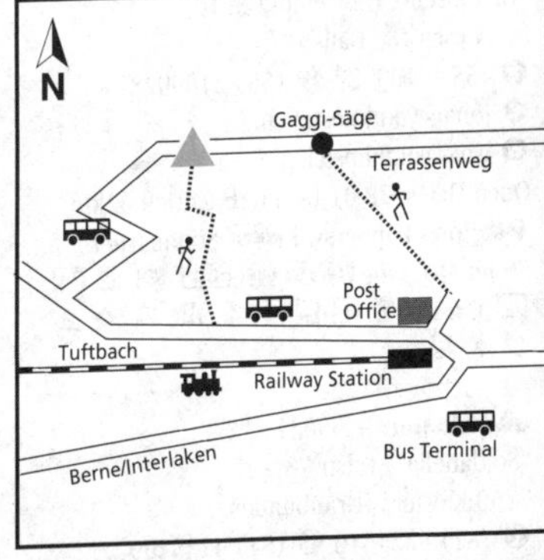

Grindelwald... Travel Tips

- **For budget eats check out...** Restaurant Sportzentrum, Memory Bistro Bar
- **For great nightlife try...** Village bars, Discos & dancing, Pubs (live performances)
- **Don't miss...** Steps to the glacier, Jungfraujoch & ice palace, Glacier gorge, First region & Männlichen/Kleine Scheidegg, First & Bussalp (panoramic views), Mountaineering Centre & guided tours, Skiing & snowboard paradise, 10 attractive bike routes of various difficulty, Interlaken, Mystery Park (only 30min from Grindelwald)

Gstaad ☛ Saanen-Gstaad

*△ **Hospental** – 55057*
Gotthardstrasse, 6493 Hospental (Uri).
(41) 8870401; (79) 4825856
(41) 8870902
hospental@youthhostel.ch
www.youthhostel.ch/hospental
Open Dates: 01.01-17.04; 09.05-15.10; 02.-31.12 Zürich 128km Hospental 500m x 60

Interlaken ☛ Bönigen

▲ Jona-Rapperswil – 55058
"Busskirch", Hessenhofweg 10,
8645 Jona (St. Gallen).
(55) 2109927 (55) 2109928
jona@youthhostel.ch
www.youthhostel.ch/jona
Open Dates: 28.01-04.11 Zürich 42km
Jona-Rapperswil Südquartier
500m x 74 CC
2 x

▲ Klosters – 55031
"Soldanella", Talstr 73,
7250 Klosters (Graubünden).
(81) 4221316 (81) 4225209
klosters@youthhostel.ch
www.youthhostel.ch/klosters
Open Dates: 01.01-23.04; 17.06-22.10;
16-31.12 Zürich 150km Klosters
Platz 500m x 84 CC
2 x

▲ Kreuzlingen – 55016
"Villa Hörnliberg", Promenadenstr 7,
8280 Kreuzlingen (Thurgau).
(71) 6882663 (71) 6884761
kreuzlingen@youthhostel.ch
www.youthhostel.ch/kreuzlingen
Open Dates: 04.03-30.11 Zürich 68km
Kreuzlingen Hafen 200m
Kreuzlingen Hafen 200m x 90
CC 1 x

▲ Langnau im Emmental – 55059
Mooseggstr 32, 3550 Langnau i.E. (Bern).
(34) 4024526 (34) 4028993
langnau@youthhostel.ch
www.youthhostel.ch/langnau
Open Dates: 01.03-17.09; 16.10-31.12
Zürich 135km Langnau 800m
x 46 CC

Lausanne – Jeunotel 55007
Ch. du Bois-de-Vaux 36,
1007 Lausanne (Vaud).
(21) 6260222 (21) 6260226
lausanne@youthhostel.ch
www.youthhostel.ch/lausanne
Open Dates: Open Times:
Beds: 264 - 44x1 20x2 14x3 37x4
Price Range: from CHF 33 BBinc
Directions: 1.5SW from city centre
Genève 65km Lausanne Ouchy
Lausanne 2 100m ap Bois-de-Vaux
Métro Ouchy x 17 CC
2 x
200m 400m

Lausanne – Jeunotel

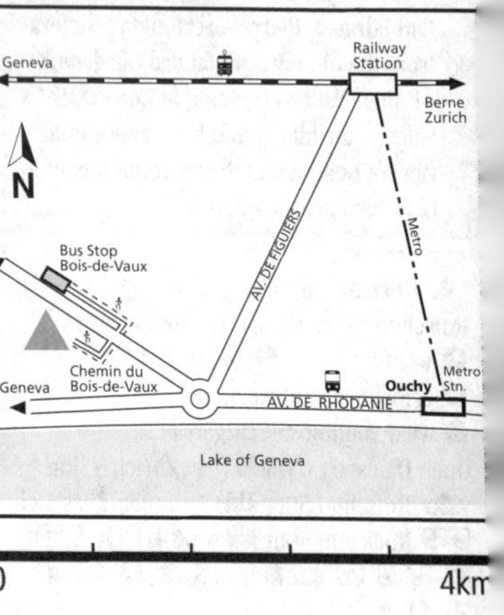

Lausanne... Travel Tips

- **For budget eats check out...** L'Éléphant Blanc, Le Barbare, Ma-Jong, Café de l'Evêché, Crêperie La Chandeleur
- **For great nightlife try...** The Dolce Vita with bar, disco and occasional live music from jazz to rap, The best scene meeting-points, cafés and music bars: The Garbo bar with DJ, Le Grand Café du Casino, similar to the famous Planet Hollywood and the Hard Rock Café, Le Latino World with Latin music, samba, salsa and merengue, The top discos in town: Le 13ème Siècle, known as the "Treize" for short, at Cité-Devant 10 with a full house on three floors, Dance music fans head for La Griffe on Place de la Gare, Students meet up in Le Bleu Lézard (cellar disco), rue Enning 2 and L'escale, Galerie Benjamin-Constant 1
- **Don't miss...** The Olympic Museum is the world's largest information centre on the Olympic Games, Musée de l'Elysée, Lausanne Museum of Photography has been dedicated to photography since 1985, La Conversion – Epesses – St. Saphorin – Vevey: the recommended route from Lausanne through the vineyards of Lavaux to Vevey promises a first-rate hike with magnificent views

▲ **Leissigen** – 55060
Albert Wander Haus, Oberfeldweg 1, 3706 Leissigen (Bern).
(33) 8471214 (33) 8471497
leissigen@youthhostel.ch
www.youthhostel.ch/leissigen
Open Dates: 14.04-15.10 Zürich 172km
Leissigen 500m Leissigen 500m
x 44

Lenzerheide ☛ **Valbella**

Liechtenstein ☛ **Schaan-Vaduz**

▲ **Locarno** – Palagiovani – 55036
Via Varenna 18, 6600 Locarno (Ticino).
(91) 7561500 (91) 7561501
locarno@youthhostel.ch
www.youthhostel.ch/locarno
Open Dates: 01.03-17.11 Agno 44km
Locarno 1.5km 31, 36 50m ap Cinque Vie Centovalli-Bahn 200m ap St. Antonio 1.5W x 188
R 3 x
1.5km 1.5km

▲ **Lugano** – Savosa – 55061
Via Cantonale 13, 6942 Savosa (Ticino).
(91) 9662728 (91) 9682363
lugano@youthhostel.ch
www.youthhostel.ch/lugano
Open Dates: 18.03-31.10 Agno 7km
Lugano 2km 5 100m ap Crocifisso
x 100 (B)

Luzern HI 55004
Am Rotsee, Sedelstr 12, 6004 Luzern (Lucerne).
(41) 4208800 (41) 4205616
luzern@youthhostel.ch
www.youthhostel.ch/luzern
Open Dates: 12 Open Times: Summer: 07.00-10.00hrs; 14.00-24.00hrs Winter: 07.30-09.30hrs; 16.00-24.00hrs
Beds: 194 - 8x2 4x3 18x4 9x6 2x6+
Price Range: from CHF 32.10 BBinc
Directions: 2N from city centre
Zürich 68km Luzern 2km
Luzern 2km 18 500m, 19 1km ap outside hostel/Rosenberg R
2 x
2km 2km

Luzern

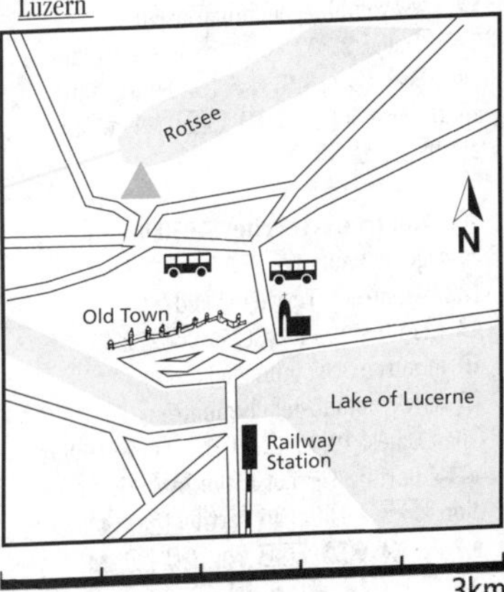

Luzern... Travel Tips

- **For budget eats check out...** Migros Restaurant, Coop Restaurant, Manor Restaurant (nice roof-deck)
- **For great nightlife try...** SEEBAR, The Loft Dance Club, Pravda Club, N8 Café, Mr Pickwick
- **Don't miss...** Kapellbrücke, Verkehrshaus (transport museum), Gletschergarten (glacier garden), Vierwaldstättersee (lake & boat trips), Blue Balls Festival (July), Löwendenkmal (Lion Memorial), Luzern Carnival, Rigi, Pilatus & Titlis (via mountain railway), Rütliwiese (origin of Swiss history), IMAX

▲ **Maloja** – 55062
Hauptstrasse, 7516 Maloja (Graubünden).
(81) 8382844 (81) 8382829
maloja@youthhostel.ch
www.youthhostel.ch/maloja
Open Dates: 01.01-02.04; 10.06-15.10 Zürich 220km St. Moritz Maloja Post 100m x 38

▲ **Mariastein-Rotberg** – 55063
Jugendburg, 4115 Mariastein (Solothurn).
(61) 7311049 (61) 7312724
mariastein@youthhostel.ch
www.youthhostel.ch/mariastein
Open Dates: 27.02-10.12 Basel-Mulhouse 6km Basel SBB 10 - Flüh 500m ap Rotberg x 81
2 x

▲ **Montreux-Territet** – 55006
Passage de l'Auberge 8,
1820 Montreux-Territet (Vaud).
(21) 9634934 (21) 9632729
montreux@youthhostel.ch
www.youthhostel.ch/montreux
Open Dates: 10.02-12.11 Genève 100km Port de Territet 150m Montreux 2km 1 100m ap Territet x 112
2 x 1km 150m

▲ **Pontresina** – 55011
Sportzentrum Tolais,
7504 Pontresina (Graubünden).
(81) 8427223 (81) 8427031
pontresina@youthhostel.ch
www.youthhostel.ch/pontresina
Open Dates: 01.01-17.04; 10.06-22.10; 09.-31.12 Zürich 212km Pontresina 20m x 130

Rapperswil-Jona ☛ **Jona-Rapperswil**

Rheinfall ☛ **Dachsen & Schaffhausen**

▲ **Richterswil** – 55033
"Horn", Hornstr 5,
8805 Richterswil (Zürich).
(44) 7862188 (44) 7862193
richterswil@youthhostel.ch
www.youthhostel.ch/richterswil
Open Dates: 04.03-26.11 Zürich 40km Richterswil 50m Richterswil 50m x 80
1 x

△ ***Romanshorn*** *– 55064*
Gottfried-Keller-Str 6,
8590 Romanshorn (Thurgau).
(71) 4631717 (71) 4611990
romanshorn@youthhostel.ch
www.youthhostel.ch/romanshorn
Open Dates: 01.03-30.10 Zürich 85km Romanshorn 500m Romanshorn 500m x 114

▲ **Rorschach** – YH Rorschach See – 55066
Churerstrasse 4, 9400 Rorschach.
(71) 8449712 (71) 8449713
rorschach.see@youthhostel.ch
www.youthhostel.ch/rorschach.see
Open Dates: 01.04-30.10 Zürich 96km Hafenbahnhof Rorschach HB 100m x 60

▲ **Saanen-Gstaad** – 55020
Chalet Rüblihorn, 3792 Saanen (Bern).
(33) 7441343 (33) 7445542
saanen@youthhostel.ch
www.youthhostel.ch/saanen
Open Dates: 01.01-12.03; 03.06-15.10; 17-31.12 Zürich 210km Saanen 800m x 72
1 x

▲ Schaan-Vaduz – 55067
Untere Rüttigasse 6,
9494 Schaan (Fürstentum Liechtenstein).
(423) 2325022 (423) 2325856
schaan@youthhostel.ch
www.youthhostel.ch/schaan
Open Dates: 11.03-29.10 Zürich 125km
Buchs 2km Postbus 500m ap Mühleholz 2SE x 110 4 x 100m

▲ Schaffhausen – 55068
"Belair", Randenstr 65,
8200 Schaffhausen (Schaffhausen).
(52) 6258800 (52) 6245954
schaffhausen@youthhostel.ch
www.youthhostel.ch/schaffhausen
Open Dates: 04.03-19.11 Zürich 50km
Schaffhausen 1km 3 100m ap Wiesli, 6 100m ap Hallenbad 1.5NW x 72 1 x

▲ Seelisberg – 55069
Gadenhaus beim Rütli, 6377 Seelisberg (Uri).
(41) 8205232 (41) 8205231
seelisberg@youthhostel.ch
www.youthhostel.ch/seelisberg
Open Dates: 15.04-29.10 Zürich 100km
Treib Brunnen or Flüelen
Cablecar Treib-Seelisberg 800m x 25 1 x

△ Sils im Domleschg – 55070
Burg Ehrenfels,
7411 Sils im Domleschg (Graubünden).
(81) 6511518 sils@youthhostel.ch
www.youthhostel.ch/sils
Open Dates: 01.04-30.10 (only)
Zürich 157km Thusis Sils 500m x 40 2 x

▲ Sion – 55008
Rue de l'Industrie 2, 1950 Sion (Valais).
(27) 3237470 (27) 3237438
sion@youthhostel.ch
www.youthhostel.ch/sion
Open Dates: 05.02-15.10 Genève 160km
Sion 50m x 83

▲ Solothurn – 55017
"Am Land", Landhausquai 23,
4500 Solothurn (Solothurn).
(32) 6231706 (32) 6231639
solothurn@youthhostel.ch
www.youthhostel.ch/solothurn
Open Dates: 04.03-25.11 Zürich 100km
Aare 1km Solothurn 200m 0.2NW x 94 1 x

▲ St. Gallen – 55015
Jüchstrasse 25, 9000 St. Gallen (St. Gallen).
(71) 2454777 (71) 2454983
st.gallen@youthhostel.ch
www.youthhostel.ch/st.gallen
Open Dates: 01.03-29.11 Zürich 86km
St. Gallen 1 500m ap Singenberg
Trogenerbähnli 200m ap Schülerhaus
1SE x 87 2 x 1km

St. Moritz Bad 55010
"Stille", Via Surpunt 60,
7500 St. Moritz Bad (Graubünden).
(81) 8333969 (81) 8338046
st.moritz@youthhostel.ch
www.youthhostel.ch/st.moritz
Open Dates: 12 Open Times: Summer: 07.00-10.00hrs; 16.00-22.00hrs Winter: 07.30-10.00hrs; 16.00-21.45hrs May/November: 07.30-09.00hrs; 17.00-19.30hrs
Beds: 220 - 20x2 44x4
Price Range: from CHF 46.50 incl halfboard BBinc
Directions: 2S from city centre
Zürich 220km St. Moritz 2km
Postbus 100m ap Hotel Sonne x 42 4 x 800m

St. Moritz Bad

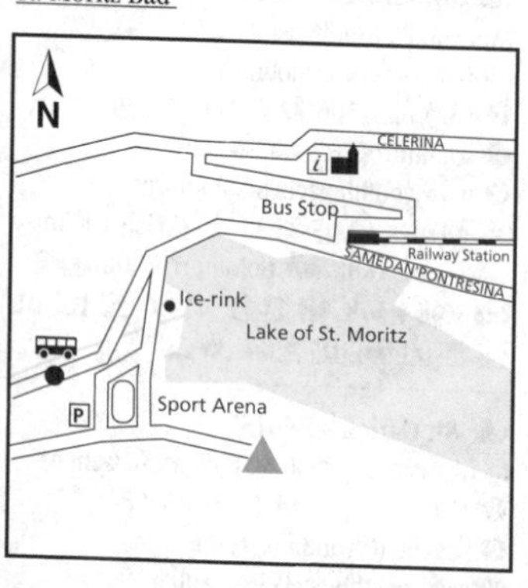

St. Moritz Bad... Travel Tips

- **For budget eats check out...** St. Mortiz Youth Hostel
- **For great nightlife try...** Muli-Bar, Bobby's Pub, Secondo, Prince, Baracuda
- **Don't miss...** Corvatsch (beautiful panorama), Oberengadin (views), Bergell & Soglio, Swiss National Park in Unterengadin, Alpine route from Grüm to Poschiavo, Glacier-Express (St Moritz - Zermatt), Zuoz & Guarda, Segantini Museum, Medicinal waters (St Moritz), Ski & snowboard paradise

▲ **Sta. Maria im Münstertal** – 55071
Chasa Plaz,
7536 Sta. Maria im Münstertal (Graubünden).
(81) 8585661 (81) 8585496
sta.maria@youthhostel.ch
www.youthhostel.ch/sta.maria
Open Dates: 01.01-13.03; 14.05-22.10; 24.-31.12 Zürich 215km Susch or Zernez Postbus x 60 CC

▲ **Ste-Croix** – 55022
18 rue Centrale, 1450 Ste-Croix (Vaud).
(24) 4541810 (24) 4544522
ste.croix@youthhostel.ch
www.youthhostel.ch/ste.croix
Open Dates: 13.04-15.10 Genève 105km Ste-Croix 200m x 63 CC 1 x

▲ **Stein am Rhein** – 55072
Hemishoferstr 87,
8260 Stein am Rhein (Schaffhausen).
(52) 7411255 (52) 7415140
stein@youthhostel.ch
www.youthhostel.ch/stein
Open Dates: 04.03-30.10 Zürich 55km Stein am Rhein 300m Stein am Rhein 800m Strandbad 50m x 112 CC 2 x

Vaduz ☛ **Schaan**

▲ **Valbella-Lenzerheide** – 55030
Voa Sartons 41, 7077 Valbella (Graubünden).
(81) 3841208 (81) 3844558
valbella@youthhostel.ch
www.youthhostel.ch/valbella
Open Dates: 01.01-17.04; 16-31.12 Zürich 150km Chur Postbus to Valbella 1.5km x 106 CC TV

Zermatt 55005
"Winkelmatten", Staldenweg 5,
3920 Zermatt (Wallis).
(27) 9672320 (27) 9675306
zermatt@youthhostel.ch
www.youthhostel.ch/zermatt
Open Dates: Open Times: 07.00-10.00hrs; 16.00-22.30hrs
Beds: 174 - 17x2 22x4 6x6 2x6+
Price Range: from CHF 47.50 incl halfboard BBinc
Directions: 0.8SE from city centre
Genève 235km Zermatt 800m Ortsbus 100m ap Luchre x 2 R CC 2 x 8 500m

Zermatt

2km

Zermatt... Travel Tips

- **For budget eats check out...** Zermatt Youth Hostel
- **For great nightlife try...** Vernissage, Grampis, Pupperla Pub, Pöstli, Hexenbar
- **Don't miss...** Matterhorn, Skiing & snowboarding (245km of pistes), World of the "Viertausender" (mountains), Fascinating glacier world, Gornergrat (3089m - view of Monte-Rosa-Massiv), Cable car (Little Matterhorn), Summer skiing (Little Matterhorn), Village atmosphere with international flair, Car-free village, Glacier-Express (Zermatt - St Moritz)

▲ **Zofingen** – 55021
General Guisan-Str 10,
4800 Zofingen (Aargau).
(62) 7522303 (62) 7522316
zofingen@youthhostel.ch
www.youthhostel.ch/zofingen
Open Dates: 27.02-16.12 Zürich 65km
Zofingen 500m x 58 CC
1 x i P

▲ **Zug** – 55009
Allmendstr 8, Sportstadion 'Herti',
6300 Zug (Zug).
(41) 7115354 (41) 7105121
zug@youthhostel.ch
www.youthhostel.ch/zug
Open Dates: 13.03-03.12 Zürich 43km
Zug 800m 6, 11 50m ap Stadium
x 88 CC
2 x i P

Zürich 55001
Mutschellenstr 114,
8038 Zürich (Zürich).
(43) 3997800 (43) 3997801
zuerich@youthhostel.ch
www.youthhostel.ch/zuerich
Open Dates: Open Times:
Beds: 281 - 16x2 51x4
Price Range: from CHF 37.50 BBinc
Directions: 3SW from city centre
Zürich 8km Zürich Wollishofen 500m Zürich 4km 33 ap outside hostel Tram No. 7 350m ap Morgental U No. 1 or 8 to Zürich-Wollishofen 500m
x 14 R CC TV
4 x i 8 P
500m 500m

Zürich

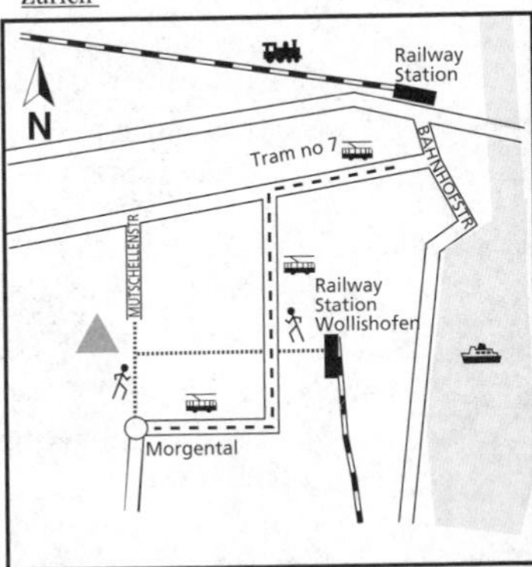

0 1.5km

Zürich... Travel Tips

- **For budget eats check out...** Zürich Youth Hostel, Mensa Uni Zürich
- **For great nightlife try...** Niederdorf (Old Town), Toni Molkerei, Kaufleuten, Cinemax cinema, Rote Fabrik (culture centre)
- **Don't miss...** Niederdorf (Old Town), Grossmünster & Fraumünster (churches), National museum, Masoala Halle & Zoo, Lake Zurich (boat trips & lakeside promenade), Uetliberg (nearest mountain), Börse (stock exchange), Bahnhofstrasse (shopping), Old Town alleys & Münsterhof (church court), Museums (art etc.)

THAILAND – THAÏLANDE – THAILAND – TAILANDIA

Thailand

Thai Youth Hostels Association,
25/14 Phitsanulok Road, Si Sao Thewet,
Dusit, Bangkok 10300, Thailand.
t (66) (2) 6287413-15
f (66) (2) 6287416
e bangkok@tyha.org; contact@tyha.org
w www.tyha.org

A copy of the Hostel Directory for this Country can be obtained from:
The National Office

National Tourist Authority/Board:	www.tat.or.th; www.tourismthailand.org
Capital:	Bangkok
Language:	Thai
Currency:	baht
Population:	66,000,000
Size:	500,000 sq km
Telephone Country Code:	66
eKit Access Number:	001-800-120-665-514

Thailand is one of Asia's most fascinating countries. The beautiful landscape, mountains and hills of northern Thailand contrast strikingly with the sprawling metropolis of the capital, Bangkok. The Thai kingdom was recognized in the mid-fourteenth century, and was known as Siam until 1939.

Today, the population of Thailand stands at approximately 66 million people, ten million of whom live in Bangkok. Thais are warm, friendly people with a deep sense of national pride. This independence has been upheld for centuries, and Thailand is the sole Southeast Asian country never to have been ruled by a European nation.

A few other Top Tips from **CULTURE SMART!**:

- Be sure to show respect to Buddha and to the King. For instance, images of the Buddha should be kept high up, in a safe place, and you should always stand up if images of the King or members of the royal family appear on the television or cinema screen.

- Thais show respect by pressing their hands gently together as if in prayer, and slightly bowing their heads in acknowledgment. This is known as the *wai*. If someone *wais* at you, it is greatly appreciated if you *wai* back at them. Many younger Thais are less formal, and are more inclined to shake hands with a foreigner.
- In Thailand, a person's social status is reflected in the manner in which they dress. This is beginning to change as the nation becomes more fashion-conscious, but many institutions and places of work have uniforms to define ranks.
- Don't wear black in Thailand, particularly if you are invited to a party or gathering, as this has a strong association with death. Black should only be worn at a funeral. Thais do not like to draw attention to themselves. Modest behaviour is appropriate.
- Pointing is considered offensive. Also, you should never show the soles of your feet: this is one of the most insulting gestures in Thailand, so be careful not to sit cross-legged or with your legs stretched out in front of your body.

Culture Smart! Top Tips © Kuperard 2005

Cultural Top Tips supplied by Culture Smart! guides. These essential guides to customs and etiquette will help you steer clear of embarrassing gaffes and sensitive issues, enabling you to discover new cultures whilst developing new friendships. Order online at www.culturesmartguides.co.uk

You can find out a lot more on our website - a visit to www.HIhostels.com is essential for planning your trip!

Pour en savoir plus, rendez-vous su notre site Internet, www.HIhostels.com une visite incontournable pour préparer votre voyage!

Viele weitere Informationen auf unserer Website: www.HIhostels.com - unverzichtbar für die Reiseplanung!

Puedes averiguar mucho más en nuestro sitio web. Es imprescindible que visites la página www.HIhostels.com para planear tu viaje.

△ ***Ayutthaya*** *– HI-Ayutthaya – 57038*
7 Moo 2. Rojana Road, Hor-Rattanachai, Ayutthaya.
(35) 241754; 210941; (1) 3668161
(35) 251124 ayutthaya@tyha.org
www.tyha.org
Open Dates: Bangkok International 50km Ayutthaya 500m Ayutthaya 500m x 20 R i P

Bangkok – HI-Bangkok 57001
25/2 Phitsanulok Rd, Si Sao Thewet, Dusit, Bangkok 10300.
(2) 2810361; 2820950 (2) 6287416
bangkok@tyha.org; contact@tyha.org
www.tyha.org
Open Dates: Open Times:
Beds: 63
Price Range: 70-350 baht
Directions: Donmuang 35km A A2 - Sanamluang 35km Tha Thewet Pier 1km Samsen 2.5km 16, 23, 43, 72, 99, 516 50m ap Thewet Market R 8 P
1km

Bangkok – HI-Bangkok

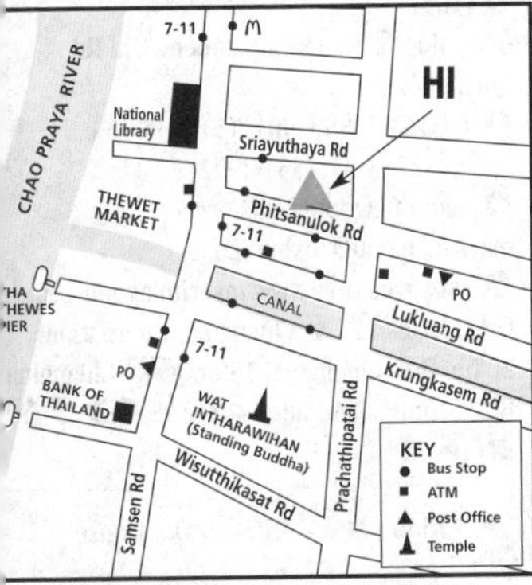

△ ***Bangkok*** *– HI-Bangkok Downtown – 37039*
395/4 Silom Road, Bangrak Bangkok 10500.
(2) 6368685; (1) 4868685
(2) 6368687 www.tyha.org
Open Dates: Bangkok International 20km Hua-Lam-Pong 5km 62, 77, 162, 164, 502, 504, 514, 544 200m; Skytrain BTS. (Chong Nonsi Station) 100m
U 1km x 49 R CC

▲ **Bangkok** – HI-Bangkok Rama Place 57020
1546 Pattanakarn Road, Suan Luang, Bangkok 10250.
(2) 7226602 (-10) (2) 7226612
bangkokrama@tyha.org; c_kiangsiri@yahoo.com www.tyha.org; www.bangkok-hotel.com
Open Dates: Bangkok International Airport 36km Klongton Pier 10mins Hua-Mark 500m 517, 206, 11 200m x 150 R 2 x P

▲ **Bangkok** – HI-Bansabai 57004
8/137 Soi Sahakorn 15, Ladphrao 71, Bangkok 10230.
(2) 9329200 to 4 (2) 5384387
bansabai@asianet.co.th; bansabai@tyha.org www.tyha.org
Open Dates: Bangkok International 10km 156 ap Sahakorn Soi 15 x 50 R TV P

▲ **Bangkok** – HI-Far East Inn 57021
20/8-9 Soi Bangkok-Bazaar, Chid Lom Rd, Bangkok 10330.
(2) 2554041 (-5) (2) 2538813
fareastinn@tyha.org; fareastinn@yahoo.com www.tyha.org; www.geocities.com/fareastinn
Open Dates: Bangkok International 15km A Al to Central World Plaza 1km Pratunam Pier 200m Hua-Lam-Pong 5km 200m x 60 R

▲ **Bangkok** – HI-Trang – 57022
99/1 Wisuthkasat Road, Bangkok 10200.
(2) 2811402 (-3); 2822141 (-4)
(2) 2803610 trangbangkok@tyha.org
www.tyha.org
Open Dates: Bangkok International 32km A A2 to Sanam-Luang 1km Thewet Pier 1km Samsen 3km x 48 R 2 x P

Bangkok... Travel Tips

- **For budget eats check out...** China Town (Yaowarach Area), Banglampoo, Sukhumvit Area, Kaosarn Road/Phra Arthit Road, Siam Square (Fast Food)
- **For great nightlife try...** Kaosarn Road, Suan-Lum Night Bazaar, Silom Road, China Town, Thonglor Area
- **Don't miss...** Grand Palace & Rattanagosin Island, Floating Market (Talingchan), Weekend Market (Jatujak), China Town, Vimanmek Royal Mansion, Siam Square Centre, Suan Pakkad Palace, Banglamphu & Kaosarn Road & Phra Arthit Road, Thai Boxing Rajdamnern Stadium, National Theatre (Thai Cultural Show)

△ ***Buriram*** *– HI-P. California 57023*
59/9 Sangkakrit Road, Nangrong, Buriram 31110.
(44) 622214; (9) 9475449
(44) 622214 buriram@tyha.org; california8gh@yahoo.com
www.tyha.org; www.geocities.com/california8gh
Open Dates: Lam-Plai-Mas 40km 30km ap Nangrong x 30 R

△ ***Chai Nat** – HI-Han Ka* Ⓗ *57025*
89 Moo 3, Ban-Nongboi, Prainokyung, Hanka, Chai Nat 17130.
(56) 401330; (2) 7565093
(2) 7565094 bankabostel@tyba.org; sunsanee_family@thai.com
www.tyba.org
Open Dates: Bangkok International 180km Hanka Bus Terminal 20km
x 20

▲ **Chiang Mai** – HI-Center Place
Ⓗ 57027
17/2 Soi l Loykroh Road, Muang, Chiang Mai 50100.
(53) 271169; 206323; (9) 9991235
(53) 208950 centerplace@tyha.org; centerplace99@hotmail.com
www.tyha.org; www.centreplace-chiangmai.com
Open Dates: Chiang Mai 3km
Chiang Mai 3km x 78

△ ***Chiang Mai** – HI-Chiang-Mai – 57005*
20 Paprao Road (21/8 Chang-Klan Rd) Chiang Mai 50100.
(53) 284046; 276737 (53) 204025
chiangmai@tyba.org; cybpeter@chiangmai.a-net.net.th; cybpeter@cmnet.co.th; peter@chiangmaiyba.com
www.chiangmaiyba.com; www.tyba.org
Open Dates: Chiang Mai 1km
Chiang Mai 1km 3.5S x 50

▲ **Chiang Mai** – HI-Five Stars – 37040
72/66-67 Tippayanet Road, Muang Chiang Mai 50000.
(53) 270091-2; (1) 8396857; (2) 3900912 (2) 7111986
hostthai@ksc.th.com; 5stars@tyha.org
www.tyha.org
Open Dates: Chiang Mai 5km
Chiang Mai 19km Chiang Mai Bus Terminal 20km x 48

▲ **Chiang Mai** – HI-Mae Rim Lagoon
Ⓗ 57037
65/1 Moo 6, Mae Rim-Samoeng Old Rd. Chiang Mai.
(53) 297288 (-90); (1) 8190963; (9) 1432723 (53) 297287
maerimlagoon@tyha.org; maerimlagoon@loxinfo.co.th
www.tyha.org; www.maerimlagoon.com/hi
Open Dates: Chiangmai Internation 20km Chiangmai 15km Chiangmai Bus Terminal (Arcade) x 45

▲ **Chiang Mai** – HI-Suan Doi House
Ⓗ 57024
38/3 Soi Chantarasap, Huay Kaew Road, Chiang Mai 50300.
(53) 221869; 406091 (53) 221869
suandoi@tyha.org www.tyha.org
Open Dates: Chiang Mai 10km
Chiang Mai 15km 10km ap Chiang Mai x 50

△ ***Chiang Rai** – HI-Sabun Nga* Ⓗ *57026*
226/50 Sankbong-Noi Road, Muang, Chiang Rai 57000.
(53) 712290; 716440 (53) 711869
chiangrai@tyba.org; sabun-nga@sabun-nga.com
www.tyba.org
Open Dates: Chiang Rai 7km
2km ap Bus Station x 60

△ ***Lop Buri** – HI-Vimolrat, Lopburi – 57007*
5/19 Moo 3. Naresuan Rd, Ampbor Mueng, Lop Buri 15000.
(36) 613390; 613731 (-3)
(36) 613390 ruj@school.net.tb; lopburi@tyba.org; lopburiiyb@botmail.com
www.tyba.org
Open Dates: Lopburi 2km 3SE
x 32

▲ **Mae Hong Son** – HI-Panorama
Ⓗ 57029
54/1 Khunlumprapas Road, Mae Hong Son 58000.
(53) 611757 (-62) (53) 611790
panorama@tyha.org; panorama@hunsa.com www.tyha.org
Open Dates: Mae Hong Son 1km
200m ap Bus Station x 20

Nakorn Ratchasima – HI-Khao Yai
57030
72/2 Moo 1 Nong-namdaeng, Packhong,
Nakorn Ratchasima 30130.
(44) 328277; (9) 6683448
(44) 311244; 313459
khaoyai@tyha.org;
srerngkiat@hotmail.com www.tyha.org
Open Dates: Bangkok International 150km Pakchong 7km x 44

***Phetchaburi** – HI-Kaengkrachan*
57031
550 Moo 1, Kaengkrachan,
Phetchaburi 76130.
(32) 461244; (1) 5872382; 6466374
(32) 461245
kaengkrachan@tyha.com;
pornrawee@hotmail.com www.tyha.org
Open Dates: Phetchaburi 54km
37km ap Phetchaburi x 82

***Phetchaburi** – HI-Phetchaburi*
57019
51/2 Tha-Hin Road,
Tharab. Phetchaburi 76000.
(32) 423671; (9) 7432146
(32) 423671 petchaburi@tyha.org;
tsiripo@hotmail.com www.tyha.org
Open Dates: Phetchaburi 2.5km
1.5km ap Phetchaburi Bus Station
x 14

***Phitsanulok** – HI-Phitsanulok*
57009
38 Sa-Nam-Bin Rd, Phitsanulok 65000.
(55) 242060; 210862-3 (55) 210864
phitsanulok@tyha.org www.tyha.org
Open Dates: 1km A No. 4 to YH
2.5km 3.5km ap YH Sign
x 40
1km

Phuket – HI-Phuket 57010
73/11 Chowfah Rd, Chalong, Mueang,
Phuket 83100.
(2) 3900912; 3916854; (76) 281325;
280103 (2) 3916854; (76) 281325
hostthai@ksc.th.com; phuket@tyha.org
www.tyha.org; www.phukethostel.com
Open Dates: Phuket 45km
A Airport Bus to City Centre 1.5km
9S x 95

Prachuab Khirikhan – HI Ban-Kruit,
Prachuab Khirikhan 57013
123 Bann-Kruit-Khoktahom Rd, Bann-Kruit,
Prachuab Khirikhan.
(2) 3900912; (32) 619103; 695525
(2) 3916854 bann-kruit@tyha.org;
hostthai@ksc.th.com
www.thailandbeach.com; www.tyha.org
Open Dates: Bann-Kruit 5km
Bangsapan Long Distance Bus Station
15km x 90
1 x

Prachuab Khirikhan – HI-Hua Hin
57032
5/15 Sasong Street, Hua Hin,
Prachuab Khirikhan 77110.
(32) 513130; 513388 (32) 514181
hihuahin@tyha.org www.tyha.org
Open Dates: Hua Hin 150m
300m ap Bus Station x 64
200m

Rayong – HI-Ban Kon Ao, Rayong –
57011
89/4 Moo 1 Mae Ram Puang Beach Rd, Phae,
Rayong 21160.
(38) 653374; (9) 7717424
(38) 621805 ban-kon-ao@tyha.org;
sukya_w@yahoo.com www.tyha.org
Open Dates: 200km Koh Samet
Ferry 6km Phu-Ta-Lung 50km
Mini Bus (Song Taew) (Light Blue
Colour) ap Hostel Sign or YHA 22E x 65
500m

Suratthani – HI-Koh Ma Dive Village
57035
Koh Ma, Koh Pha-Ngan District,
Suratthani 84280.
(77) 377068 (-9); (2) 5512058 (-9)
(77) 377032 kohmahostel@tyha.org;
chatchaphon@cpp.co.th www.tyha.org
Open Dates: Samui 15km Thong
Sala Pier 100m x 21 10m

Suratthani – HI-Pha Ngan 57034
44/65 Moo 1, Koh Pha-Ngan,
Suratthani 84280.
(77) 377068 (-9); (2) 5512058 (-9)
(77) 377032
phanganhostel@tyha.org;
chatchaphon@cpp.co.th www.tyha.org
Open Dates: Samui 14km Thong
Sala Pier 100m x 50
10m

Tunisia

Association Tunisienne des Auberges et Tourisme de Jeunes,
8 Rue d'Alger,
BP 320-1015 Tunis RP, Tunisia.
t (216) (71) 353277
f (216) (71) 352172
e ataj@planet.tn
w www.atatj.planet.tn

Office Hours: Monday-Friday 08.30-17.45hrs
Saturdays 08.30-13.00hrs

A copy of the Hostel Directory for this Country can be obtained from: The National Office.

Capital:	Tunis
Language:	Arabic
Currency:	D (dinar)
Population:	9,705,102
Size:	163,610 sq km
Telephone Country Code:	216
eKit Access Number:	Check www.hi.ekit.com for up to date Access Numbers

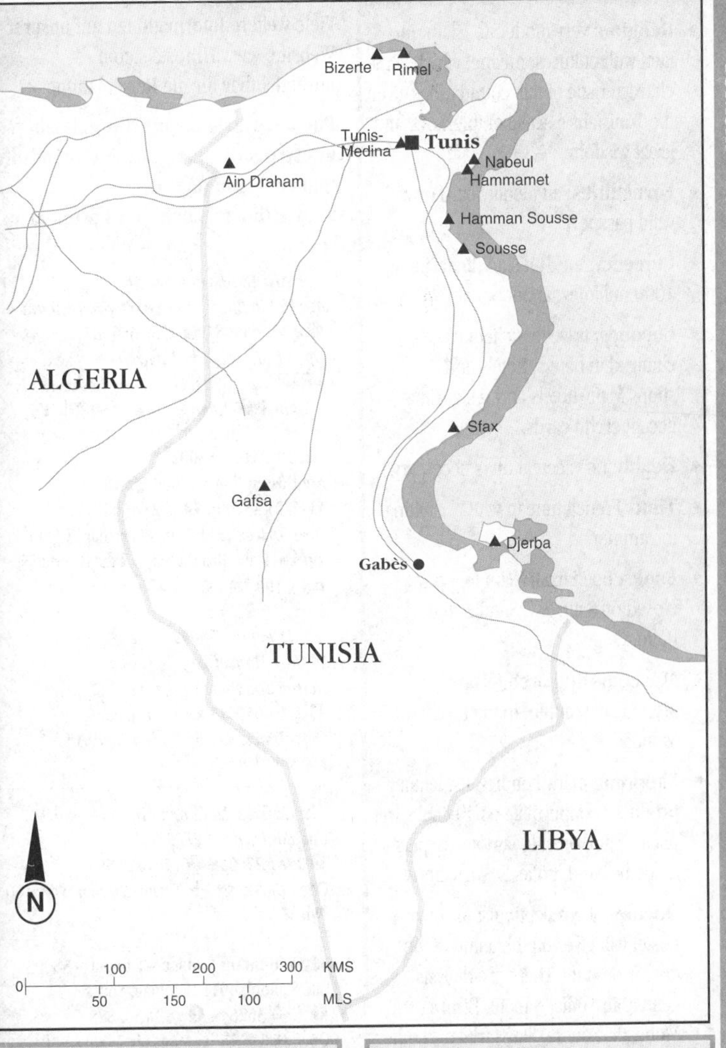

HI Suggests...

Ancient, oriental and western at the same time, backed against a cultural patrimony, exceptionally rich and three times millenary, Tunisia conveys at the highest degree the Tunisian nature characterized by broad-mindedness, wisdom and conviviality. The country joins to this point a sumptuous hospitality, a culture drawn from the Mediterranean greatest civilizations and a modern infrastructure of a high performance.

- **Geographic situation and climate:** in the heart of the Mediterranean Sea, one hour flight from Nice. Tunisia has a moderate climate, with mild winters and pleasant summers. Its sandy coasts stretching over 1300km, invite to relaxation and rest.
- **Population:** 9,705,102 inhabitants.
- **Surface area:** nearly 164.000sq km.
- **Official language:**Arabic.

- **Religion:** very moderate Islam. In fact, with cultures' mixing, which is the characteristic of this country, has given the Tunisians a sense of tolerance and great wisdom.
- **Formalities:** an identity card or a valid passport.
- **Currency:** the Tunisian dinar, i.e. 1000 millimes, about 6,5 euro
- **Cheques:** travellers cheques can be changed in banks, hotels and shops.Many hotels and restaurants accept credit cards.
- **Health:** no vaccination is necessary.
- **Time:** French time in winter, shifting in summer.
- **Banks:** open from 8 am to 4 p.m; closed on Saturday, Sunday and holidays.
- **Museums and archaelogical sites:**from 9 am to 4p.m closed on Monday.
- **Shopping:**many handicrafts, leather products, copperplate engraving, silver plates, paint on silk, famous carpets made by hand, potter's workshops.
- **Doctors:** the receptionist in your hostel will give you the name of the doctor on duty. There are dialysis centers in Tunis, Nabeul, Bizerte, Monastir, Sousse, Sfax Jerba and other places inside the country.
- For more information consult: http://www.tunisiaonline.com

You can find out a lot more on our website - a visit to www.HIhostels.com is essential for planning your trip!

Pour en savoir plus, rendez-vous sur notre site Internet, www.HIhostels.com une visite incontournable pour préparer votre voyage!

Viele weitere Informationen auf unserer Website: www.HIhostels.com - unverzichtbar für die Reiseplanung!

Puedes averiguar mucho más en nuestro sitio web. Es imprescindible que visites la página www.HIhostels.com para planear tu viaje.

△ ***Ain Draham*** *– 58001*
Ave Habib Bourguiba - 8130 Ain Draham.
(78) 655087 (78) 655087
Open Dates: [12] Tabarka
Tunis-Tabarka 170km Tunis 170km Tabarka x 150

▲ **Bizerte** – 58002
Ave Hassen Nouri - 7000 Bizerte.
(72) 431608 (72) 430561
Open Dates: [12] Tunis-Carethage 65km
Tunis-Bizerta 65km Bizerta [1N]
x 100

△ ***Djerba*** *– 58009*
11, Rue Moncef Bey,
Houmt Souk - 4180 Djerba.
(75) 650619 (75) 650619
Open Dates: [12] Djerba "Zarzis"
x 90

△ ***Gafsa*** *– La Cabaña Hostel – 58010*
Cité des Jeunes - 2119 Gafsa.
(76) 220268 (76) 225599
Open Dates: [12] Tozeur 100km x 60

▲ **Hammam Sousse** – Sahloul – 58003
Cite Sahloul, 4011 Hammam Sousse.
(73) 362644 (73) 362888
Open Dates: [12] Monastir 25km [1SE]
x 65 R P

△ ***Hammamet*** *– Centre de Sejour – 58004*
Ave Assad IBN El Fourat, 8050 Hammamet.
(72) 280440 (72) 278960
Open Dates: [12] Tunis Carthage or Monastir Tunis-Hammamet [2SE]
x 65 R P

△ ***Nabeul*** *– 58011*
Ave Mongi Slim - 8000 Nabeul Plage.
(72) 285547 (72) 285547
Open Dates: [12] Tunis Carthage or Monastir Tunis-Nabeul x 42

Rimel – 58006
7080 (Menzel Jemil)- Bizerte.
(72) 440804 (72) 440804
rimel@planet.tn
Open Dates: Open Times:
Beds: 50
Directions: Tunis "Carthage" 65km
A Tunis - Societé Regionale Bizerte
Tunis La Goulelette Tunis-Gare Centrale

Rimel

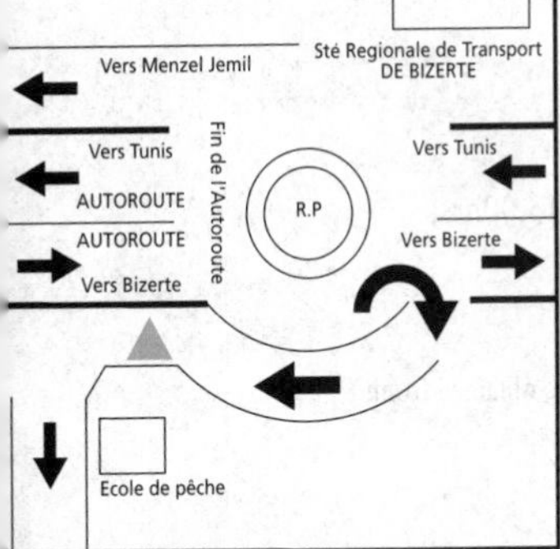

Rimel... Travel Tips

- **For budget eats check out...** Restaurant Jendoubi (Rue du 2 Mars, Bizerte), Restaurant de l'Univers (Rue Thaalbi, Bizerte)
- **For great nightlife try...** Festival International de Bizerte du 08/07 au 18/08 de chaque annee
- **Don't miss...** Maison de Culture 7 Novembre (Sidi Salem, Bizerte), Musee oceanographique la ksiba, Les Remparts de la Medina, La Medina et Vieux Port, Parc National d'Ishkeul, Elkhyam la Corniche

▲ **Sfax** – SINA – 58012
Route Menzel Chaker Km, 1 (3072) Sfax.
(74) 460888 (74) 460880
(R 2 wks before)
Open Dates: Sfax "Thyna" 7km
A 11, 13 2km 2km x 80
R (B) 500m

▲ **Sousse** – 58007
Ave Teïeb Mhiri Plage Boujaafar- 4000 Sousse.
(73) 227548 (73) 226620
Open Dates: Monastir x 90

▲ **Tunis** – Tunis Médina – 58008
25 rue saida Ajoula, Tunis: located in the old city of Médina, 500m from La Place du Gouvernement la kasbah.
(71) 567850 (71) 567850
Open Dates: Tunis Carthage x 48
R

United Arab Emirates

General Administration:
United Arab Emirates Youth Hostel Association,
39 Al Nahda Road, Al Nahda 2 Area,
P.O. Box 94141, Dubai,
United Arab Emirates.
t (971) (4) 2988151
f (971) (4) 2988141
e uaeyha@emirates.net.ae

Office Hours: Saturday-Wednesday 09.00-13.00hrs; 17.00-20.00hrs

A copy of the Hostel Directory for this Country can be obtained from:
The National Office

Capital:	Abu Dhabi
Language:	Arabic
Currency:	Dh (dirham) (US$1 = 3.7 Dhs)
Population:	2,200,000
Size:	83,600 sq km
Telephone Country Code:	971
eKit Access Number:	Check www.hi.ekit.com for up to date Access Numbers

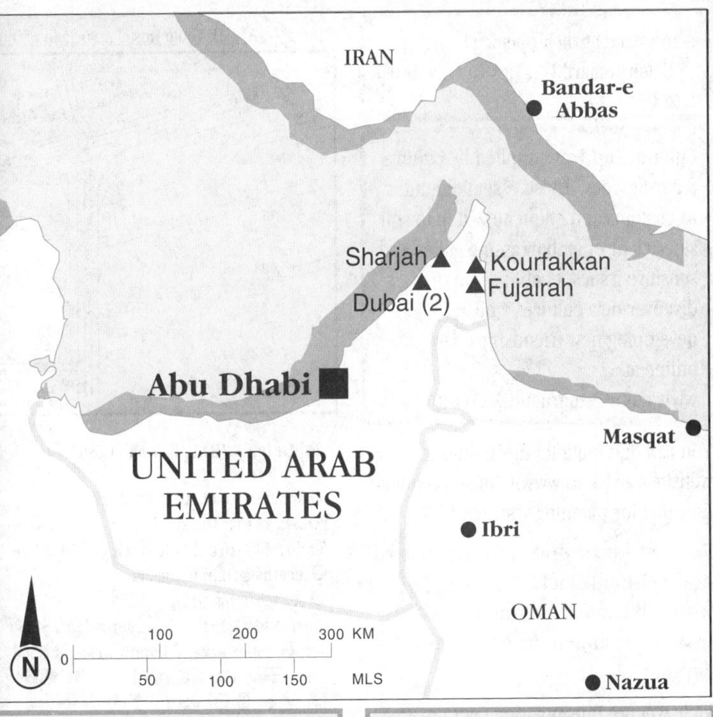

The United Arab Emirates is a federation of the seven emirates of Dubai, Abu Dhabi, Sharjah, Fujairah, Umm al-Qaiwain, Ras al-Khaimah and Ajman. This federation was officially recognized on 2 December 1971. The discovery of oil brought prosperity and employment for the population of over two million people. Non-U.A.E. nationals comprise roughly four-fifths of the population. The established religion in the U.A.E. is Islam, but Christianity, Hinduism and others are also present. Around 80 percent of the U.A.E. is desert, but there are also contrasting landscapes of lush plains and mountain ranges.

A few other Top Tips from **CULTURE SMART!**:

- Foreigners, and tourists in particular, are treated with kindness, but Emiratis expect visitors to respect local traditions, especially those that concern religion, and to adhere to the country's laws.
- Women should never appear alone in public in the U.A.E., as this would represent loose morals. Emiratis put women on a pedestal, and consider that their honour must be protected. Consequently, U.A.E. women dress carefully and completely cover themselves with a black cloak, called the *abaya.*
- Remember to be polite at all times, and you will be treated graciously in return.
- Food is regarded as a gift from God, and is accorded appropriate respect.
- During Ramadan, the Islamic holy month, meal times and waking hours change dramatically. No food or drink is consumed during the hours of daylight, and non-Muslim foreigners are required to abstain from eating, drinking and smoking in public at this time. Throughout this month, official working hours are shortened and shops may compensate for the loss of business

by extending their opening hours.
Culture Smart! Top Tips © Kuperard 2005

Cultural Top Tips supplied by Culture Smart! guides. These essential guides to customs and etiquette will help you steer clear of embarrassing gaffes and sensitive issues, enabling you to discover new cultures whilst developing new friendships. Order online at www.culturesmartguides.co.uk

You can find out a lot more on our website - a visit to www.HIhostels.com is essential for planning your trip!

Pour en savoir plus, rendez-vous sur notre site Internet, www.HIhostels.com une visite incontournable pour préparer votre voyage!

Viele weitere Informationen auf unserer Website: www.HIhostels.com - unverzichtbar für die Reiseplanung!

Puedes averiguar mucho más en nuestro sitio web. Es imprescindible que visites la página www.HIhostels.com para planear tu viaje.

Dubai – (A) UAE Youth Hostel Association (Old) – 96215
39 Al Nahda Road, Al Nahda 2 area, PO Box 94141, Dubai.
(4) 2988161; 2988151 (4) 2988141
uaeyha@emirates.net.ae
www.uaeyha.org.ae
Open Dates: Open Times:
Beds: 53
Price Range: 45 Dhs BBinc
Directions: Dubai International 5km A 3 250m Rashed 10km 3, 13, 17 30m ap Dura Bus Station R 2km 2km

Dubai – (A) UAE Youth Hostel Association (Old

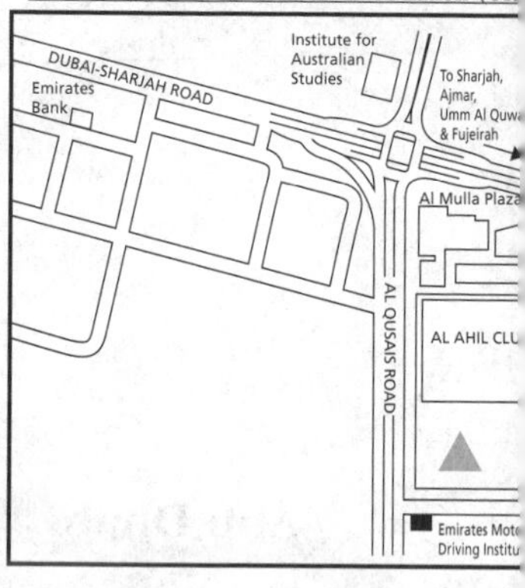

▲ **Dubai** – (B) UAE, Youth Hostel Association (New) – 96216
39 Al Nahda Road, Al Nahda 2 area, PO Box 94141, Dubai.
(4) 2988161; 2988151 (4) 2988141
uaeyha@emirates.net.ae
www.uaeyha.org.ae
Open Dates: Dubai International 5km A 250m Al Hamriya 1km; Rashed 10km 30m x 94 R 1 x 2km 2km

▲ **Fujerah Hostel** – UAE, Youth Hostel Association Fujerah – 96217
203 Al Fasil area, (next to the white village, opposite Abu Gandal primary school), Al Fujerah.
(9) 2222347 (9) 2222347
uaeyha@emirates.net.ae
www.uaeyha.org.ae
Open Dates: Fujerah x 24

▲ **Kourfakkan** – UAE Youth Hostel Association, Khorfakan – 96218
Al Kornaish Road, opposite Oceanic Hotel, next to Al Khaleej Club, Kourfakkan.
(9) 2370886 (9) 2370886
uaeyha@emirates.net.ae
www.uaeyha.org.ae
Open Dates: Fujerah x 24

▲ **Sharjah Hostel** – UAE Youth Hostel Association, Sharjah – 96219
Sharghan Area, Old Muroor r.a., In front of the old childhood & motherhood center, Sharjah.
(t) (6) 5225070 (f) (6) 5225070
(e) uaeyha@emirates.net.ae
(w) www.uaeyha.org.ae
Open Dates: 12 ✈ Sharjah International
x 32

USA

Hostelling International-USA (HI-USA),
8401 Colesville Rd, Suite 600,
Silver Spring, MD 20910,
United States of America.

(t) (1) (301) 4951240
(f) (1) (301) 4956697
(e) General enquiries & information: hostels@hiusa.org
(w) www.hiusa.org

A copy of the Hostel Directory for this Country can be obtained from:
The National Office

National Tourist Authority/Board:	www.seeamerica.org
Capital:	Washington, DC
Language:	English
Currency:	US$ (100 cents = 1 dollar)
Population:	290,000,000
Size:	9,363,123 sq km
Telephone Country Code:	1
eKit Access Number:	1800-706-1333; 1800-318-7039 (Alaska); 1800-527-6786 (Hawaii)

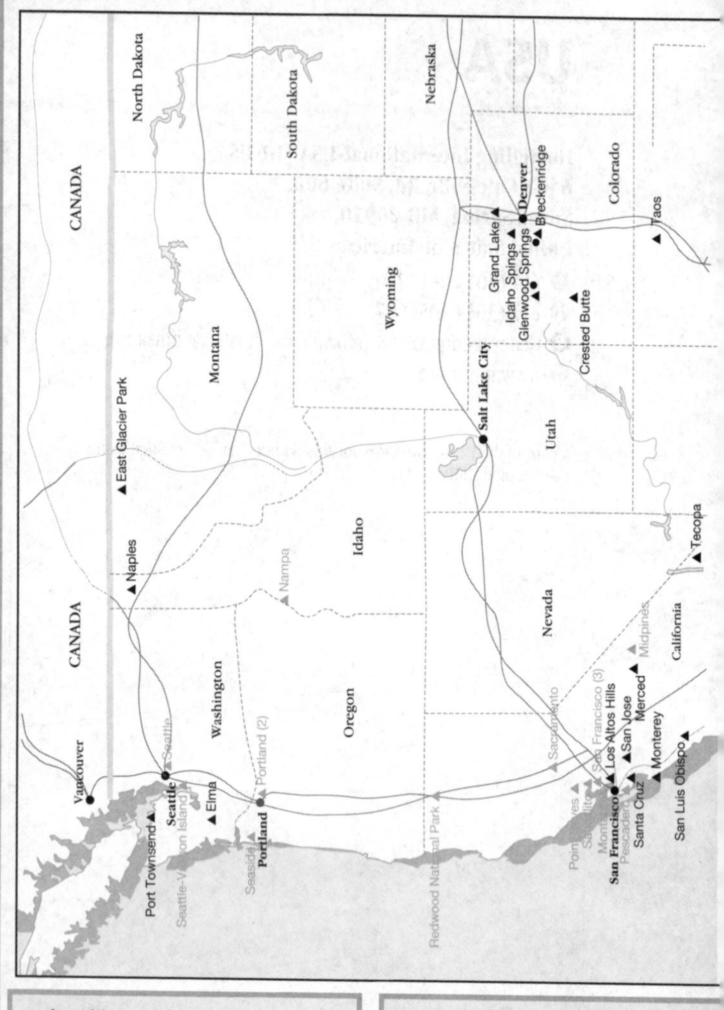

Undeniably one of the world's superpowers, the United States of America is made up of forty-eight neighbouring states plus the separate states of Alaska and Hawaii. The U.S.A. has a population of approximately 290 million. New York is the biggest city, and Washington D.C. is the capital. The American population is the product of immigration and variety; the only real natives are American Indians, and the U.S.A. has welcomed more migrants into the country than any other nation. This is reflected in the national character – the people's welcoming nature, their independence, and their strong belief in freedom.

A few other Top Tips from **CULTURE SMART!:**

- Americans are generally very direct in conversation, and this can be misconstrued as bluntness by the outside observer. However, despite their direct approach, most Americans will speak in a polite and courteous manner.
- Introductions in the U.S.A. are casual. Older people, or those in a formal or business situation, shake hands on

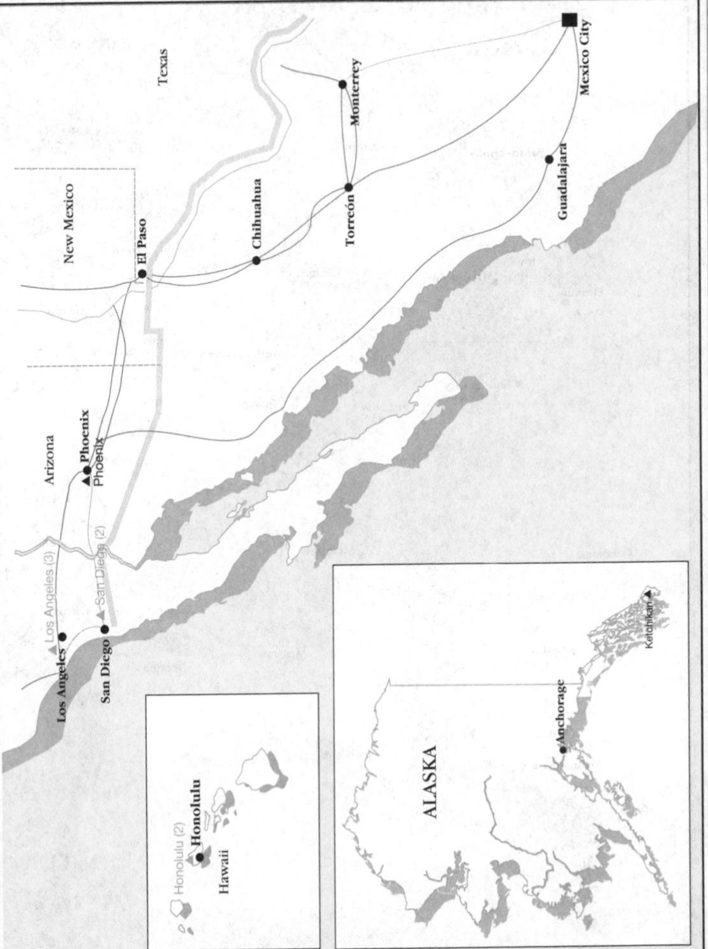

first meeting. Women greeting women, or a woman greeting a man, may meet with an "air" kiss on the cheek. Two men will shake hands. Using first names is commonplace in the U.S.A.

- A friendly approach is an American trait, intended to generate positive feelings. If somebody says "Hello!" to you in the street, they are not necessarily trying to start a conversation with you. It is simply an example of American friendliness.
- Americans have a reputation for eating a considerable amount of "fast food," but they also enjoy a vast range of foods from all over the globe. A meal is usually eaten just with a fork, held in the right hand; a knife may be used if necessary to cut or spread, and is then laid on the side of the plate. In general, table manners are informal; however it is considered impolite to rest your elbows on the table.
- Social events are often organized at short notice, so don't be surprised if you are invited to someone's house, or to see a movie or sports match, without much warning. Don't be

afraid to decline the offer if you are unable to attend. Your host will not be offended.

Culture Smart! Top Tips © Kuperard 2005

Cultural Top Tips supplied by Culture Smart! guides. These essential guides to customs and etiquette will help you steer clear of embarrassing gaffes and sensitive issues, enabling you to discover new cultures whilst developing new friendships. Order online at www.culturesmartguides.co.uk

You can find out a lot more on our website - a visit to www.HIhostels.com is essential for planning your trip!

Pour en savoir plus, rendez-vous sur notre site Internet, www.HIhostels.com une visite incontournable pour préparer votre voyage!

Viele weitere Informationen auf unserer Website: www.HIhostels.com - unverzichtbar für die Reiseplanung!

Puedes averiguar mucho más en nuestro sitio web. Es imprescindible que visites la página

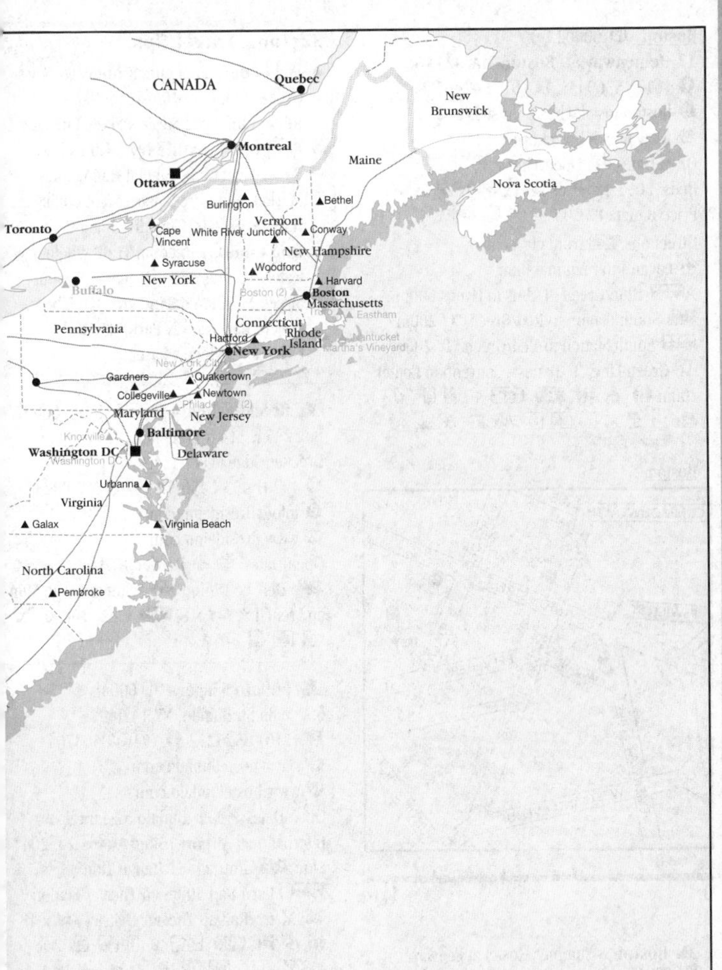

Akron ☛ **Peninsula**

▲ Austin 60035
2200 S Lakeshore Blvd, Austin TX 78741.
(512) 4442294 (512) 4442309
hostel@hiaustin.org www.hiaustin.org
Open Dates: Austin-Bergstrom 8km
Amtrak 5km 7 200m ap Burton & E Riverside x 39
1 x
2.5km

▲ Bethel – SnowBoarding House – 60132
646 West Bethel Rd., Bethel ME 04217.
(207) 8244424 207) 8248511
info@betheloutdooradventure.com
www.betheloutdooradventure.com
Open Dates: 01.04-30.09 x 30

Boston 60002

12 Hemenway St, Boston MA 02115.

(617) 5369455 (617) 4246558

bostonhostel@bostonhostel.org

www.bostonhostel.org

Open Dates: Open Times:

Beds: 205 - 1x² 6x³ 1x⁴ 9x⁵ 1x⁶

Price Range: $21.99-39.99 BB inc

Directions: 3SW from city centre

Logan International 6km

A Blue/Green "T" bus to Hynes 600m

South Station to Red/Green "T" 200m

South Station to Red/Green "T" 200m

U Green Line "T" Hynes - Convention Center 200m R CC 1 x

Boston

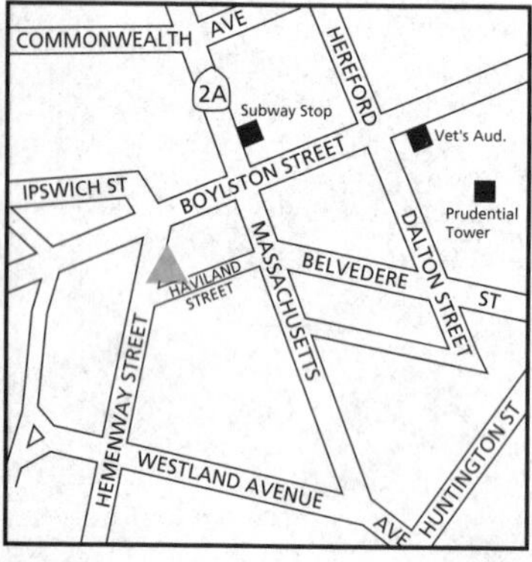

Boston – Summer Hostel at Fenway 60041

575 Commonwealth Avenue, Boston, MA 02215.

(617) 2678599 (617) 4246558

fenwayhostel@bostonhostel.org

www.bostonhostel.org

Open Dates: 02.06-13.08 Logan 8km

South Station 4.5km U Kenmore Sq 200m 1.5NW x 300 R CC 1 x

Boston... Travel Tips

- **For budget eats check out...** Woody's Grill & Tap, Pour House, No Name Restaurant, Little Stevie's Pizza, City Kitche
- **For great nightlife try...** Landsdowne Street Night Club, Fanueil Hall/Quincy Market, Kenmore Square Night Clubs, Harvard Square, The Alley Night Clubs
- **Don't miss...** Freedom Trail, Whale watching, Museum of Science, Newbury Street, Museum of Fine Arts, JFK Library, Cheers Bar, Fenway Park, Harvard University, Filene's basement

Breckenridge – Fireside Inn – 60047

Box 2252, 114 N French St, Breckenridge CO 80424.

(970) 453-6456 (970) 547-0023

info@firesideinn.com

www.firesideinn.com

Open Dates: Denver 177km

Denver 174km Summitstage 50m ap French St x 8 R CC

Buffalo Niagara 60048

667 Main St, Buffalo, NY 14203.

(716) 8525222 (716) 8563764

stay@hostelbuffalo.com

www.hostelbuffalo.com

Open Dates: Buffalo Niagara International Airport 15km A 24, 204 1km Amtrack-Exchange 2km

Metro Rail 500m ap Theater Station

Metro Rail ap Theater District x 48 R CC 1 x 2km

Burlington – Mrs Farrell's Home Hoste – 60049

Burlington, Vermont.

(802) 8653730

Open Dates: 01.04-31.10 x 6 R

Cape Vincent – Tibbetts Point Lighthouse Hostel – 60050

33439 County Route 6, Cape Vincent NY 13618.

(When shut: 535 Oak St., Syracuse, NY 13203)

(315) 6543450, (315) 4725788 (when shut) lighthousehostel@tds.net

Open Dates: 15.05-24.10 x 26 R

Chicago 60034
24 East Congress Parkway, Chicago, IL 60605.
(312) 3600300 (312) 3600313
reserve@hichicago.org
www.hichicago.org
Open Dates: Open Times:
Beds: 500 - 56x2 44x4 26x6 8x6+
Price Range: $30-35 (+ Tax)
Directions: 0.5S from city centre
O'Hare International 29km, Midway National 15km A Use Metro (CTA)
Union Station (Amtrak) 600m
Intercity Bus Terminal - Greyhound 600m U Library/Van Buren R CC 3 x

Chicago

Chicago... Travel Tips

- **For budget eats check out...** Café Giogia, Los Amigos, Millers Pub, Fast Foo's, Trattoria Caterina
- **For great nightlife try...** Second City, The Chicago Symphony Orchestra, Goodman Theatre, House of Blues, North Halsted Street
- **Don't miss...** Adler Planetarium, Field Museum, Shedd Aquarium, Museum of Natural History, Sears Tower, Hancock Observatory, Navy Pier, Buckingham Fountain, Magnificent Mile/Michigan Avenue, Sail on Lake Michigan

Clearwater Beach – 60051
606 Bay Esplanade, Clearwater Beach, FL 33767.
(727) 4431211 (727) 4431211
magillr1@juno.com
www.clearwaterbeachhostel.com
Open Dates: x 48 CC

Cleveland ☛ **Peninsula**

Collegeville – Evansburg State Park – 60052
837 Mayhall Rd, Collegeville, PA 19426.
(610) 4090113
hievansburg@hi-dvc.org
www.hi-dvc.org
Open Dates: x 18 R CC

Conway (White Mountains) – 60053
White Mountains, 36 Washington St, Conway NH 03818.
(603) 4471001 (432) 3396758
conwayhostel@yahoo.com
www.conwayhostel.com
Open Dates: Manchester 150km
Portland, ME Greyhound 500m
x 48 R CC
TV 500m

Crested Butte – 60054
615 Teocalli Ave, PO Box 1332, Crested Butte, CO 81224.
(970) 3490588; (888) 3890588
(970) 3490586
hostel@crestedbutte.net
www.crestedbuttehostel.com
Open Dates: x 50 R CC

East Glacier Park – Brownie's – 60058
1020 Montana Hwy 49, PO Box 229, East Glacier Park MT 59434.
(406) 2264426 (406) 2264426
i.m.chase@worldnet.att.net
www.brownieshostel.com
Open Dates: 01.06-14.10 (for exact dates)
Amtrak 500m x 25 R CC

▲ Eastham – Mid-Cape 60059
Mid-Cape, 75 Goody Hallet Drive, Eastham MA 02642.
(When shut: sophie@usahostels.org)
(508) 2552785
midcapehostel@yahoo.com
www.capecodhostels.org
Open Dates: 20.05-11.09 Boston 160km A Boston 160km Plymouth and Brockton 5km ap Bonanza Orleans NOT Eastham 5km x 48 (B) 30m 8km

▲ Elma – Grays Harbor Hostel – 60060
6 Ginny Lane, Elma, WA 98541.
(360) 4823119
ghhostel@techline.com
Open Dates: x 14

▲ Florida City – Everglades 60061
20 S.W. Second Ave, Florida City, FL 33034.
(305) 2481122 (305) 2457622
gladeshostel@hotmail.com
www.evergladeshostel.com
Open Dates: x 47

Fullerton ☛ **Los Angeles**

▲ Galax – Blue Ridge Mountains Hostel – 60062
Blue Ridge Pkwy 214507 (at milepost 214.5, Eastern Side), Galax VA 24333.
(276) 2364962
Open Dates: 01.04-31.10 x 20

▲ Galveston – 60063
201 Seawall Boulevard, Galveston, TX 77550.
(409) 7659431 (409) 7656545
sndpipr325@aol.com
www.sandpipermotel.com
Open Dates: Hobby-Houston 75km A Galveston Limousine Galveston 3km Houston 75km x 24 100m

▲ Gardners – Ironmaster's Mansion – 60064
Pine Grove Furnace State Park, 1212 Pine Grove Rd, Gardners PA 17324.
(717) 4867575 (717) 4865115
hiironmasters@hi-dvc.org
www.hi-dvc.org
Open Dates: 01.03-20.12 x 46

▲ HI Glenwood Springs Hostel – 60065
1021 Grand Ave, Glenwood Springs CO 81601.
(970) 945-8545
info@hostelcolorado.com
www.hostelcolorado.com
Open Dates: Denver 200km A Greyhound 500m Amtrak-4 blocks 500m Greyhound-4 blocks 500m Bus to Aspen 0.2S x 42 200m 200m

▲ Grand Lake – Shadowcliff Hostel – 60066
405 Summerland Park Rd, PO Box 658, Grand Lake CO 80447.
(970) 6279220 (970) 6279220
www.shadowcliff.org
Open Dates: 30.05-02.10 x 14

▲ Hartford – The Mark Twain Hostel – 60067
131 Tremont St, Hartford, CT 06105.
(860) 5237255 (860) 2331767
davidmarktwain@aol.com
Open Dates: x 42

▲ Harvard – Friendly Crossways – 60078
PO Box 2266, Littleton MA 01460.
(978) 4569386
info@friendlycrossways.com
www.friendlycrossways.com
Open Dates: 02.01-23.12 Boston 40km Littleton 5km x 35 2 x 5km

▲ **Honolulu** – University 60018
2323A Seaview Ave, Honolulu HI 96822.
(808) 9460591 (808) 9465904
hihostel@lava.net
www.hostelsaloha.com
Open Dates: Honolulu 10km
A 19, 20 then 4, 6 19, 20, then 4, 6 5W x 43 R CC 4km 3km

Honolulu – Waikiki 60017
2417 Prince Edward St,
Honolulu HI 96815.
(808) 9268313 (808) 9223798
ayhaloha@lava.net
www.hostelsaloha.com
Open Dates: Open Times: 07.00-03.00hrs
Beds: 60 - 4x2 8x3 4x4 1x6
Price Range: $20
Directions: 5W from city centre
Honolulu International 10km A 20 to Kings Village 100m x 2 R CC 150m 150m

Honolulu – Waikiki

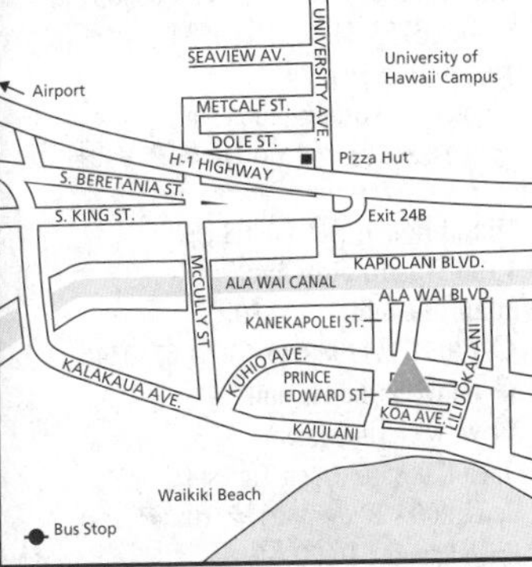

Honolulu... Travel Tips

- **For budget eats check out...** International Market Place, Ono's Hawaiian Food, Genki Sushi, Ala Moana Shopping Center
- **For great nightlife try...** Art Gallery Walk, Wave Waikiki Nightclub, Restaurant Row/Movies, Duke's Barefoot Beach Bar
- **Don't miss...** Polynesian Cultural Center, Hanauma Bay, Pali Lookout, Downtown Honolulu, North Shore Beaches, Bishop Museum, Dole Plantation, Manoa Falls hike, Pearl Harbour

▲ **Idaho Springs** – Lodge of the Rocky Mountains – 60069
1601 Colorado Blvd.,
Idaho Springs CO 80452.
(303) 5672839
innkeeperdenver@aol.com
www.innkeeperrockies.com
Open Dates: x 40 R CC

▲ **Itasca State Park** – Mississippi Headwaters – 60070
Main Park Drive - Itasca State Park, HC 5, Box 5A, Lake Itasca, MN 56470.
(218) 2663415 (218) 2663415 (call first) itascamn@aol.com
www.himinnesota.org
Open Dates: 01.01-12.03; 06.05-12.11; 26-31.12 x 31 R CC

▲ **Ketchikan** – 60071
Grant and Main St, PO Box 8515,
Ketchikan AK 99901.
(907) 2253319 (907) 2473780
ktnyh@eagle.ptialaska.net
Open Dates: 01.06-31.08 x 19 R

▲ **Knoxville** – Harpers Ferry WV
60075
19123 Sandy Hook Rd, Knoxville MD 21758.
(301) 8347652 (301) 8347652
mail@harpersferryhostel.org
www.harpersferryhostel.org
Open Dates: 16.03-14.11 x 37 R

▲ **Lincoln** – Cornerstone – 60077
640 North 16th St, Lincoln NE 68508.
(402) 4760926 (402) 4760356
hostelne@yahoo.com
Open Dates: 01.03-12.20 Lincoln 11.26km (Take Downtown exit and follow signs) ap 11th and Cornhusker (5 miles) 710 80m ap J Street @ 17th and Vine (2 miles) 11.26] x 9 R

Los Altos Hills ☛ **Palo Alto**

▲ **Los Angeles** – Fullerton 60079
1700 N Harbor Blvd,
Fullerton CA 92835. (Disneyland area).
(714) 7383721 (714) 7380925
hifull@aol.com
Open Dates: 13.06-30.09 x 20 R CC

Los Angeles – Santa Monica 60006
1436 2nd St, Santa Monica CA 90401.
(310) 3939913 (310) 3931769
reserve@HILosAngeles.org
www.HILosAngeles.org
Open Dates: Open Times:
Beds: 224 - 9x1 4x4 15x6 16x6
Price Range: $24-29 (+ Tax)
Directions: Los Angeles International (LAX) 11km Union (Amtrak) 30km Greyhound Depot 26km x 4 (B) 1 x 1km 500m

Los Angeles – Santa Monica

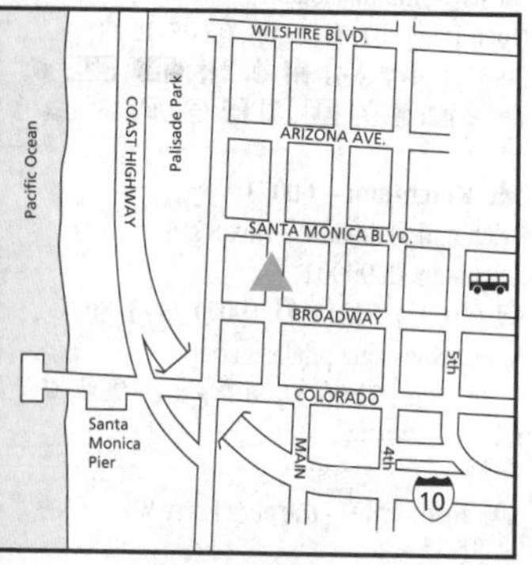

Los Angeles – South Bay 60080
3601 South Gaffey St, Building 613, San Pedro CA 90731-6969.
(310) 8318109 (310) 8314635
hisanpedro@aol.com
Open Dates: 13.06-30.09 ( ) 32S x 60 1 x

Los Angeles... Travel Tips

- **For budget eats check out...** Fat Burgers, La Salsa, McDonald's, Subway, Thai Dishes
- **For great nightlife try...** Third Street Promenade, Sunset Strip, Main Street - Santa Monica, Santa Monica Pier, Hollywood
- **Don't miss...** J Paul Getty Museum, Venice Beach, Universal Studios, Disneyland, Beverly Hills & Rodeo Drive, Hollywood Walk of Fame, Six Flags Magic Mountain/Hurricane Harbour Water Park, Olvera Street/Chinatown, Queen Mary, Disney's Symphony Hall

Lucas – Malabar Farm Hostel 60081
3954 Bromfield Rd, Lucas OH 44843.
(419) 8922055 (419) 8923055
Open Dates: 15.01-14.12 x 19

Madison 60082
141 South Butler St, Madison, WI 53703.
(608) 4410144 (801) 6594268
madisonhostel@yahoo.com
www.madisonhostel.org
Open Dates: x 28

Martha's Vineyard 60011
Edgartown Rd, PO Box 3158, West Tisbury MA 02575.
(When shut: sophie@usahostels.org)
(508) 6932665 (508) 6932699
mvhostel@yahoo.com
www.capecodhostels.org
Open Dates: 22.04-02.10 Marthas Vineyard 5km Vineyard Haven 5km Bonanza ap Woods Hole 11S x 74 (B) 5km 5km

Merced – Home Hostel – 60083
PO Box 3755, Merced CA 95344.
(209) 7250407
merced-hostel@juno.com
Open Dates: x 6

Miami Beach 60008
1438 Washington Ave, Miami Beach FL 33139.
(305) 5342988 (305) 6730346
info@clayhotel.com
www.clayhotel.com
Open Dates: Open Times:
Beds: 200 - 10x2 30x4 10x6
Price Range: $16-20
Directions: Miami International 16km A Super Shuttle to YH, "J" bus to 41st Street, then "C" bus to alighting point 200m Miami 4km Amtrak 10km Greyhound bus to "C" bus 8km ap Washington and 15th Street 200m x 10 1 x 500m 500m

Miami Beach

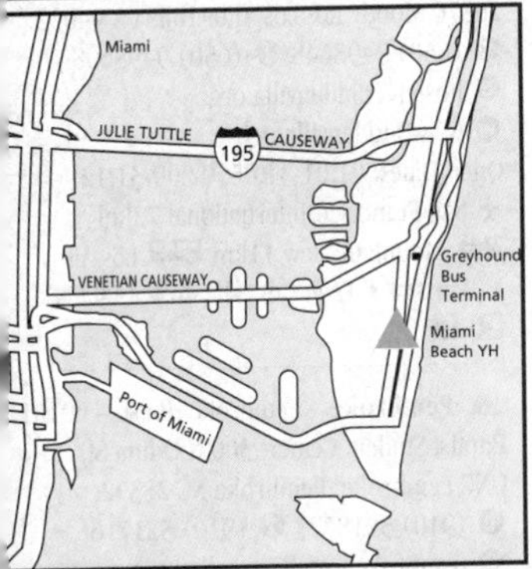

Miami Beach... Travel Tips

- **For budget eats check out...** Lincoln Road, Ocean Drive
- **For great nightlife try...** Mango's, Crobar, Score, Space, Blue
- **Don't miss...** South Beach, Bayside, Key Biscayne, Coconut Grove, Villa Viscaya & Venetian Pool, Little Havana, Parrot Jungle, Everglades, Florida Keys, Casino Boat

▲ **Midpines** – The Yosemite Bug Rustic Mountain Resort Ⓗ 60085
6979 Hwy 140, PO Box 81,
Midpines CA 95345.
(209) 9666666 (209) 9666667
bughost@yosemitebug.com
www.yosemitebug.com
Open Dates: San Francisco International 240km Yosemite Bug Stop - Amtrak 250m Yosemite Area Regional Transit System 250m ap Yosemite Bug Stop 250m x 54 3 x 90m

▲ **Montara** – Point Montara Lighthouse Ⓗ 60087
PO Box 737, 16th St at California Hwy 1, Montara CA 94037.
(650) 7287177 (650) 7287177
himontara@norcalhostels.org
www.norcalhostels.org
Open Dates: San Francisco International 50km Sam Tran 200m x 50 1 x 100m 100m

▲ **Monterey** – 60088
778 Hawthorne St, Monterey, CA 93940.
(831) 6490375
info@montereyhostel.org
www.montereyhostel.org
Open Dates: x 45

▲ **Nampa** – Hostel Boise Ⓗ 60090
17322 Can-Ada Rd, Nampa, ID 83687.
(208) 4676858 mail@hostelboise.com
www.hostelboise.com
Open Dates: Boise 25km Greyhound 5km x 11

▲ **Nantucket** – Surfside Beach Ⓗ 60091
31 Western Ave, Nantucket MA 02554.
(When shut: sophie@usahostels.org)
(508) 2280433
nantuckethostel@yahoo.com
www.capecodhostels.org
Open Dates: 13.05-02.10 Nantucket 5km Nantucket 5km Hyannis ap Surfside Bus 5SW x 49 (B) 200m 200m

▲ **Naples** – 60092
Hwy 2, Naples ID 83847.
(208) 2672947 (208) 2674118
Open Dates: x 18

New York City Ⓗ 60003
891 Amsterdam Ave at West 103rd St, New York NY 10025.
(212) 9322300 (212) 9322574
reserve@hinewyork.org
www.hinewyork.org
Open Dates: Open Times:
Beds: 624 - 16x4 22x6 38x6+
Price Range: $29-40
Directions: Kennedy 20km, LaGuardia 8km, Newark 25km A Grayline to YH Penn 4.5km Port Authority 3.5km U 1, 9 to 103rd ap St Station 200m x 7 (B) 4 x 1km

New York City

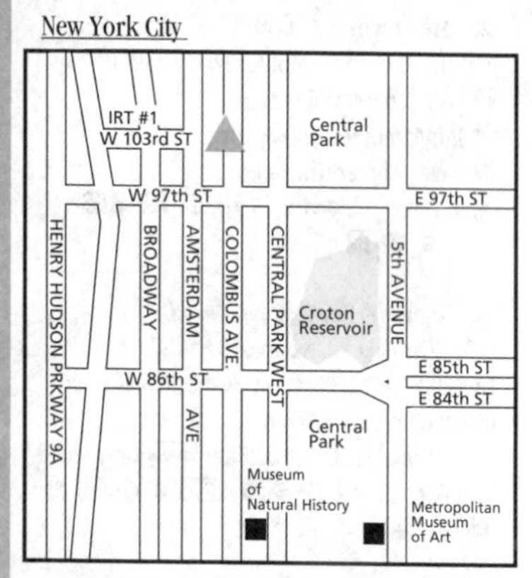

New York City... Travel Tips

- **For budget eats check out...** Pizza Parlours, Diners, New York Deli's, Little Italy, Hostel Coffee Bar
- **For great nightlife try...** See a Musical on Broadway, Lincoln Center, Midtown, East Village, Greenwich Village
- **Don't miss...** Statue of Liberty/Ellis Island Ferry, Chinatown, United Nations, Central Park, Shopping on Fifth Avenue, Empire State Building, Times Square, Rockefeller Centre, Brooklyn Bridge, Little Italy

▲ **Newburg** – Wellspring – 60094
4382 Hickory Rd, PO Box 72,
Newburg WI 53060-0072.
(262) 6756755 wellspring@hnet.net
Open Dates: x 5

▲ **Newtown** – Tyler State Park – 60095
PO Box 94, Newtown, PA 18940.
(215) 9680927 (215) 5572100
hityler@hi-dvc.org www.hi-dvc.org
Open Dates: x 25

▲ **Nordland (Marrowstone Island)** – Fort Flagler – 60098
Fort Flagler State Park, 10621 Flagler Rd,
Nordland (Marrowstone Island), WA 98358.
(360) 3851288 ffhostel@olypen.com
Open Dates: 01.06-30.09 Seattle 167km
Port Townsend 26km 1.61N x 14

▲ **Palo Alto** – Hidden Villa – 60100
26870 Moody Rd, Los Altos Hills CA 94022.
(650) 9498648 (650) 9498608
hostel@hiddenvilla.org
www.hiddenvilla.org
Open Dates: 01.01-31.05; 02.09-31.12
San Francisco International 72km
Mountain View 11km Los Altos 3.3km x 32

▲ **Pembroke** – Pembroke House – 60101
Baptist Student Center, 300 N Odum St,
UNC Pembroke, Pembroke NC 28372.
(910) 5218777 (910) 5217166
pembrokehostel@carolina.net
Open Dates: Raleigh 180km
Fayetteville 70km Lumberton 20km x 8

▲ **Peninsula** – Cuyahoga Valley Stanford Hostel – 60102
6093 Stanford Rd, Peninsula OH 44264.
(330) 4678711 (330) 4678711
hi-stanfordhostel@juno.com
Open Dates: x 30

▲ **Pescadero** – Pigeon Point Lighthouse
60103
210 Pigeon Point Rd, Pescadero CA 94060.
(650) 8790633 (650) 8799120
pplhostel@norcalhostels.org
www.norcalhostels.org
Open Dates: San Francisco International 65km x 52
1 x
100m

▲ **Philadelphia** – Bank Street Hostel
60104
32 S.Bank St, Philadelphia, PA 19106.
(215) 9220222 (215) 9224082
manager@bankstreethostel.com
www.bankstreethostel.com
Open Dates: Philadelphia (PHL) 20km
Amtrak 5km U 2nd St 250m x 70

▲ **Philadelphia** – Chamounix Mansion – 60105
3250 Chamounix Drive,
Philadelphia PA 19131.
(215) 8783676 (215) 8714313
chamounix@philahostel.org
www.philahostel.org
Open Dates: 16.01-14.12 Philadelphia 26km 30th St Station 13km Greyhound 13km x 80
12km

▲ **Phoenix** – The Metcalf House – 60106
1026 N 9th St, Phoenix AZ 85006.
(602) 2549803
Open Dates: 01.01-31.07; 01.09-31.12 Sky Harbor Phoenix 10km Red Line and 10 (45 min) 10 Bus from Central Bus Station ap 9th Street and Roosevelt, Walk N. 4 Houses to Hostel x 22
(LD)

▲ **Point Reyes National Seashore**
60109
(off Limantour Rd), Box 247,
Point Reyes Station CA 94956.
(415) 6638811 (415) 6638811
www.norcalhostels.org
Open Dates: San Francisco International 100km x 44
1km

▲ **Port Townsend** – Olympic Hostel – 60110
#272 Battery Way, Port Townsend WA 98368.
(360) 3850655
olympichostel@olympus.net
Open Dates: SeaTac 172km Port Townsend 5.6km x 27

Portland (Oregon) – Hawthorne District
60111
3031 SE Hawthorne Blvd,
Portland OR 97214.
(503) 2363380
hip@portlandhostel.org
www.portlandhostel.org
Open Dates: Open Times: 08.00-22.00hrs
Beds: 33 - 1x2 1x4 2x6 2x6
Price Range: $17-22
Directions: 3E from city centre
Portland-PDX 9.7km Union (Amtrak) and Greyhound Stations 4km SW 5th Ave. - Just Outside of the stations ap SE Hawthirne and 30th Ave.
(B)
2.9km

Portland (Oregon) – Hawthorne District

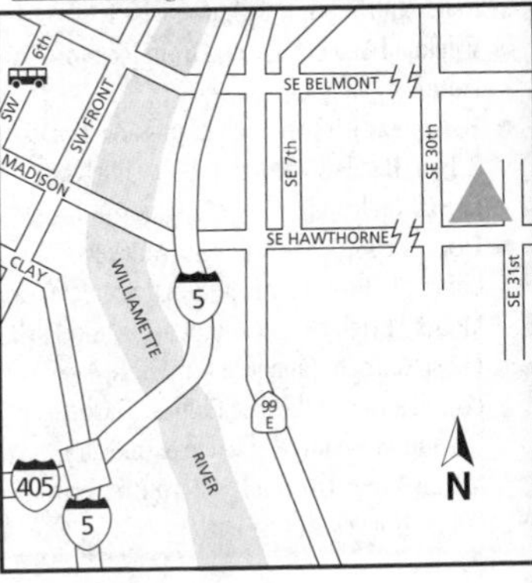

Portland (Oregon) – Northwest 60112
1818 NW Glisan, Portland, OR 97209.
(503) 2412783 (503) 5255910
hinwp@teleport.com
www.2oregonhostels.com
Open Dates: Open Times: 08.00-23.00hrs
Beds: 34 - 2x1 4x2 4x4
Price Range: $17-22
Directions: Portland International Airport 8km Red Line MAX Train 500m Amtrak 750m 17 ap NW Gibson and 19th Ave. MAX Train - Red Line 500m ap PGE Park x 2
1 x
250m

Portland (Oregon) – Northwest

Portland (Oregon)... Travel Tips

- **For budget eats check out...** NW Neighbourhood, Hawthorne District, Weekend Market, Escape from NY Pizza, Paradox Café
- **For great nightlife try...** Mission Theater & Pub, Bagdad Theater & Pub, Old Town, Crystal Ballroom, Upper Hawthorne
- **Don't miss...** The Weekend Markets, The Columbia River Gorge National Scenic Area, Mount St Helens Volcano, Washington Park (Rose Garden, Japanese Garden & Zoo), Powell's Books, Classic Chinese Gardens, Oregon Museum of Science & Industry, Mount Tabor Overlook, Micro Breweries & Coffee Houses, Forest Park

▲ **Quakertown** – HI-Weisel – 60113
7347 Richlandtown Rd,
Quakertown PA 18951.
(215) 5368749 www.buckscounty.org
Open Dates: 01.02-12.24
Allentown-Bethlehem Airport 20km
Quakertown Shopping Center 4km 4NW
x 20 R P

▲ **Redwood National Park** HI 60114
14480 Hwy 101 at Wilson Creek Rd,
Klamath CA 95548.
(707) 4828265 (707) 4824662
info@redwoodhostel.com
www.norcalhostels.org
Open Dates: 12 x 30 R
CC TV P

▲ **Sacramento** HI 60115
925 H St, Sacramento CA 95814.
(916) 4431691 (916) 4434763
hisac@norcalhostels.org
www.norcalhostels.org
Open Dates: 12 Sacramento 16km
Amtrak 1.25km x 70 R CC P 1.6km

San Diego – Downtown HI 60024 FNM
521 Market St, San Diego CA 92101.
(619) 5251531 (619) 3380129
downtown@sandiegohostels.org
www.sandiegohostels.org
Open Dates: 12 Open Times:
Beds: 142 - 27x2 3x3 8x4 1x5 2x6 3x6
Price Range: $19-29 BBinc
Directions: San Diego International 5km
A 992 to 5th & Broadway 4km
Santa Fe Depot (Amtrak) 1km
Greyhound 500m ap 6th Avenue & Market Street 300m ap 5th Avenue 300m
x 4 R CC TV
i 8 4km

San Diego – Downtown

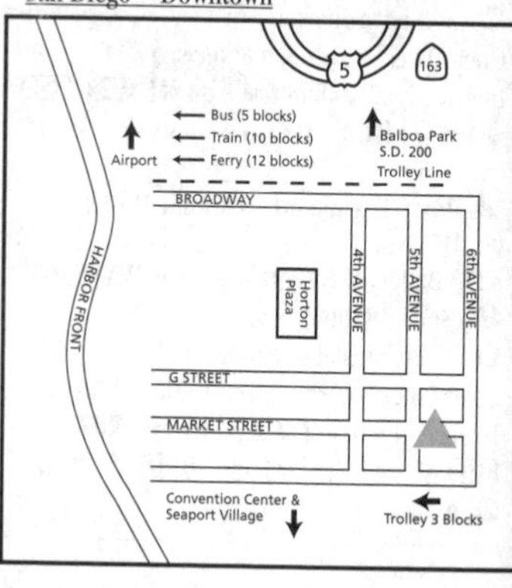

San Diego – Point Loma 60023
3790 Udall St,
San Diego CA 92107-2414.
(619) 2234778 (619) 2231883
pointloma@sandiegohostels.org
www.sandiegohostels.org
Open Dates: Open Times: 08.00-22.00hrs
Beds: 53 - 8x^{2} 3x^{3} 2x^{4} 2x^{6} 1x^{6+}
Price Range: $17-22
Directions: 10W from city centre
San Diego International 5km
Broadway Pier/Embarcadero 9km
Santa Fe Depot (Amtrak) 9km 35
200m ap Voltaire and Poinsetta 500m
Oldtown Transit Center 5km ap to M 35
x 2 R CC TV
2km 1.5km

San Diego – Point Loma

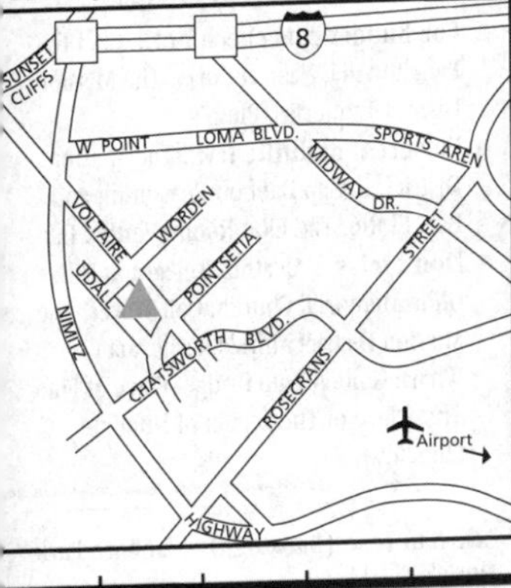

San Diego... Travel Tips

- **For budget eats check out...** Santa Monica St. @ Ocean Beach, The Ocean Walk Along Misson Beach & Pacific Beach, Pokez Mexican Restaurant (10th Ave. & E. St. Downtown), O.B. People's Co-op Café (Voltaire St., Ocean Beach), Celadon Thai Restaurant (5th Ave, University Ave, Hill Crest)
- **For great nightlife try...** Gaslamp Quarter, Pacific Beach, Ocean Beach, Le Stats Coffee House (35th Ave & Adam Ave, Normal Heights), The Whistle Stop Bar (Fern St. & Juniper St., South Park)
- **Don't miss...** The Beaches & Mission Bay, San Diego Zoo & Wild Animal Park, Tijuana - Mexico, Balboa Park, Sea World, Sea Kayaking in La Jolla Cove, Cabrillo National Monument, Mission Bay Park, Hiking in Torrey Pines Park, Whale watching

San Francisco – City Center 60036 FNM
685 Ellis Street, San Francisco,
CA 94109.
(415) 474 5721 (415) 7760775
citycenter@sfhostels.com
www.sfhostels.org
Open Dates: Open Times:
Beds: 157 - 12x^{2} 22x^{4} 9x^{5}
Price Range: $22-29
Directions: San Francisco International 22km A Aiport Shuttle San Francisco Ferry Building 5km
Amtrak/Ferry Building 5km 38
150m U Civic Center/Van Ness 2km
R CC TV
5km

San Francisco – City Center

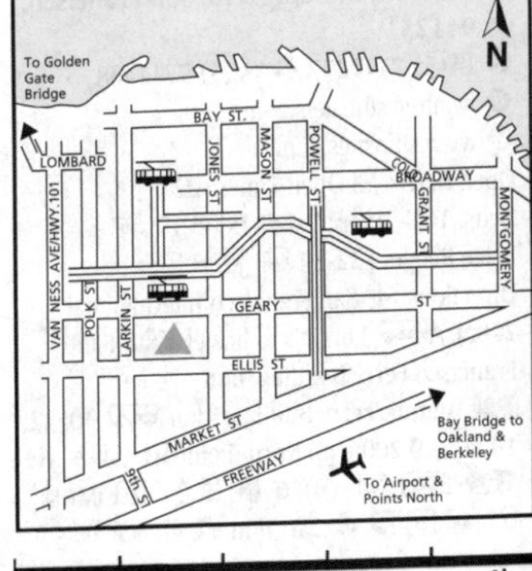

San Francisco – Downtown (Union Square)
60009
312 Mason St, San Francisco CA 94102.
(415) 7885604 (415) 7883023
dtinfo@sfhostels.com
www.sfhostels.com
Open Dates: Open Times:
Beds: 280 - 14x1 38x2 6x3 40x4 1x6
Price Range: $22-29
Directions: San Francisco International 8.7km A Airport Shuttle To Hostel Amtrak 1.5km Greyhound - Transbay Terminal to 38 100m ap Mason and Geary St Station Market & Powell 100m U Market and Powell 100m x 92 11km

San Francisco – Downtown (Union Square)

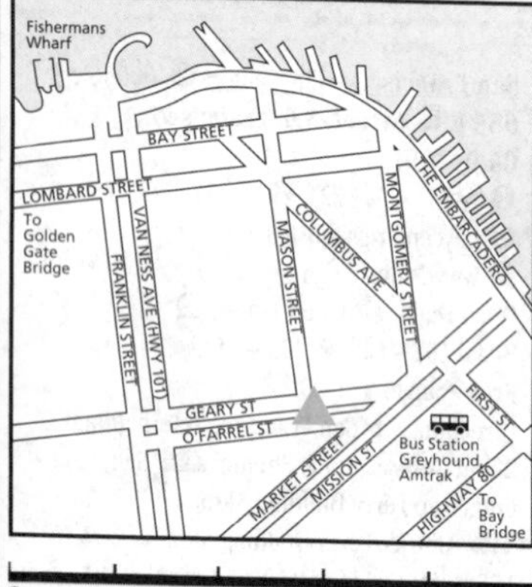

San Francisco – Fisherman's Wharf
60001
Fort Mason, Building 240, San Francisco, CA 94123.
(415) 7717277 (415) 7711468
fwinfo@sfhostels.com
www.sfhostels.com
Open Dates: Open Times:
Beds: 162 - 4x3 7x4 1x6 10x6
Price Range: $22-29 BB inc
Directions: San Francisco International 22km A Lorrie's to hostel San Francisco Ferry Building 4km Amtrak/Ferry Building 4km 30, 32, 10, 47, 49 200m ap North Point x 4 (B) 4km 4km

San Francisco – Fisherman's Wharf

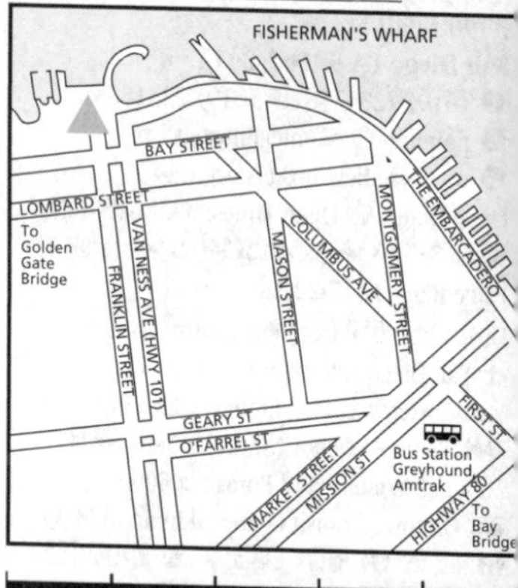

San Francisco... Travel Tips

- **For budget eats check out...** Chef Jia, Pancho Villa, Naan & Curry, The Mission District Taquerias, Pluto's
- **For great nightlife try...** The Mission District, Bissap Baobob Restaurant and Bar, El Rio, The Elbo Room, Vertigo Bar
- **Don't miss...** Alcatraz, Telegraph Hill, Glide Memorial Church, Coit Tower, The Mission District Murals, Fisherman's Wharf, Golden Gate Bridge, Place of Fine Arts, Place of The Legion of Honor, Chinatown

▲ **San Jose (Saratoga)** – Sanborn Park Hostel – 60117
15808 Sanborn Rd, Saratoga CA 95070.
(408) 7410166
www.sanbornparkhostel.org
Open Dates: San Jose International (SJC) 25km Amtrak, Caltrain in San Jose 22km VTA 6km ap Saratoga Village x 39

▲ **San Luis Obispo** – Hostel Obispo – 60118
1617 Santa Rosa St., San Luis Obispo, CA 93401.
(805) 5444678 (805) 5443142
www.hostelobispo.com
Open Dates: x 22

▲ **Santa Cruz** – Hostelling International
anta Cruz At The Carmelita Cottages – 60119
21 Main St, PO Box 1241,
anta Cruz CA 95061.
(831) 4238304 (831) 4298541
info@hi-santacruz.org
www.hi-santacruz.org
Open Dates: San Jose International (SJC) 56km Amtrak 1.25km Greyhound 1.25km x 44 2km 250m

aratoga ☛ **San Jose (Saratoga)**

Sausalito – Marin Headlands 60013
Fort Barry, Building 941,
Sausalito CA 94965.
(415) 3312777 (415) 3313568
marinhdl@norcalhostels.org
www.norcalhostels.org
Open Dates: Open Times: 07.30-23.30hrs
Beds: 104 - 3x³ 1x⁴ 3x⁵ 1x⁶ 7x⁶⁺
Price Range: $18-22 € 22-26
Directions: San Francisco International 32km A Marin Airporter 6.5km Sausalito 6.5km Amtrak - 5F Transbay Terminal 16km Golden Gate Transit 10, 50 4km 1 x 1km

Sausalito – Marin Headlands

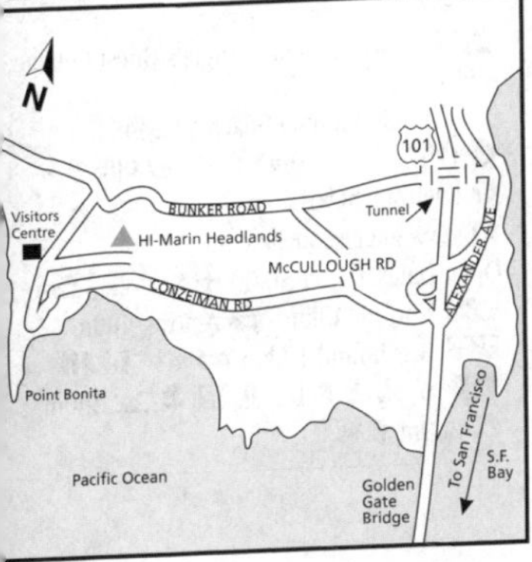

Sausalito... Travel Tips

- **For budget eats check out...** Café Trieste, Mama's Royal Café, Joe's Taco Lounge, Avatar's Punjab Burrito, Arawan
- **For great nightlife try...** No Name Bar, Sweetwater Bar, Mill Valley Sequoia Theater, San Rafael Theater, San Rafael Farmer's Market
- **Don't miss...** Golden Gate Bridge, Marin Headlands Visitors Centre, Muir Woods, Stinson Beach, Sausalito House Boats, Surf Lessons, Point Bonita Lighthouse, Sausalito Art Galleries, Kayaking, Angel Island

▲ **Seaside** 60121
930 N Holladay, Seaside, OR 97138.
(503) 7387911 (503) 7170163
seaside@teleport.com
www.2oregonhostels.com
Open Dates: Portland 100km Amtrak Bus Greyhound ap Seaside hostel x 56 1km 250m

Seattle – Downtown 60004
84 Union St, Seattle WA 98101.
(206) 6225443; (888) 6225443
(206) 6822179 reserve@hiseattle.org
www.hiseattle.org
Open Dates: Open Times:
Beds: 135
Directions: Seattle-Tacoma 24km A 194 to University St. Station Tunnel , 174 ap 4th and Union 200m Victoria Clipper 1km Amtrak 1.5km 15, 18 100m ap 1st and Union (B) 1 x

Seattle – Downtown

Seattle – Vashon Island AYH Ranch Hostel 60122
12119 Cove Rd SW, Vashon Island WA 98070.
(206) 4632592 (206) 4636157
dirk@vashonhostel.com
www.vashonhostel.com
Open Dates: 01.05-31.10 SeaTac 32km Vashon Island 9.66km Amtrak (Seattle) 54 ap Thriftway Grocery x 70 (B) 3.22km 3.22km

Seattle... Travel Tips

- **For budget eats check out...** Soundview Café, Gordito's Mexican Food, Dick's Drive-In, Jai Thai, Beecher's Handmade Cheese
- **For great nightlife try...** Theatre Sports @ Unexpected Productions, The Showbox, Crocodile Café, Re-Bar, Bada Lounge
- **Don't miss...** Pike Place Market, Pioneer Square, A walk on the waterfront, Space Needle, Boeing Aircraft Tour, Seattle Underground Tour, Fremont Neighbourhood, Local Natives American Art & Culture, Capitol Hill Neighbourhood, National Parks of The Pacific Northwest

Sitka – 60136
303 Kimsham St, PO Box 2645, Sitka AK 99835.
(907) 7478661
Open Dates: 01.06-31.08 Sitka 9.6km x 18

Syracuse – Downing International Hostel – 60124
535 Oak St, Syracuse NY 13203-1609.
(315) 4725788
Open Dates: Syracuse 10km Syracuse 5km 2NE x 35 1km

Taos – Abominable Snowmansion – 60137
Taos Ski Valley Rd, PO Box GG, Taos NM 87571.
(505) 7768298 (505) 7762107
snowman@newmex.com
www.abominablesnowmansion.com
Open Dates: x 60

Tecopa/Death Valley – Desertaire Hostel – 60125
2000 Old Spanish Trail Hwy, PO Box 306, Tecopa CA 92389.
(760) 8524580
little_egypt30@hotmail.com
Open Dates: x 10

Truro 60127
North Pamet Rd, PO Box 402, Truro, MA 02666.
(When shut: sophie@usahostels.org)
(508) 3493889
trurohostel@yahoo.com
www.capecodhostels.org
Open Dates: 24.06-05.09 Boston 180km A Plymouth & Brockton 180km Provincetown 30km Plymouth & Brockton 3km ap Truro Post Office 3SE x 49 (B) 100m 100m

Urbanna – Sangraal-by-the-Sea – 60129
907 Carlton Road, Rt. 626, Wake, VA 23176, PO Box 187, Urbanna, VA 23175
(804) 7766500
Open Dates: Richmond 140km Williamsburg 100km Williamsburg 100km ap Williamsburg x 20 1km

Vashon Island ☛ **Seattle**

Virginia Beach – Angie's Guest Cottage – 60130
302 24th St, Virginia Beach VA 23451.
(757) 4284690 (757) 4288087
angiesinvb@cs.com
www.angiescottage.com
Open Dates: 01.04-30.09 Norfolk 32km Norfolk 48km Amtrak 400m Greyhound 1.6km x 34 200m 200m

Washington, DC 60005
1009 11th St NW, Washington DC 20001.
(202) 7372333 (202) 7371508
reserve@hiwashingtondc.org
www.hiwashingtondc.org
Open Dates: Open Times:
Beds: 270 - 4x1 3x2 6x4 3x6 32x6+
Price Range: $21-29 ($34-45 01.16-22, 05.27-30, 01-04.07, 02-05.09) BBinc
Directions: 0.2N from city centre
Wash National (DCA) 8km, Dulles International (IAD) 43km, BWI 50km
A Washington Flyer/Metro/Super Shuttle
Union (Amtrak) to É 3km ap 11th & K St, NW U Metro Center 200m x 3
R CC (B)
1 x 8

Washington, DC

Washington, DC... Travel Tips

- **For budget eats check out...** Chinatown, Adams Morgan, Union Station, Post Office Pavillion, Stoney's
- **For great nightlife try...** Georgetown, Adams Morgan, Southwest Waterfront, Kennedy Center, Dupont Circle
- **Don't miss...** White House, The US Capital, The National Mall, Arlington National Cemetery, American Film Insitute, Smithsonian Museums, Six Flags of DC, Military Band performances, Screen on the green, Eastern Market

▲ **White River Junction** – 60133
The Hotel Coolidge, PO Box 515,
39 S. Main St, White River Junction, VT 05001.
(802) 2953118 (802) 2915100
reservations@hotelcoolidge.com
www.hotelcoolidge.com
Open Dates: x 26 R CC
P

▲ **Woodford** – Greenwood Lodge – 60134
VT Hwy 9, Prospect Access Rd, Woodford, PO Box 246, Bennington VT 05201.
(802) 4422547 (802) 4422547
grnwd@compuserve.com
www.campvermont.com/greenwood/
Open Dates: 19.05-24.10 Albany NY 47km
Brattleboro 32km Bennington 8km x 20 R P

Uruguay

Asociación de Alberguistas del Uruguay,
Canelones 935,
CP 11100, Montevideo, Uruguay.

- t (598) (2) 9005749; 9013587
- f (598) (2) 9013587
- e albergues@hosteluruguay.org
- w www.hosteluruguay.org

A copy of the Hostel Directory for this Country can be obtained from:
The National Office

National Tourist Authority/Board:	www.turismo.gub.uy
Capital:	Montevideo
Language:	Spanish
Currency:	$ (Peso Uruguayo)
Population:	3,061,000
Size:	176,215 sq km
Telephone Country Code:	598
eKit Access Number:	000-413-598-3143

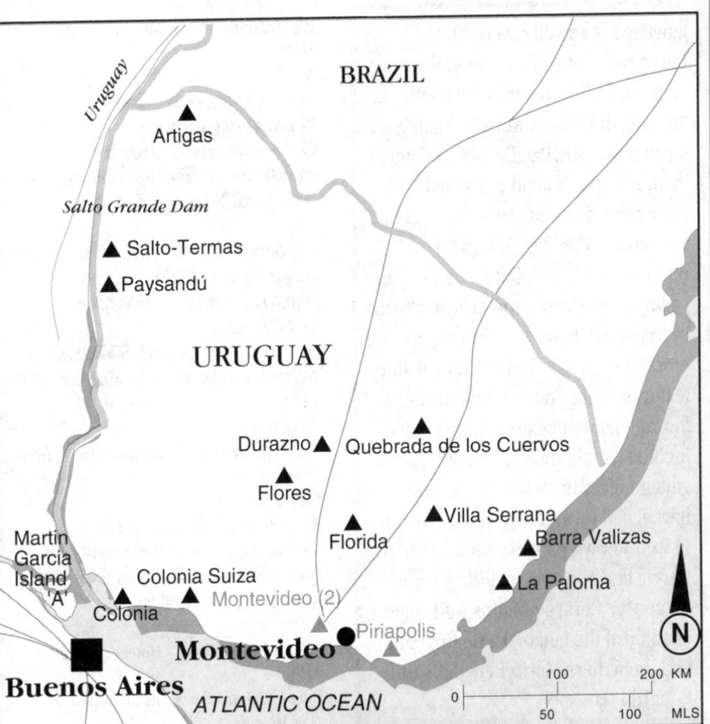

HI Suggests...

Situated in the Southern part of the American continent, Uruguay has evolved into a free, democratic and cultured society – one that is proud of its heritage and embraces other cultures. Uruguay shares its roots and destiny with the rest of the region, while retaining a unique identity and style. Uruguay is well worth a visit. Its people, varied landscape and range of activities offer something for every visitor! The country is divided into 19 provinces. The capital city Montevideo is located in the smallest and most populated of these.

Beaches beside still water or rolling waves. Coarse or fine golden sand. Fresh or salt water. Solitary or packed with people. Lush vegetation or endless sand. The Rio de la Plata (River Plate) and the Atlantic Ocean together offer 650 kilometres of coastline – that is without counting the banks of streams and rivers!

With a surface area of over 176,000 km2, Uruguay guarantees visitors the holiday of a lifetime. It is a green haven between the Atlantic Ocean and the Rio de la Plata (River Plate). Good weather and short distances allow nature lovers to make the most of this country throughout the year. Vast grasslands stretch as far as the eye can see. Uruguay is sixth in the global Environmental Sustainability Index (ESI). The main outdoor activities and natural attractions include: climbing, hiking, bird watching, rivers, caves, mountains, incomparable wildlife reserves, the countryside, national parks and a splendid coastline.

The land now known as Uruguay – which means "the river with the painted birds" in the local Guaraní language – was discovered by European explorers in the 16th century. Sailing towards the South Atlantic, these men were searching for a passage to the Pacific Ocean. Since then, Europe has had a marked influence on Uruguayan culture and traditions. The Afro-American population has also left its mark – for example the Candombe African rhythm is an important part of Uruguay's musical heritage. Other distinguishing features, comparable to the nostalgia for tango and the passion for football, include its folk music, football, the gaucho lifestyle, "maté" (tea) and barbecued meat, along with the works of well-known painters such as Torres Garcia and Juan Manuel Blanes, the composer Gerardo Mattos Rodriguez (author of the tango "La Cumparsita") and the writers Mario Benedetti and Eduardo Galeano.

You can find out a lot more on our website - a visit to www.HIhostels.com is essential for planning your trip!

Pour en savoir plus, rendez-vous sur notre site Internet, www.HIhostels.com une visite incontournable pour préparer votre voyage!

Viele weitere Informationen auf unserer Website: www.HIhostels.com - unverzichtbar für die Reiseplanung!

Puedes averiguar mucho más en nuestro sitio web. Es imprescindible que visites la página www.HIhostels.com para planear tu viaje.

△ ***Artigas*** *– Club Deportivo Artigas – 61006*
Pte. Berreta s/n, Artigas.
(77) 23860 (77) 22532
cda@artigasweb.com
www.artigasweb.com/cda
Open Dates: Bus company: Turil
x 24 R 1 x

△ ***Barra Valizas*** *– Artigas YH – 61007*
Artigas YH, Barra Valizas, Rocha.
(Montevideo 265km, Rocha 60km).
(470) 5273
Open Dates: 01.12-31.03 Rutas del Sol, Cynsa 200m x 56 R

△ ***Colonia (del Sacramento)*** *– Hotel Colonial – 61008*
Gral. Flores 440.
(52) 30347 (52) 30347
hostelling_colonial@hotmail.com
Open Dates: 200m 500m
x 18

▲ **Colonia Suiza** – Hotel del Prado – 61009
Ruta 1, Colonia Suiza, Neighbourhood "Los Hotels".
(Montevideo 129km, Colonia 58km).
(55) 44169 hotprado@adinet.com.uy
www.guiacolonia.com.uy/prado
Open Dates: Bus companies: Cot, Turil 300m x 15 R

△ ***Durazno*** *– "Hostal El Nazareno" – 61011*
Ruta 5, Km 180 (Rural).
(36) 22168
Open Dates: Bus companies: Nossar, Agencia Central, Turismar, Nunez
3S x 16

△ ***Flores*** *– Albergue Estancia "El Silencio" (Tourist Ranch) – 61012*
Ruta 14 km 166, Flores Province.
(36) 22014 silencio@adinet.com.uy
Open Dates: 01.02-20.12 1.8km
x 15 R

△ ***Florida*** *– El Ceibo (Tourist Farm) – 61034*
Ruta 5km, 97,400.
(350) 2013 www.elceibo.com.uy
Open Dates: x 12

△ ***La Paloma* – *61014***
Altena 5000' YH, Parque Municipal 'Andresito', Parada 12, La Paloma, Rocha. (Montevideo 240km, Rocha 28km).
(473) 6396
Open Dates: 01.12-31.03
Bus companies: Cynsa, Rutas del Sol, Cot 300m x 50

▲ **Montevideo** – Hotel Hispano – 61031
Convención 1317.
(2) 9003816 (2) 9003816
hotelhispano@adinet.com.uy
www.hispanohotel.com
Open Dates: Carrasco International 16km A 209, 214 2km 116, 117, 118, 164, 165, 409, 411

▲ **Paysandu** – La Posada – 61016
JP Varela Y Solis, CP 60000 Paysandu.
(72) 27879 (72) 27879
Open Dates: x 35

▲ **Salto** – Hostal Canela – 61021
Ruta 3, km.488, 300, Termas Del Dayman.
(73) 32121 (73) 32121
hcanela@internet.com.uy
Open Dates: 900m x 15

△ ***Villa Serrana* – *61023***
Los Chafas YH, Hwy 8, 145km, Molle, Villa Serrana.
(2) 9013587
albergues@hosteluruguay.org
Open Dates: 4km x 15

YOUTH HOSTEL ACCOMMODATION OUTSIDE THE ASSURED STANDARDS SCHEME

Montevideo – Schirrmann-Münker 61002
Canelones 935, Montevideo.
(2) 9081324 (2) 9081324
montevideo@hosteluruguay.org
Open Dates: Montevideo 16km A 209, 214 + Copsa Lines 700m Montevideo 2km 116, 117, 118, 164, 165, 409, 411 100m x 48 1 x

---

Piriápolis – Anton Grassl 61003
Simón del Pino 1106-36, Piriápolis, Maldonado. (Montevideo 100km).
(43) 20394 (2) 9013587
piriapolis@hosteluruguay.org
Open Dates: 200m Bus Companies: Cot, Copsa 100m x 322

Quebrada de los Cuervos – Cañada del Brujo – 61032
Local road to Quebrada de los Cuervos, Route 8 at km 306, 700 (Treinta y tres Provice).
(99) 297448; (452) 2837
cdelbrujo@latinmail.com
Open Dates: Bus companies: Nuñez, Cot 14km x 12

ADDITIONAL HOSTEL INFORMATION

The following information was received too late to be incorporated in the main part of the HI Guide.

PHILIPPINES

Youth & Student Hostel Foundation of the Philippines (YSHFP),
4227-9 Tomas Claudio St., Parañaque 1700,
Baclaran, Metro Manila.
t (63) (2) 8516934; 8522112 f (63) (2) 8522112
e yshfp@philippinehostel.com; philippinehostels@gmail.com

△ ***Baguio City*** – *Baden Powell Hall – 45001*
26 Grosvenor Park Rd.
t *(074) 4425836*
Open Dates: 12 *Naia or Centennial 246km* *Baguio 246km* x 150 45km

△ ***Baguio City*** – *Corfu Village – 45002*
92 cor Leonard Wood cor Brent Rd and Gen Luna Sts, Baguio City.
t *(074) 4422969*
Open Dates: 12 *Naia or Centennial 246km* *Baguio 246km* x 50 45km

△ ***Baguio City*** – *Zion Hostel – 45003*
18 Palma St, Baguio City.
t *(074) 4433146; 4456970*
f *(074) 4456997*
Open Dates: 12 *Naia or Centennial 246km* *Baguio 246km* 1.5E x 21 R CC 45km

△ ***Banaue*** – *Banaue View Inn YH – 45004*
Banaue, Ifugao.
t *(074) 3864078*
Open Dates: 12 *Naia or Centennial 348km* *Banaue 348km* x 30

△ ***Banaue*** – *Banaue YH – 45005*
Banaue, Ifugao.
t *(074) 3864087* f *(074) 3864088*
Open Dates: 12 *Naia or Centennial 348km* *Banaue 348km* x 60

△ ***Cagayan Valley*** – *Villa Margarita YH – 45007*
Busilac, Bayombong, Nueva Vizcaya.
t *(02) 8310627*
Open Dates: 12 *Naia or Centennial 268km* *Solano 268km* x 50

△ ***Cebu City*** – *Ecotech Center – 45008*
Lahug, Cebu City.
t *(032) 2555239* f *(032) 2547047*
Open Dates: 12 *Naia or Centennial 20km* *North Harbour 588km* *Lahug 45km* 25SW x 300 R CC 10km 50km

△ ***Cebu City*** – *Four Reasons Place – 45009*
3rd St, Happy Valley Sub Division V.Rama, Cebu City.
t *(032) 2538677*
e *cavanbarbi@yahoo.com*
Open Dates: 12 *Naia or Centennial 20km* *North Harbour 588km* *Y. Rama 35km* 1.5S x 14 R 20km 50km

△ ***Cebu City*** – *Myra's Pensionne – 45010*
12 Escario Corner, Acacia St, Brgy. Camput Haw, Cebu City.
t *(032) 2315557* f *(032) 2318405*
Open Dates: 12 *Naia or Centennial 20km* *North Harbour 588km* *Escario 30km* 0.5N x 22 R 30km 50km

△ ***Corregidor*** – *Corregidor YH – 45011*
Bataan.
t *(02) 8346857*
e *suncruises@magsaysay.com*
Open Dates: 12 *Naia or Centennial 75km* *CCP 75km* *Bataan 140km* x 60 30km 40km

△ ***Ilocos Coast*** – *D'Coral Beach Resort – 45012*
Piao Sur, Currimao: (25km S of Laoag).
t *(077) 7721133*
Open Dates: 12 *Naia or Centennial 500km* *Ilocos 500km* x 100

△ ***Malay*** *– Boracay Beach Chalets – 45013*
Manggayad Balabag, Boracay Island, Malay, Aklan.
(036) 2883993 (036) 2886313
boracaybeachchalets@yahoo.com
www.bbchalets.com
Open Dates: Naia or Centennial North Harbour 345km 200N x 15

△ ***Malay*** *– Villa De Oro – 45014*
Manggayad Balabag, Boracay Island, Malay, Aklan.
(036) 2885456 (036) 2885456
vdoboracay@yahoo.com
Open Dates: Naia or Centennial North Harbour 345km 200N x 34

△ ***Malolos*** *– Hiyas NG Bulacan Convention Center Hostel – 45015*
Malolos, Bulacan.
(044) 7910535
Open Dates: Naia or Centennial 70km Malolos 70km x 300

▲ **Manila** – International YH – 45016
4227 Tomas Claudio St, Roxas Blvd, Parañaque: (behind the Excelsior Building).
(2) 8516934 (2) 8522112
yshfp@philippinehostel.com; philippinehostels@gmail.com
Open Dates: Ninoy Aquino International 2km Baclaran Lrt 1km Baclaran 2km x 122 1 x 5km

△ ***Puerto Princesa*** *– Casa Linda Inn – 45018*
Trinidad Rd, Rizal Ave, Puerto Princesa City, Palawan.
(048) 4332606 (048) 4332309
casalind@mozcom.com
Open Dates: Naia or Centennial 400km North Harbour 400km 2NE x 35

△ ***San Pablo City*** *– Sampaloc Lake YH – 45019*
Efarca Vill., San Pablo City.
(049) 5623376
Open Dates: Naia or Centennial 82km San Pablo 82km x 40

△ ***Vigan City*** *– Villa Angela Heritage House – 45021*
#26 Ouirino Blvd., Vigan City.
(02) 3745184; (077) 7222914
(077) 7222914 info@villangela.com
www.villangela.com
Open Dates: Naia, Centennial 440km Laoag 440km x 60 20km

Affiliated Organisations

The International Youth Hostel Federation also has Affiliated Organisations in a number of other countries. These are not listed in the main body of the Guide, as they do not fulfil the minimum requirements for full membership, and hostel standards may be outside the assured standards scheme. In some instances, approval has been given for the inclusion of details on their hostel network and/or other relevant information.

These organisations which are worldwide are as follows:-

Organisations Affiliées

La Fédération Internationale des Auberges de Jeunesse a également des organisations affiliées dans un certain nombre d'autres pays. Celles-ci ne figurent pas sur la liste des pays dans la partie principale du Guide, car elles ne répondent pas aux exigences minimales régissant l'adhésion de membre à part entière et la conformité de leurs établissements aux Normes Minimales n'est pas garantie. Dans certains cas, la publication de renseignements concernant leurs auberges de jeunesse et/ou d'autres informations utiles a été approuvée.

Ces organisations mondiales sont les suivantes:-

Angeschlossene Organisationen

Der Internationale Jugendherbergsverband steht ebenso in Verbindung mit angeschlossenen Organisationen in verschiedenen anderen Ländern. Diese sind jedoch nicht im Hauptverzeichnis angegeben, weil sie zum einen keine vollberechtigten Mitgliedsverbände sind und zum anderen der Standard dieser Herbergen nicht den zugesicherten Normen entspricht. In einigen Fällen konnten jedoch Angaben über JH solcher Verbände sowie andere wesentliche Angaben ins Verzeichnis aufgenommen werden.

Diese weltweit operierenden Organisationen sind wie folgt:-

Organizaciones Afiliadas

La Federación Internacional de Albergues Juveniles (IYHF) también posee Organizaciones Afiliadas en otros países. Estas no han sido incluidas en la parte principal de la Guía, ya que no cumplen con los requisitos mínimos necesarios para ser miembros de pleno derecho y es posible que el nivel de calidad de sus albergues no corresponda al garantizado por nuestras normas. En algunos casos, se ha aprobado la publicación de información sobre su red de albergues y/u otros datos pertinentes.

Estas organizaciones que se encuentran por todo el mundo son las siguientes:-

ALBANIA

Albania YHA,
AYHA, PO BOX 8162, Tirana.
t (355) (4) 274234
f (355) (68) 2062026
e info@ayha.org
w www.ayha.org

BANGLADESH

Bangladesh Youth Hostel Association,
38 Elephant Rd, Duanmondi, Dhaka 1205.
t (880) (2) 8124479, 8628485, 8626119
f (880) (2) 8616915
e afeet@bdonline.com

BOLIVIA

Fundación Hostelling International Bolivia,
119, Calle Guillermo Loayza, Sucre.
t (591) (4) 6440471
f (591) (4) 6440471
e hostelling_international_bolivia@yahoo.com
w www.hostellingbolivia.org

BOSNIA & HERZEGOVINA

YHA of Bosnia & Herzegovina,
Cemalusa No1, 71000 Sarajevo.
t (387) (33) 208910
f (387) (33) 555590
e fsbih@bih.net.ba
w www.ferijalni.org

BULGARIA

USIT Colours Bulgaria,
35 Vassil Levski Blvd, Sofia 1000.
t (359) (2) 9811900
f (359) (2) 9819991
e sofia@usitcolours.bg
w www.usitcolours.bg

COLOMBIA

Federación Colombiana de Albergues Juveniles, Carrera 7 No. 6-10,
P.O. Box 240167, Santafé de Bogotá DC.
t (57) (1) 280 3202/3041/3318
f (57) (1) 280 3460
e hostelling@fcaj.org.co; hostels@fcaj.org.co
w www.fcaj.org.co

CZECH REPUBLIC

Česká hostelová asociace (CZYHA)
Přístavní 2, 17000 Praha 7 - Holešovice.
t (420) (2) 20805684
f (420) (2) 20806912
e office@czechhostels.com; groups@czechhostels.com
w www.czechhostels.com

Travel Sections:

GTS International
Ve Smečkách 33, 11000 Praha 1.
t (420) (2) 22211204
e info@gtsint.cz
w www.gtsint.cz

JSC Travel
Přístavní 2, 17000 Praha 7 - Holešovice.
t (420) (2) 20805684
f (420) (2) 20806912
e info@jsc.cz
w www.jsc.cz

ESTONIA

Estonian Youth Hostels Association - Eesti Noortehostelite Ühendus,
Narva Mnt. 16-25, 10120 Tallinn.
t (372) 6461 455
f (372) 6461 595
e info@hostels.ee
w www.hostels.ee

GHANA

STYO,
Opp U.N.D.P. Offices, Ring Road East,
PO Box 9732 KIA, Accra.
t (233) (21) 768257
f (233) (21) 776081; 774338

GUATEMALA

Intercambios Culturales y Académicos,
7a. Avenida 2 - 12, Zona 13,
01013 Guatemala City.
t (502) 4751230; 4752914
f (502) 4720849
e intercas@msn.com
w www.intercas.com

GUINEA

Fédération Guinéenne des Auberges de Jeunesse,
Commandayah/ Commune Dirinn, Conakry.
t (224) 453522; 349714
e dioumagueme2004@yahoo.fr

INDONESIA

Indonesian Youth Hostels Association,
Department of National Education, Gdg E Lt. 6 Dit. Kepemudann, JL. Jenderal Sudirman, Senayan, Jakarta 10270.
t (62) (21) 5725 503/504
f (62) (21) 5725 041

LATVIA

Latvian Youth Hostel Association,
17-2 Siguldas pr, Riga LV 1014.
t (371) 9218560
f (371) 7517006
e info@hostellinglatvia.com
w www.hostellinglatvia.com

LITHUANIA

Lithuanian Youth Hostels,
Filaretų Street 17, LT-01207 Vilnius.
t (370) (5) 2154627
f (370) (5) 2120149
e booking@lithuanianhostels.org
w www.lithuanianhostels.org

NEPAL

Nepal Youth Hostels Association,
Mahendra Youth Hostel, Jawalakhel, Lalitpur.
t (977) (1) 521003
f (977) (1) 220161
e buscom@wlink.com.np

NEW CALEDONIA

(In co-operation with French YHA)
Association des Auberges de Jeunesse de Nouvelle Calédonie,
51 bis rue Pasteur Marcel Ariège,
BP 767, 98845 Nouméa.
t (687) 275879
f (687) 254817
e yha.noumea@lagoon.nc

RUSSIA

Youth Hostels Association of Russia (YHAR),
11, Yakovlevskiy lane, St Petersburg, 196105.
t (7) (812) 2521867
f (7) (812) 2521867
e info@russia-hostelling.ru
w www.russia-hostelling.ru

Travel Section:
ADM Travel Agency, 9, Marata str., Office 30, St. Petersburg, 191025.
t (7) (812) 3252233; 3121143
f (7) (812) 7646894; 7176617
e info@adm.ru
w www.adm.ru

SINGAPORE

Youth Hostels Assoc. (Singapore),
1 Pasir Ris Close, Singapore 519599.
t (65) 65891637
f (65) 65846089
e nci@ntucclub.com.sg

SLOVAKIA

CKM SYTS,
Vysoká 32, 81445 Bratislava.
t (421) (2) 52731024
f (421) (2) 52731025
e ckm2000-bts@ckm.sk
w www.ckm.sk

SOUTH AFRICA

SASTS Working Adventures,
11 Bree Street , Cape Town 8000.
t (27) (21) 418 3794
f (27) (21) 418 3795
e info@sasts.org.za
w www.sasts.org.za

TAIWAN

Chinese Taipei Youth Hostel Association,
12F-10, No.50 Chuang-Hsiao West Rd, Sec 1, Taipei.
t (886) (2) 23317272; 23812550
f (886) (2) 23317272; 23316427
e iysosc@ms28.hinet.net
w www.yh.org.tw

Federal Vacation Co Ltd,
2F, No.329 Chung Hsiao E.Road, Sec 4, Taipei.
t (886) (2) 87715599
f (886) (2) 87714847
e fifa@gostudyenglish.com.tw
w www.GoByTrain.com.tw

Kang Wen Culture & Education Foundation,
Suite 504, No 142 Chung Hsiao East Rd, Sec 4, Taipei 106.
t (886) (2) 27751138
f (886) (2) 87732450
e sta@statravel.org.tw
w www.statravel.org.tw

iwan, Kaoshiung International Youth ostel,
!0 Wen Wu First Street, Kaohsiung.
(886) (7) 2012477
(886) (7) 2156322
kokiyh@ms57.hinet.net

URKEY

ençtur,
tiklal Cad. No: 212 Aznavur Pasaji K:5,
alatasaray, Istanbul.
(90) (212) 2446230
(90) (212) 2446233
genctur@genctur.com
www.genctur.com

GANDA

ternational Youth Hostels Uganda,
O Box 27270, Kampala.
(256) 7752238; (0) 71 682381
iyouthhosteluganda@yahoo.com
www.ugandayha.org

UKRAINE

Ukrainian Youth Hostel Association,
4/7, Mukachivska Street. Office 1.
Mailing address: P.O.Box 156. Kiev 01025.
t (38) (039) 4937849; (044) 4269956
f (38 (044) 426 9956; (044) 482 2297
e info@hihostels.com.ua
w www.hihostels.com.ua

VENEZUELA

Albergues HI Hostels de Venezuela,
Res. La Hacienda, Local 1-4-T, Final Av.
Ppal. de las Mercedes, Aptdo. 80160,
Caracas 1080.
t (58) (212) 9936082
f (58) (212) 9932412; 9929626
e hivenezuela@ivivenezuela.com

Ekit Access Numbers

lbania	Check www.hi.ekit.com for up to date Access Numbers
angladesh	Check www.hi.ekit.com for up to date Access Numbers
olivia	Check www.hi.ekit.com for up to date Access Numbers
osnia & Herzegovina	Check www.hi.ekit.com for up to date Access Numbers
ulgaria	Check www.hi.ekit.com for up to date Access Numbers
olombia	01800-918-0096
zech Republic	800-142-069
stonia	Check www.hi.ekit.com for up to date Access Numbers
hana	Check www.hi.ekit.com for up to date Access Numbers
reece	00800-1809-201-2429
uatemala	Check www.hi.ekit.com for up to date Access Numbers
uinea	Check www.hi.ekit.com for up to date Access Numbers
ndonesia	0018-030-113-663
atvia	800-2091
ithuania	Check www.hi.ekit.com for up to date Access Numbers
epal	Check www.hi.ekit.com for up to date Access Numbers
ew Caledonia	Check www.hi.ekit.com for up to date Access Numbers
ussia	8-10-800-2092-1012
ingapore	800-120-3480
lovakia	Check www.hi.ekit.com for up to date Access Numbers
aiwan	Check www.hi.ekit.com for up to date Access Numbers
urkey	00800-151-0788
ganda	Check www.hi.ekit.com for up to date Access Numbers
kraine	Check www.hi.ekit.com for up to date Access Numbers

BOLIVIA

Fundación Hostelling International Bolivia,
119 Calle Guillermo Loayza, Sucre.
t (591) (4) 6440471 f (591) (4) 6440471
e hostelling_international_bolivia@yahoo.com w www.hostellingbolivia.org

Travel Section:
HI-Bolivia Booking Centre, Santa Cruz de la Sierra.
t (591) (3) 3701294
e hostelling_international_boliva@yahoo.com w www.hostellingbolivia.org

Paradoxically, though one of the poorest countries in South America, Bolivia has considerable mineral wealth, including its silver mines (originally plundered by the Spanish conquistadors in the sixteenth century), copper, lead, zinc, tin, sulphur, iron and gold. Its capital, La Paz, is the highest city in the world at around 12,000 feet, sitting in the *altiplano* between the two sets of Andes near Lake Titicaca, the highest navigable lake in the world.

Bolivia, named after its independence fighter Simon Bolivar, has a huge indigenous, mostly uneducated, Indian community forming nearly fifty per cent of a total population of nine million. A constant series of coups and countercoups (over 200) since independence in 1825, causing endemic poverty, as well as the world market slumps in mineral values, have propelled the exploitation of Bolivia's vast coca resources into a major source of drugs based on cocaine.

Not surprising, Bolivia is not on the package holiday checklist. Yet it is a wonderful place to explore, a vast emptiness, most of which is untouched by man, with Inca ruins, prehistoric fossils and new bird and animal species still to be discovered.

A few other Top Tips from **CULTURE SMART!**:

- Social events tend to take place in late evening and since punctuality is not part of everyday life in Bolivia, do not turn up at a party or to dinner at the stated time. Instead, plan on being at least half an hour 'late'! Equally, in a business context, patience in often endless waiting will be required.
- When meeting socially, if you know people in the group then you should shake hands with the men and kiss the women on the left cheek whilst shaking their hands also. Avoiding eye contact is regarded as a sign of someone who is untrustworthy.
- Bolivia is a country of carnivals, which are well worth joining in, as you are welcome to do, especially the summer carnival in La Paz, which takes place in late February.
- Bolivian cuisine is basic but tasty, much of it based on soup and the one hundred varieties of potato that grow there. Main meat and chicken dishes are often garnished with spicy sauces made from the many varieties of hot peppers. You have been warned!

Cultural Top Tips supplied by Culture Smart! guides. These essential guides to customs and etiquette will help you steer clear of embarrassing gaffes and sensitive issues, enabling you to discover new cultures whilst developing new friendships. Order online at www.culturesmartguides.co.uk

ou can find out a lot more on our ebsite - a visit to www.HIhostels.com is ssential for planning your trip!

our en savoir plus, rendez-vous sur otre site Internet, ww.HIhostels.com une visite ncontournable pour préparer votre oyage!

iele weitere Informationen auf unserer Vebsite: www.HIhostels.com - nverzichtbar für die Reiseplanung!

uedes averiguar mucho más en uestro sitio web. Es imprescindible ue visites la página ww.HIhostels.com para planear tu iaje.

▲ **Cochabamba** – Hostal Versalles
HI 94017 FNM
Av. Ayacucho # S-0714 (Aroma y L.Cabrera).
t (4) 4221096 f (4) 4522653
e hiversalles@yahoo.com
Open Dates: 12 ✈ 4km 🚌 200m ap Bus Terminal 0.6SW x 50 R (B)

▲ **Copacabana** – Residencial Brisas Del Titicaca HI 94013 FNM
Av. 6 de Agosto final (Lakeside).
t (2) 8622178 f (2) 8622178
e hostellingbolivia@yahoo.com
w www.hostellingbolivia.org
Open Dates: 12 ✈ La Paz "El Alto" 120km 🚌 200m 0.4N x 105 R

▲ **Coroico** – HI Hotel Viejo Molino – 94030
Camino a Santa Barbara.
t (2) 2895506 e ventas@valmartour.com
w www.valmartour.com
Open Dates: 12 🚌 1km Yungas - La Paz 1W x 60 R

△ ***Isla del Sol** – HI - Iuka Pacja - Lago Titicaca – 94031*
Comunidad Yumani - 1km del Puerto Sur.
t *(2) 2409569*
e *hostellingbolivia@yahoo.com*
w *www.hostellingbolivia.org*
Open Dates: 12 ✈ La Paz "El Alto" 120km
Puerto Sur 1km x 20 R
(B)

▲ **La Paz** – Hotel Continental HI 94010 FNM
Av. Illampu # 626 (Plaza Eguino).
t (2) 2451176 f (2) 2451176
e hotelcontinental626@hotmail.com
Open Dates: 12 ✈ La Paz "El Alto" 15km A🚌 15km 🚌 800m ap Bus Terminal
0.3W x 120 R CC
1 x

▲ **La Paz** – Hotel Torino – 94027
Calle Socabaya #457 (Plaza Marillo - 500m).
t (2) 2406003; 409569
e hostellingbolivia@yahoo.com
w www.hostellingbolivia.org
Open Dates: 12 ✈ La Paz "El Alto" 15km A🚌 15km 🚌 1km ap Bus Terminal 0.1E
x 126 R
3 x

▲ **La Paz** – Refugio Huayna Potosi – 94018
at 42km from Zongo at 4800m in the Cordillera Real.
t (2) 2740045 f (2) 2456717
e mallku88@yahoo.com
Open Dates: 12 ✈ La Paz "El Alto" 50km 🚌 50km ap Calle Sagarnaga La Paz 50W
x 24 R (BD)

▲ **Oruro** – Hotel Samay Wasi – 94019 FNM
Av. Brasi # 232 Esq. Aroma "B".
t (2) 5276737; 5113716 f (2) 5280323
e samaywasioruro@hotmail.com
Open Dates: 12 ✈ La Paz "El Alto" 230km 🚆 1km 🚌 50m ap Bus Terminal 1SW
x 45 R
1 x 8km

▲ Potosí – Hotel Jerusalem 94004
Calle Oruro # 143.
(2) 6224633; 6226095 (2) 6222600
hoteljer@cedro.pts.entelnet.bo
Open Dates: 4km 500m ap Bus Terminal 0.5E x 61

▲ Samaipata – HI Cabañas Campeche – 94020
Barrio Campeche.
(3) 9446046 (3) 9446046
campeche@scbbs.net
Open Dates: Santa Cruz 130km 1.2km ap Taxi Parade 0.8N x 36 1 x

▲ Santa Cruz – Hotel Copacabana 94007
Calle Junin # 217.
(2) 3362770; 3321843 (2) 3330757
hisc_marco@yahoo.com
www.hostellingbolivia.org
Open Dates: Viru Viru VVI 14km A 13km 3km 500m ap Cañoto/Calle Junin 0.3E x 93 1 x

▲ Sorata – Hostal El Mirador – 94022
Calle final Muñecas, 2 cuadras de la plaza, camino a la gruta.
(2) 2895008
hostellingbolivia@yahoo.com
Open Dates: 250m ap Plaza Central 0.3NW x 25 (B)

*△ **Sucre** – Cajamarca - Centro Ecológico Juvenil – 94028*
Valle Alto de Cajamarca.
(4) 6440471 hisucre@yahoo.com
www.jbh.bolivien.de
Open Dates: Sucre 30km x 92

▲ Sucre – Hostelling International Sucre 94001
Calle Guillermo Loayza 119 (Ostria Gutierrez).
(4) 6440471 (4) 6440471
hisucre@yahoo.com
www.hostellingbolivia.org
Open Dates: 7km 150m ap Bus Terminal 1.2W x 40 (B) 1 x

▲ Tupiza – HI Valle Hermoso – 94024
Avenue Pedro Arraya 478, Tupiza.
(2) 6942370 (2) 6942592
hostalvh@hotmail.com
www.bolivia.freehosting.net
Open Dates: 100m 250m 0.25E x 45 (B)

▲ Uyuni – Hostelling International Salar De Uyuni 94023
Calle Potosí esq. Sucre (Frente a Migración).
(2) 6932228 (2) 6932228
pucara_tours@yahoo.com
www.hostellingbolivia.org
Open Dates: 200m 200m 0.3SW x 58 (B)

▲ Vallegrande – HI Teresita – 94025
C. Escalante y Mendoza #167.
(3) 9422151
hisc_marco@yahoo.com
www.hostellingbolivia.org
Open Dates: 300m 0.2N x 40

▲ Villa Tunari – Hotel Las Araras – 94029
Chapare, 161km from Cochabamba, 300km from Santa Cruz.
(4) 4114116; (7) 1066454
hisc_marco@yahoo.com
www.hostellingbolivia.org
Open Dates: Santa Cruz 300km Santa Cruz - Cochabamba 300m ap Tarada Villa Tunari 0.5SE x 35

BOSNIA & HERZEGOVINA

YHA of Bosnia & Herzegovina,
Cemalusa No1, 71000 Sarajevo.
t (387) (33) 208910 f (387) (33) 555590
e fsbih@bih.net.ba w www.ferijalni.org

HI Suggests...

Bosnia and Herzegovina has been the crossroads of ancient civilizations for a number of years. In no other place in Europe can one find such a magical mix of Europe and the Near East Orient. The Slavs settled this centrepiece of the Balkan Peninsula in the 6th century and ever since have flourished to create the most multi-ethnic society in southern Europe. Here one will find the great mystical Byzantine traditions, the Romanesque influence rooted from the Franciscan church, the small but significant traces of the Jewish communities that settled here in the 15th century, and of course the predominant oriental flavour from the Ottoman Empire.

It is a natural wonderland – blessed with rugged canyons, plush forests, crystal clear rivers and lakes, and a precious mixture of the cultures and traditions that have evolved from this mountainous region of the Southern Alps. Bosnia and Herzegovina is a place that will stun you with natural beauty, fascinate and inspire you with rich cultural heritage, and touch you with warm and genuine hospitality.

In a country that covers only 51,000 square meters it is no less than a phenomena that it hosts so many drastically various landscapes. From rugged Alpine peaks, dry and arid Mediterrenean Herzegovina, the rolling green hills of central and northern Bosnia, to the vast flatlands of Semberija in the northeast along the river Sava this tiny place offers a more fascinating array of climates, cultures, vegetation, watersheds, and wildlife than any country in southeast Europe.

The capital city of Bosnia and Herzegovina, Sarajevo, has a very long and rich history and it has always been an important crossroads of many different cultures from both east and west. All travellers should enter a buregdzenica and try the famous traditional pita dishes of burek, zeljanica, sirnica, and krompirusa. They are all made from fresh.

You can find out a lot more on our website - a visit to www.HIhostels.com is essential for planning your trip!

Pour en savoir plus, rendez-vous sur notre site Internet, www.HIhostels.com une visite incontournable pour préparer votre voyage!

Viele weitere Informationen auf unserer Website: www.HIhostels.com - unverzichtbar für die Reiseplanung!

Puedes averiguar mucho más en nuestro sitio web. Es imprescindible que visites la página www.HIhostels.com para planear tu viaje.

▲ **Sarajevo** – YH Bjelave Studentski Centar – 96401
Bardakcija 1, Sarajevo.
(33) 663355 (33) 663355
student_hotel@yahoo.com
Open Dates: 12 x 29

▲ **Sarajevo** – YH Nedjarici Studentski Centar – 96400
Aleja Bosne srebrne bb, Sarajevo.
(33) 663355 (33) 663355
student_hotel@yahoo.com
Open Dates: 17.07-14.09 x 384 TV 1 x P

COLOMBIA

Federación Colombiana de Albergues Juveniles,
Carrera 7 No. 6-10, P.O. Box 240167, Santafé de Bogotá DC.
(57) (1) 280 3202/3041/3318 (57) (1) 280 3460
hostelling@fcaj.org.co; hostels@fcaj.org.co
www.fcaj.org.co

HI Suggests...

Colombia is located in North South America, bordering the Caribbean Sea, between Panama and Venezuela, and bordering the North Pacific Ocean, between Ecuador and Panama.

Colombia lies at the gateway to South America and has been a transit point for first inhabitants who migrated from North and Central America. The pre-Columbian cultures of Colombia have been little investigated, as almost none of them left behind spectacular monuments. However, their art reveals a high degree of craftsmanship and their gold work is the best in the whole continent, both for the techniques used and for the artistic design.

Colombia is a country of geographical contrasts and extremes. It has many curiosities such as the desert of La Guajira, the peninsula in the most north-eastern tip of the country; the jungle of the pacific coast, which holds one of the world's rainfall records; and finally the Serranía de la Macarena, an isolated mountain formation of about 120 km long, rising abruptly from the eastern plains to some 2500 metres. Colombia also has several small islands. The major ones are the archipelago of San Andrés and Providencia in the Caribbean Sea, the Islas del Rosario and San Bernardo along the Caribbean coast, and Gorgona and Malpelo in the Pacific Ocean.

You can find out a lot more on our website - a visit to www.HIhostels.com is essential for planning your trip!

Pour en savoir plus, rendez-vous su notre site Internet, www.HIhostels.com une visite incontournable pour préparer votre voyage!

Viele weitere Informationen auf unserer Website: www.HIhostels.com - unverzichtbar für die Reiseplanung!

Puedes averiguar mucho más en nuestro sitio web. Es imprescindible que visites la página www.HIhostels.com para planear tu viaje.

Armenia-Quindío – Hostería mi Monaco – 13015
Finca Monaco, Vereda la Revancha, Vía Armenia, Pueblo Tapao Km 7.
(6) 7473607 (6) 7463607
isabel@mimonaco.com
Open Dates: El Edén 25km 9S x 34

Barichara-Santander – Hostal Misión Santa Bárbara – 13001
Calle 5 No. 9-12 Barichara.
(7) 7267163; (1) 2884949
(7) 7267060
Open Dates: Palonegro 118km 0.3N
x 36
1 x

Bogotá D.C. – Hostelling International de Bogotá – 13002
Carrera 7 No. 6-10, Bogotá D.C.
(1) 2803318; 2803202; 2803041
(1) 2803460
hostelling@fcaj.org.co/hostels@fcaj.org.co
www.fcaj.org.co
Open Dates: El Dorado 15km 2S
x 105
1 x

Cartagena – Hostal Santodomingo – 13003
Calle Santodomingo No. 33-46, Cartagena.
(5) 6642268 (5) 6642268
Open Dates: Rafael Nuñez 4km 1SW
x 23

Cartagena de Indias D.T. y c. - Bolivar – Hotel Costa del Sol – 13016
Carrera la No. 9-18 Bocagrande
(5) 6650844; 6650835 (5) 6653755
info@hotelcostadelsol.com
Open Dates: Rafael Nuñez 8km 1S
x 384
1 x

Medellín – Hotel Casa Dorada – 13004
Calle 50 No 47-25 Medellín, Antioquia.
(4) 5125300 (4) 5719032
Open Dates: Jose Maria Cordova 28km; Olaya Herrera 5km 1NE x 155

Medellín-Antioquia – Gran Hotel – 13017
Calle 54 No. 45-92.
(4) 5134455 (4) 5718558
mercadeo@granhotel.com.co
Open Dates: Jose Maria Cordova 25km 0.2NE x 297
1 x

Montenegro-Quindío – Hostal Portal del Samán – 13018
Finca Villa Dory, Vereda el Silencio, Km 8, Vía Armenia-Pueblo Tapao, Montenegro.
(6) 7524061
informacion@portaldelsaman.com
Open Dates: El Edén 15km 12SW
x 30

Montenegro-Quindío – La Huerta de Calocho Hostería – 13019
Vereda La Julia, Finca la Galicia, Montenegro.
(6) 7405047
Open Dates: El Edén 20km 12.5NW
x 24

Paipa – H. Cabañas El Portón – 13005
Avenida Piscinas termales, Paipa, Boyacá.
(8) 7850168; 7850864 (8) 7851391
Open Dates: El Dorado 186km; Olaya Herrera 5km 1SE x 95

Providencia Isla – *Sirius Health Centre – 13007*
Bahía suroeste,
Providencia Isla. Archipiélago de San Andrés y Providencia.
(8) 5148213 (8) 5148808
siriusbc@col1.telecom.com.co
Open Dates: El Embrujo 6km 2SW
x 40

Sabaneta-Antioquia – Sede Campestre Gran Hotel – 13020
Carrera 29 No. 84 Sur 120, Finca 105, Vereda Pan de Azúcar, Sabaneta.
(4) 5134455; 2797025 (4) 5718558; 5766030 mercadeo@granhotel.com.co
Open Dates: Jose Maria Cordova 40km 11SE x 40
1 x

△ ***San Agustín*** *– H. El Jardín – 13008*
Carrera 11 No. 4-10, San Agustín-Huila.
(8) 8373455; 8379581
Open Dates: Benito Salas (Neiva) 260km 0.2N x 36

▲ **Santa Marta** – H. Medellín – 13010
Calle 22 No. 2A-62, Santa Marta.
(5) 4212380 (5) 4212654
Open Dates: Simón Bolívar 11km 0.5N
x 37 150m

▲ **Santa Marta** – H. Medellín – 13009
Calle 19 No. 1c-30, El Rodadero.
(5) 4220220; 4220202 (5) 4228250
Open Dates: Simón Bolívar 7km 13S
x 110 200m

▲ **Santa Marta** – Hostel Tima Uraka – 13011
Calle 18 No. 2-59, El Rodadero.
(5) 4228433 (5) 4228433
Open Dates: Simón Bolívar 8km 1SW
x 25 250m

▲ **Taganga-Santa Marta** – Casa de Felipe – 13021
Carrera 5 A No. 19-13.
(5) 4219101 (5) 4219120
info@lacasadefelipe.com
Open Dates: Simón Bolivar 25km 3N
x 47

▲ **Villavicencio-Meta** – Hotel Campestre Navar City – 13014
Km. 5 Vía Bogotá. Alto de Buenavista.
(8) 6653601; 6635414 (8) 6655414
Open Dates: Vanguardia 8km 6N
x 80 1 x

CZECH REPUBLIC

Česká hostelová asociace (CZYHA)
Přístavní 2, 17000 Praha 7 - Holešovice.
(420) (2) 20805684 (420) (2) 20806912
office@czechhostels.com; groups@czechhostels.com www.czechhostels.com

Travel Sections:

GTS International, Ve Smečkách 33, 11000 Praha 1.
(420) (2) 22211204
info@gtsint.cz www.gtsint.cz

JSC Travel s.r.o., Přístavní 2, 17000 Praha 7 - Holešovice.
(420) (2) 20805684 (420) (2) 20806912
info@jsc.cz www.jsc.cz

The Czechs have a rich culture dating back to the middle ages, with Charles University (1348) the oldest in Central Europe. Indeed, culture continues to be central to Czech life, which has ensured a flourishing opera and full theatres and concert halls, widely regarded for their excellence throughout the Western world.

The Czechs are welcoming and very open, sometimes called ‘dove-like’ people and were most successful in managing their ‘velvet’ revolution following the fall of Communism; in fact, their first President, Vaclav Havel, appointed in 1990, was a distinguished writer.

Today, everyone seems to know the capital Prague – a beautiful baroque city that survived much of the destruction of the Second World War. The Czechs have a renewed energy, a growing, partly-privatised economy and are host to huge numbers of expatriates from around the world, especially the United States and Britain, who have chosen to make their home there or to set up in business. There is no doubt, too, that the Czech beer of Bohemia and the wine of Moravia are amongst the best in the world.

A few other Top Tips from **CULTURE SMART!:**

- Although the Czechs know how to enjoy the good life (famously giving the world the phrase 'Bohemian lifestyle'), they expect and respect good manners and, like the French are very fond of handshaking.
- Whether at a person's home or otherwise, you will always be greeted by a *dobry den* 'good-day', and you should reciprocate. People generally mutter the same thing as they enter any public place (including shops and offices and at the railway ticket office).
- The Czechs are largely flat-dwellers in the cities and typically remove their shoes on entering their home, padding around in socks or slippers. You may well wish to do the same but will probably be told not to bother, as a courtesy to you.
- At mealtimes always wish *dobrou chut*, the Czech equivalent of 'bon appetit' as you raise your glass *na zdravi* 'to [your] health'. The national dish is pork served with sweet-sour cabbage and dumplings. Otherwise, the Czechs eat plenty of poultry and beef and a wide variety of salamis.

Cultural Top Tips supplied by Culture Smart! guides. These essential guides to customs and etiquette will help you steer clear of embarrassing gaffes and sensitive issues, enabling you to discover new cultures whilst developing new friendships. Order online at www.culturesmartguides.co.uk

You can find out a lot more on our website - a visit to www.HIhostels.com is essential for planning your trip!

Pour en savoir plus, rendez-vous sur notre site Internet, www.HIhostels.com une visite incontournable pour préparer votre voyage!

Viele weitere Informationen auf unserer Website: www.HIhostels.com - unverzichtbar für die Reiseplanung!

Puedes averiguar mucho más en nuestro sitio web. Es imprescindible que visites la página www.HIhostels.com para planear tu viaje.

*△ **Brno** – Hotel Palacký – 15029*
Kolejní 2, 61200 Brno.
(541) 142963 (541) 142965
recepce@hotel-palaky.cz
Open Dates: 25km A Zvonarka 3km 3km 53 ap YH (1 min walk to YH) x 80

▲ **Český Krumlov** – Travellers Hostel 15031
Soukenická 43, 381 01 Český Krumlov.
(380) 711345; (731) 564144
(380) 711345 krumlov@travellers.cz
www.travellers.cz
Open Dates: 1.5km ap 10 min walk to YH x 101

△ ***Dobrošov (Dobrosov)*** *– Jiráskova turistická chata – 15060*
Dobrošov 71, Náchod.
(491) 520185
jiraskova.chata@tiscali.cz
www.volny.cz/kctnachod/dobrosov.htm
Open Dates: *Nachod-Dobrosov* x 46

▲ **Karlovy Vary** – Hostel & Backpacker "Titty Twister" 15051
Moravská 44, 360 01 Karlovy Vary.
(353) 239071
michalzidek@hostelTT.cz
www.hostelTT.cz; www.hostelTT.com
Open Dates: 3km Central Bus Station 25km ap Vymlídka 3min, 8, 11, 13, 2 to Central Station 0.5SE x 72 R

△ ***Krkonoše (Krkonose)*** *– Chata Tesla – 15059*
Krkonose, Klinove Boudy.
(732) 455911; (272) 650363
chatatesla@quick.cz
http://www.chatatesla.cz/
Open Dates: x 50

▲ **Praha** – Extol Inn Youth Hostel 15043
Přístavní 2 17000 Praha 7 - Holešovice.
(220) 876541 (220) 806752
info@extolinn.cz www.extolinn.cz
Open Dates: 17km A 119 to Dejvická, U to Vltavská Nádrazí Holesovice 800m Florenc 2km 1, 3, 5, 12, 15, 25 100m U Vltavská, Nádrazí Holesovice 800m x 132 R

▲ **Praha** – Hostel Advantage 15013
Sokolská 11-13, 12000 Praha 2.
(224) 914062 (224) 914067
hostel.advantage@jsc.cz
www.advantagehostel.cz
Open Dates: 15km Hlavní Nádrazí 2km Florenc 3km 4, 6, 10, 16, 22, 23 U I.P. Pavlova 100m x 124 R

▲ **Praha** – Pension BETA 15044
Jaromírova 46/174, 128 00 Praha 2 - Nusle.
(222) 564385 (222) 564393
pensionbeta@volny.cz
www.pensionbeta.cz
Open Dates: Praha-Ruzyně 18km A Airport Service Hlavní Nádrazí 3km Florenc 4km 7, 18, 24 ap Svatoplukova 50m U Line B - Karlovo Náméstí 2S x 56 R

▲ **Praha** – Travellers Hostel 15010
Dlouhá 33, 11000 Praha 1.
(224) 826663; 826662 (224) 826665
hostel@travellers.cz www.travellers.cz
Open Dates: Praha-Ruzyně 22km A Airport Service 5, 14 ap Revoluční U Line B - nám. Republiky 0.5N x 222 R (B)

▲ **Šumperk (Sumperk)** – Hostel Korzo – 15058
Dr.E.Benese 2871/5, Sumperk 787 01.
(583) 213072; (724) 334478/9
hostel@obchodnikorzo.cz
http://www.hostel.rej.cz/
Open Dates: x 47 (BL)

△ ***Tokán*** *– Tokán – 15056*
Tokan 91-84, 40744 Chribska.
(412) 381850 (412) 381850
info@bohemianoutdoor.com
www.bohemianoutdoor.com/
Open Dates: x 30 R

△ ***Trebíc*** *– Travellers Hostel – 15049*
Žerotínovo Nàm.
(224) 826661 (224) 826665
trebic@travellers.cz
www.travellers.cz
Open Dates: Opening June 2006 0.1S x 60 R

△ ***Vysker (Vysker)*** *– Penzion Vysker – 15061*
Vysker 71.
(605) 386286
info@penzionvysker.cz
www.penzionvysker.cz
Open Dates: x 43

△ ***Zlín (Zlin)*** *– Hostel Duo Zlín – 15062*
Rumy 1391, Zlín.
(577) 433112 (577) 056123
bajek@hotelduozlin.cz
www.hotelduozlin.cz
Open Dates: 8 min from Centre
x 120

ESTONIA

Estonian Youth Hostels Association - Eesti Noortehostelite Ühendus,
Narva Mnt. 16-25, 10120 Tallinn.
(372) 6461 455 (372) 6461 595
info@hostels.ee www.hostels.ee

Visas:
A visa may be required for entering Estonia, which in most cases will be valid for Latvia and Lithuania also. A visa is obtainable from an Estonian Embassy. For updated information see our Internet www.baltichostels.net or Ministry for Foreign Affairs of Estonia www.vm.ee. If you need any visa support we will be happy to provide you with any relevant information or documentation.

Bookings:
If possible, visit our www page for update information and/or bookings. Please allow at least a week for dealing with fax/mail bookings. Booking conditions may change - current information on the Internet. When requesting information by mail-enclosing IPRC is essential. Automated online information/booking system is available at www.baltichostels.net with secure credit cards and other forms of payment. If booking through Internet is not possible please contact hostel directly. Groups must book through EYHA office. Credit cards are accepted.

Travel Section:
Balti Puhkemajad, Narva Mnt. 16-25, 10120 Tallinn, Estonia.
(372) 6461 455 (372) 6461 595
incoming@balticbudgettravel.com www.balticbudgettravel.com

Budget travel services for incoming individuals or groups. Accommodation bookings for Estonia, Russia, Latvia, Lithuania and Finland.

HI Suggests...

Estonia lies along the Baltic Sea. Tallinn, Estonia's capital city is only about 40 miles south of Helsinki, across the Gulf of Finland. Sweden is Estonia's western neighbour across the Baltic. Russia is to the east, with St. Petersburg just across the northeastern border. To the south is Latvia with its capital city Riga. You can depart from Tallinn's international airport and in less than two hours be in Helsinki, Stockholm, Copenhagen, Riga, Moscow, St. Petersburg, or Vilnius.

If you're longing for a getaway that will give you that tingle of discovering something new and untried, something exciting and magical, you need not travel outside mainstream Europe. You need only look towards this trendy, Nordic-feeling nation of 1.4 million people. It offers you an adventure you will never forget.

In a world that can at times seem overly packaged, Estonia remains refreshingly genuine and unconstrained. Having cast off communist rule more than ten years ago, Estonia has thrown her doors back open to the world and invited visitors to come sample her charms. The country's beautiful castles, old cities, manor houses, forests, beaches and islands – as its people – speak for themselves.

This is not only a nation with a touching, visible past; it is a nation that is as progressive and hip as it is history-filled and quaint. Its spectacular progress since restoring its independence in 1991 is epitomized by its impressive Internet infrastructure, considered one of the most advanced anywhere in the world. Even in the depths of the countryside, you are almost as likely to see a villager surfing the Internet as milking a cow.

You can find out a lot more on our website - a visit to www.HIhostels.com is essential for planning your trip!

Pour en savoir plus, rendez-vous sur notre site Internet, www.HIhostels.com une visite incontournable pour préparer votre voyage!

Viele weitere Informationen auf unserer Website: www.HIhostels.com - unverzichtbar für die Reiseplanung!

Puedes averiguar mucho más en nuestro sitio web. Es imprescindible que visites la página www.HIhostels.com para planear tu viaje.

△ ***Haapsalu*** *– Endla Hostel – 92419*
Endla 5, 90504, Haapsalu.
4737999 endlahostel@hot.ee
www.hot.ee/hostelendla
Open Dates: Tallinn 101km
Tallinn 101km Haapsau 700m
0.5SW x 20 R

▲ **Harju County** – Nelijärve – 92402
Nelijärve 4, Aegviidu, Harju County.
6055940 6304500 info@hostels.ee
www.hostels.ee
Open Dates: Tallinn 55km
Tallinn 60km 2km 50SE x 182
R P

△ ***Iigaste Village, Valga County*** *–*
Kalda Holiday Farm – 92420
Tõlliste Vald , 68302.
7670512 7670151
katapuhke@hot.ee www.kaldatalu.ee
Open Dates: Tallin 260km
Tallin 260km Valga 22km
Valga 22km ap Iigaste Tee 2km 22S
x 26 R P

△ ***Pärnu*** *– Terve – 92418*
Ringi 50, 80012, Pärnu.
5077332 info@hostels.ee
www.hostels.ee
Open Dates: Tallinn 129km
Tallinn 129km Pärnu 4km
Pärnu 800m 0.5W x 12 R

▲ **Tallinn** – Academic – 92414
Acadeemia 11, Tallinn, 12611.
6202275 6202276
info@academichostel.com
www.academichostel.com
Open Dates: Tallinn 10km
Tallinn 5km Tallinn 4km
20km 6SW x 216 R CC
P

▲ **Tallin** – Baltic Hostel – 92421
Uue Maailma 19, Tallinn, 10120.
6461451 6461451
baltic@hostels.ee www.hostels.ee
Open Dates: Tallinn 4km Tallinn 1.5km Tallinn 2km x 10

▲ **Tallinn** – City Guesthouse – 92417
Pärnu Mnt 10, 10148, Tallinn.
6282236 6282236
info@cityguesthouse.ee
www.cityguesthouse.ee
Open Dates: Tallinn 4km Tallinn 1.5km Tallinn 2km 0.5SW x 80 R
(B)

▲ **Tallinn** – Mahtra – 92408
Mahtra 44, Tallinn, 13812.
t 6218828 f 6586765
e hostel@mahtra.ee w www.mahtra.ee
Open Dates: 12 ✈ Tallinn 4km ⛴ Tallinn 7km 🚆 Tallinn 6km 🚌 50m ap Mahtra 6W x 53 R P

▲ **Tallinn** – Merevaik – 92409
Sõpruse Str 182, Tallinn 13424.
t 6553767 f 6561127
e hostell.merevaik@mail.ee
w www.hostelmerevaik.ee
Open Dates: 12 ✈ Tallinn 5km ⛴ Tallinn 3km 🚆 Tallinn 3km 🚌 50m ap Linnu Tee 2SW x 62 R P

▲ **Tallinn** – Tatari – 92415
Tatari 21 B, Tallinn.
t 6466287 f 6466287
e admin@tatarihostel.ee
w www.tatarihostel.ee
Open Dates: 12 ✈ Tallinn 5km ⛴ Tallinn 1.5km 🚆 Tallinn 1.5km 🚌 50m 0.8SE x 30 R CC TV 8 P

△ ***Tallinn** – Tehnika 16 – 92416*
Tehnika 16-1, 10149 Tallinn.
t *(6) 533173* f *(6) 533173*
e *info@hostels.ee* w *www.hostels.ee*
Open Dates: 12 ✈ *8km* ⛴ *5km* 🚆 *500m* x 19 1 x P

GHANA

STYO
Opp U.N.D.P. Offices, Ring Road East,
PO Box 9732 KIA, Accra.
t (233) (21) 768257 f (233) (21) 776081; 774338

HI Suggests...

Ghana is situated in West Africa and is bounded by Burkina Faso, Togo, the Atlantic Ocean and Côte d'Ivoire.

A narrow grassy plain stretches inland from the coast, widening in the east, while the south and west are covered by dense rainforest. To the north are forested hills beyond which is dry savannah and open woodland. Ghana's coastline is dotted with sandy palm-fringed beaches and lagoons.

The capital, Accra, features the Makola Market, a large and busy open-air market. Kumasi is the historic capital of the Ashanti civilisation, where ruins of the Manhyia Palace and the Royal Mausoleum, burnt down by Lord Baden-Powell may be examined. In the northeast, the Boufom Wildlife Sanctuary contains the spectacular Banfabiri Falls. Mole National Park is recommended. Species of antelope, monkeys, lions and elephants can all be seen on guided excursions.

Local dishes include traditional soups (palmnut and groundnut), Kontomere and Okro stews that are normally accompanied by fufu (pounded cassava), kenkey or gari.

In Accra and other major cities there are nightclubs combining a selection of Western pop music and spectacular Ghanaian music and dancing.

You can find out a lot more on our website - a visit to www.HIhostels.com is essential for planning your trip!

Pour en savoir plus, rendez-vous sur notre site Internet, www.HIhostels.com une visite incontournable pour préparer votre voyage!

Viele weitere Informationen auf unserer Website: www.HIhostels.com - unverzichtbar für die Reiseplanung!

Puedes averiguar mucho más en nuestro sitio web. Es imprescindible que visites la página www.HIhostels.com para planear tu viaje.

▲ **Accra** – Pink Hostel – 93001
PO Box 9732, Accra.
t (21) 256710 f (21) 256712
e phostel@idngh.com
w www.pinkhostel.com
Open Dates: 12 ✈ Kotoka International 6km
x 54 R (BD) 5km

GREECE

The land of legendary beauty, tumultuous history, monumental architecture of times past and heir to a civilization that once enlightened the world and gave birth to the fundamental structures of democracy, the land of Plato, Pericles and Pythagoras. Greece today is greatly focused on restating its claim to excellence in all aspects of life, not least in sport (2004 Olympics), as it did 2500 years ago.

A country made up of islands (Crete being the largest) and mountains set in the delightful Aegean and Ionian seas, history has somehow made Greece a land of contradictions – both in terms of its own self-image and its relationship with the outside world, depending on the winds of change. But it is worth remembering that for 400 years up to the 1820s, it was part of the Turkish Empire.

Now part of the European Union, the old fragmentation of Greek society and way of life is giving way to a new self-belief, sense of national unity and renewal in the way Greece is and the way Greece works – all of which has to be good news for the visitor!

A few other Top Tips from **CULTURE SMART!**:

- One of the basic forms of courtesy in Greece is dressing correctly. Mostly this is to do with wearing the right quantity, rather than the right quality of clothes in public, whether on the beach (nudity is not acceptable), or in bars, cafes and restaurants, and of course, churches, it is polite to wear an appropriate top or shirt.
- Paradoxically, relationships in Greece can be surprisingly blunt, which visitors might deem to be rude; a firm but non-confrontational response is invariably the best attitude to adopt.
- Handshakes are the norm and occasional use of simple courtesies using the Greek language, 'to show willing', may or may not be appreciated: *parakaló* (please) and *efharistó* (thank you).
- It is worth remembering that there is far more to Greek cooking than *taramasalatá*, *feta cheese* and *moussaká*. For example, the *psistariá* specialise in roasted and grilled meat, the *taverna* specialise in fish (*psari*) or meat, and the formal restaurants, *estiatório*, is where you will find all of the above and much more. Persistence will also be required to discover the best of Greek wine.

Cultural Top Tips supplied by Culture Smart! guides. These essential guides to customs and etiquette will help you steer clear of embarrassing gaffes and sensitive issues, enabling you to discover new cultures whilst developing new friendships. Order online at www.culturesmartguides.co.uk

You can find out a lot more on our website - a visit to www.HIhostels.com is essential for planning your trip!

Pour en savoir plus, rendez-vous sur notre site Internet, www.HIhostels.com une visite incontournable pour préparer votre voyage!

Viele weitere Informationen auf unserer Website: www.HIhostels.com - unverzichtbar für die Reiseplanung!

Puedes averiguar mucho más en nuestro sitio web. Es imprescindible que visites la página www.HIhostels.com para planear tu viaje.

▲ **Athens** – Hostel Aphrodite 23004
12 Einardou & Mich. Voda Corner, Victoria Square.
(210) 8810589 (210) 8816574
info@hostelaphrodite.com
www.hostelaphrodite.com
Open Dates: 01.03-10.11 E. Venizelos 40km A E95 bus Syntagma, 3km from hostel Piraeus 10km Larissa (direct from Airport) 300m Telephone hostel as depends where guests are arriving from 1 150m ap Larissa - 300m U Larissa 300m; Victoria 500m x 80 R (B)

▲ **Athens** – Lozanni Hostel 23006
54 Kapodistriou Str, Vathis Sq. 10432 Athens.
(210) 5223 801; 5226161
(210) 5245506
hostellozanni@hotmail.com
Open Dates: E. Venizelos 40km A E95 Synjagma Sq. 2km Piraeus 10km Central 1km Terminal B A11; Term A051 ap A11 Vathis Sq. 051 Omonia Sq. U Omonia Sq. 200m x 81 R (B)

▲ **Athens** – Student and Travellers Inn 23005
16 Kydathineon, Plaka.
(210) 3244808; 3248802
(210) 3210065
info@studenttravellersinn.com
www.studenttravellersinn.com
Open Dates: E. Venizelos 40km A E95 bus to Syntagma 300m from hostel Piraeus 10km Larissa 3km Telephone hostel as depends where guests are arriving from 1, 2, 3, 4, 5 or 11 300m ap Syntagma U Syntagma x 120 R (B) 8 15km

▲ **Corfu** – Corfu Travellers Inn 23009
The Pink Palace, Agios Gordios Beach, Corfou 49084.
30 6974380579; 30 266105393
30 2661053985
corfutravellersinn@hotmail.com
www.corfutravellersinn.com
Open Dates: Corfu International 14km A Free pickup Corfu 14km 100m ap Agios Gordios Beach 14W x 100 R CC

▲ **Santorini** – HI Drossos 23008
Perissa Beach.
22860 81639 22860 82668
drossosh@otenet.gr
www.familydrossos.gr
Open Dates: 01.04-31.10 16km A 30m 8km x 80 R (B) P

▲ **Santorini** – Villa Holiday Beach
23007
Limnes, Perissa.
22860 81639 22860 82668
drossosh@otenet.gr
www.familydrossos.gr
Open Dates: 01.04-31.10 16km
A 50m 8km x 60 (B)

GUINEA

Fédération Guinéenne des Auberges de Jeunesse,
Commandayah/ Commune Dirinn, Conakry.
(224) 453522; 349714
dioumagueme2004@yahoo.fr

HI Suggests...

Guinea is a developing country located on the Atlantic coast of West Africa. It is bordered by Guinea-Bissau, Senegal, Mali, Côte d'Ivoire, Liberia and Sierra Leone.

The country is divided into four geographic regions: A narrow coastal belt in lower Guinea; the pastoral Fouta Djallon highlands in middle Guinea; the northern savannah and a south-eastern rain-forest region. The Niger, Gambia, and Senegal Rivers are among the 22 West African Rivers that have their origins in Guinea.

Full of strong African spirit, it is not uncommon on a Sunday stroll through Conakry to find street celebrations and dancing led by groups of men playing local instruments. The city hugs a narrow peninsula, squeezed on three sides by the sea, forcing growth back into the mainland. The attractively landscaped Ave de la République, in the heart of Conakry, is where the banks, airline offices and restaurants are clustered. Travellers who plan to stay in the capital city of Conakry should make reservations in advance.

In Guinea you can trek through beautiful highland scenery and travel along new roads into the jungles of the southeast. You can also swim at several beaches near Conakry and further a field, and the best hiking in the country is in the beautiful Fouta Djalon region.

The coastal regions of Guinea and most of the inland have a tropical climate, with a rainy season lasting from April to November, relatively high and uniform temperatures, and high humidity.

You can find out a lot more on our website - a visit to www.HIhostels.com is essential for planning your trip!

Pour en savoir plus, rendez-vous sur notre site Internet, www.HIhostels.com une visite incontournable pour préparer votre voyage!

Viele weitere Informationen auf unserer Website: www.HIhostels.com - unverzichtbar für die Reiseplanung!

Puedes averiguar mucho más en nuestro sitio web. Es imprescindible que visites la página www.HIhostels.com para planear tu viaje.

▲ **Conakry** – Auberge de Jeuesse
ommandayah – 78001
ommune de Dixinn BP 262 Conakry.
(224) 206750; 349714 (224)
93522302 dionmagueme2004@yahoo.fr
pen Dates: Glessia 6km
A Minibus and taxi's only Conakry
km 30m x 80
x 2km 3km

LATVIA

Latvian Youth Hostel Association,
17-2 Siguldas pr., Riga, LV 1014.
(371) 9218560 (international) (371) 7517006
info@hostellinglatvia.com; room@hostellinglatvia.com
www.hostellinglatvia.com

HI Suggests...

Latvia is a country located on the Baltic Sea, which has an array of ancient history and traditions. The country itself may be less famous than its capital Riga, one of the most beautiful cities in the Baltic region. Approximately a third of the Latvian population live in the capital and for all purposes it is the best base for exploring the country.

There are many things to see and do, which will accommodate a variety of interests. For the nature lovers the serene Gulf of Riga and the open Baltic Sea provide spectacular scenery, the medieval castles and culture of the ancient Latvians will fascinate the Historic enthusiasts and for the bustling traveller visit Old Riga, where you will find not only fabulous architectural monuments but also various night clubs and pubs.

Summers in Latvia are usually dry, sunny and warm with temperatures sometimes exceeding 30°C. Spring and autumn months often have unstable weather with sun and rain on the same day. Winters produce snow in the north and east from December to March.

Everything about Latvia is a contrast; the buildings, the scenery, the people, the customs and the experiences. It is just simply amazing to see and experience the surprises that crop up around every corner and in everyday life!

You can find out a lot more on our website - a visit to www.HIhostels.com is essential for planning your trip!

Pour en savoir plus, rendez-vous sur notre site Internet, www.HIhostels.com une visite incontournable pour préparer votre voyage!

Viele weitere Informationen auf unserer Website: www.HIhostels.com - unverzichtbar für die Reiseplanung!

Puedes averiguar mucho más en nuestro sitio web. Es imprescindible que visites la página www.HIhostels.com para planear tu viaje.

△ ***Riga*** *– Argonaut Hostel* 77002
50 Kaleju iela, Old Riga.
6147214 *room@hostellinglatvia.com*
www.hostellinglatvia.com
Open Dates: *15km* A *200m*
1km *400m* x 70 R
CC P

△ ***Riga*** *– Elizabeth's Hostel* *HI 77001*
101 Elizabetes iela, Riga.
t 6705476 f 7217889
e room@hostellinglativa.com
w www.hostellinglativa.com
Open Dates: 12 ✈ 15km ⛴ 1.5km
🚆 100m 🚌 300m 🛏 x 42 👪 R
CC P

△ ***Riga*** *– POSH Backpackers Hostel – 77007*
5 Pupolu iela, Riga.
t 7210917 e room@hostellinglatvia.com
w www.hostellinglatvia.com
Open Dates: 12 ✈ 15km A🚌 100m
⛴ 1.5km 🚆 200m 🚌 100m
🛏 x 60 👪 R P

▲ **Riga** – Turiba – 77005
68 Graudu Street, Riga, LV-1058.
t (371) 7617543 f (371) 7517006
e room@hostellinglatvia.com
w www.hostellinglatvia.com
Open Dates: 12 ✈ Riga 8km ⛴ Riga 10km 🚆 Riga 7km 🚌 40A 200m ap Graudu St 🚋 8 ap Graudu St 8SE
🛏 x 146 👪 R

YOUTH HOSTEL ACCOMMODATION OUTSIDE THE ASSURED STANDARDS SCHEME

Riga – Barons Guesthouse HI 77003
25 Kr. Barona iela, Riga.
t 9105939 e room@hostellinglativa.com
w www.hostellinglativa.com
Open Dates: 12 ✈ 16km A🚌 1.5km ⛴ 2km 🚆 1.5km 🚌 2km ap Dzirnav Iela 100m U 100m 🛏 x 8 👪 R

Riga – Riga Backpackers – 77008
6 Marstalu iela, Riga.
t 7229922; 8277488
e room@hostellinglativa.com
w www.hostellinglativa.com
Open Dates: 12 ✈ 15km A🚌 200m ⛴ 1km 🚌 450m 🛏 x 80 👪 R
CC P

LITHUANIA

Lithuanian Youth Hostels,
Filaretų Street 17, LT-01207 Vilnius.
t (370) (5) 2154627 f (370) (5) 2120149
e booking@lithuanianhostels.org w www.lithuanianhostels.org

Visas:
Visa free entrance for all main Western countries (Australia, USA, Canada, UK, Sweden, Finland, Norway, Croatia, Hungary, Japan, Poland, Slovenia, Portugal).

Visas are needed for citizens of Russia and CIS and some Asian and African countries - please check before travelling.

HI Suggests...

Lithuania is a small plot of land in the Baltic Sea. The west fringe of the country (approximately 100 km) is occupied by the amber coastline, which has marvellous beaches of white sand. The clean waters of the Sesupe, Dubysa, Nevezis and Nemunas flow. Sometimes Lithuania is called the Nemunas land due to the great love Lithuanians have for this river.

Lithuania's cultural life is lively. Lithuania now has 13 professional theatres, state orchestras, chamber groups and some large art collections. Some of the latter are well known to foreign experts. The Lithuanian Theatre of Youth is especially popular in both Lithuania and abroad. The Lithuanian Chamber Orchestra under Prof. Sondeckis is well known internationally.

Travelling in Lithuania presents no

real hardships, and even in well-trodden destinations the volume of visitors is low, leaving you with the feeling that there is still much to discover here. Vilnius, with its Baroque old town, is the most architecturally beautiful of the Baltic capitals, with an easy-going charm all of its own. Lithuania's second city Kaunas also has an attractive old town and a couple of unique museums, along with a handful of surprisingly good restaurants and bars. The port city of Klaipeda, despite its restored old town, is more a stopping-off point en route to the low-key resorts of Neringa, a unique spit of sand dunes and forest that shields Lithuania from the Baltic. Lithuanian Youth Hostels suggest that EU citizens carry complete health insurance or form E111.

△ ***Klaipèda*** *– Klaipèda Guests House – 92044*
Butku Juzés Street 7-4.
(46) 211879; (685) 33104
(46) 211879 guestplace@yahoo.com
www.lithuanianhostels.org
Open Dates: Klaipèda 150m 1NE
x 20 R

▲ **Vilnius** – Filaretai 92043
Filaretų str 17, 01207 Vilnius.
(5) 2154627 (5) 2120149
info@filaretaihostel.lt
www.filaretaihostel.lt
Open Dates: 01.01-23.12 Vilnius 8km
Vilnius 2km 34 100m ap Filaretų
1.2E x 54 R CC

△ ***Vilnius*** *– Old Town YH – 92045*
Aušros Vartu 20-15a, Vilnius.
(5) 2625357 (5) 2685967
oldtownhostels@lithuanianhostels.org
www.lithuanianhostels.org
Open Dates: Vilnius 6km
Vilnius 200m 0.8S x 32 R
CC

You can find out a lot more on our website - a visit to www.HIhostels.com is essential for planning your trip!

Pour en savoir plus, rendez-vous sur notre site Internet, www.HIhostels.com une visite incontournable pour préparer votre voyage!

Viele weitere Informationen auf unserer Website: www.HIhostels.com - unverzichtbar für die Reiseplanung!

Puedes averiguar mucho más en nuestro sitio web. Es imprescindible que visites la página www.HIhostels.com para planear tu viaje.

YOUTH HOSTEL ACCOMMODATION OUTSIDE THE ASSURED STANDARDS SCHEME

Zarasai – Zarasai Youth Hostel – 92046
Šiaulių 26, Zarasai.
booking@lithuanianhostels.lt
www.lithuanianhostels.org
Open Dates: 15.05-15.09 x 8 R

Zervynos – Svirnelis YH – 92047
Zervynos km, Varėnos raj.
(310) 52720 svirnelis@hotmail.com
www.lithuanianhostels.org
Open Dates: 15.05-15.09 x 12 R

NEW CALEDONIA

(In co-operation with French YHA)

Association des Auberges de Jeunesse de Nouvelle Calédonie,
51 bis rue Pasteur Marcel Ariège, BP 767, 98845 Nouméa.
(687) 275879 (687) 254817
yha.noumea@lagoon.nc

Expect to pay in the region of 11 Euros in a dormitory per person, 14.50 Euros in a doub room per person. Sheet sleeping bags are available, free of charge.

HI Suggests...

In the heart of the South Pacific lies a beautiful island surrounded by an emerald green lagoon. New Caledonia is a land like no other, offering visitors an insight to a paradise of undeniable beauty and ecological treasures, all waiting to be discovered.

New Caledonia is a fragment of an ancient continent, which drifted away some 250 million years ago. Its flora and fauna evolved in isolation, and are now quite unique: 3500 recorded species of plants, three quarters of which occur only here; 4300 species of land animals, 1000 species of fish, 6500 species of marine invertebrates.

Five hundred kilometres long, fifty kilometres wide, New Caledonia offers an endless variety of landscapes, from some of the best white sand beaches in the Pacific to spectacular mountain retreats.

Options for travellers in New Caledonia are vast, from diving in pristine reefs to dining out *à la français*, from trekking in unspoilt rainforest to having a relaxing evening in one of the many Nakamals where you can try the traditional Kava drink. With a nod to local custom and an open mind, a trip to New Caledonia will be unforgettable.

The people of New Caledonia - the Caldoches, Métros and Kanaks - staggered out of the troubles when New Caledonia was contender for the 'basket case of the Pacific' prize. They are now barrelling down the future with, if not optimism, at least one eye on putting an end to the senseless rounds of violence of the 1980s.

You can find out a lot more on our website - a visit to www.HIhostels.com is essential for planning your trip!

Pour en savoir plus, rendez-vous su notre site Internet, www.HIhostels.com une visite incontournable pour préparer votre voyage!

Viele weitere Informationen auf unserer Website: www.HIhostels.com - unverzichtbar für die Reiseplanung!

Puedes averiguar mucho más en nuestro sitio web. Es imprescindible que visites la página www.HIhostels.com para planear tu viaje.

▲ **Nouméa City Hostel** – 96142
51 bis rue Pasteur Marcel Ariège, BP 767, 98845 Nouméa Cedex, New Caledonia, South Pacific.
(687) 275879 (687) 254817
yha.noumea@lagoon.nc
Open Dates: 12 ✈ Tontouta 60km
A Direct to hostel Port Moselle 1km 0.3NE x 94 R CC TV 3km

RUSSIA

Youth Hostels Association of Russia (YHAR),
11, Yakovlevskiy lane, St. Petersburg, 196105.
t (7) (812) 2521867 f (7) (812) 2521867
e info@russia-hostelling.ru w www.russia-hostelling.ru

sas:

isa is required. This lists entry/exit dates, your invitation, passport details and requires ɔ photos. Please note, that your Russian visa is an exit permit just as it is an entry permit. ople staying in Russia for more than three working days should register at the ·partment of Passports and Visas.

·r detailed information on applying for a Russian visa please got to ww.russia-hostelling.ru/hostels.php

Travel Section:

ADM Travel Agency, 9, Marata str., office 30, St. Petersburg, 191025.
t (7) (812) 3252233; 3121143 f (7) (812) 7646894; 7176617
e info@adm.ru w www.adm.ru

After the collapse of the Soviet Union in 1991, there were hopes for a new dawn in Russia. But it was never going to be easy. New priorities and new cultural and economic freedoms have inevitably come to dominate everyday life, not least the individual and corporate quest for wealth and 'self-fulfilment' that was not possible under Communism. Traditional respects for education, the arts and the wider context of cultural pursuits generally have to be rediscovered in their own right, not because of state intervention.

There are also great social difficulties resulting from the dissolution of Russia's military culture with its high status, and its replacement with a civilian administrative class focused on a market-driven economy, which in turn has been creating even greater gaps between the 'super rich', the rich and the poor.

The Russian welcome, however, remains legendary, as does the Russian sense of humour and the delight in making merry. Even the smile is returning to the once plain-faced world of public servants and officialdom. There is reason to hope, too, that Russia's historic sense of isolation and vulnerability is giving way to a more relaxed involvement with the outside world.

A few other Top Tips from **CULTURE SMART!:**

- People greeting each other like to relate to their families and the problems of everyday life, rather than enquiring about each other's health. Contrary to the old Soviet stereotypes, Russians are open, naturally friendly people and relate to each other more personally than some of the traditionally staid northern European cultures.
- Vodka is central to the Russian way of life and you would naturally agree to enjoy a drink and of course make a toast. Making a toast, in fact, is *de rigeur* and the visitor would do well to rehearse suitable things to say. Vodka is

usually served with *zakuski* (hors d'oeuvres). Avoid homemade Vodka, which can have a very high alcohol content. An excellent non-alcoholic summer drink is *kvas*.

- There can often be significant price differences between what is charged to visitors and what is charged to Russians in places like museums, hotels, restaurants and other public amenities. The Russian economy, though making significant progress, remains fragile.
- Russia remains a patriarchy, with traditional values still obtaining in family life and the role and place of women and children. Consequently, polite society dictates that men are expected to hold open doors and offer their seat on the train to women. This conservative attitude is also reflected in fashion and style in contemporary life generally, with Russian women, for example, continuing to favour dresses and high heels more so than Western women.

Culture Smart! Top Tips © Kuperard 2005

Cultural Top Tips supplied by Culture Smart! guides. These essential guides to customs and etiquette will help you steer clear of embarrassing gaffes and sensitive issues, enabling you to discover new cultures whilst developing new friendships. Order online at www.culturesmartguides.co.uk

You can find out a lot more on our website - a visit to www.HIhostels.com i[s] essential for planning your trip!

Pour en savoir plus, rendez-vous s[ur] notre site Internet, www.HIhostels.com une visite incontournable pour préparer votr[e] voyage!

Viele weitere Informationen auf unserer Website: www.HIhostels.com - unverzichtbar für die Reiseplanung!

Puedes averiguar mucho más en nuestro sitio web. Es imprescindibl[e] que visites la página www.HIhostels.com para planear tu viaje.

▲ **Moscow** – G & R Hostel Asia Ⓗ 92159 3/2, Zelenodolskaya str., 5th Floor, Moscow, 109377.
Ⓣ (095) 3780001; 3780466
Ⓕ (095) 3782866 Ⓔ info@hostels.ru; (for groups@hostels.ru) Ⓦ www.hostels.ru
Open Dates: 12 ✈ Sheremetyevo 40km; Domodedovo 40km A 48, 49, 551 to Rechnoy Vokzal 27km; 405 to Domodedovskaya Metro 14km Rechnoy Vokzal 27km Leningradsky Vokzal 12km Kursky Vokzal 10km 69 150m ap Metro Ryazansky Prospect U Purple Line ap Ryazansky Prospect 50m 10SE x 156 R CC 8 P

▲ **Moscow** – Godzillas Hostel – 92169 6, Bolshoi Karetnyy, Apt. 5 (First Floor), Moscow, 127051.
Ⓣ (095) 2994223 Ⓕ (095) 2994223
Ⓔ info@godzillashostel.com
Ⓦ www.godzillashostel.com
Open Dates: 12 ✈ Sheremetyevo 25km A 48, 49, 551 to Rechnoy Vokzal Metro 15km Rechnoy Vokzal 15km Leningradsky Vokzal 25km; Rizhskiy Vokzal 3km U Grey Line ap Tsvetnoi Bulvar 400m 1N x 20 R 8

▲ **Moscow** – Sherstone 92150
, Gostinichnyi Proezd, korp.1, Office 324, 3rd Floor, Moscow, 127106.
(901) 7112613; (095) 7833438
(095) 7833438 info@sherstone.ru
www.sherstone.ru
Open Dates: Sheremetyevo 15km A 48, 49, 551 to Rechnoy Vokzal 7km Rechnoy Vokzal 7km Rizhskiy Vokzal 6km; Leningradsky Vokzal 10km; Kursky Vokzal 12km 88, 219 50m ap Vladykino U Grey Line ap Vladykino 800m 8N x 150 R 1 x

▲ **Moscow** – Snail – 92164
15/1 Selskokhozyaistvennaya str., Office 339, Moscow, 129226.
(095) 7952335 (095) 1890297
info@hostel-snail.ru; hostel-snail@mail.ru
www.hostel-snail.ru
Open Dates: Sheremetyevo 20km A 48, 49, 551 to Rechnoy Vokzal 12km Rechnoy Vokzal 12km Rizhskiy Vokzal 4km 33, 134, 154, 603 100m ap Botanicheskiy Sad U Orange Line ap Botanicheskiy Sad 500m 8NE x 125 R CC 1 x

▲ **Moscow** – Traveller's Guest House 92035
50, Bolshaya Pereyaslavskaya str., 10th Floor, Moscow 129110.
(095) 6314059; (095) 6804300
(095) 6807686 info@tgh.ru
www.tgh.ru
Open Dates: Sheremetyevo 25km A 48, 49, 551 to Rechnoy Vokzal Metro 15km Rechnoy Vokzal 15km Rizhskiy Vokzal 0.5km; Leningradsky Vokzal 1km 14 from Leningradsky Vokzal; 48 from Prospect Mira Metro 20m ap Bannyi Pereulok U Purple Line ap Prospect Mira 500m 4N x 54 R CC

▲ **St. Petersburg** – 5 Minutes to Hermitage 92158
11, Kazanskaya str., St. Petersburg, 191186.
(812) 3151917 (812) 3150495
travelspb@hotmail.com
www.discount-travel-petersburg.ru
Open Dates: Pulkovo II International 15km A 13 to Moskovskaya Metro Station 10km Gavan 7km Moskovsky Vokzal 2km 3, 22, 27 100m ap Kanal Griboedova 5, 10, 17 100m ap Kanal Griboedova U Blue Line 2/Green Line 3 ap Gostiny Dvor/Nevsky Prospect 500m 0.1S x 30 R (B)

▲ **St. Petersburg** – All Seasons 92152
11, Yakovlevskiy Lane, St. Petersburg, 196105.
(812) 3271070 (812) 3271033
info@hostel.spb.ru www.hostel.ru
Open Dates: Pulkovo II International 8km A 13 to Moskovskaya Metro Station 3km Gavan 6km Vitebsky 7km; Moskovsky 7km 3 350m ap Kuznetsovskaya str. 16, 25, 29, 43, 45 150m ap Blagodatnaya str. U Blue Line 2 ap Elektrosila/Park Pobedy 500m 5S x 60 R CC

▲ **St. Petersburg** – Menshikovskiy 92165
8, Menshikovskiy Prospect, St. Petersburg, 195067.
(812) 2499806; 2498977
(812) 2498977 info@mhostel.ru
www.mhostel.ru
Open Dates: Pulkovo II International 30km A 13 to Moskovskaya Metro Station 3km Gavan 15km Finlyandskiy 7km 123, 102, 106, 178 200m ap Piskarevka 18, 38, 7 , 14, 22, 46, 51 300m ap Piskarevka U Red Line 1 ap Ploshad Muzhestva 9NE x 200 R 1 x

▲ **St. Petersburg** – Metro-Tour 92153
47, Blagodatnaya str., St. Petersburg, 196105.
(812) 3896451; 3885969
(812) 3885969
admin@hostelmetro.spb.ru
www.hostelmetro.spb.ru
Open Dates: Pulkovo II International 8km A 13 to Moskovskaya U 3km Gavan 6km Vitebsky 7km; Moskovsky 7km 3 300m ap Kuznetsovskaya str. 16, 25, 29, 43, 45 100m ap Blagodatnaya str. U Blue Line 2 ap Elektrosila 400m 5S x 90 R CC TV i 8 P

▲ **St. Petersburg** – Ostrovok 92154
130, Bukharestskaya str., korp. 2, 13th Floor, St. Petersburg, 192288.
(812) 7762349; 7762340
(812) 7762340
ostrovok-13@yandex.ru
www.ostrovok-spb.by.ru
Open Dates: Pulkovo II International 6km A 13 to Moskovskaya U 6km Gavan 9km Vitebsky 4km 56, 57 20m ap Yaroslava Gasheka 45, 62 20m ap Yaroslava Gasheka U Blue Line 2 ap Kupshino 2km 9S x 42 R TV i 8 P

▲ **St. Petersburg** – The St. Petersburg Travellers Hostel 92168
25, Sadovaya Str., St. Petersburg, 191023. (Entrance from Bankovskiy pereulok)
(812) 3140814 (812) 3140814
tenzorspb@mail.ru; yana@namuchnom.ru
www.hostel.spbtraveller.ru
Open Dates: Pulkovo II International 15km A 13 to Moskovskaya Metro Station 10km Gavan 7km Moskovsky Vokzal 2km 3, 22, 27 300m 14 200m U Blue Line 2/Green Line 3 ap Gostiny Dvor/Nevsky Prospekt 300m 0.3S x 100 R CC (B) TV i 8 P

▲ **Ulan-Ude** – Baikal International Hostel – 92167
3A, Sukhe-Batora str., Ulan-Ude, 670000.
(3012) 213651 (3012) 213748
e_center@burnet.ru
www.hostel.bsu.ru
Open Dates: 01.06-20.08 Ulan-Ude 10km A 77, 55 10km Ulan-Ude 1km 36, 63 100m ap Soviet Square 7, 4 300m ap Soviet Square 1N x 40 TV i 8 P

▲ **Velikiy Novgorod** – Kruis – 92151
11, Prusskaya str., Velikiy Novgorod, 173007.
(8162) 775487; 772283 (8162) 772283 nsm_kruis@mail.natm.ru
www.russia-hostelling.ru/hostels.php
Open Dates: 800m 9, 26 100m ap Central Market 0.3SW x 60 R TV 1 x i 8 P

SINGAPORE

Youth Hostels Assoc. (Singapore),
1 Pasir Ris Close, Singapore 519599.
(65) 65891637 (65) 65846089
nci@ntucclub.com.sg

Singapore, covering an area of just 250 square miles, is a unique melting pot of Chinese, Indian, Southeast Asian and European cultures. The visitor will have an extraordinary and magical experience on arriving in the midst of this striking combination of very different cultures.

Singapore is particularly tolerant towards different religions: Buddhism, Islam, Taoism, Christianity, Hinduism and Sikhism are just some of the faiths that are welcomed in this cosmopolitan society. English, Malay, Chinese and 'amil are the four main languages. As well as its cultural contrasts, the city itself is full of dramatic physical differences. Skyscrapers adorn the skyline, contrasting with the city's nature reserve at Bukit Timah – a last remaining pocket of primary tropical rainforest.

A few other Top Tips from **CULTURE SMART!**:

- Beware of touching someone in Singapore. This can be misinterpreted, especially when it comes from the opposite sex. In the West, a pat on the back or a hand on the shoulder is usually seen as a friendly gesture, but in Singapore it may be regarded as aggressive or flirtatious.
- To some Singaporeans, displaying the sole of your foot (or shoe) is considered disrespectful and rude. Don't cross your legs unless you are seated behind a table or a desk.
- Always use the right hand when dealing with Indians or Malays. Among Muslims, the left hand is used only for personal hygiene, and is considered unclean.
- It's better to use the whole of the palm with the four fingers folded if you need to point at something. Using the forefinger to point, even at an object, is considered very rude.
- The Chinese regard finishing everything on your plate at meal times as rude to the host: it would imply that you are not content with the meal provided. A clean plate suggests that you are still hungry, or, even worse, greedy.
- It is polite to use the right-hand door when entering a temple, and the left when leaving.

Cultural Top Tips supplied by Culture Smart! guides. These essential guides to customs and etiquette will help you steer clear of embarrassing gaffes and sensitive issues, enabling you to discover new cultures whilst developing new friendships. Order online at www.culturesmartguides.co.uk

You can find out a lot more on our website - a visit to www.HIhostels.com is essential for planning your trip!

Pour en savoir plus, rendez-vous sur notre site Internet, www.HIhostels.com une visite incontournable pour préparer votre voyage!

Viele weitere Informationen auf unserer Website: www.HIhostels.com - unverzichtbar für die Reiseplanung!

Puedes averiguar mucho más en nuestro sitio web. Es imprescindible que visites la página www.HIhostels.com para planear tu viaje.

▲ **Costa Sands Resort (Downtown East) YH** Ⓗ 95002
1 Pasir Ris Close, Singapore 519599.
Ⓣ (65) 65891865 Ⓕ (65) 65829535
Ⓔ dmcsde@costasands.com.sg
Ⓦ www.costasands.com.sg
Open Dates: 12 (R required via www.HIhostels.com) ✈ Changi International 12km (15 min by taxi) Pasir Ris MRT Feeder bus 354 from Pasir Ris Interchange ap YH x 200 R CC

▲ **Costa Sands Resort (Pasir Ris) YH**
HI 95001
159m Jalan Loyang Besar, Pasir Ris Park, Singapore 509404.
t (65) 65892184 f (65) 65822098
e dmcspr@costasands.com.sg
w www.costasands.com.sg
Open Dates: 12 (R required via www.HIhostels.com) ✈ Changi International 12km (15 min by taxi) Pasir Ris MRT Feeder bus 354 from Pasir Ris Interchange ap YH x 200 R CC

▲ **Costa Sands Resort (Sentosa) YH**
HI 95003
30, Imbiah Walk, Sentosa, Singapore 09953
t (65) 62751034 f (65) 62751074
e dmcsrs@costasands.com.sg
w www.costasands.com.sg
Open Dates: 12 (R required via www.HIhostels.com) ✈ Changi Internation 31km (40mins by taxi) Harbourfront MRT From Sentosa take "blueline" bu service to Underwater World stop for a free shuttle service to Costa Sands Resort x 6
R CC

▲ **Mount Emily – Hangout@mt.emily** HI 95007
10a Upper Wilkie Road, Singapore 228119.
t (65) 64385588 f (65) 63396008
w www.hangouthotels.com
Open Dates: 12 ✈ 20km 280m
U Little India 400m x 195

SLOVAKIA

CKM SYTS,
Vysoká 32, 81445 Bratislava.
t (421) (2) 52731024 f (421) (2) 52731025
e ckm2000-bts@ckm.sk w www.ckm.sk

HI Suggests...

Slovakia has a considerably long list of interesting natural and historical sights, and is now getting on the list for travellers as a new destination, with surprisingly nice landscapes and moderate prices for tourist services.

Its position in the very centre of Europe makes it easily accessible. Bratislava, the Slovak capital, is only 60 km from Vienna, 255 km from Budapest, 323 km from Prague and 410 km from Berlin, to mention just a few nearest capitals. Also the cross-border cooperation within the so called Danube triangle (Vienna-Budapest-Bratislava) makes it touristically more and more attractive.

For nature lovers Slovakia can offer several natural parks including High Tatras and Slovak Paradise, plenty of natural lakes and other unspoiled areas for sports and relaxation. Even the cyclists are nicely surprised as the Slovak and Austrian Danube cycle-route is now connected by a regular boat service from Devin to Heinburg, allowing bikes on board.

For the culture and history lovers there are many castles such as Bratislava castle, Devin, Cerveny Kamen, Beckov and Bojnice and many national cultural heritage sights such as the ancient mining town of Banská Štiavnica or the Eastern Slovakia's jewel Levoca.

The main communication language, English and German are more and

nore widely spoken among its 5.5 nillion population, breaking the nguage barriers and making the tay for all foreigners more njoyable.
After Slovakia became a member of he European Union on May 1st 2004, travelling to this small and nteresting country has become really easy and comfortable.

You can find out a lot more on our website - a visit to www.HIhostels.com is essential for planning your trip!

Pour en savoir plus, rendez-vous sur notre site Internet, www.HIhostels.com une visite incontournable pour préparer votre voyage!

Viele weitere Informationen auf unserer Website: www.HIhostels.com - unverzichtbar für die Reiseplanung!

Puedes averiguar mucho más en nuestro sitio web. Es imprescindible que visites la página www.HIhostels.com para planear tu viaje.

▲ **Banská Bystrica** – Hotel Dixon – 92082
Švermova 32, 974 00 Banská Bystrica.
(48) 4130808 (48) 4231191
toppromo@dixon.sk www.dixon.sk
Open Dates: Bratislava 210km Banská Bystrica 3km ap Banská Bystrica 3km 1 100m ap Štiavničky x 110

▲ **Bojnice** – Penzión Signál – 92083
Rekreačná 1561, 972 01 Bojnice.
(905) 859468; (46) 5430187
signalbojnice@post.sk
www.signal.host.sk
Open Dates: Prievidza 3km x 29

▲ **Bratislava** – Down Town Backpackers' Hostel 92091
Panenska 31.
(2) 54641191 (2) 54641191
info@backpackers.sk
www.backpackers.sk
Open Dates: A Trolleybus 208 ap 4 stops (7min to YH) 15mins walk to YH 2km (3mins by 81, 91, 95) x 7

▲ **Bratislava** – Hotel Spirit – 92084
Vančurova 1, 831 01 Bratislava.
(2) 54777817; 54777561
(2) 54777817 info@hotelspirit.sk
www.hotelspirit.sk
Open Dates: Bratislava 10km A 61 10km Bratislava 100m x 40 1 x

▲ **Demänovská Dolina** – Penzión Limba – 92085
Demänovská Dolina 22, 032 51, Demänovská Dolina.
(44) 5548205 (44) 5548209
limba@liptour.sk www.liptour.sk
Open Dates: Liptovský Mikuláš 9km x 60

△ ***Hrabušice** – Hotel Petra – 92086*
Gaštanová 18, 053 15 Hrabušice.
(53) 4490259; 4490438; 4299264
(53) 4490438; 4299265
petraroyal@hotelpetra.sk
Open Dates: Poprad 15km x 45

△ ***Liptovský Trnovec*** – *Chatky Aqua Therm – 92087*
Liptovský Trnovec 271, 032 22.
(905) 500876 (44) 5524144
miro@liptour.sk www.mara.sk
Open Dates: Liptovský Mikuláš 5km x 22

▲ **Nitra** – Hotel AX – 92088
Vihorlatská 10, 949 01 Nitra.
(37) 6534541 (37) 6534545
Open Dates: Nitra 6km 14, 15, 16, 19, 32 200m ap Výstavná x 122

▲ **Poprad** – Hotel Gerlach – 92089
Hviezdoslavova 2, 058 01 Poprad.
(52) 7721945 (52) 7763663
hotelgerlach@hotelgerlach.sk
www.hotelgerlach.sk
Open Dates: Poprad 300m x 1

▲ **Žilina** – Hotel Garni – 92090
Vysokoškolákov 4, 010 08 Žilina.
(41) 7246153 (41) 5655122
vystavy@domtechza.sk
Open Dates: Žilina 2km 6 50m ap Dom Techniky x 65 1 x

TAIWAN

Chinese Taipei Youth Hostel Association,
12F-10, No. 50 Chuang Hsiao West Rd, Sec 1, Taipei.
(886) (2) 23317272; 23115067 (886) (2) 23317272; 23316427
iysosc@ms28.hinet.net www.yh.org.tw

Expect to pay in the region of US$10-US$20 per night. It is essential to book in advance during peak periods.

N.B. For Chinese address in detail, please contact the head office in Taipei.

Not surprisingly, Taiwan is often referred to as the *Ilha Formosa*, the "Beautiful Island." Beyond the busy cities is a glorious coastline, and much of the country is covered in spectacular mountain ranges.
Taiwan has a population of approximately twenty-two million people, who have preserved their independence from mainland China, despite continuing friction between the People's Republic of China and the Democratic Progressive Party on Taiwan. This tension dates back to the Chinese revolution of 1949, when Communists, led by Chairman Mao, wrested control of mainland China, thereby forcing Nationalist leader Chiang Kai-shek to withdraw to Taiwan along with two million refugees. Resentment escalated between the millions of native Taiwanese and the mainland refugee newcomers, and climaxed with Chiang imposing a "perpetual" martial law over the island for the next thirty-eight years.
A few other Top Tips from **CULTURE SMART!**:

- The majority of Taiwanese wear Western-style clothing. They like to look neat and tidy, and many of them keep up to date with the latest fashions. Traditional Chinese clothing is worn only at special celebrations.
- The Taiwanese seldom speak very frankly, or express their emotions publicly, in order not to cause offence or loss of face to themselves or others. Smiles and graciousness are expected. Most Taiwanese are familiar with Western customs, and are forgiving

of any *faux pas* that you may make.

You should never talk about dying or accidents. The Taiwanese are superstitious about death, and avoid its symbols – white and the number four.

When meeting people, shaking hands is becoming more widespread and is now probably the customary means of greeting; however, a nod of the head is usually adequate. It is unusual to hug and kiss when greeting.

The elderly are greatly respected in Taiwan, and it is particularly important to treat them politely. In a group, acknowledge and address older people first; and in all ways behave respectfully towards them by opening doors for them, giving them your seat, and so on.
Culture Smart! Top Tips © Kuperard 2005

ultural Top Tips supplied by ulture Smart! guides. These ssential guides to customs and tiquette will help you steer clear of mbarrassing gaffes and sensitive ssues, enabling you to discover new ultures whilst developing new iendships. Order online at ww.culturesmartguides.co.uk

can find out a lot more on our site - a visit to www.HIhostels.com is ential for planning your trip!

ır en savoir plus, rendez-vous sur re site Internet, w.HIhostels.com une visite ontournable pour préparer votre age!

e weitere Informationen auf unserer Website: www.HIhostels.com - unverzichtbar für die Reiseplanung!

Puedes averiguar mucho más en nuestro sitio web. Es imprescindible que visites la página www.HIhostels.com para planear tu viaje.

▲ **Chiayi** – A Li Shan Youth Activity Center – 92201
106, Erh Wan Ping, Hsiang Lin Village, A Li Shan Hsiang, Chiayi County.
t (5) 267-9874 f (5) 267-9562
Open Dates: x 260 (B)

△ ***Chinmen*** – *Chinmen Youth Activity Center – 92202*
1, Huan-Tao-North Road. Chin Cheng Town, Chinmen County.
t *(82) 325-722* f *(82) 328-606*
Open Dates: x 102

▲ **Hualien** – Hualien Farmtastic YH – 92203
No. 19-58, Kang-leh Tsuen, Shincheng, Hualien
t (3) 8263672 f (3) 8263659
e roger4@ms67.hinet.net
Open Dates: Hualien 5km Hualien 9km Hualien bus to Tienshian or Tailuge ap Kang-Leh Tsuen 9N x 16

△ ***Hualien*** – *Tienhsiang Youth Activity Centre – 92204*
30, Tienhsiang Rd. Hsiu Lin Hsiang, Hualien County.
t *(3) 869-1111-4* f *(3) 869-1171*
Open Dates:

△ ***I-Lan*** – *92206*
125 Gainhsing Rd. Tocheng Town.
t *(3) 9772222* f *(3) 9778688*
e *tcfarm@e-lan.net.tw*
w *www.tcfarm.com.tw*
Open Dates: *Gueishen 3km* x 450 1 x

△ ***Kaohsiung*** – *Cheng Ching Lake Youth Activity Center – 92207*
140, Wen-Cheng Road. Niao Sung Hsiang, Kaohsiung County.
t *(7) 371-7181-4* f *(7) 371-9183*
Open Dates: x 450

△ ***Kaohsiung*** *– Chuan-His-Jai Study and Training Center – 92208*
32-2, Da-Pi Rd. Niao Sung Hsiang, Kaohsiung County.
(7) 731-2608 (7) 733-6235
cychzwac@mszl.hinet.net
Open Dates: Kaohsiung 20km
Kaohsiung Kaohsiung City Bus 60 ap Chien Shiu Technical College
x 186

△ ***Kaohsiung*** *– Meishan Youth Activity Center – 92212*
55, Meishan Village, Taoyuan Hsiang, Kaohsiung County.
(7) 6866057 (7) 6866167
Open Dates: x 120

▲ **Miao-Li** – Li Tian Chuang Youth Hostel – 92215
17-2, Shiao-ton-ho, Nan Chuang, Miao Li County.
(37) 824978 (37) 821537
Open Dates: x 30 (B)

△ ***Nantou*** *– Chitou Youth Activity Center – 92216*
15, Sen Lin Lane, Nei Hu Village, Lu Ku Hsiang, Nantou Country.
(49) 261-2160-3 (49) 261-2322
Open Dates: x 500

▲ **Nantou** – Sun Moon Lake Youth Activity Center – 92220
101, Chung-Cheng Road. Sun Moon Village. Sun Moon Lake, Yu Chin Hsiang, Nantou County.
(49) 285-0071 (49) 285-0037
Open Dates: x 484

▲ **Taichung** – Taichung International Youth Hostel – 92223
628 Pu-Tze Rd. Taichung
(4) 22399809 (4) 22394133
ttyh88@hotmail.com
www.ttyh.adsldns.org
Open Dates: Shui Nan 20km
Taichung 15km Renyo Bus 1 from 2.2km ap Da-Kon Ci 15N x 40
1 x 8

△ ***Tainan*** *– Tsengwen Youth Activity Center – 92227*
70-1, Mi-Chih Village, Nan His Hsiang, Tainan County.
(06) 5753431 (06) 5753455
Open Dates: x 350

▲ **Taipei** – Chientan Youth Activity Center 92228
76, Chung Shan N. Rd. Sec. 4, Taipei.
(2) 2885-2551-9 (2) 2885-3360
Open Dates: CKS International
Direct Bus from Taipei Guo-guong Bus Station ap YH x 696

△ ***Taipei County*** *– Chinshan Youth Activity Center – 92230*
1 Ching Nien Rd. Chin Shan, Taipei County
(2) 24981190~4 (2) 24983621
Open Dates: x 700
1 x

△ ***Taoyuan*** *– Fuhsing Youth Activity Center – 92231*
1, Chung-Shan Rd. Tse-Jen Village. Fusing Hsiang, Taoyuan County.
(3) 3822276 (3) 3822789
Open Dates: x 468
1 x

YOUTH HOSTEL ACCOMMODATION OUTSIDE THE ASSURED STANDARDS SCHEME

Kaohsiung – Kind YH – 92211
257 Chung-Sun Rd. Sec. 1, Kaohsiung.
(7) 288 9131 (7) 288 9139
Open Dates: x 100 (B)

Kaohsiung – Modern Plaza Hotel – 92213
Modern Plaza Hotel, No 332 Chiu-Ru 2nd Rd San-Mon, Kaohsiung City.
(7) 3122151 (7) 3218282
Open Dates: Kaohsiung 10km A Airbus to Kaohsiung 7km 3 50m 1N x 128 R CC

Kenting – Wu Fong YH – 92214
No 12 Fon-kuan Lane, Kenting Li, Hengchun, Ping-tung County.
(8) 8861061 (8) 8861661
Open Dates: x 26 CC

ıntou – Hotel Ti Lun Tonpo Spa – 92217
› Land Kaikao, Tung-Pu, Hsinyi,
ıntou County
› (49) 702789 (49) 701360
ɔen Dates:

ıntou – Pu-Li Nan-Hsin YH – 92218
1 Nan-Hsin St. Pu-Li, Nantou County.
› (49) 2989232 (49) 2982622
ɔen Dates:

ıntou – Shangrila Noble Hanging Garden &
ıuntry Club – 92219
› 8 Rongguang Lane, Datong Village,
ı-ai Town, Nantou County.
› (49) 2802166 (49) 2802169
› wgloria@ms9.hinet.net
› www.shangrila-resort.com.tw
ɔen Dates: Kuo Kuan bus to Pu-Li,
ɛn transfer Nantou bus to Tsuefon.
Chingjing Farm 70E x 62 R

nghu – Penghu Youth Activity Center –
221
, Chieh-Shou Rd, Ma Kung, Penghu County.
(6) 927-1124-7 (6) 927-4565
ɛn Dates: x 224
ı 1 x

Pingtung – Kenting Youth Activity Center – 92222
17 Ken-Ting Road. Heng Tsum Chen, Pingtung County.
(8) 886-1221-4 (8) 886-1110
Open Dates: x 650

Tainan – Hwa-Jou Hotel – 92224
9, Lane 181, Sec. 1, Min Sheng Road. Tainan City, Taiwan.
(6) 2283151 (6) 2208911
Open Dates: Tainan 2.7km A 1 Hsimen Tainan 850m 2, 5, 7, 11, 14, 17, 18, 26 50m ap Hsimen x 51 (BL)

Tainan – Kwan Hwa YH – 92225
No. 115 Section 1, Beimen Rd, Tainan.
(6) 2263171 (6) 2263175
Open Dates: x 63

Tainan – Tainan Student Hostel – 92226
1, Lane 300, Fu-Non St. Sec.1, East District, Tainan.
(06) 2670528 (06) 2689018
Open Dates: x 92

TAIWAN

Taiwan, Kaoshiung International Youth Hostel,
120 Wen Wu First Street, Kaohsiung.
(886) (7) 2012477 (886) (7) 2156322
kokiyh@ms57.hinet.net

YOUTH HOSTEL ACCOMMODATION OUTSIDE THE ASSURED STANDARDS SCHEME

ıohsiung – Taiwan Kaohsiung International
ı Wu YH – 92209
20 Wen wu First St, Kaohsiung, Taiwan ROC.
(7) 2012477 (7) 2156322
kokiyh@ms57.hinet.net
ɛn Dates: 8km A 1.2km
1.2km 1.2km 82, 83 1.2km
x 28 R

Kaohsiung – Taiwan Kaohsiung International Wu Chiang YH – 92210
#7 Wu Chian St, Kaohsiung, Taiwan ROC.
(7) 2411120 (7) 2156322
kokiyh@ms57.hinet.net
Open Dates: 8km A 1.2km 1.2km 1.2km 82, 83 1.2km x 12 R

TURKEY

Gençtur, Istiklal Cad No: 212 Aznavur Pasaji K:5, Galatasaray, Istanbul.
t (90) (212) 2446230 f (90) (212) 2446233
e gencturgenctur.com w www.genctur.com

Turkey has a remarkable past, and, after thirteen successive civilizations extending 10,000 years, it is bursting with historic treasures. Also known as Anatolia and Asia Minor, Turkey was settled as early as 7000 BC. Ancient sites such as Ephesus and Troy are there, along with rock villages in Cappadocia and biblical sites such as Tarsus. Turkey is surrounded by four seas: the Mediterranean to the south, the Aegean to the west, the Sea of Marmara between the European and Asian landmasses, and the Black Sea to the north.

Modern Turkey sits between the contrasting worlds of East and West, with elements from both sides integrated into its rich culture. The Turks, whether from the city or the rural areas, are known to be patriotic and romantic. They are also very friendly to visitors, and see it as a pleasant duty to make them welcome in their country.

A few other Top Tips from **CULTURE SMART!:**

- The Turkish body language may be confusing to the visitor. A shake of the head to the side means, "I don't know," and elevated shoulders and a protruded lip normally accompany this. A shrug of one shoulder means, "I don't care," and lifting the eyebrows and tutting means, "no."
- To address the Turks in a polite manner, add "*Bey*" for a man and "*Hanim*" for a woman, after the given name.
- When bargaining, start from the lowest possible price. The trader will start from a high figure, and after much haggling you should reach a price somewhere in the middle.
- In Turkey the acceptable attire is very similar to that of most wester European countries. Other than fo visiting a mosque, when you shou cover up, there are no strict dress codes. However, be prudent.
- Turkish food is unique, influence as it is by the Middle East and the Mediterranean. A meal may start with *meze*, a variety of small dish that may include yoghurt, olives, pureed aubergines and goat's cheese. A popular main course is grilled fresh fish or meat accompanied by bread, rice, tomatoes and salad. Slow-cooked meat dishes and stuffed vegetables are delicious.

ou can find out a lot more on our
ebsite - a visit to www.HIhostels.com is
sential for planning your trip!

our en savoir plus, rendez-vous sur
otre site Internet,
ww.HIhostels.com une visite
contournable pour préparer votre
yage!

ele weitere Informationen auf unserer
ebsite: www.HIhostels.com -
nverzichtbar für die Reiseplanung!

uedes averiguar mucho más en
uestro sitio web. Es imprescindible
ue visites la página
ww.HIhostels.com para planear tu
aje.

▲ **Istanbul** – Cordial House Hostel
HI 92314
Peykhane Sk. No:29 Çemberlitas - Istanbul.
t (212) 5180576; 5172727
f (212) 5164108
e bookings@cordialhouse.com;
enquiries@cordialhouse.com
w www.cordialhouse.com
Open Dates: 12 ✈ Atatürk Airport 12km A Esenler 10km; Airport Shuttle Stop in Aksaray 3km Karaköy Limani 4km Sirkeci 2km Intercity in Sirkeci 2km 40m ap Çemberlitas Tram Stop U Metro Line from ✈ to Çemberlitas 40m x 142

▲ **Istanbul** – Orient International Hostel
HI 92313
Akbiyik Cad. No:13, Sultanahmet/Istanbul.
t (212) 5179493 f (212) 5183894
e orienthostel@superonline.com
w www.orienthostel.com
Open Dates: 12 ✈ 15km A Shuttle and or tram available - Havas 15km Karakoy 1km Sirkeci 500m Esenler 10km Aksaray to Sultanahmet 150m U Aksaray 3km; Taksim 6km x 92 R CC

▲ **Istanbul** – Sultan Hostel HI 92312
Akbiyik Caddesi, Terbiyik Sokak No.3,
Sultanahmet 34400, Istanbul.
t (212) 5169260; 5169262
f (212) 5171626
e enquiries@sultanhostel.com
w www.sultanhostel.com
Open Dates: 12 ✈ Atatürk 18km A Havas 18km Karaköy 1km Sirkeci 500m Esenler 10km x 81

▲ **Istanbul** – Sultanahmet - Yücelt
Interyouth Hostel HI 92309
Caferiye Sok. No:6/1 Sultanahmet - Istanbul.
t (212) 5136150 f (212) 5127628
e info@yucelthostel.com
w www.yucelthostel.com
Open Dates: 12 R info@yucelthostel.com or www.yucelthostel.com ✈ Ataturk 11km A Havas/Airport-City Centre Bus to Aksaray Aksaray to Sultanahmet 150m x 320 R

UGANDA

International Youth Hostels Uganda,
PO Box 27270, Kampala.
(t) (256) 77552238; (0) 71682381
(e) iyhouthosteluganda@yahoo.com
(w) www.ugandayha.org

HI Suggests...

On the elevated basin between the eastern and western branches of the Great Rift Valley, Uganda is where the dry savannah of East Africa meets the dense rainforest of West Africa, whilst to the north is arid semi-desert. A fertile country of dramatic mountain ranges, beautiful lakes, rivers and waterfalls, and abundant wildlife including a remarkable diversity of bird life, it is no surprise that Uganda is considered one of the most diverse and fascinating of the East African countries.

Uganda has a pleasant tropical climate. Straddling the equator there is little year round fluctuation in temperature with a daytime maximum of 25 to 30°C and a night time minimum of 12 to 18°C. The wet seasons are generally mid-September to November and March to May but with between 1,000 - 2,000 millimetres of rain every year it can rain at almost any time.

It is a country with one of the fastest growing economies in Africa thanks to the increase of travellers flowing to experience Uganda's beautiful 241,039 square kilometres of land. Uganda offers the inquisitive traveller an array of attractions, which range from trekking opportunities through national parks to motor biking, bird watching, or white water rafting.

You can find out a lot more on our website - a visit to www.HIhostels.com is essential for planning your trip!

Pour en savoir plus, rendez-vous su[r] notre site Internet, www.HIhostels.com une visite incontournable pour préparer votr[e] voyage!

Viele weitere Informationen auf unserer Website: www.HIhostels.com - unverzichtbar für die Reiseplanung!

Puedes averiguar mucho más en nuestro sitio web. Es imprescindibl[e] que visites la página www.HIhostels.com para planear tu viaje.

△ ***Kampala*** *– International Youth Hostels Uganda – 75001*
PO Box 27270, Kampala.
(t) *077 552238; 71 682381*
(e) *iyouthhosteluganda@yahoo.com*
(w) *www.ugandayha.org; www.hostelworld.com*
Open Dates: 12 ✈ *Entebbe 15km*
A *500m* *500m* *50m*
ap Main Gaba Road, American Embassy Head Office in Sambia *500m*
ap Cardinal Snuduga Social Center - Sambia x 130 TV i 8 P 1km 2km

UKRAINE

Ukrainian Youth Hostel Association,
4/7, Mukachivska Street. Office 1.
Mailing address: P.O.Box 156. Kiev 01025.
(38) (039) 4937849; (044) 4269956
(38 (044) 426 9956; (044) 482 2297
info@hihostels.com.ua www.hihostels.com.ua

ease note: there is no visa requirement to Ukraine until 2008 for the citizens of the uropean Union, Switzerland, Canada and Japan.

Ukraine, although covering a large area of land, is one of Europe's lesser-known countries, but its beautiful landscapes and welcoming people make it a wonderful place to visit. Historically, the area has been a strategic battleground, owing to its location between the Black Sea, the Sea of Azov and the Baltic Sea, and it was the focus of several battles between Russia and Germany in the Second World War. Ukraine was also the location of the world's most damaging nuclear accident – the Chernobyl disaster – in 1986. Today, the country is undergoing somewhat of a transformation as it tries to step out of the Soviet shadow, and there is still a blurring between Russian and Ukrainian culture. For the last century or more the official language was Russian, but since independence, Ukrainian is being upheld as the state language. Regardless of this, the Russian language remains the most widespread, especially in the business world and in the major cities.

A few other Top Tips from **CULTURE SMART!:**

- Visitors are advised to take along Russian and Ukrainian phrasebooks, as learning the basics will make your stay a lot easier. It will also help you to understand important basic signs.
- The Ukrainians are extremely hospitable. Remember to remove your shoes on entering a Ukrainian home – you may be provided with some *tapochky* (slippers). It is customary to bring a present such as alcohol, flowers or chocolates. The number of flowers should be *odd* – even numbers are reserved for funerals.
- Drink bottled water, or sterilize tap water by boiling. Water supplies were polluted during the environmental neglect of the Soviet era, and there may be contamination by radioactivity.
- Be prepared to drink vodka! This is part of Slavic tradition, and some Ukrainians adhere to numerous points of etiquettes. For example, one should not drink before the first toast is made, and a new glassful is poured for each separate toast. The first toast is usually downed in one gulp!

Cultural Top Tips supplied by Culture Smart! guides. These essential guides to customs and etiquette will help you steer clear of embarrassing gaffes and sensitive issues, enabling you to discover new cultures whilst developing new friendships. Order online at www.culturesmartguides.co.uk

You can find out a lot more on our website - a visit to www.HIhostels.com is essential for planning your trip!

Pour en savoir plus, rendez-vous sur notre site Internet, www.HIhostels.com une visite incontournable pour préparer votre voyage!

Viele weitere Informationen auf unserer Website: www.HIhostels.com - unverzichtbar für die Reiseplanung!

Puedes averiguar mucho más en nuestro sitio web. Es imprescindible que visites la página www.HIhostels.com para planear tu viaje.

▲ **Kiev** – International Youth Hostel "Kiev" – 74005
52-a, Artema street, Korpus (Building. #2).
(067) 985 1173; (044) 426 9956
(044) 426 9956
info@hihostels.com.ua
www.hihostels.com.ua
Open Dates: Boryspil International 45km A Shuttle 'Atass' bus to the Southern Train Station Terminal Kiev Central 4km 16, 18 3km ap Poltavska 16, 18 3km ap Poltavska U Lukyanivska 1km x 100 R 1 x

▲ **Kiev** – International Youth Hostel "Yaroslav" – 74006
Podil. 10, Yaroslavska street in the inner yard
(039) 493 7849; (044) 426 9956
(044) 482 2297
info@hihostels.com.ua
www.hihostels.com.ua
Open Dates: Boryspil International 45km A Shuttle 'Atass' bus to the Southern Train Station Terminal Kiev Central 10km 18 ap Kontraktova Square U Kontraktova 100m x 10 R

▲ **Lviv** – International Youth Hostel "Afena" – 74007
49-a, Khymychna Street.
On crossroad with Chornovola Ave.
(032) 296 5734; (097) 433 2866
(032) 296 5734
info@hihostels.com.ua
www.hihostels.com.ua
Open Dates: Lviv International 20km Lviv Central 5km 66 ap Khymychna x 12 R

▲ **Lviv** – Seasonal Hostel Banking Academy – 74002
14 Kopernika str. Lviv.
(39) 4937849 (44) 2192297
info@hostel.org.ua
www.hostel.org.ua/hostel_ba
Open Dates: 01.07-01.09 Lviv International 10km Lviv 6km x 20 R

YOUTH HOSTEL ACCOMMODATION OUTSIDE THE ASSURED STANDARDS SCHEME

Sevastopol – International Youth Hostel Balaclava – 74004
18 Drapushko str, Balaklava, Sevastopol, Crimea.
(67) 3987888 (44) 4822297
info@hihostels.com.ua
www.hihostels.com.ua
Open Dates: Simferopol International 83km Sevastopol 12km Sevastopol 12km 9 ap Kadykovka x 105 R 3km

VENEZUELA

Albergues HI Hostels de Venezuela, Res. La Hacienda, Local 1-4-T,
Final Av. Ppal. de las Mercedes, Aptdo. 80160, Caracas 1080.
Ⓣ (58) (212) 9936082; 9929626 Ⓕ (58) (212) 9932412
Ⓔ hivenezuela@ivivenezuela.com

Travel Section:

Projectos IVI Venezuela C.A., Res. La Hacienda, Local 1-4-T,
Final Av. Ppal. de las Mercedes, Aptdo. 80160, Caracas 1080.
Ⓣ (58) (212) 9936082; 9929626 Ⓕ (58) (212) 9932412
Ⓔ info@ivivenezuela.com Ⓦ www.ivivenezuela.com

Venezuela is a country of stark contrasts. From the Andes to the Caribbean, Venezuela's beautiful landscape encompasses snowy peaks, flat-topped mountains, glorious beaches and Amazonian jungle. It has also witnessed major political upheavals and military coups since emerging from the fall of Gran Columbia in 1830. Venezuela's historical national pride is marked by the many statues of Simón Bolivar, one of South America's supreme generals, whose victories over the Spaniards won independence for Bolivia, Panama, Colombia, Ecuador, Peru and Venezuela.

Most of Venezuela's major cities are situated along the coast. These coastal regions provide the basis of the country's wealth through pearls, fishing and oil. Oil is the most important industry in Venezuela and the country was the world's major exporter prior to 1970. Caracas, Venezuela's capital, was built on oil money and is a large, bustling city. There is a marked contrast between the wealthy areas complete with skyscrapers and the poor population who live in shantytowns on the outskirts of the city. Venezuela has a population of approximately 25 million and modern day Venezuelans are a real mix of nationalities from Mestizo, European, African and Indian descent. The vast majority of Venezuelans speak Spanish. English is more frequently spoken in the more urban areas.

A few Other Top Tips from **CULTURE SMART!:**

- Venezuelans are outgoing people and often use quite expressive body language, which can be misinterpreted. They may seem to be angry because they use demonstrative gestures and raised voices, but soon after they will be laughing and smiling. Do not be surprised if you hear people hissing, as this is sometimes used to catch someone's attention.
- The normal greeting is a kiss on either cheek. Women kiss both women and men, but men only kiss women. A common handshake is the usual grip succeeded by another shake with the hand being wrapped around the wrist. This greeting is very informal and should only be used among friends. It is advisable not to use this handshake with someone in a position of authority!
- Appearance is very important in Venezuelan culture and the pressure to dress up is evident wherever you go. Make-up is meticulously applied and clothes are always fashionable.

Most of the clothing is heavily influenced by the fashion in the US and designer labels are easy to find.

- "If you are dieting, Venezuelan food is not the cuisine to be eating, as it tends to be high in cholesterol and cooked in plenty of oil. The *arepa* , which is a cornmeal patty, is perhaps the most popular food. These thick doughy discs made from *harina pan* (pre-cooked cornmeal) are cooked on a hot plate or fried in a pan and are usually stuffed with meat bologna, scrambled eggs or cheese. Although quite heavy and not particularly appetising to the eye, they will grow on you! Sweet desserts are also very popular and one of Venezuelans speciality cakes is the *Bienmesabe* , a soft sponge cake soaked in a sweet coconut cream sauce. It's name literally means "tastes good to me".

Culture Smart! Top Tips © Kuperard 2005

Cultural Top Tips supplied by Culture Smart! guides. These essential guides to customs and etiquette will help you steer clear of embarrassing gaffes and sensitive issues, enabling you to discover new cultures whilst developing new friendships. Order online at www.culturesmartguides.co.uk

You can find out a lot more on our website - a visit to www.HIhostels.com is essential for planning your trip!

Pour en savoir plus, rendez-vous sur notre site Internet, www.HIhostels.com une visite incontournable pour préparer votre voyage!

Viele weitere Informationen auf unserer Website: www.HIhostels.com - unverzichtbar für die Reiseplanung!

Puedes averiguar mucho más en nuestro sitio web. Es imprescindibl que visites la página www.HIhostels.com para planear tu viaje.

▲ **Ciudad Bolívar** – Posada Angostura – 76001
Calle Boyaca, entre Venezuela y Bolívar.
(285) 6324639 (285) 6324639
hivenezuela@gmail.com
Open Dates: Ciudad Bolívar 2km
2km ap Bus Terminal x 23

▲ **Laguna de Tacarigua** – Tortuga Lodge – 76002
Parque Nacional Laguna de Tacarigua.
(414) 9361426
hivenezuela@gmail.com
Open Dates: Caracas 120km 5km ap Tacarigua x 46 25km

▲ **Los Roques** – Cacao Village – 76003
Gran Roque.
(414) 2085707
hivenezuela@gmail.com
Open Dates: Gran Roque 500m
x 14

▲ **Puerto Ayacucho** – Campamento Orinoquia – 76004
Carretera Pto., Ayacucho-Samariapo (Km 20 - Garcitas).
(248) 5214882; (414) 4865923
(248) 5214882
hivenezuela@gmail.com
Open Dates: Puerto Ayacucho 20km
4, Samariapo Line 3km ap main road
x 36

▲ **Río Caura** – Caura Lodge – 76005
Las Trincheras, Caura river.
(285) 6324639 (285) 6324639
hivenezuela@gmail.com
Open Dates: Ciudad Bolívar 250km
90km ap Maripa x 42

EUFED

(European Union Federation of Youth Hostel Associations)

EUFED is the Federation that represents the interests, at European Union level, of the national Youth Hostel Associations of Europe, and the young people who stay at Youth Hostels.

There are currently 17 European countries represented within EUFED. At present, Youth Hostel Associations within EUFED, taken together, account for approximately:

- 1,800 Youth Hostels across Europe;
- 2.8 million members (many of whom are young people); and
- 23 million overnight stays within Europe.

EUFED was founded in 1987 and its main activities are:

- to promote the youth hostelling movement at the EU level, and thereby to gain financial and political support for the cause;
- to assist national Youth Hostel Associations to access EU funding, to help them in the development of their work;
- to facilitate on-going performance improvement within Youth Hostels. Staff training and environmental sustainability at Youth Hostels are two key areas in this respect.
- EUFED, with the support of the IYHF and national Youth Hostel Associations, has been awarded funding from the EU Leonardo da Vinci II Programme to develop new training modules;
- running European-wide projects and programmes for the benefit of young people, and with the financial support of the EU YOUTH Programme; and
- assisting the national Youth Hostel Associations of the EU accession and candidate countries to make the most of the opportunities arising from EU enlargement.

EUFED is run by an Executive Committee, who are the elected representatives of the Youth Hostel Associations of the European Union. The Executive Committee comprises a President, a Vice-President and three Members. The Secretariat is based in Brussels.

EUFED contact details are as follows:

Hoogstraat 25, rue Haute
B 1000 Brussels
BELGIUM

t +32 (0)2 502 80 66
f +32 (0)2 502 55 78
e info@eufed.org
w www.eufed.org

What is FIYTO?

The Federation of International Youth Travel Organisations is a leading global membership association and trade forum devoted exclusively to the youth travel industry. Partnering with leading national, official and private tourism organisations, FIYTO provides its members and the industry with a voice for advocacy, business & networking opportunities and focused industry intelligence.

Membership is open to organisations actively engaged in youth travel that adhere to the Federation's established Code of Conduct that signifies competence, fair dealing and high integrity.

FIYTO boasts over 450 members in 80 countries worldwide that serve approximately 20 million young travellers and account for an annual turnover of some 10 billion USD. The Federation's greatest strengths lie in its dedication to serving its members and the industry, and the continued commitment to its founders' ideals.

FIYTO is an affiliate member of the World Tourism Organization (WTO), a member of the Pacific Asia Travel Association (PATA), and a member of the International Bureau for Social Tourism (BITS). Additionally it enjoys operational relations with the United Nations Educational, Scientific and Cultural Organisation (UNESCO).

The Federation manages three product-driven associations; the Association of Language Travel Organisations (ALTO); the International Au Pair Association (IAPA), and the Global Work Experience Association (GWEA). Each association specialises in a unique sector of youth travel providing a platform for trade and quality control.

In addition, FIYTO co-hosts and organises the annual World Youth and Student Travel Conference (WYSTC) in conjunction with - The International Student Travel Confederation (ISTC). WYSTC is the youth travel industry's premier annual event. Providing intense trading, pre-booked business appointments, association meetings, seminars and workshop opportunities.

The mission of the Federation is "*To promote youth mobility and protect the identity of youth travel.*"

FIYTO members' provide a wide range of services and products to the student and youth travel industry. These include:

- Activity holiday groups
- Adventure travel providers
- Au pair agencies
- Education travel providers
- Financial services providers
- Homestay providers
- Hotel groups
- Language travel providers
- National tourism authorities
- Specialist student travel agencies
- Student travel bureaus
- Student/youth card providers
- Technology/communication
- Theme parks and restaurants
- Tour operators
- Tourism boards
- Transportation providers
- Travel publishers
- Travel insurance providers
- Work and study abroad programs
- Work experience providers
- Youth accommodations providers

For more information about FIYTO, please contact:

FIYTO, Bredgade 25H
DK-1260 Copenhagen K, Denmark
e mailbox@fiyto.org
w www.fiyto.org
t +45 3333 9600
f +45 3393 9676

International Student Identity Card (ISIC) & International Student Travel Confederation (ISTC)

The ISIC is carried by up to 4 million students around the world wherever they travel. ISIC is the only *globally accepted* proof of full-time student status and is endorsed by UNESCO (the United Nations Educational, Scientific and Cultural Organisation) as a tool for furthering education through travel and cross-cultural opportunities for young people.

.part from being a handy ID, the ISIC is also the key to more than 35,000 iscounts, benefits and services, at home and abroad, specially negotiated for tudents and youth. These include deals on airfares, rail and bus travel, .ccommodation, work exchange programmes, travel insurance, museums, ntertainment, restaurants, shops and telephone calls.

SIC holders are supported by a service network of 5000 student travel agencies n 116 different countries and an Emergency Help Line that provides 24-hour ıssistance for legal or medical emergencies.

ın ISIC can be obtained on-the-spot by taking a passport photo, proof of student status, and the ISIC fee to your nearest student travel agency (check on www.isic.org for your nearest issuing office – they will give you details of the fee n your country). Cards are also available for Youth Under 26 (IYTC) and Teachers (ITIC). For more information, visit www.isic.org.

The International Student Travel Confederation (ISTC), a global network of the world's leading student travel organisations, produces the ISIC, IYTC and ITIC.

UNESCO

IYHF-UNESCO Peace volunteers

UNESCO is an agency of the United Nations, with its international headquarters in Paris, France.

IYHF and UNESCO are two international organisations that share a common mission – to improve intercultural understanding amongst all in the pursuit of peace. Both organisations have made a commitment to undertake actions to promote greater Peace and International Understanding. This IYHF-UNESCO initiative forms part of the International Decade for a Culture of Peace and Non-Violence for the Children of the World.

The basic mission of UNESCO is to:

contribute to sustainable human development in a culture of peace, underpinned by tolerance, democracy and human rights, through programmes and projects in UNESCO's fields of competence – education, the natural and social sciences, culture and communication and information.

In 2003 IYHF and UNESCO sent 11 selected peace volunteers to Youth Hostels, which were identified as 'Learning Centres for Peace' in Australia, Brazil, Costa Rica, France, Germany, Italy, Japan, Northern Ireland, Israel, Tunisia and the USA. In 2004 300 young people gathered in Seoul, Korea to celebrate the first UNESCO/IYHF Youth Festival for Peace.

IYHF encourages every national Youth Hostel Association and affiliated organisation to be in close contact with their National Commission to UNESCO. Youth Hostels are encouraged to support and host UNESCO activities and programmes.

Find out more at www.unesco.org/youth or www.HIhostels.com/peace

WE WANT TO HEAR FROM YOU...

... help us to implement our assurance of standards at hostels by writing to us or by using the reply slip in this Guide to tell us what you think of our hostels.

Just tick the boxes to indicate how well the hostel did in the five areas, and remember to let us have your comments on how you found your stay.

Simply put your reply in an envelope and post to us at the address shown on the slip. You can also find this form on our website at www.HIhostels.com

NOUS AIMERIONS CONNAITRE VOTRE OPINION...

... aidez-nous à mettre en place les normes garanties dans nos auberges en nous faisant part de ce que vous pensez d'elles, soit en nous écrivant, soit en remplissant la fiche prévue à cet effet que vous trouverez dans ce guide.

Il vous suffira de cocher les cases pour évaluer la performance de l'auberge dans les cinq domaines indiqués, sans oublier d'ajouter vos observations sur votre séjour.

Envoyez-nous votre fiche sous enveloppe, à l'adresse indiquée dessus. Vous la trouverez également dans notre site Web sur www.HIhostels.com

WIR MÖCHTEN IHRE MEINUNG HÖREN...

... helfen Sie uns, unsere zugesicherten Standards zu gewährleisten, indem Sie uns wissen lassen, was Sie von unseren Herbergen halten. Bitte schreiben Sie uns oder benutzen Sie dazu die am Ende dieses Führers beigefügte Antwortkarte.

Kreuzen Sie bitte Ihre Beurteilung für die jeweilige Kategorie in dem entsprechenden Kästchen an, und vergessen Sie nicht, uns Ihren Kommentar über Ihren Aufenthalt mitzuteilen.

Ihre Antwort ganz einfach in einen Umschlag stecken und an die auf der Antwortkarte angegebene Adresse schicken. Diese Antwortkarte finden Sie auch auf unserer Website www.HIhostels.com

QUEREMOS SABER LO QUE USTED OPINA...

... ayúdenos a implementar nuestras normas garantizadas en los albergues. Escríbanos, o haga uso de las hojas provistas en la Guía, para comunicarnos lo que piensa de nuestros albergues.

Sólo tiene que marcar las casillas según la opinión que le merezca el albergue en lo que respecta a los cinco apartados de consulta. No olvide añadir comentarios sobre su estancia en el recuadro de las observaciones.

Envíe su comunicación en un sobre dirigido a la dirección indicada. También encontrará este impreso en nuestra página Internet: www.HIhostels.com

TELL US WHAT YOU THINK!

DITES-NOUS CE QUE VOUS EN PENSEZ!
SAGEN SIE UNS IHRE MEINUNG!
¡DIGANOS LO QUE OPINA!

Hostel Name-Address/
Nom de l'Auberge-Adresse/
Name der Jugendherberge Anschrift/
Nombre y Dirección del Albergue

City/*Ville*/Stadt/*Ciudad*

Country/*Pays*/Land/*País*

Date(s) stayed/
Dates du séjour/
Daten des Aufenthaltes/
Fechas de la Estancia

Please return to:
INTERNATIONAL YOUTH HOSTEL FEDERATION,
2nd Floor, Gate House, Fretherne Road,
Welwyn Garden City,
Hertfordshire AL8 6RD. ENGLAND

	☺	☺	😐	☹	☹
Welcome/*Accueil*/ Aufnahme/*Recibimiento*	☐	☐	☐	☐	☐
Comfort/*Confort*/ Komfort/*Comodidad*	☐	☐	☐	☐	☐
Cleanliness/*Propreté*/ Sauberkeit/*Limpieza*	☐	☐	☐	☐	☐
Security/*Sécurité*/ Sicherheit/*Seguridad*	☐	☐	☐	☐	☐
Privacy/*Intimité*/ Privatsphäre/*Intimidad*	☐	☐	☐	☐	☐

COMMENTS/*COMMENTAIRES*/BEMERKUNGEN/*OBSERVACIONES*

Name/*Nom*/
Name/*Nombre*

Address/*Adresse*/
Anschrift/*Dirección*

Discounts & Concessions

Hostelling International Membership enables you to claim discounts and concessions on everything from travel and museums, to eating and entertainment! The top discounts are included here – for the full story check out **www.HIhostels.com**. Simply present your Hostelling International Membership Card to claim a discount – and begin recovering the cost of Membership!

Discounts are sorted by **Country**. Within each country, discounts are listed alphabetically by **City** – national discounts are listed first. Within each city, discounts are listed by **Discount Category** – Entertainment, General, Museums and Culture, Retail, or Travel. For each discount, we list: discount provider's name, address and telephone number, along with a brief description of the discount available.

FreeNites & More - **www.HIhostels.com/FreeNites**
FreeNites & More rewards you every time you visit a participating hostel! Earn points on overnight stays, meals, drinks – and redeem points for a free overnight etc. The more points you earn, the more money you save! All HI members with a valid national or HI card who live in a participating country can join FreeNites & More. For the most up-to-date list of these countries check out **www.HIhostels.com/FreeNites**

Please note: The information about discounts has been supplied by the Youth Hostel Association of each country represented. Every effort has been made to ensure that this information is correct, and Hostelling International can accept no responsibility for any inaccuracies or for changes subsequent to publication.

Remises et réductions

Votre adhésion à Hostelling International vous permet de profiter de nombreuses remises et réductions sur presque tout, des transports aux entrées de musées en passant par la restauration et les spectacles! Seules les remises les plus importantes sont citées ci-après. Pour la liste complète, faites donc un tour sur notre site Internet, **www.HIhostels.com.** Présentez votre carte d'adhérent Hostelling International pour bénéficier d'une réduction et commencez à amortir le coût de votre adhésion!

Les différents avantages que l'on vous propose sont d'abord répertoriés par **Pays** puis en ordre alphabétique par **Ville** – les offres qui sont valables à l'échelle nationale sont en tête de liste. Elles sont ensuite classées par **Catégorie** – Voyages ✈ *(Travel)*, Magasins et Restaurants *(Retail)*, Spectacles et Activités *(Entertainment)*, Musées et Culture *(Museums and Culture)* ou Général ⓖ. Pour chaque remise, nous fournissons le nom de l'entité qui la propose, son adresse et numéro de téléphone, ainsi qu'un bref descriptif de l'offre en question.

FNM FreeNites & More - **www.HIhostels.com/FreeNites**

FreeNites & More vous récompense À CHAQUE FOIS que vous séjournez dans une auberge participante! Accumulez des points FNM sur des séjours, des repas, des boissons et échangez-les contre une nuitée GRATUITE etc. Plus vous gagnez de points FNM, plus vous économisez!

Tout titulaire d'une carte nationale d'adhérent ou d'une carte internationale HI en cours de validité, et résident de l'un des pays participants peut s'inscrire à FreeNites & More. Pour la liste la plus à jour de ces pays, rendez-vous sur **www.HIhostels.com/FreeNites**

Remarque: Les renseignements sur ces remises nous sont communiqués par l'Association d'Auberges de Jeunesse de chaque pays représenté. Tout a été mis en oeuvre pour s'assurer que ces données sont correctes mais Hostelling International ne peut accepter aucune responsabilité pour toute inexactitude ou tout changement intervenant ultérieurement à la publication du présent ouvrage.

Rabatte & Ermäßigungen

Die Mitgliedschaft bei Hostelling International sichert Ihnen Anspruch auf Rabatte und Ermäßigungen bei Reisen und Museen, in der Gastronomie und Unterhaltung! Die interessantesten Preisnachlässe findet ihr hier – weitere Ermäßigungen unter **www.HIhostels.com**. Legen Sie einfach Ihre Hostelling International Mitgliedskarte vor, um einen Nachlass in Anspruch zu nehmen – und fangen Sie an, den Mitgliedsbeitrag wieder einzuholen!

Die Rabatte sind nach **Ländern** *(Country)* und innerhalb jedes Landes nach **Städten** *(City)* in alphabetischer Reihenfolge geordnet. Die nationalen

Preisnachlässe *(National)* sind zuerst aufgeführt. Sie sind für jede Stadt nach **Rabattkategorien** *(Discount Category)* – Unterhaltung *(Entertainment)*, Allgemeines ⓖ *(General)*, Museen und Kultur *(Museum and Culture)*, Einzelhandel *(Retail)* sowie Reisen ✝ *(Travel)* – systematisiert. Für jeden Nachlaß ist, neben dem Namen des Anbieters, dessen Adresse und Telefonnummer, eine kurze Beschreibung des verfügbaren Rabattes *(Discount Discription)* aufgeführt.

(FNM) FreeNites & More - **www.HIhostels.com/FreeNites**

FreeNites & More belohnt Sie JEDES MAL, wenn Sie in einer beteiligten Herberge übernachten! Sammeln Sie FNM - Punkte für Übernachtungen, Mahlzeiten, Getränke – und lösen diese gegen eine KOSTENLOSE Übernachtung usw. ein. Je mehr FNM - Punkte Sie sammeln, desto mehr Geld sparen Sie! Alle HI-Mitglieder mit einem gültigen Mitgliedsausweis von HI oder ihrem nationalen Verband, die ihren Wohnsitz in einem der Teilnehmerländer haben, können bei FreeNites & More mitmachen.

Die aktuelle Liste dieser Länder finden Sie auf der Website **www.HIhostels.com/FreeNites**

Bitte beachten Sie: Die Informationen über die Rabatte wurden von den Jugendherbergsverbänden jedes aufgeführten Landes zur Verfügung gestellt. Wir haben alles unternommen, um sicherzugehen, dass diese Informationen korrekt sind. Hostelling International kann keine Verantwortung für jegliche Ungenauigkeiten oder Änderungen im Anschluss an die Veröffentlichung übernehmen.

Ofertas y Descuentos

Su afiliación a Hostelling International le permite disfrutar de ofertas y descuentos de todo tipo: en los transportes y entradas de museo, restaurantes y espectáculos – ¡la lista es interminable! A continuación se relacionan los descuentos más importantes solamente. Los mejores descuentos se detallan aquí. Para ver toda la información, echa un vistazo a **www.HIhostels.com**. Para conseguir un descuento, no tiene más que presentar su tarjeta de socio de Hostelling International y así ir amortizando el coste de la misma.

Los descuentos están clasificados en primer lugar por **país** y en segundo lugar por **ciudad o población**, ambos en orden alfabético. Los que son válidos a nivel nacional aparecen primero y todos están ordenados por **categoría**, a saber: Viajes ✝ *(Travel)*, Tiendas y Restaurantes *(Retail)*, Actividades Recreativas *(Entertainment)*, Museos y Cultura *(Museums and Culture)*, y General ⓖ. Para cada uno de ellos, se indica el nombre de la organización o compañía que concede el descuento, su dirección y número de teléfono, y una breve descripción del mismo.

FreeNites & More - **www.HIhostels.com/FreeNites**

¡Nuestro programa FreeNites & More (noches gratuitas y más) te recompensa cada vez que te hospedas en un albergue participante! Puedes acumular puntos FNM al abonar tu alojamiento, comidas y bebidas, y canjear puntos por una noche gratis, etc. ¡Cuantos más puntos FNM acumulas, más dinero te ahorras! Todos los miembros de HI que sean titulares de un carné de alberguista nacional o una tarjeta HI vigentes y que residan en uno de los países participantes pueden adherirse a FreeNites & More:

Para ver la lista actualizada de estos países, consulta **www.HIhostels.com/FreeNites**

Importante: La información sobre estos descuentos nos ha sido suministrada por la Asociación de Albergues Juveniles de cada país representado. Hemos hecho todo lo posible por asegurarnos de que los datos son correctos y Hostelling International no se responsabiliza de ninguna inexactitud ni de ningún cambio que se produzca en fecha posterior a la publicación de la presente guía.

Explanation of Symbols

- FreeNites and More
- Entertainment
- General
- Retail
- Museums and Culture
- Travel

- FreeNites and More
- Spectacles et Activités
- Général
- Magasins et Restaurants
- Musées et Culture
- Voyages

- FreeNites and More
- Unterhaltung
- Allgemeines
- Einzelhandel
- Museen und Kultur
- Reisen

- FreeNites and More
- Actividades Recreativas
- General
- Tiendas y Restaurantes
- Museos y Cultura
- Viajes

GLOBAL

GLOBAL

Columbus

www.columbusdirect.net/HI

Special rates available for Hostelling Intenational members. Conditions apply.

lonely planet

Lonely Planet Guide Books

www.lonelyplanet.com

Lonely Planet, the world's leading publisher of independent travel information, offer £2 off on Lonely Planet Guide Books! Postage to the United Kingdom and Northern Ireland is free. Please note that you will need a code when ordering, by calling Lonely Planets promo order line – (44) (0)20 7841 9111. Email your membership details to Hostelling International: contact@HIhostels.com and you will receive the code you need for taking advantage of this special offer.

Taxback

www.taxback.com

If you have worked abroad while travelling, you probably qualify for an income tax refund! Hostelling International has teamed up with specialist Taxback.com to help you make savings even when your trip is finished! Taxback.com makes it easy and hassle-free for you to receive a tax refund - they take care of the necessary paperwork and deal with the foreign tax authorities on your behalf. So, why not visit www.HIhostels.com to find out just how much you can claim back? You will find it in the HI Shop in the main menu on www.HIhostels.com.

Travelex worldwide money

Travelex

www.travelex.com

COMMISSION FREE CURRENCY EXCHANGE - A SPECIAL OFFER FOR HOSTELLING INTERNATIONAL MEMBERS. TRAVELEX - the world's largest airport and passenger terminal bureau de change - has offered Hostelling International members a very special service to reduce the cost of international travel. By showing your membership card and quoting "Hostelling International" or "IYHF" you can enjoy Commission Free Currency exchange at any of the 650 Travelex offices world-wide. The list of their offices can be found on the Travelex website at www.travelex.com Conditions apply.

EUROPEAN

EUROPEAN

Hertz

Call one of the following Reservation Hotlines or contact your local reservation office:
Belgium: (32) 2 717 3625,
France: (33) 1 41 919 525,
Germany: (49)1805 938814,
Italy: (39) 199 11 77 11,
The Netherlands: (31) 020 201 3512

www.hertz.com

Hertz are offering Hostelling International members a discount of between 10-25% (sometimes more) on standard car rental rates depending on the make and model of the car and length of hire. The discount is available on both business and leisure rentals in Europe and when travelling from Europe to North America, Australia, Asia and South Africa. Simply quote CDP number 532239 when making your booking. You may be asked to show your membership card upon collection of vehicle. Normal restrictions apply.

Argentina

National

FreeNites & More promotions are available on www.HIhostels.com/FreeNites!

Don Otto - Bus
10% off all destinations. Collect discount voucher from YH

Flechabus - Bus
10% off all destinations. Collect discount voucher from YH

Que Bus - Bus
10% off all destinations. Collect discount voucher from YH

Ruta Patagonia - Bus
15% off all destinations. Collect discount voucher from YH

Tigre Iguazu - Bus
10% off all destinations. Collect discount voucher from YH

Transportdora Patagonica - Bus
10% off all destinations. Collect discount voucher from YH

Via Bariloche - Bus
(54) 11 4511 8723
hiargentina@hostels.org.ar
10% off all destinations. Collect discount voucher from YH

Buenos Aires

Hard Rock Café
Av. Pueyrredon 2501, 2° piso
(54) 11 4807 7625
15% off selected items - Nearest hostel; Buenos Aires Milhouse YH

Patagonia Region

Chalten Travel - Bus
10% off all destinations. Collect discount voucher from YH

Australia

National

Conservation Volunteers Australia
10% off becoming a member of Conservation Volunteers Australia. Enjoy the opportuntiy to travel and help the environment.

Jetta Excess Baggage
10% off all charges (Exclusions apply)

Luggageline
Free cartons and packing materials when sending your stuff home.

The Travel Doctor
10% off all Travel Doctor products, vaccines and medical kits

Travel Clinics Australia
(61) 13 0036 9359
10% off travel health products. Free pocke medical guide and international vaccinatio certificate (value $9.90). Free country medical report (value $22.00)with first consultation

American Express Foreign Exchange
(61) 13 0013 9060
Commission free exchange of travellers cheques and currency at American Express Foreign Exchange outlets

Aussie Disposals
www.aussiedisposals.com.au
10% off everything instore (exclusions apply)

Camera House
Save 50% - have your images burnt to CD for half price. Save 10% - film, batteries, and standard developing & printing (includes passport photos). Not to be used with any other offer

Columbia Sportswear
www.columbia.com.au
10% off everything instore (excludes discounted/sale stock)

Downtown Duty Free
Vouchers available at selected YHA Travel and Membership Centres. Spend $100 and get $10 off, spend $200 and get $20 off.

Kathmandu
(61) 18 0033 3484
www.kathmandu.com.au
25% off full-price Kathmandu travel packs, rucksacks, daypacks, travel accessories, goosedown sleeping bags and tents. 10% off all full-priced stock. Conditions apply

Mountain Designs
www.mountaindesigns.com
10% off everything instore (excludes discounted and sale stock)

City Sightseeing
www.citysightseeingtours.com.au
$5 off on City Sightseeing Tours in Sydney, Melbourne, Canberra, Adelaide and Gold Coast

Europcar
(61) 13 0013 1390
www.europcar.com.au
Special rates for YHA members

Greyhound Australia
www.greyhound.com.au
10% off all Greyhound passes and point-to-point tickets

Oz Experience
www.ozexperience.com
5% off selected Oz Experience passes in Australia

Suncoast Pacific Coaches
10% off all coach fares

Adelaide

Heading Bush
(61) 8 84143000
$205 off Adelaide to Alice tours when booked through YHA Travel - Nearest hostel; Adelaide Central YHA

Prime Mini Tours
(61) 8 84143000
$3.00 off all tours when booked through YHA Travel - Nearest hostel; Adelaide Central YHA

Alice Springs

Alice Springs Cultural Precinct
(61) 8 8951 1132
20% off full entry fee - Nearest hostel; Alice Springs

Blue Mountains

Australian School of Mountaineering
166 Katoomba St, Katoomba NSW
(61) 2 4782 2014
10% off Blue Mountains based abseiling, canyoninng and rockclimbing courses, adventures and tours - Nearest hostel; Blue Mountains YHA

Blue Mountains Walkabout
(61) 0408 443 822
$5 off full price ticket - Nearest hostel; Blue Mountains YHA

Fantastic Aussie Tours
(61) 2 4782 1866
Concession rate on all tours - Nearest hostel; Blue Mountains YHA

High 'n' Wild Adventures
(61) 2 4782 6224
$5 off half day/$10 off full day abseiling - Nearest hostel; Blue Mountains YHA

Brisbane

Australian Day Tours
Level 3 Transit Centre Roma Street
(61) 7 3236 4155
10% off day tours (excludes Theme Park tours) - Nearest hostel; Brisbane City YHA

XXXX Ale House Brewery Tours
Cnr Black & Paten Streets
(61) 7 3361 7597
$1.50 off full adult rate - Nearest hostel; Brisbane City YHA

Byron Bay

Sundive
Cnr Byron & Middleton Sts, Byron Bay
(61) 2 6685 7755
10% off - Nearest hostel; Byron Bay YHAs

Surfing Byron Bay
Shop 5, 84 Jonson St, Byron Bay
(61) 2 6685 7099
$5 off full price lesson - Nearest hostel; Byron Bay YHAs

Cairns

Cairns Tropical Zoo
Captain Cook Highway, Palm Cove
(61) 7 4055 3669
10% off entry fee - Nearest hostel; Cairns Central YHA

Passions of Paradise
(61) 0 4051 1368\ 0 4031 1919
$5 off ticket price - Nearest hostel; Cairns Central YHA

Reef Magic Cruises
(61) 0 4051 1368\ 0 4031 1919
Free introductory scuba dive worth $60, or free guided marine snorkel tour - Nearest hostel; Cairns Central YHA

Canberra

Cockington Green Gardens
11 Gold Creek Rd, Nicholls
(61) 2 6230 2273
20% off general admission - Nearest hostel; Canberra YHA

Darwin

Territory Wildlife Park
(61) 8 8999 3824
20% off any full paying entry fee - Nearest hostel; Darwin International YHA

Hervey Bay/Fraser Island

Fraser Venture Tours
$5 off Fraser Venture day tour, $10 off 2 day safari (quad only), $15 off 3 day safari (quad only) - Nearest hostel; Colonial Cabins Resort YHA

Hobart

Penitentiary Chapel Ghost Tour
6 Brisbane Street
(61) 3 6231 0911
10% off entry fee - Nearest hostel; Adelphi Court YHA

Kakadu/Katherine

Gecko Canoeing
(61) 8 8981 2560
10% off - Nearest hostel; Kookaburra Backpackers YHA

Launceston

Escape Tours Tasmania
10 Morris Street, Prospect
(61) 1 800 133 555
5% off all tours - Nearest hostel; The Devi[l's] Playground YHA

Melbourne

IMAX Theatre
Rathdowne St, Carlton Gardens, Carlton South
(61) 3 9663 5454
20% off full price ticket - Nearest hostel; Melbourne Metro YHA

Backpackers Auto Sales
500 Elizabeth Street, Melbourne
(61) 3 9663 6622
Upgrade RACV cover to Extracare includin[g] towing and five nights accommodation in case of breakdown and a full tank of petro[l] - Nearest hostel; Melbourne Metro YHA

Melbourne Aquarium
Cnr Queenswharf Rd and King St
(61) 3 9923 5994
10% off all tickets - Nearest hostel; Melbourne Metro YHA

Melbourne Zoo
Elliott Avenue, Parkville, 3052
(61) 3 9285 9300
Concession price on presentation of YHA Membership Card - Nearest hostel; Melbourne Metro YHA

Perth

Brass Monkey
Corner William and James Street, Northbridge
(61) 8 9227 9596
10% off bottleshop purchases, 10% off caf[é] bar & lounge - Nearest hostel; Perth City YHA

Surfing Lessons
14 Andrew St, Scarborough
(61) 8 9203 5678
2 for 1 on private lessons - Nearest hostel; Indigo Net Café and Lodge YHA

Active Safaris
(61) 8 9427 5100
5-10% off brochure price - Nearest hostel; Perth City YHA

Easyrider Backpackers
(61) 8 9427 5100
$10-$40 off tours -
Nearest hostel; Perth City YHA

Sydney

Australian National Maritime Museum
2 Murray St, Pyrmont
(61) 2 9298 3777
20% off any ticket -
Nearest hostel; Sydney Central YHA

Chinese Garden
Exhibition Place, Darling Harbour
(61) 2 9281 6863
$4.50 adult entry (usually $6) -
Nearest hostel; Sydney Central YHA

IMAX Theatre
Southern Prm Darling Harbour
(61) 2 9281 3300
20% off regular admission prices. Not vaild with any other offers -
Nearest hostel; Sydney Central YHA

Museum of Sydney
Cnr of Phillip & Bridge Sts, Circular Quay
(61) 2 9251 5988
Concession rate -
Nearest hostel; Sydney Central YHA

Sydney Aquarium
Aquarium Pier, Darling Harbour
(61) 2 8251 7800
25% off admission -
Nearest hostel; Sydney Central YHA

Sydney Observatory
Watson Rd, Millers Point, The Rocks
(61) 2 9217 0485
$12 night tours (usually $15), $4 day tours (usually $6) -
Nearest hostel; Sydney Central YHA

Taronga Zoo
Bradleys Head Rd, Mosman
(61) 2 9969 2777
20% off adult & children admisson. Not valid with any other existing Zoo offer/concession or transport pass including Zoo Pass -
Nearest hostel; Sydney Central YHA

Sydney Jet
Cockle Bay Wharf, Darling Harbour
(61) 2 9938 2000
20% off all rides - Nearest hostel; Sydey Central YHA

Sydney Skydivers
Book at YHA Travel
(61) 2 9261 1111
Free return shuttle, 50% off full weekend rates - Nearest hostel; Sydney Central YHA

Whitsundays

Prosail
(61) 7 4946 7533
$4 off America's Cup Challenge tickets (usually $79) - Nearest hostel; Airlie Beach YHA

Austria OJHV

National

FNM FreeNites & More promotions are available on www.HIhostels.com/FreeNites!

There are discounts available on transport, tours, tourism and cultural activities for Hostelling International members. For details of discounts please ask at the Hostel.

Salzburg

FNM 250 FNM for a ticket to the Sound of music Tour (4 hours tour, incl. the famous "Edelweiß-cocktail" and the movie shown daily in the Youth Hostel Salzburg-Nonntal)

Belgium LAJ

National

Please see www.laj.be for full list of discounts

Aywaille

Monde Sauvage Safari Park
Fange de Deigne 3, 4920 Aywaille
(32) 0 4360 9070
www.mondesauvage.be
20% off entry fee - Nearest hostel; Liege Georges Simenon

Dinant

Bateaux Bayard
Bd W. Churchill, quai 10, 5500 Dinant
(32) 0 8222 3042
15-20% off entry fee - Nearest hostel; Namur Felicien Rops

Brazil

National

FreeNites & More promotions are available on www.HIhostels.com/FreeNites!

São Paulo

Fue Brazil Brazilian Food
Shopping Moto Aventura - 2nd floor
10% off - Nearest hostel; Sao Paulo Downtown YH

Gil Guta (Percussion teacher)
Rua Barao de Campinas, 94 - Centre
(55) 11 3225 0623
Free Brazilian percussion classes. Tues at 7pm - Nearest hostel; Sao Paulo Downtown YH

Paparoti Italian Fast Food
Shopping Moto Aventura - 2nd floor
(55) 11 3331 2434
paparoti.italian@pop.com.br
10% off lunch. Mon to Sat - Nearest hostel; Sao Paulo Downtown YH

Odyssey South America
Largo do Arouche, 63 - Centre
(55) 11 3331 0278
info@odysseysouthamerica.com
20% off guided walking tours - Nearest hostel; Sao Paulo Downtown YH

Chile

National

FreeNites & More promotions are available on www.HIhostels.com/FreeNites!

Pacific Fitness Club Gym
Multiple Locations
(56) 0 2373 9155
marketing_1@pacificoclub.cl
30% off all services

Restaurant Pura Carne
Multiple Locations
(56) 0 2212 9496
e.fell@lomiton.cl
10% off food and drink

Bus Company Alsa
Multiple Locations
(56) 0 2776 0101
15% off bus fares

La Serena

Café el Patio
Prat 470
(56) 5121 0759
cafeelpatio@gmail.com
20% off all services (excluding Happy Hou and menu items)

San Pedro de Atacama

Restaurant El Milagro
Caracoles 241
(56) 5585 7575
10% off food and drink

Desert Adventure Agency
Caracoles s/n
(56) 5585 1067
desertsp@ctcinternet.cl
15% off tourist services

Santiago

Bar el Tunel
Sto. Domingo # 439 Santiago
(56) 0 2639 4914
info@bareltunel.cl
30% off entry fee

Buin Zoo
Panamericana Sur km.32 # 01730, Buin
(56) 0 2821 5511
administracion@buinzoo.cl
25% off entry fee

Sala Murano lounge bar
Av. Las Condes 14950 - Las Condes
(56) 0 2217 0959
20% off entry fee

Clínica Odolontológica Integral
Pio X 2460 Of 704-Providencia
(56) 0 2321 8941
40% off clinincal dental services

Figaro Café -Lounge
Guardia Vieja 181 loc 4 -Providencia
(56) 0 2374 0413
figarocafe@hotmail.com
10% off breakfast and afternoon snacks

Language Institute Mapamundi
Merced 346 piso 3C, Santiago Centro
(56) 0 2441 9076
mapamundi@mapamundi.cl
10% off Spanish lessons

Medical Body Art
Gilberto Fuenzalida 185. Loc 110, Las Condes
(56) 0 2212 7207
medicalbodyart@hotmail.com
10% off all services

Sportime
Av: larrain 9700- La Reina
(56) 0 2275 1297
info@sportime.cl
15% off all services

Woodward
Av Apoquindo 4248- Las Condes
(56) 0 2263 3847
info@woodward.cl
25% off language classes

Comercial V-Tec
Av Irarrazaval # 5180-Ñuñoa
(56) 0 2277 8783
ventas@v-tec.cl
15% off car accessories

Innova Ltda
Las Urbinas 53 local 46-Providencia
(56) 0 2335 1213
innova_chile@entelchile.net
10% off all products

Photonew
Av. Providencia 2198 loc 33 , Providencia
(56) 0 2231 4404
info@photonew.cl
10% off film processing and purchases

Chile Montaña Mountain Tourism
Leonardo Da'Vinci 6928 - La Reina
(56) 0 2325 1288
info@chilemontana.cl
15% off all products and services

Extrem Tourism Office Lo Tuyo.cl
Diagonal Paraguay 160 Of .1109 Santiago
(56) 0 2370 1079
info@lotuyo.cl
20% off trekking, 15% off cabalgatas & 10% off canyoning

Full Famas Rent a Car
Av Bilbao 1049- Providencia
(56) 0 2343 0665
fullfama@chilesat.net
20-30% off car hire

GTS Travel
Cienfuegos 151, Santiago Centro
(56) 0 2699 7892
info@gts.cl
Special rates for tourist services

Pacifico Divers Ltda
Av Cristobal Colón 5328- Las Condes
(56) 0 2202 3680
pacificodivers@vtr.net
Special rates for courses

Radio Taxi Providencia
Av Irarrazaval # 3054 of 404-A-Ñuñoa
(56) 0 2209 0445
gerencia@radiotaxiprovidencia.cl
10% off taxi services

Ski Total
Av. Apoquindo 4900 loc 40- Las Condes
(56) 0 2246 0156
skitotal@skitotal.cl
10-20% off ski hire and transportation

The New Ski & Sport Ltda
Alonso de Camargo 7612- Las Condes
(56) 0 2211 4101
10-15% off all services

Transfer Delfos
Av Armando Cortínez s/n
(56) 0 2766 2303
Special rates for airport transport services

Windsurfing Chile
Las Carmelitas # 30 -Las Condes
(56) 0 2211 1959
info@windsurfingchile.com
10% off all services

Yak Expediciones
Nocedal 7135, La Reina
(56) 0 9892 8761
info@yakexpediciones.cl
10% off selected services

Viña del Mar

Café Internet Rue Valparaiso
Av. Valparaiso 286
(56) 3271 0140
286@ruevalparaiso.zzn.com
Up to 40% off Internet services

Pasteleria Viale
Av. Valparaiso 498
(56) 3271 0596
10% off all products

Restaurant Pura Carne
5 Norte 132
(56) 0 2212 9496
e.fell@lomiton.cl
10% off food and drink

Salón de Belleza Daniel ^O
Av Valparaiso 515. Loc 102
(56) 3268 6660
10% off all services

Rainbow Tours
San Antonio 1287
(56) 3268 6968
10% off all services

Estonia

Tallinn

Key Travel
(372) 646 1455
inc@balticbudgettravel.com
www.BalticBudgetTravel.com
Up to 5% off all products (Flight/ferry/bu tickets, on car/bike rent, accommodation insurance, guidance etc). Conditions appl

Finland

Åland Islands/Vårdö

Bomans Gästhem B&B/Hostel
Vårdöbyvägen 75, 22550 Vårdö.
(358) 184 7821
bomans.gasthem@aland.net
€ 2 off bike hire

Espoo

Budget Hotel Matinlahti
Rantamäki 3, 02230 Espoo
(358) 9 88761
hotelli.matinlahti-reception@sodexho.fi
Free movie channels and internet access in private rooms

Helsinki

Eurohostel
Linnankatu 9, 00160 Helsinki
(358) 9 622 0470
eurohostel@eurohostel.fi
10% off tickets to Serena, the largest tropical water park in Europe. Purchase tickets from reception

Hostel Satakuntatalo
Lapinrinne 1 A, 00180 Helsinki
(358) 9 6958 5232
ravintola.satakunta@sodexho.fi
10% off snacks and non-alcoholic drinks sold at reception

Eckerö Line Ab Oy
Mannerheimintie 10, 00181 Helsinki
(358) 9228 8544
info@eckeroline.fi
20% off route fare and day cruise. Discount card must be shown when booking - Nearest hostel; all Helsinki hostels

Helsinki, Rovaniemi

Eskelisen Lapin Linjat (Bus Company)
Koskikatu 49-53, 96100 Rovaniemi
(358) 1 6342 2160
esk.lapinlinjat@co.inet.fi
50% discount on adult's normal bus ticket Helsinki-Rovaniemi. 30% discount on adult's normal bus ticket from Rovaniemi to Norway (Nordcape, Tromsö, Vadsö and Kautokeino). Discounts valid only on the Finnish side of the border. Tickets from the driver - Nearest hostel; all Hesinki hostels, Rovaniemi Hostel Rudolf

Helsinki, Vantaa, Turku, Lahti, Tampere, Oulu, Rovaniemi

Transvell
Ormuspellontie 5, 00700 Helsinki
(358) 9350 5590
rent@transvell.fi
15% off car hire at Transvell Car Rental (Helsinki, Vantaa, Turku, Lahti, Tampere, Oulu, Rovaniemi) - Nearest hostel; all Helsinki hostels

Inari/Kaamanen

Kaamasen Kievari
99910 Kaamanen
(358) 1667 2713
kaamanen@kaamasenkievari.fi
10% off snow-shoe and cross-country ski equipment hire. Free use of rowing boat in summer

Kemi

Gemstone Gallery
Kauppakatu 29, 94100 Kemi
(358) 1625 9690
kemin.matkailu@kemi.fi
20% off entry fee

Kuopio

Hostel Puijon Maja
Puijontornintie, 70300 Kuopio
(358) 1 7255 5250
puijo@sakky.fi
Free entrance to the Puijo Lookout Tower. 5% discount at the Puijo Tower Restaurant (revolving panoramic restaurant)

Oulu

Kesähotelli Oppimestari
Nahkatehtaankatu 3, 90100 Oulu
(358) 8884 8527
oppimestari@merikoski.fi
Free use of washing machine (usually € 2)

Rantasalmi

Country Hotel SaimaanSydän
Ohitustie 5, 58900 Rantasalmi
(358) 1544 0761
countryhotel@saimaaholiday.net
10% off stays longer than one night. 10% off sightseeing boat trip in Linnansaari national park

Sulkava/Kaartilankoski

Partalansaaren Lomakoti
Hirviniementie 5, 58720 Kaartilankoski
(358) 1547 8850
arjaschenkwein@partalansaarenlomakoti.com
Free use of row-boat, canoe, bicycle and kick sled

Tervola

Wild Lapland
Kätkävaara, 95300 Tervola
(358) 1643 9148
info@wildlapland.net
10% off tours and safaris. Free fishing license - Nearest hostel; Tervola Wild Lapland

Turku

Hostel Turku
Linnankatu 39, 20100 Turku
(358) 2262 7680
hostel@turku.fi
20% off TurkuCards sold at YH which offers free entrance to most museums in Turku, and discounted sight-seeing tours and bus journeys on Turku public buses

France

AJ Aix les Bains

ST2a
Aix les Bains
€ 2.50 off (tickets on sale at the YH)

AJ Boulogne sur Mer

Aqualud (Aquatic Leisure Park)
Bld de la Mer 6252 Le Touquet
(33) 3 2190 0707
contact@aqualud.com
10% off

Bowling
Impasse Quéhen 62200 Boulogne, Boulogne sur Mer
(33) 3 2180 6580
contact@bowling-de-boulogne.com
€ 2.50 off (tickets on sale at the YH)

Char à Voile (Sand Yacht)
272, bld St Beuve 62200 Boulogne sur Mer
(33) 3 2183 2548
cvcco@wanadoo.com
1 hour free bike hire

Château musée
Vieille ville 62200 Boulogne sur Mer
(33) 3 2110 0220
Discounts for groups

AJ Brive

Adventure Parc
Aubazine
(33) 5 5527 2110
Discounted rates

Boutique du CABC
Brive
(33) 5 5517 1532
10% off the rides

Cinema Rex
Brive
(33) 5 5574 2051
Discounted rates

Golf de Brive
Brive
(33) 5 5585 5757
Discounted rate: € 20

Golf du Coiroux
Aubazine
(33) 5 5527 2566
25% off day rental

Le Roc équitation (Horse Riding Center)
Sainte Féréole
(33) 5 5585 7757
10% off

Tour of the Cesar Tower
Allassac
(33) 5 5524 0880
Discounted rate: € 4

Château de Turenne (Castle)
Turenne
(33) 6 8159 9778
Free audioguided tour

Cinema CGR
Brive
(33) 8 9268 0445
10% off

Musée Edmond Michelet (Museum)
Brive
(33) 5 5574 0608
Discounted rates until 3pm daily and all day Mon

Musée Labenche (Museum)
Brive
Free book "l'homme de la Chapelle aux saints"

Tour of the city centre
Brive
(33) 5 5524 0880
Free for the 2nd person

Ardoisières de Travassac (Salt Quarry)
Travassac
(33) 5 5585 6633
5% off when you spend € 15

Musée de l'Homme de Néandertal (Museum)
La Chapelle aux Saints
(33) 5 5591 1800
€ 1 off the audioguided tour of the city

AJ Carcassonne

Cité Nature (bio grocer)
2, rue porte d'Aude, 11000 Carcassonne
(33) 4 6826 3464
€ 2 off (€ 4 instead of € 6)

Giant Gulf of Cabrespine
11160 Cabrespine, Carcassonne
(33) 4 6826 1422
€ 2 off (€ 6.50 instead of € 8.50)

Lastours Castle
Usine Rabier 11600 Lastours, Carcassonne
Tél/fax : (33) 4 6877 5602
€ 1 off (€ 2.50 instead of € 3.50)

Limousis Cave
Carcassonne
€ 1 off (€ 7.00 instead of € 8)

Puilaurens Castle
Château 11140 Lapradelle-Puilaurens, Carcassonne
Tél/fax : (33) 4 6820 6526
€ 1 off (€ 2.50 instead of € 3.50)

Abbaye de St Hilaire
Ancien Presbytère 11250 Saint Hilaire, Carcassonne
Tél/fax : (33) 4 6869 6276
€ 1 off (€ 7 instead of € 8)

Australian Park
Carcassonne
€ 1 off (€ 3 instead of € 4)

Chalabres Castle
Carcassonne
€ 1 off (€ 2.50 instead of € 3.50)

Cruise on the "Canal du Midi"
Carcassonne
€ 2.50 off entry

d'Arques Castle
Carcassonne
€ 1.50 off (€ 11 instead of € 12.50)

Knighthood Museum
Carcassonne
Free

Middle Age Museum
Carcassonne
€ 1 off (€ 4 instead of € 5)

Quéribus Castle
Carcassonne
€ 1 off (€ 3 instead of € 4)

Sainte Marie d'Orbieu Abbey
Carcassonne
€ 1 off (€ 2.50 instead of € 3.50)

Saissac Castle
Carcassonne
€ 1 off (€ 4 instead of € 5)

School Museum
Carcassonne
€ 1 off (€ 3 instead of € 4)

La Cité des Oiseaux (the birds city)
Colline de Pech Mary, 11000 Carcassonne
(33) 4 6847 8899
10% off

Fine Arts Museum
Carcassonne
€ 1 off entry fee

AJ Colmar

Unterlinden Museum
1, rue d'Unterlinden, Colmar
€ 1.15 off entry

Swimming Pool
rue Schuman, Colmar
€ 1.50 off entry

Bartholdi Museum
30 rue des Marchands, Colmar
€ 2 off entry

Centre de réintroduction des cigognes et des loutres
1 free "kir breton" (French aperitif)

AJ Grenoble Echirolles

A2C Shop Photo
116 Cours Jean Jaurès, Grenoble 38000
(33) 4 7696 9229
Free shoe hire except on Sat after 8pm, public holidays and days before public holidays

Adrénaline Sport (sports equipment shop)
26-28 place Paul Vallier, Grenoble 38000
(33) 4 7686 0606
€ 8 off bungee jumping

Bowl Center (bowling, games, bar)
19 av Grugliasco, Echirolle 38130
(33) 4 7623 4090
10% off

Etrier du dauphiné (horse riding center)
1 route de Champagnier, Echirolle 38130
(33) 4 7698 5566
10% discount (excl. on special offers) 15% off day rental, 20% off ski-snow maintenance

Crêperie de Gordes (restaurant)
3, place de Gordes, Grenoble 38000
(33) 4 7651 3667
€ 1 off a take-away pizza

Le Globe Trotter (resto du monde)
49 av Alsace Lorraine, Grenoble 38000
(33) 4 7647 2120
10% off

Le Kiosque Thaï (Thai restaurant)
40, av Victor Hugo, Echirolle 38130
(33) 4 7622 8355
10% off

Le Stambouliote (kebab)
57 Cours Jean Jaurès, Echirolle 38130
(33) 4 7609 7590
1 free kir (aperitif)

Les Daux Savoie (regional restaurant)
33 av Félix Viallet, Grenoble 38000
(33) 4 7687 1476
20% off

Pizzeria Tic et Tac (restaurant)
46 Cours Jean Jaurès, Echirolle 38130
(33) 4 3849 3404
1 free cocktail & 5% discount

Vertige Aventure
45 Route de Lyon, Grenoble 38000
(33) 4 7687 7288
10% off second-hand clothes except on special offers; 1 free coffee or a juice whe you buy any CD

AJ Ile de Groix

Bikini Bike
Le port, Groix
5-20% off depending on the time of year

AJ La Foux D'Allos

Ski Lift (contact the YH for more infomation)
5% off collective ski classes for adults and children registering at YH

AJ Lanslebourg Val Cenis

ESF
73480 Lanslebourg
10% off in winter and 30% off in summer. Ski pass on sale at YH

AJ Les Deux Alpes

Cinema le Slalom
rue des Vikings, les Deux Alpes
(33) 4 7679 0688
22% off kayak tour

Deux Alpes Loisirs
Immeuble le Meijotel, les Deux Alpes
(33) 4 7679 7501
info@2alpes.com
Free entry with the ski pass sold at YH

Deux Alpes Loisirs
Immeuble le Meijotel, les Deux Alpes
(33) 4 7679 7501
info@2alpes.com
Free entry with the ski pass sold at YH

Sport Emotions
33 avenue de la Muzelle, les Deux Alpes
(33) 4 7679 2093
sportemotion@wanadoo.fr
50% off. Tickets on sale at YH

Deux Alpes Loisirs
Immeuble le Meijotel, les Deux Alpes
(33) 4 7679 7501
info@2alpes.com
40% off ski/snow equipment hire. Tickets on sale at YH

AJ Nîmes

Golf 18 holes
1075 chemin du golf 30900 Nîmes
50% off entry

Ghraphicaderme (tattoos and piercing)
27 rue Vincent Faita 30000 Nîmes
10-20% off tattoos

La Croquignole (pizzeria)
rue Vincent Faïta, 30000 Nîmes
15% off meals

India

Connaught Place - Delhi

M. Ram & Sons
21-E Connaught Place, New Delhi
(91) 11 2332 0558
mram@bol.net.in
12% off

Stic Pvt. Ltd.
G-55 Connaught Place, New Delhi
(91) 11 2336 8161
stictrvl@del2.vsnl.net.inc
5% off

Travel Corporation of India
C-35, Connaught Place, New Delhi
(91) 11 2331 9992
www.tcindia.com
5-10% off - Nearest hostel; New Delhi International YH

Malcha Marg - Delhi

Lazeez Affairs
Malcha Marg, Chanakyapuri, New Delhi
10% off

Orissa

Hotels & restaurants of Orissa run by Hotel and Restaurant Association of Orissa
10% off

Pragati Maidan - Delhi

Appu Ghar
International Amusement Limited
(91) 11 2337 1446
50% off

Talkatora Garden - Delhi

Shah-En-Shah
Talkatora Garden, New Delhi
(91) 11 2309 3127
shahenshahdelhi@indiatimes.com
20% off

Israel

Acco

Track Yam
10% off - Nearest hostel; Shlomi

Afula

Maayan Harod National Park
50% off - Nearest hostel; Maayan Harod, Beit Shean

Beit Shean

Gan Guru Australian Park
10% off - Nearest hostel; Maayan Harod, Beit Shean

Beit Shean National Park
25% off - Nearest hostel; Maayan Harod, Beit Shean

Beit Shean/Afula

Beit Alfa Antique Synagogue
25% off - Nearest hostel; Maayan Harod, Beit Shean

Ein Gedi

Botanical Garden
20% off - Nearest hostel; Ein Gedi, Massada

Ein Gedi SPA
20% off - Nearest hostel; Ein Gedi, Massada

Ein Gedi Nature Reserve
15% off - Nearest hostel; Ein Gedi, Massada

Ein Gedi/Massada

Massada Site
25% off - Nearest hostel; Ein Gedi, Massada

Haifa

Carmelit Cable
50% off - Nearest hostel; Haifa

Haifa Theatre
2 for the price of 1 - Nearest hostel; Haifa

Municipality Museums
Special price - Nearest hostel; Haifa

Jerusalem

Biblical Zoo
10% off

Time Elevator
20% off

Biblical Museum
25% off

Israel Museum
30% off

Kiryat Shmona

Canada Center
20% off - Nearest hostel; Tel Hai, Karei Deshe

Manara Cable
15% off - Nearest hostel; Tel Hai, Kaiei Deshe

Tel Hai Yard
10% off - Nearest hostel; Tel Hai

Mitzpe Ramon

Jeep Tours
10% off - Nearest hostel; Mitzpe Ramon

Visitors Center
10% off - Nearest hostel; Mitzpe Ramon

Naharia/Acco

Monfort Lake
10% off - Nearest hostel; Shlomi

Rosh Hanikra
20% off - Nearest hostel; Shlomi

Tiberias

Abu Kajak
10% off - Nearest hostel; Tiberias, Karei Deshe

Rob Roy (Canoe)
10% off - Nearest hostel; Tiberias, Poria

Tiberias Hot Springs
40% off - Nearest hostel; Tiberias, Poria, Karei Deshe

Italy

National

Please see www.ostellionline.org for full list of discounts

Sixt rent-a-car
www.sixt.it
Special rates for HI members. Quote E110100123 - all Italian YH

Vacupan Dental Care
Special rates for HI members - Nearest hostels; Milan, Roma, Turin

Brek Restaurants
www.brek.com/eng/index.htm
10-15% off depending on hours - Nearest hostels; Milan, Turin, Venice, Padua, Verona, Vicenza, Bologna, Rome

Trenitalia Italian Railways
www.trenitalia.com/en/index.html
Discounts on selected services

Genoa

Genoa Aquarium
(39) 01 0234 5678
€ 1 off entry fee - Nearest hostel; Genoa YH

Roma

Hard Rock Café
Via Veneto 62
(39) 0 6420 3051
rome_sales@hardrock.com
Free gadget for HI members - Nearest hostel; Rome YH Foro Italico A.F. Pessina

Japan

National

FreeNites & More promotions are available on www.HIhostels.com/FreeNites!

Aichi

Youth Holiday Adventure
(81) 0 568 67 3710
10% discount on selected activities with valid HI card

Hokkaido

Higashi-Nihon-Ferry
(81) 0 11 518 2718
10% off selected tours - apply to following routes; Tomakomai-Oarai, Muroran-Naoetsu, Naoetsu-Hakata, Muroran-Hachinohe, Muroran-Aomori, Hakodate-Ouma, Hakodate-Aomori

Kyoto

Tenryu-ji (Temple)
(81) 0 75 881 1235
100 yen off entry fee with valid HI card

Nagano

Henry Miller Museum
(81) 0 261 23 5002
100 yen off entry fee with valid HI card

Osaka

Club CRANE (horse-riding)
(81) 0 723 62 3450
30% off selected services - applies to Horse-riding, one-ride course

WTC Cosmo Tower
(81) 0 6 6615 6000
100 yen off entry fee with valid HI card

Hankyu-Ferry
(81) 0 6 6345 6341
10-20% off regular fare. Conditions apply

Kansai-Kisen
(81) 0 6 6572 5181
20% off regular fare. Conditions apply

Meimon-Taiyou-Ferry
(81) 0 6 6531 5511
20% off regular fare. Conditions apply

Tokyo

Asakusa Hana-Yashiki Amusement Park
(81) 0 3 3842 8780
30% off selected services with valid HI card

Sanyo-do
(81) 0 3 3580 3410
5% off suitcases, 20% off travel goods with valid HI card

Japaren (Rent-a-Car)
(81) 0 3 3356 3900
10% off selected hire with valid HI card

Lebanon

Beirut

Expeditions International
Beirut
(961) 329 3210
15% off tours and activities

Luxembourg

Beaufort

Castle in Beaufort (Amis de l'ancien Château a.s.b.l.)
L-6313 Beaufort
(352) 836002
40% off with valid HI card - Nearest hostel; Beaufort YH

Bettembourg

Wonderland Parc
rte de Mondorf L-3260 Bettembourg
(352) 5110481
guy.feidt@parc-merveilleux.lu
15% off with valid HI card - Nearest hostel; Luxembourg City YH

Binsfeld

Land Museum "A Schiewesch" (Tourist Office Beaufort)
Maison 20 L-9946 Binsfeld
(352) 979820
museebinsfeld@netscape.net
25% off with valid HI card - Nearest hostel; Wiltz YH, Vianden YH

Bourscheid

Castle in Bourscheid (Château de Bourscheid)
L-9140 Bourscheid
(352) 990570
50% off with valid HI card - Nearest hostel; Lultzhausen YH

Christnach

Golf Club Christnach
Am Lahr L-L-7641 Christnach
(352) 878383
gcc@gms.lu
20% off with valid HI card - Nearest hostel; Beaufort YH, Larochette YH

Clervaux

Museum of Battle of the Ardennes (Château de Clervaux)
Montée du Château L-9712 Clervaux
(352) 920072
info@tourisme-clervaux.lu
50% off with valid HI card - Nearest hostel; Wiltz YH, Vianden YH

Museum of Toys
9, Grand Rue L-9710 Clervaux
(352) 920228
30% off with valid HI card - Nearest hostel; Wiltz YH, Vianden YH

Diekirch

Military Museum
10, rue Bamertal L-9208 Diekirch
(352) 808908
mnhmdiek@pt.lu
40% off with valid HI card - Nearest hostel; Lultzhausen YH

Grevenmacher

Exotic Butterfly Garden
rte de Trèves L-6793 Grevenmacher
(352) 758539
info@bernard-massard.lu
10% off with valid HI card - Nearest hostel; Echternach YH, Bourglinster YH

Junglinster

Golf of Luxembourg
Domaine de Belenhaff L-6141 Junglinster
(352) 780 0681
10-50% off with valid HI card - Nearest hostel; Bourglinster YH

Larochette

Castle in Larochette (Amis de la Ville Larochette)
L- 7612 Larochette
(352) 837497
15% off with valid HI card - Nearest hostel; Larochette YH

Luxembourg City

Casino Luxembourg
41, rue Notre Dame L-2240 Luxembourg
(352) 225045
25% off with valid HI card

Bock Casemates (Luxembourg City Tourist Office)
Montée de Clausen L-1343 Luxembourg
(352) 222809
touristinfo@luxembourg-city.lu
40% off with valid HI card

Petrusse Casemates (Luxembourg City Tourist Office)
Boulevard Roosevelt L-2450 Luxembourg
(352) 222809
touristinfo@luxembourg-city.lu
40% off with valid HI card

CK Sport Center S.A.
20, rte de Bettembourg L-1899 Kockelscheuer
(352) 472285
info@ck-online.lu
20% off with valid HI card

Swimming Pool (Parc-Hotel)
120, rte d'Echternach L-1453 Luxembourg
(352) 435643
info@parc-hotel.lu
30% off with valid HI card

Swimming Pool Coqué Aquacenter
2, rue L. Hengen L-1745 Luxembourg
(352) 436 0601
info@coque.lu
15% off with valid HI card

Guided City Promenade (Luxembourg City Tourist Office)
Place d'Armes L-2011 Luxembourg
(352) 222809
touristinfo@luxembourg-city.lu
15% off with valid HI card

HOP & OFF Bus Tour
B.P.39 L-4901 Bascharage
(352) 2362 6410
marion.lauer@sales-lentz.lu
50% off with valid HI card

Petrusse Express (Sales-Lentz)
Place de la Constitution L-2450 Luxembourg
(352) 236261
25% off with valid HI card

Sightseeing (Sales Lentz)
Place de la Constitution L-2450 Luxembourg
(352) 236261
25% off with valid HI card

Mersch

Swimming Pool "Krounebierg" (Commune de Mersch)
L- B.P. 93 L-7501 Mersch
(352) 328823
wantz.commune@mersch.lu
50% off with valid HI card - Nearest hostel; Hollenfels

Munshausen

Living Rural Museum "A Robbesscheier" (Syndivat d'Initiative)
Frummeschgaas L-9766 Munshausen
(352) 9217 4511
info@robbesscheier.lu
25% off with valid HI card - Nearest hostel; Wiltz YH, Vianden YH

Remich

St. Martin Wine Cellars (Vinum Veritas)
53,rte de Stadtbredimus L-5570 Remich
(352) 699744
20% off with valid HI card - Nearest hostel; Luxembourg City YH

Vianden

Castle in Vianden (Les Amis du Château)
Montée du Château L-9408 Vianden
(352) 849291
info@castle.vianden.lu
25% off with valid HI card - Nearest hostel; Vianden YH

Wiltz

Battle of the Bulge Museum
L-9516 Wiltz
(352) 957442
30% off with valid HI card - Nearest hostel; Wiltz YH

Museum of the Art and Handicraft (Château de Wiltz)
L-9516 Wiltz
(352) 957442
25% off with valid HI card - Nearest hostel; Wiltz YH

Tennis Club (Tennis Club Wiltz a.s.b.l.)
rue Joseph Simon L-9550 Wiltz
(352) 957056
50% off with valid HI card - Nearest hostel; Wiltz YH

México

Cancún

Coco Bongo
Kukulcan Km. 9. Zona Hotelera
15% off Bar and Boutique

Gray-Line
Kukulcan Km. 3.5. Local 43 Zona Hotelera
10% off

Hooters
Kukulcan Km. 9. Zona Hotelera
10% off

The City Night Club
Kukulcan Km. 9. Zona Hotelera
15% off Open Bar and T-shirts. 20% off Boutique

Carlos & Charles
Kukulcan Km. 9.5. Zona Hotelera
Express Pass

Hard Rock Café
Kukulcan Km. Lotes 10 y 10 c.
Free national drink

Margarita Ville
Kukulcan Km. 115. Zona Hotelera
15% off

Outback Steak House
Centro Comercial Flamingo
10% off

Pato O´Brians
Centro Comercial Flamingo
15% off

Planet Hollywood
Kukulcan Km. Lotes 10 y 10 c.
Free national drink

Rain Forrest
Kukulcan Km. Lotes 10 y 10 c.
Free national drink

Sr. Frogs
Kukulcan Km. 9.5. Zona Hotelera
Express Pass

Playa del Carmen

AllTourNative
Av. 38 Norte
20% off

Norway

Evje

Troll Mountain
Setesdal Rafting og Aktivitetsenter, 4735 Evje
(47) 3793 1177
post@heidalrafting.no
10% off all activites - Nearest hostel; Evje YH

Sjoa

Heidal Rafting
Sjoa, 2670 Otta
(47) 6123 6037
tim@troll-mountain.no
10% off rafting daytrips - Nearest hostel; Sjoa YH

Stryn

Olden Aktiv Briksdalsbreen a
6792 Briksdalsbre
(47) 5787 3888
info@oldenaktiv.no
10% off glacier trips - Nearest hostel; Stryn YH

Peru

Colca Canyon, starts from Lima

Alternative Wheels Expeditions
info@culturetrack.ca
www.culturetrack.ca
20% off with valid HI card - Nearest hostel; Lima YH

Cuzco

Camping Equipment
Mercado Rosaspara Jiron Abel Landeo P -1
10% off camping equipment hire and repair - Nearest hostel; Cuzco YH

Lima

De rompe y Raja
Manuel Segura 127 Barranco
(51) 1247 5271
derompeyraja@infonegocio.net.pe
Free entry until 10:30pm. 2 for 1 on drink for couples - Nearest hostel; Lima YH

Del Carajo
Calle San Ambrosio 328 Barranco
(51) 1247 7023
reservas@del-carajo.com
10% off restaurant meals. 2 for 1 on drinks. Free Pisco Sour if you enter between 12am and 1am - Nearest hostel; Lima YH

El SOL - Spanish School
Grimaldo del Solar 469 Miraflores
(51) 1242 7763
elsol_info@idiomasperu.com
10% Spanish lessons - Nearest hostel; Lima YH

Si Señor
Bolognesi 706 Miraflores
(51) 1445 3789
sisenor@terra.com.pe
10% off menu items. Free Margarita - Nearest hostel; Lima YH

Washios Barranco
Boulevard de los Bomberos Barranco
(51) 1247 2832
washiosbar@yahoo.com
Free Pisco Sour. Free snack - Nearest hostel; Lima YH

Washios Chacarrilla
C:C:El Tambo de Monterrico
(51) 1247 2832
washiosbar@yahoo.com
Free Pisco Sour. 2 for 1 on drinks

IPM
Paseo de la republica 6099 Miraflores
(51) 1241 5505
informesipm@yahoo.com
50% off Marketing Programme - Nearest hostel; Lima YH

Switzerland

Basel

YH Basel
(41) 06 1272 0572
basel@youthhostel.ch
Mobility Ticket for checked-in guests for free transportation in Basel.

YH Basel City
(41) 06 1365 9960
basel.city@youthhostel.ch
Mobility Ticket for checked-in guests for free transportation in Basel.

Davos

YH Palace Davos
(41) 08 1410 1920
davos@youthhostel.ch
Mobility Ticket for checked-in guests for free transportation in Davos.

Locarno

YH Locarno
(41) 09 1756 1500
locarno@youthhostel.ch
Discounted entry fee to local swimming pool. Summertime only

YH Locarno
(41) 09 1756 1500
locarno@youthhostel.ch
Free digestive at the local Pizzeria St. Antonio.

YH Locarno
(41) 09 1756 1500
locarno@youthhostel.ch
50% off cable car to Cardada-Cimetta. March to October

Pontresina

YH Pontresina
(41) 08 1842 7223
pontresina@youthhostel.ch
25% off indoor pool entry fee

St. Moritz

YH St. Moritz
(41) 08 1833 3969
st.moritz@youthhostel.ch
10% off sports equipment hire and purchase

Zermatt

YH Zermatt
(41) 02 7967 2320
zermatt@youthhostel.ch
Discounted ski, snowboard and bike hire

USA

National

FNM FreeNites & More promotions are available on www.HIhostels.com/FreeNites!

eKit Communications Card
(1) 800 706 1333
www.hiusa.ekit.com
Save up to 70% for long distance phone calls, free email access and voicemail

Greyhound/Greyline
(1) 888 454 7277 (in USA & Canada only)
www.greyhound.com
25% off specific city sightseeing tours. 10% Greyhound Discovery Pass (N American wide)

Trek America
(1) 800 221 0596 (in USA only)
info@trekamerica.com
5% off any tour package